Plant Physiology

The Wadsworth Botany Series

William A. Jensen and Leroy G. Kavaljian, Series Editors

PLANT PHYSIOLOGY
Salisbury and Ross

AN EVOLUTIONARY SURVEY OF THE
PLANT KINGDOM
Scagel, Bandoni, Rouse, Schofield, Stein, and Taylor

PLANT DIVERSITY: AN EVOLUTIONARY APPROACH
Scagel, Bandoni, Rouse, Schofield, Stein, and Taylor

Fundamentals of Botany Series

Jensen: THE PLANT CELL

Cook: REPRODUCTION, HEREDITY, AND SEXUALITY

Doyle: NONVASCULAR PLANTS: FORM AND FUNCTION

Salisbury and Parke: VASCULAR PLANTS:
FORM AND FUNCTION

Billings: PLANTS AND THE ECOSYSTEM

Baker: PLANTS AND CIVILIZATION

Bell: PLANT VARIATION AND CLASSIFICATION

Plant Physiology

Frank B. Salisbury

Utah State University

Cleon Ross

Colorado State University

Wadsworth Publishing Company, Inc., Belmont, California

L. C. Cat. Card No.: 68-17381

Printed in the United States of America

To Marilyn and Gloria

Preface

Preparation of this text was most enlightening. It demonstrated to us how much the science of plant physiology has changed in recent years and how rapidly it is presently changing. It is evident that, while the specialist must continue to probe his narrow field in depth, much of modern biological science is intimately intertwined with the rest of science. The main topic of this book is the functioning systems of higher plants, but we occasionally found it necessary to discuss the lower plants, particularly algae and bacteria—and even animal physiology where appropriate. The profound impact of molecular genetics is clearly evident in plant physiology as well as the whole of biology.

It was difficult to decide what should be included in the text. We could take only a small fraction of the available material—what we considered the highlights of modern plant physiology. We expect that no teacher who uses this text will completely agree with us. Teachers will want to add material from their own fields of interest, especially as new data become available. They will also want to subtract from our material, since we have included more than can be conveniently covered, at least in a single-quarter course. We believe the extra material in this text will be a valuable reference for students even if it is not covered in lectures. An example is the rather detailed discussion of growth chambers in the last chapter.

We have been especially concerned about current trends in plant physiology. We wrote to about fifty of our scientific colleagues for suggestions about recent areas of high interest. Many of their suggested topics had already been discussed in the text, but we felt that a summary of some recent trends might be helpful to the student. Thus after we read page proofs, we prepared an essay titled *Advancing Frontiers;* this appears at the end of the text.

Many topics logically fit in more than one place in the organization of this book. We tried to avoid redundancy to some extent, but we consciously included a certain amount of repetition for its value in the learning process. We also included cross references to other chapters and to specific sections. This should illustrate to the student the extreme complexities and overlap of modern plant physiology.

We are assuming that the student has had a basic background in botany, chemistry, and algebra. Often our review of basic mathematics or chemistry has been at a level more elementary than might be justified by the rest of the text and these assumptions. These discussions are presented as reviews of material to which the student has already been exposed and not as original instruction in basic science. It has been our experience that this can be valuable to many students, and those who don't need this material can skip over it quickly.

Boldface type is used for new terms and to emphasize terms summarized in a discussion. Often we defined a term rather formally the first time it appeared in boldface. This convention, combined with the index, should serve the purpose of a glossary.

To give some historical and even personal perspective to plant physiology, we tried to mention the locations and dates (publication, usually) of fairly important discoveries as well as the name or names of the discoverers. Unless they appear at widely separate places in the book or there is otherwise a chance for confusion, given names are used only once.

The references at the end of the book are separated into general review articles and books, and specific articles. Most of the papers implied by the names and dates mentioned in the chapter can be found in these lists, although work referred to more generally (without names and dates) must be sought in the review articles and books. It was simply impossible to include all pertinent references, but we hope that we have at least opened some doors to the literature for the student.

We are grateful to the following reviewers: William Jackson, Russell Jones, James Lockhart, Peter Ray, Tom Scott, and Joseph Varner. We are especially grateful to William Jackson and Peter Ray. Dr. Jackson tested the material in his class at Dartmouth and provided us with his comments and those of his students. Dr. Ray carefully examined the page proofs and made valuable suggestions that we incorporated.

The book has truly been a joint effort. Both of us have edited all chapters several times, and we have each contributed to virtually every section. Yet Salisbury was primarily responsible for Section One and Ross for Section Two. Ross almost completely rewrote Salisbury's versions of Chapters 3 and 8. In Section Three, Salisbury originally prepared Chapters 19, 22, 24, 25, and 26, and Ross Chapters 20, 21, 23, and 27. Salisbury contributed the last section of Chapter 23 and both chapters of Section Four. We finally managed to agree on all points, including philosophy of approach! In a field as fluid as modern plant physiology, we feel this is no simple accomplishment, made possible no doubt by the fact that our committee consisted of two chairmen.

Using original material, data from the literature, and rough sketches supplied by Ross for his chapters, the illustrations were prepared under the direction of Salisbury.

In many cases, these were prepared in nearly final form, and then traced in ink by Karen Barozzi, Kathleen Steffen Hoth, Clifford Sroka, David Steffen, or Brian Taylor. Kathleen Steffen Hoth "specialized" in graphs and metabolic diagrams (e.g., 15-2, 15-3, 15-4). Karen Barozzi prepared several delightful drawings in the first part of the book (e.g., 2-2, 4-1, 5-4, 5-5, 6-1, 7-2, 24-1). All these artists, especially David Steffen, finished many other graphs and figures. Salisbury finished a number of figures in ink, including many of the graphs and free-hand drawings toward the end of the book (e.g., 6-4, 21-1, 21-12(a), 22-2, 22-7, 27-1, 29-7, 29-9, 29-10). Julian Maach, Head of the Department of Medical Illustration at the University of Utah, prepared many biological drawings (e.g., all of the halftone drawings). His talents, and those of the others who helped illustrate the book, are greatly appreciated.

We are deeply grateful to the many scientists who have read all or part of the manuscript. Each contributed something, and in several cases the contributions have been substantial. The following individuals studied the entire manuscript at our request and were especially helpful: Alice Denney, Irving B. McNulty, and Herman Wiebe. It was also read in part by Martyn Caldwell, William Campbell, Bert Drake, John Evans, Karl Hamner, Paul Kramer, J. L. Monteith, Ivan Palmblad, Herbert Papenfuss, Klaus Raschke, Roy Sachs, the late Sterling Taylor, and David Walker. The Plant Science Department staff at Utah State University was especially helpful with Chapter 28.

Several typists have worked on the manuscript, but Patricia Hagius and Annelee Donnelly were especially helpful. Alice Denney and Bert G. Drake helped with a host of small details, such as finding material in the library, preparing plants for photographs, and even performing experiments to provide data for figures.

Our wives and children also contributed, not only by long-suffering patience, but often in highly tangible ways.

Even with all this help, we have not accepted every suggestion and must remain completely responsible for the book as it stands.

Contents

1

The Marvel of Plant Function

Plants, though they appear commonplace and passive, prove to be complex and fascinating functioning systems, and understanding them is a difficult but challenging task, both for the student and for the scientist.

Comprehension of even the rudiments of plant *function* depends upon some knowledge of plant *structure* at the microscopic level, and real understanding even requires knowledge of molecular function. The curious person who would achieve this understanding is faced with a stimulating mystery to solve. He must dissect the over-all problem into a number of smaller problems, insight upon insight, until finally the solution becomes clear. This is the process of analysis. Of course, the task is beyond any one individual, and many scientists have long been engaged in it. Activity has become especially intense in recent years.

The purpose of this book is to outline some high points in this human endeavor, laying the foundation for future steps by a summary of the present status of our knowledge and an indication of some of the important problems remaining to be solved.

We can gain some impression of where we now stand in biology by considering engineering, which is more of a synthetic science. In biology, the organisms were there, and our task was to understand them by analysis, but engineering principles were worked out *de novo* more by invention than by analysis. Our intricate technological civilization is the result of these inventions. A moon lander with its launching system represents a pinnacle in man's ability to combine the elements of his physical environment to reach his own ends. We can define the complexity of such a system, and hence it serves as an excellent comparative model for a biological system, such as a plant.

1.1 THE PLANT AS A SELF-SUSTAINING MECHANISM RESPONDING TO ENVIRONMENT

Let us consider plant function in terms of a far-fetched engineering analogy. Say that we have achieved the ability to explore deep space. We discover a planet having the same physical environment as Earth: the same temperature, light intensity, atmosphere, water, soil, seasons, etc. There is, however, no life on the planet (a highly unlikely situation, since the environment of our planet is strongly influenced by life). We must take steps to prepare it for colonization. We assign our engineers the task of designing and building a special robot that can be landed on the planet in advance of manned ships. It must meet the following specifications:

1.1.1 Metabolic Synthesis

The robot must be capable of synthesizing organic compounds (including carbohydrates, fats, and proteins) for the colonizers. The future inhabitants will need a variety of other special substances, such as vitamins, pigments, hormones, and the like. Cellulose will be required as structural material. The robot must produce these as well.

Although various elements will be available to the robot primarily as salts, it must make all of the organic substances from two principal raw materials: water and carbon dioxide. Since the carbon dioxide is present in quantities of only about three parts in 10,000 parts of air (by volume), the robot will have to process about 8,050 kg (6,222 cubic meters—the volume of a room $10 \times 20 \times 31$ meters!) of air, removing *all* of its carbon dioxide, to get one kilogram of carbon for incorporation into organic compounds. In some way it must capture the energy of sunlight to drive these synthetic processes. All the robot's water must be obtained from the soil, even though moist soil is sometimes fairly scarce. Some of the essential minerals are present in rather small quantities, while other, less essential or nonessential ones are overabundant; so the robot must obtain and process minerals selectively.

If our analogy is to be complete, the designers cannot be allowed unlimited factory space for all this chemical engineering. In fact, they must work with a basic unit only about as large as a grain of dust. They are not restricted as to kinds of these "cells" but can utilize in the final robot an almost unlimited variety of basic units combined in large numbers and in many ways.

1.1.2 Growth, Differentiation, and Reproduction

Payload on this rocket venture is extremely limited, and thus the package will have to start out at only about the size of a small pearl; this includes the robot itself and its stored supplies. It must increase its size upon arriving by making more of itself. That is, it must exhibit the property of growth. In this process it may use the products formed in answer to the first specification, but some must be left over for the colonizers who will follow. Oxygen is abundant, and the robot may utilize it for the growth process.

In its initial condition, the robot may be relatively simple, endowed primarily with the ability to increase its size by using some fairly elaborate materials sent with it, but as it becomes larger, it must become less dependent upon its stored supplies, until it is finally able to operate using only materials and energy sources in its environment. It must become more *complex* as well as larger, and all of its final potential must be programmed within the initial simple structure.

As it increases in size, it must provide itself with a supply and transport system between its parts in the soil and its parts in the air, but if it gets too large it may become cumbersome and exhaust all the raw materials from its immediate vicinity. Thus the designers must build into it the capacity to construct other units like itself—to reproduce. The new units should be capable of becoming dispersed over the entire surface of the planet.

1.1.3 Adaptation to Environmental Change

The intricacy of the robot's structure might result in a rather delicate mechanism that must be protected from certain violent forces and changes in the environment on the planet. It must withstand the heating effects of full sunlight, the shearing effects of storms, and the destructive effects of rapid temperature changes and sharp temperature gradients from one of its ends to the other.

In order to thrust part of itself into the soil

and the other part into the atmosphere, it must be capable of sensing and responding to gravity. It must also sense and respond to the direction of light rays to present its light-absorbing surfaces most efficiently and, if necessary, to move out of shaded areas.

It must respond to seasonal changes by changing itself *in anticipation of* coming seasons. It may detect the season by measuring time, the length of day or night. To do so it may have to be sensitive to very low light intensities and specific light qualities, and this mechanism must be largely unaffected by changes in temperature. It may also use the extended low temperatures of winter to prepare itself for the coming spring or the high temperatures of summer to prepare for fall.

It must be programmed so that detection of season and anticipation of coming season lead to the development of resistance to freezing temperatures or to dry periods and to the production of its reproductive structures at a time when conditions will be favorable. By the same mechanisms, the robot or its reproductive units should become inactive during unfavorable times and resume their activity only at appropriate times.

Obviously the specific responses to environment will depend upon where on the planet's surface the robot is allowed to land, and it should contain a capacity to become gradually adapted, with time through several generations, to its specific environment.

These are the basic specifications; and when the committee of scientists and engineers really settle down to work, other details will no doubt develop.

Of course our engineers would be completely incapable of constructing this "robot," but they might recognize that it has the specifications of the seed of a higher plant, and send one of those instead. Our engineers could now duplicate some of the required chemistry, but far from all of it, and not in a volume as confining as the plant cell. We can make devices to respond to gravity and to light and to measure time and temperature, but again the requirement for miniaturization would make such a project presently impossible. We can do little more than offer suggestions about the functions of growth and reproduction. How can a machine construct itself, adding complexities to meet special needs, all in accordance with instructions built into the original machine?

We are far from the point of constructing such a robot, having the properties of life, but the biologist of today is involved in the fascinating process of trying to understand how the living organism is itself capable of such prodigious feats. The essential assignment of the biological scientist is to study the structure of living organisms (the machinery) and then to discern how it all operates. We have made enough progress in doing these things to have discovered that living organisms are unique in their machinery and in its functions. This uniqueness provides a definition of life.

1.2 VITALISM VERSUS MECHANISM

The problem of understanding life as a functioning machine has sometimes proved so difficult that philosophers have proposed an alternative: that life functions depend upon something beyond the limits of physics, chemistry, and engineering—a spirit or entelechy. This is known as the **vitalistic theory**, as contrasted to the concept of **mechanism**. Mechanism states that life can be understood on the basis of physical and chemical events. Vitalism has been completely unproductive in science, as we shall see in subsequent chapters, while mechanism provides the only approach that allows experimentation and application of the scientific method. We will take the mechanistic approach here.

This is not to say that certain vitalistic principles may not be true—only that there is no way to study them in the laboratory. The student may have his own convictions (as do the authors), based upon other kinds of evidence, relating to the existence of an immortal spirit, and of a god.

1.3 THE NATURE OF LIFE

Specifications for our robot were essentially those relating to function. They constitute the functions often listed in basic biology and botany textbooks as being characteristic of life: metabolism, irritability, growth, and reproduction. Movement seems to be characteristic of living things if we consider the movement of subcellular particles as well as the movement of the organisms themselves. Yet these functions are not themselves a sufficient basis for a definition of life. We must realize that the functions of life arise because of the structure of living things. The marriage between structure and function is absolutely incapable of dissolution. The structures function; and, at the same time, the functions create the structures.

The relationship between structure and function in living organisms is highly complex, but it is this very complexity that provides the uniqueness of the phenomenon we recognize as life. We can better understand the situation by attempting to organize the complexity. A convenient approach is to think of several levels of organization from the simplest at the bottom to the most complex at the top. In each case, the functions associated with the structural level of organization can also be considered. The approach is illustrated in Fig. 1-1.

It is important to note that not all of the levels in the figure are characteristic of all life. Certain of the lower levels are characteristic of all life, and all levels taken together provide an organizational description of the entire phenomenon of life as we see it on the earth.

1.3.1 The Atomic and Small-Molecule Level

The physical and chemical activities of atoms and small molecules are not restricted to living organisms. Yet, living things are primarily atoms and molecules organized in such a way that their functions become the functions of life. Indeed, a great many of the activities of living things are simply the activities of ions, atoms, and small molecules *in solution*. The first section of this textbook will deal with these events.

1.3.2 The Macromolecules of Life

In recent years scientists have given a great deal of concentrated attention to the study of the large molecules found in protoplasm. Some of these, such as **starch**, **cellulose**, and **pectins**, are not really greatly different from the large molecules, such as crystals, found in the nonliving world. That is, they consist of *repeating* identical building blocks or units. Even here we must recognize, however, that starch, cellulose, and pectins are *not* found in the inorganic world, and they are of an order of complexity considerably higher than that encountered in most crystals. The sugar building blocks of these compounds are themselves fairly complex molecules, particularly since each asymmetric carbon atom may exist in two forms ("right" and "left"), but only one form (stereoisomer) occurs in a given sugar molecule.

Certain of the macromolecules of life, namely, the **proteins** and the **nucleic acids**, have a structural feature that is quite characteristic of life and that is not, so far as we know, encountered in any nonliving system. These molecules are also made of smaller building blocks (the amino acids and the nucleotides), but these building blocks are not all identical, nor are they arranged in a repeating fashion as are the units in a crystal. The order of these units might appear random, yet this order is

ORGANIZATIONAL LEVELS CHART
OF THE PROPERTIES OF LIVING ORGANISMS

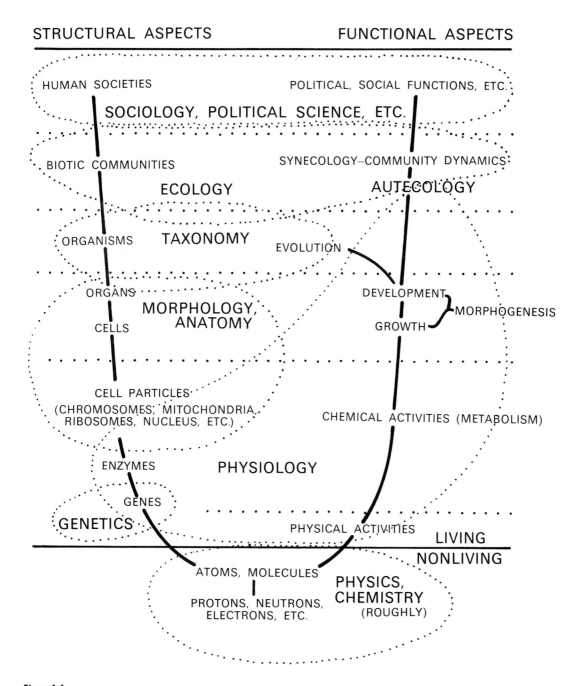

STRUCTURAL ASPECTS   FUNCTIONAL ASPECTS

HUMAN SOCIETIES   POLITICAL, SOCIAL FUNCTIONS, ETC.

SOCIOLOGY, POLITICAL SCIENCE, ETC.

BIOTIC COMMUNITIES   SYNECOLOGY—COMMUNITY DYNAMICS

ECOLOGY   AUTECOLOGY

ORGANISMS   TAXONOMY   EVOLUTION

ORGANS   DEVELOPMENT

MORPHOLOGY,   MORPHOGENESIS

CELLS   ANATOMY   GROWTH

CELL PARTICLES
(CHROMOSOMES, MITOCHONDRIA,
RIBOSOMES, NUCLEUS, ETC.)   CHEMICAL ACTIVITIES (METABOLISM)

ENZYMES   PHYSIOLOGY

GENES

GENETICS   PHYSICAL ACTIVITIES

LIVING

NONLIVING

ATOMS, MOLECULES   PHYSICS,
                        CHEMISTRY
PROTONS, NEUTRONS,   (ROUGHLY)
ELECTRONS, ETC.

Figure 1-1
The organizational levels of natural science and the main branches of science (within dotted lines) that study them.

highly specific, is characteristic of a given molecule, and is preserved from generation to generation as these molecules are duplicated. Written language provides a good analogy. The letters in this sentence are not arranged in any repeating fashion, and their order would appear quite random to anyone not familiar with the concept of written language. Yet this order is not really random at all but is an order containing information. With language, the information is a concept or idea. With protein (the **enzymes**), the information provides the ability to perform some specific catalysis (to control some specific chemical reaction). The information in the nucleic acids is basically a code capable of governing the synthesis of the proteins.

At the level of the protein molecule, structure and function are intimately related. An enzyme is able to govern a chemical reaction because of its particular arrangement of amino acids. A nucleic acid has a structure that allows the molecule to reproduce itself. The structure at the same time carries the information for the synthesis of protein. All of this will be discussed at some length in Chapter 17.

Present studies on the origin of life imply (although they certainly do not prove) that molecules as complex as protein and nucleic acid might come into being by the chance processes of inorganic nature. If this is true, then such molecules could exist on the surface of planets we would otherwise consider quite devoid of life. So the presence of molecules of a certain complexity cannot alone constitute a definition of life. If these molecules, however, are further organized according to the levels discussed below and if they actually are performing their functions of catalysis, information transfer, and reproduction, then their presence and action may indeed come very close to defining life in a way that would eliminate all manifestations of nature we intuitively consider nonliving, while including all those manifestations we consider to be a part of life.

1.3.3 The Cellular Organelles

Within the cellular structure, other organized bodies can be discerned: The nucleic acids are organized to form the **chromosomes**, which in turn, are all found within the **nucleus** with its **nucleolus**. Many of the enzymes are organized into highly active bodies called **mitochondria**. Enzyme synthesis is apparently intimately connected with still smaller bodies called **ribosomes**. And the process of photosynthesis depends upon an organization of certain protein molecules with chlorophyll and other pigments in an association of **grana** and **stroma** inside bodies called **chloroplasts**. Other structures are also recognized within the cell, such as the **endoplasmic reticulum**, **leucoplasts**, and **Golgi apparatus**.

Each of these cellular organelles performs some kind of vital function. As a rule, these functions are metabolic, relating to the chemical processes within the cell. Typically, part of the organization of these subcellular particles involves a surrounding **membrane**, a structure with other important functions (see Chapter 8).

In our definition of life, we must take the viruses into special account. They have much in common with things more obviously living, and consequently many workers feel that viruses should be thought of as a part of life. Yet, it is probable that a comprehensive definition of life should be limited by some of the structures and functions above the organelle level, although the viruses are no more complex than a relatively simple cellular organelle (e.g., a chromosome).

1.3.4 The Cell

The **cell theory**, which states that this unit of organization is fundamental to life, was formulated in the middle of the 19th century. In spite of a few exceptions (e.g., certain slime molds), our present knowledge of biology provides strong support for this fundamental concept. The cell is a complete and sufficient integration of the three levels discussed above. This integration is capable of virtually all of the functions specified for our robot, and organisms consisting of a single cell are both highly efficient and highly prevalent on the earth's surface.

Many of the activities of cells, as well as those of cellular organelles and of molecules within the cell, come within the broad category of functions known as **metabolism** (all of the chemical functions of life). The second section of this textbook is concerned with metabolism.

The viruses do not reach the cellular level of organization. Yet they are completely dependent upon it if they are to function. Usually they metabolize and reproduce within a living cell, using the organization of this cell and the metabolic products of this organization to carry out their own life function—which is hardly more than the function of reproduction. When a virus is cultured in a test tube in the absence of living cells, it must still be provided artificially with the conditions found in cells. As a matter of fact, it would be provided with these conditions by a virologist who himself consists of cells! So even virus "life" is dependent upon the level of organization of the cell, and we will include the cellular level in our definition of life.

1.3.5 Tissues and Organs

Groups of cells, constituting tissues, are organized into organs in the plant: the **root**, the **leaf**, the **stem**, the **flower**, and some other specialized examples. Although single-celled organisms do not really have the ability to differentiate and produce organs, many do become specialized in ways that remind us of organ structure. In this course of study, we are concerned primarily with the higher plants, and they do consist of organs. It is the many functions of these organs, mostly specialized aspects of the functions already listed, that make the study of higher plants (and animals) so interesting.

1.3.6 The Organism

In the organism itself, all of the functions of the lower levels become integrated to produce the functions of the higher plant. Only at this level can we consider the transport of materials over fairly large distances, or the alignment of leaves or stems in reponse to gravity or light. Furthermore, growth and reproduction become far more complex, and therefore interesting, when considered at the level of the entire organism. The steps from the cell (the fertilized egg) to the mature organism are many and complex. The study of how an entire organism can develop from a single cell is the study of **morphogenesis**. The third section of this textbook is devoted to the many and varied aspects of morphogenesis.

1.3.7 Populations

Much of modern biology is concerned with the study of groups of like individuals. Their functions are many, including all of those of each individual organism. **Adaptation** to environment is a function that goes beyond the abilities of a single individual. Through the process of natural selection, the genetic constitution of a population may be gradually changed through time from generation to generation. This is **evolution** in at least one sense of the word.

1.3.8 Communities

On the surface of the earth, populations of different living organisms occur together in organizations that have been called **biotic communities**. This becomes a very high level of organization, quite difficult for the scientist to study. The boundaries of a given biotic community are seldom sharply defined but typically grade imperceptibly into other biotic communities in such a way that it may be better to speak of a **continuum** of changing biotic composition rather than of discrete biotic communities. The dynamics of the community consist of the specific functions of all the individuals, again changing continuously through both time and space and superseding in a broad sense the functions of each individual (as in plant succession).

The study of the structures and functions of populations and biotic communities belongs properly to the field of **ecology**. But the dividing line between physiology and ecology may be as vague as that between communities. Since the functions of groups of organisms are dependent upon the functions of the organisms themselves, which in turn are dependent upon the functions of their organs, cells, organelles, and molecules, we may be able to gain more understanding of population and community function in nature by studying the functions of the individuals. Such an approach would be far too complex for inclusion in a textbook in plant physiology. Yet the topic is an important one, and we will deal with some of its basic concepts in the fourth section of this text.

1.3.9   Human Communities

Because of the capability of the human brain, it is probably quite valid to consider the ecology of human populations as a level of organization higher than those discussed above. Study of these populations is probably one of the most difficult and challenging aspects of human endeavor. In a sense we are all involved in it, because we are all a part of it. Indeed, when we are engaged in any field of modern science we are probably contributing to the study of human ecology.

1.4   DEFINITION OF LIFE

Although future research is bound to bring about some modifications, we might begin to formulate a definition of life:

Life is a peculiar series of functions associated with a peculiar series of organized structures in which certain macromolecules, having building blocks arranged in apparently random but reproducing order, have the ability of reproduction, transfer and utilization of information, and catalysis of metabolic reactions; all of this being organized to a level allowing the functions of growth, metabolism, irritability, and reproduction.

As indicated above, the viruses would not fit this definition because they are organized only to the level of the cellular organelles. To manifest one property of life (reproduction), they must be associated with a cellular organization. If one insists upon stating whether the viruses are to be considered as alive or dead, he might have to be content with the statement that they are by themselves dead but a part of life when surrounded by the proper cellular environment.

Indeed, we begin to realize that all of our definitions are dependent upon *structure functioning within environment*. The protein and nucleic acid molecules synthesized in response to electrical discharges in an atmosphere of methane, ammonium, and water and lying on the surface of a primordial planet would not be considered alive. Life is not just an organization of matter, but it is a proper organization able to function.

1.5   EXOBIOLOGY

At the time that this textbook is being written, a new science of exobiology is being formulated. This science deals with the question of life on planets other than Earth. Since such life has yet to be studied directly, we can only study Earth's life and use the results as the basis for philosophical discussion in preparation for an eventual encounter with extraterrestrial life. Much of this discussion necessarily revolves around the nature of life itself. Would life on Mars, or on Planet X revolving in the α-Centauri system, fit the definition of life as we have stated it above? Would the "proteins" be built of amino acids and would the "nucleic acids" be built of nucleotides?

Although such questions can only await future discovery, present studies are beginning to indicate that their answers may well be positive. It is mostly a matter of confidence. The physicist has gained enough confidence in his statements about the physical interactions of matter that he thoroughly expects them to be valid anywhere in the universe (that is, given a specified set of conditions anywhere in the universe, the same events will occur). The biologist is not yet far enough along in his speculations to make such statements with equal confidence. Yet he is approaching this station. He discovers, for example, that when electrical discharges are caused to occur in artificial mixtures of methane, ammonium and water, amino acids and purines and pyrimidines (particularly the nucleotide precursor adenine) are by far the most predominant products. Based upon these experiments and on our rapidly growing knowledge of life function, we almost have the courage to predict that extra-terrestrial life will, in many fundamental respects, be quite similar to life as we know it here.

1.6 FIELDS OF PLANT SCIENCE

Our analysis of plant function and structure as illustrated in Fig. 1-1 makes it possible to define the various fields of biological science—and also to see the expanding overlap in some of these traditional fields.

Physics is concerned with the various manifestations of matter.[1] This is usually contrasted

with biology, but it should be readily apparent that **biology** is in a sense really a branch of physics, a branch concerned with the manifestations of matter known as life. This is becoming more apparent in our use of the terms biophysics and biochemistry.

The science of **physiology** is concerned with the functions of living things. In its present context, this means the functions of living things from the level of atoms and small molecules to that of the whole organism. At the level of the nucleic acids and the enzymes, structure and function are so intimately related that the physiologist is at least as concerned with the structure of these macromolecules as he is with their function.

The science of **genetics** has, since its inception around the turn of the century, been concerned primarily with the outward manifestations of the genes, now equated with one of the nucleic acids. In recent years, however, geneticists have become more and more concerned with the mechanisms of inheritance and gene action, and in this respect they completely overlap the interests of the physiologist.

Anatomy or **morphology** is traditionally the science of structure. There are still many scientists engaged in trying to describe structure better at the tissue and organ level. The anatomist specializing in the structure of cells and subcellular particles may be called a **cytologist**. But his activities are now becoming more and more involved in the *functions* of the structures he is studying. Furthermore, today's physiologist can hardly study cellular function without becoming deeply involved in the structure. Thus the traditional areas of anatomy and physiology are not only overlapping, but they are becoming integrated into a single approach at the cellular level.

Taxonomy is the classification of the different kinds of organisms. In this endeavor, it, like anatomy, is concerned primarily with structure. The modern taxonomist, however, finds himself

---

[1] There may really be only one science: physics. It is concerned with the manifestations of matter, and **chemistry** is concerned with those manifestations involving the exchange or sharing of electrons, that is, chemical reactions.

increasingly fascinated by the problem of relationships between the different organisms he studies. This takes him deeply into the field of function concerned with adaptation and change through time and space. In some cases, he even uses modern biochemical techniques to better his understanding of taxonomic relationships.

Ecology is the study of organisms in relation to environment and to each other. **Autecology** is the study of individual organisms in relation to their environment, and **synecology** is the study of the relationships of groups of organisms to their environment and to each other. There is a structural side to ecology as the ecologist attempts to improve his descriptions of the structure of biotic communities. He is, however, continually interested in the functional aspects of these communities, such as plant succession. As he pursues the science of plant autecology, he is working largely in the field of physiology, since this is basically the problem of individual plant function in relation to environment. On the other hand, the work of the physiologist may contribute a great deal to the understanding of the autecologist.

Sociology, **political science**, etc., are infant sciences dedicated to the study of human societies from both a structural and a functional aspect. Although this level seems highly removed from plant physiology, it is so broad and inclusive that little if anything is really omitted. Man's relationship to his environment, including both plants and animals, is an extremely important part of man's sociological function.

The sciences indicated in Fig. 1-1 are essentially the basic sciences of biology. Usually five are listed: physiology, genetics, anatomy, taxonomy, and ecology. We have mentioned a number of other divisions, however. The sciences of **botany** and **zoology** do not show up on the chart, since they would require another dimension. One might visualize the chart as being split in the plane of the paper from the top

toward the bottom (although the split could not be complete at the bottom) with plants on one side of the split and animals on the other. At the level of structure and function studied by physiologists, plants and animals are, indeed, very much alike. All is based on physics and chemistry. Actually, most of the efforts of physiologists, both plant and animal, during the past century, have been directed toward understanding some general principles of function that apply to virtually all species of plants and animals. As we shall see later on, the chemical reactions of respiration are essentially the same in all living things, both plant and animal.

We are now, after this century of unification in biology, beginning to have time and tools to consider the diversity. Surely the physiology of one plant will differ from the physiology of another, and it may be the assignment of coming generations of plant physiologists to describe and understand this situation. Most of the discussion in this text will be based upon the assumption that the physiology of all plants is essentially the same. This is only true about a first approximation, but that it is true about the first approximation is in itself a very impressive discovery of modern biology. We may be equally impressed as we gradually gain deeper insights into the diversity of living things as well as their uniformity.

Plant physiology is, then, a basic science. As such, it is seldom extremely rewarding to one who would use it only as a tool. Unfortunately, its direct application to applied problems such as those of agriculture is still somewhat limited. We lack sufficient information about the specific functions of specific species of plants. Yet the study of life, as manifested in plants, is itself a very rewarding undertaking, and furthermore, it provides an essential frame of reference for the work of the applied scientist.

Many applied plant sciences are contributing to man's well-being and comfort. Indeed, we might differentiate between basic and applied sciences on the grounds that basic sciences pursue knowledge for its own sake, while applied sciences attempt to use this knowledge in providing a better life for man. This might hold in theory, but in practice such differentiation is seldom possible. The basic scientist would certainly not pass up a chance to apply his findings for the benefit of himself or of civilization, and the applied scientist often finds himself engaged in the pure pursuit of knowledge, always with the hope that he will some day be able to find application for it, but often when such application is not at all apparent.

Forestry, agriculture, engineering, horticulture, and **agronomy** are examples of sciences that are mostly applied and that are often concerned with plants. **Pathology** studies the abnormal features of life structure and function, and traditionally its efforts have been directed toward application of these findings to the use of man, to the control of diseases in man or agriculture. But again we are beginning to catch up on some of this, so that pathologists have a little more time to think about the basic nature of things and consider the plant and its pathogen in an ecological sense, rather than as something "abnormal." In doing so, their activities are becoming more and more related to those of other biologists in both basic and applied fields.

The classical boundaries of the sciences are in the process of collapse. In a sense, this is all rather paradoxical, providing a tremendous challenge to the modern student. Really to contribute to our fund of knowledge, he must specialize more and more, yet at the same time he must become more and more aware of the activities of his colleagues in the other sciences. Obviously, the only way that he can become both more specialized and at the same time broader in his outlook is by a continuing effort on his own part and by an intensive effort on the part of his teachers. They must present things in a broader context, relating them at every opportunity to all science, while at the same time going into deeper and more intricate detail within his field of specialization.

Water, Solutions, and Surfaces
in the Plant

2

The Water Milieu

2.1 THE IMPORTANCE OF WATER TO LIFE

Biological function is completely dependent upon water, and the properties of life are often directly a result of the properties of water. It is the most abundant molecule in living organisms. It is possible, then, to learn a great deal about life by learning about water, and in our subsequent discussions we shall have occasion to refer to the unique physical and chemical properties of water. Consider the following ways in which water takes part in the functions of living organisms.

2.1.1 The Reactions of Protoplasm

The very essence of life is found in the biochemical, enzymatically controlled reactions of protoplasm. The reactive components in these metabolic pathways are in water solution, that is, surrounded by water molecules. This greatly facilitates chemical reactions. In addition to this, water molecules themselves interact directly with these reactive components of metabolism, often by entering into chemical reactions such as photosynthesis or fat breakdown.

2.1.2 The Structure of Living Things

2.1.2A Protoplasmic structure The macro-molecules of protoplasm, including the protein enzymes that catalyze the metabolic reactions of life, the nucleic acids that contain the "information of life," and others, such as starch and pectins, form a unique structure by being associated with water molecules. The colloidal state, one feature of this structure, to be discussed in Chapter 4, provides the protoplasmic framework upon which life depends.

2.1.2B A hydraulic system Water is essentially incompressible at the pressures encountered in living tissues. Thus it provides a very literal supporting structure to virtually all plant parts not supported by relatively large quantities of wood. Herbaceous stems, young roots, leaves, flower parts, fruits, and buds all owe their form to the turgidity produced by water under pressure within their cells. This becomes very evident whenever any of these tissues wilt or dry out (Fig. 2-1). Indeed, the animal body also owes much of its normal form to water pressure, as witness the dry and shriveled mummies exhibited in museums.

Not only do hydraulic pressures within the plant tissue account for plant form, but changes in hydraulic pressure result in growth and movement of plant parts. In some instances movement is a result of growth. In other instances, no growth may be involved but only a change of hydraulic pressure within the tissues, as in the opening and closing of certain flower

Figure 2-1
Normal (left) and wilted (right) bean plants. The normal appearance of a plant is dependent upon sufficient water in the cells to provide turgidity. (Photograph by F. B. Salisbury.)

parts or the rolling of certain leaves due to changes in water pressure within the water-filled **bulliform** (bubble-shaped) **cells**. In a sense, the most important opening and closing phenomenon in the plant is that of the guard cells in the leaf and stem epidermis. This stomatal movement is also a response to changes in pressure within these guard cells (see Chapter 6).

2.1.2C A transport system Movement of many substances within the plant occurs as these substances diffuse through membranes and cell walls saturated with water, or as materials are carried along in a bulk flow of sap through phloem and xylem elements and through other tissues.

2.1.3 Heat Stabilization and Transfer

The extremely high specific heat and heats of fusion and vaporization of water tend to stabilize plant (or animal) temperature. The high specific heat first provides a considerable buffering capacity by absorption of fairly large quantities of heat with only relatively small changes in temperature. Furthermore, when the plant is absorbing heat from the environment in the form of radiant energy, some of this heat may be returned to the environment by evaporation of water from the plant's surfaces.

2.2 MOLECULAR STRUCTURE OF WATER—THE HYDROGEN BOND

Most of the unique properties of water can be ascribed to the interesting fact that the lines connecting the centers of the two hydrogen atoms with that of the oxygen atom do not form an angle of 180°. The angle is instead about 105°[1]—closer to a right angle than to a straight

---

[1] This angle is exact only in the crystal structure of ice. In liquid water the angle is more flexible but averages about 105°.

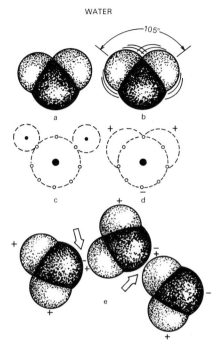

WATER

105°

a   b

c   d

e

Figure 2-2

Water molecules, indicating (a and b) the angle between the two hydrogen atoms (lighter) attached to the oxygen atom (darker). As shown, the angle is not absolutely stable (b) but represents an average sharing of electrons and distribution of charge (c and d). Attraction of the negative side of one water molecule to the positive side of another produces the hydrogen bond (e). Arrows indicate hydrogen bonds.

line (Fig. 2-2). The two electrons that fill the first shell of the hydrogen atom (one of the hydrogen's own and the other borrowed from the oxygen) are not equally distributed around the hydrogen nucleus but tend to be closer to the oxygen nucleus. Thus the hydrogen atoms approximate naked protons on the surface of the oxygen atom. While the net charge for the molecule as a whole is, of course, neutral, the presence of the protons distributed at their 105° angle on the surface of the oxygen atoms provides a slight positive charge on one side of the molecule. This must be balanced by a negative charge on the other side of the molecule.

Thus the molecule is said to be **polar**.[2] The result of this unequal distribution of charge on the water molecule is that the positive side of one molecule can be attracted to the negative side of another (Fig. 2-2), approaching quite closely, since the hydrogen nucleus is essentially a naked proton. The bond formed between the two molecules is somewhat stronger than the van der Waals forces or bonds that occur between the molecules of liquids or solids (Table 2-1). Such bonds found in water are called **hydrogen bonds**.

Actually, in any body of liquid water all of the molecules are hydrogen-bonded to each other. In a rather specialized sense, then, all of the world's connected oceans form a single giant molecule.

2.3 SOME PROPERTIES OF WATER IMPORTANT TO LIFE

2.3.1 Liquid at Room Temperature

As a general rule, the higher the molecular weight of an element or a compound, the greater the likelihood that this material will be a liquid or a solid at a given temperature, say room temperature. The lower the molecular weight, the greater the likelihood of its being a liquid or a gas. The larger the molecule, the more energy (heat) is required to cause it to break its binding forces with surrounding molecules and become a liquid or a gas. For example, the low-molecular-weight hydrocarbons are gases or liquids, while the higher ones are liquids or solids (see Fig. 2-3). But compare water, having a molecular weight of 18, with ammonia (mol. wt. = 17) or methane (mol.

[2] Molecules with no surface distribution of charge are said to be **nonpolar**. Nonionic nonpolar molecules may bear little attraction for water and are said to be **hydrophobic** (water "fearing") as contrasted to molecules (or surfaces) that are attracted to water and are said to be **hydrophilic** (water "loving").

TABLE 2-1

BOND ENERGIES (kcal/mole)[a]

Ionic bonds: (Crystal energies)		Covalent bonds (continued):	
LiF	240	N—H	93
NaF	213	C—O	84
NaCl	183	C—C	83
NaBr	174	S—H	81
KCl	165	C—Cl	78
NaI	163	C—N	70
CsI	139	C—S	62
Covalent bonds:		O—O	33
$C\equiv C$	198	**Hydrogen bonds:[b]**	
C=O	173		2 to 10
C=C	145		
O—H	110	**Van der Waal's attractive forces:[c]**	
H—Cl	103		about 1.0
C—H	99		

[a] From L. Pauling, *The Nature of the Chemical Bond,* 3rd ed., 1960, Cornell Univ. Press, Ithaca, New York, p. 85, F. Daniels and R. Alberty, *Physical Chemistry,* John Wiley & Sons, Inc., New York, 1955, p. 122, and *Handbook of Chemistry and Physics,* 45th Edition 1964–5, Chemical Rubber Co., Cleveland, Ohio.

[b] Strengths of hydrogen bonds usually lie in the range 2 to 10 kcal/mole, depending on the electronegativity of the atoms with which H is associated. With the fluorine atom (which is the most electronegative atom known), the strongest H bonds are formed. Oxygen, nitrogen, chlorine, and sulfur are believed to form hydrogen bonds decreasingly stable in the order given.

[c] These weak forces arise in neutral molecules ordinarily considered to be nonpolar. They result from the fact that electrons are continuously in motion, and the centers of negative charges thus do not continuously correspond exactly with the centers of positive charges in the molecules. Such a molecule approaching another very closely can induce a slight polarization in it; the ends of unlike charge then attract each other. For normal alkanes the forces amount to about 1.0 kcal/mole per carbon atom in the molecule. These forces account for the increases in boiling points among molecules in a given homologous series.

wt. = 16), or even carbon dioxide (mol. wt. = 44). Only water is a liquid at room temperature, while the others are gases and must be cooled to very low temperatures before they become liquids or solids. The explanation is the hydrogen bond, which provides a disproportionately high attractive force between water molecules.

It is interesting to note that other liquids with low molecular weights also have hydrogen bonding. Good examples are the lower alcohols (methyl = CH_3OH) or the lower organic acids (formic = CHOOH, or acetic = CH_3COOH). The presence of the oxygen atom makes hydrogen bonding possible in these compounds.

2.3.2   Latent Heat of Vaporization

Some 539 calories are required to convert one gram of water to one gram of water vapor at

100°C. This unusually high **heat of vaporization** can again be ascribed to the tenacity of the hydrogen bond, and it is of considerable importance in the cooling of plants and other organisms by transpiration, as mentioned above.

2.3.3   Heat of Fusion and Expansion upon Freezing

To melt one gram of ice at 0°C, 80 calories must be supplied. This is also a high **heat of fusion**, due again to the hydrogen bonds, although ice has fewer per molecule. Each molecule of water in ice is surrounded by *four* others, forming a tetrahedral structure (each oxygen atom attracts two extra hydrogen atoms). The tetrahedrons are arranged in such a manner that the ice crystal is basically hexagonal (as demonstrated in the pattern of snowflakes).

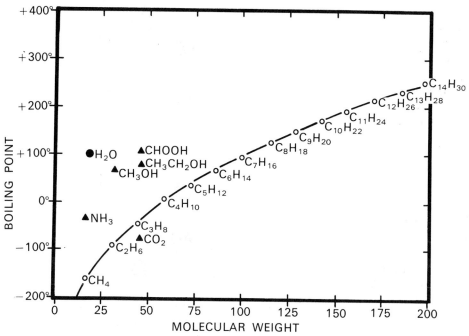

Figure 2-3

Boiling points as a function of molecular weight for several hydrocarbons (connected points), and several other compounds (triangles). Water and some other compounds, because of hydrogen bonding, lie at some distance from the curve.

As is the usual situation during conversion from the solid to the liquid state, molecules of water during melting move farther apart (from an average distance of 2.72 Å to 2.90 Å). Yet water is extremely unusual, in that the total volume decreases at melting. This is because packing of the molecules in the liquid is more efficient than it is in the solid. Each molecule in the liquid is surrounded by *five* or more others (each oxygen attracts three or more extra hydrogens).

The expansion of water as it turns to ice is quite significant. As a result, ice has a lower density than water. This keeps ice floating on top of lakes in the winter rather than going to the bottom, and the expansion may also result in damage to plant or animal tissue during ice crystal formation. Because water expands upon freezing, increased pressure will make ice melt at a *lower* temperature (pressure lowers the melting point). With other substances, increased pressure usually results in a raised melting point.

The high heat of fusion also makes freezing occur less readily than would be the case with other liquids under comparable conditions. Sometimes crops may be sprayed with water to keep them from freezing.

2.3.4 Specific Heat

To increase the temperature of one gram of water one degree centigrade, about one calorie must be supplied (the exact amount is slightly dependent upon temperature). This specific heat of one calorie per gram is higher than that measured for any other substance except liquid ammonia. It comes about because the arrangement of molecules in liquid water is such that the hydrogen and oxygen atoms are allowed to vibrate very freely, almost as if they were free ions. Thus, they can absorb large quantities of energy without much temperature increase (see discussions of energy in Chapter 3). A result is a tendency toward more stable temperatures in living organisms and more stable metabolic rates.

2.3.5   Viscosity

Since hydrogen bonds must be broken for water to flow, one might expect a viscosity considerably higher than that encountered. But in liquid water each hydrogen bond is shared on the average by two other molecules, and thus the bonds are somewhat weakened and fairly easily broken. In ice there are fewer bonds per oxygen; hence they are stronger.

2.3.6   Adhesive Forces of Water

Because of its polar nature, water is attracted to many other substances; that is, it wets them. The cellulose, starch, and protein of living tissues constitute excellent examples. This **adhesion** or attraction between unlike molecules (water and other molecules) is very important to water movement in the plant (see Chapters 6 and 7).

2.3.7   Cohesive Forces of Water

Primarily because of the hydrogen bond, water molecules are strongly attracted to each other (they have high **cohesion**—attraction between like substances). Thus water has an unusually high tensile strength. In a thin, confined column of water such as that in the xylem elements of a plant stem, this tensile strength may reach very high values. By this mechanism, water is lifted to the tops of tall trees. We shall discuss this in Chapter 7.

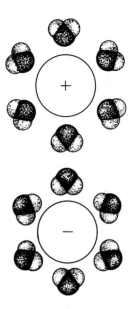

Figure 2-4

A schematic representation of the arrangement of water molecules around positive or negative ions in solution.

2.3.8   Water as a Solvent

Water will dissolve more substances than any other common liquid. This is partially because it has a very high dielectric constant, one of the highest known. (The **dielectric constant** is a measure of the capacity to neutralize the attraction between electrical charges.) Because of this property, water is an especially powerful solvent for electrolytes. The positive side of the water molecule is attracted to the negative ion and the negative side to the positive ion. Water molecules thus form a "cage" around the ions so that they are unable to unite with each other (Fig. 2-4).

If water contains dissolved electrolytes, then these will carry a charge, and water becomes a good conductor of electricity. If water is absolutely pure, however (and pure water is extremely difficult to obtain), then it is a very poor conductor. Hydrogen bonding makes it too rigid to carry a charge readily.

In recent years it has been discovered that water is a better solvent for some nonelectrolytes than might have been foreseen. Careful theoretical studies of the structure of liquid water provide a probable explanation. Water molecules may be arranged to form two basic kinds of cubic lattices (one of these has 46 molecules and the other has 136). These cubic "units of water" contain holes of various sizes and shapes. There may be, for example, from 12 to 16 "walls" or "faces" making up these holes. Various completely nonionic or non-polar substances have the right spatial dimensions to fit into these holes, explaining how certain hydrophobic molecules may still dissolve in water—not because they are attracted to water molecules but precisely because they are not. Such molecules could be an important part of protoplasm.

Although water is the best solvent known, it is still rather inert and innocuous, entering into only a relatively few chemical reactions. This allows it to function even better as the milieu for protoplasmic activities.

2.3.9   Ionization of Water

Some of the molecules in water separate into hydrogen and hydroxyl ions. The tendency for these ions to recombine is a function of the chances for collisions between the ions; that is, recombination depends upon the relative numbers of ions present in the solution. This **mass law relationship** may be expressed mathematically by saying that the product of the molar concentrations equals a constant: $[H^+] \cdot [OH^-] = K$. Near to room temperature the value of K is 10^{-14}. In pure water, then: $[H^+] = 10^{-7} M$ and $[OH^-] = 10^{-7} M$. Water is seldom pure enough to allow such an exact distribution between hydrogen and hydroxyl ions. Presence of dissolved carbon dioxide, the usual case, may raise the hydrogen ion concentration as high as $10^{-4} M$. The hydroxyl ion concentration is then determined at $10^{-10} M$,

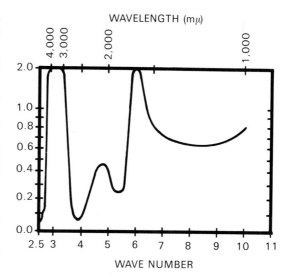

Figure 2-5

The absorption spectrum of water in the infrared part of the spectrum.

since the product of these two concentrations must be equal to 10^{-14}

The hydrogen ion concentration is indicated by the pH scale, on which $pH = -\log [H^+]$. For example, when $[H^+] = 10^{-4} M$, then $pH = 4$. Neutrality is expressed by $pH = 7$. We should remind ourselves that the pH units are multiples of 10 on a logarithmic scale and should therefore not be added together or averaged. Only a tenth as many H^+ ions need to be added to change the pH from 7 to 6 as from 6 to 5.

2.3.10   Light Absorption by Water

Water is essentially transparent to visible light, although the slight absorption of red makes large bodies of it appear bluish-green. The hydrogen bond absorbs very efficiently at infrared wavelengths of about 3 microns (Fig. 2-5). The strong absorption at this wavelength (liquid water is densely "black") is a good direct evidence for the presence of the hydrogen bond, known to absorb at 3 microns. Long-wavelength thermal radiation (10 to 30 microns) is also strongly absorbed by water molecules (and by most other substances). This is important in the absorption of radiant heat energy by water vapor in the atmosphere or by water in the plant itself.

2.4 WATER AND LIFE

It should be apparent that water is uniquely well suited to the functions of living things. Scientists are currently speculating about the possibilities of life on other planets in the universe. Frequently the question arises as to whether life might be based upon some other solvent, liquid ammonia, for example. Considering the many special properties of water and the widespread occurrence of hydrogen and oxygen in the universe, it is probably safe to predict that life as a general rule depends upon the presence of water.

3

Energy Relations and Diffusion

A great deal of modern science is based upon **kinetic theory**, the concept that all particles of atomic or molecular size are in constant motion at all temperatures above absolute zero. Much of physics and chemistry is based upon this picture of matter, and nearly everything that we presently know about the functions of plants can be better understood with its help. The assumption that gas molecules are constantly moving about in straight lines until they strike the wall of the container or another gas molecule allows physical chemists to explain much about diffusion, chemical reactions, and pressures of gases. Although considerably less is known about solids and liquids (especially liquids containing dissolved solutes), we have been able to explain many of their properties by extrapolation from our knowledge about gases. The knowledge from quantum mechanics that energy occurs in discrete units is also very valuable, and the concepts of thermodynamics are especially useful to us.

Before discussing the physiology of plants, a brief review of these principles is in order. The discussion leads directly into an examination of the important aspects of water in the plant and thus into several topics of the following chapters.

3.1 ENERGY LEVELS IN MOLECULES

A practical consequence of the fact that energy exists in discrete, indivisible packets is that a given atom, ion, or molecule may absorb or give up energy only in a restricted number of discrete quantities. It is not possible for a molecule to undergo gradual and continuous changes in energy from one level to another, but it instead changes levels by definite jumps.

Gas molecules possess straight-line movements, which account for their **translational kinetic energy**.[1] Those having two or more atoms possess, in addition to energies of translation, components of **rotation** and **vibration** (movement of atoms in the molecule with respect to one another). In liquids the motion is primarily translational and vibrational, while in solids the only type of motion possible is vibration of the molecules about their equilibrium positions. Increasing the temperature may raise the energy of the atoms through effects upon all three of these components.

---

[1] The quantity of translational kinetic energy (e) in ergs is given by the formula $e = 1/2\, mu^2$, where m is the mass in grams, and u is the root-mean-square velocity in cm/sec. Note that, for molecules with a given energy, small molecules will have a higher velocity than large ones.

Another part of the energy of a molecule arises from the status of particles making up the nucleus. Changes in **nuclear energy** are extremely large (e.g., as in a thermonuclear bomb) and are not encountered in physical and chemical reactions occurring in the plant.

A further important contribution to the energy of a molecule is the movement of electrons in specified orbitals about the nucleus (**electronic energy**). At the lowest energy level (the **ground state**), these electrons are as close to the positively charged nucleus as is possible. Two electrons may be present in any given orbital, if they have opposite spins. Because the electrons appear to move with a wave motion and a specific velocity and because the waves must synchronize with each other in each orbit (wavelength must be an integral factor of orbital perimeter), the electrons can occur only in certain orbits—only at certain distances from the nucleus. Upon absorption of a definite amount of energy, an electron may jump to a higher orbital. Its spin may now be either the same as or opposite to that of the electron with which it was paired. Shifting of an electron to a higher energy level is accompanied by vibrational and rotational changes in the molecule. **Electron excitation** cannot be accomplished simply by increasing the temperature, at least over temperature ranges in which life exists. Visible light does possess sufficient energy to cause such changes, and this fact is important in photosynthesis, phototropism, phototaxis, and various light-stimulated alterations in plant development discussed in later chapters. In addition, of course, all chemical reactions involve changes in electronic energy levels.

3.1.1 Distribution of Energy among Molecules in a Homogeneous System as Affected by Temperature

In a system of molecules of a single kind, for example those of oxygen, we can calculate an average translational velocity that depends upon the temperature.[2] The actual velocity of a given molecule within the group will probably be larger or smaller than the average, depending upon its immediately previous history. It may have gained or lost energy by colliding with other molecules or with the container wall, depending upon the mechanics of the collision.

The distribution of velocities among a statistically large population can be calculated from the Maxwell–Boltzmann distribution equation given in physical chemistry texts. Application of this equation gives curves like those shown in Fig. 3-1. These curves indicate that there are only a few molecules with very low or very high velocity, while the majority have energies close to the mean. Note that increasing the temperature from 300°K to 310°K (27°C to 37°C) raises the average energy only a small amount, but the proportionate number of molecules with high velocities increases considerably.

Similar distribution curves probably apply for the energies of molecules in water solutions, although they are less easy to calculate. This could account for the sizable increases in rates of physiological reactions following a 10°C increase in temperature. The student has probably learned that chemical rates may approximately double or triple with a 10°C temperature rise. It is believed that before molecules can undergo such reactions, they must reach a certain critical activation energy, which varies for each reaction. If we assign this arbitrary critical energy at the point indicated in Fig. 3-1, then by measuring the area to the right of this point under both curves, we see that approximately twice as many molecules at the higher

---

[2] The root-mean-square velocity of perfect gases (a value close to but not identical with the average velocity) in cm/sec is equal to $\sqrt{3RT/M}$, where R is the gas constant (8.34×10^7 ergs/mole deg), T is the absolute temperature, and M is the molecular weight (grams/mole).

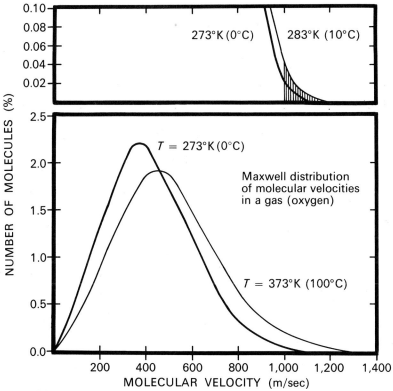

Figure 3-1

The Maxwell–Boltzmann distribution of molecular velocities in a gas at two temperatures 100°C apart. The curves at the top show the high-velocity portion for a gas at two temperatures 10°C apart. The area indicated by the vertical lines can be seen to approximately double in going from the lower to the higher temperature.

temperature have energies equal to or greater than the critical needed. We assume that these excited molecules are the ones most apt to melt, evaporate, or react chemically, while those having lower energies will be the ones to freeze or to condense from vapor to the liquid state.

The influence of temperature upon physiological processes is often expressed by a value called the Q_{10}. This is a quotient obtained by dividing the rate of a reaction measured at one temperature by the rate measured at a temperature 10° (centigrade or Kelvin scale) lower. If it is impossible to measure the rates at temperatures exactly 10° apart, the following equation is used to calculate the value from rates measured at any two temperatures:

$$Q_{10} = \left(\frac{k_2}{k_1}\right)^{\frac{10}{T_2 - T_1}} \quad \text{or}$$

$$\log Q_{10} = \left(\frac{10}{T_2 - T_1}\right) \log \frac{k_2}{k_1} \quad (1)$$

where:

T_1 = lower temperature
T_2 = higher temperature
k_1 = rate at lower temperature
k_2 = rate at higher temperature

Reactions having high activation energies have greater Q_{10} values than those with smaller activation energies. Most chemical reactions have Q_{10}'s between 2 and 3, while such physical processes as diffusion often have Q_{10}'s only slightly greater than 1.0. Such processes may be related to absolute temperature (e.g., gas diffusion is proportional to $\sqrt{T}$), and a 10° change at room temperature (approximately 300°K) is small compared to the entire range. Other effects, however, may complicate the picture (e.g., effects on viscosity of a liquid).

Under many conditions, photochemical processes also have Q_{10} values approximately equal to 1.0. These processes depend upon energy supplied only by light, and moderate temperature increases cannot cause the electronic displacements necessary for the reaction to occur. By determining the Q_{10} for a complex physiological process, such as photosynthesis or nutrient uptake into plant roots, one can sometimes obtain an indication of whether the rate-limiting step is a physical or a chemical reaction.

3.1.2 Excitation of Molecules by Radiant Energy

Radiation has two characteristic properties. *First*, it appears to travel as a stream of tiny particles called **photons**. The energy present in an individual photon is referred to as a **quantum** (plural, **quanta**). *Second*, light also appears to be propagated through space as a wave. It travels in a vacuum or in air at a velocity of 3.0×10^{10} cm/sec, and the number of wave crests (peaks in energy) passing a given point in a given interval of time is called the **frequency** (v), expressed as cycles/sec. If the **velocity** (c) is divided by the frequency, the **wavelength** (λ, often measured[3] in nanometers, nm, or milli-

---

[3] One micron is equal to 10^{-6} meter, and thus one mμ is equal to 10^{-9} meter, a value called a nanometer (abbreviated nm). Nanometers are increasingly being used in the scientific literature to indicate wavelengths. In some applications, Ångstrom units (Å) are used as a measure of the wavelength of radiation, where one Å is equal to 0.1 mμ or nm. Since mμ has long been used but nm now seems preferable, the student should be familiar with both.

microns, mμ) or distance between wave crests, is obtained:

$$\lambda = \frac{c}{v} \quad \text{or} \quad v = \frac{c}{\lambda} \qquad (2)$$

The energy (E) present in each photon is directly proportional to its frequency, according to Planck's equation:

$$E = hv \qquad (3)$$

where h is **Planck's constant** (1.58×10^{-34} cal sec or 6.624×10^{-27} erg sec). Because of this formula, it is customary in some applications to refer to a quantum or a photon of light simply as hv. Since frequency and wavelength are inversely related ($v = c/\lambda$), energy in a photon is inversely proportional to the wavelength:

$$E = \frac{hc}{\lambda} \qquad (4)$$

When using this equation with c in units of cm/sec, it is also necessary to convert λ into cm units. Frequently **wave number** ($\bar{v}$) is used instead of frequency. This is the reciprocal of the wavelength in centimeters. Multiplied by the velocity of light, it is equal to the frequency:

$$v = c\bar{v} \qquad (5)$$

Hence the energy equation may be written:

$$E = hc\bar{v} \qquad (6)$$

We are generally able to measure only those energy changes that involve many excited molecules, and so we often wish to apply the above equations [(3), (4), or (6)] to an entire mole of a substance (Avogadro's number, 6.02×10^{23}, of molecules, atoms, or ions). If an entire mole of any substance is excited by radiation (one photon for each molecule), Avogadro's number of photons will be required. This number of photons is defined as an **einstein** of radiation (Example 3-1).

The wavelength spectrum of electromagnetic radiation is very broad, extending from the high energy **gamma rays** of $\lambda = 0.0001$ nm up through the **radio waves**, which may have wavelengths of

Example 3-1

Calculate the amount of energy in an einstein of red light having a frequency of $4.545 \times 10^{14} \, sec^{-1}$ ($\lambda = 660 \, nm$, $\bar{v} = 15{,}150 \, cm^{-1}$) and determine how much less energetic this radiation is than blue light of $v = 6.67 \times 10^{14} \, sec^{-1}$ ($\lambda = 450 \, nm$, $\bar{v} = 22{,}222 \, cm^{-1}$). Using equation (3):

$$E = (1.58 \times 10^{-34} \, cal \, sec/photon)(4.545 \times 10^{14} \, sec^{-1})(6.02 \times 10^{23} \, photons/einstein)$$
$$= 43{,}200 \; calories/einstein.$$

Or, using equation (4):
$$E = \frac{(1.58 \times 10^{-34} \, cal \, sec/photon)(3.0 \times 10^{10} \, cm/sec)(6.02 \times 10^{23} \, photons/einstein)}{(660 \times 10^{-7} \, cm)}$$
$$= 43{,}200 \; calories/einstein.$$

Since blue light has a frequency $6.67/4.545$ times that of red, its energy will be 1.466 times that of the red, or 63,400 calories/einstein.

several kilometers. Of this tremendous spectrum (16 orders of magnitude), the wavelengths detectable by the human eye as light consist of a very narrow zone (a fraction of one order of magnitude). Visible light varies in wavelength from about 390 to 760 nm. This region covers the wavelengths effective in photosynthesis in higher plants and algae, although in photosynthetic bacteria, wavelengths as long as 900 nm can cause photosynthesis. Figure 3-2 shows the relation of wavelengths of visible light to other electromagnetic radiation and gives the approximate wavelength region corresponding to each color in the visible spectrum.

Biologists have developed the habit of speaking of light in terms of wavelength, but for several reasons frequency (or wave number) should be used more often. For one thing, the energy of a photon is *directly* proportional to frequency, while its relationship to wavelength is inverse. Absorption bands tend to have the same widths at various parts of a frequency scale but are much narrower at shorter wavelengths on a wavelength scale. Areas under these absorption curves are meaningful only on a frequency scale. The biologist should make an effort to become familiar with both wavelength and frequency. Study of the comparative curves

in Fig. 3-3 should make some of the relationships clear. The wave number is presently used extensively by those who identify compounds by their characteristic absorption of infrared radiation.

The wavelengths of sunrays that actually strike the earth's surface cover a range of approximately 310 to 2,300 nm. Wavelengths as short as 225 nm (ultraviolet) are also radiated by the sun, but these highly energetic photons, which are harmful to many living things (Chapter 23), are screened out by a layer of ozone in the upper atmosphere. Rays longer than 2,500 nm (2.5 microns) emitted by the sun are largely removed by water vapor and carbon dioxide in the atmosphere. About half of the sun's energy that penetrates to the earth's surface is in the infrared region, not visible to the eye.

For radiation to cause a response, the affected molecule must absorb the photon. Absorption of the sun's infrared wavelengths causes changes only in the vibrational and rotational energy levels in molecules. The shorter (visible and ultraviolet) rays, however, possess sufficient energy to cause electron excitations as well as vibrational and rotational changes.

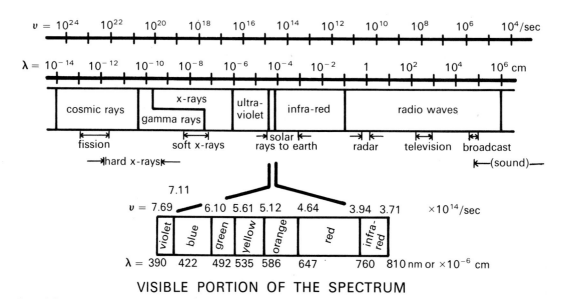

VISIBLE PORTION OF THE SPECTRUM

Figure 3-2

The electromagnetic spectrum, using both wave number (v) and wavelength (λ) in centimeters. Various portions of the spectrum are shown, and the visible portion is expanded to indicate the region that appears to the human eye to have various colors.

Molecules absorbing visible light are colored or black (**pigments**). The electrons that become excited are usually particularly mobile electrons associated with unsaturated double bonds. Chlorophyll, for example, has a high degree of unsaturation and efficiently absorbs light, especially blue and red. The blue light possesses more energy per photon than does the red, and so it raises the electron to a higher energy level.

The **excitation energy** induced in a molecule or an atom by a photon may be lost in any of three ways. *First*, it may be immediately lost as heat (translational, vibrational, or rotational energy). *Second*, it may be partially lost as heat, with the remainder emitted as visible light of a wavelength longer than that absorbed. This is called **fluorescence**. When fluorescence occurs, it usually does so very rapidly, generally within 10^{-9} to 10^{-7} sec after absorption of the original radiation. *Third*, the energy may be used to cause a chemical reaction. Photosynthesis occurs as a

result of this third process. Fluorescence of chlorophyll can also readily be observed as the red light emitted when a concentrated solution of the pigment is illuminated with white or ultraviolet light. Fluorescence of the chlorophyll in a leaf is not as readily seen, because most of the excitation energy is instead used to cause photosynthesis.

3.2 THERMODYNAMICS AND PLANT PHYSIOLOGY

In the second half of the 19th century, certain quantitative measurements of changes in heat and other forms of energy (especially in steam engines) led to the formation of a comprehensive theory known as the **science of thermodynamics**. This science describes the laws governing energy changes occurring in physical and chemical processes, including, of course, those occurring in living cells. An acquaintance with the thermo-

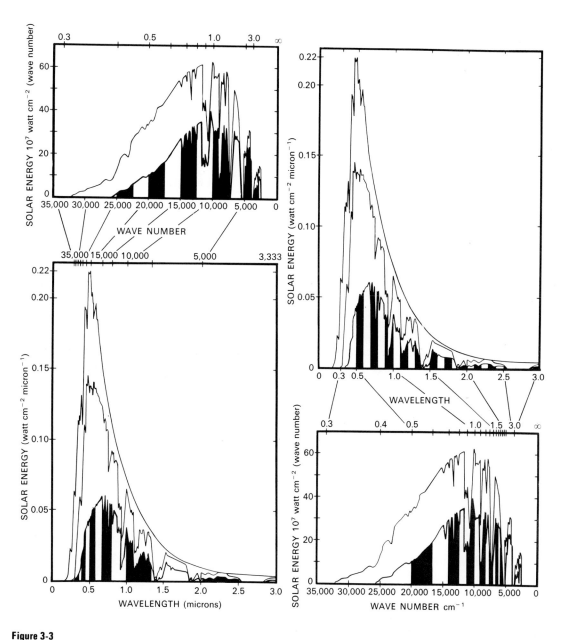

Figure 3-3

A comparison between the wavelength and the wave number systems of plotting the spectrum. To help the student to intuitively understand the difference between these two methods, sections under the curve have been darkened for equal intervals of wave number in the two graphs on the left. Such equal intervals on a wave number scale become increasingly wider with increasing wavelength on a wavelength scale. When equal intervals of wavelength are indicated, as in the two graphs on the right, the intervals appear to expand with increasing wave number on the wave number scale.

dynamic principles and some of their consequences is necessary for adequate understanding
of water movement throughout the plant,
nutrient uptake by roots, and the many biochemical reactions that keep the plant alive and
allow it to grow. A more detailed discussion
than the one below is presented in physical
chemistry courses.

3.2.1 Thermodynamic Laws

The **first law of thermodynamics** states that
*energy can be converted from one form to another,
but it cannot be created or destroyed.* This law
further states that the energy of work can be
completely converted into heat, but it says
nothing about the amount of work that can be
obtained from a given quantity of heat. The
second law of thermodynamics states that *heat
cannot be completely converted into work without
leaving a change on some part of the system.* By
proper application of the second law, one can
often predict whether a process can occur
spontaneously, that is, whether it can occur
without the addition of energy from an external
source. Examples of spontaneous processes
include the transfer of heat from a hot to a cold
body, the uncoiling of a watch spring, the flow of
water downhill, the dissolving of sugar in water,
and the expansion of a gas in a vacuum. None
of these processes can be reversed at a constant
temperature without introduction of work from
the outside. Each process can be made to do
work if properly harnessed; for example, movement of hands on the watch by the spring and
the turning of a paddlewheel by the falling water.
However, even if these processes are not
accompanied by the performance of work, *a net
loss in the capacity to do work occurs.* This is
illustrated by the gas that expands in a vacuum.
No work is performed, yet the gas can never
undergo exactly the same process again without
the intervention of an outside agency to re-
compress it. A final property in common to each
of these processes is *a change toward a more*

random arrangement in which the molecules or
energy become less highly ordered. This is most
easily seen in the case of the dissolving sugar
and the expanding gas, in which the molecules
become randomly distributed throughout the
system. In the case of the flow of thermal energy
from the hot to the cold body, an equal distribution of molecular motion is finally attained in
both.

3.2.2 The Entropy

The greatest significance of the second law is
perhaps that spontaneous processes are accompanied by increases in the randomness or dis-
order of the entire system under consideration,
and that they are accompanied by a loss in
ability to perform work. The extent of randomness is expressed by a term called the **entropy**,
mathematically abbreviated by the symbol S,
which has units of energy per degree (often
cal/deg). The **third law of thermodynamics** tells
us that *the absolute entropy of most substances
is zero at the temperature of absolute zero*
(minus 273.16°C). Although this temperature
has never been reached, it is assumed that the
crystalline structure of these materials would
then be ordered in the highest manner possible.
It is then possible to calculate the entropy of
these at any higher temperature. However, it is
difficult to predict the exact entropies for
dissolved substances not present in the pure
state, but we can accurately measure entropy
changes accompanying many processes of interest. These changes are expressed by the symbol
ΔS, and, for a process occurring at constant
temperature, multiplication of the absolute
temperature by ΔS for the process gives a
quantitative measure in calories of the loss in
ability to do work.

3.2.3 Free Energy

The energy isothermally (constant temperature)
available for conversion to work is called the

Gibbs free energy, G. The free energy is a thermodynamic property, and for a single component it may be defined by the following equation, which is valuable for our purposes:

$$G = E + PV - TS \qquad (7)$$

where:

E = **internal energy** (the sum of the translational, rotational, vibrational, electronic, and nuclear energies of the substance)

PV = the pressure-volume product. (If P is expressed in atmospheres and V in liters, these may be converted to calories, since one liter-atmosphere equals 24.2 calories.)

T = absolute temperature

S = entropy

Since S and E are a part of G, absolute values of G are difficult to calculate, but in any chemical or physical process, ΔG represents the *difference* in free energy between the final and the initial state $(G_2 - G_1)$. This can be calculated for reversible processes at constant temperatures in several ways. If the final state has a lower free energy than the initial state, ΔG is *negative*, and the process is spontaneous and **exergonic** (energy releasing). If G_2 is greater than G_1, ΔG is *positive*, and the process is an uphill (**endergonic**) one. If G_2 is equal to G_1, ΔG is zero and we have a condition of equilibrium in which there is no net change. Indeed, *at constant temperature, equilibrium is reached only when* $\Delta G = 0$.

Although a knowledge of ΔG for a particular reaction allows us to predict whether it is spontaneously possible, it does not give any information about the rate at which it will occur. Even a reaction having a very large negative ΔG may proceed too slowly to be measured. Thermodynamics predicts that under most circumstances water will evaporate from plant leaves with a loss in free energy, but if the stomates are closed, transpiration rates may be low or undetectable. Stomatal aperture thus controls rates of transpiration but always within the limits set by thermodynamics. Similarly, the combination of oxygen with glucose to produce carbon dioxide and water is a spontaneous process, but it hardly proceeds at all in the absence of living cells. However, cells possess the proper enzymes necessary to catalyze the reactions involved. The role of enzymes in plant physiology is discussed in Chapter 11. Either reactants (A and B) or products (C and D), or both, may be introduced into such a reversible system:

$$A + B \underset{}{\overset{enzyme}{\rightleftharpoons}} C + D \qquad (8)$$

An equilibrium will eventually be reached in which $\Delta G = 0$. It can be intuitively seen that if products are initially absent, the reaction can only proceed to the right. If the reactants are present at concentrations much higher than those of the products, the same thing is expected. Physical chemists have derived a general equation to define the free energy changes accompanying such reactions. From this it is possible to predict whether they should proceed from right to left or from left to right under any condition of concentration of each chemical species involved:

$$\Delta G = 2.3RT \left[\log \frac{(C)(D)}{(A)(B)} - \log K \right] \qquad (9)$$

where:

R = the gas constant (often in cal/mole deg)

T = absolute temperature (must be constant)

K = the equilibrium constant

The parentheses indicate the effective concentrations of each chemical present.[4] This equation

---

[4] If any product or reactant is formed or used in a ratio of more or less than one mole for each mole of the others, its concentration must be raised to the appropriate power. That is, for: $K_2SO_4 \rightleftharpoons SO_4^{=} + 2K^+$,

$$\Delta G = 2.3RT \left[\log \frac{(SO_4^{=})(K^+)^2}{(K_2SO_4)} - \log K \right]$$

By effective concentration is meant, strictly speaking, the activity or chemical potential of each substance (see below, section 3.2.4).

Example 3-2

The hydrolysis of an ester into an alcohol and an acid is usually a slightly exergonic process. The following reaction, for example, has an equilibrium constant of about 2.1 when carried out in an aqueous solution at 38°C:

$$\text{glucose-6-phosphate} + H_2O \rightleftharpoons \text{glucose} + \text{phosphoric acid}$$

Suppose that in a plant the concentration of glucose-6-phosphate is 0.01 M, that of glucose is 0.001 M, and that of phosphoric acid is 0.05 M. What will be the energy change upon hydrolysis of one mole of glucose-6-phosphate under these conditions?

It is customary in reactions such as this where water is a participant in the reaction and is also the solvent (and thus is present at an unchanging value of about 55.5 M) to ignore it in determining the equilibrium constant and in the free energy equation below. Thus,

$$\Delta G = 2.3RT \left[\log \frac{(0.05\ M)(0.001\ M)}{(0.01\ M)} - \log(2.1) \right]$$

$$= 2.3RT \left[\log \frac{5 \times 10^{-3}}{2.1} \right] = 2.3RT(-2.624)$$

if R is expressed in units of cal/mole deg,

$$\Delta G = (2.3)(1.987\ \text{cal/mole deg})(311\ \text{deg})(-2.624) = -3,730\ \text{calories}$$

shows that if the ratio of products to reactants is very low, ΔG will probably be negative, and the reaction from left to right will proceed spontaneously, while the reverse will be true if the ratio of products to reactants is sufficiently high. We can see immediately that this ratio alone is not sufficient to predict the sign and magnitude of ΔG, since the equilibrium constant must also be known. Equilibrium constants have been measured for a large number of chemical reactions and are listed in various tables. With the use of these and knowledge of the concentrations of products and reactants, we can predict the direction in which any reaction will tend to proceed (Example 3-2).

In Example 3-2 the low hypothetical concentration of glucose relative to the glucose-6-phosphate was of greater importance than the relatively high concentration of phosphoric acid, and under these conditions the reaction was driven toward the right with a release of energy. Under certain cellular conditions, the concentrations of reactants and products present may be quite different, and this reaction and others may then require an input of energy in order to proceed. As we shall see in Chapter 11, the energy for biosynthesis of many large molecules in the plant is provided by such molecules as adenosine triphosphate (ATP).

3.2.4 The Chemical Potential and Water Potential

The free energy of a substance in any system is dependent upon the amount of substance present, that is, upon the number of molecules having a particular internal energy and entropy under the defined conditions of temperature and pressure. To understand water movement in plants (and most other processes, as well), we are usually concerned with the free energy present in a specified number of molecules in one condition compared to their energy after undergoing some change. Free energy is usually therefore stated in terms of energy per mole or per gram of the substance in question (i.e., cal/mole). The **free energy per mole** of any particular chemical species in a multicomponent system is defined as the **chemical potential** of that species. The larger the chemical potential of a substance, the greater will be its tendency to undergo chemical reactions and other processes, such as diffusion.

Salts like sodium chloride are completely ionized, even in the crystalline state. When these are dissolved, the attractive force between the oppositely charged ions is reduced by the high dielectric constant of water, and the ions are free to move about and to react chemically. It is found, however, that increasing the concentration of a salt from a very dilute value does not usually lead to a proportionally large increase in particles able to undergo reaction. This is apparently partly because the attraction among ions in concentrated solutions prevents free activity. This **effective concentration** or **activity**, as well as the chemical potential of these ions is therefore dependent upon their concentration. In general, even uncharged molecules undergo chemical potential changes with changes in concentrations and with addition of other substances.

The chemical potential of water is a property of considerable importance to our understanding of water and its movement in the plant and the soil. For convenience, we will refer to the chemical potential of water (free energy per mole) as the **water potential**. As we shall see in Chapter 5 (5.1.1B), water potential, usually expressed in energy terms, may by a simple conversion be expressed in terms of pressure. Regardless of how it is expressed, if water potential differs in various parts of a system, water will tend to move to the point where water potential is lowest. A common example of this is the condensation of water around particles of a hygroscopic salt. As we shall see, many factors besides salts influence water potential, and these are of primary importance in water movement through the plant.

Tendency for water to react or to move within a system may also be expressed in terms of **water activity**. The water activity of a given part of a system is equal to the relative humidity of a closed volume of air in equilibrium with that part of the system, expressed as a decimal fraction. For example, at a relative humidity of 68 percent, the water activity of the air equals 0.68. This simple system is extremely valuable for some applications, but in this text we shall use only the concept of water potential. (Water activity and water potential are interconvertible by the appropriate equation. See footnote 2, Chapter 5.)

3.3 DIFFUSION

With the above background, consideration of the process of diffusion becomes relatively simple. **Diffusion** is usually defined as the net movement of a given substance from one point to another due to the random kinetic motions of its particles (molecules, atoms, ions, etc.), such as the ions of potassium permanganate diffusing from a crystal placed in a beaker of water. In terms of concentration, it is not difficult to understand this process in an intuitive way. Imagine two rooms connected through an opening and having perfectly elastic walls. One room contains perfectly elastic white balls in free motion, while the other room contains perfectly elastic black balls in motion. Obviously, the chances of a black ball hitting the opening and going through into the other room in a given amount of time will depend upon the speed and concentration of black balls. At the beginning, the concentration of black balls in the one room is much higher than it is in the other, but some go through the opening; so the concentration builds up in the other room.

Gradually a condition of equilibrium will be approached in which the number of black balls is the same in both rooms. At this time, the chances of a black ball going in one direction through the opening are the same as the chances of a black ball going in the opposite direction. Of course the same would be true for the white balls, and indeed the direction of diffusion of each will be independent of the other.

In terms of the entropy concept, there was a relatively high degree of order existing when the balls were separated in the two different rooms (or when any concentration gradient exists, such as the gradient from the potassium permanganate crystal to the surrounding pure water). Because of the high degree of order, the level of entropy is low. At equilibrium, there is much less order; a maximum state of randomness has developed [the black and the white balls are equally mixed, or the ions of potassium permanganate have become equally distributed (concentrated) throughout the entire beaker]. The entropy of the entire system (both rooms, or the beaker) has increased to a maximum level, as is proper for spontaneous, chance-directed processes.

The free energy of the black balls (or the potassium permanganate ions) is initially very high in the one room (or in the immediate vicinity of the potassium permanganate crystal) and very low in the other (or in the water in the beaker). Difference in quantity of free energy in different parts of the system is due to differences in concentration. We might also say that the free energy of the entire system (contents of both rooms or the beaker) is high. As diffusion occurs from the point of high free energy toward the point of low free energy, a state is reached in which free energy content throughout the system becomes equal. At this point, the change in free energy from one part of the system to the other is zero, and indeed the free energy content for the system *as a whole* has decreased. For all parts of the system, ΔG has now become zero. This is, as described above, equilibrium.

Up to this point, we arrive at the same result whether we consider diffusion as a tendency toward equal concentration throughout the system or as a tendency toward equal free energy. The free energy approach is more general, however, since it includes other factors besides concentration. We can define diffusion more exactly in terms of free energy:

Diffusion of any substance will tend to occur downward along any free energy or chemical potential gradient, regardless of how the gradient is established.

Of course, whether diffusion actually does occur will depend upon whether movement along the gradient is otherwise possible, that is, not obstructed by some barrier, such as the closed leaf stomates in the transpiration example mentioned earlier.

3.3.1 Establishment of the Free Energy or Chemical Potential Gradient

There are a number of ways to establish a free energy gradient. We will consider the somewhat more specific case of a water potential gradient, although the same principles apply to any free energy or chemical potential gradient. Suppose a completely enclosed and rigid container full of water is separated into two compartments by a rigid membrane through which only water can diffuse (Fig. 3-4). Initially, of course, there will be no net movement of water in either direction across the membrane.

3.3.1A Temperature Suppose molecules on one side of the membrane are warmer than those on the other. Thermodynamic considerations indicate that raising the temperature increases the free energy or chemical potential. Diffusion will thus occur toward the cooler side of the container. It is likely that water movement in the plant is sometimes caused by temperature

FACTORS AFFECTING DIFFUSION (ΔG)

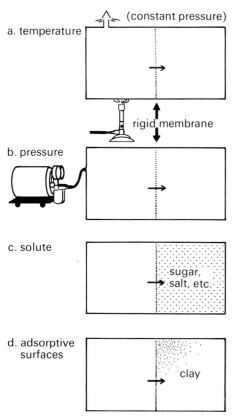

Figure 3-4

Models of diffusional systems as discussed in the text.

cell membranes greatly influence water movement in the plant.

3.3.1C Presence of dissolved solutes Suppose that a small amount of sugar (a typical **solute**) is added to the water (the **solvent** of most importance in plants) in one compartment of the apparatus of Fig. 3-4, accompanied by the removal of an amount of water which keeps the pressure constant. It is now found that water will diffuse into this compartment, again because of a difference in water potential across the membrane. What has caused this difference in water potential? A straightforward explanation is not readily apparent, but the water molecules are interacting with the solute particles in such a way that the *free energy of the water molecules is decreased.* If there are no chemical interactions between the water and the solute (compound formation), and if solutions are fairly dilute (approaching "perfect" solutions), then this effect of solute upon free energy of solvent is independent of the *kind* of solute particle, be it ion, small molecule, or even a large molecule like a protein. Only the *number* of solute particles compared to the *number* of solvent particles is important. This relationship between number of particles is conveniently given by the **mole fraction**[5] as expressed in equations (10) and (11).

gradients from one cell to another, since temperature differences do occur among individual neighboring cells. The importance of these, however, remains to be determined. (The equations introduced here are valid only at constant temperature.)

3.3.1B Pressure The free energy equation indicates that a pressure increase in one side of this system will increase the pressure-volume product and raise the water potential [equation (7)]. This will cause diffusion of water toward the side exposed to a lower pressure. As will be shown in Chapter 5, pressure gradients across

---

[5] In practical laboratory work, this relationship is given by solution concentrations expressed in terms of **molality**. A **molal solution** (abbreviated *m*) is stated in terms of moles of solute per 1,000 g of water. The more common **molar** solutions (abbreviated *M*) are expressed in terms of moles of solute per liter of final solution volume. Since the change in solution volume upon addition of solute varies and is a function of the kind of solute, only the molal convention expresses a constant proportion between number of solute and number of solvent particles. If there is *no* change in volume upon addition of solute, then molal and molar concentrations are equivalent. Dilutions are most easily carried out with molar solutions where the $M_1 V_1 = M_2 V_2$ relationship holds (M_1 and M_2 equal molarities of initial and final solutions; V_1 and V_2 equal initial and final volumes). With molal solutions, the grams of water and the moles of solute present in the volume at hand must be calculated. This can be done by knowing the volume change upon addition of solute. Knowing this, the appropriate grams of water may then be added.

In one sense, then, the effect of solute particles upon free energy of solvent particles is a dilution effect. Solute particles "dilute out" water particles by decreasing the mole fraction of solvent. Yet in the exact sense of dilution this is not true. Dilution implies a decrease in the *concentration*, in this case, of the water molecules. Yet **concentration** is by definition *quantity per unit volume*, and the quantity of water per unit volume will be changed upon addition of solute only if the final solution volume is different from the original volume of solvent. Sometimes it is not; other times it is greater or less. Thus addition of solute may make water in the true sense more or less concentrated or may not influence its concentration at all. In any case, the effect of solute upon water concentration has virtually nothing to do with the effect on free energy, but this effect is directly related to the mole fraction of solvent. Gradients in water potential established by this effect are of extreme importance to movement of water in plants (Chapter 5).

3.3.1D Adsorption Imagine that the compartment of one side of the membrane in Fig. 3-4 is filled with nearly dry particles of clay, and the other compartment is filled with pure water. Water will diffuse across the membrane into the clay. There is a great tendency for water molecules to become adsorbed onto the surfaces of the clay particles (see next chapter), and so there is a steep gradient in water potential between the water molecules in pure water and the surfaces of the clay particles. The result of this water potential gradient is diffusion of water toward the clay. This is of obvious importance to a plant in the soil, and there are

also many water adsorbing surfaces (protein, cellulose, starch, etc.) within the plant itself. These may or may not be completely **hydrated** (saturated with adsorbed water molecules).

3.3.2 The Rate of Diffusion

The entropy and free energy concepts define only the *tendency* for diffusion to occur. Other factors may strongly influence whether diffusion does in fact occur and at what rates:

3.3.2A Steepness of the free energy gradient
Differences in chemical potential (or in the case of water, water potential) per unit distance will strongly influence rate of diffusion. The steeper this gradient, the more rapidly diffusion will tend to occur, other factors remaining equal. Of course, as equilibrium is approached, the gradient approaches zero.

3.3.2B Resistance or permeability of the medium through which diffusion occurs The less resistance offered by the medium (the more permeable the medium is to the diffusing substance), the more rapidly diffusion will occur. This resistance may often be related to viscosity of the solvent.

3.3.2C Temperature The velocity of the diffusing particles (and hence the rate of diffusion) is, for perfect gases, proportional to the square root of the absolute temperature (see footnote 2). In general, raising the temperature always increases the rate of diffusion. Sometimes temperature effects on permeability are as important as effects on diffusion *per se*, however.

$$\text{mole fraction of solvent} = \frac{\text{moles of solvent}}{\text{moles of solvent} + \text{moles of solute}} \tag{10}$$

$$\text{mole fraction of solute} = \frac{\text{moles of solute}}{\text{moles of solvent} + \text{moles of solute}} \tag{11}$$

3.3.2D Size of the diffusing particles
As indicated in footnote 1, the smaller the particle at a given temperature, the higher its velocity and hence the greater the diffusion rate of this particle, all other factors being equal.

3.4 COLLIGATIVE PROPERTIES OF SOLUTIONS

Four important properties of solutions bear a direct relationship to the free energy or chemical potential of the *solvent* as it is influenced *only* by the presence of solute particles. These **colligative properties** are, *for dilute solutions*, always a function of the mole fraction.

3.4.1 Vapor Pressure of the Solvent

At a given temperature, the number of solvent particles that can exist in the vapor state in a closed volume above a free surface of the solvent will be a function of the free energy or chemical potential of the solvent. The higher the chemical potential of the solvent, the higher the pressure produced by the solvent molecules in the vapor state (the **vapor pressure**). Since the presence of solute particles decreases the chemical potential of the solvent, the presence of such particles decreases the vapor pressure. **Raoult's law**, formulated in 1887, states that the relative lowering of the vapor pressure is proportional to the mole fraction of solute. Since the mole fraction of solute added to the mole fraction of solvent must equal unity, then the actual vapor pressure of the solvent is directly proportional to its mole fraction:

$$p = x_1 p^o \qquad (12)$$

where:

  p = vapor pressure of the solution
  x_1 = mole fraction of solvent [see equation (11)]
  p^o = vapor pressure of pure solvent

The law holds only for ideal solutions, but it holds approximately for any dilute solution. It is of considerable importance in modern methods of determining water potential of plants (Chapter 5), and it was used to derive expressions for the effects of solutes on osmotic pressures, a topic to be discussed in Chapter 5.

3.4.2 Boiling Point

The addition of solute to a liquid lowers the chemical potential of the solvent and consequently raises its boiling point. Addition of pressure raises the free energy of both vapor and liquid, and this increases the boiling point of the solvent. In the balance between effects on liquid and vapor, there is a slight increase in solvent vapor pressure due to increasing pressure on the total system.

3.4.3 Freezing Point

The addition of solute lowers the freezing point, and this is again proportional to the mole fraction of solute and hence to the chemical potential of the solvent. An increase in pressure also causes water to freeze at a lower temperature. The effect is due to the expansion of water when it freezes.

3.4.4 Osmotic Pressure and Osmotic Potential

As indicated in the example above (Fig. 3-4), diffusion will occur down a water potential gradient established by the presence of a solute that is restricted to one part of a system. If diffusion of the solute in the opposite direction is restricted by a membrane, then pressure will tend to build up in the solution. As this occurs, water potential of the solution may increase until the gradient no longer exists (if the membrane is strong enough to withstand the pressure), and net diffusion of water will cease. (Water molecules will still be moving across the membrane but at equal rates in both directions.) The pressure that can be built up with a given solution is a function of the mole fraction of solvent (the free energy, chemical potential, or water potential). The **osmotic pressure** of a solution is equivalent to that real pressure that may be built up as described above. The **osmotic potential** is that component of water potential resulting from the presence of solute particles. It is equivalent to osmotic pressure in concept but opposite in sign. It may also be expressed in energy terms, while osmotic pressure is always expressed in pressure terms. **Osmosis** is the topic of discussion in Chapter 5.

4

Reactive Surfaces

At the level of the cell and below, two outstanding structural features seem to be highly typical of living things. One of these includes the special kinds of molecules found in protoplasm, and these are discussed in much of this book. The other feature is the physical nature of protoplasmic structure. There is in protoplasm a large amount of interface between different kinds of materials. This excludes single atoms or small molecules but refers to the surfaces between bulk materials, some of these materials being as small as large molecules. The interactions between substances at these interfaces are for the most part not strictly chemical (not a sharing or transferring of electrons), but they involve primarily physical and always electrical forces.

The large amount of surface comes about because of the small volumes of the entities under discussion. Consider, for example, a volume of material, cuboidal in structure and one cubic centimeter in volume. It will have six surfaces of one square centimeter each or a total surface area of 6 cm². As the cube is cut into smaller pieces, the total volume stays the same, but each cut produces more surfaces (Fig. 4-1). After cutting a cubic centimeter of solid material into minute cubes, 1×10^{-6} cm on a side (100 Å—the approximate dimensions

of a small protein molecule), we will have produced 600 square meters of surface area.

It is interesting that almost all of the highly reactive and important complex reactions in nature take place at these submicroscopic surfaces, particularly in soil and in cells. These surfaces strongly influence water relations in the soil–plant–air continuum, and since these relationships and their related functions are the topic of discussion in Chapters 3 to 9, it is important that we consider surface effects as soon as possible. Some principles have already been introduced (Chapter 3, 3.3.1D). It is logical also to present in this chapter several of the physical principles the protein chemist applies in his separations and other manipulations of proteins. Chapter 11 is devoted to the chemistry of the protein enzymes, but their physical behavior is considered here.

4.1 COLLOIDS

The properties of very small particles with their concurrent large surface areas have been studied since the 19th century. Since suspensions of these small particles in water are sometimes glue-like, the particles have been termed **colloids** from the Greek word for glue. For individual particles suspended in a liquid, the features

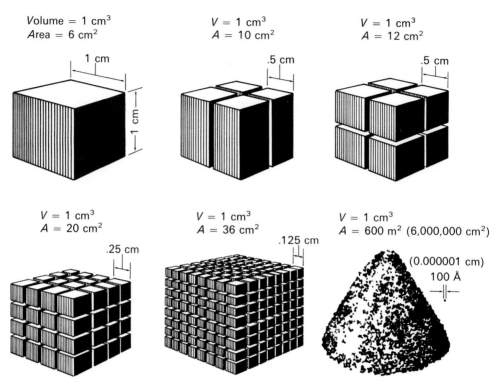

Figure 4-1
An illustration of the relationship between surface area and volume as particle size decreases.

resulting from large surface area can be observed only when the particles are smaller than some maximum size (approximately so large that gravity will cause them to settle out of solution) and larger than some minimum size (a size below which particles begin to have all of the properties of atoms, ions, and small molecules). That is, in reference to their behavior in a liquid, they are *smaller than "suspension" particles and larger than true solute particles.*

4.1.1 Some Colloidal Properties Related to Size

Three properties of colloids are a direct function of their minute size.

4.1.1A Visibility through a microscope Due to interference phenomena, objects smaller than about half of the wavelength of the light with which they are being observed cannot be resolved (seen) in the microscope. This is an absolute lower limit independent of the degree to which lenses are perfected or the microscope is otherwise technologically improved. Different authors place the upper size range of colloids at values of 0.1 to 2.0 microns (μ) or 1,000 to 20,000 Å. The smallest are on the order of 100 Å. Light waves in the visible part of the spectrum are 3,850 to 7,760 Å long, so only the largest colloidal particles (larger than about 2,000 Å) are visible in the light microscope. If the upper size limit of 1,000 Å is accepted, no colloids are visible in the light microscope. Ultraviolet light consists of shorter wavelengths (2,000 to 3,850 Å), and so particles as small as 1,000 Å begin to appear distinctly on photographs taken through an ultraviolet microscope. Electrons move in beams with extremely short wavelengths (less than 1 Å), but the lower limits of resolution in an electron microscope are set by technological problems such as spherical aberration. With biological specimens, objects as small as 10 Å have been photographed, although 20 to 40 Å is a more practical lower limit of resolution.[1] Hence most colloidal particles are readily visible in photographs through an electron microscope. Yet the smallest protein molecules at the bottom of the size scale of colloidal particles are not commonly observed even in the electron microscope.

4.1.1B Brownian movement Although colloidal particles do not appear as distinct bodies when viewed through the light microscope, if illumination is correct (strong illumination from the side), light waves are disturbed so that the position of the particle becomes apparent as a point of light. This is known as the **Tyndall effect**, since it was first noticed by John Tyndall. He observed the beam of light passing through a colloidal suspension of particles in liquid, or of dust particles in air.

Properly illuminated, colloidal particles can be observed in the field of the microscope as points of light dancing rapidly with a random motion (Fig. 4-2). This movement is called **Brownian movement** after its discoverer Robert Brown. It comes about because at this size range there is a high statistical probability that

a particle will be struck by the molecules of the liquid with more force on one side than on the other. This can be observed to happen several times per second. The smaller the particle, the greater the chances for unequal collisions and the more rapid its Brownian movement. Its size may be apparent from the brilliance of the point of light that indicates its position.

Brownian movement keeps colloidal-sized particles from settling out in response to gravity. They are said to *remain in suspension.*

Brownian movement is also the most direct evidence we have for the kinetic theory discussed in Chapter 3. It could occur only if molecular-sized particles are in continuous motion and if this motion is distributed over a range of velocities (as in the Maxwell–Boltzmann curve—Fig. 3-1).

4.1.1C Filtration properties Colloidal particles are of such a size that they will pass through pores of filter paper but not through those of cellophane. Solute particles, on the other hand, will pass through the pores of cellophane, making it possible to separate colloidal particles (usually protein) from true solute particles such as electrolytes and small molecules. In this separation process, called **dialysis**, the mixture is placed in a cellophane bag which is then held under running water or perhaps in a large beaker of water stirred with a magnetic stirrer (Fig. 4-3). Solute particles will diffuse out through the cellophane into the surrounding water (which is continually renewed) until their concentration in the cellophane bag is reduced to an insignificant level.

Colloidal particles will settle out in a centrifuge which produces very high accelerational fields (about 100,000 × gravity or more). The rate of settling in such an **ultracentrifuge** will be a function of the size and shape of the particle and the viscosity of the medium. In an **analytical ultracentrifuge**, an optical system is

---

[1] At the time of this writing, rapid advances are being made in electron microscope technology. Humberto Fernandez-Moran at the University of Chicago has obtained resolutions in the 2–4 Å range (see article by Susan Winer in *Scientific Research*, a magazine published by McGraw-Hill Publishing Co., Jan. 8, 1968, p. 29). Even molecules as small as glucose may be resolved soon.

Figure 4-2
Brownian movement of colloidal particles, as observed with lateral illumination.

often used to observe differences in index of refraction of the spinning liquid containing the colloid so that the rate of settling of an individual kind of colloidal particle (again usually protein) can be directly observed.

4.1.2 Some Typical Colloidal Systems

Table 4-1 summarizes a number of different kinds of colloidal systems. Two systems typical of protoplasm will be discussed.

4.1.2A Emulsions When two immiscible liquids are mixed so that droplets of one are suspended in the other, the system is called an **emulsion**. To be a stable emulsion, the droplets must be so small that they do not **coalesce**

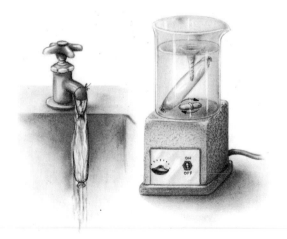

Figure 4-3
Laboratory methods of dialysis.

TABLE 4-1

POSSIBLE KINDS OF COLLOIDAL SYSTEMS WITH EXAMPLES

Particles of colloidal size		Continuous phase	Examples
gas	in	liquid	some foams, whipped cream
gas	in	solid	floating soap, some precious stones, whipped egg
liquid	in	gas	fog, mist
liquid	in	liquid	emulsions: milk, cream, mayonnaise
liquid	in	solid	gels: jello, jellies; some minerals, pearls
solid	in	gas	smoke, fine dust clouds, blue haze
solid	in	liquid	most sols, protoplasm, egg white, Mississippi River
solid	in	solid	some types of stained glass, alloys, black diamonds

(blend together). Sometimes these droplets are of the size range mentioned above, but probably more typically they are somewhat larger, perhaps visible in the light microscope. There are two fundamental kinds of emulsions.

When droplets of oil are dispersed in water, the system is said to be a **cream-type emulsion**. In this case the water, a polar liquid, is continuous. The oil droplets are hydrophobic (see footnote 2, section 2.2) or lypophilic (fat "loving") and usually nonpolar. Hence polar solutes dissolve in the water, lowering its surface tension so that the tendency for water droplets to form is less than the tendency for oil droplets, and the water remains continuous. Sodium soaps (the sodium salts of long-chain fatty acids) are relatively polar, dissolving more in the water than in the oil and producing a cream-type emulsion.

When droplets of water are suspended in a continuous oil phase, the system is said to be a **butter-type emulsion.** Such an emulsion forms when the lipid, nonpolar oil becomes the continuous phase upon the addition of relatively nonpolar solutes, such as calcium soaps. As we shall see in Chapter 8, the membranes of living organisms resemble in certain respects a butter-type emulsion.

4.1.2B Sols and gels Certain nonspherical colloidal particles suspended in water may form a **sol–gel system**. We are all familiar with the manner in which gelatin dessert is prepared. The gelatin, consisting of nonspherical protein gelatin molecules (many other proteins act in a similar manner) to which a considerable quantity of sugar has been added, is combined with hot water. The gelatin molecules go into suspension, forming a so-called **sol**. The presence of the sugar decreases considerably the water potential so that the gelatin molecules become somewhat less hydrated. As the temperature decreases, the gelatin begins to "set." That is, it takes on a semisolid condition known as a **gel**.

It was long thought that the gelatin molecules had formed cells enclosing minute droplets of water, but solutes diffuse through the gel system nearly as rapidly as they diffuse through the sol system. This would seem to imply, not only that the gelatin phase has become continuous (providing a certain degree of rigidity to the system—the gel), but that the liquid phase has also remained continuous. This model of a sol–gel system is called the **brush-pile model or theory**, in which the gelatin molecules are analogous to the sticks in a pile of brush. In the sol system these particles are unable to adhere to each other because of their high kinetic energy. As the temperature drops (kinetic energy decreases), the particles begin to contact each other at various places until finally all have become attached (probably by van der Waals forces) to each other, and the system has the tenuous rigidity of a pile of brush. As small animals move readily through the brush pile, so will small particles diffuse through the gel.

Sol–gel systems have a number of interesting properties that have been enumerated and studied by physiologists for several decades now. Typically, a sol–gel system is **reversible**, its state depending upon temperature, but a blood clot may be an example of a nonreversible gel. In the property of **syneresis**, a gel forces out droplets of liquid as it shrinks upon standing. In terms of the brush-pile model, we can think of the "sticks" as tending to contact and pull together at more points. **Thixotropic gels** are reversible in a special way, forming a gel upon standing but a sol upon being disturbed. In **hysteresis**, a gel exhibits a property of "memory." If one gel is made up with a large quantity of water and another with less water, and both are allowed to dry to complete dryness, the one originally made up with the most water will reabsorb the most water. This property has been applied in certain theories put forth to explain drought hardiness of some plants. The property of **hydration** or **imbibition** (the adsorption of water by hydrophilic surfaces) is an important characteristic of sol–gel and other systems and is discussed separately below.

In the present terminology, a suspension of colloids in liquid should not be referred to as a solution, but as a *sol*. It is common practice, however, to speak of *protein solutions*.

4.2 SURFACE REACTIONS IN GENERAL

Many of the properties of colloids are exhibited by systems not truly colloidal. That is, a great deal of surface area may be available, even though the particles contact each other as in a gel. The **endoplasmic reticulum** of a cell consists of a system of membranes permeating the cytoplasm of a cell, sometimes with attached particles called **ribosomes**. The system constitutes a high interfacial surface within the cytoplasm. The cell wall consists of minute fibers of cellulose, arranged somewhat as in the brush-pile model. To a good first approximation, we may think of a cell wall as a highly hydrated, hydrophilic gel. The clay particles in a soil are

of colloidal size but, being in close contact with each other, exhibit more of the properties of a gel than a sol.

4.2.1 Surface Charge

In either case, whether we are concerned with dispersed colloidal particles or with a continuous system having a large amount of interfacial surface area, certain properties are a function of this surface area. Most of these arise because such interfacial systems typically involve an electrical charge at the surface. In clay particles, the atoms are bound together in a crystal lattice making up the bulk of the particle. At the edge of the particle the crystal lattice is broken, and the ionic electrical charges are exposed. In proteins (Chapter 11), there are free amino groups (basic) and carboxyl groups (acidic). These may (depending upon the pH—see below) account for surface charge on protein. Some of the cell wall constituents, such as the pectins, also contain ionic carboxyl groups. The three systems mentioned above are perhaps the most common colloidal systems encountered in nature, and as a general rule all three of these have a net excess of negative charge at the surface. It is possible to observe positive charges at the surface, but negative charges are most common in nature.

4.2.2 Water Adsorbed on Colloids

The negative charge on colloidal surfaces tends to attract the positive pole of water molecules. It also attracts dissolved cations (positively charged), and these in turn are hydrated, adding to the layer of water on the surface of the colloid. The negative surface plus the positive cations constitute the **electrical double layer**, and the result is a layer of water molecules due partially to their direct attraction by the negative surface and partially to the "osmotic" effect resulting from the presence of the cations (Fig. 4-4). As

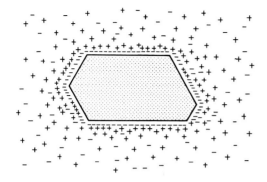

Figure 4-4

The electrical double-layer of ionic distribution around a charged colloidal particle. Charges next to the surface of the particle are meant to indicate surface charge. This is mostly negative but is interrupted at three points with positive charge. Distribution of ionic charge is statistically opposite to the distribution of surface charge, but a few irregularities are apparent.

the distance between the surface and the water molecules increases, the attractive forces with which these molecules are held decrease.

Such hydrated colloids suspended in a sol do not settle out because they are unable to contact each other, due both to their repelling negative charge and to the shells of water around them. To overcome this, something must be added that will both remove the water and neutralize the charge. Certain hydrophilic liquids, such as alcohol and acetone, will remove the water layer by decreasing the water potential of the surrounding water, and usually an excess of electrolytes is added to neutralize the charge. The particles will then contact each other, adhere, and settle out—a process called **flocculation**.

4.2.3 The Lyotropic Series

If, in a flocculation experiment, cations are used to neutralize the negative charges on the colloidal surfaces, it becomes apparent that some cations are much more effective than others. This is because different cations are adsorbed to the charged surfaces with different degrees of tenacity. Using **equivalent solutions** (the same number of cationic charges per unit volume), the cations can be arranged in the order of their effectiveness in neutralizing the colloidal charge. This arrangement, the **Hofmeister or lyotropic series**, with the most efficient cations listed first, is as follows:

$$Al^{+++}, H^+, Ba^{++}, Ca^{++}, Mg^{++}, K^+$$
$$= NH_4^+, Na^+, Li^+$$

When one is dealing with the minerals readily available in soils, usually the list is shortened as follows:

$$H^+, Ca^{++}, Mg^{++}, K^+ = NH_4^+, Na^+$$

Anionic systems have also been worked out as they apply to positively charged surfaces.

4.2.4 Examples of Lyotropic Adsorption

4.2.4A Flocculation In hydrophilic colloidal systems, aluminum ions are most tightly adsorbed and are consequently the most effective flocculators. Lithium ions are least effective. Such statements always assume comparison at equivalent concentrations. The practice of flocculation by addition of electrolytes is often referred to as **salting out**. This is a procedure frequently used to flocculate proteins from a sol without denaturing them. Usually, ammonium sulfate is added as the salting-out material, partly because of its high solubility.

4.2.4B Sol – gel relationships The properties of sols and gels listed above are influenced by the presence of electrolytes. With the usual negative proteins, the effectiveness of the added cations falls into the lyotropic series. In the property of hydration to be discussed below, for example, aluminum ions are most effective in inhibiting the process, while lithium ions are least effective.

4.2.4C Cation exchange Since the cations are adsorbed on colloidal surfaces with differing degrees of tenacity, it is possible at equivalent concentrations for one cation to replace another. In such a reaction (common on clay particles in soils), the adsorbing surface or particle may be thought of as one reactant in a typical chemical equilibrium reaction [see (R4-1)].

$$2NH_4^+ + clay \cdot Ca \;\rightleftharpoons\; Ca^{++} + clay \cdot (NH_4)_2$$
$$(R4\text{-}1)$$

At equivalent concentrations, calcium is more tenaciously adsorbed than ammonium, and so reaction (R4-1) as written would tend to move strongly to the left. If the ammonium concentration is increased far above the calcium concentration, however, the reaction may be driven toward the right. One may think of such a process as a typical equilibrium reaction with its equilibrium constant (K):

$$K = \frac{[Ca^{++}][clay \cdot (NH_4)_2]}{[NH_4]^2[clay \cdot Ca]} \qquad (13)$$

The negative surfaces such as clay, cell walls, and protein are all capable of this **cation exchange**, and in many instances this is an important consideration. Much of soil science is based upon the cation exchange properties of clay colloids. In areas of high rainfall, for example, the incoming moisture contains dissolved carbon dioxide, which reacts with the water to produce carbonic acid. The hydrogen ions of carbonic acid are more effective in the lyotropic series than any other ion except aluminum, and so they gradually tend to replace all of the other ions of the soil, as these are produced by breakdown of minerals. The result is that in areas of high rainfall the soil becomes highly acidic, and the nutrient ions are leached down to the water table.

Cation exchange also normally takes place at cell wall and protein surfaces in living tissue (Chapter 8, 8.6.3).

Home water softeners are based on the cation exchange principle. A highly effective, colloidal-like material (usually zeolite) is first charged with a high concentration of sodium ions which displace other cations. As water is then run through the system, the "hard" calcium ions replace the "soft" sodium ions on the exchange material.[2]

The principle of cation exchange is often used in the laboratory for the purification and separation of various plant constituents.

4.2.4D Donnan equilibrium In systems where relatively large, nonmobile, charged surfaces exist, the concentrations of electrolytes become influenced by these surfaces. If the surface is negative (a nonmobile anion), then the concentration of cations in the vicinity of this surface will be higher than the concentration at some distance from the surface. The concentration of anions will be lower close to the surface. Of course, at a distance beyond the influence of the surface, the concentration of cations will equal that of anions, but in any case, the total of anions and cations will be highest near the surface. This relationship was worked out in mathematical terms by F. G. Donnan in 1911, using a somewhat less general system in which large anions (typically proteins) were separated from the rest of the system by a membrane that allowed free passage of small anions and cations (electrolytes). Assume a system containing a quantity (a) of nondiffusible anion and an original quantity (b) of diffusible cation with an equal quantity (b) of diffusible anion. Now assume that a quantity (x) of diffusible cation and an equal quantity (x) of diffusible anion move to the vicinity of the non-

---

[2] Calcium ions are "hard" because they form an insoluble calcium soap and hence a butter-type emulsion (the ring around the bathtub—difficult to wash off), while sodium ions form a water soluble cream-type emulsion. Hence water containing sodium ions is "soft" compared to water containing calcium ions.

diffusible anion (a). The final concentrations of both cation and anion beyond the influence of the nondiffusible anion will then be ($b - x$), and their concentrations near the surface will be ($a + x$) for the cation and (x) for the anion. Donnan showed that the products of the anions and the cations near the surface will equal their products at a distance:

Surface: Solution:

$$(a + x)x = (b - x)^2$$

For sodium chloride, for example:

$$(Na^+)_a(Cl^-)_a = (Na^+)_s(Cl^-)_s$$

or

$$\frac{(Na^+)_a}{(Na^+)_s} = \frac{(Cl^-)_s}{(Cl^-)_a} \quad (14)$$

where the subscript a refers to the vicinity of the surface, and the subscript s refers to the solution beyond the influence of the surface. Representative concentrations might be:

	Surface:	Solution:
Na^+	9.00	8.00
Cl^-	7.12	8.00
Products	64.00	64.00
Sums	16.12	16.00

The principle is of broad general application in both plants and animals, although application of the above equations is extremely complex due to the presence of many kinds of anions and cations, both diffusible and nondiffusible, and the various degrees with which these substances may pass through membranes or otherwise be restricted in their movement. Some of the consequences of the Donnan phenomenon include gradients in pH (due to hydrolysis), gradients in anions and cations, and gradients in water potential that result from these solute gradients. The phenomenon could be especially important in plants, not only because of the presence of proteins, but also because of the

negative charge on cell walls. Indeed, the processes discussed in Chapter 8 are always complicated by these manifestations.

4.2.5 Amphoteric Surfaces

Proteins and clay particles (but *not* cell walls) may have either a positive or negative charge at the surface, depending upon pH. Such systems are called **amphoteric**. Under conditions of low pH (high acidity), the free carboxyl groups on the surface of protein will be neutral because of the abundance of hydrogen ions. The surface of the protein will then have a positive charge from the amino groups and their adsorbed protons (Fig. 4-5). As the pH increases (acidity decreases), fewer protons will be attached to amino groups, and more carboxyl groups will ionize. Eventually, few if any of the amino groups will have a positive charge, and many of the carboxyl groups will be ionized, producing a negative charge and hence a predominantly negative protein surface. At some point between these two extremes, the surface will exhibit a net neutrality, with positive charges exactly balancing negative ones.

Colloidal charge can be observed because the properties of such systems are a function of the charge and consequently an indication of it. Figure 4-5, for example, shows the "solubility" of two hypothetical proteins as a function of pH. At both acid and alkaline pH values, the proteins are more "soluble," because either a positive or a negative charge on the surface increases their ability to adsorb water (the electrical double layer becomes thicker). At the pH at which they are neutral, they will adsorb the least water and consequently be the least "soluble." This pH is called the **isoelectric point**. As is indicated by the difference in the two curves in Fig. 4-5, both the isoelectric point and the general shape of the solubility curve are characteristic of the particular protein at hand.

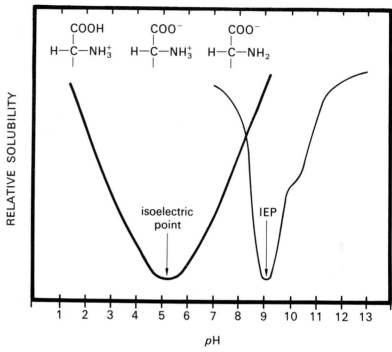

Figure 4-5
The relative solubility of amphoteric colloids as a function of pH. Note that specific shape of a curve will depend upon the specific protein, as will the exact position of the isoelectric point. Conditions of the carboxyl and amino groups of protein are indicated at the top of the graph.

Systems of colloids in suspension may often be separated from each other by the process known as **isoelectric precipitation**. In this process the pH is adjusted so that one amphoteric material is highly soluble while another is quite insoluble. In **electrophoresis**, an electrical potential is established across a sol or a gel or across some medium, such as filter paper, that can support a sol. The colloidal particles will migrate in the electrical field according to the charges on their surfaces (negative charges will migrate toward the positive pole) and according to their sizes and tendencies to be adsorbed by the medium if it exists. Such methods are very important in protein chemistry.

4.3   HYDRATION

4.3.1   The Nature of Hydration

As indicated above, a very significant property of charged surfaces is their adsorption of water molecules, the process of **hydration** or **imbibition**. Materials capable of hydration, such as the proteins and cellulose in living material, cause seeds to swell by imbibition when they are placed in water, or wood to swell in water or in air of high humidity. Pure proteins (such as gelatin), nearly pure proteins (such as those found in the stipe of various brown algae— kelp), and many other growing plant parts (such as fungal hyphae or meristematic cells) are also powerful imbibants. In these last-named cases, growth (an increase in plant size—see Chapter 19) is often a hydration phenomenon, in which hydrophilic materials are synthesized by the metabolic activity of the tissue, and these then cause the tissues to swell as they become hydrated.

Adsorption of water in the soil accounts for much of its water-holding capacity, permitting a volume of soil to hold water sufficient to supply several days to several months of plant growth.

The tenacity with which water molecules are held on an imbibing surface is a function of their water potential, the nature of the surfaces (especially the charge), and the distance between the water molecules and the surface. The closer the molecules are to the surface, the more firmly they will be held. The tenacity with which they are held may be expressed in terms of chemical potential or water potential. If a hydrating surface comes into equilibrium with a solution in which water potential (3.2.4) is decreased below zero by the presence of solute, the water potential at the hydrating surface will be equal to the water potential of the solution (the osmotic potential at zero pressure, see Chapter 5). The hydrating, often highly irregular and porous surface (colloid or gel-like material, such as the cell wall) is referred to as the **matrix**, and its water potential is called the **matric potential**. As osmotic potential is that component of water potential influenced by the presence of solutes, so matric potential is that component of water potential influenced by the presence of a matrix. All of these values may be expressed in terms of either energy or pressure (see Chapters 3 and 5). By convention, pure water at atmospheric pressure is said to have a water potential of zero. The matric potential will, then, be zero or some value *less* than zero; that is, a negative number. It will be lowest (most negative) for a dry material; and, as the

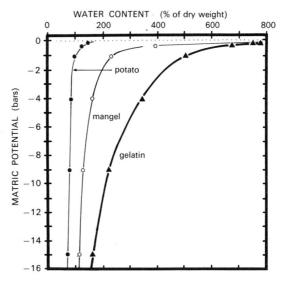

Figure 4-6

Moisture release curves for two plant materials and gelatin. (From H. H. Wiebe, 1966, *Plant Physiol.* 41:1439. Used by permission.)

matrix adsorbs water, it will increase toward a maximum value of zero when it is in equilibrium with pure water at atmospheric pressure. The relationship between degree of hydration and matric potential is called the **moisture release curve** (Fig. 4-6).

There are several ways to measure matric potential, as we shall see in Chapter 5. The simplest in principle is to find a solution in which the substance in question will neither gain nor lose water. For such a system, $\Delta G = 0$, and so the water potential of the solution is equivalent to the matric potential. For example, the minimum (most negative) matric potential for a given material may be determined by introducing the dry material into solutions of various concentration (water potential) until one is found from which the material is unable to adsorb water. Dry cocklebur fruits were used in such an experiment by C. A. Shull in 1916. He found that only saturated lithium chloride solutions would prevent hydration, indicating minimum matric potentials of nearly $-1,000$ bars.[3] We should note that while this experiment is simple in principle, it is strongly complicated by the effects of the ions on the hydrating surfaces. Hence this approach is not used in modern methods of measuring matric potential.

The phenomenon of hydration has three important characteristics that not only help define it but also help us understand its nature:

4.3.1A Volume change

In the course of hydration, the volume of the system increases; that is, swelling occurs. What happens at the molecular level, however, is not so clear. Careful measurements seemed to indicate that the total volume of the water imbibed plus the hydrating material is actually less after imbibition than before. This might be partially because water goes into micropores in the matrix, but the best present evidence indicates that there is an actual compression of water. That is, the water molecules, by being arranged on the surface of the imbibant, occupy less volume than the same molecules do when they are free in the normal liquid. On the other hand, some workers feel that the water molecules might take the ice crystal structure on the surface of the imbibant. This would result in an *expansion* of the water volume. The problem remains to be solved.

4.3.1B Production of heat

As the water molecules are arranged on the surface of the imbibant, they lose some of their kinetic energy, which then appears as heat in the system. This **heat of hydration** is analogous to the heat of fusion, the 80 cal/g given off when water freezes. In the process of hydration, most of the temperature

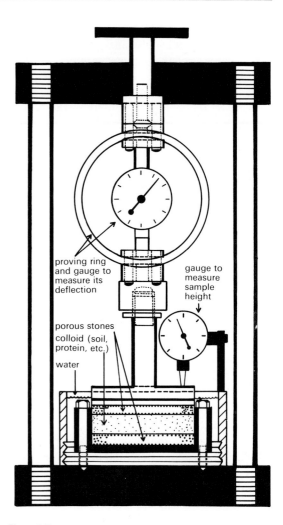

Figure 4-7

A mechanical apparatus that may be used to determine hydration pressures in the laboratory.

increase occurs at first, since the molecules closest to the imbibing surface are held the tightest.

4.3.1C Development of pressure

If a hydrating system is confined, great pressures may be developed by the swelling. This can be mechanically demonstrated in the laboratory (Fig. 4-7),

---

[3] 1.0 bar = 1,000 millibars (mbars)
         = 0.987 atmosphere = 10^6 dyne/cm^2
         = 1,019.7 g/cm^2 = 14.5 lb/in^2.

but such demonstrations are in certain respects less spectacular than those occurring in nature. For example, grass seeds may be trapped under an asphalt pavement, and when rain finally seeps under the edge of the pavement to the seeds, they will often develop enough imbibitional force to push the developing seedlings up through the asphalt. In the 1940s in Salt Lake City, Utah, a group of mushrooms caused a concrete driveway to shatter. Enough stress was developed in the concrete before breaking took place that, upon release of this stress, a noise like a rifle shot was produced, and pieces of concrete were actually displaced around a small "crater" containing the group of mushrooms. Imagine the forces necessary to cause such a phenomenon.

No one has yet devised a completely satisfactory mechanical system for measuring these forces, but the maximum pressures which could be developed should be numerically equal to the minimum matric potential expressed as pressure. This maximum pressure may exceed 3,000 bars. It approached 1,000 bars in the above example using cocklebur fruits.

4.3.2 Factors Influencing the Degree of Hydration

Since the hydration phenomenon is basically a response to free energy gradients, factors that will influence free energy gradients will also influence hydration. For example, with increasing temperature the rate of hydration is increased (at higher kinetic molecular activity, water molecules "find their place" sooner on the hydrating surface), although the total quantity of water imbibed is decreased (water molecules are harder to hold on the hydrating surface when they have higher kinetic activity). Thus, in the making of wheat or oatmeal mush, a softer product can be obtained if the material is allowed to imbibe water for a long period of time (overnight) at low temperature, but the mush can be prepared faster if it is boiled gently during preparation.

The presence of ions will influence the hydration process by their effect on water potential, but they will also influence the process in a specific way, depending upon their adsorption on the imbibing surface (i.e., according to the lyotropic series). The pH will also influence the ability of an amphoteric surface to become hydrated because of its effect on charge, as indicated above.

4.4 CONTACT CATALYSIS

Of the many responses of surfaces we have discussed in this chapter, one important one remains. This is the process of **contact catalysis**, whereby the rate of a chemical reaction is controlled by the presence of an adsorbing surface. In our biological application, protein enzymes adsorb reactants on their surfaces, thereby greatly hastening the speed with which the reaction can occur. In these systems, it is highly characteristic that *specific* proteins will adsorb strongly only highly *specific* molecules, catalyzing their further reaction. All of this will be discussed at length in Chapter 11 on protein chemistry.

5

Osmosis and the Components of Water Potential

Several factors within the plant influence water potential, and gradients in water potential may result in diffusional movements of water, if movements are not prevented by water-impermeable barriers.

Because in the plant there are many restrictions upon the free diffusion of solutes, the special diffusional water transfer called osmosis is of particular importance. There are cellular membranes, vacuolar membranes, nuclear membranes, membranes around plastids such as chloroplasts, and even membranes around the mitochondria. In each of these examples, water molecules may pass through the membranes more rapidly than solute particles, and thus the essential features of an osmotic system are present. The consequences include not only the development of pressures (turgor) within the cells but also the bulk movement of solutions within the plant. We will have occasion to consider a number of these manifestations in detail in subsequent chapters. The purpose of this chapter is to examine the components of water potential and the process of osmosis, particularly as they apply to plant cells.

5.1 THE OSMOTIC SYSTEM

A system in which osmosis occurs is called an **osmometer**. This may be a laboratory device,

or a living cell may be thought of as an osmometer. Both are illustrated in Fig. 5-1. In either case, two things are essential: *First*, solutions or pure water must be isolated by something that restricts the movement of solute particles more than it restricts the movement of solvent molecules. This could be a vapor gap or a layer of liquid with which the solutions are immiscible but through which solvent molecules may move more readily than solute particles. In most cases, however, the restriction is a membrane (see below). *Second*, an osmometer includes some means of allowing pressure to build up. Such an increase in pressure is not essential for osmosis to occur, but it is typically a part of a laboratory osmometer and an extremely important part of the plant cell osmometer. In the laboratory osmometer, pressures usually build up hydrostatically by the lifting of solution in a tube. Other means have also been used, such as a device for automatically increasing the external pressure on the system as soon as the volume of liquid begins to expand by the first small increment. This expansion may trip a microswitch, for example, or break a beam of light that falls on an electric eye, activating a pressure pump that shuts off when volume has decreased. In the cell, pressure can be built up because of the rigidity of the plant cell wall. It is important to differentiate between the cell wall and the membrane. The membrane allows water molecules to pass more readily than solute particles; the cell wall normally allows both to pass readily. It is the plant cell membrane that makes osmosis possible but the cell wall that provides the rigidity to allow a build-up in pressure. Animal cells do not have walls, and consequently pressure does not build up in them nearly as much as in plant cells.

In the initial part of the discussion below, we will consider a **perfect osmometer**. In such a device, the membrane is perfect, allowing ready passage of solvent (water), but *no* passage of solute, and the solution is so confined that movement of water into the osmometer causes no significant increase in solution volume. A nearly perfect osmometer can be constructed in the laboratory, but a cell is never a perfect osmometer.

5.1.1   The Process of Osmosis

As already indicated in Chapter 3, restriction upon the diffusion of solute particles compared to solvent molecules can result in the establishment of a water-potential gradient. If there is pure water on one side of the membrane and a solution on the other side (typically inside the laboratory osmometer or the cell), then the water potential of the solution will be lower than that of the pure water. By definition,

water potential of the pure water at atmospheric pressure is equal to zero, and so the water potential of the solution will be some negative number (less than zero).

Water molecules will diffuse "down" this water-potential gradient into the solution. The result will be a build-up of pressure within the osmometer, either a raising of liquid in the tube of the laboratory osmometer or a pressure upon the plant cell wall. *Increasing pressure will raise the water potential,* and so the water potential

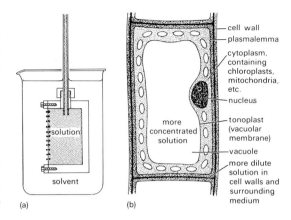

Figure 5-1

A mechanical osmometer (left), and the cell as an osmotic system (right). (From Salisbury and Parke, 1965, *Vascular Plants: Form and Function*, Wadsworth Publishing Company, Inc., Belmont, California, p. 25. Used by permission.)

within the osmometer will begin to increase toward zero. This is illustrated by Fig. 5-2.

The situation is analogous to the scale of a thermometer, but in this case we are dealing almost exclusively with values below zero. Addition of solute decreases the water potential level to some value below zero, and addition of pressure raises this level back toward zero. If pure water is on one side of the membrane, pressure on the other side will increase until the water potential of the solution is equal to zero; that is, equal to the water potential of the pure water on the other side. When water potentials are equal on both sides, the water potential difference between the two sides of the membrane is zero, and equilibrium has been achieved.

If on one side of the membrane there is a solution and on the other side another solution but of different concentration, osmosis will still occur. The more concentrated solution will have the lower (more negative) water potential. Water will diffuse from the other solution into this one until pressure has been built up to the point where the water potential in the more

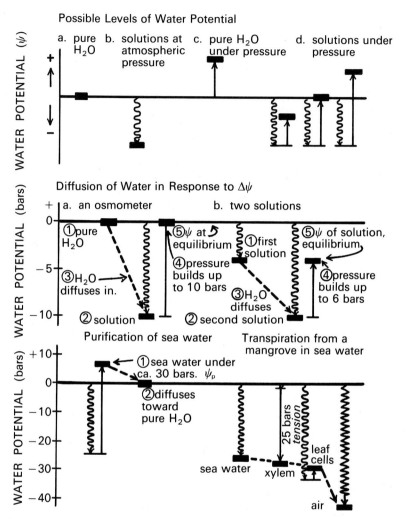

Figure 5-2
Effects of various conditions on water potentials, and diffusion of water in response to gradients' in water potential.

concentrated solution is equal to the water potential of the less concentrated solution, upon which there is no pressure. At this time, both solutions will have a water potential of some negative but equal value. Equilibrium will have been reached. Actually, the process is completely general. There could be pressure on both solutions, or the solution outside the osmometer might be more concentrated (water would move out as in plasmolysis, see below), but *when equilibrium is achieved, water potential will be equal in all parts of the system.*

5.1.1A The components of water potential
In the above paragraph, we have considered **water potential** (ψ) and two of its components:

pressure potential (ψ_p), which is due to the addition of pressure, and **osmotic potential** (ψ_π), which is due to the presence of solute particles. At constant temperatures, the water potential results from the combined action of the pressure potential and the osmotic potential:

$$\psi = \psi_p + \psi_\pi \qquad (15)$$

The pressure potential may be any value, either positive or negative. Addition of pressure results in a positive pressure potential, and tension (see Chapter 7) results in a negative pressure potential. The osmotic potential, within our experience, is always negative. That is, addition of solute particles always results in a decrease in water potential and never in an increase. Since pressure potential can be positive and very high, and osmotic potential can be either zero or negative, water potential can be either negative, zero, or positive. In pure water at atmospheric pressure, water potential is defined as zero. In a solution at atmospheric pressure, water potential will be negative. In pure water under some external pressure above atmospheric, water potential will be positive. In a solution under some pressure other than atmospheric, water potential may be negative (pressure potential less negative than osmotic potential), zero (pressure potential equal to osmotic potential), or positive (pressure potential exceeding osmotic potential).

5.1.1B Expression of water potential as energy or as pressure

Water potential and its components may be thought of either in terms of energy or of pressure. In energy terms (joules/kilogram, ergs/gram, or calories/mole), the value expresses the ability of the part of the system under consideration to do work compared with the ability to do work of a comparable quantity of water at atmospheric pressure. The osmotic potential of a solution is negative because the ability of the water in the solution to do work is *less* than the ability of pure water

to do work. As pressure on the solution increases, the ability of the water in the solution to do work also increases. In practice, the work is usually performed by movement of pure water into the solution. In a laboratory osmometer, for example, a 1.0 m sugar solution at 28°C has an osmotic potential of -10.77 calories/mole, and this indicates (but doesn't necessarily equal) the work done as pure water comes into equilibrium with the solution in the osmometer. This indicates the energy required to raise the level of the liquid to the point in the laboratory osmometer where the pressure exerted increases the water potential of the solution to zero. This pressure will be equal to 25 bars in a perfect osmometer. A column of mercury 18.75 meters high would be supported. In the case of the cell, the work is done by stretching the cell wall. It is important to realize that the work is actually done by the pure water, which has the higher water potential.

When water potential or its components are expressed in terms of energy, this is equivalent to the chemical potential defined as the free energy/mole. Thus, water potential expressed as energy might more accurately be referred to as **molar or specific water potential** (-10.77 calories/mole for the 1.0 m sugar solution above). Dividing this value by the molar volume (18 ml) or specific volume (1 ml/g) of water changes the expression to units of pressure.[1] The result may

---

[1] For example:

$$\frac{ergs/g}{ml/g} = ergs/ml = dyne\ cm/cm^3$$

$$= dyne/cm^2,$$

the dimensions of pressure. Specifically, since 1.0 erg $= 2.389 \times 10^{-8}$ cal, and 1.0 mole $H_2O = 18$ g, then

$$-10.77\ cal/mole \times \frac{1.0\ erg}{2.389 \times 10^{-8}\ cal} \div 1.0\ ml/g$$

$$= -25.4 \times 10^6\ ergs/ml \quad or \quad dyne/cm^2$$

and

$$-25.4 \times 10^6\ dyne/cm^2 \times \frac{1.0\ bar}{10^6\ dyne/cm^2} = 25.4\ bars.$$

be thought of as the **volumetric water potential** (-25 bars for the same solution). For many applications in plant physiology, expresssion of water potential and its components in terms of pressure offers important advantages. The examples of problems given at the end of this chapter utilize exclusively pressure units (bars, the most convenient metric unit for our application).

There are certain simple guidelines that should help the student in considering the phenomenon of osmosis. Regardless of whether the potentials are expressed as energy or pressure, under isothermal conditions

water will always tend to diffuse "down" a water potential gradient toward lower (more negative) values. At equilibrium, water potential will be the same throughout an entire system.

If one part of this system contains pure water at atmospheric pressure, equilibrium water potentials will be equal to zero. Under other circumstances, equilibrium water potentials might have any value, either positive or negative. It is often convenient to consider the **water potential difference** ($\Delta\psi$) between different parts of an osmotic system

$$\Delta\psi = \psi_1 - \psi_2 \qquad (16)$$

Another way of saying that water potentials are equal in two parts of a system at equilibrium is to say that $\Delta\psi = 0$ when $\psi_1 = \psi_2$.

5.1.1C Effects of dilution

We have neglected one factor that may be very important in a real osmotic system as contrasted to a perfect osmometer. As water moves across the membrane, it will not only cause an increase in pressure, but it will also tend to dilute the solution. This will increase the osmotic potential in the solution (make it less negative), and so the pressure required to reach equilibrium will be somewhat less than might have been predicted from the original osmotic potential. In studying the

water relations of plant cells, the dilution effect should be taken into account whenever possible by measuring the volume before and after osmosis has taken place and correcting the osmotic potential by the laws of dilution indicated in Chapter 3 (footnote 5).

The relationship between water potential and its two primary components is well illustrated by the so-called Höfler diagram (Fig. 5-3). The concept of this diagram was devised by K. Höfler in Germany in 1920. It indicates the magnitudes of water potential, pressure potential, and osmotic potential as a function of cell volume, assuming that the cell expands by taking in water and that no solutes pass out during cell expansion. The curve for osmotic potential is derived by the simple dilution relationship that holds to a close approximation for dilute molal solutions ($\psi_{\pi 1} V_1 = \psi_{\pi 2} V_2$). The curve for pressure potential, on the other hand, is purely hypothetical. It will depend upon the stretching properties of the cell wall, being very steep if the wall is very rigid and much less steep if the wall is less rigid. The water potential curve is the summation of the pressure potential and the osmotic potential curves as predicted by equation (15).

5.1.2 Inadequacy of the Concentration of Water Explanation for Osmosis

It may be noted that the explanation for the process of osmosis presented above (and in Chapter 3) differs somewhat from that often encountered in textbooks in biological fields. Usually, it is stated that osmosis occurs because the presence of solute particles *decreases* the concentration of water molecules. In the sense of the mole-fraction, this explanation is valid: the mole-fraction of solvent has been decreased by addition of solute. In terms of the definition of concentration as quantity per unit volume, however, the water concentration explanation

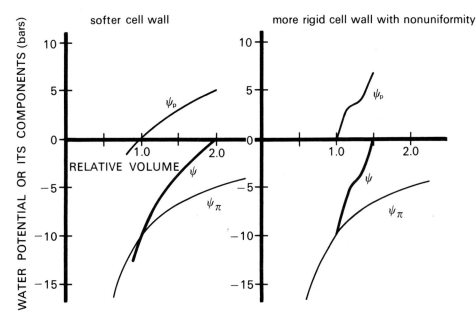

Figure 5-3

The Höfler diagram, using the concept of water potential as discussed in the text. The components of water potential are shown as they change with changing volume: for a cell with a soft cell wall (left) and for one with a more rigid cell wall and with nonuniform expansion properties (right).

simply does not apply (also discussed in section 3.3.1C). Diffusion occurs in response to a gradient in water potential, and this is influenced by presence of solutes (osmotic potential) and pressure potential, but it is virtually independent of water concentration in the usual sense. This becomes especially clear when we realize that water concentration is influenced in many different ways upon addition of different kinds of solutes. Volume may increase slightly, change not at all, or in a few cases, actually decrease. In the last-named case, water concentration *increases*, although osmotic potential decreases (becomes more negative). Some examples are shown in Table 5-1 and compared to the effects of solute mole-fraction upon osmotic potential. Clearly, the osmotic effect cannot be predicted on the basis of water concentration.

5.1.3 The Membrane

Membranes exist in a wide variety, but osmosis will occur regardless of how the membrane functions so long as solute movement is restricted compared to water movement (Fig. 5-4). As indicated above, the "membrane" could consist of a layer of liquid immiscible in the solvent of the osmotic system, but allowing more solvent molecules than solute particles to pass through. A layer of air between two water solutions provides a perfect osmotic barrier. Water will pass between different parts of the system in the vapor state, but nonvolatile solutes will not. We can imagine a membrane filled with small pores containing air, or a membrane in which the solvent molecules can dissolve, as in the layer-of-liquid analogy. The third membrane mechanism we

TABLE 5-1

THE RELATIONSHIP BETWEEN OSMOTIC POTENTIAL AND WATER CONCENTRATION OR MOLALITY OF SOLUTE

Solute	Molality (m)	Ψ_π (van't Hoff) (bars)	Ψ_π (empirical) (bars)	Solution volume (% of pure H_2O)	Water concentration (C_{H_2O}) (moles/liter)	$\Psi_\pi C$[a]	Ψ_π/mi[b]
pure H_2O (20°C)	0	0	0	100%	55.408 M	—	—
$MgSO_4$	0.08 m	5.80 ($i = 2$)	—	99.870%	55.437 M	321.0	24.15
NaCl	0.10	4.83 ($i = 2$)	—	100.165%	55.310 M	267.0	24.15
NH_4Cl	4.73	114.4 ($i = 2$)	—	118.3%	46.9	5,360.0	24.15
sucrose (20°C)	0.1	2.42	2.62	102.08%	54.280	143.0	26.2
	0.5	12.08	12.90	110.32%	50.225	643.0	25.8
	1.0	24.17	27.00	120.68%	45.912	1,240.0	27.0

Data from several sources. See especially A. S. Crafts, H. B. Currier, and C. R. Stocking, 1949. Water in the Physiology of Plants. *Chronica Botanica*, Waltham, Mass. (For $MgSO_4$, see T. Kohlrausch and W. Hallwawch, 1894, *Ann. Physk.* 53:14.)

[a] If Ψ_π is *inversely* proportional to water concentration (C_{H_2O}), then $\Psi_\pi \cdot C_{H_2O}$ = Constant. For sucrose, empirical values of Ψ_π are used.

[b] If Ψ_π is *directly* proportional to molality (m) times the correction for ionization (i), then Ψ_π/mi = Constant. For sucrose, empirical values of Ψ_π are used.

can visualize would be a sieve-type membrane with holes of such a size that water molecules could pass but not solute particles. It is conceivable that all three of these kinds of membranes or barriers exist in plants, or at least in the soil-plant-air system.

In the perfect osmometer, solvent molecules would penetrate the membrane readily while solute particles would not penetrate at all. We will define this as a truly **semipermeable membrane**. The vapor "membrane" is a good example. It is found, however, that most and probably all of the true membranes occurring in plants allow some solute to pass as well as the solvent. In such cases we are dealing with **differentially permeable membranes** rather than truly semipermeable ones. This introduces an important complication in our consideration of osmosis. Clearly, the rates of osmotic water movement and equilibration will be determined

by the nature of the membrane. The more permeable the membrane is to water molecules, the more rapidly osmotic water movement will occur. Hydrated membranes may be more permeable to water than dry membranes (e.g., as in seeds). The permeability of the membrane to solute particles will determine the rate at which the equilibrium established by concentration and pressure will gradually shift as osmotic potentials on either side of the membrane change in response to the passage of solute particles. Several conventions have been adopted in an attempt to express quantitatively the relationship between the permeability of the membrane to water molecules and its permeability to solute particles. The **reflection coefficient** (σ) is one of them. When $\sigma = 1$, the membrane is semipermeable (all solutes are "reflected"). When $\sigma < 1$, for a particular solute, it can pass through the membrane, and

MEMBRANE MECHANISMS:

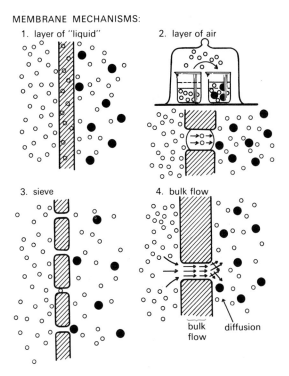

Figure 5-4
A schematic diagram illustrating the four conceivable membrane mechanisms discussed in the text.

if $\sigma < 1$ for all solutes, then ultimate equilibrium will be achieved only after osmotic potentials have become identical in all parts of the system.

In recent years, Peter Ray (then at the University of Michigan), and other workers as well, brought an interesting problem to the attention of plant physiologists. This concerns the mechanism of osmotic movement of water across a membrane. Calculations of the thickness of certain membranes and the rate of osmotic water movement across them show that this movement cannot occur strictly by diffusion. Rates are too high. It is said that to account for the rates, water must move through these pores by bulk flow. In diffusion, individual molecules move according to their random kinetic energy, but in **bulk flow**, volumes of water (or other fluid or gas) molecules move together in response to some pressure gradient. Ray has suggested that the actual zone of diffusion is very thin—an interface, say, between water in the pores of the membrane and the solution inside of the osmometer. At this interface, the water-potential gradient would be extremely steep, resulting in a very rapid diffusion. This rapid movement of water across the interface into the solution would create a tension in the water in the pore, pulling it along in a bulk flow (Fig. 5-4). Clearly, this is just another complication in our consideration of membrane mechanisms. Ultimate control of osmotic water movement is thermodynamic through the diffusion resulting from a water-potential gradient, even though part of the actual movement of water in the membrane may be due to a bulk flow mechanism.

It is interesting to note that use of the vapor barrier model of an osmotic system contributed to the early development of quantitative expressions relating to osmotic potential. Considering the vapor pressure above pure water and above a solution, according to Raoult's law [Chapter 3, equation (12)], it was possible to derive expressions for the osmotic potential. This was an important early confirmation of developing thermodynamic principles.

5.1.4 The Rate of Osmotic Water Movement

So far, we have considered the thermodynamic conditions that can result in osmotic water movement, and the conditions that will exist at equilibrium. The actual rate of water flow across the membrane is determined by two factors (in a manner exactly analogous to Ohm's law for the flow of an electric current across a resistance). **Flow** (J, flow per unit cross-sectional area) is proportional to the **driving force** (the water-potential difference, $\Delta\psi$) and inversely proportional to the **resistance** of the membrane (r):

$$J = \frac{\Delta\psi}{r} \qquad (17)$$

In dealing with osmotic movement, it is more convenient to think of the *reciprocal* of resistance, namely, **permeability** (L_w), a parameter expressing the rate at which *water* (indicated by the subscript *w*) can move through the membrane under a given driving force (Chapter 8):

$$L_w = \frac{1}{r} \qquad (18)$$

Flow then becomes equal to the driving force times the permeability:

$$J = \Delta\psi L_w \qquad (19)$$

From the concepts of equations (15) and (16):

$$\Delta\psi = \Delta\psi_p + \Delta\psi_\pi \qquad (20)$$

Substituting in equation (19), we then obtain for the flow:

$$J = L_w(\Delta\psi_p + \Delta\psi_\pi) \qquad (21)$$

Or, including the reflection coefficient (σ), for a real membrane:

$$J = L_w(\Delta\psi_p + \sigma\Delta\psi_\pi) \qquad (21A)$$

Permeability is a parameter with the following units: quantity of water per unit cross section of membrane per unit time per unit driving force. The driving force in the permeability will cancel the units of ($\Delta\psi_\pi + \Delta\psi_p$), giving flow in units of quantity/area/time. From the above formula it can be seen that permeability (of a membrane to water) can be determined by measurements of the rate of flow and the driving force:

$$L_w = \frac{J}{\Delta\psi} = \frac{J}{\sigma\Delta\psi_\pi + \Delta\psi_p} \qquad (22)$$

5.2 THE TRADITIONAL OSMOTIC SYSTEM OF PHYSIOLOGISTS

The phenomenon of osmosis was discovered before the principles of thermodynamics had been worked out. The German plant physiologist W. F. P. Pfeffer made some extremely careful measurements of the pressures that could be developed in an osmometer by solutions of various concentrations, and these data, published as early as 1877, were applied in the subsequent development of thermodynamics. Pfeffer had used highly rigid, virtually semipermeable osmometers made by precipitating cupric ferrocyanide in the pores of a porous clay cup. The cups were soaked first in potassium ferrocyanide and then in cupric sulfate. Columns of mercury were used to determine pressure. Perfection of such osmometers in subsequent years allowed the development of real pressures as high as 273 atmospheres. In 1915, the German plant physiologist Otto Renner introduced the concept of water potential, realizing that diffusion of water occurred not only in response to differences in solution concentration, but that pressure was also important. He used the term *Saugkraft* or suction force for the water potential concept.

The principles of the system developed by the physiologists are identical in every important respect to those described above in relation to water potential and its components. The sign, however, was in each case applied in an opposite way. The **osmotic pressure** was defined as a property of a solution expressed in pressure terms equivalent to the real pressure that could be developed in a perfect osmometer when this was placed in pure water at 1 atmosphere pressure. It was natural to think of the osmotic pressure in a positive sense, because it was measured by determining a real and positive pressure in the osmometer. The effect of the pressure in the osmometer was subtracted from the osmotic pressure to arrive at the value we have expressed as water potential but that was a positive number in this system when water potential is negative (as is typically the case).

The system has been perfectly adequate for a great many studies until about the time of the writing of this book, at which time soil scientists and plant physiologists are converting to the water potential terminology. This is advantageous in that water potential and the chemical potential of thermodynamics are identical, a potential to do work is expressed, and the concept of diffusion of water "*down*" a water-potential gradient seems (to some, at least) to be a better analogy than diffusion "*up*" a gradient.

One of the greatest difficulties encountered in the osmotic system of physiologists has been terminology. Table 5-2 summarizes some of the terms that have been used for the concept of water potential and its components and the combining of these terms into the osmotic equation.

The term osmotic pressure has itself been confusing to many students, since it seems to imply a real pressure while it is actually only a property of a solution expressed in pressure terms. To overcome this problem, some authors have suggested use of the terms **osmotic concentration** or osmotic potential. In this book we will restrict use of the term osmotic potential to the component of water potential that becomes increasingly negative with the addition of solute. The term osmotic pressure may be used for the same conceptual idea, except that it becomes increasingly positive with the addition of solute.

Even the pressure terms have provided some confusion. Thermodynamically, the simple term pressure is quite adequate. Pressure at a point in a fluid has no direction but is equal in all directions. The effect in an osmotic system is upon the free energy of the solvent molecules, again quite independent of direction. Nevertheless, physiologists have long differentiated between **turgor pressure**, the protoplast pushing against the wall, and **wall pressure**, the equal and opposite pushing of the wall against the cell contents. This usage has been taken from Newton's third law of *equal* and opposite reactions. Yet, it has been stated that growth of a cell occurs when turgor pressure *exceeds* wall pressure. It would be better to say that growth occurs when pressure exceeds the resistance of the cell wall to plastic deformation (Chapter 19). In this text, wall pressure will not be used, but **turgor pressure** will be used exclusively to refer to the pressure within plant cells.

By far the greatest confusion has come about in relation to the terminology of the water-potential concept. Originally, the term **suction force** (*Saugkraft*) or **suction pressure** was applied. It was thought that the solution in the osmometer had an attractive or suction effect upon the water outside. Although this does appear to be the end result, it is not a completely correct way to look at things. Diffusion of water molecules is occurring "down" a water-potential gradient. The molecules are not being *pulled* into the osmometer any more than a vacuum pulls molecules of air out through a leak in a container. Water molecules do have a tendency to *escape* from a liquid (to be pushed), and this is fortified not only by the leaky-container analogy, but also by the vapor pressure. If vapor pressure is thought of as arising from the escape tendency of the water molecules, then we can imagine that the escape tendency of pure water is greater than that of a solution and explain osmosis in these terms (as in the derivation for osmotic potential from Raoult's law). This escaping tendency has been referred to as a **diffusion pressure**, and since the solution has a lower diffusion pressure than the pure water, we might say that it has a **diffusion pressure deficit**. This explanation and terminology were put forth by Bernard S. Meyer at Ohio State University in 1938. The explanation is in every important respect equivalent to the explanation from thermodynamics presented above, but the language is somewhat different. The term

TABLE 5-2

TERMINOLOGY FOR THE OSMOTIC QUANTITIES AS USED BY SEVERAL AUTHORS

	This text, others[a]	Meyer and Anderson, many others[b]	Bonner and Galston[c]	Levitt[d]	Steward[e]	Salisbury and Parke[f]	James[g]	Fogg[h]	Renner[i]	Harder, Firbas, Schumacher, von Denffer[j]
Osmotic Potential Ψ_π (or π)		Osmotic Pressure OP	Osmotic Concentration OC	Osmotic Potential O	Osmotic Pressure P	Osmotic Potential ϕ	Osmotic Pressure O.P.	Osmotic Pressure P_i (internal) P_o (external)	Osmotischer Druck (Osmotic Pressure) P	Osmotischer Saugwert (suction value) oder Osmotische Potenz (potential) S_i
Pressure Potential Ψ_p (or P)		Turgor Pressure (equal and opposite to Wall Pressure) TP	Turgor Pressure TP	Wall Pressure p	Wall Pressure W	Pressure P	Wall Pressure W.P.	Turgor Pressure T	Hydrostatischer Druck oder Turgordruck T (hydrostatic or turgor pressure)	Gegendruck der Zellwand W (Opposing pressure of the cell wall)
Water Potential Ψ		Diffusion Pressure Deficit DPD	Diffusion Pressure Deficit DPD	Osmotic Equivalent E	Suction Pressure S	Enter Tendency E	Suction Pressure S.P.	Diffusion Pressure Deficit S	Saugkraft (suction force)	Saugkraft S_z
Water Potential Difference $\Delta\Psi$	$\Psi = \Psi_\pi + \Psi_p$	$DPD = OP - TP$	$DPD = OC - TP$	Osmotic Potential Difference P — $E = O - p$	$S = P - W$	$E = \phi - P$	$S.P. = O.P. - W.P.$	$S = (P_i - P_o) - T$	Saugkraft = $P - T$	$S_z = S_i - W$

[a] Gardner, W. R. 1965. Dynamic aspects of water availability to plants. *Ann. Rev. Pl. Physiol.* 16:323–342.
Kramer, P. J., Knipling, E. B., and Miller, L. N. 1966. Terminology in cell water relations. *Science* 153:889–890.
Slatyer, R. O. 1967. *Plant Water Relationships*, Academic Press, New York.
Taylor, S. A., and Slatyer, R. O. 1962. Proposals for a unified terminology in studies of plant-soil-water relations. *UNESCO Arid Zone Res.* 16:339–349.

[b] Devlin, R. M. 1966. *Plant Physiology*. Reinhold Publishing Corporation, New York.
Ferry, J. R., and Ward, H. S. 1959. *Fundamentals of Plant Physiology*. The Macmillan Co., New York.
Kramer, P. J., and Kozlowski, T. T. 1960. *Physiology of Trees*. McGraw-Hill, New York, Toronto, London.
Kozlowski, T. T. 1964. *Water Metabolism in Plants*. Harper & Row, Publishers, New York, Evanston, and London.
Meyer, B. S., Anderson, D. B. and Bohning, R. H. 1960. *Introduction to Plant Physiology*, D. Van Nostrand Co., Inc., Princeton, N.J., Toronto, London, New York.

[c] Bonner, James, and Galston, A. W. 1952. *Principles of Plant Physiology*. W. H. Freeman and Co., San Francisco.

[d] Levitt, J. 1954. *Plant Physiology*, Prentice-Hall, Inc., Englewood Cliffs, N.J.

[e] Steward, F. C. 1964. *Plants at Work*, Addison-Wesley Publishing Co., Inc., Palo Alto, London, and Reading, Massachusetts.

[f] Salisbury, F. B., and Parke, R. V. 1964. *Vascular Plants: Form and Function*. Wadsworth Publishing Co. Inc., Belmont, California.

[g] James, W. O. 1963. *An Introduction to Plant Physiology*. Clarendon Press, Oxford.

[h] Fogg, G. E. 1963. *The Growth of Plants*, Penguin Books Ltd., Harmondsworth, Middlesex. U.S.A.: Penguin Books Inc., Baltimore. Md.

[i] The paper in which the concept of water potential (Saugkraft) was proposed:
O. Renner. 1915. Theoretisches und Experimentelles zur Kohäsionstheorie der Wasserbewegung. *Jahrbuch für Wissenschaftliche Botanik* 56:617–667.

[j] A textbook in wide use in Germany: Harder, R., Firbas, F., Schumacher, W., and Von Denffer, D. 1962. *Lehrbuch Der Botanik. Für Hochschulen.* Gustav Fischer Verlag, Stuttgart, Germany.

diffusion pressure deficit (DPD) reached by far the widest acceptance in the United States of any of the available terms for the water-potential concept. Like osmotic pressure, it is typically a positive term rather than a negative one.

The student should be fully aware of the traditional system, but the thermodynamic approach to osmosis and the water-potential concept that develops logically from it offer many advantages. This system is followed exclusively in this textbook.

5.3 PROPERTIES AND MEASUREMENTS OF THE COMPONENTS OF WATER POTENTIAL

Soon after formulation of the water-potential concept, methods were developed for the measurement of water potential and its components. These methods were used for many years, but recently newer methods have been introduced. The older methods are instructive in terms of our understanding of plant-cell-water relations, but the newer methods are more valuable for current research applications. We will summarize a few of the original as well as the newer methods in the following paragraphs.

5.3.1 Water Potential

Probably the most meaningful property we can measure in the soil-plant-air system is the water potential. This is the final determinant of diffusional water movement; and, as suggested above, bulk water movement may also occur in response to pressure gradients set up by diffusional movement under the control of a water-potential gradient. Furthermore, both in principle and in practice, water potential is probably the simplest component of an osmotic system to measure. As indicated above, at equilibrium $\Delta\psi = 0$, or ψ is equal throughout all parts of the system. Thus, a plant part can be introduced into a closed system, and after equilibrium has been achieved ψ may be known or determined for any other part of the system, indicating its value for the plant part. There are several possibilities for applying this principle. Three general approaches are most widely used (Fig. 5-5).

5.3.1A Volume change Sample pieces of the tissue in question are placed in a series of solutions of varying concentration. The object is to find that solution in which the volume of the tissue does not change, indicating neither a gain nor a loss in water. Such a situation would imply that the tissue and the solution were in equilibrium to begin with, and so the water potential of the tissue must be equal to that of the solution. (At atmospheric pressure, $\psi = \psi_\pi$.)

In practice, the primary problem concerns the determination of volume change. This may be done volumetrically by measuring the volume of the tissue before placing it in a solution (usually standard volumes are cut), and then measuring the volume again after time has been allowed for exchange of water. Sometimes only one dimension is measured, as length of a cylinder of potato tuber tissue. Volume change may be plotted as a function of solution concentration, indicating a gain of volume in relatively dilute solutions and a loss of volume in relatively concentrated ones. On such a plot (Fig. 5-6), the point at which the volume curve crosses the zero line indicates the tissue water potential.

In some cases it may be more convenient (e.g., with leaves) to determine the weight of the tissue rather than its volume. This method might be somewhat less reliable, however, since one must be certain that all excess moisture has been blotted from the tissue before weighing, and it is very difficult to be sure that no test solution has infiltrated into the intercellular spaces of the tissues. In an attempt to overcome these problems, tissue samples have been allowed to equilibrate in small closed containers with the

Chardakov's method:

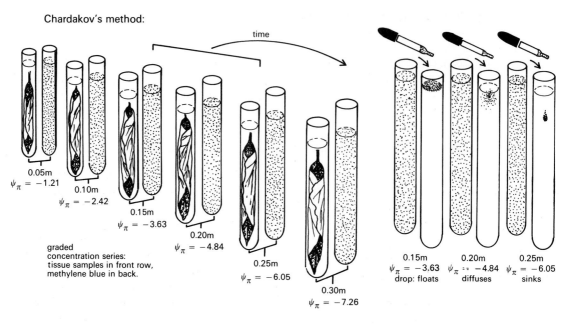

graded
concentration series:
tissue samples in front row,
methylene blue in back.

0.05m
$\psi_\pi = -1.21$

0.10m
$\psi_\pi = -2.42$

0.15m
$\psi_\pi = -3.63$

0.20m
$\psi_\pi = -4.84$

0.25m
$\psi_\pi = -6.05$

0.30m
$\psi_\pi = -7.26$

0.15m
$\psi_\pi = -3.63$
drop: floats

0.20m
$\psi_\pi = -4.84$
diffuses

0.25m
$\psi_\pi = -6.05$
sinks

Constant Volume Method:

Vapor Pressure Method:

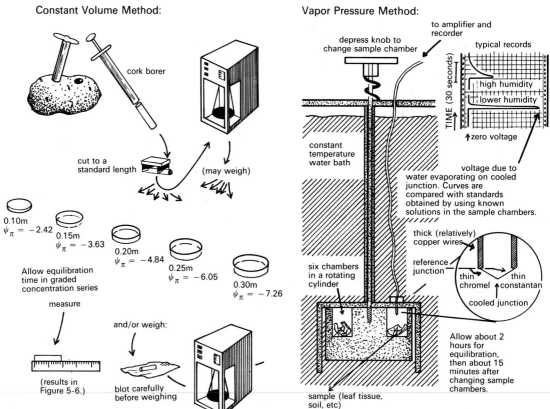

cork borer

cut to a
standard length

(may weigh)

0.10m
$\psi_\pi = -2.42$

0.15m
$\psi_\pi = -3.63$

0.20m
$\psi_\pi = -4.84$

0.25m
$\psi_\pi = -6.05$

0.30m
$\psi_\pi = -7.26$

Allow equilibration
time in graded
concentration series

measure

and/or weigh:

(results in
Figure 5-6.)

blot carefully
before weighing

depress knob to
change sample chamber

to amplifier and
recorder

typical records

TIME (30 seconds)

high humidity

lower humidity

zero voltage

constant
temperature
water bath

voltage due to
water evaporating on cooled
junction. Curves are
compared with standards
obtained by using known
solutions in the sample chambers.

thick (relatively)
copper wires

reference
junction

thin
chromel

thin
constantan

cooled junction

six chambers
in a rotating
cylinder

Allow about 2
hours for
equilibration,
then about 15
minutes after
changing sample
chambers.

sample (leaf tissue,
soil, etc)

Figure 5-5
The three different ways to measure water potential, as discussed in the text.

vapor over solutions of known concentration rather than with the solutions themselves. There is a problem in maintaining constant temperature, and there are problems with equilibrium times and changes that might take place in the tissue during equilibration.

5.3.1B Changes in concentration of the test solution
Rather than measuring the tissue itself, one might measure the test solution. If it becomes more concentrated, the tissue will have absorbed water; if it becomes less concentrated, the tissue will have lost water. Several methods might be used in this approach. Sugar solutions may be tested with a refractometer, for example, the index of refraction being a sensitive indication of concentration.

A Russian scientist, V. S. Chardakov, devised in 1953 a very simple yet efficient method of determining the test solution in which no change in concentration occurs. His method may conveniently be used in the field. Test tubes containing the graded solutions of known concentrations are colored slightly by the addition of a very small crystal of methylene blue (addition of the crystal does not change osmotic potential significantly). Tissue samples are placed in test tubes containing equivalent solutions but with no dye. Some time is allowed for exchange of water. It is not essential that the tissue reach equilibrium with the solution, but only that a certain amount of exchange of water occurs. This may happen within a few minutes, perhaps as short a time as 5 to 15 minutes. After this time, tissue is removed, and a small drop of the comparable colored solution is added to the test tube. If the colored drop stays on top of the liquid in the test tube, then the solution has become more dense, indicating that the tissue has taken up water. Thus the tissue has a lower (more negative) water potential than the original solution. If the drop sinks, the solution is now less dense than originally, having absorbed some water from the tissue.

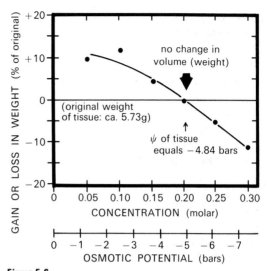

Figure 5-6

Weight of plant tissue samples as a function of the concentration of solutions with which the samples have been allowed to come into equilibrium. (Data from a student plant physiology laboratory report, Colorado State University.)

The solution, then, has a lower water potential than the tissue. If the drop diffuses evenly out into the solution without sinking, then no change in concentration has occurred, and the water potential of the solution equals that of the tissue. To insure fairly rapid changes in osmotic potential of the test solutions, relatively large amounts of tissue are used in small volumes of test solution.

The main errors involved in these methods result from contamination of the test solution by solutes on the surface of the tissue or released at the cut surfaces of the tissue. Substances may also diffuse out of the intact cells of the tissue, changing the concentration of the test solutions. These errors may be avoided to some extent by using as much uncut tissue as possible and making measurements after as short a time as possible.

5.3.1C Vapor pressure measurement
If a tissue is placed in a small, closed volume of air,

the water potential of the air will come into equilibrium with the water potential of the tissue. The water potential of the air is measured by measuring vapor pressure (humidity) at a known temperature.[2] The principle is quite simple, yet in practice a number of difficulties are involved, and these have been solved only relatively recently. Now the approach is coming into much wider use and may well be the predominant method in future years. To begin with, temperature must be controlled within a thousandth of a degree centigrade, if the method is to be sufficiently accurate. (Slight changes in relative humidity indicate large changes in water potential.) Such temperature control is now possible if the test chamber is submerged in a suitable water bath. The second problem involves measurement of the humidity inside of the test chamber. If a wet-bulb thermometer is used, the humidity in the chamber will probably come into equilibrium with the wet bulb rather than the tissue. An ingenious method was first developed in 1951 by O. C. Spanner in England. It has since been improved by several workers. Two thermocouple junctions are built into the chamber. One of these has a relatively large mass and thus remains at the temperature of the air in the chamber (water-bath temperature). The second is very minute, and when a weak current is passed in the right direction through the two junctions, the small one cools rapidly by the Peltier effect. As this

thermocouple cools, a minute drop of moisture condenses on it from the air inside the chamber. This very small point of moisture then acts as the "wet bulb," and the difference between its temperature and that of the dry thermocouple indicates the water potential of the air in the chamber. In practice, the drop evaporates so rapidly that actual temperatures cannot be measured. Rather, the system is arbitrarily calibrated using solutions of known concentrations. Typically, measurements (which require less than a minute) are made at regular intervals until they become stabilized after an hour or two, indicating that the tissue has reached equilibrium with the air in the chamber (Fig. 5-5).

5.3.2 Osmotic Potential

As implied from the definition of osmotic potential, this property of a solution may be measured directly in an osmometer. Initially, many measurements of this type were made (as indicated earlier, particularly by the plant physiologist Pfeffer). With our developing understanding of the colligative properties of solutions, it became apparent that other, simpler measurements could be made, and the data then could be converted by calculation to terms of osmotic potential. Excellent ways of doing this with free liquids have been developed, but no completely satisfactory method is yet available for measuring the osmotic potential of the liquid in plant cells. Attempts to measure it almost invariably result in changing it.

---

[2] Knowing the absolute temperature (T), the vapor pressure of pure water at that temperature ($p°$), the vapor pressure in the test chamber (p), and the molar volume of water (V_1 in liters/mole), water potential is calculated from the following formula derived from Raoult's law:

$$-\psi = \frac{RT}{V_1} \ln \frac{p°}{p}$$

This simplifies to:

$$-\psi \text{ bars} = 10.7T \log_{10}\left(\frac{100}{\text{RH}}\right)$$

where RH = relative humidity.

5.3.2A The van't Hoff Law

Plotting osmotic potential from direct osmometer readings as a function of solution concentration, J. H. van't Hoff discovered in 1887 an empirical relationship that resembles exactly the law for perfect gases:

$$-\psi_\pi = miRT \qquad (23)$$

where:

    m = molality of the solution

    i = a constant which accounts for ionization of the solute and/or other deviations from perfect solutions

    R = the gas constant (0.083 liter bars/mole degree, or 0.082 liter atmospheres/mole degree, or 0.0357 liter calories/mole^2 degree)

    T = absolute temperature

If i and m are known for a given solution, then osmotic potential may be readily calculated for dilute solutions in the absence of highly active colloids. For nonionized molecules such as sucrose or mannitol, i may be equal to one, but in other cases i may vary with concentration (activity), partially because the extent to which a salt or acid ionizes may depend upon its concentration. Tables of empirically determined osmotic potentials are available (some examples are shown in Tables 5-1 and 5-3).

The van't Hoff law stated that osmotic potential (actually, osmotic pressure) will be equivalent to the pressure of a gas under equivalent conditions. That is, if the solute particles were suspended in an equivalent volume as a gas, they would exert a pressure on the walls equivalent to the absolute value (positive) of the osmotic potential. Under standard conditions, the pressure of 1 mole of a gas in 1 liter would be 22.7 bars, and −22.7 bars is the osmotic potential developed by a 1 molal solution of nonionizing solute. This interesting relationship caused considerable confusion. The relationship is now generally accepted as essentially coincidental; it is incorrect to think of solute particles as exerting pressure on the walls of the container as though they were a gas. Obviously, such pressures are not exerted, and at best we have only a good analogy.

5.3.2B Vapor pressure method
The method described for the measurement of water potential by equilibration of the sample with air in a closed container applies equally well to the measurement of osmotic potential, provided a sample of liquid at approximately atmospheric pressure (zero pressure potential) is used instead of intact tissue. At $\psi_p = 0$, $\psi = \psi_\pi$. As an application of this principle, a tissue may be frozen and then its water potential measured by the vapor pressure method. Rapid freezing in the laboratory produces ice crystals that rupture all the membranes,[3] so that pressure within the cells becomes zero and $\psi = \psi_\pi$. The treatment could also result in some mixing of cytoplasm and vacuolar sap with a consequent change in osmotic potential. The method is in frequent current use.

5.3.2C Cryoscopic method
Since the freezing point, as well as the vapor pressure, is one of the colligative properties of solutions, when it is determined, osmotic potential can be calculated. Of course, boiling points would provide the same information, but they are less satisfactory because some solutes may be destroyed or changed by boiling. Freezing point is perhaps the easiest of the colligative properties of solutions for us to determine using presently available equipment.

As mentioned above, the osmotic potential of a molal nonionized solution is ideally −22.7 bars. Its freezing point (Δ_f) proves to be −1.86°C. Thus the osmotic potential of an unknown dilute solution may be estimated from its freezing point by the relationship:

$$\frac{\psi_\pi}{-22.7} = \frac{\Delta_f}{-1.86}$$

or

$$\psi_\pi = 12.2\Delta_f \qquad (24)$$

---

[3] Natural freezing in the out-of-doors seldom if ever is rapid enough to result in rupturing of cell membranes. See discussion in Chapter 29 (29.4.3).

TABLE 5-3

SOME EXAMPLES OF EMPIRICALLY DETERMINED OSMOTIC POTENTIALS

Species	Osmotic potential Ψ_π (atmos.)	Species	Osmotic potential Ψ_π (atmos.)
atriplex *(Atriplex confertifolia)*[a]	24–202	dandelion *(Taraxacum officinale)*[c]	14
pickleweed *(Allenrolfea occidentalis)*[b]	88	cocklebur *(Xanthium spp.)*[c]	12
sagebrush *(Artemisia tridentata)*[a]	14–73	marestail *(Hippuris vulgaris)*[d]	11
salicornia *(Salicornia rubra)*[a]	32–72	small white water lily *(Nymphaea dentata)*[d]	8.6
blue spruce *(Picea pungens)*[b]	51	chickweed *(Stellaria media)*[c]	7.3
mandarin orange *(Citrus reticulata)*[b]	47	wandering Jew *(Zebrina pendula)*[c]	4.8
willow *(Salix babylonica)*[b]	35	herbs of moist forests[e]	6–14
velvet plant *(Gynura aurantiaca)*[b]	21	herbs of dry forests[e]	11–30
cottonwood *(Populus deltoides)*[c]	21	deciduous trees and shrubs[e]	14–25
white oak *(Quercus alba)*[c]	20	evergreen conifers and Ericaceous plants[e]	16–31
sunflower *(Helianthus annuus)*[c]	19	herbs of the alpine zone[e]	7–17
red maple *(Acer rubrum)*[c]	17		
water lily *(Nymphaea odorata)*[c]	15		
blue grass *(Poa pratensis)*[c]	14		

[a] J. A. Harris. 1934. *The Physico-chemical Properties of Plant Saps in Relation to Phytogeography. Data on Native Vegetation in its Natural Environment.* University of Minnesota Press, Minneapolis. See pp. 65, 70, 110. Harris made thousands of measurements. The ranges shown indicate the variability he encountered within a single species, in a single state (e.g., Utah), and within a single year. Obviously, little certainty can be attached to the specific values shown for individual species.

[b] Student reports, Plant Physiology class, Colorado State University, Ft. Collins.

[c] B. S. Meyer and D. B. Anderson. 1939. *Plant Physiology.* D. Van Nostrand Co., New York.

[d] E. Hannig. 1912. Untersuchungen uber der Verteilung des osmotischen Drucks in der Pflanze im Hinsicht auf die Wasserleitung. *Ber. Deutschen bot. Ges.* 30:194.

[e] Arthur Pisek. 1956. Der Wasserhaushalt der Meso- und Hygrophyten. *Encyclop. Plant Physiology* 3:825–853.

In practice, there are two problems in applying this method to the determination of the osmotic potentials of plant saps: measurement of the freezing point, and obtaining a representative sample of sap. Determination of the freezing point proves to be relatively simple. Highly accurate mercury thermometers are commercially available for this purpose,[4] and thermocouples can be even more sensitive and easier to operate.

Obtaining a pure plant sap is far more difficult. One may squeeze out the sap with a press, freeze the tissue to rupture the cells and then squeeze out the sap, or homogenize the tissue in a blender and filter the sap. All of these methods applied to the same tissue may give different results, and often the differences are fairly high (Table 5-4). The principal problem is that the various methods involve different degrees of mixing of cytoplasmic contents and other substances with the vacuolar sap, which is primarily responsible for the osmotic behavior of plant tissue. In spite of the limitations, the cryoscopic method has been widely used for many years.

5.3.2D Plasmolytic method
If the sap within plant tissue were in osmotic equilibrium with some outside surrounding solution ($\Delta\psi = 0$) and *no pressure or tension existed within the*

---

[4] The thermometer has a very fine capillary, so that temperature can be read to 0.01°C. A time–temperature curve is determined to account for supercooling and the subsequent warming upon freezing due to release of the heat of fusion. Results are compared with those using pure water.

TABLE 5-4

CRYOSCOPICALLY DETERMINED OSMOTIC POTENTIALS FOR PLANT EXTRACTS OBTAINED IN SEVERAL DIFFERENT WAYS

Plant and method of extraction	Freezing point	Osmotic potential (atm)
potato tuber[a]		
frozen, diced, squeezed through cloth	−0.65	7.8
homogenized in blender, filtered	−0.70	8.4
sap expressed from fresh tissue in a plant press	−0.63	7.6
potato tuber[b]		
hydraulic press, 5,000 psi, fresh tissue		3.5–4.2
hydraulic press, 5,000 psi, frozen tissue		3.2–3.9
hand squeezed through cloth, fresh tissue		2.2–3.0
hand squeezed through cloth, frozen tissue		2.5–3.2
blended, filtered, fresh tissue		3.0–5.0
blended, filtered, frozen tissue		3.0–6.0
carrot root[b]		
hydraulic press, fresh tissue		2.5–3.7
hydraulic press, frozen tissue		3.2–4.1
hand squeezed, fresh tissue		3.1–4.4
blender, fresh tissue		4.0–5.5
blender, frozen tissue		4.0–4.4
turnip root[b]		
hydraulic press, fresh tissue		3.8–4.0
hydraulic press, frozen tissue		2.0–2.8
hand squeezed, fresh tissue		2.8–4.4
blender, fresh tissue		3.1–5.5
blender, frozen tissue		4.3–4.7

[a] Student report, Colorado State University: Gary Jones, Alan Batten, Dave Wallingfor, and Gary Propp. A differential mercury thermometer was used. The students concluded that values for the three methods were not significantly different from each other.
[b] Student report, Colorado State University: Tom Bargston, and Bert Drake. A thermocouple was used to determine freezing points. Some 85 samples were tested; each range of figures represents five samples. Note that blender values are consistently higher but more heterogeneous. Hand squeezed values are typically lower. Values for fresh tissue are on the average about 0.5 atm lower than for frozen tissue. The wide range of values demonstrates the difficulties of using the method.

tissue, then the osmotic potential of the sap would be equal to the osmotic potential of the solution. The problem in this kind of a measurement is to obtain zero pressure within the tissue without changing the other osmotic properties any more than necessary. This is the method of observing **incipient plasmolysis**. Strips of tissue are placed in a graded solution series of known osmotic potentials. Sucrose solutions may be used, but mannitol or other substances have the advantage of not penetrating or being changed metabolically as readily by the tissue. After an equilibration period (usually 30 minutes to an hour), the tissue is examined under a microscope. It has been arbitrarily assumed by plant physiologists that tissue in which about half of the cells are just beginning to **plasmolyze** (protoplasts are just beginning to pull away from the cell wall) represents a zero internal pressure. If this assumption is true, then the osmotic potential of the solution that produced incipient plasmolysis is equivalent to the osmotic potential of the cells within the tissue, *after they have come to equilibrium with the solution.*

If this is true for the tissue at equilibrium (and its being true depends only upon the assumption that incipient plasmolysis truly represents zero pressure), then we must question how much the tissue changed as incipient plasmolysis developed. Pulling away of the protoplasts from the wall is a shrinkage or decrease in volume, and so the sap solution inside, by becoming more concentrated, developed a more negative osmotic potential. If careful volume measurements of original tissue and tissues at incipient plasmolysis are made (either the over-all volume of the tissue or, better still, the dimensions of a fairly large sample of protoplasts), then the change in osmotic potential due to change in volume can be calculated. When this is not done, values of osmotic potential obtained by the plasmolytic method are too high, often by a value of one to several bars (5–10 percent or more).

A severe limitation to this method is the detection of incipient plasmolysis. In many tissues it is very difficult to see the protoplasts and whether they are plasmolyzed. In spite of the difficulties, this method is really the only one presently available for determining the osmotic potential of nearly *intact* cell sap (as contrasted to the vapor pressure measurements above tissue that has been frozen, as described earlier).

Another serious problem with the plasmolytic method is that the osmotic potential within the cell may change during the measurement due to penetration of solutes from the outside solution. This is usually avoided somewhat by using solutes like sucrose or mannitol, which are known to penetrate slowly, but the principle has also been put to practical advantage in the measurement of the rate of penetration of solutes. When cells are placed in a fairly concentrated solution of some solute, water will tend to move out rapidly so that plasmolysis occurs sometimes within seconds or minutes. As the solute particles then begin to penetrate the cell, adding to those already present (and probably not leaking out, due to factors discussed in Chapter 8), water potential inside becomes more negative than that of the outside solution, and water begins to move back into the cell. Measuring the rate of **deplasmolysis** (swelling of the plasmolyzed protoplasts) indicates the rate of penetration of the solute.

5.3.2E Osmotic potentials of some plant saps
Measurements of osmotic potentials by the above methods have yielded results varying from very low values of one bar or less in aquatic plants to very high values, 200 or more bars in salt-containing halophytes. Typically, osmotic potentials of plant saps lie between 4 and 20 bars (see Table 5-3).

5.3.3 Pressure Potential

In a laboratory osmometer, pressure is measured directly, but direct measurement of pressure in plant cells is much more difficult. Usually the pressure is calculated after water potential and osmotic potential have been determined:

$$\psi_p = \psi - \psi_\pi \qquad (25)$$

In a recent report (1967), Paul B. Green and Frederick W. Stanton at the University of Pennsylvania describe a method for the direct measurement of turgor pressure in large cells, such as those of the alga *Nitella axillaris*. A minute manometer is made by fusing closed one end of a capillary tube (diameter $40\,\mu$) and fashioning the other end into a tip like that of a syringe needle. As the tube is observed with the microscope, some of the water surrounding the cell will be seen to enter the open end due to capillarity, compressing the air inside the tube somewhat. The position of the meniscus inside the tube is noted and the volume of air calculated.

As the open end of the tube punctures the cell, pressure in the cell will be transferred to the air in the tube, compressing it further as indicated by movement of the meniscus. The final pressure in the tube will be equal to the pressure before penetration of the cell multiplied by the ratio of the original to the final volume. The pressure before penetration can be determined by multiplying atmospheric pressure by the ratio of the original volume to the volume after entrance of water by capillarity. There will be a slight change in pressure within the cell upon penetration of the tube, but even this can be ascertained by penetrating a cell with a second tube while observing the change in pressure in the first. The method measures actual pressure in the cell, but according to convention this will be one atmosphere higher than the turgor pressure or the pressure potential.

Green and Stanton found a turgor pressure of 5.1 atm in a *Nitella* cell in equilibrium with pure water. As the cell was allowed to equilibrate with sugar solutions of increasing concentration (more negative osmotic potential), turgor pressure decreased exactly as predicted. It reached a value of zero with the cell in a solution of $\psi_\pi = -5.3$, although visible plasmolysis did not occur until $\psi_\pi = -5.7$, confirming that the cell must shrink before incipient plasmolysis becomes apparent.

5.3.4 Matric Potential

The matric potential was discussed in the preceding chapter. It was pointed out that colloidal hydrophylic surfaces may adsorb water, and that the tenacity with which the molecules of water are adsorbed will be a function of the distance between the surface and the molecules. Molecules located directly on the adsorbing surface will be held more tightly, and molecules some distance above the surface will be held much less tightly. The **matric potential** (ψ_m) is a measure at atmospheric pressure of the tenacity with which the least tightly held molecules are adsorbed, or of the tendency for the matrix to adsorb water molecules further. A dry colloid may have an extremely low matric potential (as low as $-3{,}000$ bars), while a colloid in pure water at atmospheric pressure will have a matric potential of zero (it is completely saturated). When the colloid at atmospheric pressure has come into equilibrium with its surroundings, its matric potential will be equal to the water potential of the surroundings.

The most common modern means of measuring matric potential is instructive from the standpoint of the osmotic relationships. A colloid may be enclosed in a container, one side of which is a membrane permeable to solutes and water but not the colloid. This membrane must be supported, probably by a fine screen, so that it can withstand very high pressures. Compressed air under controlled pressure is then introduced into the system. Increasing the pressure potential raises the water potential of the adsorbed moisture toward and finally above zero, so that water begins to diffuse out through the membrane. Further increases in air pressure on the colloid result in additional but smaller increments of water movement from the colloid out through the membrane.

Water on the colloid under pressure will be in equilibrium through the membrane with water (or solution) at atmospheric pressure on the outside of the membrane. That is, the water potential of the least tightly adsorbed water molecules on the colloid under pressure will be equal to zero if pure water at atmospheric pressure exists on the outside of the membrane, and so water potential of these least tightly adsorbed molecules will also be zero. If pressure potential and the matric potential are the only components influencing water potential inside the membrane, as indicated by the following formula:

$$\psi = \psi_p + \psi_m \tag{26}$$

then when water potential is zero, the absolute value of the negative matric potential will be equal to the positive pressure potential ($-\psi_m = \psi_p$). The pressure is known and positive, so the matric potential is also known but negative.

Usually, after equilibrium has been reached at a given pressure, water content of the colloid is determined by weighing before and after drying in an oven. Matric potential plotted as a function of water content provides the moisture release curve (Fig. 4-6).

A test of the assumption that the pressure in the pressure membrane apparatus is a measurement of matric potential is to measure the water potential of the colloid at atmospheric pressure by the vapor method described above. The two measurements agree closely, indicating the validity of the approach.

It has been frequently stated in the current literature that matric potential is a component of water potential according to the following equation:

$$\psi = \psi_p + \psi_\pi + \psi_m \qquad (26A)$$

The assumption is that water potential is determined by pressure potential, osmotic potential, and matric potential all acting additively. Data that seem to support this assumption have been obtained by empirical studies using clay colloids or agar in combination with solutions of various osmotic potentials. Furthermore, it is easy to see that colloid and solute may interact in their effects on water potential. If dry colloid is added to a solution, water will be adsorbed and thus removed from the solution, and water potential of the system will become more negative. But in a sense, solute concentration will also increase.

It is difficult, however, to see how matric and osmotic potentials can add together in a given system as components of the water potential of the system as a whole, as is implied by equation (26A). This does not seem consistent with our discussions and definitions of matric

potential above and in Chapter 4. The problem is that the solution and the colloidal material in a given system may constitute two different phases in equilibrium with each other rather than adding together to constitute a water potential for the system as a whole. In Chapter 4 (4.3.1), we discussed the measurement of the matric potential of cocklebur fruits. The procedure was to find a solution so concentrated that the fruits could not adsorb water from it. This is the procedure described in 5.3.1A for determining water potential. It was assumed that the *only* component of water potential of the dry cocklebur fruit was the matric potential, and further that the matric potential of the fruits came into equilibrium with the osmotic potential ($\psi_\pi = \psi$ at $\psi_p = 0$) of the surrounding solution. Shouldn't the situation remain exactly the same if we think of protein molecules surrounded by cytoplasmic solution rather than cocklebur fruits surrounded by salt solution?

Of course, as pointed out in Chapter 4, electrolyte particles will influence the matric potential by being adsorbed on the colloids and thus influencing their ability to adsorb water. Furthermore, removal of the ions by adsorption on the colloids will change the concentration and hence the osmotic potential of the surrounding solution, theoretically at least. So there is always an important interaction between the osmotic and the matric components of a system in which solution is in direct contact with colloid, but there is no reason to believe that this interaction will be expressed by the simple arithmetic addition implied by equation (26A). Hence this equation may be an indication of an important interaction, but it is not valid in an arithmetic sense, as is the simple equation for water potential ($\psi = \psi_\pi + \psi_p$).

If the colloids and the solution constitute two separate but intimate phases in a cell-like system, then the water potentials of each will be in equilibrium with each other, and the pressures applied to both systems will be equal due to their intimacy. Hence the following equations for the solution (subscript s) and the colloid (subscript c) should apply:

$$\psi_s = \psi_{ps} + \psi_{\pi s}$$
$$\psi_c = \psi_{pc} + \psi_{mc}$$

but:

$$\psi_c = \psi_s$$

so:

$$\psi_{ps} + \psi_{\pi s} = \psi_{pc} + \psi_{mc}$$

and:

$$\psi_{ps} = \psi_{pc}$$

so:

$$\psi_{\pi s} = \psi_{mc}$$

The conclusion is that matric and osmotic potentials must be equal in a given system at equilibrium (and not additive components of water potential). This should be true at equilibrium after both osmotic and matric potentials have mutually influenced each other by adsorption of ions on the colloidal surfaces. So equation (26A) might be more correctly written as:

$$\psi = \psi_p + (\psi_\pi = \psi_m) \qquad (27)$$

In soils, the matric potential may become much more negative than the minimum possible osmotic potential, as this is limited by the maximum possible concentration of solutes in the soil solution. Pressure is zero because the system is not confined. Under these conditions, osmotic potential in the usual sense is not a component of water potential, although solutes will be an integral part of the layer of water adsorbed on the colloids and hence will contribute to matric potential. It is impossible, so far, in a practical way to separate the effects of solute from those of the colloid in such a system. Perhaps a similar situation exists in certain plant cells, particularly in seeds or cells of the

meristematic region, where solutes may not be readily separated from the water adsorbed on colloids. This must be the case if growth occurs due to imbibitional forces as suggested in Chapter 4. We must regard our current concepts relating to matric potential [equations (26) and (27)] as highly tentative. They seem reasonable at the moment but could easily be changed by future research.

5.4 NONOSMOTIC WATER UPTAKE

For some years it was argued that water might be pumped into cells against a water-potential gradient by the expenditure of metabolic energy, in close analogy with the accumulation of solutes by cells against a concentration gradient (Chapter 8). Two evidences were presented in favor of this possibility. *First*, values of osmotic potential obtained plasmolytically were lower (more negative) than those obtained for the same tissue cryoscopically. Since the plasmolytic measurement involved living tissue, while the cryoscopic method measured extracted sap, it was suggested that a metabolic component was a part of the osmotic potential as measured in the plasmolytic method. *Second*, the rate of water uptake can often be correlated with respiration and inhibited by respiration inhibitors. This is especially true during growth of entire plants or even in water-uptake studies utilizing excised tissues.

Most workers now agree that such **metabolic or active[5] or nonosmotic water uptake** does not

[5] The term *active water uptake* has been widely used for the phenomenon in recent years, but it was used earlier in another sense by Renner (1912), and in an important book on plant-water relations by Paul Kramer at Duke University. Renner distinguished between *passive* uptake as in transpiration (Chapter 7) and *active* uptake, in which ions are moved into the cell by the expenditure of metabolic energy (Chapter 8), and this results in a greater osmotic uptake of water.

occur significantly in higher plants, and that water uptake follows strictly osmotic principles. Three arguments are cited: *First*, values of osmotic potential obtained plasmolytically might be expected to be too negative because estimates of volume decrease during plasmolysis were lacking or were too low. This was well substantiated by the direct measurements of Green and Stanton discussed earlier (5.3.3). *Second*, the relationship between water uptake and respiration is probably an indirect one. That is, a number of processes require respiratory energy, and these often go hand in hand with water uptake. *Third*, the permeability of cell membranes to water molecules has been studied in many ways, most recently by utilization of tritium-labeled water. This permeability proves to be extremely high, and enormous quantities of energy would be required to maintain a water potential gradient across a membrane with such high permeability to water. Jacob Levitt, at the University of Missouri, showed this quite clearly in 1947, basing his demonstration upon the principles of thermodynamics. For several years after Levitt's paper the argument about active water uptake continued until the other evidences made it apparent that active water uptake was not a significant phenomenon in plant tissue.

5.5 PROBLEM SOLVING WITH THE OSMOTIC QUANTITIES

To illustrate procedures that might be followed in solving problems involving osmosis, two broad examples are discussed. These include most of the manipulations that can be carried out with the osmotic quantities. To simplify matters, we will use only the subscripts for osmotic and pressure potentials (i.e., $\psi_\pi = \pi$, $\psi_p = P$).

5.5.1 Strips of Tissue Are Allowed to Equilibrate with Mannitol Solutions of Known Molality

5.5.1A Calculation of osmotic potential and water potential for the solutions This may be carried out by application of the van't Hoff law. If the mannitol solutions ($i = 1$) have concentrations of 1.2 *m*, 1.0 *m*, 0.8 *m*, 0.6 *m*, and 0.4 *m* at 28°C, then we may calculate the osmotic potential of the most concentrated one by the following relationship:

$$T = \deg C + 273 \deg = 28 + 273 = 301 \deg$$

$$-\pi = miRT \, [\text{equation (23)}]$$

$$-\pi = \left(1.2\frac{\text{moles}}{\cancel{l}}\right)(1.0)\left(0.083\frac{\cancel{l} \text{ bars}}{\text{mole deg}}\right)(301\,\cancel{\text{deg}})$$

$$\pi = -30 \text{ bars}$$

The other solutions will have osmotic potentials proportionate to this one as follows:

$$\frac{m_1}{\pi_1} = \frac{m_n}{\pi_n}$$

$$\frac{1.2}{-30} = \frac{1.0}{\pi_{1.0}} = \frac{0.8}{\pi_{0.8}} = \frac{0.6}{\pi_{0.6}} = \frac{0.4}{\pi_{0.4}}$$

$$\pi_{1.2} = -30 \text{ bars}$$

$$\pi_{1.0} = -25 \text{ bars}$$

$$\pi_{0.8} = -20 \text{ bars}$$

$$\pi_{0.6} = -15 \text{ bars}$$

$$\pi_{0.4} = -10 \text{ bars}$$

The ψ values for these solutions are identical to the osmotic potentials. This is because we arbitrarily agree to assign zero P to solutions exposed to the atmosphere. The same assignment is made for the P of water in soils.

5.5.1B The "no-change-in-volume" tissue

The tissue that shows no change in volume must be in a solution having a water potential equal to that of the tissue at the time it was placed in the solution. Assuming that this happened in the solution with $\pi = -15$ bars, then for that tissue, $\psi = -15$ bars.

5.5.1C Incipient plasmolysis

If incipient plasmolysis is observed in the tissue in the solution having $\pi_e = -25$ bars (subscript e = external; i = internal), then the assumption is made that in the tissue $P_i = 0$. Since $P_e = 0$, the π_e for the solution will be equal to π_i for the cell sap, or $\pi_e = \pi_i = -25$ bars. (For change-in-volume correction, see 5.5.1F below.)

5.5.1D The osmotic quantities, first approximation

If $\pi_i = -25$ bars, and $\psi_i = -15$ bars, then, from equation (25):

$$P_i = \psi_i - \pi_i = -15 \text{ bars} - (-25 \text{ bars})$$

$$= +10 \text{ bars}$$

Because π_i obtained above is too negative, P_i obtained in this equation is higher than the true value by the same amount.

5.5.1E Cryoscopic determination

If sap is expressed from the tissue and its freezing point determined to be -1.637 deg C, then:

$$\pi_i' = \left(12.22 \frac{\text{bars}}{\text{deg}}\right)(-1.637 \text{ deg}) = -20 \text{ bars}$$

This is 20 percent less negative than the plasmolytically determined osmotic potential (π_i).

5.5.1F Volume change

If the volume of the protoplast was measured at the beginning and at the end of the incipient plasmolysis experiment and seen to decrease to a value of 90 percent of the original, then we can calculate the original osmotic potential by the following relationship:

$$\pi_i V_1 = \pi_2 V_2$$

$$\pi_i 100 = (-25)(90)$$

$$\pi_i'' = -22.5 \text{ bars (the corrected } \pi \text{ for the incipient plasmolysis tissue)}$$

5.5.1G Temperature correction

From the van't Hoff law it can be seen that osmotic potential is proportional to absolute temperature. Since the cryoscopic determination of osmotic potential occurs near the freezing point, it may be advisable to correct to room temperature. The correction may be obtained as follows:

$$\frac{\pi_1}{\pi_2} = \frac{T_1}{T_2}$$

$$\frac{-20 \text{ bars}}{\pi_2} = \frac{271.6 \text{ deg}}{301.0 \text{ deg}}$$

$$\pi_i''' = -22.2 \text{ bars}$$

Using the corrected π_i values ($\pi_i'' = -22.5$ bars, and $\pi_i''' = -22.2$ bars), our second approximation values for the osmotic quantities are:

$$\pi_i = -22.5 \text{ bars or } -22.2 \text{ bars}$$

$$\psi_i = -15.0$$

$$P_i = +7.5 \text{ bars or } +7.2 \text{ bars}$$

5.5.1H Probable errors

The student should be able to discuss the assumptions and probable errors involved in the above steps. In 5.5.1A, the value of i must be known exactly for the concentration of each solution and for the particular solute. In 5.5.1B, ψ may be slightly in error because the concentration of the test solution changes as solutes are absorbed by or released from the tissue. In 5.5.1C, the plasmolytic method suffers from the difficulty of detecting incipient plasmolysis microscopically and from the volume change. In 5.5.1E, the cryoscopic method suffers from concentration changes due to mixing vacuolar sap with cytoplasm and other materials. In 5.5.1F, the correction for volume change assumes that the $\pi_1 V_1 = \pi_2 V_2$ relationship held exactly and that no exchange of solute between the tissue and the external medium had occurred. Both assumptions are only approximately correct.

5.5.1I   Ionization

Assuming that the cell sap consists of substances ionized 10 percent, what is its approximate molality? We will use the corrected value for osmotic potential, $\pi = -22.2$ bars. If no ionization occurs, we may think of i in the van't Hoff formula as equal to one. Assuming that our salt or acid ionizes into two particles, and if ionization is 100 percent, for every 100 molecules before ionization, there will be 200 after ionization, and i will be equal to 2. If ionization is 10 percent, for every 100 original molecules, 90 will remain unionized, and 10 will ionize, producing 20 ions. The total number of particles will be 110, and i will approximate 1.10. We can then substitute our known values in the van't Hoff formula as follows:

$$-\pi = miRT$$

$$m = \frac{-\pi}{iRT}$$

$$m = \frac{-(-22.2 \text{ bars})}{(1.10)\left(0.083\dfrac{1 \text{ bars}}{\text{mole deg}}\right)(301 \text{ deg})}$$

$$= 0.807\frac{\text{moles}}{1} = 0.807 \ m$$

5.5.2   Movement of Water Between Cells

Assuming that in cell A, $\pi = -10$ bars, and $P = 4$ bars; while in cell B, $\pi = -6$ bars, and $P = 3$ bars:

(1) *If the two cells are placed in contact, which way will water flow and why?* To answer this, $\Delta\psi$ between the two cells must be understood. For cell A, $\psi = P + \pi = 4 - 10 = -6$ bars. For cell B, $\psi = 3 - 6 = -3$ bars. For the two cells $\Delta\psi = \psi_A - \psi_B = -6 - (-3) = -3$ bars. Water will move toward the more negative water potential, or from cell B to cell A.

(2) *Cell A is placed in a solution with $\pi = -2$ bars, cell B is placed in a solution with $\pi = -5$ bars. What are P and ψ of the cells at equilibrium, assuming no change in their volume? If the cells are placed in contact, what is $\Delta\psi$ and which way will water flow?* Cell A at equilibrium will have $\psi_A = -2$ bars, since it will have to be the same as the water potential of the solution with which it is surrounded ($\Delta\psi = 0$ at equilibrium). Thus for this cell $P_A = \psi - \pi = -2 - (-10) = 8$ bars. Cell B at equilibrium will have $\pi_B = -5$ bars, and $P_B = -5 - (-6) = 1$ bar. Water will move from cell A to cell B because the water potential is lowest (most negative) in cell B ($\Delta\psi = 3$ bars).

(3) *Assuming cell A doubles in volume and cell B increases only 10 percent, when placed in the solutions of part (2), what are the osmotic quantities at equilibrium? If the cells are placed in contact, what is $\Delta\psi$ and which way will water flow?* The new osmotic quantities can be calculated from the dilution relationship:

$$\pi_1 V_1 = \pi_2 V_2$$

For cell A $(-10)(1) = (\pi_A)(2)$

$$\pi_A = -5 \text{ bars}$$

For cell B $(-6)(100) = (\pi_B)(110)$

$$\pi_B = -5.45 \text{ bars}$$

The water potentials will still be the same as their surrounding solutions (assuming that these solutions were of large volume and not changed by the small amount of water taken up by the cells). Pressure potentials will be:

$P_A = \psi_A - \pi_A = -2 - (-5) = 3$ bars

$P_B = \psi_B - \pi_B = -5 - (-5.45) = 0.45$ bars

$\Delta\psi$ between the two cells will be the same as for part (2) (+3 bars), and water will still move from cell A to cell B.

(4) *Assuming that the volume of the cells changes by an unknown amount, but the cells are allowed to come to equilibrium with the solutions [part (2)] and then placed in contact, what is $\Delta\psi$ and which way will water flow?* Regardless of any changes in pressure or concentration of the cells at equilibrium, their water potentials will have to be the same as the solutions (large volume) in which they are placed. Thus $\Delta\psi$ will be the same as for part (2) (+3 bars), and water will still move from cell A to cell B.

6

Transpiration and Heat Transfer

6.1 INTRODUCTION

Transpiration is the loss of water by evaporation from plants. It differs from the general process of evaporation, because the water vapor does not evaporate from a free surface but must pass through the epidermis with its cuticle or through the stomates.

Relatively large quantities of water are transpired by typical plants. A corn plant, in growing to a final volume of two liters, absorbed and lost by transpiration some 200 liters of water. Actually, the amount of water absorbed and lost by various species differs considerably, as indicated in Table 6-1 (data shown in grams per square decimeter of leaf surface per hour).

We will discuss in some detail the effects of environment upon transpiration, but fundamentally there are two principal effects: one upon the evaporation of water and the other upon the stomatal aperture. Increasing leaf temperature, for example, promotes evaporation but may eventually cause stomates to close. Light causes stomates to open but increases temperature. Increasing humidity decreases transpiration, but relative humidity is a function of temperature, and this in turn is influenced by light. Wind blows away the vapor, causing an in-

crease in evaporation, but if the leaf is warmed by sunlight, wind will lower its temperature, causing a decrease in transpiration. When soil moisture becomes limiting, transpiration may be inhibited. So transpiration, although basically a simple process, is the resultant of a number of interacting factors and therefore is rather complex in practice.

Modern consideration of transpiration must be based upon quantitative data; so we will first consider a few methods involved in measurement of transpiration. Then we will ask four fundamental questions about the process: *First*, how can so much water pass through such small pores? *Second*, is transpiration beneficial to the plant? *Third*, how important is water at a given tension or water potential to plant function? *Fourth*, how is the plant in its transpirational processes related to its environment, particularly to the exchange of energy and the gradients of water potential?

6.2 MEASUREMENT OF TRANSPIRATION

Many methods have been suggested for measurement of transpiration. The basic and often

TABLE 6-1

SOME REPRESENTATIVE TRANSPIRATION DATA FOR DIFFERENT SPECIES AND DIFFERENT CONDITIONS[a]

Plant	Temperature (deg C)	Relative humidity[b] (%)	Water loss[c] (g/dm^2/hr)
tobacco *(Nicotiana tabacum)*	37–38	68	3.6
tobacco *(Nicotiana tabacum)*	23–26	68	1.5
sunflower *(Helianthus annuus)*	38	22	1.2
oak *(Quercus rubra)*	38	32	0.8
sycamore *(Platanus occidentalis)*	38	32	0.8
buckeye *(Aesculus glabra)*	38	32	0.7
peach *(Prunus persica)*	21–38	40–98	0.7
box elder *(Acer negundo)*	38	32	0.6
orange *(Citrus sinensis)*	21–38	40–98	0.2
germander *(Teucrium scorodonia)*			
sun leaves—in sunshine	26–30	38–46	0.7
shade leaves—in sunshine	26–30	38–46	0.4
sun leaves—in shade	18–19	75–76	0.3
shade leaves—in shade	18–19	75–76	0.1

[a] Data from: William S. Spector (ed.). 1956. *Handbook of Biological Data.* W. B. Saunders, Philadelphia and London.
[b] Humidity is less important than temperature in its effect on transpiration. See discussion in text.
[c] To be truly comparable, all values should be obtained under the same conditions of air temperature, radiation load, light, humidity, wind velocity, time of day, and atmospheric pressure. In no case, were all of the factors specified. The 36-fold range for different species is nevertheless impressive.

limiting problem is to measure the process without influencing it. For example, in a demonstration often performed in basic botany and general biology teaching laboratories, a piece of dry (blue) cobaltous chloride paper is placed in contact with the leaf. After some time the paper turns pink, indicating that it has absorbed moisture. Yet it is quite apparent that nearly all of the factors influencing transpiration have been affected by this procedure: heat transfer by convection is upset, the leaf is shaded on one side, humidity increases between the paper and the leaf, and the leaf is protected from wind. Such a method can have little or no quantitative value, although it does show that water is indeed being given off by the leaf. We will see that it is virtually impossible to measure transpiration both accurately and without influencing it. One can, however, sometimes measure and account for the influence of the measurement upon transpiration.

6.2.1 Measurement of Transpiration in the Laboratory

Potometers have often been used as an indication of transpiration in the laboratory (see Fig. 6-1). In this approach, a cut stem or perhaps the roots of a small plant are inserted through a cork and placed in a reservoir of water. Loss of water from the reservoir is usually measured by movement of a bubble through a small capillary. The problem is that the plant must be cut or its roots immersed in water, either treatment an abnormal one. There is evidence that transpiration is affected. Furthermore, absorption of water as indicated by the potom-

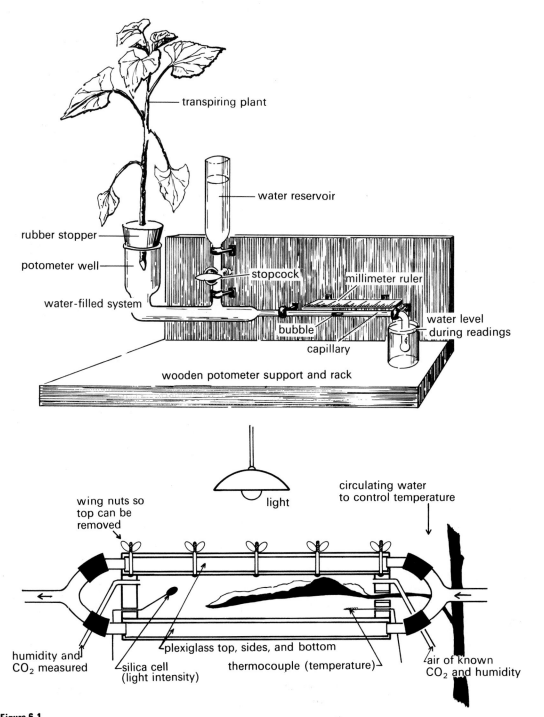

Figure 6-1

Two laboratory methods for measuring transpiration: a potometer (top) and a cuvette enclosing a leaf (bottom). With the cuvette method, humidity of air entering and leaving the leaf must be measured. The cuvette method is often used for the study of photosynthesis as well as transpiration.

eter is not always equal to transpiration (see 7.3.3E).

With a small **potted plant,** the pot may be sealed with water-proof plastic and/or aluminum foil and weighed during transpiration. Of the methods discussed here, this one probably influences transpiration the least. One difficulty is that the plant will continuously increase in weight as it grows, but the rate of growth is usually insignificant compared to the rate of transpiration. It is possible, by careful measurements of plant size, to account for this, if necessary.

The plant may be placed in a **closed container,** and the amount of water vapor in a measured volume of ingoing air can be compared with the amount of water vapor in the outgoing air. There are several methods for measuring humidity of ingoing and outgoing air: the hair hygrometer, the electrical resistance of some hygroscopic (water absorbing) material, the psychrometer (difference in temperature between a wet and dry surface), or the amount of infrared light of suitable wavelength absorbed by the water in the air. The closed-chamber or **cuvette method** has been used rather widely in the laboratory. We are faced with a typical paradox of measurement, however: as the chamber is made smaller it becomes more difficult to provide a desired environment around the leaf (e.g., air must be circulated faster to remove heat); while as the chamber becomes larger, readings are less accurate because of the lag brought about by the larger volume of air. Nevertheless, environment in the near vicinity of a leaf in such a cuvette can be quite accurately measured, allowing fundamental studies of transpiration to be carried out.

6.2.2   Measurement of Transpiration in the Field

By measurement in the field, we imply that transpiration must be measured without changing the environment in any way. As indicated above, such an assignment is extremely difficult if not impossible. Yet a number of methods are used (Fig. 6-2). "**Tent methods**" attempt to duplicate the closed-chamber approach under field conditions. Some sort of transparent tent or container is placed over a branch or even an entire plant, and air is passed through with humidities and volumes being monitored. One limitation is that no material yet used for such a "tent" is 100 percent transparent to all wavelengths of radiation. Polyethylene comes fairly close, transmitting more of the infrared wavelengths than most other readily available materials. Yet all materials absorb a certain portion of the incoming and outgoing radiation and thus upset the radiation balance, which affects transpiration by influencing the leaf temperature and the stomatal opening.

The **potted plant method** can be used in the field in some cases. If the plant is small enough, this is probably the best approach. The method has even been used on a large scale with so-called **lysimeters,** in which large plants or even groups of plants are grown in large containers (on the order of several cubic yards) placed on an underground balance. The method is expensive, but fairly accurate data have been obtained this way. A recent, less expensive approach is to place the lysimeter on a large plastic bag filled with fluid (water-antifreeze) which extends into a stand pipe at the surface. The level of liquid in the pipe is a measure of the weight of the lysimeter, and so it changes with the water content of the soil in the lysimeter.

A method that has been widely used in field studies is to **detach a leaf** from a transpiring plant and weigh it with a delicate balance at frequent intervals, beginning as nearly as possible at the time of detachment. The rate of water loss during the first few moments is thought to be typical of the rate of water loss occurring while the leaf was still on the plant (Fig. 6-3). Of course, no one feels very secure about the assumption that transpira-

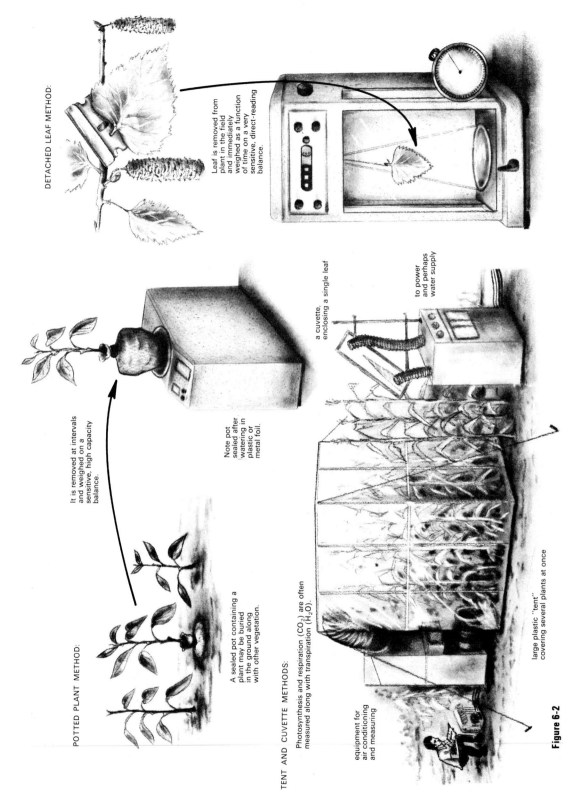

DETACHED LEAF METHOD:

Leaf is removed from plant in the field and immediately weighed as a function of time on a very sensitive, direct-reading balance.

POTTED PLANT METHOD:

It is removed at intervals and weighed on a sensitive, high capacity balance.

A sealed pot containing a plant may be buried in the ground along with other vegetation.

Note pot sealed after watering in plastic or metal foil.

TENT AND CUVETTE METHODS:

Photosynthesis and respiration (CO_2) are often measured along with transpiration (H_2O).

a cuvette, enclosing a single leaf

to power and perhaps water supply

equipment for air conditioning and measuring

large plastic "tent" covering several plants at once

Figure 6-2 Some methods of measuring transpiration in the field.

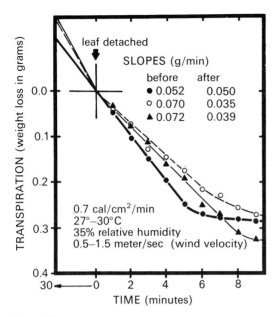

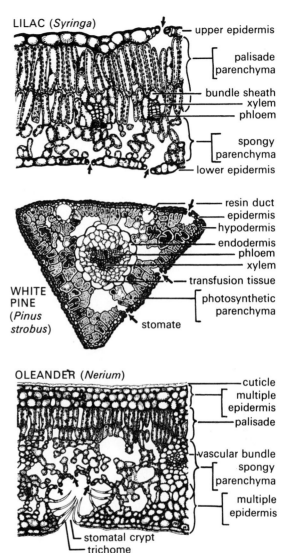

Figure 6-3

Results of three experiments in which a potted plant with a single leaf (the pot and stem wrapped with aluminum foil) was weighed at the beginning and end of a 30-minute interval to determine transpiration rate. At the end of the 30-minute period (time 0), the leaf was removed and weighed at one-minute intervals on a sensitive balance (as in Fig. 6-2). In one experiment, the rate remained almost the same before and after removal of the leaf. In the other two, rates were considerably decreased after removal of the leaves. (Data original, obtained by B. G. Drake using *Xanthium strumarium.*)

tion is uninfluenced for the first few moments by detaching the leaf from the plant. Typically, the release of tension (Chapter 7) results in rates that are slightly high compared to the potted-plant method. Yet this is one of the most practical methods so far devised for the study of natural vegetation in the field.

6.3 THE PARADOX OF PORES

Transpiration from the leaf is strongly a function of the leaf's anatomy. Figure 6-4 shows the cross sections of a "typical" leaf, one with sunken

Figure 6-4

Cross-sections through three representative leaves, one (top) with "normal" stomates, one (middle) with slightly sunken stomates, and another (bottom) with stomates deeply sunken in a substomatal cavity. Note other details of differing leaf anatomy. It is important to note that even the palisade cells are not tightly packed but contain many air spaces. A section (not shown) parallel to the surface and through the palisade cells indicates that virtually every cell is in contact with an air space.

stomates, and a conifer needle. Of importance to transpiration are the **cuticle**, the **epidermal cells**, the **guard cells** constituting the **stomatal apparatus** (conveniently called the **stomate**, although this term refers only to the opening) and the surfaces of the **mesophyll** and **spongy parenchyma cells** from which water evaporates into the **intercellular spaces**, which are continuous with the outside air, through the stomates. The stomates vary somewhat in anatomy, and in some plants most are located on the underside of the leaf, while in others (e.g., grasses) both sides of the leaf have about an equal number of stomates. Photographs of representative types are shown in Fig. 6-5. Some water passes through the cuticle, but most (typically 90–95 percent) passes through the stomates.

Table 6-2 gives the results of a simple experiment in evaporation. Water was allowed to evaporate from a free surface and from a surface covered by a membrane perforated with minute pores. Of course the evaporation from the covered surface was less than that from the free surface, but considering the area of the pores as compared to the area of the free surface, evaporation through the pores was far more efficient. The open stomates of a leaf may occupy only 1 percent of the leaf area, but approximately 50 percent as much water may transpire from such a leaf as will evaporate from a free water surface of equal area.

This may best be understood by thinking of evaporation as a diffusion process from water surface to atmosphere. The rate of diffusion, all other factors being equal, will be strongly influenced by the steepness of the water-potential gradient. Water molecules evaporating from the free surface will be part of a relatively dense column of molecules extending above the surface and not having a very steep concentration gradient from surface to atmosphere. Water molecules diffusing through a pore, however, can go in any direction within an imaginary hemisphere centered on the pore. In such a situa-

tion, the concentration gradient from pore to atmosphere will be relatively much steeper than above the free water surface (Fig. 6-6). The imaginary hemisphere has been referred to as the **diffusion shell** around the pore, but if stomates are close enough together, the "shells" may overlap so completely that they no longer have any significant meaning.

Early experiments using single pores of fairly large dimensions seemed to indicate that diffusion through the pore was proportional to its perimeter (or diameter) rather than its area. Recent measurements on actual leaves, where stomates are very close and diffusion shells overlap, show clearly that transpiration may be nearly proportional to the total pore *area* of the leaf (as stomates open, transpiration increases nearly proportionately to the area). Transpiration is as rapid as it is, considering the small pore area, simply because the diffusion gradient across these pores is extremely steep.

6.4 THE PHYSIOLOGY OF STOMATAL ACTION

6.4.1 The Mechanics of Stomatal Action

Frequently the inner wall of the two stomatal guard cells is somewhat thickened compared to the outer wall. The epidermal cells surrounding the guard cells are usually turgid, pushing against the guard cell. As the guard cells absorb water and expand, they tend (partially because of the thickened inner wall) to bow outward, separating at the middle and causing the stomate to open (Fig. 6-7). So opening is a turgor phenomenon in which *stomates open as the guard cells take up water*.

6.4.2 Special Features of Guard Cells

In contrast to other epidermal cells, the guard cells contain some chloroplasts with functional

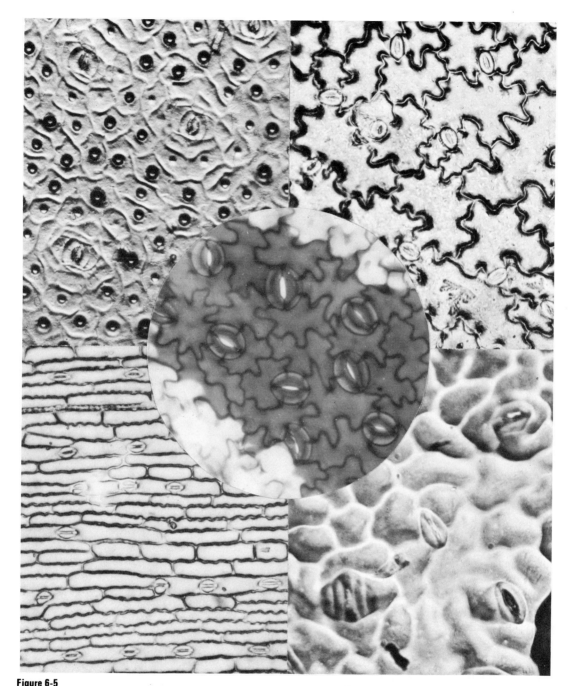

Figure 6-5

Surface views of stomates. The insert is a photomicrograph of epidermal tissue removed from a cocklebur leaf. All others are photomicrographs of collodian (or silicon rubber negative, then collodian positive, lower right) which has been allowed to harden on the surface of a leaf and then removed. Different lighting techniques account for the different appearances. Upper left appearance is of a collodian negative. Invert to see illusion of a collodian positive. "Ridges" become "valleys." Note that stomates are open in some cases and closed in others. Upper left: cactus; upper right: tobacco; lower left: corn; lower right: cocklebur. Note different cell shapes in center and lower right, both cocklebur. (Photos courtesy of B. G. Drake and B. W. Poovaiah, Utah State University.)

TABLE 6-2

EVAPORATION OF WATER FROM AN OPEN SURFACE AND THROUGH PORES[a]

Total surface area		Number of pores	Area for evaporation	Water evaporated	% water lost[b] % area for evap.	mg lost[c] mm^2 of pore area
(1)	400 mm^2	(open)	400 mm^2 (100%)	2.4580 g (100%)	1	6.145 (1.0)
(2)	400 mm^2	196	18.20 mm^2 (4.55%)	0.9219 g (37.1%)	8.15	50.65 (8.25)
(3)	400 mm^2	49	4.55 mm^2 (1.14%)	0.2735 g (11.2%)	9.82	60.08 (9.78)
Oft-quoted data for leaves						
open water surface			100%	100%	1	
leaf with open stomates			1%	50%	50	

[a] Original data of F. B. Salisbury and B. G. Drake. Three small identical aluminum pans, filled with water, were left for 15 hours in a room at about 25°C. One was left open (area = 400 mm^2). One was covered by a thin layer of metal (0.762 mm) perforated with 196 small holes (area of pore = 0.0929 mm^2, diameter = 0.345 mm) spaced on a square grid; the other was perforated with 49 holes. Evaporation was determined by weight loss.

[b] This is the ratio of observed/expected evaporation. The pan covered with the sheet containing 49 holes lost 9.82 times as much water as would have been expected on the basis of the percentage of area available for evaporation. According to data often quoted, a leaf can lose up to 50 times as much water as would be expected on this basis (indicating a more optimal size and spacing of pores—stomates).

[c] On the basis of area available for evaporation, the 49 holes lost 9.78 times as much as might have been expected. This comparison differs from (b), since total area (400 mm^2) is not part of the calculation.

chlorophyll. It has been demonstrated that they are capable of photosynthesis, can synthesize starch, and can carry out a number of other chemical reactions. There are **plasmodesmata** in the guard cell walls contacting mesophyll cells, but not in those contacting the immediately surrounding epidermal cells, called the **accessory cells**. These contacting walls are very thin, so perhaps plasmodesmata are not essential. Various studies have shown that the guard cells are more resistant to toxic substances, but that they are more sensitive to water stress. After wilting, for example, the rest of the leaf may recover while the guard cells remain damaged and closed.

6.4.3 Regulation of Stomates by Environment

Much headway has been made in describing the response of stomates to environment. We are still, however, a long way from understanding the actual mechanisms of regulation; that is, the manner in which environmental changes may cause turgor changes in the guard cells. Consider a few environmental factors as they influence stomatal opening and closing.

6.4.3A Carbon dioxide Low partial pressures of carbon dioxide cause the stomates to open, and this response can be observed both in the light and in the dark. Conversely, high carbon dioxide partial pressures cause the stomates to close, and this occurs in the light as well as the dark. The carbon dioxide *inside* the leaf controls this response. For example, if the stomates are completely closed, *external* carbon-dioxide-free air has no effect. There is considerable reason to believe that various other environmental factors may have their effects upon stomatal opening

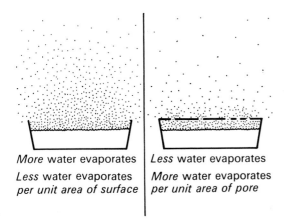

More water evaporates | *Less* water evaporates
Less water evaporates | *More* water evaporates
per unit area of surface | *per unit area of pore*

Figure 6-6
A schematic illustration of evaporation from an open surface and through small openings.

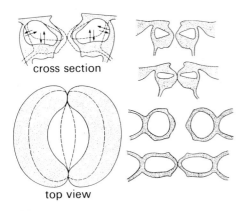

cross section

top view

Figure 6-7
Illustrations of three kinds of stomates, showing how stomates open as guard cells take up water.

and closing by acting indirectly through the internal carbon dioxide partial pressures.

6.4.3B   Light   Stomates typically close in darkness and open in light. Opening generally requires about an hour, while closing is usually somewhat faster (Fig. 6-8). Some exceptions are known, such as certain succulents (cacti, *Kalanchöe*, *Bryophyllum*, etc.) that open their stomates at night, fix carbon dioxide into

organic acids in the dark, and close their stomates during the day. Much study has gone into an attempt to understand the opening phenomenon in the usual plants. There appears to be a minimum intensity for opening of around 100 to 300 ft-c. (approximately equivalent to the compensation point—Chapter 13). The light intensity under which the test plant is placed influences not only the rate of opening but also the final size of the aperture (Fig. 6-8), which is also influenced by various other factors, such as the physiological age of the leaf or leaf tissue.

Opening in light appears to be brought about by a photosynthetic lowering of the carbon dioxide partial pressure within the leaf. Red light at 660 mμ is highly effective in causing opening, as it is in photosynthesis. On the other hand, blue light is more efficient in causing stomatal opening than might be expected on the basis of its efficiency in photosynthesis. It has now been quite conclusively shown that chlorophyll in the guard cells is absolutely essential to their opening in response to light. Opening will not occur, for example, in albino barley plants devoid of chlorophyll. Yet the light effect is translocated very rapidly from an illuminated part of a leaf to a nonilluminated part, and thus experiments with variegated leaves (a portion of the leaf lacks chlorophyll) are somewhat less meaningful. It has been shown by careful measurement that there is a close correlation between light, the photosynthetic lowering of carbon dioxide, and stomatal opening.

In spite of such good evidence, some evidence also exists for a direct effect of light on the stomates through a pathway independent of carbon dioxide. Perhaps the energy of light is converted into chemical energy, which is then used to move ions from surrounding cells into the guard cells. This increase in ionic concentration would cause water to move in osmotically.

6.4.3C   Water stress   The water potential in the leaf proves to have a powerful control over

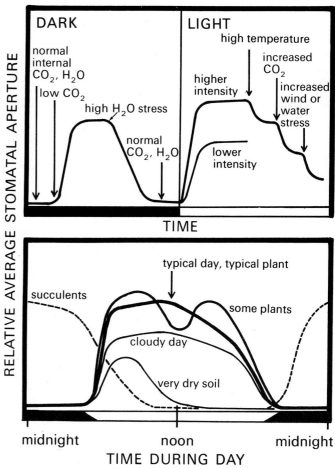

Figure 6-8

A summary diagram of stomatal response to several environmental conditions.

stomatal opening and closing. As water potential decreases (water stress increases), the stomates close. This effect can predominate over low carbon dioxide levels and bright light. The effect may be a direct one, due to loss of water by the guard cells themselves, since such loss is the actual mechanism of closing.

6.4.3D Temperature High temperatures (30° to 35°C) usually cause stomatal closing. It has been suggested that this might be due to a rise in respiration rate causing an increase in carbon dioxide within the leaf. This is probably the correct explanation, since closing in response to high temperatures can be prevented by flushing the leaf continuously with carbon-dioxide-free air. In some experiments, high temperatures cause stomatal opening instead of closing (see end of chapter).

6.4.3E Wind Sometimes stomates close when the leaf is exposed to high wind velocities. This may be because the guard cells themselves lose water by transpiration, or the effect may be indirect through leaf temperature.

6.4.4   The Mechanism of Stomatal Regulation

How do the above environmental effects actually cause turgor changes in the guard cells? The turgor changes must come about in response to changes in water potential within the guard cells, but how is this brought about? The problem remains to be solved, but some four possibilities have been considered, and each appears to have its own merits.

6.4.4A   Increase of sugar in the guard cells due to photosynthesis   This would be an easy way of solving the problem, except that the magnitude is simply not great enough. Not enough sugar is produced to change the water potential of the cells sufficiently to cause opening. Furthermore, why should the guard cells open in carbon-dioxide-free air in the dark, if the only mechanism of opening were photosynthesis?

6.4.4B   A change from starch to sugar   The so-called classical theory of stomatal function was formulated in 1923 by J. D. Sayre and extensively studied by G. W. Scarth in subsequent years. Sayre suggested that carbon dioxide accumulating in the guard cells in the dark caused a reduction in pH (increase in acidity) of the cytoplasm. As the lights came on, this carbon dioxide was removed by photosynthesis, raising the pH. In response to this pH change, the enzyme that catalyzes the hydrolysis of starch to sugar became more active. Large starch molecules have little osmotic effect, but the increase in the sugar concentration would make the water potential of the cell more negative. As predicted by this theory, increasing pH (as by exposing leaves to ammonia vapor) does cause stomates to open. One of the main arguments against this theory, however, is that some guard cells contain no visible starch but still respond to light. Furthermore, it was said that conversion of sugar to starch might be too slow to account for observed rates of closing. Nevertheless, many researchers still believe that this mechanism is, in some species at least, an important one (see 6.4.4E). For example, carbon-dioxide-free air in darkness would cause an increase in pH (carbonic acid would diffuse out of the cells as CO_2), causing the guard cells to open.

6.4.4C   Permeability changes   It has been suggested that pH changes in the cytoplasm might change the permeability of cell membranes. If the permeability to solutes suddenly increased, for example, solutes leaking out of the guard cells would increase their osmotic potential (make it less negative), causing them to lose water and close. Solutes might also move in and out of chloroplasts or mitochondria within the guard cells. It is not conceivable that increasing permeability to *water* could result in an opening of stomates. Guard cell membranes are always so permeable to water that this cannot limit rate of opening.

6.4.4D   Direct metabolic responses   Perhaps ions are taken up from surrounding cells by the use of metabolic energy, accounting for a more negative water potential and the resultant opening. Active water uptake has also been suggested, but the inadequacy of this concept was discussed in the preceding chapter. At any rate, some evidence exists for metabolic participation in stomatal function, even though we do not know exactly how it might work. For example, stomatal function is inhibited by metabolic inhibitors. Oxygen pressure (always important in respiration) could also be important, although it has not yet been studied in a satisfactory manner.

Except for the Sayre theory, none of these mechanisms readily explains why the stomates open in carbon-dioxide-free air in the dark.

The regulation of stomatal action by environmental conditions has been well described, but the mechanisms of response remain a mystery. It is often suggested that a combination of the above theories might eventually account for stomatal action. There is considerable current interest in the idea of active or metabolic processes in stomatal regulation. Probably the role of carbon dioxide needs clarification more than any other aspect of the problem.

6.4.4E Levitt's modified classical theory

In a paper that came to our attention only as the manuscript for this book was being prepared for final submission to the printer, Jacob Levitt (1967) provides a very penetrating and logical examination of the mechanism of stomatal action. He reasons that, of the conceivable mechanisms of stomatal control, only a formation of solutes in the guard cells could account for observed rates of stomatal action. Active absorption of water cannot occur, and even an active absorption of solutes followed by passive osmotic absorption of water is too slow to account for observed rates. Conversion of some polymerized compound such as starch or inulin to its soluble components (glucose or fructose) would be rapid enough (an enzyme molecule may convert as many as 1,000 molecules per second—see Chapter 11) and energetically feasible. Of the objections to the classical theory, Levitt eliminates on the basis of factual data all but one, namely that removal of CO_2 by photosynthesis would not change the pH of the guard cells as much as has been observed or enough to control the hydrolysis of starch to sugar or the synthesis of starch from sugar. He then modifies the classical theory by suggesting that removal of CO_2 by photosynthesis would not only have a direct effect upon pH, but that it would have a much more important indirect effect by influencing other equilibria, particularly the formation and breakdown (decarboxylation) of organic acids. When CO_2 in the guard cells is high, formation of organic acids is strongly favored. These acids provide a low (acid) pH, sugar is converted to starch, osmotic potential is less negative, and the guard cells lose water, closing the stomates.

On the basis of this modified classical theory, Levitt is able to explain all of the presently known facts relating to stomatal opening and closing. Opening of succulent stomates at night appears at first to be an exception, since increasing organic acids leads to opening instead of closing. In this case, however, the organic acids increase to such a concentration that they themselves can make the osmotic potential more negative by as much as 5 bars, accounting for the uptake of water in the guard cells and opening of the stomates. During the day, these organic acids are converted by the photosynthetic process to starch, allowing the stomates to close. Levitt points out that the major remaining deficiency in our understanding of stomatal action is in relation to the actual enzymes and substrates controlling the conversion of polymer to solutes, and that research should be concentrated in this area.

The subject of stomatal action remains highly controversial. Levitt remains convinced that his modified classical theory will prove to be correct, but other scientists (e.g., Klaus Raschke, now at Michigan State University) disagree and feel that an active transport of ions, particularly potassium ions, will prove to be the deciding factor in production of the osmotic potential differences that are the basis of stomatal action.

6.4.5 Feedback Regulation

In recent years, some interesting new data relative to stomatal action have been obtained. For example, a component of stomatal action appears to be controlled by an internal timing mechanism (the biological clock—see Chapter 24) almost independently of the external environment.

Other careful studies by Klaus Raschke in Giessen, Germany, using a recording **porometer,** have been especially interesting. Raschke used isolated sections from leaves of *Zea mays* (corn), which have about an equal number of stomates on both sides of the leaf. The status of the stomates is sampled at frequent and regular intervals by very briefly contacting the leaf on opposite sides with two open tubes, one of which has a slightly higher pressure than the other. Passage of air (or any controlled atmosphere) through the leaf indicates the status of the stomates. Data from as many as 24 samples can be recorded simultaneously on a strip recorder.

Raschke analyzes his results in terms of a **feedback system** (Fig. 6-9), and this approach is proving to be very valuable in the study of many plant and animal processes. As a thermostat detects the temperature in a room, reacting by calling for heat from a furnace if the temperature is too low or cooling from an air-conditioner if the temperature is too high, so the stomates appear to react to the levels of CO_2 in the air. As the thermostat is set manually for a desired temperature value, so light intensity seems to determine the optimum CO_2 levels within the leaf and consequently the stomatal aperture under given conditions. Light may also provide the energy for the response of the regulatory mechanism (as electricity may activate the thermostat). Typically, feedback or **servo control systems** (a more correct term for systems in which a desired value may be set, as on the thermostat) tend to oscillate by temporary overcompensation. Raschke and others have been able to detect the same kind of momentary oscillations in the stomatal mechanism (Fig. 6-10).

6.5 THE ROLE OF TRANSPIRATION IN PLANT GROWTH

Plant physiologists have argued about whether transpiration benefits the plant or not. It was assumed that since transpiration happens it must be good for the plant, as though a plant function could not exist if it did not contribute to the plant's betterment and well-being. Most philosophers reject the idea that all things in the universe must have their purpose; that is, they reject the **teleological argument**. Nevertheless, much progress has been made in biology by taking essentially this approach. This is apparently because in the world of living things, natural selection operates very strongly, so that those functions that confer the most advantageous features upon their possessors will be the functions most likely to survive.

Apparently, transpiration is *not* essential for some species, because they have been grown successfully in atmospheres of 100 percent relative humidity (RH) where transpiration is negligible. As a rule, plants do grow better at high humidities. So why does transpiration occur? We may think of it as a compromise with the plant's need to exchange carbon dioxide and oxygen with the atmosphere. Since these gases must pass in and out of the leaf, water in the vapor form will also pass in and out of the leaf. The situation is not so simple, however, since some plants are known that will not grow at 100 percent RH (e.g., the buds on a pear tree). Furthermore, as we shall see below, the light essential for photosynthesis will warm the leaf above air temperature, and transpiration will occur even in atmospheres of 100 percent RH.

Proponents of the advantages of transpiration have suggested three possible values of the process. Each of these brings up an important topic for our discussion:

6.5.1 Transport of Minerals from the Soil in the Transpiration Stream

Minerals absorbed by the plant from the soil often move up through the plant in the transpiration stream. But is the transpiration stream *essential* for this movement? Actually, there is always *some* water movement through the plant.

A SIMPLE FEEDBACK SYSTEM:

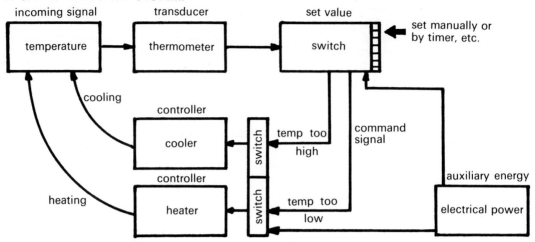

SOME POSSIBLE ELEMENTS OF A
STOMATAL FEEDBACK SYSTEM (Levitt's modified classical theory):

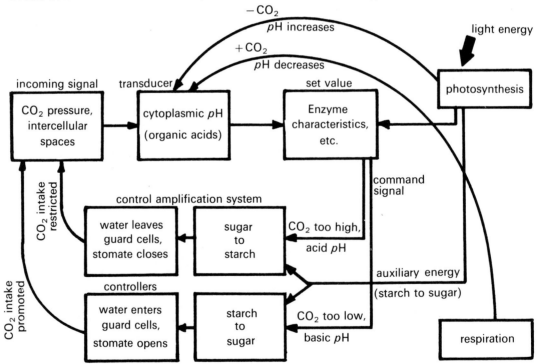

Figure 6-9

A simple mechanical feedback system (top), as it might be used to control the temperature in a room, compared to a possible feedback system that might control operation of the stomates (bottom).

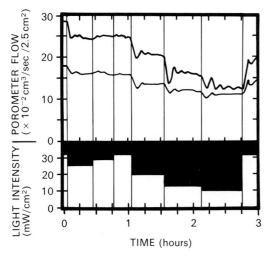

Figure 6-10

Oscillations in stomatal aperture (upper two curves) in response to changing light intensity (bottom of figure). Oscillations are apparent immediately following the change in light intensity but damp out within a fairly short time (e.g. 15 minutes). (Data from K. Raschke, 1966, "Die Reaktionen des CO_2—Regelsystems in den Schliesszellen von *Zea mays* auf weisses licht," *Planta* 68:111. Berlin–Heidelberg–New York: Springer, 1966. Used by permission.)

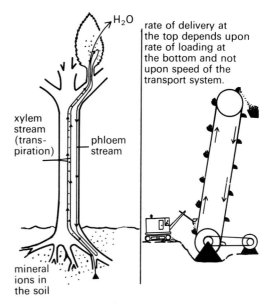

Figure 6-11

An illustration of how rate of delivery depends upon rate of supply rather than rate of transport.

Water is used in photosynthetic processes in the leaves, and it is moved back down to the roots in the phloem system, actually circulating throughout the plant (Chapter 9). Assuming such a constant flow through the plant, the quantity of minerals reaching the leaves will depend upon the rate at which they enter the roots and not upon the rate of flow of water through the plant. The idea is illustrated in Fig. 6-11. This problem will be discussed in more detail in the next chapter in relation to the pathway of water from the soil to the air through the plant. In general we shall conclude that under conditions of limiting minerals in the soil, wide ranges in transpiration rate make little difference in the uptake of minerals; but, when soil minerals are abundant, uptake may then be related to the rate of transpiration.

6.5.2 Optimum Turgidity

It has been suggested that there is an optimum level of water potential (water stress) within the plant. The various plant functions are said to be slower or less efficient both above and below this level. If transpiration is not allowed to occur, the plants will become overly "turgid" and thus will not grow as well as when water potential is more negative. Some plants grown in atmospheres of 100 percent relative humidity do appear abnormal. We will discuss in section 6.6 the effects of water stress on metabolism and other aspects of plant growth.

6.5.3 Evaporative Cooling of the Leaf

Transpiration removes a certain amount of heat from the leaf, namely, about 600 calories per gram of evaporated water. Often this is a very sizable proportion of the heat lost from the leaf. There are, however, other ways for this heat to be removed if it is not removed by evaporation. Considerable space is devoted to discussion of this topic (section 6.7).

6.6 THE PHYSIOLOGY OF WATER DEFICITS

Is the concept of **optimum turgidity** really meaningful? In the next chapter we will discuss the water potential of the soil, defining certain arbitrary points along the scale of tensions with which water is held (the scale of soil matric potentials). One of these is the field capacity (soil water held only against gravity); another is the **permanent wilting point**. It has long been said that water between these two tensions is equally available to the plant; that the plant grows with equal efficiency provided that soil water is held anywhere within this range. Yet water stress in the plant is influenced by water stress in the soil, and so this old generalization is oversimplified.

The status of water in the plant may be measured by measuring the water potential of the tissue, as discussed in Chapter 5. Another approach is to place a detached leaf in pure water at atmospheric pressure (or the stem in pure water, the rest of the leaf in a saturated atmosphere) and measure the amount of water absorbed (the change in leaf weight). This second method of measurement of **water deficit** has been used rather widely, especially in field studies.[1]

Although there are some complications, as we shall see, it has now been rather conclusively demonstrated that the water potential

does influence a number of physiological processes. Let us consider a few examples:

6.6.1 Transpiration and Stomatal Aperture

As mentioned above, stomatal opening is strongly influenced by water deficit, and this will influence transpiration and probably photosynthesis and respiration, which in turn may influence still other processes. Hence there may be an *indirect* effect of water stress (*via* the stomates) on various plant functions.

6.6.2 Photosynthesis

Certain authors have reported little influence of water stress on photosynthesis until the wilting point is reached. Others show clear decreases of photosynthesis at stresses well above the permanent wilting point. We might expect that there would be species differences, but probably the most important influence is the indirect one on stomatal aperture as mentioned above. The problem is far from solved, but there does appear to be some evidence that an inhibition of photosynthesis may occur because of water stress in the cell rather than simply because of an effect upon the stomatal mechanism.

6.6.3 Respiration

This process can be studied somewhat easier than photosynthesis, since the process can be observed in the dark where stomates may remain closed under all conditions of water stress. There appears to be a fairly clear relationship between respiration and the water stress within the tissue. As a matter of fact, some good experiments indicate that there is an optimum, showing *increasing* respiration with decreasing water potential down to a certain value, after which respiration *decreases* with further decreases in

---

[1] The concept of water deficit (*Wasser Defizit*) was introduced by O. Stocker in 1929. It is calculated as follows:

$$\text{Water deficit} = \frac{\text{Saturated wt.} - \text{Original fresh wt.}}{\text{Saturated wt.} - \text{Oven dry wt.}} \times 100$$

water potential. Here we may have at least one good example of optimum turgor.

6.6.4 Other Effects

Several studies document various effects of water stress on such factors as the chemical composition of the tissue, nitrogen metabolism, etc. Considerable study has gone into the relationship between growth and water stress. It is quite apparent that water stress is extremely important. Tree ring studies indicate this clearly, for example. In years when water is limiting, growth is strongly restricted. There are actually many examples showing that water stress may clearly control the growth of plants, even at levels well above the permanent wilting point. Tomato plants, for example, grow much better when the soil is maintained near field capacity than when it is allowed to dry periodically nearly to the permanent wilting point before watering. Water potential is of considerable importance in the physiology of the plant.

6.7 HEAT TRANSFER BETWEEN THE PLANT AND ITS ENVIRONMENT

Transpiration is an important component of energy transfer between the plant and its environment, and so it should be discussed in the broad heat-transfer context. Furthermore, heat transfer is itself an interesting and important topic, and its discussion brings up a number of important biophysical principles which should be part of a plant physiologist's background.

Our discussion of heat transfer may conveniently be centered around the heat-balance equation and the various factors making it up, which must add up algebraically to zero:

$$0 = Q + C + V + B + M \qquad (28)$$

where:

Q = net radiation. When the term is negative, this indicates that the leaf is radiating more energy to its surroundings than it is absorbing from them, and when the term is positive, the leaf is absorbing more radiant energy.

C = convection. When C is negative, heat is moving from the leaf to the air, and when it is positive, from the air to the leaf.

V = the rate of heat consumption as latent heat of vaporization. This is the transpiration term. When it is negative, water is vaporizing, and when it is positive, water (or frost) is condensing on the leaf.

B = storage. When this term is positive, the leaf temperature is increasing as the leaf stores heat; when negative, leaf temperature is decreasing.

M = metabolism and other factors. This term includes the metabolic heat produced or absorbed by reactions like photosynthesis and respiration, the water arriving from the soil at some temperature other than that of the leaf, and perhaps other factors.

To simplify matters, heat-transfer studies are usually carried out under steady-state conditions where leaf temperature is constant, and so B is equal to zero. Factors constituting M are also usually ignored because they are very minor compared to radiation, convection, and transpiration (usually less than 2 or 3 percent of the others). Hence the equation may be written:

$$0 = Q + C + V \qquad (29)$$

Since the terms must balance to zero, if two are positive, the third must be negative; or if two are negative, the third must be positive. In the usual daytime conditions most often studied, Q is positive, and C and V are negative. Under such conditions, we may think of the net absorbed radiation (Q_{abs}) as being equal to the heat lost by convection and transpiration:

$$- Q_{abs} = C + V \qquad (30)$$

At night, however, the leaf might be losing heat by radiation to its surroundings but gaining heat by convection from the surrounding air and by condensation of dew. Hence equation (28) is very general, and equation (29) is also quite general under steady-state conditions, but equation (30) is more limited in application. In nature, steady-state conditions may be somewhat rare, but consideration of the highly complex exchanges found in nature can be profitably based upon an initial study under steady-state conditions. We will consider in some detail the parameters of radiation, convection, and transpiration.

6.7.1   Radiation

The laws governing absorption and emission of radiant energy have been known for nearly a century, although they are only now coming into use by plant physiologists. We will consider first the absorption of incoming radiation and then the loss of radiant energy by the plant.

6.7.1A   Absorption of incoming radiation   A perfect **black body** absorbs all incoming radiation. Consider, for example, a hollow body painted as nearly black as possible on the inside and with a small hole for incoming radiation. Radiation entering through the hole will be largely absorbed by the first surface it strikes, and whatever is reflected will be absorbed by the next surface so that eventually all is absorbed but a minute amount, which reflects back out through the hole.

Over much of the spectrum, the leaf is far from being a black body. Figure 6-12 shows one example of the quantity of light energy absorbed by a leaf as a function of the wave-length of that light energy. In the visible spectrum, there is an important "**window**" in the green portion (much of this light is not absorbed by the leaf). There is another, even more striking "window" in the near-infrared part of the spectrum. Only a small amount of this part of the spectrum is absorbed by the leaf, and the rest is either transmitted or reflected. Plants photographed with infrared film sensitive to this part of the spectrum appear quite white in the photograph. Virtually all of the radiant energy at wavelengths greater than three microns is absorbed.

Since the quantity of light energy absorbed by a leaf is so strongly dependent upon the nature of the incoming radiation, it is appropriate that we consider the radiation produced by various sources.

(1) *Sunlight.* Sunlight is very rich in the near-infrared and in the green (Fig. 6-12), those wavelengths least absorbed by most leaves. So a considerable portion may not be absorbed by the leaf. Depending upon the species, as much as 50 percent of the incoming radiation may be reflected or transmitted.

As shown in Fig. 3-3 (section 3.1.2), the form of the curve for a spectrum depends upon whether it is plotted as energy per unit increment of wavelength, or as energy per unit increment of frequency (for discussion of the relationship between wavelength and frequency, see section 3.1.2). The peak of the curve shifts toward the infrared when it is plotted on a frequency instead of a wavelength basis.

(2) *Thermal radiation.* All objects above absolute zero emit radiation, the quantity and the wavelength being dependent upon their temperature (see below). Objects in a plant's environment, such as the soil, other plants, clouds in the sky, and carbon dioxide in the air, are no exception. Since these objects are mostly at relatively low temperatures, they emit mostly very long wavelengths (Fig. 6-13). The plant

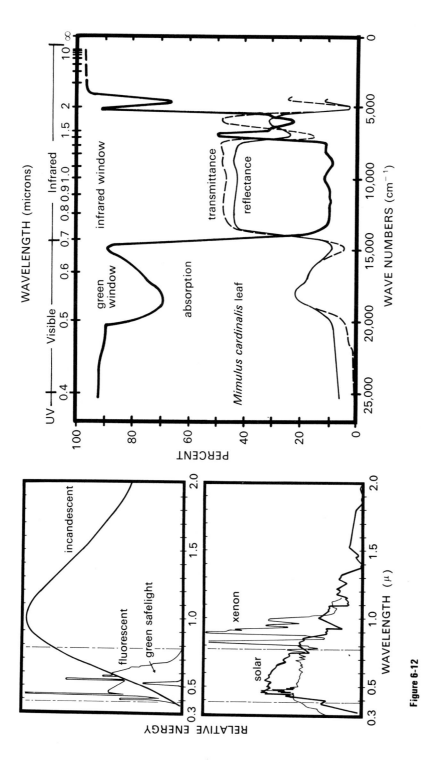

Figure 6-12

(left) Emission spectra for five sources. Note incandescent lamp peak at about 1.0 micron; mercury emission lines in fluorescent lamp spectra; infrared peaks (0.85 to 1.05 microns) from the xenon lamp; and solar peak in the midpart of the visible (indicated by dashed vertical lines). (right) Absorption, transmission, and reflection spectra of a leaf. Note especially the "windows" in the green and in the near-infrared portions of the spectrum. The leaves are thin and light green. (From Gates et al., 1965, *Applied Optics* 4:11. Used by permission.) Note that emission spectra are plotted on a linear wavelength scale for the sources and a linear wave number scale for the leaf spectra.

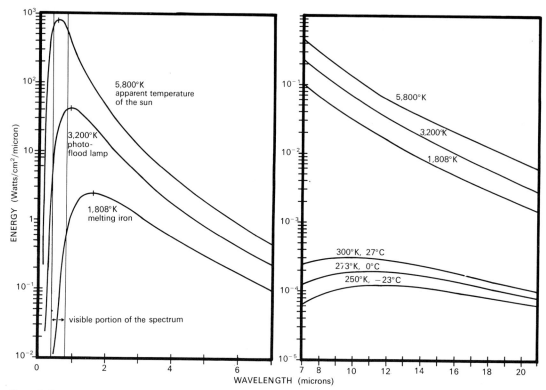

Figure 6-13

Black body emission spectra compared over a wide range of energy emission and wavelength. The spectra would apply for any perfect black body radiator. Note shift in the peaks toward longer wavelengths, flattening of the curves, and decrease in total energy as temperatures decrease.

will absorb virtually all of this, and in some situations the total incoming radiant energy absorbed by the plant from surrounding objects may be as high as that absorbed from the sun.

(3) *Incandescent light.* The spectral distribution of light from an incandescent lamp is also shown in Fig. 6-12. Most of the radiant energy from such a light source is in the infrared, and only a relatively small portion is in the visible. Since the near-infrared is not absorbed, a significant portion of the incandescent light will not be absorbed by the leaf. Much will be absorbed, however, since the leaf absorbs effectively red and far-infrared, both of which are present in considerable quantities in incandescent light.

(4) *Visible light.* Fluorescent light has virtually no infrared but only visible radiation (Fig. 6-12). Light from other sources can be filtered (e.g., through copper sulfate solutions) so that only visible light results. A plant exposed to such light will absorb a relatively high percentage, considerably more than from an incandescent lamp (Table 6-3).

Since light quality varies so much with different sources, and since plants absorb differently at different wavelengths, a simple measurement of total incoming radiation will be

TABLE 6-3

APPROXIMATE QUANTITIES OF "VISIBLE"[a] AND "VISIBLE PLUS NEAR INFRARED"[b] RADIATION ABSORBED BY A LEAF OF
XANTHIUM STRUMARIUM, **AND THE RESULTING LEAF TEMPERATURES AND TRANSPIRATION RATES[c]**

Parameter	"Visible"[a]	"Visible plus infrared"[b]
total energy falling on leaf	0.34 cal/cm^2/min	0.34 cal/cm^2/min
foot-candle readings (visible light)	7,950 ft-c	2,150 ft-c
approximate light absorbed, calories	0.24 cal/cm^2/min	0.15 cal/cm^2/min
approximate light absorbed (percent)	70	45
air temperature	$15 \pm 0.5°C$	$15 \pm 0.5°C$
relative humidity (percent)	86–90	86–90
leaf temperature	$21.0°C$	$17.6°C$
transpiration rate	3.12 g/dm^2/hr	0.82 g/dm^2/hr

[a] Incandescent light filtered through 8 cm of copper sulfate solution (20 g/1), transmitting wavelengths from about 400 nm to 650 nm.

[b] Incandescent light filtered through 4 cm of water (wavelengths from about 400 nm to 1,400 nm).

[c] Data from Robert S. Mellor, Frank B. Salisbury, and Klaus Raschke, "Leaf Temperatures in Controlled Environments," *Planta* 61:56–72 (1964).

virtually useless from the standpoint of plant response. Expression of light energy only in terms of foot-candles is even worse than the measurement of total energy and nothing else. A foot-candle meter is constructed to respond only to the wavelengths of light to which the human eye is sensitive. The plant absorbs other wavelengths, and some of the light to which the eye is sensitive (notably the green) is not absorbed strongly by the plant. Data are still presented by plant physiologists in terms of foot-candles, because foot-candle meters are readily available, and since a detailed analysis of the spectral distribution of incoming light is difficult and quite beyond the instrumentation available to most workers. But instruments are becoming available, and they should be used in any serious photobiological study. If foot-candles must be used, then the light source should be described as carefully as possible.

6.7.1B Emission of radiant energy by the leaf

The extent of the plant's environment is as broad as can be imagined. The leaf is in immediate contact with the surrounding air, exchanging heat through molecular conduction. It is also receiving a large portion of its energy from the sun some 93 million miles away. It is emitting radiant energy not only to the objects around it, but some of the radiation given off by the plant will extend into outer space, and a certain portion of it may continue unabsorbed to the ends of the universe! So the plant's environment includes everything from the closest molecule of air to the infinite distances of unending space.

This loss of energy by radiation is governed by two characteristics of the body under consideration: its temperature and its emissivity.

(1) *Temperature and radiation.* Both the quantity and the quality of radiant energy emitted from a body are dependent upon temperature. The **quantity** emitted is a function of the fourth power of the absolute temperature, according to **Stefan's law**:

$$Q = e\delta T^4 \qquad (31)$$

TABLE 6-4 ,

deg C	deg K	T^4	Q = Cal/cm^2/sec	% of Q at 0° C
0°	273°	5.55 × 10^9	0.00718	100%
20°	293°	7.38 × 10^9	0.00954	133%
30°	303°	8.42 × 10^9	0.01085	151%
5,477° [a]	5,750° [a]	1.10 × 10^{15}	1,415.0	19,700,000%

[a] Average surface temperature of the sun.

where:

Q = the quantity of energy radiated (in calories, using δ as below)

e = the emissivity (about 0.95 for leaves at growing temperatures—see below)

δ = the Stefan–Boltzmann constant (1.36 × 10^{-12} cal/cm^2 sec deg K^4)

T = the absolute temperature

The fourth power of absolute temperature in the above equation means that the emission of radiant energy will increase very rapidly as temperature increases. In the normal range of temperatures encountered by plants, this will not be an overwhelming increase, because on the absolute temperature scale, this range is very narrow. Yet as shown in Table 6-4, radiant energy emitted will increase from an arbitrary value of 100 percent at 0°C to 151 percent at 30°C. When the temperature increases to the level encountered at the surface of the sun, the amount of energy radiated is increased to nearly 20 million percent of that given off at 0°C.

The **quality** of radiation emitted by a body is also strongly influenced by temperature. This is illustrated in Fig. 6-13. As the temperature increases, the peak of the emitted spectrum shifts toward the shorter wavelengths at the same time that the total area under the curve (the total energy emitted) increases according to Stefan's law as discussed above. The shift toward shorter wavelengths with increasing temperature is called **Wien's law**. In accordance with this law, one may speak of "**color temperature**" of light,

expressing light quality in terms of degrees Kelvin. Such an expression implies that the spectral distribution of the light under consideration is essentially equivalent to that produced by a black body at the indicated temperature. This notation is used in color photography. As color temperature increases, light balance shifts more toward the blue.

(2) *Emissivity* (*e*). The curves shown in Fig. 6-13 all assume a perfect black-body radiation. Actually, such an ideal is seldom achieved. In practice, as objects fail to absorb all wavelengths, they also fail to emit all wavelengths, the curve for emission being the same as the curve for absorption.

The leaf is nearly a perfect black-body radiator at wavelengths beyond 3 μ. The emissivity is about 95 percent, or $e = 0.95$. Since leaves at their normal temperatures emit essentially all of their radiant energy beyond the 3 μ limit, we need not be concerned at these temperatures with the wide deviations from a black body encountered in the green and the near-infrared.

The atmosphere is far from a perfect black body, even in the far-infrared (Fig. 3-3), and this must be taken into account in calculating either the thermal radiation coming from the atmosphere or that absorbed by the atmosphere after being emitted by the leaf.

6.7.1C Radiant heat transfer from the leaf

The heat loss from the leaf in the form of radiation may, since the leaf is a nearly perfect black body at moderate temperatures, be calculated to a good approximation by equation (31) on the basis of leaf temperature alone ($e = 0.95$).

In the heat balance equations, (28) and (29), the radiation term, **Q**, refers to **net radiation of the leaf**, that is, the difference between the amount of radiation absorbed by the leaf and the amount radiated from it. This must be calculated by multiplying the incoming radiation by the **absorptivity coefficient** (a decimal fraction indicating the portion of energy absorbed by the leaf) and subtracting from this the thermal energy radiated by the leaf as calculated by Stefan's law [equation (31)]. The absorptivity coefficient will depend upon both the leaf and the quality of the incoming radiation. It is one of the most difficult unknowns in the experimental study of heat transfer in plants. Values range from 0.44 to 0.88.

Often the net radiation in the *environment* can be measured directly. A net radiometer has two black-body absorbers insulated from each other and protected from convection (usually by a polyethylene dome, which is nearly transparent in the infrared). The one black-body absorber faces upward, its temperature being influenced by incoming radiation, while the other faces downward, absorbing outgoing radiation from the soil, plants, etc. The difference in temperature between these two is measured electrically, and this is an indication of net radiation.

To measure either incoming or outgoing radiation, the actual temperature of an insulated black-body absorber (often a minute thermistor covered with lamp black) is measured. A highly reflective funnel directs incoming radiation from a certain solid angle onto the absorber. The instrument is calibrated by aiming it at black-body surfaces of known temperature.

The emissivity of air is low, being due almost exclusively to carbon dioxide and water vapor. Hence on a clear night and when the atmosphere is extremely dry, little long-wave thermal radiation will be coming in from the atmosphere (some will come from the carbon dioxide), and so the leaf will radiate more energy out into space than it receives. Under such conditions, the leaf temperature may drop below the air temperature, sometimes causing the formation of dew or frost. During the daytime when the balance is reversed, leaf temperatures may climb as high as 20°C above the surrounding air temperature (Fig. 6-14). Of course, the actual difference between leaf and air temperature will also depend upon factors in the heat balance equation besides radiation.

6.7.2 Convection

In discussions of heat transfer between the leaf and the environment, the concepts of conduction and convection are usually included under the single term convection. **Conduction** is a molecular transfer of heat (analogous to diffusion), in which the molecules transfer kinetic motion to each other. In **convection**, groups of molecules in a gas or a liquid move together due to pressure gradients resulting from density differences caused by the expansion or contraction brought about by temperature differences. This is a **bulk transfer** of material rather than a molecular one. The differences are analogous to those relating to the movement of water: there is a diffusional flow in response to free energy gradients and a bulk movement in response to density differences or pressure gradients. True convection, which depends completely upon density (pressure) differences, would not occur in the weightless state,[2] although conduction is independent of gravity. In heat transfer from the leaf to the surrounding air, heat energy (sensible heat) is

[2] For this reason, a flame does not burn brightly in an earth-orbiting satellite, even in a pure oxygen atmosphere. It soon becomes enveloped in a layer of CO_2 and H_2O vapor. Oxygen must diffuse through this layer to support the flame.

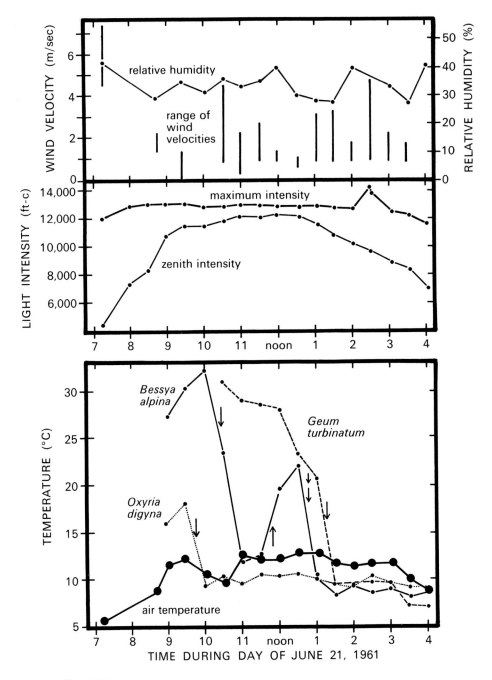

Figure 6-14

Some leaf temperatures of Alpine plants in the field compared to the status of several environmental factors. Maximum light intensity indicates that photocell was aimed directly at the sun. Lower curves indicate leaf temperatures as measured by thermocouples in the leaf tissues. Arrows indicate that shadows moved over the leaf. (From F. B. Salisbury and G. G. Spomer, 1964, *Planta* 60:497. Used by permission.)

first transferred from the leaf to the contacting layer of air molecules by conduction and then away from the leaf by convection. The entire process will be referred to as convection.

Discussions of convection are greatly aided by the concept of the boundary layer. This is of help not only in our intuitive understanding of convection but also in the mathematical approach to this problem. The concept has further application in the discussion of transpiration.

The **boundary layer** may be defined as a transfer zone of gas or liquid in contact with an object (in this case the leaf), in which the temperature, vapor pressure, or velocity of the gas or liquid are influenced by the object. Beyond the boundary layer there is no influence of the object upon the medium (Fig. 6-15). In general, heat convection (or the transfer of water vapor) will occur more rapidly through the boundary layer if the boundary layer is thin. The heat (and vapor) gradients are then steeper.

The kind of formula given above (equation 17) for rate of flow of water through a membrane in osmosis applies also to diffusional and convective transfer of heat. Transfer of heat through the boundary layer by convection (C) is proportional to the driving force and inversely proportional to the resistance of the air to convective heat movement (r_a). In this case, the driving force is the difference in air temperature between the leaf (T_L) and the air beyond the boundary layer (T_a):

$$C = \frac{T_a - T_L}{r_a} \qquad (32)$$

Again as in osmosis, a permeability constant is sometimes more useful than a resistance term. This permeability factor is called the **heat transfer coefficient** (h_c), and it is inversely proportional to the resistance:

$$h_c = \frac{1}{r_a} \qquad (33)$$

In terms of the heat transfer coefficient, the formula for convective loss or gain of heat by the leaf becomes:

$$C = h_c(T_a - T_L) = h_c(\Delta T) \qquad (34)$$

If ΔT is positive, the air is warmest and the leaf is gaining heat (C is positive); if negative (C is negative), the leaf is warmest and losing heat by convection. The heat transfer coefficient, which is an expression of the thickness of the boundary layer, is strongly influenced by two factors: *first,* leaf size and shape, and *second,* wind velocity.

6.7.2A Shape and size of the leaf

Where the moving medium (the air) first touches the leaf, the boundary layer is the thinnest. As distance from the edge of the leaf increases, so does the thickness of the boundary layer. So the boundary layer for a leaf is not uniform, and neither is h_c. It is strongly influenced both by size and by shape of the leaf. By making a few assumptions, one may calculate an *average* value for h_c for a given leaf.

In general, the boundary layer is thickest to the leeward of the center of large leaves. The thinnest boundary layers are encountered near the margins (both windward and leeward) and with small leaves, particularly the needles of conifers.

6.7.2B Wind velocity and the boundary layer

As the wind velocity increases, the boundary layer becomes thinner. Consequently the boundary layer is the thinnest for small leaves in high wind velocities, and under these conditions, convective heat transfer will be the most effective (Fig. 6-16). Leaf temperatures will approach air temperatures as the wind increases, and this will occur faster at constant wind velocity for smaller leaves.

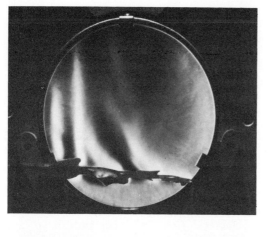
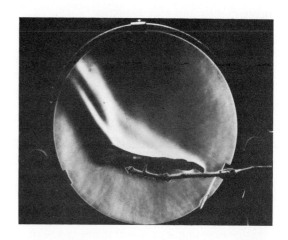

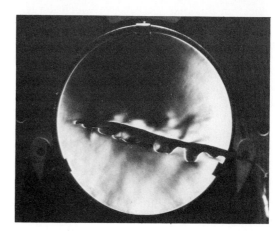

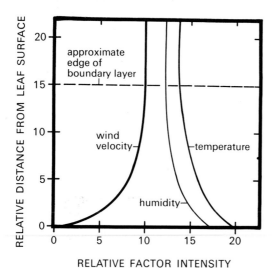

Figure 6-15

(top) Schlieren photographs of leaves losing heat by convection. The schlieren technique utilizes a high-quality concave mirror in a manner that makes air of different densities appear light or dark on the photographs. The light areas near the leaf indicate warmer (less dense) air. This is the boundary layer. (Photographs courtesy of D. M. Gates, Missouri Botanical Garden.) (bottom left) Relative factor intensities as a function of distance from a surface, illustrating the principle of the boundary layer.

6.7.3 Transpiration

Transpiration (V) is also proportional to the driving force and inversely proportional to resistance.[3] The driving force is the gradient in partial pressure of water vapor (or water vapor concentration) in the boundary layer. This gradient is determined by the thickness of the boundary layer and the difference between the partial pressure (p_L) of water vapor in the internal air of the leaf and the partial pressure (p_a) of water vapor in the bulk air outside. The resistance has at least two terms: that of the leaf (r_L) and that of the boundary layer (r_a). The value r_a is equal to that discussed above in relation to heat convection through the boundary layer. The leaf resistance could be further divided into resistance of the mesophyll cells and evaporation at their surfaces, resistance of the cuticle, and resistance of the stomates. Stomatal resistance is especially important because it may vary widely with opening and closing of the stomates. The equation for transpiration, including a constant (k) that depends upon the desired units of V, becomes:

$$V = \frac{(p_L - p_a)k}{r_L + r_a} = \frac{\Delta p k}{r_L + r_a} \qquad (35)$$

6.7.3A Factors determining the water-potential gradient
We will now consider factors that influence these various parameters.

(1) *Temperature.* In Fig. 6-17 vapor pressure is shown as a function of temperature. The vapor pressure approximately doubles for each 10°C (or 20°F) increase in temperature. The **relative humidity** (RH) of air is the actual humidity of the air compared to the potential humidity (vapor pressure) of the air at the given temperature. Since potential humidity of the air is so strongly dependent upon temperature,

---

[3] In discussions of transpiration, resistance is more commonly used than permeability.

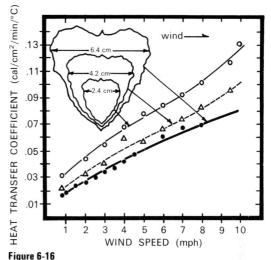

Figure 6-16

Heat transfer coefficients for leaves of different sizes as a function of wind speed. (From B. G. Drake, 1967, Master's thesis, Colorado State University, Fort Collins. Used by permission.)

relative humidity is likewise strongly influenced by temperature. For example, air saturated at 20°C (100 percent RH) has only approximately 50 percent RH if its temperature is increased to 30°C.

From the standpoint of the transpiration rate, the difference between the actual humidity and the potential humidity is of primary importance. And this will also be a strong function of temperature. As the temperature of a given volume of air increases, there is an increase in the so-called **vapor pressure deficit** (the difference between the actual vapor pressure and the potential vapor pressure at saturation).

The gradient in vapor pressure deficit between the leaf and the air (related to the water-potential gradient) is strongly influenced by temperature differences between the leaf and the air. Usually it is assumed that the relative humidity immediately next to the mesophyll cell walls inside the leaf is 100 percent—that is, that the internal air of the leaf is saturated with water vapor at the temperature of the leaf. If the leaf temperature is higher than the air temperature, the vapor pressure in the leaf will be high and the gradient to the air steep.

The main cause of temperature difference between the leaf and the air will be absorbed radiation. Convection will reduce this difference, and so will transpiration. So far as the vapor pressure difference goes, radiation and wind will have their influence through temperature. Here the properties of heat transfer directly influence transpiration.

(2) *Atmospheric humidity.* The actual concentration of vapor in the air will establish one end of the gradient. In some situations (particularly very low humidities and high air temperatures), this may be of major control in the rate of transpiration. Often, however, the difference in temperature between the leaf and the air will be a more important factor than atmospheric humidity. In air at 20°C, for example, an atmospheric humidity of 10 percent will establish a vapor pressure difference of about 21 mbars between the leaf and the air, providing both are at the same temperature. If the leaf is at 30°C, however, and the atmospheric humidity is *90 percent* (at 20°C), there will still be a vapor pressure difference of about 22 mbars.[4]

A striking illustration of this phenomenon is transpiration into air having a relative humidity of 100 percent. This may occur under high radiant heat loads where leaf temperature is elevated above the air temperature. The air in the boundary layer (warmer than beyond the boundary layer due to convection from the leaf) will have a relative humidity below 100 percent,

---

[4] This calculation is based upon Fig. 6-17. At 20°C, vapor pressure at saturation is about 23 mbars. Ten percent of this is about 2 mbars Hg, leaving a gradient of 21 mbars. At 30°C, vapor pressure is 43 mbars, 90 percent of 23 mbars (20°C air) is 21 mbars; this subtracted from 43 mbars leaves a gradient of 22 mbars.

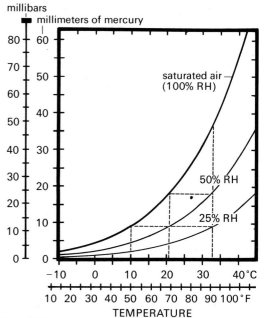

Figure 6-17

Relationship between moisture in the atmosphere (partial pressure of water vapor) and temperature for saturated air and for air at 50 percent and 25 percent relative humidity. Dashed lines indicate, for example, that air at 10°C, 100 percent RH has the same amount of moisture as air at 21°C, 50 percent RH, and air at 33°C, 25 percent RH.

constituting a gradient between the leaf and the air. As this vapor goes beyond the boundary layer, it may condense. This phenomenon can be seen in the steaming of forests following a rainstorm as the sun breaks through the clouds.

(3) *Other factors.* Substances dissolved in the cell-wall water will influence the water potential. As a rule these effects are considered rather minor, but they might be significant. Furthermore, water under tension (see next chapter) may have a fairly low water potential. As a general rule this is completely ignored, although the hydrational tensions with which water is held to the cell walls may be very high, as discussed in Chapter 4. The result of these factors

might be that relative humidity next to the evaporating cell walls could be a few percent less than 100 percent.

6.7.3B The resistance to transpiration

Both boundary layer and leaf resistance are influenced by a number of factors.

(1) *The boundary layer resistance* (r_a). The boundary layer resistance to transpiration is very similar to, if not identical with, the resistance to convective heat transfer. This similarity often provides a close coupling between convection and transpiration. When r_L is small r_a is controlling, and both processes are almost equally influenced by wind (increasing wind decreases resistance), by leaf shape and size (smaller leaves have less boundary layer resistance), and by difference in temperature between the leaf and the air.

(2) *Leaf resistance* (r_L). The actual resistance encountered by water in moving from inside the plant to the boundary layer consists of a number of components. There is a resistance to diffusion and bulk movement of water in the cytoplasm, the cell membranes and walls, and in the cuticle on the outside of the epidermis. Water evaporating from the moist surfaces within the leaf must pass through the substomatal cavities, and particularly through the stomates themselves. So far as we know, most of these resistances remain relatively constant, but the stomatal aperture is highly variable and thus primarily responsible for changes in leaf resistance. Under some circumstances there are also slight changes in the resistances encountered in the cuticle.

A recent method for measuring transpiration in the field involves measurement of leaf resistance (r_L) with a sensitive hygrometer contained in a cup clamped on the leaf.

(3) *The relationship between the boundary layer and the leaf resistance.* At constant relatively low r_L, transpiration and convection are closely coupled. As r_L increases, an uncoupling begins to occur, so that factors influencing convection have less influence on transpiration. The term α may be used as the ratio between the boundary-layer resistance (influencing convection) and the total resistance (influencing transpiration):

$$\alpha = \frac{r_a}{r_a + r_L} \qquad (36)$$

With a wet body, such as an open surface of water or a piece of wet filter paper, $r_L = 0$, and consequently α = 1.0. Convection and transpiration are completely coupled. With a leaf, r_L is never 0, and it may vary over a wide range of values as the stomates close. When the stomates are completely shut, r_L reaches a very high value, and the ratio becomes a small fraction approaching zero. Under these conditions, convection and transpiration have become uncoupled from each other. Changing wind velocity, for example, will influence convection as always but has little effect upon transpiration. Essentially the same thing happens as the boundary layer resistance r_a gets smaller. Hence transpiration and convection are less closely coupled for small leaves or with increasing wind velocities.

Considering a wet body of the same shape and size as the leaf ($r_L = 0$), as the wind increases, the temperature of the body approaches the psychrometric (wet bulb) temperature. This temperature will be below the air temperature at humidities of less than 100 percent. With a real leaf, ($r_L > 0$), as wind increases, leaf temperature approaches air temperature, and transpiration tends to become uncoupled from convection as convection becomes increasingly efficient.[5]

---

[5] The discussion in this section is based upon an unpublished manuscript written by Dr. Klaus Raschke.

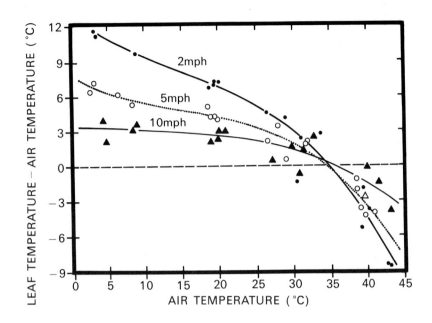

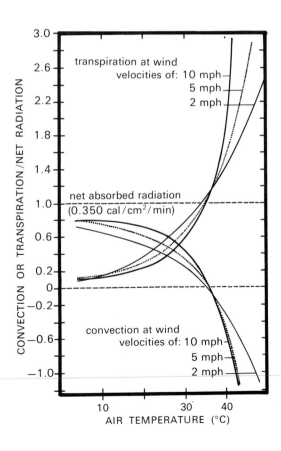

Figure 6-18

(top) The difference between leaf and air temperatures as a function of air temperature for three wind velocities. Light intensity 1.3 cal/cm²/min. Curves are third order polynomials drawn by computer to match the data. (right) The ratio of convection or transpiration to net radiation as a function of air temperature and at three wind velocities. (Data for both figures from B. G. Drake, 1967, Master's thesis, Colorado State University, Fort Collins. Used by permission.)

6.8 TRANSPIRATION IN TERMS OF THE HEAT TRANSFER CONCEPTS

At the beginning of this chapter, we briefly introduced the effects of various environmental factors upon transpiration. These may be summarized again in terms of concepts developed in the above paragraphs. We have, for the most part, considered the leaf in an environment where net radiation is positive, that is, the leaf is absorbing radiant energy. Thus equation (30) applies:

$$- Q_{abs} = C + V$$

From equations (34) and (35), this may be expanded to:

$$- Q_{abs} = h_c(T_a - T_L) + \frac{(\Delta p)k}{r_L + r_a} \qquad (37)$$

Figure 6-18 illustrates two sets of experimental results obtained by Bert G. Drake, a graduate student of Salisbury, first at Colorado State University and then at Utah State University. One part of the figure shows the effects of increasing wind at various air temperatures on the difference between leaf and air temperature ($T_a - T_L = \Delta T$), and the other part indicates the effects of these factors upon transpiration and convection. We can summarize the influence of environment upon transpiration in terms of equation (37), and several of these effects are illustrated by the data of Fig. 6-18. To provide practice for the student, the discussion in the following few paragraphs will utilize exclusively the symbols that have been introduced in this and previous chapters.

6.8.1 Air Temperature

Air temperature strongly influences Δp (via relative humidity), but it also influences ΔT and r_L (via stomatal aperture). In the data of Fig. 6-18, $\Delta T = 0$ for all wind velocities at an air temperature of about 35°C. Drake could explain

this phenomenon on physical principles, but its advantage to the leaf seems quite evident. At low temperatures, T_L values under Drake's conditions (high Q_{abs}) were considerably above T_a, but at elevated T_a, T_L was actually below T_a. It is also evident that this was due to extremely high transpiration rates. Convection was actually *adding* heat to the leaf at these temperatures.

6.8.2 Radiation

Incoming radiation, by its effect upon leaf temperature, influences both ΔT and Δp. Light also may tend to lower r_L by causing the stomates to open, but closing of the stomates in response to elevated T_L may tend to increase r_L. (Incidentally, in Drake's data, stomates were seen to *open* at the highest temperatures. Transpiration rates under these conditions were extremely high.)

6.8.3 Humidity

This will determine one component of Δp, but always as a function of T_a.

6.8.4 Wind

Effects of wind upon transpiration are complex and interesting. Increasing wind, by reducing the thickness of the boundary layer, lowers r_a both for convection and transpiration (the heat transfer coefficient, h_c, is increased by increasing wind). With high Q_{abs}, wind by its effect on h_c will lower T_L, and this will tend to reduce transpiration. Thus wind may *decrease* transpiration by lowering T_L but *increase* it by decreasing r_a. The actual effect will depend upon conditions. With high r_L and high Q_{abs}, effects upon T_L will predominate, and wind will *decrease* transpiration. With low Q_{abs} and low r_L, leaf and air temperature will be about equal, and wind will *increase* transpiration (as evaporation from a piece of wet blotter paper). As the various factors change, situations between these will occur. The

TABLE 6-5

A THEORETICAL ENERGY BUDGET FOR A COCKLEBUR LEAF, 5 CM LONG, WITH WIND BLOWING ACROSS THE LEAF PERPENDICULAR TO THE MID VIENS[a]

Environment	Air temperature (°C)	Leaf temperature (°C)	Relative humidity (%)	Wind (cm/sec)	Transpiration (g/dm²/hr)	Absorbed radiant energy (cal/cm²/min)	Energy radiated from leaf (% of energy absorbed)	Transpiration energy (% of energy absorbed)	Convection energy (% of energy absorbed)
Temperate zone: bright, warm day, high humidity	29.0	33.1	76	225	−1.77	1.04	−71	−17	−12
Temperate zone: bright, warm day, low humidity	30.6	29.2	14	225	−4.03	1.06	−58	−38	+4[b]
Desert: bright, hot, dry, windy day	40	39.7	20	500	−6.85	1.40	−53	−49	+2[b]
Alpine: bright, cold damp, windy day	15	19	35	500	−2.10	1.40	−40	−15	−45
Northern Rain Forest: low light, cool, wet still air (inside canopy)	15	17	100	10	−0.12	0.60	−90	−2.0	−8
Tropical Rain Forest: low light, hot, wet, still air (inside canopy)	30	29	100	10	+0.11[c]	0.60	−108	+2.0[c]	+10[b]
Alpine: cold, wet, windy night	0	−0.6	100	500	+0.16[d]	0.33	−121	+5.0[d]	+16[b]

Note that, If Absorbed energy = +100%, then:
Absorbed Energy + Reradiated Energy + Transpiration + Convection = 0

[a] This information obtained in part from the laboratory of Dr. David Gates at the Missouri Botanical Gardens in St. Louis. The data on radiant energy exchange between the atmosphere and the leaf were so obtained, but the convection and transpiration data were calculated from the energy budget equation by B. G. Drake.

[b] Leaf is *gaining* heat by convection because it is below air temperature.

[c] Dew is forming on the leaf, hence the plus sign.

[d] Frost is forming on the leaf.

apparently conflicting results in the literature relating to effects of wind on transpiration are now being nicely resolved.

In Fig. 6-18, increasing wind decreased transpiration at $T_a < 35°C$ but increased it at $T_a > 35°C$. At the lower temperatures convection was negative (the leaf was being cooled by the wind), but at the elevated temperatures convection was actually positive, so that increasing wind was *warming* the leaf with increasing efficiency!

The effect of wind is dependent upon its degree of turbulence. Turbulent air flow over the leaf transfers heat with higher efficiency than does laminar flow. Unfortunately, little is known about the aerodynamics of leaves, and even less is known about the aerodynamics of leaves on plants surrounded by other plants.

6.8.5 Soil Moisture

Soil moisture exercises its influence upon transpiration via the water stress (free energy or water potential) within the plant. This effect upon ψ should have an important influence upon Δp. So far, study of this effect has emphasized effects of water stress upon the stomatal aperture (r_L) rather than upon the gradient itself. It is helpful, in considering these various terms as they interact with each other, to examine an energy budget sheet as shown in Table 6-5.

It should be evident in conclusion that application of physical principles allows considerable understanding of the plant, its function, and its relationship to its environment. In these terms, the time-honored argument as to whether transpiration is beneficial to the plant seems of little interest. To summarize: transpiration is not essential to dissipate heat from the leaf. If it doesn't occur, the temperature of the leaf will increase, and convection and radiation will become more effective in dissipation of the heat. Under normal conditions, however, much heat (about 600 cal/g H_2O) is removed by the transpiration process, and this may, as indicated in Table 6-5, constitute a very sizable portion of the total amount of heat lost from the leaf to the environment. In Fig. 6-18, at elevated temperature heat lost by transpiration was actually more than the absorbed radiation and included heat absorbed by the leaf by convection ($-V = Q_{abs} + C$)!

The Ascent of Sap

7.1 THE PROBLEM

A suction pump can lift water only to the **barometric height**, which is that height supported by atmospheric pressure from below (about 10.3 m or 34 ft at 1 atm pressure). If a long, horizontal pipe is filled with water, sealed at one end, and then placed in an upright position with the open end down and in water, the pressure at the barometric height equals zero, and above this the water will turn to vapor; that is, it will **vacuum boil**, even at 0°C. This formation of water vapor when the pressure reaches the vapor pressure of liquid water or below is called **cavitation** (the water is said to cavitate). If water does exist as a liquid at lower pressures it is said to be in a **metastable state** (any state that would normally not be expected under the specified conditions: a supersaturated solution or a supercooled liquid).

Yet some trees are on the order of 130 meters (400 ft) tall from their water-collecting roots in the soil to the upper tips of their branches. If the water is lifted to that height by pushing from below, some 13 atm or bars of pressure would be required in addition to that required to overcome the resistance and to maintain the flow.

Can the water be raised to the top of such trees by **capillarity**? Such a rise of water in small tubes comes about because of the **adhesion** be-tween water molecules and the wall of the tube (or other porous material) in which the process is taking place. This adhesion forms a **meniscus** in which the water tends to "climb" up the side of the container. The angle between the water and the side of the container indicates the degree of lift (Fig. 7-1). By simple geometric considerations, it can be seen that the perimeter of a capillary tube decreases less rapidly than the cross-sectional area as the diameter decreases. Consequently, the smaller the diameter of the tube, the greater is the lifting force of the meniscus compared to the amount of water to be lifted. Hence the smaller the tube, the higher the column of capillary water will rise (see calculation in Fig. 7-1).

But in plants the water-conducting xylem elements do not contain such open menisci. Although there are many empty tubes or air bubbles in partially filled tubes, those that are functional are completely filled with water from top to bottom. Thus capillarity in the usual sense does not operate in plants. Furthermore, if it did, it would be an insufficient force. Water is lifted less than one meter in glass or cellulose tubes the size of xylem elements anyway. And what about cavitation?

So how does the water get to the top of a tree?

CAPILLARITY:

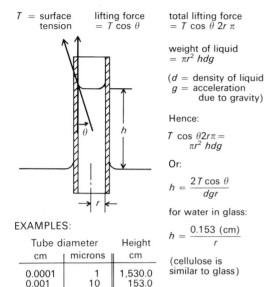

T = surface tension

lifting force = $T \cos \theta$

total lifting force = $T \cos \theta \, 2r \, \pi$

weight of liquid = $\pi r^2 \, hdg$

(d = density of liquid
g = acceleration due to gravity)

Hence:

$T \cos \theta 2r\pi = \pi r^2 \, hdg$

Or:

$$h = \frac{2T \cos \theta}{dgr}$$

for water in glass:

$$h = \frac{0.153 \, (cm)}{r}$$

(cellulose is similar to glass)

EXAMPLES:

| Tube diameter | | Height |
cm	microns	cm
0.0001	1	1,530.0
0.001	10	153.0
0.01	100	15.3
0.1	1,000	1.53
0.004	40	38.3 ←typical tracheid

Figure 7-1
The principle of capillarity and the mathematics to predict the height a liquid may be expected to reach in a tube. Examples of calculated heights are also shown.

7.2 INADEQUATE IDEAS

Many suggestions have been made to answer the problem, but most of these are not completely satisfactory. They are quite instructive.

7.2.1 Root Pressure

The most logical way to solve the problem of cavitation is to force the water up from below. Rather high pressures might be required, but at least the water in the columns would never reach negative pressures and be in danger of cavitation.

Such pressures from below, produced by the roots, have been observed in several species. Grapevines, for example, are capable of exhibiting fairly high root pressures (5 or 6 bars) in a

mercury manometer attached to the cut stem as in Fig. 7-2. Furthermore, one might always suggest that the pressures would be even higher if the system were not disrupted by cutting the stem.

Yet no one now seriously considers root pressure as a mechanism for the ascent of sap in tall trees. To begin with, it is observed only under certain conditions, typically a very moist soil and a high atmospheric humidity. During the time of year or time of day when pressures would be most needed to maintain plant turgidity (during a hot, dry summer), root pressures cannot be detected. Instead, the water in the stem seems to be under *tension*. Furthermore, root pressures are not observed in conifers, although some of the tallest trees are conifers. Recent experiments have indicated that conifer roots isolated in culture may build up slight pressures, but these would be far from adequate to push the water to the top of a sequoia tree.

7.2.2 Liquid Moving as Vapor Through the Tree

It has been suggested that water might essentially distill through the tree by changing to the vapor state at the bottom and condensing out again in the leaves at the top. Or perhaps the water moves as water of hydration up through the cell walls of the tree. These two theories are simply contrary to our experience. The trunk of a tree is filled not with vapor but with moving water, as has been repeatedly observed by microscopic examination of plants under living conditions. Observed rates and quantities also indicate that the tubes are filled (see below, 7.4.2B and 7.4.2E).

7.2.3 Vitalistic Ideas

To meet these severe problems, it has often been suggested that the water is moved through the tree in response to some of the living functions of the cells in the stem. That is, some sort of

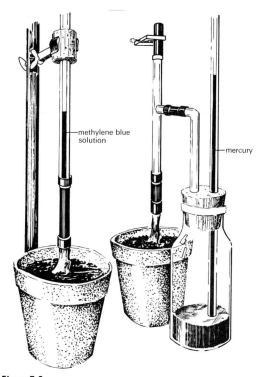

methylene blue
solution

mercury

Figure 7-2
The principle and measurement of root pressure. The stem
has been removed a short distance above the soil line of a
potted plant to which the tubes have been attached. The
bottle is filled with water above the mercury.

pumping action due to the processes of life is
postulated. We can lift water to any height by
pumping it over successive intervals, each one
less than the barometric height.

But careful anatomical study has failed to
reveal any sort of pumping cells. As a matter of
fact, all indications are that most water moves in
the *dead* xylem elements. This has been elegantly
demonstrated by the use of radioactive (tritiated)
water. Furthermore, it is possible to kill all of the
cells of the trunk and observe that water will
continue to flow. Stems have been killed by heat
treatment. In another experiment, a tree was
allowed to absorb picric acid, which diffused
out from the xylem elements, killing all of the

cells of the bark as well as the scattered living
cells in the wood. Water continued to move up
through the trunk, although eventually, after the
leaves had been killed, water flow did cease.

There are a number of vitalistic ideas still
being considered by a few plant physiologists,
but none of these is very convincing, and the
evidence against the entire vitalistic theory
seems quite overwhelming.

In one sense, however, the ascent of sap
clearly depends, although indirectly, upon living
cells. All of the transporting xylem elements are
produced by the living, water-filled **cambial cells**.
Furthermore, it is transpiration from the living
leaves at the top of the plant that ultimately
results in water movement through the plant.
Although the actual flow is not occasioned by
vitalistic forces in the transporting cells, we
should not forget that the plant is fundamentally
a living system.

7.3 THE PATHWAY OF TRANSPORT

Before we further pursue the question of water
movement, we should better define the anatomical aspects of the problem and consider the
pathway of water movement from soil to air
through the plant. The plant structure makes
this function possible. This structure consists
primarily of the elements of the **vascular system**:
the **stele** with its **tracheids**, **vessels**, **fibers**, **pith**,
parenchyma, and other components of the **xylem**
(Fig. 7-3). In Chapter 9 we will consider also the
phloem system in this transport complex.

7.3.1 Water in the Soil

Certain terms and concepts, based upon the
tension with which water is held by a soil, are
used by both plant physiologists and soil
scientists. The tension is the matric potential of
Chapters 4 and 5. It may be expressed in energy
terms or as a negative term with an absolute
value equivalent to the pressure required to

increase the water potential in a pressure membrane apparatus to the point where water will leave the soil particles (see the moisture release curve of Fig. 4-6). Measured in a centrifuge, it may be expressed in terms of the gravity constant.

Soil water potential will increase toward zero with increasing pressure (Chapter 4) and decrease with increasing tension. It will also be influenced by the presence of solutes and by temperature. A centrifuge method of measurement will not measure the influence of solutes, and thus this component can be separated from the hydrational component by combining a centrifuge measurement with a pressure membrane measurement of matric potential. Increasing temperature increases the free energy (water potential), thus decreasing the tension with which water is held by the soil. As we shall see below, some of the water in the soil can be removed only by very high temperatures. Figure 7-4 shows moisture release curves for several soils. The following descriptive terms have been applied to various arbitrary points on these curves.

7.3.1A Gravitational water When all of the pores of a soil are completely filled with water, a certain portion of this water is held by forces weak enough to be overcome by the earth's gravity (by forces of $1\,g$). This **gravitational water** normally moves out of the root zone within a few days. Gravitational water is held with a tension of less than about $-\frac{1}{3}$ bar (ψ is less negative than $-\frac{1}{3}$ bar). A soil containing all of its gravitational water is said to be **saturated**.

7.3.1B Capillary water After the gravitational water has drained out in response to gravity, a certain relatively large quantity of water remains in the soil, held against the force of gravity by capillarity, involving menisci as discussed above. A soil containing its full complement of **capillary water** is said to be at **field capacity** and is

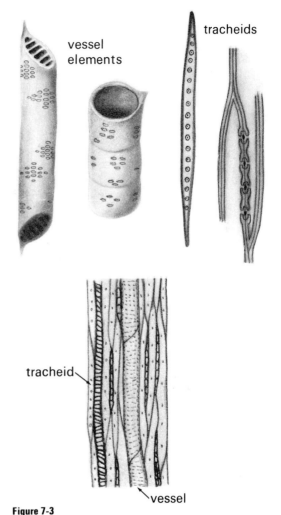

Figure 7-3

Some examples of xylem cells. The anatomy of the xylem is very important to the mechanics of movement of water within the plant. Note especially pits in the cell walls.

usually holding its water with about $-\frac{1}{3}$ bar of tension.

Saturation and field capacity are examples of soil moisture constants. The relation between moisture content and the tension with which the water is held is a characteristic of the soil. The quantity of water is expressed as a percent of the oven-dry weight of the soil (not as a percent of the weight of the original sample). The field capacity may be measured on a sample of soil in the field by waiting until the rate of downward flow has become negligible (usually one or two days). Approximately the same constant is obtained in the laboratory by centrifuging an artificially wet sample of the soil (1,000 × *g* for 30 minutes: a time much shorter than that required for equilibration in the field, but the accelerational force is much greater). The soil moisture content obtained in this way is called the **moisture equivalent**.

As the menisci between the soil particles become more curved, the tension with which the water is held increases. (Curvature indicates the tension but does not cause it.) The pore size will influence strongly the amount of water held with a given tension.

7.3.1C Hygroscopic or bound water

As water is removed from the soil, a point is reached at which it becomes unrealistic or at least impractical to think of menisci. In this condition, water is distributed in the electrical double layer on the surfaces of charged clay colloids and held by hydrational forces. This **hygroscopic or bound water** can be removed from the soil by raising the temperature to 106°C.

7.3.1D Water of crystallization

After the hygroscopic water has been removed, certain water molecules are still held *within* the crystal lattice of the soil minerals. To remove this **water of crystallization,** the temperature must be raised as high as 600°C.

7.3.1E The permanent wilting percentage

As capillary water is removed by the plant's roots, and as the tension of the remaining water increases, a point is finally reached beyond which the plant can no longer remove appreciable quantities of water. This point may be measured by allowing a plant to wilt in a soil to the point

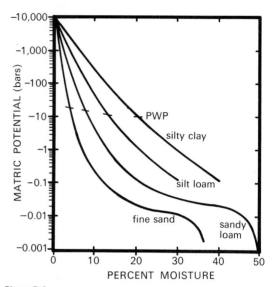

Figure 7-4
Moisture-release curves for four different kinds of soils. (Redrawn from M. B. Russell, 1939, *Soil Sci. Soc. Amer. Proc.* 4:51–54.)

where it will no longer recover when placed in an atmosphere having 100 percent relative humidity.[1] After the **permanent wilting point** or **percentage** has been reached, the amount of water in the soil is determined by first weighing the soil sample and then driving off the remaining bound water at 106°C and weighing again.

The permanent wilting point is an important soil moisture constant. The amount of water left in the soil at this point will vary considerably with the kind of soil, being highest in soils having a high clay content and thus considerable bound water. But water remaining at this point is unavailable to plants in quantities or at a rate to maintain turgidity of the plant.

Many early experiments seemed to indicate that the tension with which water was held at the permanent wilting point was quite constant,

---

[1] Frequently, a sunflower seedling is grown in a pot of soil along with wheat seedlings. The roots of the wheat seedlings penetrate the soil very extensively, but wilting is easier to detect in the sunflower seedling.

even when measured with many different species of plants. We now know that this is not quite true; some species can remove water against considerably higher tensions than others. Yet actual quantity removed by one plant as contrasted to another is relatively small. As a general average, most plants are able to remove water from a soil only until the tension reaches a value of about -15 bars.

7.3.1F Mobility of water in the soil Soil physicists and engineers have devoted considerable study to the principles of soil water mobility. As their results become more widely known and appreciated, plant physiologists will have a much better understanding of the water pathway both in the soil and in the plant. We will examine here only a few fundamental principles.

Consider a soil that is being wet by rain. Water will move downward in response to gravity, tending to fill the pore space as it goes. That which can be moved by gravity will continue to move, and that which can be held by capillary forces will remain. So there will be a moving front of water downward through the soil, behind which the soil will be saturated and then wet to field capacity and beyond (below) which the soil will remain completely dry. Thus it is essentially impossible to wet a soil in place to anything but field capacity (or saturation).

Given sufficient time, there will also be some capillary and vapor movement of water through the soil from the wet regions toward the dry regions. Rates and distances are limited, however. As water is removed by plant roots (and by evaporation from the surface), the soil will gradually approach the permanent wilting percentage near to the roots. Roots, then, to obtain water must grow into regions where it is more plentiful. Obviously, roots cannot grow to every minute volume of soil containing water. If they did, there would not even be enough water to account for the root volume itself, let alone any to be moved to the top of the plant. So as the

root penetrates new volumes of moist soil, water moves toward it along the water potential gradients that are established by water absorption into the roots. It is important to note that water moves about 10,000 times as fast at the field capacity as at the permanent wilting point.

7.3.2 Transfer of Water from Soil to Root

As indicated in Chapter 5 [equation (26A)], most soil scientists believe that when soil water (the **soil solution**) is in contact with the root, two components of soil water potential must be considered: the matric potential (ψ_m) and the osmotic potential (ψ_π). Yet the plant may absorb the solutes responsible for osmotic potential. When this occurs, the effect of solutes on the soil water potential is transferred along with the solutes to the region inside the root. In view of this, H. Walter of Stuttgart, Germany, suggested several years ago that we should ignore the osmotic potential of soil water so far as its effect on water uptake goes.

In actual measurements, carried out particularly at the salinity laboratory in Riverside, California, it appeared that the solutes cannot, under many circumstances, be ignored, but do provide a significant contribution to soil water potential. How can we resolve this apparent paradox?

To begin with, ψ_m and ψ_π may not be additive; ψ_m may be a *function* of ψ, of which ψ_π is one component. The results of the Riverside work may have other interpretations. In addition, it was suggested by John Philip of Canberra, Australia, that when the soil dries out so roots are less able to reach liquid moisture, water may move across the short gap from the soil to the root in the vapor state (i.e., it may distill across). This vapor gap would act as a perfect semipermeable membrane, allowing water but not solutes to pass. The actual importance of this possible mechanism remains to be determined, but it might well play a role. In practice we might expect a varying portion of the water that enters a plant to distill across a vapor barrier, but there would always be certain portions of the root system in contact with water and able to absorb solutes as well as water.

7.3.3 Pathway of Water in the Plant

Based upon the plant's anatomy, we can formulate the problem. In the cortex of the stem and in the leaf mesophyll, there are many cells consisting mostly of water-filled vacuoles surrounded by a relatively thin layer of cytoplasm. It would be logical to expect water to move across the membranes from vacuole to vacuole. This may well be the most direct "straight-line" route. But we have become aware of the connected system of cell walls surrounding these vacuolated cells, and this provides an alternate pathway for the flow of water. If there are two possible pathways for the flow of a liquid, it will follow the one that offers the least resistance. Our question is then: is there less resistance to water flow in the direct path from cell to cell or in the more tortuous path through the cell walls?

7.3.3A The concept of free space Immerse a tissue in a solution. Assume that a portion of the tissue volume is open to free diffusion of solute particles. At equilibrium, the concentration of solute particles inside the tissue (inside the volume open to free diffusion: the **free space** or **diffusion space**) will equal the concentration of solute particles in the surrounding solution. This is true if we assume that the process of entry of the solute into the tissue is purely by diffusion.

After the tissue has come to equilibrium, and before absorption by processes other than diffusion can take place, the amount of solute in the tissue might be measured. If the volume of liquid outside is relatively small, the convenient way to measure this is by measuring the loss of solute from the surrounding solution. Measurements might be made in other ways,

however, such as by using radioactively labeled ions and measuring the radioactivity in the tissue itself.

Knowing the quantity of solute inside the tissue, and assuming that its concentration there is the same as in the surrounding solution, the volume it must occupy can be calculated (Fig. 7-5) since concentration (C) equals quantity or amount (A) per unit volume (V):

$$C = \frac{A}{V} \qquad (38)$$

Hence:

$$V_d = \frac{A}{C} \qquad (39)$$

where:

V_d = volume within the tissue available to diffusion.

Expressing this volume as a percentage of the total tissue volume (V_t) and referring to this percentage as the **apparent free space** (S_d), we have the following relationship:

$$S_d = \frac{100V_d}{V_t} = \frac{100A}{V_t C} \qquad (40)$$

So the apparent free space is that portion of the volume of a tissue which, according to the assumptions of the method of measurement, can be in diffusion equilibrium with an outside medium. It may or may not be exactly equal to the actual free space.[2]

Many measurements of the type indicated above have been made, and values of S_d on the order of 7–10 percent of the volume of the tissue have been obtained after suitable corrections. In early experiments of this type, values as high as

---

[2] The so-called free space has also been called the "outer space," as contrasted to the "inner space," that volume of the tissue *not* in free diffusion equilibrium with an external medium. The term "inner space" has value in plant physiology perhaps, but "outer space" has different connotations in our modern usage!

THE EXPERIMENT:

10 cm^3 of plant tissue is added to 100 ml of 0.2014 M $SO_4^=$:

time for equilibrium

THE RESULTS:

Solution is 0.2000 M $SO_4^=$;
so tissue contains 0.00014 moles
of $SO_4^=$ (0.0134 grams)

THE CALCULATION OF AFS (Apparent free space):

1. Assume that $SO_4^=$ in the free space is in diffusion equilibrium with outside solution—hence it is at the same concentration (0.200 M $SO_4^=$).

2. How much volume does it occupy?

$$\text{Concentration} = \frac{\text{Quantity}}{\text{Volume}} \text{ or } C = \frac{A}{V}$$

Hence: $V = \frac{A}{C} = \frac{0.00014 \text{ moles}}{0.2 \text{ moles/liter}} = 0.0007 \text{ liters}$

or $\boxed{0.7 \text{ cm}^3}$

3. So 0.7 cm^3 of 10 cm^3 is occupied by 0.200 M $SO_4^=$, or

$$\text{AFS} = \frac{0.7 \times 100}{10} = \boxed{7.0\%}$$

But

4. This 7% is distributed throughout the tissue, probably in cell walls and intercellular spaces.

Figure 7-5
The measurement and calculation of apparent free space.

20–25 percent or even higher were reported. Actual observations of the anatomy of plant tissue indicated that such volumes would have to include not only the cell walls and intercellular spaces but also the cytoplasm of the cells. The implication was that the plasmalemma or plasma membrane was freely permeable to outside solutes. Certain workers, notably Jacob Levitt at the University of Missouri, questioned this conclusion and reexamined the techniques used. It was found that the amount of solute measured in the tissue often included solute in solution on the outside of the tissue that had not been properly removed by blotting (clearly a very difficult task for finely divided root systems, for example). Certain high values for S_d do remain valid, but in no case can we conclude that the plasmalemma is an ineffective membrane.

Microscopic observation indicates that the cell walls and water-filled intercellular spaces of many tissues do constitute about 7 to 10 percent of the total tissue volume. Hence the apparent free space quite probably consists of cell walls and intercellular spaces. Furthermore, the resistance to diffusion of solutes (and surely water) would be low in these regions and probably much higher through the protoplasts.

Certain microscopic studies performed using various dyes and other tracer materials seem to substantiate this idea. These materials penetrate plant tissue primarily through the cell walls and intercellular spaces.

7.3.3B The apoplast-symplast concept   E.
Münch of Germany introduced a terminology in 1932 that proves valuable in our discussion of the pathway of water movement through the plant (Fig. 7-6). He suggested that the interconnecting cell walls and intercellular spaces, including the water-filled (or air-filled) xylem elements, should be considered as a single system and called the **apoplast**. In terms of our above discussion, this would be approximately but not exactly equivalent to the free space. The remaining part of the plant consists of the protoplasts of the cells. Evidence based upon electron micrographs now indicates that the cytoplasm may be connected from cell to cell via the **plasmodesmata**, also constituting an interconnected system. We have evidence indicating that dissolved materials can move across these plasmodesmata, and so the system is a functional one. This system of interconnected protoplasm (excluding the vacuoles) was termed by Münch the **symplast** (Fig. 7-6).

7.3.3C A proposed mechanism of root pressure
Based upon the apoplast-symplast concept,

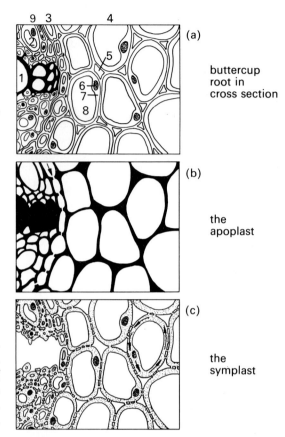

(a)

buttercup root in cross section

(b)

the apoplast

(c)

the symplast

Figure 7-6
Anatomical drawings illustrating the apoplast-symplast concept. Note xylem cell (1), phloem cell (2), endodermal layer (3), cortex (4), intercellular space (5), nucleus (6), cytoplasm (7), vacuole (8), pericycle (9), and break in the apoplast due to casparian strips around endodermal cells [arrow in (b)]. (Redrawn from F. B. Salisbury, 1966. In W. A. Jensen and L. G. Kavaljian (eds.), *Plant Biology Today: Advances and Challenges*, Wadsworth Publishing Company, Inc., Belmont, California.)

Alden S. Crafts and Theodore C. Broyer in 1938 proposed a mechanism to account for root pressure. The suggestion seems reasonable. In the root, the **endodermal layer** of cells around the stele constitutes a barrier to free movement of water and solutes through the cell walls. The **Casparian strips** around each cell are suberized and thus less permeable to water than other cell walls. This being the case, the apoplast, which by our definition above includes the

Casparian strips, would not be equivalent to the free space.

Let us assume that the root is in contact with a soil solution (i.e., that there is no vapor barrier). Ions will diffuse into the root via the apoplast across the **epidermis**, through the **cortex**, and up to the endodermal layer. Along the way, ions will be passing across the cell membranes from the apoplast into the symplast. This is largely an active, respiration-requiring process (Chapter 8). The result is a build-up in concentration of ions inside the cells within the symplast to levels higher than those outside in the apoplast. The symplast is continuous across the endodermal layer, and so ions can move freely into the **pericycle** and other living cells within the **stele** (Fig. 7-6). This probably occurs by diffusion across the plasmodesmata, and the velocity of movement inward might well be increased by **cytoplasmic streaming** within the cells, a circular flowing of the cytoplasm often observed in cells of this type.

Within the stele, oxygen tensions would be lower than in more external cells. This could result in a less efficient active absorption or even retention, and ions might leak into the apoplast (xylem) inside of the stele. The result of this would be a build-up in concentration of solutes within the apoplast to levels higher than that in the soil solution. Because water must pass through the protoplast of the endodermal layer, this layer would act as a differentially permeable membrane, and the root becomes an osmometer. The build-up in pressure due to this osmotic system can account for the phenomenon of root pressure. (See section 8.7.1 for confirmation.)

7.3.3D An argument against water movement only through the free space A number of workers have measured the rates of diffusion of labeled (tritiated) water into plant tissue, using both intact root systems and excised pieces of solid tissue like potato. If diffusion is more limited at one point than another, as at the cuticle or at the epidermis, or even at cell membranes (movement from the apoplast to the symplast), then the rate of diffusion of water into the tissue should follow Fick's first law of diffusion.[3] If, on the other hand, diffusion occurs as though the resistances encountered by it were equal throughout all the tissue (cell walls, membranes, vacuoles, etc., all essentially alike), then the rate of diffusion should follow Fick's second law.

The experimental results show that diffusion of labeled water into tissue follows Fick's *second* law (Fig. 7-7). The conclusion is that water apparently diffuses equally well throughout all the tissue, both the apoplast and the symplast! These experiments are set up in such a way that they do not really say much about the endodermis, but to a first approximation they seem to imply that the permeability of all parts of plant tissue to water is essentially equal and very high.

Normally, in discussing the pathway of water through the plant, we are talking about movement in response to a pull from above brought about by transpiration. This is a bulk flow rather than a molecular diffusion. In such a case we are faced more with the problem of *resistances* to bulk flow than to diffusion. Thus the conclusions based on Fick's laws do not really contradict the idea that the apoplast, the free space, is the main pathway of water movement in the plant. We shall present some interesting evidence in favor of this idea in the next section.

7.3.3E Some experiments on the pathway of water movement P. E. Weatherley at the University of Aberdeen in Scotland sought an approach to the question of whether the water goes through the vacuoles or around the cells, particularly in the cortex and leaf mesophyll of *Pelargonium* shoots. He established two hypotheses or model systems that might apply to the pathway of water through an excised piece of stem with its associated leaves:

---

[3] See physical chemistry textbooks for exact information about Fick's laws.

First, assuming that the water must pass through the cells, a tension is built up during transpiration due to the resistances in these cells. When transpiration is stopped suddenly, the tension is relieved only gradually as water continues to enter the system and to overcome the resistance of the entire system. Such a hypothesis has been described mathematically, the result being an equation that predicts curves such as those in Fig. 7-8. As the tension is gradually relieved, the rate of water uptake will drop off logarithmically with time (plotting the log of the rate, the drop-off will be expressed by a straight line).

Second, if the water passes around the cells, there will not only be the resistance of the pathway itself, but a secondary resistance of water movement from the pathway (apoplast) into the cytoplasm and vacuoles (symplast). If this is so, then when transpiration is stopped suddenly, the uptake will be determined not only by the tension established in the pathway but also by the tension established between the pathway and the vacuoles. As a result, there will first be an instantaneous or very rapid drop in the rate of uptake as the water potentials become adjusted to the reduced demand for water, after which the rate will again drop off logarithmically. This is also illustrated in Fig. 7-8.

Weatherley attached a leaf to a potometer (Chapter 6), allowed a constant rate of transpiration to become established, and then stopped transpiration by suddenly immersing the plant in a beaker of medicinal paraffin. (Immersing the plant in water proved to have the same effect.) Some representative results, shown in Fig. 7-9, make it apparent that the second and not the first hypothesis is supported. Although the drop in rate was not *exactly* vertical, this can be understood because the pathway itself had a water deficit to be satisfied.

From the shape of the curves, Weatherley could calculate the extent of the water deficit in the pathway and in the "inner space" (probably

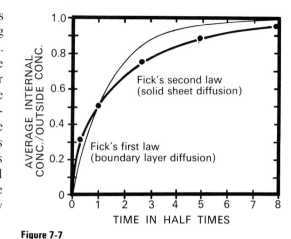

Figure 7-7
A comparison of predicted curves for penetration of tritiated water into plant tissue as predicted by Fick's first or second laws with actual data as shown by points. Data closely match prediction based on Fick's second law. (From J. Bonner, 1959, *Science* 129: 447. Data from L. Ordin and J. Bonner, 1956, *Plant Physiol.* 31:53. Used by permission.)

the vacuoles and the symplast). According to these calculations, water can move through the pathway about 60 times faster than into the cells. The pathway itself becomes saturated in about 20 minutes, while the "inner space" requires several hours for saturation. Uptake by the pathway proves to be quite insensitive to temperature, as one might imagine if it were simply the apoplast. Movement into the "inner space," on the other hand, can be virtually stopped by a temperature of 3°C, which may imply that permeability depends upon the metabolic functions of the cytoplasm.

7.3.3F Movement of water into the root
Because of the presence of the endodermal layer, movement of water into the root is more complicated than movement through the rest of the plant. It might involve a bulk flow in response to transpiration pull and/or an osmotic flow brought about because the root may be considered an osmometer (7.3.3C). Weatherley studied the problem, concluding that the ratio

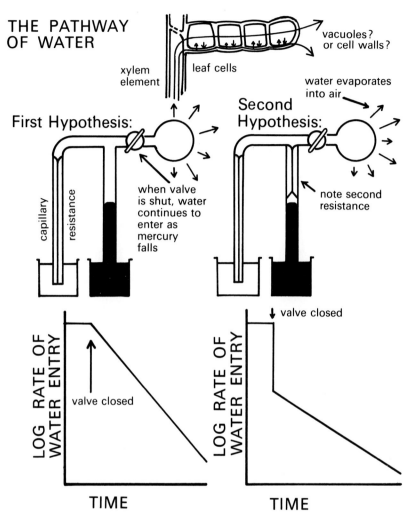

THE PATHWAY OF WATER

xylem element   leaf cells   vacuoles? or cell walls?

First Hypothesis: Second Hypothesis:

water evaporates into air

when valve is shut, water continues to enter as mercury falls

note second resistance

capillary   resistance

LOG RATE OF WATER ENTRY

valve closed

TIME

↓ valve closed

LOG RATE OF WATER ENTRY

TIME

Figure 7-8

Illustrating the principles of Weatherley's experiments on the pathway of water in the plant. (After P. E. Weatherley, 1963. In A. J. Rutter and F. A. Whitehead (eds.), *The Water Relations of Plants*, John Wiley & Sons, Inc., New York. Used by permission.)

of bulk to osmotic flow is responsive to an applied pressure gradient across the root, but his results are not completely clear-cut and need verification.

Many questions come to mind that must be answered by future research. Under conditions of water tension in the plant, could water be pulled through the endodermal cells by bulk flow? Endodermal cells having thinner walls have been observed in contact with the cells inside the stele. What is the role of these so-called "**passage cells**" in water transport? The endodermal cylinder is being formed near the root tip and hence is essentially open there.

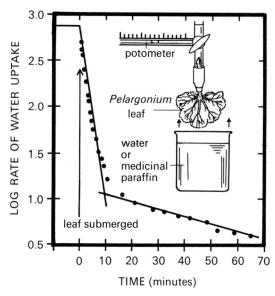

Figure 7-9

The results of Weatherley's experiment with a *Pelargonium* leaf. (From P. E. Weatherley, 1963. In A. J. Rutter and F. H. Whitehead (eds.), *The Water Relations of Plants*, John Wiley & Sons, Inc., New York. Used by permission.)

Could water move in readily at the "open" end? Evidence indicates that relatively little water enters near the root tips, and when tensions are highest in the plant, more water enters through the more mature regions of the root. Apparently the apoplast is only poorly developed in the young and thin cell walls near the root tip.

So we remain in doubt about many aspects of water movement into the roots. The importance of the endodermis seems clear. Except for the stomates, it may be the only necessary living link in the chain of water flow from soil through the plant into the air. The possibility that the permeability of the endodermis may respond to tension is an intriguing one.

7.3.4 The Catenary Sequence of Resistances to Water Movement

In a *steady state* of transpiration and absorption of water from the soil, the amount of water transpired from the leaves will be equal to the amount moving through a complete cross section of the stem, and also to the amount moving through a complete cross section of the roots, and also to the total amount removed from the soil. Furthermore, it becomes apparent that the quantity transported through the system is proportional to the driving force ($\Delta\psi$) and inversely proportional to the resistance (r) encountered along the way, as in the cases of osmotic flow [equation (17)], transpiration [equation (35)], and even convective heat transport through the boundary layer [equation (32)]. This may be expressed for the various links in the system as:

$$\frac{dJ}{dt} = \frac{\Delta\psi}{r_t} = \frac{\Delta\psi_1}{r_1} = \frac{\Delta\psi_2}{r_2} = \cdots \frac{\Delta\psi_n}{r_n} \quad (41)$$

where:

dJ = an increment quantity of water transported

dt = an increment of time

r_t = the total resistance

$\Delta\psi_1$ = the water potential gradient for part 1 of the system

r_1 = the resistance for part 1 of the system

The significance of this expression is that at a given rate of flow (dJ/dt), the *ratio between the driving force and the resistance* will not only be a constant for the system as a whole, but it *will be equal for each link in the chain* of steps making up the pathway. This is because, in the steady state, the same amount of water will move through each link in a given time interval. Hence, when r_n for any part of the system is very large, then $\Delta\psi_n$ for *that* part of the system must also be very large. As the resistance of any part of the system increases, the driving force will have to increase proportionately to maintain the flow. In practice, it is easier to measure $\Delta\psi$ than any r, but because of the constant ratio, the relative driving forces ($\Delta\psi_n$) will imply the magnitudes of the resistances (r_n).

In Table 7-1, typical values of $\Delta\psi$ across various parts of the plant's water pathway are

TABLE 7-1

DRIVING FORCES ($\Delta\psi_n$) AND RELATIVE RESISTANCES (r_n) FOR A HYPOTHETICAL WATER PATHWAY THROUGH A PLANT

	$\Delta\psi$ [a]	Relative r
Water to root	−1.5 bars	1.0
Root to leaf	−18.0 bars	12.0
Leaf to air (20°C, 50% RH)	−915.0 bars	602.0

[a] Hypothetical soil solution with $\psi_\pi = -0.5$ bar, hypothetical root with $\psi = -2.0$ bars, hypothetical leaf with $\psi = -20$ bars.

shown. The value of $\Delta\psi$ is relatively low from the soil to the root, from the root to the stem, and from the stem to the leaf, but very high from the leaf to the air. Thus it becomes obvious that at steady state the step from the cells to the air is the one with the highest resistance, and consequently the one that limits the process. This conclusion should also be quite apparent from our discussion of transpiration in the preceding chapter. We must remember that steady-state conditions are not always present in the field (under many conditions they may be rare), but the conclusions are probably valid to an approximation under nearly all conditions.

7.4 THE COHESION HYPOTHESIS OF THE ASCENT OF SAP

To discuss the ascent of sap, it is now necessary only to bring together a number of points already presented and to consider further the cohesive properties of water.

7.4.1 The Theory

7.4.1A The driving force As indicated in the section immediately above, the force driving transpiration is the gradient in water potential ($\Delta\psi$) between the water in the soil and that in the air. Typically, this gradient is established be-

cause incoming solar radiation warms the leaf and the air, resulting in an atmosphere with a vapor pressure deficit greater than zero and a consequent very negative value of ψ, while vapor pressure within the leaf may be very high, near to the saturation value (100 percent RH, $\psi = 0$).

7.4.1B Hydration as the water-holding force in the cell walls The moist cell walls in the substomatal cavities of the leaves remain moist because water is attracted to them by the adhesive hydrational forces discussed in Chapter 4. The water molecules farthest from the imbibing surface are held with the weakest tensions (on the order of a few bars). These will evaporate into air, even when the air has a high relative humidity. At 20°C and 99 percent relative humidity, for example, the water potential of the air is already −13.5 bars (Fig. 7-10). Thus even when leaf and air temperatures are nearly identical, if atmospheric humidity is even slightly below saturation, evaporation will tend to occur.

The molecules close to the imbibing surfaces may be held with tensions approaching −1,000 bars (Chapter 4). Yet fairly dry air will have an even more negative water potential. For example, for air at 20°C and 10 percent RH, $\psi = -3,108$ bars. Obviously, a plant would continue to dry out when the air is dry until virtually all of the water had been removed, even from regions quite close to the hydrating surfaces.

7.4.1C Cohesion and the ascent of sap Henry H. Dixon (1914) in Ireland and independently Otto Renner (1911) in Germany suggested that the tensions created by evaporation and the subsequent hydration of water by the cell walls, drawing water from the pathway within the plant, were relieved by an upward flow of water from below. Of course, in plants shorter than the barometric height, and providing the resistances within the plant are not too high, such a mechanism is quite feasible. Suction is created at the top by evaporation and hydration, and water is

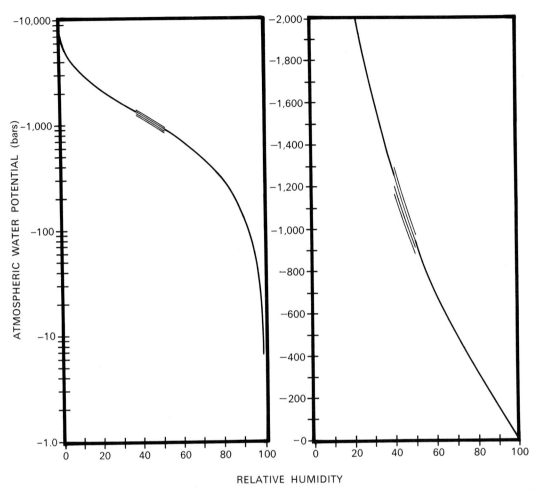

Figure 7-10

The relationship of atmospheric water potential (20°C) to relative humidity plotted on a logarithmic scale (left) and on a linear scale (right). The four thin lines are for different temperatures: 0° (bottom line), 10°, 20°, and 30°C (upper line). (See footnote on p. 66.)

pushed up from below by atmospheric pressure. Such a mechanism would suffice nicely for a great many of the plants on the earth's surface.

But what about tall trees? Dixon and Renner[4] suggested that in trees taller than the

---

[4] The idea had been developing at least as early as 1894 when Henry Dixon and John Jolly independently advanced the basic concept. It was further supported by E. Askenasy in 1895.

barometric height, the water is pulled up from below in continuous columns (Fig. 7-11) that do not cavitate simply because of the inherent tensile strength of water, a property arising from **cohesion** of the water molecules (the forces of attraction between water molecules).

For a tree 130 meters from the water-absorbing roots to the tips of the uppermost leaves (as a sequoia or a eucalyptus), about − 13 bars of tension in the system (or pressure from

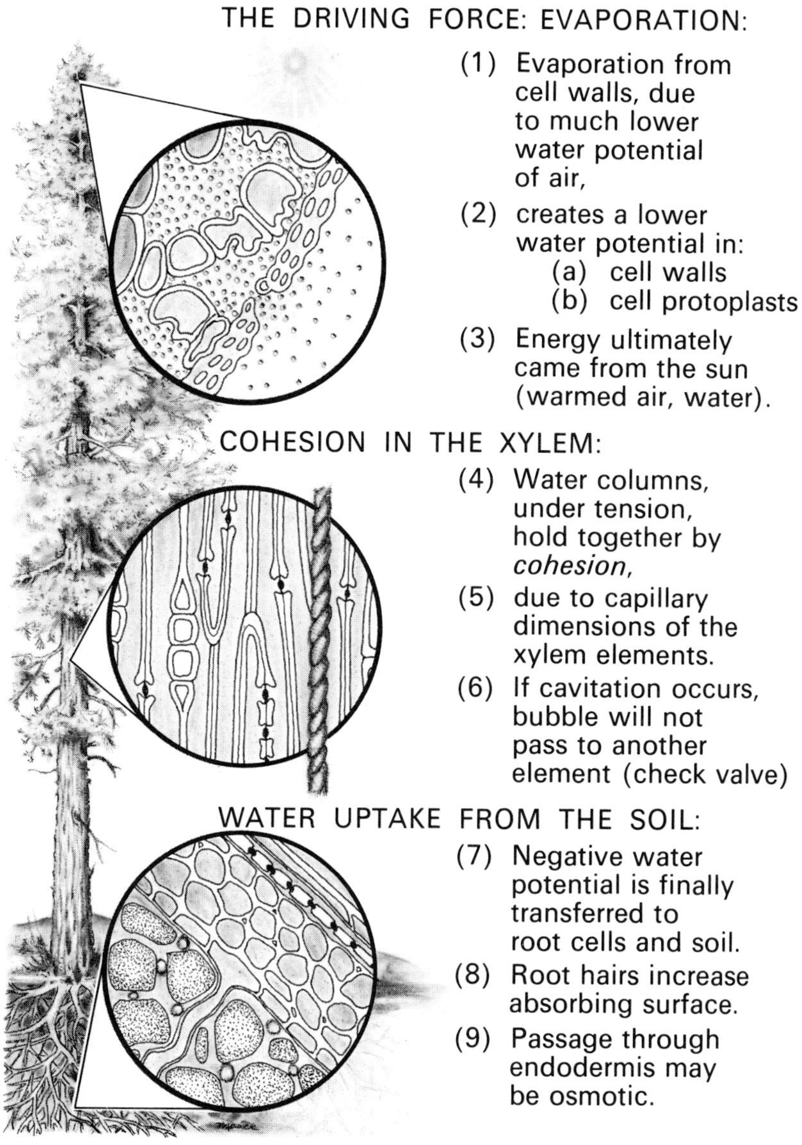

THE DRIVING FORCE: EVAPORATION:

(1) Evaporation from
cell walls, due
to much lower
water potential
of air,

(2) creates a lower
water potential in:
    (a) cell walls
    (b) cell protoplasts

(3) Energy ultimately
came from the sun
(warmed air, water).

COHESION IN THE XYLEM:

(4) Water columns,
under tension,
hold together by
cohesion,

(5) due to capillary
dimensions of the
xylem elements.

(6) If cavitation occurs,
bubble will not
pass to another
element (check valve)

WATER UPTAKE FROM THE SOIL:

(7) Negative water
potential is finally
transferred to
root cells and soil.

(8) Root hairs increase
absorbing surface.

(9) Passage through
endodermis may
be osmotic.

Figure 7-11
The cohesion theory of the ascent of sap summarized.

below) would be required to hold up the column of water. More tension (or pressure from below) would be required to overcome the frictional drag (the resistance) of the pathway. The resistance and therefore the driving force will depend upon the nature of the pathway, and perhaps various other factors, but measurements indicate that an upper value of another -13 bars is reasonable.

We might assume, then, that something on

the order of -30 bars tension in the water columns would be a minimum negative value required to maintain the transpirational flow.

7.4.1D Other complications

Of course we would also have to consider various other factors discussed earlier, such as the endodermal cells and their possible mechanism of action, the apoplast-symplast system of the plant, and the movement of water from the soil into the root. Yet most of these complications fit well into the cohesion theory as presented here.

7.4.2 Critical Tests of the Cohesion Hypothesis

Since the original formulation of the cohesion theory by Dixon and by Renner, plant physiologists all over the world have attempted to devise experiments capable of testing it critically. Some of these experiments are suggested by the nature of the theory, others arise because of objections to it, and still others were formulated to test possible alternatives. The Dixon–Renner hypothesis succeeds very well at suggesting experimental approaches to its investigation.

7.4.2A Does water have a high enough tensile strength?

The problem is whether water can sustain tensions of up to -30 bars without cavitating; whether the cohesive forces of water are as negative as -30 bars. Determination of the tensile strength of water has proved to be an extremely difficult task, and the many approaches have produced a mass of conflicting data over the several decades since the cohesion theory first appeared. There seem to be three general kinds of conclusions, and the third may provide us with a final solution:

First, it is possible, based upon available information relating to the nature of the water molecule, to calculate the potential cohesive strength under ideal conditions. Using this approach, values as negative as $-15,000$ bars have been obtained.

Second, several experimental approaches have been taken. The force required to separate steel plates held together by a water film has been measured. Fern annuli which are pulled apart by water under tension have been studied. Glass tubes have been sealed while full of hot expanded water, and then cavitation has been observed as the water cools and contracts. These and still other methods have produced values for the tensile strength of water on the order of -100 to -300 bars, although a few workers have reported lower values, on the order of only -1 to -30 bars. These methods measure both cohesion and adhesion of water to the container. Results represent minimal tensile strengths for either adhesion or cohesion.

Third, the most clear-cut approach is probably one introduced by Lyman Briggs in 1950, using capillary glass tubes bent in the form of a "Z." These tubes are centrifuged, and the tension on the water at the center of the tube can easily be calculated (Fig. 7-12). Such observations have produced a very important conclusion: the smaller the capillary, the higher the tensile strength of water. With rather fine capillaries, values as negative as -264 bars have been measured. Using a capillary tube with a diameter of 0.5 mm (considerably thicker than most xylem elements), air-saturated tap water does not cavitate under tensions of -20 bars, although cavitation did occur when the center of the Z-tube was frozen with solid CO_2. The cohesive forces in water seem to be quite sufficient for the cohesion mechanism of the ascent of sap, providing that the water is held in tubes of small enough diameter.

It is important to realize that the tensile strength of water is strongly a function of the distance to an interface between the water and its container. It is not yet readily apparent why this should be the case, but we can think of the statement above that the tenacity with which water was held by an imbibing surface was ex-

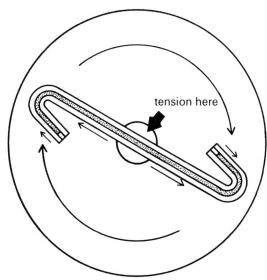

Figure 7-12
Method of measuring the cohesive properties of water utilizing a centrifuged Z-tube. Small arrows indicate direction of centrifugal force and principle of balancing due to the Z-tube.

pressed in the degree of curvature of the meniscus produced. The phenomenon of water in small pores or capillaries is being studied by hydraulic engineers and by soil physicists. Their results could contribute a great deal to future discussions of this topic.

7.4.2B Are the water columns really continuous? Again, it is easy to find much contradictory evidence in the literature. Some direct observations indicate continuity while others do not. We must remember that virtually any method of observation is itself quite likely to introduce discontinuity. The observed rates of flow in stems[5] clearly imply that the xylem

elements are indeed filled and continuous. Moving the observed quantities at the observed rates requires the entire cross-sectional area of the functional xylem. To move the quantities observed in the vapor phase or only in the walls of the xylem elements, would require rates of movement one or two orders of magnitude greater than those observed.

7.4.2C Are the columns really under tension?
Tension of the water in the stem of the transpiring plant is not difficult to demonstrate. For example, the stem of such a plant may be immersed in a dye solution and cut. The dye instantaneously moves a considerable distance both up and down the stem inside the xylem elements and then stops rather suddenly. It is difficult to interpret this in any way other than a sudden relief in the tension on the walls of the xylem tubes. The sudden movement is due to the elasticity of the cell walls.

Renner in 1911 performed an elegantly simple experiment that is difficult to interpret on any basis other than high tension in the stem. He attached a leafy branch to a burette and measured the uptake of water. He constricted the stem of the branch with a clamp to produce a high resistance. After measuring uptake under these conditions, he cut off the leafy end and applied suction with a pump (such a pump could only produce a tension of about −1 bar). In response to the pump, only about one-tenth as much water moved as in response to the leafy branch. We seem compelled to conclude that the leaves must exert a pull of some −10 bars.

Such tensions in the stem are also indicated by many careful measurements of trunk diameters in the field. During the heat of the day, the trunk actually shrinks by a measurable amount, apparently in response to the increased internal water tension.

The clearest answer to many of the problems concerned with the ascent of sap might come through actual measurement of water tensions

---

[5] Modern measurements of rate apply a pulse of heat at one point on the stem, measuring the time it takes to detect the warmed water at some level above. Rates vary greatly depending upon environmental conditions, but values based upon various methods of measurement ranging from 50–4,360 cm/hr have been reported.

in the stem. For years, attempts to develop a suitable methodology met with failure. No available manometer measures tensions in a liquid, and even indirect methods, such as finding a sugar solution of such a concentration that it will not be absorbed by a stem containing water under tension, produced unsatisfactory and unlikely results. (The sugar solutions indicated gradients in tension as high as 44 bars per meter!) In 1965 Per Fredrik Scholander and his colleagues at the Scripps Institute of Oceanography in California finally published a method which is elegantly simple and apparently quite satisfactory. As a matter of fact, as we shall see in subsequent sections, Scholander has contributed a considerable body of highly significant information to our modern understanding of the ascent of sap in tall trees and vines.

Scholander reasoned that when a stem containing water under tension is cut, the water recedes from the cut because, before the cut is made, the pressure on the outside was much higher than the pressure on the inside. If the same difference could be reestablished, the meniscus would move back exactly to the cut. The method, then, consists of cutting a branch or twig from a tree or shrub, placing the branch in a pressure bomb, and increasing the pressure on the branch until water in the xylem tubes can be observed through a binocular microscope to come back to the cut surface (Fig. 7-13). The pressure in the bomb should then be equivalent to the absolute value of the tension in the stem before the cut. The method is closely analogous to the measurement of matric potential already discussed (5.3.4). Using this method, Scholander was able to obtain measurements of tension in tropical mangroves and other plants that were entirely consistent with the principles being presented here (see 7.5.3A and Fig. 7-17 below).

7.4.2D How can such high tensions be maintained in the stem without cavitation? The explanation apparently lies in the anatomy of the plant and in the nature of water in close

proximity to hydrophilic (hydrating) surfaces, as discussed above. The lateral walls and the ends of the vascular elements (the tracheids plus the vessels in angiosperms) are typically perforated by minute holes, and these holes may be closed by thin membranes with such a fine porosity that bubbles of air cannot pass through them. Liquid water can move through these holes and these membranes and indeed through the wall itself, but the system forms a **check valve** against the passage of air.

We can understand this somewhat better by thinking of the surface-tension properties of small droplets of liquid in air. As a drop of liquid gets smaller, its surface/volume ratio increases, and the forces of surface tension on it become stronger, compressing the droplet more and more. This increase of pressure in the droplet increases the free energy, and this in turn results in a higher vapor pressure. As one watches such a small droplet under a microscope, it tends to shrink (dry) faster and faster, until, as the vapor pressure increases to the point where the drop boils at room temperature, it suddenly disappears.

A bubble of air in liquid also exhibits the powerful force of a curved meniscus. When the bubble is very small, the interfacial tensions acting on it are proportionately very large, giving it a high stability against deformation. The result is that the surface of a bubble cannot be bent enough to pass through a very small pore.

Because of the high surface tension of water, if the water in one column should cavitate, producing a bubble of air or vapor, this break will not be transformed laterally to another xylem element or tube. So long as some tubes remain filled, water will continue to move upward. Scholander has said that the water transport system of a plant "combines capillary dimensions with check-valved compartmentalization." He has further suggested that no other solution of the movement of water to the top of tall trees may be possible.

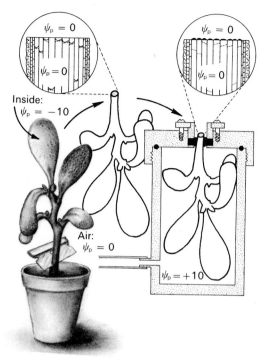

Figure 7-13
Method of measurement of tension within a plant stem utilizing a pressure bomb as described in the text. (Modified after Scholander et al., 1965, *Science* 148:339. Used by permission.)

7.4.2E Do field observations agree with the cohesion hypothesis?

Perhaps the most important question raised by plant physiologists in regards to the cohesion hypothesis concerns the question of what would happen if the continuous columns of water should in some way be broken. Say, for example, that strong wind disturbance causes the columns of water in the stem to cavitate, or that the water in the tree trunk freezes, forming bubbles of gas. (Air is completely insoluble in ice.) Or what would happen if the columns are broken by sawing part way through the trunk?

Many investigators have taken many approaches to these and other problems. We will consider some further elegant experiments of Scholander and his coworkers.

Several of their experiments are summarized in Fig. 7-14. They used the tropical rattan vine (*Calamus*) from an equatorial area at the northern tip of Queensland, Australia. These vines reach the canopy of the tallest jungle trees, 30 to 50 m above the ground. Water moving up through these vines should have tensions of at least −5 to −10 bars. Furthermore, the vines do not grow straight up but often form loops of 10 to 20 m hanging from the branches. These loops can be manipulated in various ways.

Scholander's group started by investigating cavitation caused by freezing. They cut off a vine near its base, attached a burette, and measured the rate of water uptake. A section of the vine above the burette was then placed between two pieces of dry ice. No decrease in the rate of water uptake could be detected! Apparently water was moving too fast through the vine to freeze. Rate of uptake through these vines was approximately 12 ml/min, for vines of 1.5 to 2.0 cm thickness.

When the burette was stoppered, water continued to be absorbed by the vine at essentially the same rate, even though a vacuum was produced in the burette so that the water vacuum boiled.

In order to freeze the water in the vine, it was necessary to let the cut end of the vine take up air until all of the passages had been blocked by air bubbles, and water uptake finally ceased. After this treatment, the vine could then be frozen with the dry ice some distance above the cut end where water was still present. The air-filled section (approximately 2 m) was then cut off under water, and the vine with the frozen section was reconnected to the burette, showing no uptake of water and confirming that the section of stem was really frozen. The frozen section was then hoisted some 11 m above the ground (above the barometric height) and allowed to thaw. There was still no water uptake from the burette, although some water ran from the vine out into the burette. This demonstrated that the vine was now completely vapor locked by the gas

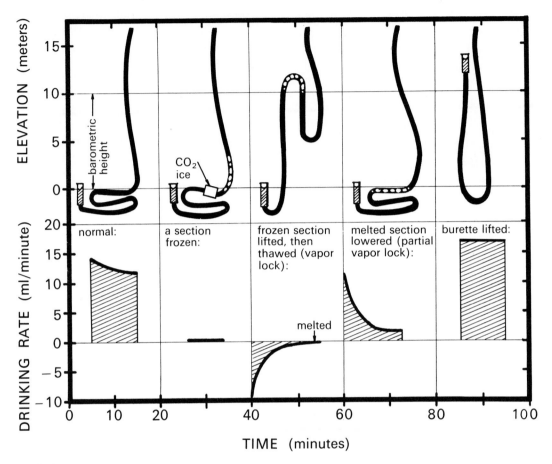

Figure 7-14
Scholander's experiments with tropical rattan vines as described in the text. (From P. F. Scholander et al., 1961, *Science* 134:1835. Used by permission.)

released by exclusion upon freezing. The weight of water below the previously frozen section, and the transpiration pull from above, kept the water in the previously frozen section in all parts of the pathway in the vapor state.

The loop with the frozen section was then lowered to the ground. There was an initial rapid uptake as the vapor condensed and some of the channels previously filled with vacuum were filled with water. Then there was a steady uptake at about 20 percent of the original rate. The decrease in rate of water uptake indicated

that some vapor lock remained. Probably some of the vessels were air-filled, or perhaps water vapor remained in portions of the stem well above the ground level.

When the burette was elevated to 11 m, the rate of water uptake increased to the original, indicating that the vapor lock had now been eliminated completely.

These observations fit the picture we have described of the ascent of sap, but they would be very difficult to interpret in terms of any other theory.

Scholander had previously experimented with grapevines and with tropical lianas. He had made crosscuts in the vines in such a way that *all* large vessels were disrupted (see Fig. 7-15). Yet water uptake continued at a rapid rate! It could be shown, however, that this occurred only at the expense of a much higher tension gradient across the treated section of stem. Apparently the stem consists of a system made up of macropores (the vessels and tracheids) surrounded by micropores (probably the cell walls). Resistance is considerably less through the macropores, but movement can occur through the micropores, providing the force gradient is high enough. In experiments in which the stem is cut off and allowed to take up air, such as those described for the rattan vines above, even the micropores become vapor locked and blocked.

7.4.2F What about air excluded from solution in the stem by freezing in northern trees?
Microscopic observation has shown that air blockage occurs when trees in cold climates are frozen, just as when water was frozen in the spinning Z-tube by dry ice (7.4.2A). Inability to restore the water columns in the spring may well be the factor that excludes certain trees and especially vines with large vessels from these regions. How can the water pathway be restored in trees that do grow in cold climates? The answer is not yet clear, but we do have some suggestions. Perhaps the transpiration stream is simply reversed by the heavy spring rains which are absorbed by the leaves, bringing the gases back into solution and refilling the channels. Or it is conceivable that root pressures or other metabolic pressures during the favorable time of year might refill the channels with water. In all cases, the cambium cells divide in the spring, producing new water-filled xylem elements. In some ring-porous trees, virtually all of the water moves in these newly formed tubes. In other species, however, even the old elements conduct water during the summer, and so in some way they must become refilled in the spring.

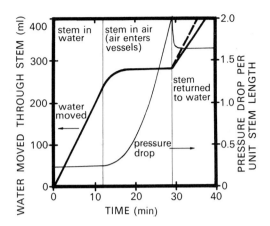

Figure 7-15
Scholander's experiment with a tropical liana. Heavy curve indicates quantity of water moved as a function of time. At about 12 minutes, air was allowed to enter the stem. Amount of water taken up immediately decreased. After 29 minutes, the stem was returned to water. Water uptake continued but at a rate less than the original (dashed line). Thin line indicates the increase in pressure drop per unit stem length. When the stem was returned to water, the pressure drop per unit stem length fell but not to the original level, accounting for the decreased rate of water uptake. (Modified after J. Bonner, 1959, *Science* 129:447. Data from P. F. Scholander et al., 1957, *Plant Physiol.* 32:1. Used by permission.)

Cosmic rays cause cavitation in the bubble chambers used by physicists in which liquid is under slight tension. A strong cobalt-60 source of ionizing radiation failed to cause cavitation in a spinning Z-tube, however, and there is no evidence that cosmic rays cause cavitation in trees.

7.5 SOME CONCLUSIONS

7.5.1 A Well-Adapted Water Transport System

Check-valved compartmentalization is an extremely impressive adaptation, solving the problems posed by trees growing taller than the barometric height. We should also not forget that the plant is a living system, and that new cells are continually being formed by the growing cambium as part of this system.

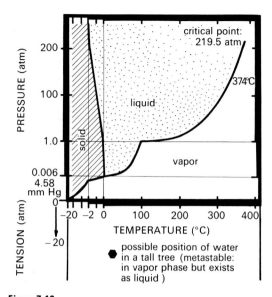

Figure 7-16

Phase diagram for water. To show the shape of the curves close to 0°C and also at much higher temperatures and pressures, it was necessary to change the scales sharply. Note that negative pressures must always result in water in the vapor state, in which state negative pressures cannot be maintained. Yet water in the tree exists under tension.

7.5.2   Life in the Metastable State

The metastable state as defined at the beginning of this chapter is a state of matter other than what might be expected under the given conditions of temperature and pressure. In the laboratory, water under negative pressures (tensions) vacuum boils, producing water vapor in which tension cannot exist. Based upon the experiments used to produce the phase diagram for water (Fig. 7-16), water in the tree should be a vapor, yet it is clearly a liquid. As we have seen, the apparent secret of this metastable state of water is the small dimensions of the channels in which it flows. Do these small dimensions make it so that equilibrium cannot be reached (such as in a supersaturated solution or a supercooled liquid)? Or does the nearness of the cell

walls, the hydrating surfaces, change the properties of water in such a way that it can exist in a state we would otherwise consider metastable? In any case, it is only metastable in terms of the usual phase diagram. Conditions in the xylem are such that the normal state of water is liquid.

It is interesting to consider the extent of water in this state on the earth's surface. All of the trees, taller than perhaps half of the barometric height (hydrostatic lift plus resistance), must contain "metastable" water. Perhaps even herbaceous plants contain "metastable" water when high resistances and tensions cannot be relieved by barometric pressure (as in Renner's tension experiment with the branch). Low soil moisture may produce "metastable" water in any plant.

7.5.3   A Final Problem

We may wonder how a *turgid* plant (positive pressures in the mesophyll cells) can contain water under *tension* (negative pressures in the xylem). Obviously, as we have discussed above, it does, but how? Water in the transpiration pathway will have a low water potential due to its negative pressure. Why doesn't water move into the pathway from surrounding cells, so that they lose turgor and wilt?

Since turgor is maintained in the surrounding cells, their osmotic potential must be equal to that of the water in the pathway. The osmotic potential of typical leaf cells has been measured and found to be on the order of -20 to -30 bars. It would appear, then, that the water potential of the water in the pathway will of necessity be higher (less negative) than -20 to -30 bars (Fig. 7-17).

In the experiments of Scholander and his co-workers referred to above (7.4.2C), the validity of this principle was clearly demonstrated. They studied a situation in which tensions must always be present in the xylem elements to

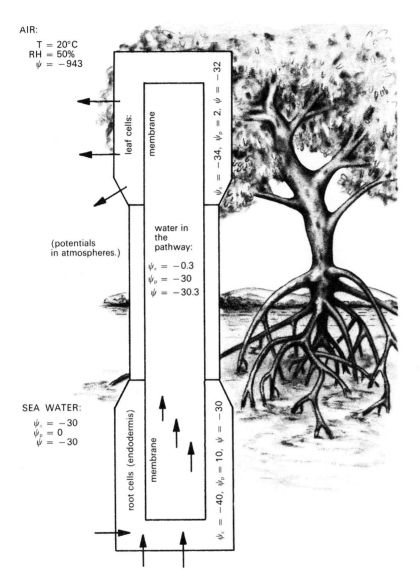

AIR:
T = 20°C
RH = 50%
$\psi = -943$

leaf cells:

membrane

$\psi_\pi = -34, \psi_p = 2, \psi = -32$

(potentials
in atmospheres.)

water in
the
pathway:
$\psi_\pi = -0.3$
$\psi_p = -30$
$\psi = -30.3$

SEA WATER:
$\psi_\pi = -30$
$\psi_p = 0$
$\psi = -30$

root cells (endodermis)

membrane

$\psi_\pi = -40, \psi_p = 10, \psi = -30$

Figure 7-17
Water relations of a mangrove tree growing with its roots immersed in sea water. The diagram indicates the "essential" parts of the mangrove tree from the standpoint of water relations, particularly the membranes of the endodermis and of the leaf cells. It is important to note that if leaf membranes should suddenly cease to be differentially permeable, salt and subsequently water would move from leaf cells into the pathway due to the high tension of water there, and thus the leaf cells would collapse. (Data from Scholander et al., 1965, *Science* 148:339. Used by permission.)

maintain equilibrium. Tropical mangrove trees grow with their roots bathed in sea water, which has an osmotic potential of about -30 bars. As water enters the tree through the roots, salts are excluded, probably by the endodermal layer, so that the xylem sap is almost pure water with an osmotic potential of nearly zero. (This is a property of certain halophytes to be discussed in Chapter 29, section 29.4.4.) The reason that the xylem sap remains in the tree and does not move out through the roots into the sea water is that it has a water potential of -30 bars or lower. This is achieved by xylem tensions of -30 bars or less. Scholander was able to measure the predicted tensions. He also successfully tested our concepts of water tensions in conventional tall trees by shooting branches off douglas fir trees at various heights with a rifle and measuring their sap tensions in his pressure bomb.

Obviously, if the xylem sap in mangroves has a water potential of -30 bars, the protoplasts of leaf cells must also have water potentials of -30 bars if they are to remain turgid. If they have pressure potentials of about 5 bars, then their osmotic potentials will have to be about -35 bars, values that can be readily measured.

In any case, the importance of osmosis in the plant is clearly demonstrated. Without the differentially permeable membranes around the living cells in the mangrove leaves and the highly negative osmotic potentials of the sap inside, the high tensions in the xylem system would lead to collapse of the living tissues. So without osmosis, plants would collapse!

Transport across Membranes

8.1 INTRODUCTION

Osmosis occurs because transport of solutes across membranes is typically much slower than movement of water (solvent). We have been primarily concerned with water transport, and as a general rule it has been to our advantage to ignore the movement of solutes. But solutes also move in the plant. Many are essential for the biochemical processes that go on within the cell. Others are harmful and must be excluded.

The striking thing about transport of solutes across membranes is that some are actively moved across, building up higher concentrations inside the cell than outside, while others are actively excluded. The end result is a concentration and distribution of soluble materials within the cell fundamentally well suited to plant function, but possibly radically different from the composition of the surrounding medium. For the higher plant this external medium is usually the soil solution; for marine algae, it is the ocean. In neither case is this a desirable solution in which to carry out the chemical reactions of life; so both kinds of plants have mechanisms by which their internal composition is appreciably altered from that around them.

8.2 MEMBRANES OF PLANT CELLS

For many years it was supposed that plant cell membranes consisted of only a **plasmalemma** (or **ectoplast**) and a membrane dividing the vacuole from the surrounding ground cytoplasm, the **tonoplast**. Nuclei, plastids, and mitochondria could easily be detected with the light microscope, which has a limiting resolution of approximately 0.2 micron, yet it was not until the 1950s, when electron microscopes came into wide use, that it became clear that these bodies also possess limiting organized membranes. An entirely new viewpoint of the cell was opened up with these instruments, most of which have limiting resolutions of about 5 to 15 Ångstrom units.

Pictures taken with the electron microscope (**electron micrographs**) clearly show the above-mentioned membranes, and others, too (Fig. 8-1). The nucleus is surrounded by two membranes, through which pores extend. These pores appear to be continuous across both membranes, as illustrated in cross-sectional or surface-view preparations (Fig. 8-2). These pores are usually 500 to 900 Å in diameter and thus, if continuous, would allow diffusion of many

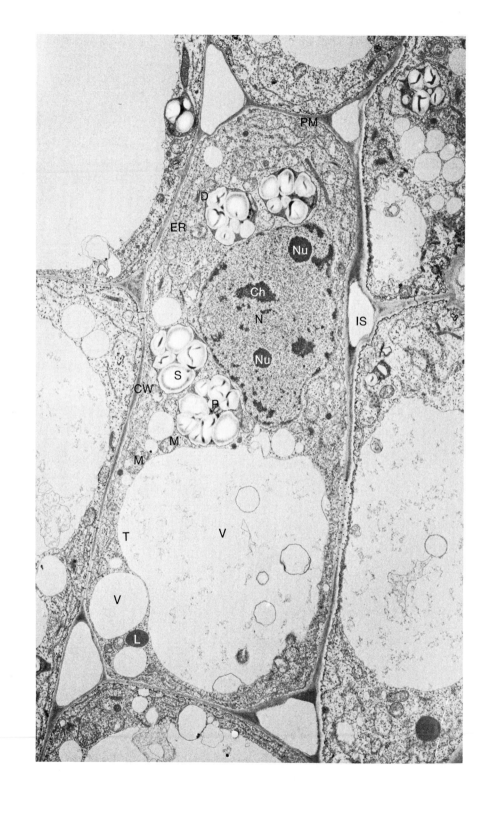

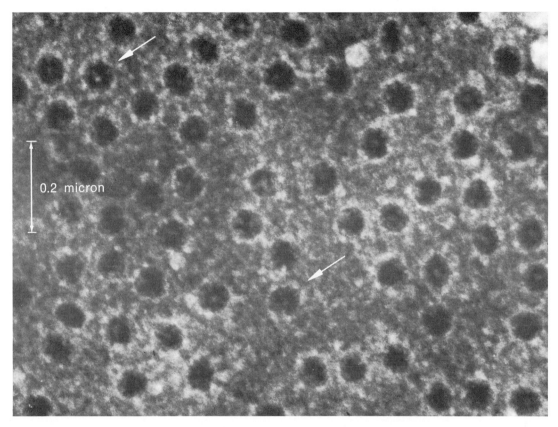

Figure 8-2
Electron micrograph of part of an onion root nuclear membrane in surface view, showing pores (dark areas). (From W. W. Franke, 1966, *J. Cell Biol.* 31:619. Used by permission.)

molecules between the nucleus and the ground cytoplasm. This is believed to be important in genetic control of hereditary characteristics, since large compounds with genetic information must pass from the nucleus to the cytoplasm.

Another discovery of electron microscopy was the existence of the **endoplasmic reticulum**, abbreviated ER. The ER appears in cross-sectional views as a series of ultrastructural canals extending throughout the cells, but the depth of the third dimension cannot be shown in such sections. It may be visualized as a deflated sac so extensively folded that it extends throughout the ground cytoplasm. The cavity (**lumen**) appears to be continuous in all parts of the ER, even though this continuity is not

Figure 8-1
Parenchyma cell from a cotton style (× 6,000) illustrating several features common to many plants cells (PM, plasmalemma; N, nucleus; Nu, nucleolus; P, plastid, containing starch grains, S; V, vacuole; T, tonoplast; CW, cell wall; M, mitochondrion; ER, endoplasmic reticulum; D, dictyosome; L, lipid droplet; Ch, chromatin; IS, intercellular space. (Photograph courtesy W. A. Jensen, University of California, Berkeley.)

apparent in a single cross-sectional electron micrograph. The lumen is bounded on each side by a single membrane. These membranes are presumed to be extensions of the outer nuclear membrane, since direct connections between them can often be seen, as indicated in Fig. 8-3. The ER is extensive and clear in young cells and others having an active metabolism, but in older, less active cells, it appears to have "dissolved" into the ground cytoplasm.

When the cells are properly fixed for electron microscopy (i.e., using glutaraldehyde followed by osmium tetroxide but not potassium permanganate), the ER can often be seen to possess small, beadlike objects attached to the outside of each membrane. These are called **ribosomes**, and, as discussed in Chapter 17, they are active in protein synthesis. Ribosomes also occur free in the ground cytoplasm. Functions of the ER are not yet fully established, although there are indications that in addition to participating in protein synthesis, small vesicles are pinched off from it during mitosis. These vesicles move to the **cell plate** and there release constituents needed in synthesis of a new **middle lamella** and perhaps the primary wall. In yeast cells and in the nectar hairs of *Abutylon* flowers, anaerobic conditions cause a remarkable increase in ER development. This suggests that reactions of respiration that can proceed under anaerobic conditions (fermentation and glycolysis—Chapter 15) occur in the ER. Another role of the ER seems to be in fat synthesis. Certain tiny vesicles, sometimes pinched off from the ends of the ER, soon expand and develop into bodies called **spherosomes** (Fig. 8-4). They are surrounded by a membrane that was originally part of the ER. They are approximately 0.5 to 1.0 micron in diameter and are stained by

several dyes used to detect fats. Their abundance in cells rich in fats is indicative that the ER is indeed active in fat production.

An Italian microscopist, Camillo Golgi, discovered in the 1880s a network of special membranes in nerve cells. This network has become known as the **Golgi apparatus**, or as **dictyosomes** (from Greek *dictyes*, or net). Electron micrographs showed the Golgi apparatus to be present in several plant and animal cells, including fungi and algae. It consists of several stacks of adjacent flattened vesicles as shown in Fig. 8-5. Each such stack is referred to as an individual dictyosome. The membranes surrounding the lumen of each vesicle in any dictyosome contain no ribosomes, as contrasted to those of the ER. A function of the Golgi apparatus in plants is apparently to secrete carbohydrate materials (except cellulosic substances) of the developing middle lamella and primary wall, and perhaps even of secondary walls. As with the ER, small vesicles pinched off from the ends of the membranes move to their sites of utilization and release the necessary cell wall materials. In addition, the large central vacuole found in mature parenchyma cells is formed by the fusion of smaller vacuoles that may arise from dictyosomes. The origin of the Golgi apparatus is not clear, but it may arise, like the ER, from the nuclear envelope.

Other subcellular bodies that can be seen with a light microscope but that have a fine structure visible only by electron microscopy are the **mitochondria** (Greek *mitos* = thread, and *chondria* = granules). Mitochondria undergo changes in shape and size but are generally seen as small rods 0.5 to 1.0 micron in diameter and 1 to 2 microns long. They are normally found in all cells except those of bacteria and blue-

Figure 8-3

Parenchyma cell from the nucellus of cotton (× 5,460) showing continuity of the outer nuclear membrane and the endoplasmic reticulum, ER (P, plastid; CW, cell wall; S, starch; M, mitochondrion; N, nucleus; Ch, chromatin; V, vacuole; and D, dictyosome). (Photograph courtesy W. A. Jensen, University of California, Berkeley.)

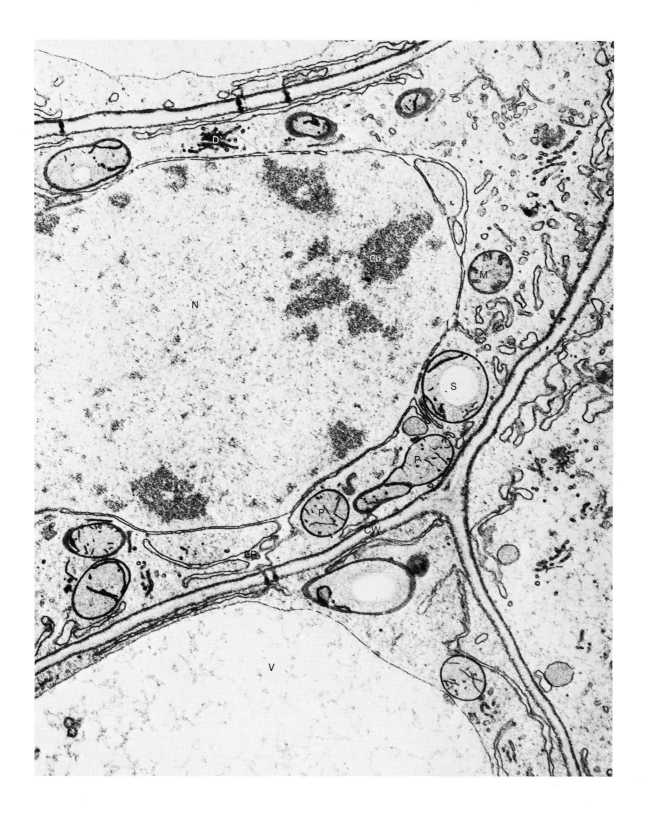

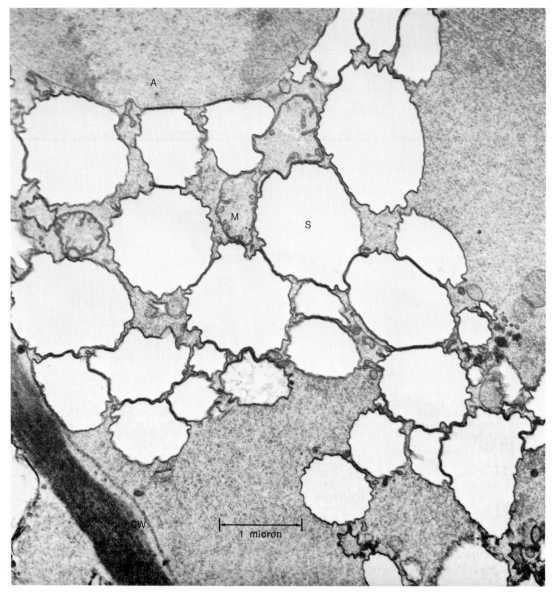

Figure 8-4

(top) Electron micrograph of section through a peanut seed
after imbibing water for one day. S, spherosomes; A,
aleurone grain; M, mitochondrion; CW, cell wall. (From
T. J. Jacks et al., 1967, *Plant Physiol.* 42:585. Used by
permission.) (bottom) Suggested mechanism for origin
and development of spherosomes. (a) Terminal portion of a
vesicle of the endoplasmic reticulum; (b) detached immature
spherosome; (c), (d), (e), stages in development of mature
spherosomes (f). (From A. Frey-Wyssling and K. Muhlethaler, 1965, *Ultrastructural Plant Cytology*, Elsevier Publishing Company, New York, p. 171. Used by permission.)

green algae. They possess a double membrane, the inner one being extensively infolded to form shelflike projections called **cristae** or fingerlike (tubular) projections called **microvillae** (Fig. 8-6). Oxidative reactions of respiration collectively called the Krebs cycle apparently occur between these membranes and on the extended surface of the inner membrane. Several theories are available on the origin of mitochondria. They are known to divide (and even to fuse) and also seem to arise from smaller bodies called mitochondrial initials. They also seem to bud off from chloroplasts.

Still other subcellular structures found in various plant cells are the **plastids**. Various kinds of plastids exist, including the colorless **leucoplasts**, which may accumulate starch to form **amyloplasts**, fats and oils (**elaioplasts**), proteins (**aleuroneplasts**), and the colored **chromoplasts**, including the orange or yellow carotenoid-containing chromoplasts of tomato fruits, various flowers, and carrot roots, and the green **chloroplasts** of photosynthetic cells. Plastids often arise from tiny plastid initials, although in most mature cells chloroplasts are produced by the division of existing chloroplasts. Carotenoid-containing chromoplasts not only arise from plastid initials (as in carrot roots), but also from chloroplasts by loss of chlorophyll and accumulation of carotenoids (as in various flowers and fruits).

As to plastid membranes, primary emphasis will be given to those of chloroplasts in the present chapter, because much more is known about the movement of solute particles across these than across the membranes of other plastids. The chloroplasts of higher plants, such as the mosses, ferns, and seed plants, are somewhat disc-shaped, with diameters of about 5 microns and widths and thicknesses of 1.0 micron. They are thus easily discernible by regular light microscopy. They are bounded by a double membrane, the inner layer of which is branched in places to become continuous with

an extensive series of membranes inside called **lamellae** (Fig. 13-6). The fine structure of these lamellae and their role in photosynthesis is discussed in Chapter 13. Because chloroplasts are the sites of photosynthesis, carbon dioxide must rapidly penetrate, and oxygen and certain sugars and other photosynthetic products must be able to diffuse out across the boundary membranes. Various ions must also cross these membranes, as well as others in the cell, to insure that metabolism occurs in a proper manner.

8.3 PERMEABILITY

The discussion of the movement of materials across membranes is basically a discussion of permeability. In Chapter 5, permeability was defined as being the reciprocal of resistance. It was discussed in relation to osmosis [equation (18), 5.1.4] and heat transfer [Chapter 6, equation (34), 6.7.2].

8.3.1 The Concept of Permeability

We speak of a membrane *being permeable to* some material. The more permeable the membrane, the more rapidly the material is able to pass through it. The term permeability is applied to the *medium*, in the context of this chapter, the membrane, and not to the material being transported.

In quantitative terms, membrane permeability is usually expressed as a *rate*. It may be expressed as the quantity of material that passes through a unit cross-sectional area of membrane in a unit interval of time (e.g., dimensions of moles/cm^2/min.). In the study of permeability, then, we are concerned primarily with changes in concentration on opposite sides of a membrane having known surface area, all as a function of time.

Of course, different substances exhibit greatly different degrees of permeability. Pure water is highly permeable to virtually any

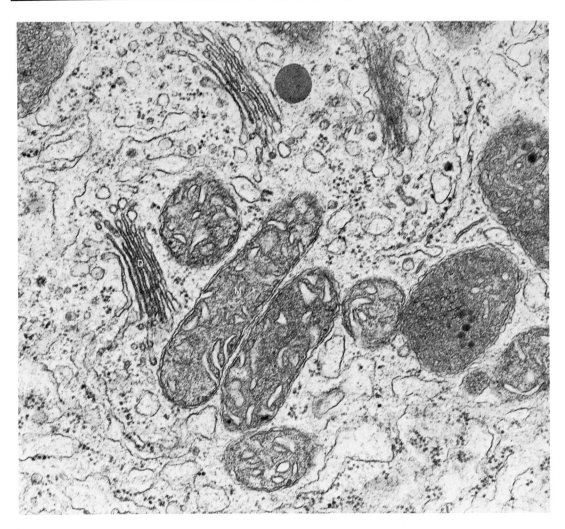

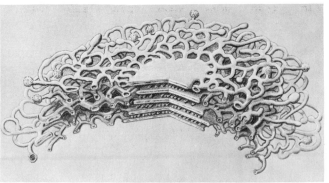

solute that is soluble in it. The vacuole in a cell is essentially a water solution and is therefore highly permeable to many solutes. The cell wall, which we have referred to as a hydrophilic gel, is also quite permeable to water and to its solutes. Cytoplasm is perhaps somewhat less permeable to many materials but still stands relatively high on the scale. The membranes are the least permeable of the barriers that must be traversed by materials moving within living systems. The effectiveness with which membranes act as barriers to solutes is indicated by a calculation that showed that urea diffused through the plasmalemma of an alga one million times less rapidly than through water. The plasmalemma, tonoplast, and the membranes surrounding the nucleus, chloroplasts, mitochondria, and various other cellular inclusions all seem to have differential permeability.

8.3.2 Methods of Measuring Permeability

There are several ways to study the relative solute concentrations on opposite sides of the membrane and how these change as a function of time.

Either the contents of the cell or the changes in concentration of the surrounding medium can be monitored. In cases where the cell contains an extremely large vacuole, such as occurs in the algal cells of *Chara*, *Valonia*, *Halicystis*, or *Nitella*, the vacuolar sap may be extracted with a hypodermic needle and analyzed directly. In studies of higher plant roots or storage tissues such as potato or Jerusalem artichoke tubers, vacuolar sap must be expressed in a press or by some other means. Yet extraction of this sap usually involves a considerable contamination of the vacuolar contents by the dissolved materials in the cytoplasm and even by substances in the free space surrounding the protoplast (section 7.3.3A).

There are various ways of monitoring the changes in concentration of some solute in the solution surrounding the absorbing cells or tissue. These same methods can often be used in analyzing the sap within the tissue. The concentration of a solute in the surrounding medium may be studied by applying the traditional methods of analytical chemistry to samples taken at regular intervals. The ionic concentration of a surrounding solution may be implied from electrical conductivity measurements. These are relatively easy to carry out, and the data may be recorded continuously on a moving chart. There is sometimes danger in interpretation of conductivity measurements, however, since we know that plant tissues often release certain ions in exchange for those absorbed. If hydrogen or bicarbonate ions are being given off as various anions or cations are being absorbed, conductivity of the surrounding solution will not be a valid measure of absorption.

Many modern studies have utilized radioisotopes. In such cases it is often possible to distinguish between ions of a given species that are entering a tissue and ions of the same species leaving it in exchange. Concentration changes both inside and outside of the tissue may easily be detected by measuring the radioactivity of appropriate samples taken at appropriate times. It is even possible in such cases to monitor concentration changes continuously (e.g., by circulating a sample of the external liquid through the instrument used to measure the radioactivity).

Figure 8-5
(top) Electron micrograph showing typical appearance of dictyosomes in plant cells. D, dictyosomes; M, mitochondrion. (Photograph courtesy of W. A. Jensen, University of California, Berkeley.) (bottom) Diagrammatic interpretation of a portion of a plant dictyosome composed of five cisternae. (From H. H. Mollenhauer and D. J. Morré, 1966, *Ann. Rev. Plant Physiol.* 17:27. Used by permission.)

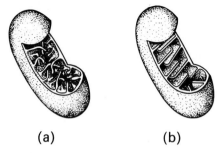

Figure 8-6

An interpretation of the fine structure of mitochondria. (a) inner membrane forming tubuli or microvillae, (b) inner membrane forming cristae.

8.3.3 Some General Permeability Features of Plant Membranes

Permeability studies have been carried out with plant materials since the second half of the 19th century. In many ways the results are conflicting and even confusing, but this is largely due to the complications of metabolically controlled uptake of materials, which we shall discuss in the second half of this chapter. Ignoring these extremely important features for the moment, we can arrive at a number of fairly concrete generalizations relating to the permeability of membranes.

8.3.3A Relation of permeability to metabolism

Physiologists studying both animals and plants have established that as long as cells are healthy and metabolizing rapidly, their permeability to solutes is relatively low. If these cells are injured in any of a number of ways (i.e., by heat, ionizing radiations, extensive pH change, excess electrical stimulation, or by placing them in improperly balanced salt solutions), the permeability rises. If the injury is minor the permeability increases only a little, but if it is more severe the permeability rise is larger. As the cells approach death they become very permeable. From this standpoint, death is therefore a quantitative process.

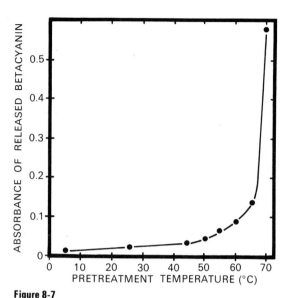

Figure 8-7

Influence of various pretreatment temperatures on leakage of betacyanin from red beet root sections. Sections (0.13 cm × 1.0 cm × 2.5 cm) were cut and washed briefly in water to remove pigments adhering to the cut cells. Pretreatments were given by placing sections at 5°C and at 26°C for 1 hour and by immersing those receiving higher temperatures 1 minute in distilled water at the indicated temperature. Sections were then placed in water for 1 hour, during which the betacyanin diffused into the water. Absorbancies of resulting solutions were measured with a Bausch and Lomb Spectronic 20 colorimeter at 425 nm. (Data of Ardell Halvorson and Ervin Forgy, 1967, Colorado State University, plant physiology class.)

Most of the above factors influence respiration rates, and the effect on the membrane could often be an indirect result of this. In addition, removal of oxygen or addition of respiratory poisons increases membrane permeability. Not enough is yet known about membranes to explain these effects fully, but it might be that respiration continuously provides an energy supply to the membrane that keeps it in proper repair. When respiration is altered too severely, the membrane would begin to leak. Figure 8-7 shows an example of the effects of brief temperature treatments upon leakage of betacyanin compounds (the purple-colored pigments) from sections of red beet roots. The compounds are normally held in the cell vacuoles, but when the sections are exposed to temperatures near 55° to 60°C, the membranes become altered so that the pigments later diffuse out very rapidly, even at common physiological temperatures.

8.3.3B Further temperature effects

The temperature has significant effects (independent of the injury effects above) upon rates of penetration of molecules through membranes. The solutes diffuse faster through the water in which they are dissolved as the temperature is raised. The Q_{10} values for this process are usually in the range of 1.2 to 1.4. Solute transport across the membrane itself usually has a higher Q_{10} and has even been found to be as high as 4.7 for movement of certain solutes into *Arbacia* eggs. The Q_{10} for water movement into these eggs was calculated to be 2.4, which is similar to values for uptake of several substances by plant cells. The reason the Q_{10} values are so much higher than for simple diffusion could be that chemical bonds in the membrane must be broken to let the substance pass through. As shown by the Maxwell–Boltzmann distribution curve (Fig. 3-1, 3.1.1), a 10°C temperature rise could greatly increase the number of energetic molecules in which such bonds could be broken.

8.3.3C Dissolved gases and water molecules

Dissolved carbon dioxide, oxygen, nitrogen, and other gases will penetrate most membranes with a rapidity that is exceeded only by the penetration of the water molecules themselves. This allows exchange of oxygen and carbon dioxide at suitable rates during respiration and photosynthesis.

8.3.3D Hydrophilic, nonionized compounds

It was observed as early as 1867 (by Moritz Traube in Germany) that the penetration of nonionic, water-soluble materials into cells occurred at rates inversely related to the *size* of the penetrating particles. The smaller the particle, the faster it penetrated.

8.3.3E Lipid materials

It was also observed in Switzerland by Charles E. Overton, at least as early as 1895, that fat-soluble materials passed through membranes at rates roughly proportional to their fat solubility. That is, molecules having a high lipid solubility penetrated cells more rapidly than less lipid-soluble molecules. The size of the penetrating particle is less significant, although there is a tendency for small particles to penetrate faster than larger ones if their lipid solubility is comparable. Overton's observations have been well documented by studies of others.

As a general rule, molecules will penetrate cells more rapidly than will ions. Figure 8-8 illustrates the penetration of carbon from carbonic acid or bicarbonate ions as a function of *p*H, and the relation of *p*H to ionization of carbonic acid. As ionization increases, penetration decreases. The general rule that molecules penetrate better than ions has been applied to practical situations such as those involving chemical weed killers or growth regulators. If the material can be applied at a *p*H at which most of it exists in the molecular instead of the ionic form, the likelihood of penetration, and consequently effectiveness, is greatly increased. The rule is far from infallible, however, since a number of exceptions are known.

8.3.3F Electrolytes

The penetration of electrolytes is complex, as we shall see. A very approximate and general rule, however, states that the permeability of membranes to electrolytes is inversely related to the charge on the electrolyte, after the increase in size of the ion due to its water of hydration is accounted for.

8.3.3G Effect of lipid solvents

Materials like acetone, ether, benzene, or chloroform will often greatly increase the permeability of membranes to many different substances. For example, briefly exposing red beet roots to a solution of equal parts acetone and water allows large

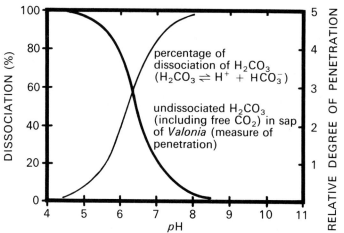

Figure 8-8

Influence of pH upon absorption of a weak electrolyte in the alga *Valonia*. After Osterhout and Dorcas, in A. C. Giese, 1962, *Cell Physiology, 2nd ed.*, W. B. Saunders Company, Philadelphia, p. 233. Used by permission.)

amounts of the betacyanin pigments to leak out, even after the roots are placed back in water. It is thought that this is because the acetone dissolves some of the lipids from the membranes, thus destroying them.

8.3.3H Type of cell As might be expected, there is considerable variation in permeabilities as a function of species and of tissue. One species or tissue may be highly permeable to a given material, while another may be much less so. For example, permeability of cells normally found in conditions of low oxygen (e.g., rice roots) may be expected to respond to oxygen partial pressures differently from other cells. Such differences have been essentially ignored in the above generalizations, but they are certain to prove more and more interesting and important as we document them more thoroughly and begin to understand what they mean in terms of natural ecological relationships.

8.4 THE NATURE OF MEMBRANES

A primary problem of physiology concerns the nature and function of membranes. We have

begun to develop some information about this problem by making deductions based upon the permeability measurements summarized above, by direct chemical analysis of certain membrane systems that can be isolated, and by electron microscopy.

8.4.1 Deductions from Permeability and Other Studies

The observation that penetration of hydrophilic molecules is inversely related to molecular *size* seems to suggest that the membrane acts essentially like a sieve. That is, the molecules must be penetrating the membrane through minute holes that may vary in size. The smaller the molecule, the greater the chance that it could encounter a suitable hole in its random kinetic motion. This idea, formulated by Traube in 1867, is referred to as the **molecular sieve hypothesis**.

In 1898, Overton suggested that the membrane consisted primarily of lipid material. This suggestion accounted for his above-mentioned observation that lipid soluble molecules penetrate membranes at rates related to their lipid solubility and faster than those soluble only in water. This idea was called the **lipid hypothesis** of solute penetration.

These two hypotheses could be reconciled by making the assumption that the membrane consisted of a **lipid matrix, perforated by watery holes.** A number of variations on this idea have been developed, and perhaps they reach some sort of epitome in the statement of A. Frey-Wyssling, that the membrane consists of "regularly arranged globular mucoproteidic or lypo-proteidic macromolecules in a reticulum of lipoid chains." On the other hand, authorities such as R. Collander felt that the situation was just the opposite: a protein (hydrophilic) framework with lipid molecules arranged in the protein *mesh.* As we shall see below, none of these early hypotheses are really very satisfactory in the light of all of the observations relating to permeability of living membranes.

Evidence that proteins form part of membranes was deduced from studies in which cells (from which the walls had been removed) and subcellular organelles were subjected to electrophoresis. The results indicated that the surfaces of these bodies behave as amphoteric substances, since they moved as cations at pH values below 3 or 4 and migrated toward the cathode, while they had a negative charge above pH 4 and migrated toward the anode. Since proteins were well-recognized amphoteric compounds, it was logical to believe that they were responsible for this property of the membranes. That membranes contained proteins was also indicated by the observation of K. Mothes in 1933 that the tonoplast of an alga was destroyed by papain, a protein-digesting enzyme from the papaya tree.

8.4.2 Chemical Analysis

It has been possible in a few cases to separate membranes from the other cellular materials. In plants, the chloroplast membranes have been isolated and analyzed, and in animals the membrane surrounding the erythrocytes (so-called **erythrocyte ghosts**) have been removed intact. Plasma membranes from muscle cells and from marine organisms have also been analyzed. Finally, the membranes surrounding animal mitochondria have been extensively investigated in the past few years.

In most of these cases, the primary constituents prove to be proteins and lipids, as suggested in the above discussion. Some of the proteins are composed of aliphatic amino acids and are rather water insoluble; part seem to be structural rather than catalytic in nature, but even these may be responsible for numerous enzymatic reactions occurring in and on membranes. The lipids of chloroplast membranes make up approximately half of their total dry weight, although they represent only one-third or less of other membranes. In many membranes phospholipids are common, but in the chloroplast membranes galactolipids are even more abundant (see Chapter 18). Various sterols and other complex lipids are also present, depending on the kind of membrane and cell involved.

8.4.3 Electron Microscopy and Other Physical Studies

Electron micrographs show that most membranes, regardless of their source, have generally similar appearances. Cross sections (which are easier to prepare than surface-view sections) indicate a thickness of 75 Å up to more than 100 Å. The membranes usually appear as two dark (electron dense) lines, each often about 20 Å thick, separated by a lighter (electron transparent) layer roughly 35 Å thick (Fig. 8-9). The complete structure of three apparent layers is referred to as a **unit membrane.** In many cells of both plants and animals the two outer layers are of equal thickness, and the membrane is then symmetrical. Cases are known, however, where the tonoplast and plasmalemma of plant cells are asymmetrical. For example, the inner dark layer next to the vacuole was found to be much

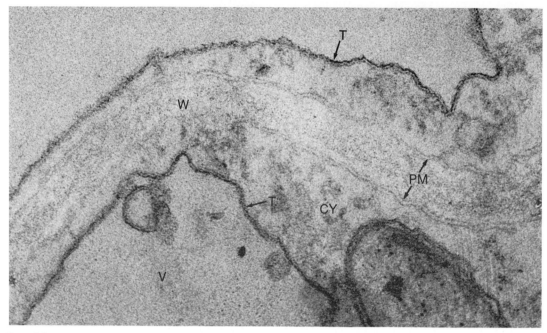

Figure 8-9
The three-layered appearance of the tonoplast (T) and plasmalemma (PM) in root tip cells of potato. The cell wall (W), cytoplasm (CY), and part of the vacuole (V) are also shown (× 131,000). (Photograph courtesy Paul Grun, from 1963, *J. Ultra. Res.* 9:198.)

thicker than the layer adjacent to the cytoplasm when the tonoplasts of potato root tip cells were studied. In these cells the plasmalemma was symmetrical, but in cells of orange rind the outer dark layer of the plasmalemma adjacent to the cell wall was thicker than the inner one. The plasmalemma and tonoplast are single-unit membranes, as is that surrounding spherosomes, and each of the double membranes of the nucleus, mitochondria, chloroplasts, endoplasmic reticulum, and Golgi apparatus has a similar structure.

For many years it was supposed that the two dark-appearing (electron dense) layers of the unit membrane were made of protein, and that these were bound by ionic forces to charged portions of lipid molecules sandwiched between them. More recent evidence summarized in

1966 by David Green and James Perdue at the University of Wisconsin and by Edward Korn in Bethesda, Maryland, indicated that this interpretation is not correct. They suggested that the protein and lipids are held together partly by ionic bonds between oppositely charged portions and partly by van der Waal forces between hydrophobic regions of the two substances, but that no distinct separation of protein into one layer and lipid into another occurs.

It has been possible to fragment subunits off from the membranes by various techniques, such as by treatment with detergents or by ultrasonic vibrations. Loss of these subunits does not disrupt the continuity of the membrane, even though they are a normal part of its structure. Sometimes it is even possible, if the detergents are removed, for the subunits to become re-

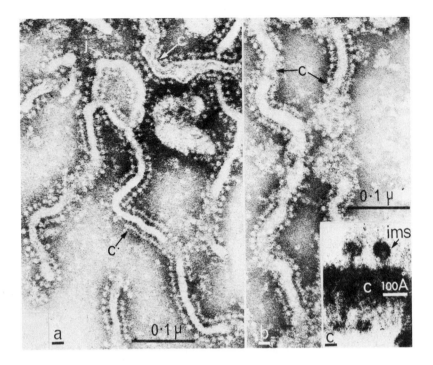

Figure 8-10
(a) Projecting subunits associated with the inner membranes or cristae (c) of mitochondria
from mouse liver (× 192,000). The cristae are occasionally branched (j). Such subunits have been
referred to by Fernandez-Moran as "elementary particles" and by others as "oxysomes."
(b) Similar cristae and subunits from rat liver mitochondria (× 192,000). (c) Higher magnification
(× 770,000) of a few subunits from (b). Spherical heads of the subunits are 75 to 80 Å in diameter,
and the stems are 30 to 35 Å wide and 45 to 50 Å long. (From D. F. Parsons, 1963, "Mitochondrial
Structure; Two Types of Subunits on Negatively Stained Mitochondrial Membranes," *Science*
140:985–987, May 31. Copyright 1963 by the American Association for the Advancement of
Science.) Parsons also found similar particles on cristae from plant mitochondria.

attached to the remainder of the membrane, apparently in the same way that they were originally held. As the techniques of electron microscopy improved, it was possible in 1961 for H. Fernandez-Moran to detect tiny bead-like particles on mitochondrial membranes that apparently correspond to one of the subunits separable by detergent treatment (Fig. 8-10). Subunit particles of various other kinds are suspected to exist on still other membranes.

Green and Perdue suggested a tentative model, shown in Fig. 8-11, for membrane structure based on the above observations. Each membrane is thought to consist of subunits that differ somewhat in form and size, depending upon the kind of membrane. These subunits are a headpiece (as seen by Fernandez-Moran), a stalk, and a basepiece, the latter being the part which keeps the membrane continuous when the other parts are removed. The subunits not only vary in structure but also apparently in function. In mitochondrial membranes, various oxygen-requiring reactions of respiration seem to be divided among these units. In chloroplast

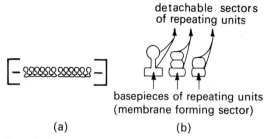

detachable sectors
of repeating units

basepieces of repeating units
(membrane forming sector)

(a)   (b)

Figure 8-11

(a) Representation of part of a unit membrane as a fused continuum of repeating units. The shapes of the subunits depend upon the membrane involved. The repeating particle in (a) with a spherical headpiece and a stalk may apply only to mitochondrial membranes. (After D. E. Green and J. F. Perdue, 1966, *Proc. Natl. Acad. Sci.* 55:1295. Used by permission.)

membranes, photosynthetic reactions may be so divided. The primary function of the plasmalemma and tonoplast is probably regulation of solute transport, although this property is also common to mitochondria and chloroplast membranes. Furthermore, the plasmalemma is involved in formation of the cell wall, which is, of course, deposited around it.

It should be emphasized that the model of Green and Perdue does not fully account for the three-layered appearance of membranes seen in electron micrographs, although when the chemistry of fixing and staining tissue for electron microscopy is better understood, this layering pattern may be explained. It at least seems certain that the proteins and lipids are not separated into discrete layers as previously thought, but that both are present in each subunit described. It should also be noted that the lipid-sieve model is not yet supported by electron microscopy.

8.5 ANTAGONISM

In our discussion of membrane permeability, we omitted certain observations that tend to complicate the picture. We are now ready to consider in some detail these complications.

If a seedling, for example, is placed with its roots in a dilute solution of potassium chloride, it will show severe toxicity symptoms in a relatively short period of time. That is, potassium ions are accumulated and chloride ions along with them, and the result is injury or death of the seedling. But if a small quantity of calcium chloride is added to the potassium chloride solution, then neither the potassium nor the calcium ions are taken up in toxic amounts, and symptoms fail to develop. The small quantities of calcium ions are said to **antagonize** the toxic effects of the potassium ions. Many such examples are known. Calcium ions will also antagonize the toxic effects of sodium ions, or potassium or sodium ions will antagonize the toxic effects of calcium ions.

Some years ago this area of research was very active, and a number of interesting facts were accumulated. Unfortunately, we are essentially as unable to explain these facts now as we were when the work was done. It was noted, for example, that the less closely ions are related in the periodic table, the more effective they are as antagonists. Thus, sodium and potassium do not antagonize each other as effectively as do sodium and calcium or potassium and barium. Furthermore, only *traces* of the antagonizing ions are required to produce the effect. This is one of the most perplexing aspects of the entire problem. If three cations are all present in a solution, it becomes impossible to demonstrate for any one of them the kind of toxicity being discussed here.

Suggestions put forth to account for antagonism have been varied and unsatisfying. It was proposed, for example, that the membranes had the properties of emulsions. Thus calcium ions produced a butter-type emulsion while sodium ions produced a cream-type emulsion (section 4.1.2), thus influencing permeability. Yet the quantities required to reverse these kinds of emulsions were much higher than the trace amounts effective in antagonism. Below we shall discuss competitive effects in the active uptake of ions from solution. Again, however, we shall be speaking of ions present in relatively high and almost equivalent concentrations. Antagonism remains a mystery.

8.6 ACCUMULATION

By the analytical methods discussed at the beginning of this chapter, it was discovered that the concentration of many solutes often became higher inside plant cells than in the surrounding medium. Such solutes are said to be **accumulated** by the cells. For example, small amounts of plant roots or storage tissue (such as potato tubers) placed in considerably larger volumes of nutrient solutions often deplete the concentrations of the various ions to nearly zero within a day or two. During this time some of these ions attain concentrations inside the cell vacuoles considerably higher than those that originally occurred in the nutrient solution. Sap from the vacuoles of certain green algae was found to have up to a thousand-fold higher concentration of potassium than was present in the surrounding water.

Although potassium and certain other ions are commonly present in higher concentrations inside than outside plant cells, still others may not be. Sodium is often not accumulated, and sometimes neither is calcium. Table 8-1 presents results of measurements of the levels of certain monovalent ions of sea water and the concentrations that existed in algae growing therein. Note that one alga weakly accumulated sodium, while in the other the internal concentration of this ion was less than in the sea water. Both species effectively accumulated potassium, and one accumulate chloride, while the other did so only very weakly. It is thus apparent that different species accumulated various ions to different extents. The same is true for roots of various higher plants, as will be shown later. Furthermore, several elements not essential to

plants, including some not usually found in the soil or in plant cells, can be accumulated.

8.6.1 Passive and Active Solute Transport

If a substance is moving across a cell membrane, the number of particles moving per unit time through a given area of the membrane is referred to as the **flux**. The flux (J) is equal to the permeability (L_a) of the membrane multiplied by the driving force (ΔG) causing diffusion, as in equation (19) for the flow of water through a membrane (5.1.4).

$$J = L_a \Delta G \qquad (41A)$$

If an *uncharged* molecule, such as glucose, is diffusing across, the driving force is due to the difference in concentration, or strictly speaking, the chemical potential, of that molecular species on the two sides of the membrane. If the chemical potential of the solute is higher outside the membrane than inside, the transport inwardly is said to be **passive**. If, however, a cell is to accumulate molecules *against* a chemical potential gradient, it must provide energy sufficient to overcome this difference in chemical potential. Transport against such a gradient is said to be **active**. As we shall see, the cells must be actively metabolizing in order to carry out active solute uptake.

Both passive and active transport of molecules commonly occur from one subcellular compartment to another within individual cells, as well as into the cell. For example, sucrose synthesized inside chloroplasts during photosynthesis could be transported passively into the surrounding cytoplasm where its chemical potential is lower, and from there to a neighboring cell, such as a sieve tube element. Active transport within cells is thought to take place when the purple anthocyanin molecules so abundant in leaves of red cabbage or flowers of many species are moved across the tonoplast from the cytoplasm into the vacuoles where they accumu-

TABLE 8-1

CONCENTRATIONS OF MAJOR IONS IN SEA WATER COMPARED WITH THEIR CONCENTRATIONS IN VACUOLES OF ALGAE LIVING THERE

Ion	*Nitella obtusa*[a]—Baltic Sea		*Halicystis ovalis*[b]	
	Vacuole conc.	Sea water conc.	Vacuole conc.	Sea water conc.
Na^+	54 mM	30 mM	257 mM	488 mM
K^+	113 mM	0.65 mM	337 mM	12 mM
Cl^-	206 mM	35 mM	543 mM	523 mM

[a] Data for *Nitella* are from J. Dainty, *Ann. Rev. Plant Physiol.* 13:379, 1962.
[b] Data for *Halicystis* are from R. W. Blount and B. H. Levedahl, *Acta Physiol. Scand.* 49:1, 1960.

late. It should be noted that although passive and active transport of molecules are usually distinguished on the basis of whether a chemical potential difference exists across the membrane, there are probably many cases in which cells expend energy moving solutes across only by passive transport. Here the flux is increased by the use of metabolic energy, perhaps to break bonds in the membrane, which facilitates solute movement, or chemically to alter the solute in such a way that the membrane is more permeable to it. If the membrane is at all permeable to the solute, the chemical potential will eventually become the same on both sides of a membrane by passive transport whether or not metabolic energy speeds up the process.

When *ions* are transported across membranes, the driving force is not simply due to the chemical potential gradient as it is with molecules, but to an **electrochemical potential** gradient across the membrane. The electrochemical potential gradient is made up of the chemical potential difference and an electrical potential difference. The latter usually arises from the fact that although one ion of a salt tends to move across a membrane along with its oppositely charged counterpart, the diffusion rates are almost always different. If the cation diffuses across more rapidly than the anion, the inside will become positive with respect to the outside, and vice versa. Electrical potential differences between the external solution and the vacuoles of several plant cells have been determined by inserting tiny electrodes directly into the vacuoles. The vacuoles are usually found to be negatively charged, potentials between − 70 and − 150 millivolts being common. In a few cases similar potentials were found to exist across the plasmalemma between cytoplasm and surrounding solution, implying that there is little difference in potential between the vacuole and cytoplasm.

Whether the transport of an *ion* is active or passive depends upon the contribution of the electrical potential difference and the chemical potential difference. Sometimes these two factors will act in the same direction, while in other cases, they act oppositely. For example, a cation might have a higher concentration inside the cell and yet be transported in passively with no energy expenditure on the part of the cell if the electrical potential is sufficiently negative. On the other hand, anion absorption against both a chemical potential gradient and a negative electrical potential would always necessarily be an active process.

When equilibrium has occurred with respect to an ion, its flux outwardly (**efflux**) is equal to its **influx**, and its electrochemical potential is the same on the inside of the membrane as on the outside; i.e.,

$$\mu_i = \mu_e \qquad (41B)$$

where μ is the electrochemical potential, and the subscripts i and e refer to the values inside and external to the membrane. From this fact, an equation has been derived that relates the difference in ionic activity (i.e., effective concentration, see section 3.2.4) to the electropotential difference, $\Delta\varepsilon$, across the membrane at equilibrium:

$$\Delta\varepsilon = -\frac{2.3RT}{zF}\log\frac{a_i}{a_e} \qquad (42)$$

where:

$z =$ the net charge on the ion and is preceded by a negative sign for anions

$F =$ the Faraday constant (23,060 calories/volt equiv.)

$a_i/a_e =$ the ratio of activity of the ion inside to that outside the membrane

$R =$ the gas constant in units corresponding to those of F, in this case 1.987 calories/mole degree

$T =$ the absolute temperature

Using this, the **Nernst equation**, plant physiologists have determined whether several ions were absorbed passively or actively in certain situations. Data of N. Higinbotham, B. Etherton, and R. Foster obtained in 1966 at Washington State University with roots of oat and pea seedlings are given in Table 8-2. Excised roots were placed in a balanced nutrient solution for periods up to 48 hours, then the absorbed ions were extracted and the amount of each ion was measured in the extract so that its concentration in the tissue could be calculated. Nearly all of the ions were accumulated in the cells of both species, as indicated by accumulation ratios greater than 1.0. The ratio of 78 for potassium in pea roots was highest of all. The pea roots accumulated sulfate much more effectively than did the oat roots, again showing a difference between species in ability to transport ions. The interior of the cells of pea roots had $\Delta\varepsilon$ values of about -110 millivolts relative to the outside solution, and for oats the value was about -84 millivolts. When the measured activity ratios were compared with those calculated by substituting these values for $\Delta\varepsilon$ into the Nernst equation, only potassium gave similar experimental and theoretical values based upon electrochemical equilibrium. The measured ratios for all of the other cations were lower than those calculated by the equation, indicating that they were not in equilibrium and could move passively toward the negative potential inside the tissue. On the other hand, each of the anions was not only accumulated internally, but this occurred against the electrical potential. It was therefore concluded that only the anions were actively accumulated, and that the cations were carried along passively.

This is one of only a few such measurements that have been made with roots of higher plants, and many more are needed before it can be generalized that anion uptake into root cells is more typically an active process than is cation uptake. Further information is also needed about accumulation of ions used by plants only in trace amounts, such as zinc, copper, manganese, and iron. One of the first studies to determine whether the accumulation of such ions is active or passive was performed with zinc ions and barley roots in 1965, and it indicates that those ions were indeed accumulated, but that this was due to exchange adsorption (Donnan accumulation) and formation of stable compounds in the cells. Both processes lower the internal chemical potential of zinc; so it presumably diffuses passively into the roots.

TABLE 8-2

USE OF THE NERNST EQUATION TO PREDICT WHETHER IONS ARE ABSORBED PASSIVELY OR ACTIVELY

	Ion concentrations in tissues (μ equiv./g water content)			
	Pea roots		Oat roots	
Ion	Predicted conc.	Measured conc.	Predicted conc.	Measured conc.
K^+	74	75	27	66
Na^+	74	8	27	3
Mg^{++}	2,700	3	350	17
Ca^{++}	10,800	2	1,400	3
NO_3^-	0.0272	28	0.0756	56
Cl^-	0.0136	7	0.0378	3
$H_2PO_4^-$	0.0136	21	0.0378	17
$SO_4^=$	0.000094	19	0.00071	4

Values for measured ion contents were determined on water extracts of roots 24 hours after roots were placed in solutions having known ion concentrations. The predicted values were obtained by assuming that electrochemical equilibrium exists and using the Nernst equation to calculate a_i/a_o. Knowing a_o, a_i could be predicted and tabulated above. Electropotential value (compared to solution) for pea roots was minus 110 millivolts and for oat roots, minus 84 millivolts (data of N. Higinbotham et al., *Plant Physiol*. 42:37, 1967). Example for K^+ in pea roots:

$$\log(a_i/a_o) = \frac{(0.110 \text{ volts}) (1.0) (23,060 \text{ cal/volt equiv.})}{(2.3 \quad 1.987 \text{ cal/mole deg}) (298 \text{ deg})} = 1.86$$

$$a_i a_o = 73$$

Since a_o for K^+ was 1.0 μ moles/ml = 1.0 μ equiv./g, a_i = 73 μ equiv./g.

8.6.2 *p*H Changes Accompanying Ion Accumulation

It is sometimes found that the uptake of nutrient cations from a solution into roots exceeds that of the anions, while with other solutions the reverse is true. As discussed previously, monovalent ions usually penetrate membranes more rapidly than do divalent ions. Potassium, ammonium, nitrate, and chloride ions, for example, are usually absorbed rapidly in comparison to many other mineral ions. Electrical neutrality seems to be maintained in these cases in two ways. *First*, if uptake of nutrient anions exceeds cation uptake, hydroxyl and bicarbonate ions are transported outwardly from inside the cells. This usually raises the *p*H of the external solution, but the cells are so well buffered that their *p*H may hardly change. If

cation absorption is more rapid than that of anions, some hydrogen ions are exchanged by the cells, so that the external solution remains electrically neutral while its *p*H decreases. Furthermore, excess cation (compared to anion) uptake is probably accompanied in part by the simultaneous absorption of bicarbonate and hydroxyl ions, while excess anions may be taken up with hydrogen ions.

Second, A. Ulrich discovered in 1942 that when excess cation (compared to anion) absorption by barley roots occurred, large amounts of organic acids, especially malic acid, were produced by the cells. Similar results have now been observed with roots or other tissue from several plants. The *p*H of the cell sap normally does not decrease under this condition, because the hydrogen ions associated with the organic acids are exchanged for the excess cations absorbed. The formation of the additional organic acids depends, in part, upon bicarbonate ions coming in with the cations. It is now well known that bicarbonate ions (or CO_2) react with certain 3-carbon organic acids having only one carboxyl group, such as phosphoenolpyruvic acid to form oxaloacetic acid which has two carboxyl groups (see Chapter 15). Oxaloacetic acid, in turn, is quickly converted to malic, citric, and other acids, which accumulate under this condition. Kenji Torii and George Laties found that in barley roots, the acid anions (such as malate) are moved along with the excess cations into the vacuoles, where they accumulate. They suggested that as this process occurs, further CO_2 fixation into organic acids occurs in the cytoplasm, maintaining the normal level there.

8.6.3   Time Studies of Ion Accumulation

Considerable information about the mechanism of ion transport across membranes has been obtained from studies in which absorption into plant tissues is followed over long periods of time under different physiological conditions (Fig. 8-12). When temperatures are suitable and the tissue receives sufficient oxygen, a rapid uptake lasting several minutes is observed, and this is followed by a less rapid but quite steady rate of absorption often lasting many hours. The ions move into the tissue against an electrochemical potential gradient during the time represented by the linear part of the curve, while, as we shall see, the initial rapid phase is due to passive uptake. Since the concentration of ions in the external solution decreases steadily over the linear phase, the absorption rate is then not directly proportional to the concentration gradient. Instead, the cells seem to be able to absorb the ions with increased efficiency as time progresses, since the rate stays constant as the external concentration decreases.

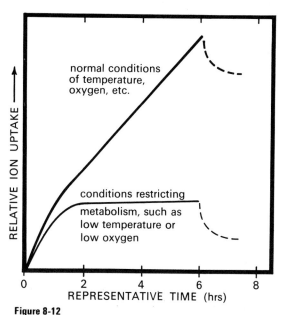

Figure 8-12

Uptake of ions by plant tissue under conditions in which an active metabolic accumulation is possible and under conditions in which this is largely prevented. Dashed lines indicate release of ions when tissues are placed in water (for explanation, see text).

Figure 8-12 also indicates the low rate of ion absorption under conditions in which aerobic respiration is prevented. This may be caused by temperatures just above the freezing point, by an absence of oxygen, by starving the cells, or by adding respiratory poisons, such as cyanide, azide, or fluoride ions. The absorption represented by this curve must be almost entirely passive, because nonphotosynthetic tissues like these have no way of effectively providing energy for active uptake except by aerobic respiration. If the ion is negatively charged, its chemical potential inside the cells under these conditions becomes essentially the same as that outside and remains constant for long periods of time, during which a continuous influx and efflux occurs. If the ion is positively charged, its concentration becomes slightly higher in the tissue than outside because of

Donnan equilibrium effects (see section 4.2.4D). Such cations are attracted to free negatively charged carboxyl groups of pectic compounds and certain other substances in the cell walls, and probably to negative sites upon the outer surface of the plasmalemma itself. Few positive sites are available to attract and accumulate anions.

8.6.4 Nonexchangeability of Actively Absorbed Ions

If the tissues represented in Fig. 8-12 are removed from the solutions at the time indicated by dashed lines and are placed in a large volume of distilled water, the ions absorbed passively (except for those held on Donnan sites) will leak out. However, those absorbed actively (especially those taken into the vacuoles) do not readily leak out as long as the cells remain healthy, nor will they exchange with similar ions in the external medium (indicated by radioactive labeling of those in the tissue). As discussed below, these observations are important in suggesting possible mechanisms to explain active uptake.

8.7 POSSIBLE MECHANISMS OF ACTIVE SOLUTE ABSORPTION

Although it is well recognized that accumulating molecules against a chemical potential gradient or ions against an electrochemical gradient requires respiratory energy, it is not yet understood how respiration and active absorption processes are coupled. A number of theories have been proposed, but most of them employ in one way or another the mechanism of a **carrier**. For example, it is conceivable that an ion might be unable to penetrate a membrane because of the lipophylic nature of the membrane and the large shell of water associated with the charged ion. If the charge could be neutralized, penetration might occur. This neutralization might come about as the ion is attached to some

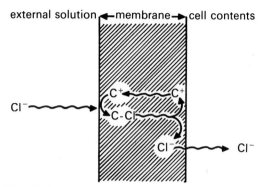

Figure 8-13

Hypothetical model to explain how carriers might cause ions to be accumulated inside cells. Wavy lines indicate diffusion paths, solid curved arrows, chemical reactions. In the present example, Cl^- diffuses to the membrane, where it reacts with a carrier molecule, C^+, to form a complex, C–Cl. This reaction is catalyzed by a specific enzyme, which is a part of the outer portion of the membrane. C–Cl diffuses toward the inner side, where it encounters a second, different enzyme, which catalyzes only the breakdown of C–Cl, releasing Cl^-, which diffuses into the cell contents, and C^+. C^+ diffuses back toward the outer side of the membrane, where its concentration is maintained low by incoming Cl^- and the enzyme on the outer surface. (C^+ is presumably continuously supplied to the membranes by the actively metabolizing cell contents to regenerate C^+ molecules, which, as various experiments seem to indicate, are subject to destruction or loss.) If the two enzymes are fixed in space and catalyze only the synthesis or the breakdown of C–Cl, depending upon their positions, then the Cl^- so accumulated cannot leak out of the cells.

molecular entity that is fundamentally a part of the membrane. The ion attached to this carrier might then diffuse readily across the membrane, being released on the opposite side. To account for the facts of accumulation, it is further necessary to postulate that attachment requires the expenditure of metabolic energy and can occur on only one side of the membrane, while release can occur only on the other side of the membrane. A simple hypothetical carrier model is outlined for anion accumulation in Fig. 8-13, and a similar one could be constructed for cations.

Three indirect evidences that ion carriers exist in plants are recognized. *First*, the fact

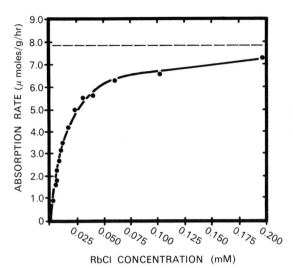

Figure 8-14
Absorption rate of rubidium ions at different concentrations of RbCl by excised barley roots. (From E. Epstein, 1965. In J. Bonner and J. E. Varner (eds.), *Plant Biochemistry*, Academic Press, New York, p. 458. Used by permission.)

discussed above that ions absorbed by active processes do not readily leak out of the cells is quite consistent with a carrier mechanism. The *second* and *third* evidences are discussed under the next two headings.

8.7.1 Concentration Kinetics

Emanuel Epstein, then working at the United States Department of Agriculture laboratories in Beltsville, Maryland, studied ion accumulation as a function of external salt concentrations. He found that rates of accumulation increased with concentration of the ion in the external medium up to a certain point after which further increases in concentration did not result in additional increases in rates of accumulation (Fig. 8-14). That is, a **saturation concentration** exists. This is what one might predict if accumulation consisted of movement of materials across the membrane by a carrier. When all of the carrier molecules were being

utilized in the accumulation process, further increases in concentration of external ions could not increase the rate of uptake.

These observations prove to be analogous to enzyme action to be discussed in Chapter 11. An enzyme controls a reaction rate by first becoming attached to a substrate molecule. Increasing the concentration of substrate molecules will not increase rates of reaction if all of the enzyme molecules are already occupied. A mathematical equation expressing this qualitative statement was developed and tested in ion uptake studies by comparing the curves it predicted with the curves for reaction rates obtained experimentally. (If they did not match, the theory would have to be rejected or modified; if they did match, the theory was supported but not proved, since the match could be coincidental.)

Epstein and his coworkers used the developed equation in a study of accumulation and showed that the predicted curves were indeed realized. The curve as shown in Fig. 8-14 is difficult to evaluate mathematically, but the data of such a curve form a straight line when the reciprocal of the rate is plotted as a function of the reciprocal of the concentration, as in Fig. 8-15. This is good circumstantial evidence that molecules, such as carriers, do combine with ions and facilitate their absorption, just as enzymes combine with substrates during catalysis.

By comparing the curves obtained during cation absorption, Richard Smith and Epstein obtained evidence that various ion carriers present in barley roots and corn leaf tissues are very similar or identical, even though the tissues are quite different. Other research by Epstein and by George Laties indicates that although similar carriers may be present in different plants, the situation is more complicated, because often two or more carrier systems for a given ion exist in the same cells. Torii and Laties performed uptake experiments with very

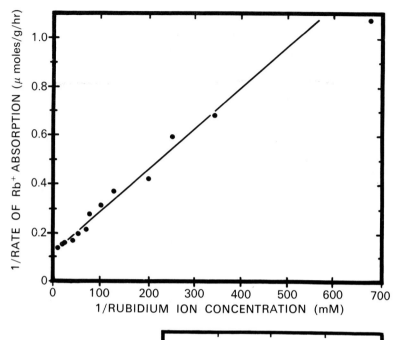

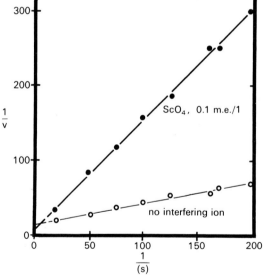

Figure 8-15

Double reciprocal method of plotting data like those in Fig. 8-14 to aid in mathematical analysis. When the data form a straight line like this, an estimate of what is thought to be the affinity between an ion and its carrier can be obtained. (Plotted from the data of E. Epstein shown in Fig. 8-14). See Fig. 11-10 for further explanation. (right) Double reciprocal method, showing inhibition of sulfate uptake in the presence of selenate. From the slopes and intercepts of the curves, it can be calculated that sulfate and selenate compete for a common carrier site. (Data of J. E. Leggett and E. Epstein, 1956, *Plant Physiol.* 31:222. Used by permission.)

young corn root tips in which the vacuoles had not developed and with older vacuolated root sections. Their results suggest that the carrier with the greatest affinity for the ion (that which is effective at low ion concentrations similar to those normally existing in the soil) is present in the plasmalemma, while the carrier with the lower affinity (effective only when the ion concentration is much higher) is in the tonoplast. Laties later found that the rate of translocation of both chloride and rubidium (which behaves in absorption experiments in the same way as does potassium) from the roots to the shoots of corn seedlings is controlled by the high-affinity plasmalemma carrier in the roots, indicating that ions must penetrate a cytoplasmic barrier but need not ever enter the root cell vacuoles as they move toward the xylem transport system (as postulated by Crafts and Broyer—see section 7.3.3C).

8.7.2 Competitive Effects

Epstein showed that potassium or cesium ions inhibited the uptake of rubidium, but that sodium or lithium had little effect upon this process. Bromide and iodide ions inhibited chloride absorption and vice-versa, but ions less similar chemically, such as nitrate and phosphate, were not competitive with the halides. Certain ions apparently competed for specific sites on the carrier, while other ions were moved on other carriers or other sites. This phenomenon was also known in relation to enzymes, where certain substrates can compete for a given site on an enzyme molecule. Characteristic curves are obtained when the rate of an enzyme-catalyzed reaction is plotted as a function of concentration of the substrate in the presence of some given concentration of the competing material (Figs. 8-14 and 8-15). Using this approach, Epstein outlined certain groups of ions that apparently competed for the same sites or the same carriers (see Table 8-3).

This is reminiscent of the phenomenon of antagonism mentioned above. The presence of one ion appears to antagonize the uptake of another. Yet, in order to observe the competition during ion absorption, essentially equal concentrations must be present, but antagonism can be observed when one ion is present only in trace amounts.

8.7.3 Transport of Sodium

As mentioned earlier in this chapter, many algae take up surprisingly little sodium, even though species living in the oceans may be exposed to a

TABLE 8-3

COMPETITION AMONG IONS DURING ABSORPTION[a]

Plant tissue	Ion	Competing ion	Ion not competing
barley roots	rubidium	potassium, cesium	sodium, except at high conc.
barley roots	chloride	bromide, iodide	nitrate
barley roots	calcium	strontium, barium	magnesium
barley roots	sulfate	selenate	nitrate, phosphate

[a] Data summarized by E. Epstein, *Ann. Rev. Plant Physiol.* 7:1, 1956.

NaCl concentration as high as 0.49 M. The ion is absorbed rapidly by the roots of many higher plants, but it is usually only poorly transported to the stems and leaves. For example, after bush beans were kept in a solution containing 10^{-4} M NaCl for 24 hours the sodium concentration in the roots was 2.3 micromoles per gram of dry tissue while in the stems and leaves the concentrations were only 0.04 and 0.01 micromoles per gram, respectively. It is because of such low amounts of sodium in plant shoots that diets of grazing animals must be supplemented with sodium chloride.

Arthur Wallace, of the University of California in Los Angeles, obtained evidence that sodium is very effectively accumulated into the vacuoles of root cells and is moved out with great difficulty. He also noted that when the ion was applied directly to bush bean leaves, it appeared to be deposited in the vacuoles of these cells and was not easily translocated to the roots. It seems, in general, that vacuoles represent storehouses for ions, but that the normal flow from the soil to the leaves bypasses the root cell vacuoles, as indicated in Chapter 7 (7.3.3). Other ions are probably not as easily trapped in the vacuoles as is sodium, but apparently once any ion is absorbed into these compartments its removal is slow.

Transport of sodium from roots to leaves is not restricted in some species. In most strains of sugar beet (*Beta vulgaris*) this ion is abundant in the shoots. This is also true for certain desert plants and a few other species that may require sodium as an essential element (see Chapters 10 and 29).

From the above discussion, it is clear that many higher plants and various algae have mechanisms to maintain low cytoplasmic concentrations of sodium. In the algae this cannot simply be due to a slow rate of absorption, because the ion would eventually penetrate the cells even though a long time were required. Furthermore, certain algal species maintain a low internal ratio of sodium to potassium in the light, but in darkness the ratio slowly increases as the supply of compounds produced during photosynthesis is depleted by respiration. This and other facts indicate that a low cytoplasmic concentration of sodium is due to an active mechanism that pumps it out as it is passively absorbed. Similar low sodium levels are maintained in some species of yeast (i.e., *Saccharomyces cerevisiae*) and in several animal cells. Here there is evidence that a **sodium pump** indeed exists and that it is dependent upon energy provided by respiration (ATP—Chapter 15). Extrusion of sodium by a carrier of the pump system is thought to be coupled to potassium uptake, although the latter process can also occur by another mechanism. Perhaps a comparable sodium pump exists at the tonoplast to discharge this ion into plant vacuoles, thus removing it from the mainstream of metabolic activity in the cytoplasm.

8.7.4 Transport of Organic Compounds

Although the absorption of organic compounds from the soil may not be important to most plants, the proper distribution of such molecules inside plant cells and from one tissue to another requires that membranes be somewhat permeable to them. Unfortunately, relatively little is known about whether the transport is an active or a passive process in most cases.

Absorption of amino acids is probably an active process in microorganisms, since the internal concentration of these molecules can greatly exceed that of the external medium when respiration occurs normally. Many experiments have been performed in which molecules chemically very similar to naturally occurring amino acids were investigated. It was often found that absorption of chemically similar amino acids was mutually inhibitory. This could be due to a simple competition for a site on a carrier molecule, but various observations suggest that this hypothesis is too simple. For example, both in plants and in microorganisms one amino acid may inhibit the absorption of another, but the reverse inhibition may not occur. This fact alone suggests that there is not always competition for a common carrier. Furthermore, extensive studies of L. M. Birt and F. J. Hird with carrots show that one amino acid sometimes inhibits the transport of others that have quite different structures. If separate carriers exist for these amino acids, it is difficult to understand why one inhibits the absorption of another.

Results similar to these were obtained by Joseph Miller and Cleon Ross, who determined the influence of *p*-fluorophenylalanine (a protein synthesis inhibitor) upon absorption of the naturally occurring amino acids phenylalanine, glycine, and leucine by cocklebur leaf sections. It inhibited the uptake of phenylalanine (which is structurally very similar), but was equally inhibitory to the uptake of the others, which bear little structural resemblance. Phenylalanine did not appreciably affect the absorption of *p*-fluorophenylalanine, however. The results suggest that if carriers participate in amino acid transport, they have poor specificities or can be altered by one compound to such an extent that their ability to transport another is affected.

The transport of such sugar molecules as glucose, fructose, and sucrose, and of sugar phosphates across membranes is an important process in plants, but, as with the amino acids, it is only poorly understood. Research upon yeast cells, bacteria, and erythrocytes from animals indicates that carriers probably do exist to transport free sugars. Yeast cells, for example, are relatively impermeable to several sugars, including lactose, galactose, sorbose, and arabinose, although they will readily absorb fructose, mannose, and glucose. This ability to transport some sugars but not others (which are chemically similar) is certainly suggestive of specific carriers. In fact, evidence exists that sugars are temporarily converted into sugar phosphates as they pass through the membrane and are then reconverted as they are released inside. When sugar phosphates are added to plant and microbial cells, they seem to be dephosphorylated before the free sugar can be released inside. Further evidence that marked chemical changes in sugars can occur at membranes comes from studies of translocation in the phloem. Sucrose is commonly produced in leaf cells, but some plants convert this molecule into larger ones such as stachyose, which are then transported to other parts of the plant where they act as energy sources. Stachyose is found primarily in the phloem transport stream, suggesting that it arises from sucrose at the boundary of the phloem.

8.7.5 The Relation of Respiration to Ion Absorption and the Nature of Carrier Molecules

It is thermodynamically necessary to absorb only one member of a salt actively (since the other should follow passively along the electrical potential gradient established), but Epstein and others obtained evidence that both cations and anions may be accumulated by a carrier mechanism. Still others, however, suggested that only cations are actively accumulated, and

that the anions move through the membrane by diffusion, thus maintaining electrical neutrality. Nevertheless, since most of the direct measurements indicate the cell contents to be electronegative relative to the external medium, it is possible that anions are usually actively transported and that cations may or may not be, depending upon their chemical potentials inside and outside the cells.

Considerable study has been given to the phenomenon of accumulation of ions by such cellular organelles as chloroplasts and mitochondria. Since about 1960, a theory that may partially explain how respiration drives cation accumulation has been developing from studies with mitochondria isolated from both plant and animal cells. P. Mitchell suggested in 1961 that cation uptake occurred in exchange for hydrogen ions released in respiration. As will be seen in Chapter 15, much of the respiratory process occurs directly in the membrane subunits of the mitochondria, and, during this, hydrogen ions and electrons are transported from one compound to another along the mitochondrial electron transport (or cytochrome) system until they ultimately combine with oxygen and hydrogen ions to form water. It appears that when mineral salts are abundant, the hydrogen ions released during oxidation of the organic acids immediately move out of the mitochondria in exchange for cations coming in (Fig. 8-16). During this process the mitochondrial contents become measurably more basic, while the solution in which they are suspended becomes more acidic.

High-energy phosphate molecules formed during respiration also play an important role in transfer of ions across the membranes of both plant and animal mitochondria. Chloroplasts also take up ions, and light energy drives this process. It appears that active ion absorption across the plasmalemma into cells, across the tonoplast into the vacuoles, and into mitochondria and chloroplasts may occur by some-

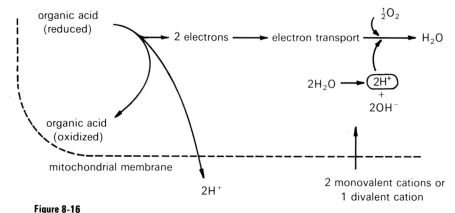

Figure 8-16
Hypothetical model showing absorption of cations in exchange for hydrogen ions produced in respiration. An actual accumulation of cations could presumably occur by such a method, thus partially accounting for the relation between active ion uptake and respiration.

what similar processes. Critical studies indicate that respiration is needed for active transport of ions into cells and into the mitochondria partly because it produces high-energy phosphate molecules, such as adenosine triphosphate (ATP, see Chapters 13–15). Thus arsenate, an ion chemically similar to phosphate and one that prevents ATP formation, and dinitrophenol, which stimulates the breakdown of ATP in the mitochondria, strongly inhibit ion absorption. At proper concentrations, neither of these molecules interferes with oxygen absorption nor, presumably, with the CO_2 release process of respiration. Their primary effect is to reduce the amount of available ATP or other high-energy, phosphate-containing molecules. Since respiration and ATP production occur principally in mitochondria, it seems likely that high-energy phosphate molecules are transported from these bodies to the plasmalemma and tonoplast where the energy they contain can be used to drive active ion absorption. Chloroplasts do not depend upon such an energy supply from mitochondria, since they take up ions primarily in the light, and photosynthesis then provides an

adequate supply of ATP and other high-energy phosphate compounds.

Although it thus seems that high-energy phosphate molecules supply the energy needed to drive active absorption, it is not yet apparent how this occurs. It has been suggested that the carrier molecules are subject to rapid destruction, and that the energy in the phosphate bonds is constantly necessary to reform them. For example, the carriers themselves might be phospholipids, which, as mentioned previously, are probably very abundant in all membranes except those of chloroplasts. According to this idea, a positive portion of the phospholipid attracts and transports an anion, while a negative portion transports a cation. Although phospholipids do possess both negative and positive sites (Chapter 18), and although ATP is needed to synthesize them, there is no direct evidence that they perform a carrier function.

More recently, evidence that carrier molecules may be proteins was obtained by Arthur Pardee and his colleagues at Princeton University. They found a substance in extracts of the bacterium *Salmonella typhimurium* that tightly

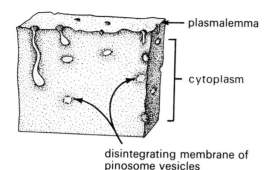

Figure 8-17

Origin and breakdown of pinocytotic vesicles from the plasmalemma.

binds sulfate and which appears to be normally involved in the absorption of this ion. This binding substance is almost surely a protein. A protein that transports lactose into *Escherichia coli* cells has also recently been discovered. It will be interesting to learn whether such proteins are common to other organisms and are involved in absorption of other solutes. If carriers are proteins that are constantly being broken down and resynthesized, this could account for the requirement for ATP in ion uptake, since ATP is essential to protein synthesis. ATP might also be needed to form a temporary bond between the protein carrier and the solute being transported, thus facilitating absorption in that way, too.

8.7.6 Pinocytosis

We also know that much larger particles, such as viruses, proteins, and nucleic acids, can penetrate membranes and can sometimes be transported from one part of the plant to another. Such particles can be absorbed by cells and their presence or effects detected internally; moreover, several enzymes are secreted from various plant organs, especially roots. Enzyme

secretion is extremely common in microorganisms, and often this facilitates the absorption of food by both saprophytic and pathogenic organisms. We can perhaps account for movement of such substances through the plant as occurring from cell to cell across plasmodesmata, in which case they would not necessarily go through any membrane. Yet observations indicate that they can also be taken into the cytoplasm of cells of roots and other organs when added externally. How can such large substances penetrate the plasmalemma?

It was observed in 1925 that *Amoeba*, which very effectively absorb and digest substances with high molecular weights, do so by a process now known as **pinocytosis** (Greek: *pinein*, to drink). The plasmalemma of these organisms is greatly irregular due to extensive infoldings in various regions. It was noticed with the light microscope that at the ends of these infoldings small vesicles named **pinosomes** appear to be pinched off (Fig. 8-17). These pinosomes contain substances that were formerly only in the channel between the infolded membrane. Inside the cell the membrane surrounding the pinosome is presumably digested or otherwise broken, thus releasing the contents.

This process is of considerable importance in certain kinds of animal cells, and it has been looked for in plant cells as a mechanism to explain absorption of molecules such as those mentioned above. Electron micrographs of plant cells show that the plasmalemma is not stretched tightly against the cell wall, but that it, too, is invaginated. In a few cases, what appear to be pinosomes close to these invaginations have been observed, suggesting that pinocytosis can occur in plants. It is likely, however, that its occurrence here is far less common than in other organisms, especially those that often depend upon polymeric substances as energy sources. It should be noted that although pinocytosis is an energy-dependent process, it probably does not usually lead to active absorption against a chemical potential gradient. The absorption of solutes by this method could not explain the marked selectivity that usually is found in solute absorption by plants, since the pinosomes presumably have no way of restricting the kinds of substances that are present at the time they are pinched off from the plasmalemma. These facts suggest that pinocytosis may be important in special cases of solute transport in plants but certainly cannot generally account for penetration across membranes.

9

The Translocation of Solutes

The plant, thrusting its roots into the soil and its leaves into the atmosphere and sunlight, must be a complex of specialized organs. For the plant to function properly, a balanced and integrated transfer of materials must take place among the various parts of its over-all structure. Materials absorbed by the roots must be moved to the leaves to be available for assimilation. We have considered at length the movement of water in this direction, but inorganic salts also take part. As photosynthesis proceeds, the products elaborated must move out of the leaves toward other parts of the plant. Roots will require them for growth and other metabolic activities, and developing fruits and flowers will either metabolize these photosynthates or store them. Special compounds, such as hormones and growth regulators, may be synthesized only in certain parts of the plant, and often they move to other parts.

Plant physiologists have devoted considerable effort to the study of this movement or **translocation** of dissolved materials throughout the plant. To begin with, we need descriptive information. In which tissues does the movement take place? Is the movement of certain solutes restricted to certain tissues? Then we can ask: what are the mechanisms of translocation?

With the consideration of these problems we arrive at a level of plant function about as complex as we can go without devoting a major part of our approach to biochemistry. Biochemistry is certainly involved in the transport of materials across membranes, as discussed in the previous chapter, and in the translocation of solutes throughout the plant as well. But the net result is essentially a physical process and not a chemical reaction: substances are moved by a variety of mechanisms from one position in space to another. In the case of translocation, however, these substances are sometimes chemically changed during the process of movement. Here is a borderland where the main problems remain physical, but where we cannot really consider the topic without discussing chemistry. In chapters following this one, we will concern ourselves almost completely with the chemical approach.

9.1 SOME METHODS OF STUDY AND THEIR RESULTS

Perhaps the ultimate goal in the study of this topic is to understand *how* things are happening. Yet we must first have a considerable body of information relating to *what* happens, and this is often rather closely a function of the methods of approach used in the experimental study of the problem.

9.1.1 Surgical Methods: Girdling

Some of the earliest experiments in the study of translocation involved the removal of certain plant tissues, usually the bark. Experiments of this sort were carried out by the Italian anatomist and microscopist, Marcello Malphighi, as early as 1675 and by Stephen Hales in 1727. Indeed, these were some of the first experiments performed in the field of plant physiology. Experiments of this type are still used as demonstrations, but for the most part they have been replaced by other approaches. In their most sophisticated development, however, they have been applied quite recently and often combined with radioactive tracers. In such cases bark may be surgically separated from wood, or wood may even be removed, leaving the bark virtually intact. Three very general conclusions (and many more particular ones) may be derived from these surgical experiments.

9.1.1A Water with its dissolved minerals moves primarily upward in the plant through xylem tissue

In the earliest experiments, it became apparent that the bark (containing the phloem) could be removed from the stem or trunk (the xylem) with no immediate effects upon growth of the shoot or loss of water by transpiration from the leaves. In the most advanced experiments, water labeled with some radioactive solute or with tritium can be observed to move readily through the wood in the transpiration stream, even though the bark has been removed. Detailed studies show that the solution moving in the xylem contains not only dissolved minerals, but also small amounts of such organic compounds as sugars and amino acids. We think of the xylem sap, however, as primarily an aqueous solution of inorganic anions and cations.

9.1.1B Products of photosynthesis move primarily in the phloem

In Malphighi's and Hales' experiments, it was apparent that the bark below the girdle dried up and eventually died, while the bark above the girdle swelled somewhat and remained healthy (Fig. 9-1). From this observation we can conclude that food materials produced in the leaves moved to the roots through the phloem tissues. Modern studies show that the sap in the phloem cells may contain as much as 5–10 percent dissolved sugars, and that other organic molecules are present as well. These include amino acids, growth regulators and various other classes of compounds. Mineral elements are also present, but they are far less concentrated than the organic compounds. Even in the very early experiments, it became apparent that the root system would not survive longer than several weeks when its food supply was cut off by girdling the trunk. This was a definitive way to kill the roots of otherwise resistant trees, such as willows or poplars.

9.1.1C Materials move from source to sink

Various parts of the plant have been girdled besides the main stem. It is possible, for example, to remove the bark between a leafy branch and a developing fruit. Again, sugars will accumulate on the side of the leafy branch. Or the girdle may be placed below the shoot tip between the leaves on the stem and the developing tip. In this case sugars will accumulate on the side of the leaves or at the *bottom* of the girdle. Gravity has nothing to do with movement of materials in the bark, but the controlling relationship is the relative positions of the **source** and the **sink**. The leaves with their photosynthetic capacity typically constitute the source. (An exporting storage organ would also constitute a source.) Any nonphotosynthesizing, growing, or metabolizing tissue might constitute the sink. Roots, developing fruit or flowers, or growing stem tips are the common examples. Since the roots are

Figure 9-1
Effects of removing a strip of bark from around the trunk of a tree. The drawing represents a tree about two years after girdling.

a very important sink, we tend to think of movement in the phloem as being *downward* from the leaves to the roots. Typically, however, materials also move in the phloem *upward* from the leaves to such sinks as the growing stem tips, seeds, or fruits.

9.1.2 The Balance Sheet Approach

Several studies were carried out in which the quantities of material moved from a given part or to a given part were determined by dismembering the plant and measuring dry weights. Of course, dry weights are influenced by processes other than translocation, notably photosynthesis and respiration. The complication of photosynthesis could be eliminated by carrying out the experiment in the dark. Respiration could be accounted for by dismembering a statistical sample of plants at the beginning of the experiment, keeping them moist and able to respire, and then determining their dry

weights. A comparable statistical sample of plants is kept under comparable conditions and dismembered at the close of the experiment. Results of an experiment of this type are summarized in Fig. 9-2. It can be seen from these data that the older leaves export by far the most material. About half of this goes to the roots, a third to the stem and the remainder to the young, developing leaves.

A refinement of this kind of experiment is to measure net respiration and photosynthesis directly by measuring carbon dioxide and oxygen exchange. This is more difficult, and results are somewhat less clear-cut. In general, it may be concluded, however, that the source-to-sink relationship clearly holds under conditions of both light and dark, and that the greatest quantities of photosynthate are typically translocated during the daytime when they are being produced. That is, as we might expect, the greatest concentrations of sugar in the leaves due to photosynthesis result in the greatest quantities of sugar being exported from the leaves in the translocation process.

It is possible in experiments like this to analyze for specific materials including sugars and other compounds. Complications arising from temperature and other factors may also be studied. But the tracer methods to be discussed below are better suited to these problems.

In 1944, Alden S. Crafts and O. Lorenz at the University of California at Davis used this method to arrive at an estimate of the rate of movement of materials in the phloem. Their method is impressive in its simplicity and elegance. They measured the growth of 39 Connecticut field pumpkin fruits from August 5 to September 7. Considering the total amount of dry weight accumulated in the fruits over this period of time, they calculated that the dry assimilates would have to move at an average of 11 centimeters per hour to account for the growth of the pumpkins. Of course, assimilates would not move in the dry form, and if they

THE EXPERIMENT:

Time interval:

dawn ⟶ noon
noon ⟶ dusk
dusk ⟶ midnight
midnight ⟶ dawn

A. dismembered, dried:

(At least ten plants are used for each treatment.)

B. left intact

6 hours

B. dismembered, dried:

C. parts placed in stand:

C. separate parts dried:

Roots in dark

Weight change of parts
from A to B due to:
  photosynthesis
  respiration
  translocation
from A to C due to:
  photosynthesis
  respiration
hence:

$$(B - A) - (C - A) = \text{translocation}$$
$$B - C = \text{translocation}$$
$$(A - C = \text{metabolism})$$

THE RESULTS (Summer):
(Figures in % of loss or gain.)

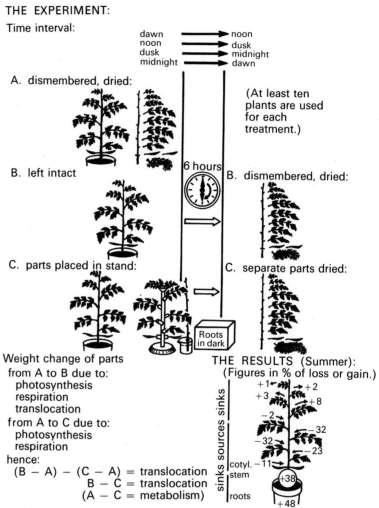

+1 +2
+3 +8
−2
  −32
−32 −23

cotyl. −11
stem
roots

+38
+48

sinks sources sinks

Figure 9-2

An experiment performed by D. W. Goodall to study movement of assimilate within a tomato plant. In (C) the plants are dismembered and placed in a stand so that the leaves are provided with water and held in a position in relation to sunlight similar to their position on the intact plant. (Data from D. W. Goodall, 1946, *Ann. of Botany* 10:304–338.)

moved in a solution of 10 percent concentration, their average velocity would be 110 cm/hr. Of course, it would be unusual if the flow rate were maintained the same day and night. It is quite likely that, at peak flow, velocities over 200 cm/hr would be reached. Measurements on a summer squash gave a value of 134 cm/hr with an assumed 10 percent phloem sap concentration.

9.1.3 The Tracer Approach

It has long been the aim of plant physiologists

to measure translocation directly by following the actual movement of marked materials in the transport system. Some attempt was made to use dyes several decades ago, and indeed the dye fluorescein was found to move predominantly in phloem cells and was used as an effective tracer.

In the 1930s and the 1940s, a number of studies utilized viruses. A leaf was inoculated with a virus, and its movement could be followed by the development of symptoms in the rest of the plant. These studies bore out the conclusions mentioned above, particularly that movement occurs predominantly from assimilate source to assimilate sink. In some cases, it was possible to observe movement of virus particles against their own concentration gradient, but along with the bulk carbohydrate flow from source to sink.

With the discovery of the herbicide 2,4-D in the early 1940s, a new avenue of approach was opened up. Growth regulators, such as 2,4-D and several other related compounds, could be applied to the plant at a given point and their movement followed by the development of characteristic symptoms in the plant (e.g., bending of petioles). Again, it was found that movement occurred almost completely in the assimilate stream from source to sink. And again, movement would occur against the concentration gradient of the substance in question, but along with the assimilate stream.

A number of interesting facts have become apparent in relation to the movement of compounds of this type (discussed in Chapters 21 and 28). For example, the mobility of various growth regulators varies considerably in the cytoplasm of plant tissue (e.g., maleic hydrazide is more mobile than 2,4-D), and some compounds (e.g., monuron) will not move in the cytoplasm at all, but only in the apoplast.

In a few of the very early studies, particularly those utilizing dyes, movements of different materials in opposite directions in the stem were reported. No really convincing case of **bidirectional movement** within the same cells has been reported, but some observations do seem to imply this.

By far the most important application of tracers has involved the radioactive nuclides made available by the development of atomic energy following World War II. Radioactive phosphorus, sulfur, chlorine, calcium, strontium, rubidium, potassium, hydrogen (tritium), and carbon have been used in these studies. A rather extensive body of literature has developed relating to this approach, and a fairly involved technology has also grown up around this fundamental method.

Radioactive tracers may be applied in several different ways (Fig. 9-3). A typical approach is to place a small ring of vaseline or lanolin on a leaf, perhaps over a vein, and then to apply a drop of solution containing the tracer inside of the ring. The ring is essential, since without it the drop of solution may spread on the surface of the leaf without penetrating. Another method is to remove the leaf blade and insert the petiole, still attached to the plant, into a test tube containing a solution of the radioactive tracer. Again, the precaution must be taken of ringing the petiole with a hydrophobic material such as vaseline. A widely used approach exposes the leaf in a closed container to carbon dioxide labeled with carbon-14 (^{14}C). The carbon dioxide is then incorporated into the plant materials by photosynthesis, and in this form it will be exported from the leaf in the translocation stream.

A complication involves the nature of the material actually being translocated. Often the radioactivity must be isolated from extracts of the plant tissue and studied by chemical analysis to determine the kind(s) of molecule(s) in which it resides. As a rule, the inorganic ions, such as phosphate, sulfate, potassium, or rubidium, remain unchanged, while most of the carbon dioxide is converted to sucrose. Of

Figure 9-3
Two methods of applying radioactive (and other) materials to a plant. A leaf may be removed and the petiole inserted in a vial of solution. A ring of vaseline around the petiole prevents surface movement. A drop of solution may also be placed on the leaf inside a ring of vaseline or other suitable material. (Photograph by F. B. Salisbury.)

course, many exceptions are known, particularly the compounds into which radioactive carbon dioxide may be incorporated.

Much of the technology involves detection of the radioactive tracer after it has been transported. A perfectly simple approach is to bring a Geiger tube into contact with the plant stem or other part. Sometimes this is sufficient to give an indication of the position of the tracer. A much more widely used approach is the application of **autoradiography** (Fig. 9-4). The plant is placed in contact with a sheet of X-ray film,

sometimes for periods of time as long as several months, and the film is then developed to show the location of the radioactivity. An immediate problem is to make the measurement without allowing the radioactivity to move within the plant after the time of harvest. Frequently, this is accomplished by freeze-drying the material. Plants may be placed between blocks of dry ice and then, while still frozen, subjected to a vacuum, allowing the water to sublime away. It is assumed that little movement of material will occur in the frozen or dried state. Another way of guarding against movement is to dismember the plant before making the auto-radiographs.

Several elegant techniques have been developed. It was possible, for example, for Orlin Biddulph and S. R. Cory at Washington State University to distinguish between radioactive phosphorus and radioactive carbon by placing a film of aluminum foil between the plant and the X-ray film for the first exposure. (The strong beta particles—electrons—from phosphate will penetrate the aluminum, but the weak beta particles from carbon will not.) They then waited several months for the phosphate to decay away, after which they were able to make the auto-radiograph showing the position of the carbon. (^{14}C has a much longer half-life than ^{32}P.) In this study they were able to show that the carbon and phosphate usually moved together in the assimilate stream, but in a few instances they would move in opposite directions in the same, very young, vascular bundles.

The tracer technique has been applied to virtually all of the problems of translocation. Rates can be determined nicely by removing sections at different distances from the point of tracer application at some interval of time (Fig. 9-5). These rates support the values indicated above. Typically they lie in the neighborhood of 100–200 cm/hr, but rates as high as 300 cm/hr have been measured; and, as we shall see, certain aspects of the translocation phenomenon may involve rates even considerably higher than

Figure 9-4

Results of an experiment in which autoradiography is used. In this experiment, which was not designed to test translocation, seeds were soaked for 24 hours in a solution of radioactive herbicide (EPTC—eptam). Seeds were then allowed to germinate and grow for 2 weeks into small plants, which were harvested, pressed, dried, and placed in contact with a piece of x-ray film for 21 days. The film was then developed, showing the location of radioactive materials within the plant. Note the high concentration in the cotyledons. (Note, also, that the left leaf of the upper right plant was broken off and moved after the autoradiograph was made.) (Plants and film courtesy of J. LaMar Anderson, Utah State University, Logan.)

these. A phloem element in angiosperms is typically on the order of 0.5 mm long (gymnosperm elements are about 1.4 mm long), and at rates of translocation of 180 cm/hr, an entire element could be emptied in one second. Even under fairly low magnification, an entire phloem element could not be seen at once in a microscope field. Thus, if one could watch movement of particles of tracer dye through the microscope in phloem cells, rates would be too rapid to follow conveniently with the naked eye. Slow motion moving pictures would have to be used! Without magnification, movement at 100 cm/hr would be equivalent to the tip of a 16 cm (6.3 inches) minute hand on a clock. Such movement could easily be detected with the unaided eye.

9.2 NECESSITY FOR ACTIVE METABOLISM

One of the most important observations of translocation, substantiated by all of the methods described above, is that movement in the phloem tubes is dependent upon these cells being alive and metabolizing. Any treatment that kills the cells (e.g., treating a section of the stem with steam) or inhibiting their metabolism (e.g., excluding oxygen or adding respiration inhibitors) stops the movement of assimilates through the cells. Furthermore, translocation has a temperature response quite similar to that of other metabolic processes. Study of this is complicated with whole plants, because temperature will influence production and utilization of assimilates as well as their translocation. A typical temperature curve for translocation, with minimum, optimum, and maximum, may also be observed when only a leaf petiole is subjected to various temperatures, and the rest of the plant remains at a constant temperature. Translocation of assimilates seems to be clearly dependent upon metabolism.

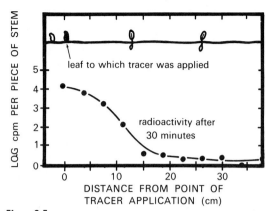

Figure 9-5

Results of an experiment in translocation using application of $^{14}CO_2$ applied to the leaf of a sunflower plant as indicated. $^{14}CO_2$ was incorporated into the leaf by photosynthesis. Radioactivity was measured 30 minutes after beginning of photosynthesis time. (From C. D. Nelson, 1963. In L. T. Evans (ed.), *Environmental Control of Plant Growth*, Academic Press, New York and London, p. 159.)

9.3 MECHANISMS OF ASSIMILATE TRANSLOCATION

Knowing some of the facts about the movement of assimilates in plants, we can now consider the mechanisms of movement. We must account for several observations, such as the concentrations of materials, the rates of movement, the requirement for living phloem cells, the pattern of movement from source to sink, and the interactions with temperature and other environmental factors.

Frequently, in discussions of this sort, it is assumed by the participants that *the* mechanism is the object of the search, as though only one mechanism of movement could account for translocation in the plant. This approach has led to relatively heated (and consequently often very interesting) controversies between the proponents of the various possible mechanisms. Looking back at these discussions, it now becomes apparent that we might very well expect more than a single mechanism to take part in assimilate translocation. Certain mechanisms might apply to certain tissues, and other mechanisms might apply to others. Or for that matter, a number of processes might be acting concurrently to account for movement of a single substance throughout the plant. Rapid long-distance transport through phloem sieve tube cells remains the most difficult and interesting problem.

It appears at this stage of our scientific endeavor that certain aspects of the translocation problem have indeed been solved, but that a number of highly intriguing problems still remain. Let us consider several of the postulated mechanisms.

9.3.1 Cytoplasmic Streaming

It was suggested as early as 1885 by the Dutch botanist, Hugo de Vries, that movement of solutes might be accelerated by streaming of the cytoplasm. The idea was strongly championed beginning in 1929 by Otis F. Curtis, an American plant physiologist. The mechanism is basically very simple: diffusion occurs from cell to cell according to concentration gradients (source to sink), but rate of movement is much higher than might be expected on the basis of diffusion alone because of the streaming of the cytoplasm. The theory is basically so simple that apparently only two requirements must be met for the mechanism actually to operate in a plant: *first*, it must be possible for diffusion to occur from cell to cell, and *second*, the cytoplasm within the cell must stream.

There is ample evidence, based upon studies with dyes and various other materials, that diffusion can occur from cell to cell.

Furthermore, cytoplasmic streaming has long been observed in the cells of living tissues. Demonstrations of the phenomenon are commonly a part of basic laboratories in high school or college biology courses. We must conclude, then, that materials may indeed be moved through living tissue according to this mechanism. Any concentration gradient that would result in diffusion would suffice to make the process possible, providing cytoplasmic streaming is taking place.

As is indicated in Fig. 9-6, different substances might go in different directions at the same time and in the same cells by the cytoplasmic streaming mechanism. They would always follow their own concentration gradients, their rate of movement being accelerated by the streaming of the cytoplasm.

The mechanism surely operates in many plant tissues, such as those of the root cortex (we mentioned the mechanism in our discussion of root pressure—section 7.3.3C), or in the parenchyma cells of leaves. But does it operate in phloem cells? This question is much more difficult to answer, since the phloem cells are extremely difficult to observe in the living condition. To consider this question and others relating to translocation, we need some background relating to the anatomy of phloem tissues.

There are four kinds of cells in phloem tissue: **sieve-tube elements**, **companion cells**, **fibers**, and **parenchyma**. The sieve-tube elements are connected end to end, forming cellular aggregations called **sieve tubes**. The end walls separating two adjacent sieve-tube elements are specialized as **sieve plates**. These have groups of openings or pores lined with a special carbohydrate, **callose**, and connecting strands of cytoplasm pass through these openings in the sieve plate. The phloem fibers lend support to the tissue but seem to play no role in translocation, while the thin-walled, living parenchyma cells perform such functions as food storage and lateral transport of solutes and water. Function of the companion cells is not known.

Figure 9-7 shows schematically the development and maturation of a sieve-tube element and its companion cell. The young element is similar to other young undifferentiated cells. It

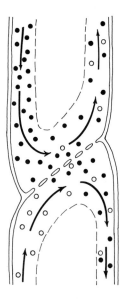

Figure 9-6

A schematic illustration of the cytoplasmic streaming hypothesis of solute translocation. Note that diffusion of white or black particles across the sieve plate will occur in response only to their own concentration gradients. Movement of the two materials might occur simultaneously in opposite directions. Rate of movement is accelerated by streaming. (From F. B. Salisbury, 1966. In W. A. Jensen and L. G. Kavaljian (eds.), *Plant Biology Today: Advances and Challenges*, Wadsworth Publishing Company, Inc., Belmont, California, p. 81. Used by permission.)

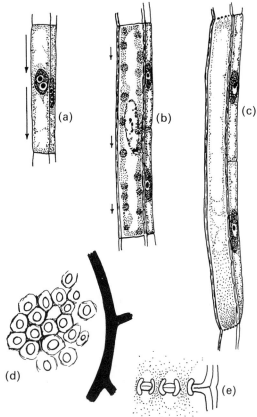

Figure 9-7

Some morphological aspects of sieve-tube elements. (a) Young sieve-tube element with companion cells. Long arrows indicate considerable cytoplasmic streaming. (b) Sieve tube of intermediate maturity. Slime bodies are evident, the nucleus is beginning to disappear, and cytoplasmic streaming is no longer readily evident. (c) Mature sieve-tube element. The nucleus, tonoplast, and cytoplasmic streaming are no longer evident. (d) Cross section through a sieve tube near the sieve plate, showing pores. (e) Longitudinal section of sieve tube through a sieve plate, showing cytoplasmic connections through the pores. (From F. B. Salisbury, 1966. In W. A. Jensen and L. G. Kavaljian (eds.), *Plant Biology Today: Advances and Challenges*, Wadsworth Publishing Company, Inc., Belmont, California, p. 77. Used by permission.)

contains a large visible nucleus, considerable cytoplasm, and obvious vacuoles. Cytoplasmic streaming may occur. As the cell matures, the nucleus begins to disappear, so-called **slime bodies** appear in the cytoplasm, and cytoplasmic streaming is less active. Finally, the nucleus disappears, cytoplasmic streaming apparently stops, and the demarcation between cytoplasm and vacuole is not readily apparent. The slime bodies have essentially disintegrated, but their remains can often be observed. Recent electron micrographs seem to indicate that fluids could flow through the sieve plate perforations. The much smaller plasmodesmata form interconnections between sieve-tube elements and their companion cells. The nucleus remains clearly distinguishable in the companion cells.

There is no convincing observational evidence that cytoplasmic streaming occurs in mature phloem elements. Furthermore, the rates of cytoplasmic streaming in cells in which it occurs are on the order of only two or three centimeters per hour (readily observable under low-power magnification in the microscope) and, consequently, far too slow to account for the measured rates of transport indicated above. (Could movement of the invisible liquid be faster?)

It appears, then, that translocation by cytoplasmic streaming does indeed occur in the plant but not in the assimilate conduction system consisting of the phloem tubes.

9.3.2 The Pressure Flow Hypothesis of Münch

In 1930 E. Münch in Germany published a book in which he proposed a model system to account for the movement of assimilates in plants. Many model systems used in science are purely formal, in the sense that they require perfect springs, absolutely rigid walls, or other features that make them impossible to construct in a physical sense (e.g., the "connected rooms" in the diffusion model—section 3.3). Münch's model, however, is simple and straightforward and can be built in the laboratory.

It consists of two osmometers connected to each other with a tube (Fig. 9-8). Both osmometers may be immersed in the same solution or in different solutions, which may or may not be connected. The first osmometer contains a solution (1) considerably more concentrated than the surrounding solution, while the second osmometer contains a solution (2) less concentrated than that in the first osmometer, but either more or less concentrated than the surrounding medium. Because $\Delta\psi$ between the medium and solution (1) is very great, water will tend to move into the first osmometer. Water may also tend to move into the second osmometer, but in this case $\Delta\psi$ is less, and so the rate of entry will be less. Pressure will build up in the first osmometer more rapidly than in the second. Since the two are connected, pressure will be transferred from the first osmometer to the

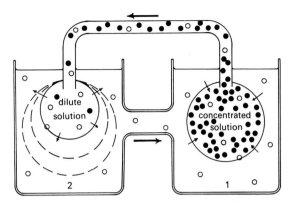

Figure 9-8

A model illustrating the pressure-flow theory of solute translocation as proposed by Münch. Note that concentration of black particles will control the rate and direction of flow, but white particles (which are much more dilute) will move along in the resulting stream. Dashed lines on the left imply that flow may occur due to expansion (growth) of the second osmometer (tissue), as well as movement out through the membrane. (From F. B. Salisbury, 1966. In W. A. Jensen and L. G. Kavaljian (eds.), *Plant Biology Today: Advances and Challenges*, Wadsworth Publishing Company, Inc., Belmont, California, p. 82. Used by permission.)

second (with the velocity of sound—basically a pressure-transference phenomenon). Soon the pressure in the second osmometer will result in a reverse-gradient of $\Delta\psi$, so that the surrounding medium has a more negative water potential than solution (2). The result will be a diffusion of water *into* the first osmometer and *out of* the second osmometer. Solution (1) with its solutes will be carried along in a **bulk or mass flow** to the second osmometer.

As a matter of fact, it is not even necessary for water to move out of the second osmometer. If its walls are elastic (or plastic, stretching irreversibly), pressure will be relieved as the second osmometer swells.

In Münch's model, the mass flow will cease when enough solute has been moved from the first osmometer to the second to equalize the concentration of both solutions (or when solute has passed through the membrane making $\Delta\psi = 0$). If some mechanism could be devised to keep the concentration high in the first osmometer and low in the second, flow would continue indefinitely.[1] Münch's model has been constructed as a demonstration in many teaching laboratories, and if its few basic requirements are met, it will invariably function perfectly.

Münch suggested that the living plant contained a system comparable to his physical model (Fig. 9-9). The photosynthesizing cells in the leaves constitute the first osmometer. Here concentrations are maintained high by the production of assimilates in photosynthesis. These are the source cells. The sink cells, those in the roots, fruits, developing buds, etc.—which are removing assimilates by the processes of assimilation, growth, or storage—represent the second osmometer. The connecting link between the source and the sink consists of the phloem system with its phloem tubes. The surrounding solution is that of the apoplast, with its dilute solutions present in the cell walls, intercellular spaces and xylem elements of the plant. Indeed Münch proposed the concepts of the symplast and the apoplast in the course of his discussion of the mass flow hypothesis.

If the model system will work in the laboratory when certain conditions are established, it will work in the plant if all of the same conditions are also established. The conditions are: *first*, a difference in concentration of solutions, as in the two osmometers; *second*, a functional connecting system between the two solutions, as the tube between the two osmometers, and *third*, a surrounding medium of lower concentration than those in the two osmometers. If these conditions are met, Münch's system must work in the plant.

---

[1] For example, the first osmometer might be filled with crystals that continue to go into solution, and the second osmometer might contain crystals of another salt with a lower saturation concentration that reacts with the first one to produce a precipitate.

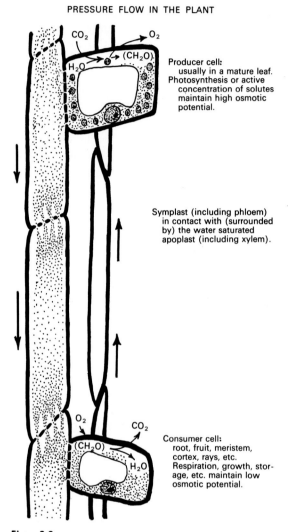

PRESSURE FLOW IN THE PLANT

Producer cell: usually in a mature leaf. Photosynthesis or active concentration of solutes maintain high osmotic potential.

Symplast (including phloem) in contact with (surrounded by) the water saturated apoplast (including xylem).

Consumer cell: root, fruit, meristem, cortex, rays, etc. Respiration, growth, storage, etc. maintain low osmotic potential.

Figure 9-9
The pressure-flow theory of Münch as it may be applied to the plant. (From F. B. Salisbury, 1966. In W. A. Jensen and L. G. Kavaljian (eds.), *Plant Biology Today: Advances and Challenges*, Wadsworth Publishing Company, Inc., Belmont, California, p. 82. Used by permission.)

9.3.2A Osmotic gradient This condition seems to be readily met in the plant. We have already discussed the osmotic potentials of root cells as compared to leaf cells (Table 7-1, 7.3.4).

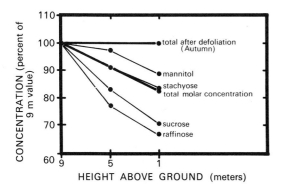

Figure 9-10
Some data relating to concentration of certain sugars as a function of height above the ground in the trunk of a white ash tree. (After M. H. Zimmerman, 1957, *Plant Physiol.* 32:399. Used by permission.)

The mere facts of photosynthetic manufacture of assimilates in certain cells and utilization of these assimilates in other cells argue quite convincingly in favor of the osmotic gradient. In addition, many measurements have been made of such gradients in plants, and they are not difficult to demonstrate. Figure 9-10 shows the results of one such study performed by Martin Zimmerman, of Harvard University. Although we could dwell on this topic at length, it has been investigated so thoroughly that we are quite safe in accepting it without further discussion.

9.3.2B The connecting system Here is the real crux of the application of Münch's model to the plant. To begin with, the phloem elements contain considerable quantities of cytoplasmic material. Indeed, recent electron micrographs from Germany indicate that the entire cell contents may consist of these viscous materials, which are (at least as we conceive of the situation) not likely to flow readily. Furthermore, phloem elements are connected by the sieve plates, which have only very minute perforations. Could a viscous liquid under pressure be forced to flow through such small holes *at the observed velocities?*

Some workers wondered if the phloem elements could even be capable of acting as the osmotic tubes required by the Münch model. There is considerable evidence, for example, that **lateral transport** from phloem tubes is a common phenomenon. How could these tubes contain liquid under pressure? It was shown, in a series of careful experiments, that phloem elements could be plasmolyzed. This settled the question. Sieve tube elements are enclosed in the usual plasma membrane, which is differentially permeable. Phloem cells do not leak. One might expect a slower lateral transport through plasmodesmata, however, since sieve tubes are just one part of the symplast, and other parts nearby may well draw nourishment from them.

The main problems do not concern the ability of phloem tubes to contain pressure but have to do with the reality of flow through the tubes. Can a pressure gradient be observed in the connecting system? Although it may *seem* unlikely, does bulk flow of materials actually occur through the sieve tubes?

The question of pressure in the phloem system is very difficult to answer in quantitative terms of gradients. How does one accurately measure the pressure in tubes as small as the phloem tubes? Yet it is not difficult to see that the phloem tubes do indeed contain liquid under pressure. There is a vast body of literature relating to studies on the phloem exudate which oozes out of phloem tubes when they are cut, or tapped in some other way. In many cases, this phenomenon is of commercial importance. When the bark of the sugar palm is cut, as much as 10 liters of sugary sap may drip out of the cut phloem tubes in a day. The Palmyra palm in India produces on the order of 11 liters of sap from cut phloem each day, and this sap consists of 10 percent sucrose and 0.25 percent mineral salts. Flow rates required to produce these quantities of sap range from 100 to 500 cm/hr. (These flow rates may be higher than normal, due to the release of pressure by cutting the phloem.)

In recent years, phloem exudates have been studied by the use of aphid and other insects' stylets. These insects selectively penetrate phloem tubes with their stylets. They normally rely on the pressure within the tube for their nourishment, since they are incapable of exerting active sucking motions. The sap is simply forced into their bodies, sometimes exuding through their bodies to the surface where it is further utilized by ants. The stylet may be cut from an insect which has penetrated the phloem tubes, and the insect body is then discarded. Sap will exude from the cut end of the stylet for long periods, on the order of several days. Again, movement through the phloem tubes must be occurring at rates of approximately 100 cm/hr to account for the flow from the stylet and, in the instances studied, this is equivalent to the contents of approximately 100 sieve tube elements per minute.

Most of these studies with insect stylets have not been directly concerned with the fact that the phloem elements contain liquid under pressure; rather this is taken for granted, and the investigations are directed toward an analysis of the material exuded. These analyses are interesting, but for our purpose we may summarize them by saying that phloem sap consists as a rule of a fairly concentrated solution of sucrose, although various other sugars are often involved. Reducing sugars are typically not present, but such substances as amino acids, hormones, or minerals in solution may be present in varying quantities.

We have answered in a positive way the most important part of the question relating to the connecting system. The phloem elements do indeed contain liquid under pressure, and this liquid is capable of flowing through the system. We may not understand how such viscous material can flow at such high rates and particularly through such small apertures as those in the sieve plate, but the fact that this does indeed occur seems to be beyond dispute.

9.3.2C The surrounding medium The apoplast also seems to be a reality. At any rate, assimilating cells in the leaves are in contact with phloem tubes, are never far from xylem elements, and are surrounded by moist cell walls. So our studies of anatomy make it possible, tentatively at least, to accept the third condition. So long as there is a surrounding solution of less negative water potential than that in the producing cells (the counterparts of the first osmometer of Münch's model), the system will tend to operate.

Either the consuming cells (second osmometer) must be capable of losing water in response to the reverse $\Delta\psi$ gradient (caused by utilization of sugars in respiration; conversion to starch, etc.), or else it must be capable in some other way of relieving the pressure. Growth of meristems or expanding fruit may provide as effective a mechanism for relieving the pressure as pressure release via the osmotic process.

9.3.2D Complications of pressure flow in the plant We have in principle, then, accepted the pressure-flow model of Münch as it applies to the plant. All of the conditions seem to have been met, and so pressure flow must operate. As mentioned earlier, this is not to say that some other mechanism such as cytoplasmic streaming cannot operate in the plant where conditions for its operation are also met. Nor is this to say that operation of mass flow in the plant proceeds as smoothly and as simply as it does in a laboratory model of the Münch system. The plant osmometers are far more intricate and complex, and the connecting system poses certain problems that still baffle us. Let us consider a few of the complications.

One test of the pressure-flow hypothesis is the extent to which materials other than sugar move with the sugar. We mentioned above that viruses, growth regulators, and tracers typically move in the assimilate stream even though direction of movement may be against their own concentration gradient. The conclusion has always been that sugars move from source to sink, and other materials follow along.

A number of recent tracer studies have shown, however, that the *rates* of movement of various substances may not all be the same. So one of the first complications encountered in applying Münch's model to the plant is that the nature of the channels influences the rates of flow. We can think of the channels as being somewhat similar to a chromatogram (Chapter 11). Some substances might be more soluble in phloem sap than others or more tightly adsorbed to the solid materials in the phloem tubes or their walls. Even in a mass flow, there might be a diffusional interaction of the moving materials with the matrix of the tubes. Companion cells, since they are universally present, may also play a role.

More than anything, we are concerned with the phenomenal rates of movement in the phloem and how these might relate to the requirement that the phloem cells be alive and metabolizing. Is some sort of metabolic activity responsible for the rate of movement? Crafts considers the possibility that the molecules move through the sieve tube plates in a superfluid condition. When some fluids, such as liquid helium, are cooled to extremely low temperatures, their molecules become arranged so that they will slide over each other with a virtual lack of friction. Viscosity reaches an extremely low value. Is it possible that the metabolic activity of the phloem and perhaps the companion cells some way orders the molecules as they go through the sieve plates so that they can move with less friction? Rates of flow through the sieve plates are so high[2] that skepticism about the concept of flow is easily

developed. Yet as we saw above, flow does indeed occur, and we must simply learn enough about the system to be able to account for it.

9.3.3 Electro-osmosis

It was suggested that materials move across the sieve plate in response to an electrical-potential gradient. This was supposedly established by the circulation of potassium ions, which were moved across the sieve plate actively, creating the electrical gradient. Perhaps at some distance from the center of the sieve tube pores (possibly even in the companion cells), they would move back, ready to be circulated again. This would account for the necessity for metabolism, and it might even account for the rates. The theory has been strongly criticized, however, on the basis that the required potentials would be too great. One English investigator calculated that enormous voltages, on the order of 100,000 volts, would have to be developed to make the system workable. He wryly commented that "we should be able to detect such voltages."

9.3.4 Translocation Via Tubules

R. Thaine in England suggested in 1963 that substances might move through the phloem in **tubules** connected from pore to pore through the sieve tube elements, as shown in Fig. 9-11. He claimed to have evidence for such structures, obtained by observation of living cells through the light microscope. Globular materials seem to be moving along in the strands, as illustrated in the figure. The mechanism was supposed to help solve the problem by reducing the friction involved, since the entire tubule moved as a unit rather than liquid flowing through the sieve tubes.

His theory has been sharply criticized, primarily on two grounds. *First*, it was suggested that the observations in the light microscope were basically artifacts. Movement was claimed

---

[2] If over-all velocities are on the order of 150 cm/hr, rates through the restricted area of the sieve plates might be at least 11 times as high, or on the order of 16 *meters* per hour (4.4 mm/sec).

by Thaine's critics to be due to cytoplasmic streaming in cells other than the phloem elements, cells that were out of focus and thus gave the impression of bright spots of light (the globules). *Second,* many workers wonder how the existence of a tubule could really cut down the friction. Wouldn't there be friction between the tubule and its surroundings? It is, however, too early to make a positive decision about Thaine's hypothesis.

9.3.5 Rapid Movement

C. D. Nelson in Canada has made measurements of extremely rapid movement of radioactive carbon in plant stems. By taking sections of a stem at different distances from the point of application of radioactive carbon dioxide to a leaf, he finds the usual logarithmic decrease in activity with distance, predicted by the mass flow hypothesis (considering adsorption and metabolic losses), but beyond this there is a discontinuity and a second peak of activity, indicating that some material has moved out at rates much faster than the sucrose (Fig. 9-12).

Nelson refers to this phenomenon as **rapid translocation** and speculates about its mechanism. He considers the possibility that material in a certain form (the substance involved in rapid translocation has not been identified) might move at some interface within the phloem system. This suggestion is based on the fact that interfacial movement is essentially the only movement known that could account for the extremely high rates observed, but interfaces in the anatomy of phloem cells are not readily apparent. Some of his critics have suggested that the material involved in rapid translocation is moving as a gas through intercellular spaces. This phenomenon is also known, particularly in aquatic plants, which have long, open, gas-filled tubes in their stems. The presence of such gas-filled tubes in the stems of soybeans, and other plants used by Nelson, is not so well established,

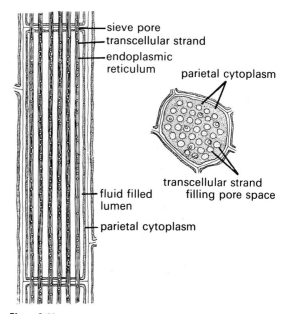

sieve pore
transcellular strand
endoplasmic reticulum
parietal cytoplasm
transcellular strand filling pore space
fluid filled lumen
parietal cytoplasm

Figure 9-11

An illustration of Thaine's proposal relating to phloem translocation via transcellular strands. (From R. Thaine, 1964, *Jour. Exptl. Botany* 15:470. Used by permission.)

however. Again, we must simply wait for the results of future studies.

9.3.6 The Importance of Accumulation and Metabolism

A number of investigators throughout the world (especially A. L. Kursanov in Moscow, Russia) are concerned with the metabolic changes that take place in the phloem tubes as materials move through them. The makeup of sugars, for example, can be seen to change with distance from the source.

There is good evidence that sucrose is moved into the beginning of the phloem translocation system by active processes of accumulation. It may also be removed at the sink end of the system by comparable processes. This could be very important in establishing the required osmotic gradient in the phloem system itself.

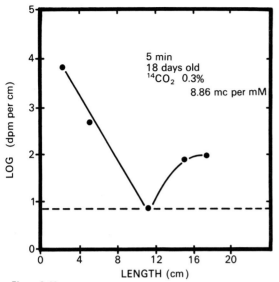

Figure 9-12
A figure indicating "rapid translocation." A single soybean leaf is allowed to photosynthesize in the presence of $^{14}CO_2$ for five minutes, after which samples are taken at different distances from the photosynthesizing leaf as indicated. The peak of radioactivity at about 16 cm illustrates the principle of rapid translocation. (After C. D. Nelson, 1963. In L. T. Evans (ed.), *Environmental Control of Plant Growth*, Academic Press, New York and London, p. 157. Used by permission.)

9.4 FURTHER PROBLEMS RELATING TO TRANSLOCATION

We are probably justified in concluding that cytoplasmic streaming is one mechanism for speeding the movement of dissolved substances in plants, but that this process is probably fairly well restricted to cells outside of the phloem distribution system, such as cortex cells in roots and stems. We might further conclude that the movement of dissolved materials is accelerated within the plant by pressure differences that come about according to the mechanism suggested by Münch. Here, however, the system involved is probably much more complex than Münch's laboratory model. Metabolism surely has something to do with maintaining the sieve tubes in a suitable condition, and a pumping action of some sort across the sieve plates cannot be completely excluded. It is even possible that certain substances move with extreme rapidity along interfaces in the system—interfaces unfortunately still awaiting our discovery.

There are still other complications and problems. We need to know more, for example, about why potassium, sulfur, nitrogen, and phosphorus move readily within the plant, while calcium, magnesium, iron, and cobalt are relatively immobile once they have arrived via the xylem transportation stream at the living cells. Various organic molecules show the same kind of **mobility series**. These problems will probably clear up as we increase our knowledge about the chemistry of plant tissue.

Such substances as phosphorus, nitrogen, and potassium are so mobile within the plant that they actually circulate. This has been clearly demonstrated, using radioactive tracers, in plants like sugar cane. Phosphorus in this plant has been shown to move from leaves to the roots (in the phloem) and back to the leaves (in the xylem) several times. Russian workers provide evidence that sugars can circulate in this way, and there is also reason to believe that other organic compounds such as maleic hydrazide and dalapon can circulate within the plant. It has long been known that certain minerals are exported before leaves drop from the tree in the fall. It is interesting that we now consider a **circulatory system**, primarily for inorganic ions, in the plant (one direction in the xylem the other in the phloem) after having looked for it with negative results in the 1600s shortly after the discovery of blood circulation in animals.

Certain compounds, particularly α-methoxyphenylacetic acid, may be applied to plant leaves and subsequently appear in the neighborhood of the roots in the soil solution. They may be further absorbed by neighboring plants. The **excretion** by the roots appears to be a metabolically controlled process.

SOME RATES OF MOVEMENT OF
SUBSTANCES IN PLANTS:

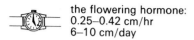 the flowering hormone:
0.25–0.42 cm/hr
6–10 cm/day

(tip of an *hour hand* about
1.0 to 1.5 cm long)

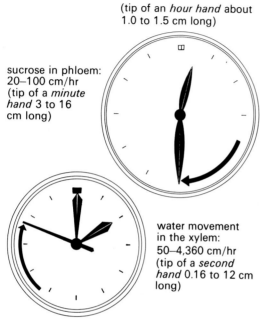

sucrose in phloem:
20–100 cm/hr
(tip of a *minute
hand* 3 to 16
cm long)

water movement
in the xylem:
50–4,360 cm/hr
(tip of a *second
hand* 0.16 to 12 cm
long)

Figure 9-13
An illustration of rates of movement of various substances.
The clocks are drawn to scale to show maximum rates of
movement as indicated. (Modified after F. B. Salisbury,
1966. In W. A. Jensen and L. G. Kavaljian (eds.), *Plant
Biology Today: Advances and Challenges*, Wadsworth Publishing Company, Inc., Belmont, California.)

Some substances, notably the auxins (plant
stem growth hormones), to be discussed in
Chapter 21, are translocated at physiological
concentrations only in *one direction* through
living tissue. In the stem, this is the direction
from the tip toward the base. There is some
evidence that sugars also exhibit this **polar transport** as they are being exported from the leaves.

As a matter of fact, translocation may, in
some as yet mysterious manner, be dependent
upon the presence of certain hormones. Kinetin,

for example (Chapter 21), seems to cause leaf
tissue to act as a center of accumulation for
nitrogen compounds. If one half of an excised
tobacco leaf is sprayed with kinetin, this not
only prevents the yellowing that results from a
loss of soluble nitrogen compounds from this
part of the leaf, but such compounds move into
the sprayed area from the rest of the leaf.

Light has an interesting influence on translocation. Not only is the most sugar exported
from photosynthesizing leaves during the light
period, but most of it goes to the stem tip or
other parts of the shoot rather than to the roots.
In the dark, on the other hand, translocation to
the root system is strongly favored over translocation to the stem tip.

There are further intriguing problems in the
field of translocation. Why does the flowering
hormone (Chapter 26) move so much more
slowly than anything else? Is this because it is a
large, virus-like molecule? How can we understand the movement of the excitation stimulus
in *Mimosa*, the sensitive plant? This stimulus
has been shown to be chemical in nature, and
yet its rate of movement through the plant is
extremely rapid and interesting compared to
the movement of other substances, such as
sugars. Figure 9-13 indicates the magnitude of
velocities observable in plant translocation.

9.5 SUMMARY OF WATER AND SOLUTES IN THE PLANT

Building upon the concepts and terminology
developed in Section I on water, solutions, and
surfaces in the plant, it is possible to condense
into a fairly limited space a rather comprehensive
picture of plant water relations, those primarily
physical events occurring within the plant.
Figure 9-14 summarizes some of these ideas.

The water potential of water in the xylem
system may be very low (negative) when the
water is under tension or somewhat positive

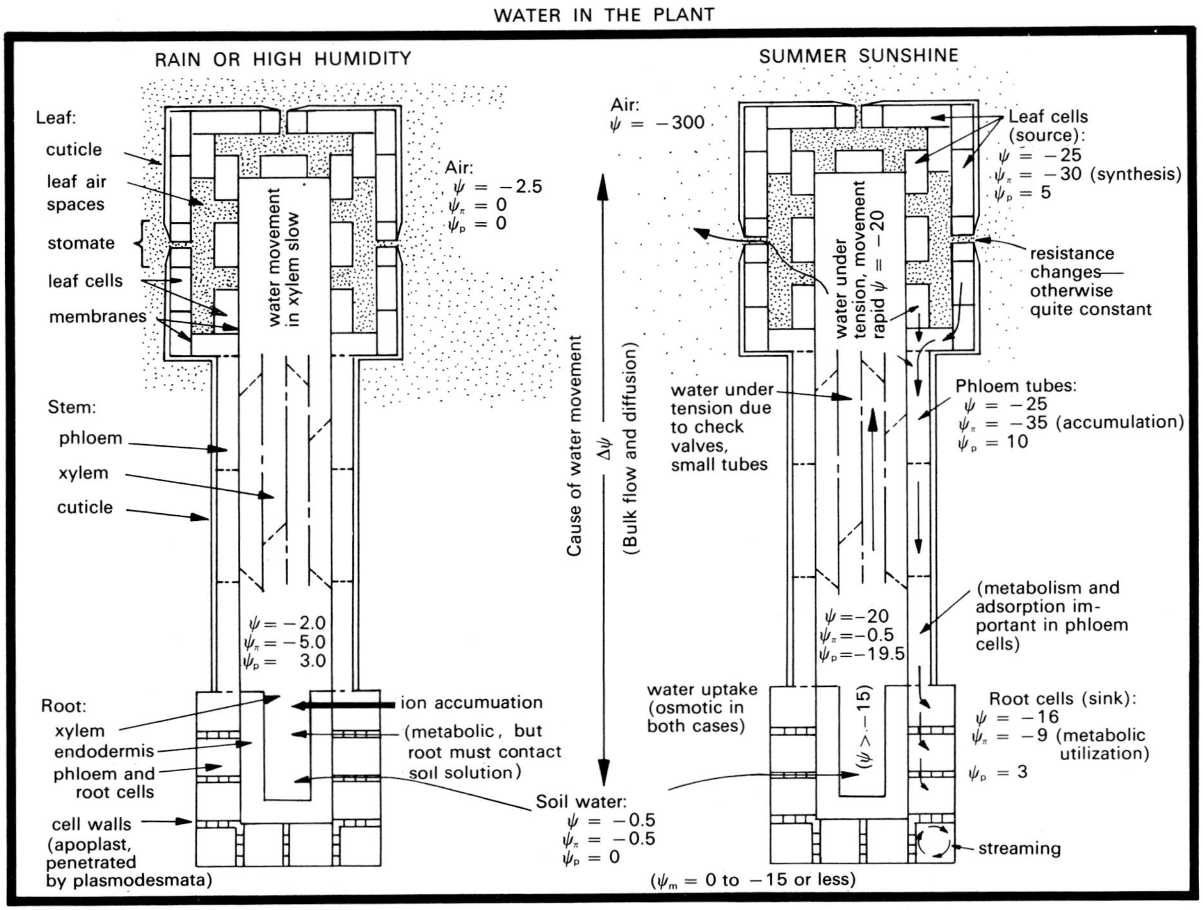

WATER IN THE PLANT

Figure 9-14
Summary of water and solutes in the plant.

when the plant is exhibiting root pressures, or perhaps during a rainstorm when the tops may actually be absorbing water. If the plant is not transpiring, water may be moving only very slowly in the xylem (in the general circulation system), but under conditions of high transpiration water may move very rapidly upward through the xylem. Pressure potential will be the principal component of water potential in the xylem, but since xylem sap contains small quantities of dissolved minerals, osmotic or solute potential will also contribute to water potential.

Since nonosmotic or active water uptake apparently does not operate in the plant (membranes are too permeable to water), root pressure must be accounted for by some mechanism similar to that proposed by Crafts and Broyer in which solutes from the soil are moved actively into the xylem (apoplast) system, allowing the plant, particularly because of the endodermal layer of cells with their Casparian strips, to operate as an osmometer. The nonosmotic uptake of ions and other substances is known to be an important process in plants, and it will always contribute to the osmotic relationships, as will any other mechanism that results in gradients in concentration of dissolved substances. The Donnan phenomenon is an example of such a mechanism.

When tall trees, or even shorter plants with high resistances to flow of xylem sap, are transpiring rapidly, water remains in a continuous column in the xylem tubes, probably because of the property of cohesion. Cohesive forces between water molecules are potentially very high, especially in tubes of small diameter. If cavitation does occur in one xylem element, the system as a whole maintains its integrity because of the check-valved compartmentalization afforded by the anatomy of the conducting xylem cells.

The degree of tension in the xylem elements will be a function of the rate of transpiration, the height of the system (the hydrostatic head), and the resistance to flow. In all cases of transfer of material within the plant, both diffusional and bulk flow and for both water and solutes, the rates of movement will be proportional to the driving force and inversely proportional to the resistance or directly proportional to its reciprocal, the permeability. The driving force in transpiration will be established thermodynamically by the energy balance between water in the soil and water in the air. The resistances within the plant will be for the most part relatively stable, but stomatal resistance may vary over a wide range, often in response to changing environment.

Movement of water into the roots will be in response to a more negative water potential inside the root than in the soil. Water may move in response to this gradient in the liquid state, both by diffusion of water molecules and by bulk flow in response to pressure gradients set up by the diffusional movement. Water could also quite conceivably move from soil to root in the vapor state, but the movement of solutes into the soil will be greatly influenced by whether water moves into the root as a liquid or as a vapor. In any case, movement of solutes into the root may be influenced by the anatomy and the metabolism of the root itself. Movement of both water and solutes may occur primarily through the apoplast (the free space) of the root tissue, although movement into the symplast will also be important. Individual cells will accumulate relatively high concentrations of solutes into their vacuoles, resulting in the negative water potentials essential to maintain turgidity. Under any conditions, if water is to enter the root, water potentials inside (in the apoplast as well as the vacuoles) must be more negative than water potentials in the soil. Since the permanent wilting point of the soil is approximately -15 bars, water potentials within the root must approach -15 bars as the soil dries out if the plant is to obtain water. If the matric potential of the soil becomes more negative than −15 bars, then water potentials within the plant will also drop below, −15 bars, and the plant will wilt. In wilting, water moves out of the normally turgid cells into the air or into the apoplast and finally into the air, or possibly even to a certain extent into the soil. The effects of water tensions more negative than −15 bars on plant growth and metabolism may be highly significant, although in tall trees under conditions of high transpiration, water potentials in the xylem may become more negative than −15 bars.

When a plant does not wilt, the implication is that the water potential of leaf and other living cells is more negative than the water potential of the xylem (apoplast). So if a minimum water potential of cells, due primarily to the osmotic component, is about −30 bars, then tensions in the xylem of a turgid plant will never result in water potentials more negative than about −30 bars. Of course, these generalizations may not hold in such special cases as halophytes (plants, such as the mangrove, adapted to soil solutions with a high salt content).

For the phloem system to operate according to the model of Münch, pressures within the system must always be positive, at least in the vicinity of the assimilate source. Hence the water potential of phloem tubes near the source must be more negative than the surrounding apoplast. This will be due to an accumulation of solutes (primarily sugars) in these cells, and this accumulation may be an active one, dependent upon metabolism. For water to move out of the phloem system near the assimilate sink, water potential within the cells must be less negative

than in the surrounding apoplast. This will be partially due to pressure transferred through the phloem system from sieve tubes near the source, but it will also be due to a lower solute concentration in the cells near the sink. Some solute will be lost in the transport system along the way, due to metabolism and movement to nearby living cells (also sinks), but a considerable portion will be lost to the sink itself. The picture is probably complicated somewhat by interactions between the moving solutes and the sieve tubes. Adsorption may play a role, and metabolic changes could also be important. In the symplast system other than mature phloem tubes, movement of solutes may often be accelerated by cytoplasmic streaming.

As in the case of the leaf mesophyll cells and all cells responsible for the turgid form of a plant, a functioning phloem transport system must be able to withdraw water from the apoplast even when water potentials in the apoplast are very negative due to tensions caused by transpiration. If tensions become so high that the phloem system can no longer absorb water from the apoplast, then the sieve tubes themselves might "wilt," and the system would cease to function in transport. On the other hand, if the xylem system is under pressure (root pressure), then it might seem that water would not tend to move out of the phloem system in the roots (at the root sink). But the pressure in the xylem would also be transferred to the apoplast near the source and hence into the phloem system near the source. Thus, the phloem system should operate under all conditions except wilting severe enough to cause a loss of water and pressure from phloem tubes near the source.

SECTION TWO

Plant Biochemistry

10

Mineral Nutrition of Plants

If plants are heated to approximately 100°C for several hours, the water is driven off, and the remainder represents the so-called dry matter of the plant. The dry weights of various plants and plant parts vary greatly, ranging from some 90 percent of the original fresh weight of the tissue in the case of dormant seeds to near 5 percent in very succulent tissues. An average of approximately 20 percent of the total fresh weight of many herbaceous plants is dry matter.

Much of this dry material consists of organic compounds, largely carbohydrates, proteins, amino acids, organic acids, and lipids. Also present are several mineral elements (inorganic ions), many of which are essential to the growth of the plant. These elements and their functions in plants are discussed in the present chapter. The following eight chapters are devoted to discussions of the kinds and functions of organic molecules.

10.1 EARLY STUDIES IN PLANT NUTRITION

As early as the third century, B.C., Aristotle, observing plants growing in soil, suggested that soil is the material of which plants are made. His views were largely accepted until the results of a now-famous experiment by Jan Baptista van Helmont (1577–1644) became available. This work was published by van Helmont's son in 1684. Van Helmont planted a small willow tree weighing five pounds in 200 pounds of dry soil and patiently watered it with rain water for five years, during which it grew to a final weight of 169 pounds. The soil weighed only two ounces less than at the start of the experiment, and so he logically, but erroneously, concluded that his tree was made from water. At that time nothing was known of the important role of atmospheric carbon dioxide in plant nutrition (or even of the existence of this gas), nor of the plant's absorption of various elements from the soil. We now know that van Helmont's willow was indeed made partly from water, since essentially all of the hydrogen and some of the oxygen in the plant is provided by this molecule, and that the soil and the air also contributed to its weight.

Slightly later (1699), in England, John Woodward performed an experiment indicating that the soil may contribute in a direct way to the weight of a plant. He performed perhaps the first recorded experiment in which plants were grown with their roots immersed in water. His mint plants survived for some time growing only in rain water, but they grew better in water from the Thames River, and best in a watery extract of soil. He therefore disagreed with van Helmont and suggested that plants are composed of soil.

In 1727, Stephen Hales correctly suggested that plants obtain part of their nourishment from the air, but it was not until the quantitative work of N. T. deSaussure in 1804 that people became aware of the true role of the soil in plant growth. De Saussure grew plants in distilled water and in dilute salt solutions. He found that those not given salts did not gain appreciably in ash (inorganic) content, but that the others did. His work also first showed the need for nitrate salts in the culture solution.

With the advancement of chemistry in the 1800s, agricultural chemists such as von Liebig in Germany, Boussingault in France, and Lawes and Gilbert in England systematically discovered the necessary supplements to agricultural soils necessary to maintain good growth. At this time, European plant physiologists, such as Julius Sachs and W. Knop, taking advantage of the technique of growing plants in aqueous solutions in the absence of soil, were discovering some of the essential elements. Other essential elements were discovered from outgrowths of their experiments, and the proper concentrations of these elements were determined for various plants.

10.2   THE ELEMENTAL COMPOSITION OF PLANTS

Although soils are composed largely of oxygen, silicon, and aluminum, plants growing in soil by no means reflect this composition. Carbon and oxygen, followed by hydrogen, make up the bulk of the dry weight of plants. These elements are obtained from carbon dioxide and water. Nitrogen ranks next in quantitative importance, followed by such elements as potassium, calcium, magnesium, phosphorus, sulfur, and silicon, all of which are absorbed from the soil.

At least 60 elements have been found in various plants, compared to the total of 92 known natural elements. It is, in fact, likely that plant roots will absorb to some extent from the surrounding solution any element existing in a soluble form. Nevertheless, as pointed out in Chapter 8, plants do have the partial ability to select the rate at which they absorb various ions, so that absorption is usually not in direct proportion to nutrient availability. Furthermore, different species vary in their ability to select particular ions. Table 10-1 shows the varying contents of five elements in sunflower, bean, wheat, and barley plants all grown on the same soil. In general, members of the grass family seem to take up more potassium and less calcium than do legumes. This differential absorption may lead to potassium deficiency and poor yields of legumes growing in pastures together with grasses. Yields of these legumes can be improved by adding potassium fertilizers to soils low in potassium.

10.2.1   Criteria for Essentiality

In 1939, two American plant physiologists, Daniel Arnon and Perry Stout, made an important contribution to mineral nutrition studies by introducing three criteria of essentiality by which elements may be judged. These critera are as follows: *First*, the element must be essential for normal growth or reproduction, neither of which can occur in its complete absence. *Second*, the requirement must be specific and cannot be replaced by substituting some other element. *Third*, the element must be acting directly inside the plant and not simply causing some other element to be more readily available or simply antagonizing a toxic effect of another element.

Because of the trace amounts of certain elements needed for plant growth, it is difficult to demonstrate positively that an element is not essential. Experimenters thus sometimes state that if an element is necessary it is required only at concentrations less than a particular value, a

TABLE 10-1

PERCENTAGE OF CALCIUM, POTASSIUM, MAGNESIUM, NITROGEN, AND PHOSPHORUS IN THE TOPS OF SEVERAL SPECIES OF PLANTS GROWN IN A GREENHOUSE IN AN ALBERTA LOAM SOIL[a]

Species	Percent of dry weight				
	Ca	K	Mg	N	P
sunflower	1.68	3.47	0.730	1.47	0.080
bean	1.46	1.19	0.570	1.48	0.053
wheat	0.46	4.16	0.225	2.26	0.058
barley	0.68	4.04	0.292	1.94	0.125

[a] Data of Newton, *Soil Science*, 26:86, 1928.

value determined by the sensitivity limits of their detecting instruments. For example, it was reported that if silicon is essential for the growth of tomatoes, the amounts needed are less than 0.2 μg per gram of dry plant tissue. With regard to the second criterion, several examples are known in which nonessential elements can partially satisfy the need for one that is essential. The occasional partial replacement of potassium by sodium, calcium by strontium, molybdenum by vanadium, and chlorine by bromine are examples illustrating this. Direct action of an element inside the plant is usually demonstrated by the discovery of an essential metabolic process to which the element is necessary or at least stimulatory. For many elements several such processes are known.

10.2.2 Elements Believed Essential for All Higher Plants

In spite of the relatively large number of elements available in soils, only approximately 16 are thought to be actually essential to the growth of most plants. Table 10-2 lists these 16 elements, the chemical forms most commonly available to plants, the concentration in the plant considered adequate, and the number of

atoms of each element needed compared to molybdenum. They are arbitrarily divided into the **macronutrients**, those needed in relatively large quantities, and the **micronutrients**, those needed in considerably smaller amounts.

The macronutrients include carbon, hydrogen, oxygen, nitrogen, phosphorus, calcium, sulfur, potassium, and magnesium. The micronutrients include chlorine, iron, manganese, boron, zinc, copper, and molybdenum.

Actually there is no sharp distinction between macro- and micronutrients. Differences between required amounts of some of the elements within either group are larger than the difference between the groups.

10.2.3 Other Elements

Although most higher plants are thought to require only those elements mentioned in Table 10-2, certain species may need others. The fact is that the mineral nutrient requirements of various members of the plant kingdom differ to some extent, both qualitatively (the kinds needed) and quantitatively (the optimal amounts). For example, certain desert species such as *Atriplex vesicaria*, accustomed to growing in salty soils of Australia, and *Halogeton glomeratus*, common on certain soils of the western United States, apparently require sodium; and many other plants, such as turnips, beets, sugar beets, and celery, grow better in the presence of sodium and may actually require it. Some blue-green algae also seem to require this element.

Silicon is another element that is probably present in all plants but is particularly abundant in monocots, especially members of the grass family. *Equisetum* species also contain large amounts of silicon. The available form in soils is primarily undissociated silicic acid (H_4SiO_4). Small quantities of silicon stimulate the growth of several plants and may even prove to be essential for some. For certain marine algae (diatoms), which are surrounded by a silicious

TABLE 10-2

ELEMENTS ESSENTIAL FOR MOST HIGHER PLANTS AND INTERNAL CONCENTRATIONS CONSIDERED ADEQUATE[a]

Element	Chemical symbol	Form available to plants[b]	Atomic wt	Concentration in dry tissue		Relative no. of atoms compared to molybdenum
				ppm	percent	
Molybdenum	Mo	$MoO_4^=$	95.95	0.1	0.00001	1
Copper	Cu	Cu^+, **Cu^{++}**	63.54	6	0.0006	100
Zinc	Zn	Zn^{++}	65.38	20	0.0020	300
Manganese	Mn	Mn^{++}	54.94	50	0.0050	1,000
Iron	Fe	Fe^{+++}, Fe^{++}	55.85	100	0.010	2,000
Boron	B	**$BO_3^=$**, $B_4O_7^=$	10.82	20	0.002	2,000
Chlorine	Cl	Cl^-	35.46	100	0.010	3,000
Sulfur	S	$SO_4^=$	32.07	1,000	0.1	30,000
Phosphorus	P	**$H_2PO_4^-$**, $HPO_4^=$	30.98	2,000	0.2	60,000
Magnesium	Mg	Mg^{++}	24.32	2,000	0.2	80,000
Calcium	Ca	Ca^{++}	40.08	5,000	0.5	125,000
Potassium	K	K^+	39.10	10,000	1.0	250,000
Nitrogen	N	**NO_3^-**, NH_4^+	14.01	15,000	1.5	1,000,000
Oxygen	O	O_2, H_2O	16.00	450,000	45	30,000,000
Carbon	C	CO_2	12.01	450,000	45	35,000,000
Hydrogen	H	H_2O	1.01	60,000	6	60,000,000

[a] Modified after P. R. Stout, *Proc. 9th Ann. Calif. Fertilizer Conf.*, pp. 21–23, 1961.
[b] If one of two forms is more common than the other, this is indicated by boldface type.

wall, or sheath, silicon is required. Silicon, though not essential to rice, increases the yields of thick stands, primarily because it makes the straw stiffer, and the plants thus grow more erectly.

Aluminum, like silicon, is found in most plants, and in concentrations of a few mg per liter (parts per million, ppm) it stimulates the growth of some species. Definite demonstrations that it is essential to any plant have not been made.

Cobalt is a necessary element for the growth of the blue-green algae, but it has not been shown to be essential for other algae or for higher plants, except that it is required by certain legumes to fix atmospheric nitrogen. Here, however, the ion is necessary to the symbiotic bacteria present in the nodules associated with the roots (see Chapter 16), and if the plants are provided with suitable forms of nitrogen (such as nitrate), they grow well without cobalt. For the bacteria, cobalt is essential because it is a part of vitamin B_{12}. Since there are scattered reports that vitamin B_{12} is also found in certain higher plants, it is possible that cobalt in extremely low concentrations will prove essential to these species.

Several authors have reported that a few other elements are essential for certain species. Vanadium, for example, is apparently required by one species of green algae, *Scenedesmus obliquus*, and it can partially substitute for molybdenum in certain bacteria. Its function in *Scenedesmus* is not understood, and other plants grow well without detectable amounts of vanadium.

In addition to the 16 elements listed in Table 10-2, higher animals require iodine, sodium, cobalt, and selenium. Iodine functions as a component of the hormone thyroxine and is a part of a very few amino acids. Iodine-containing amino acids exist in certain higher plants, yet there is no evidence that these are essential to their growth.

Selenium is readily absorbed by certain plants in the genera *Astragalus, Stanleya, Oonopsis,* and *Xylorrhiza,* but it is taken up poorly by others growing on the same soils. Growth of some species in the above genera is stimulated by selenium, and they thus serve as valuable indicators of seleniferous soils. They are also of importance because, especially with *Astragalus* species, they absorb so much selenium that they become toxic to livestock. The toxic forms of selenium are apparently organic compounds, including certain amino acids, in which this element has replaced the sulfur normally present (see Chapter 11).

10.3 METHODS OF STUDYING PLANT NUTRITION

10.3.1 Hydroponic Plant Growth

The German plant physiologists Julius Sachs and W. Knop recognized during the middle of the 19th century the desirability of performing nutritional studies in as well-defined a medium as possible. Most elements could not be clearly demonstrated as essential for plants grown in a medium as complex and heterogeneous as the soil. Furthermore, Sachs and Knop also desired to establish the amounts of the elements needed. They therefore grew their plants by immersing the roots in an aqueous nutrient solution, the chemical composition of which could be largely controlled. Growth of plants in this way is often called hydroponic culture, and an example is shown in Fig. 10-1. F. C. Steward later found that many plants grow far better in such solutions if oxygen is provided to the roots by forcing

air bubbles through the solutions, as in Fig. 10-1.

Sachs and Knop established the essentiality of most of the macronutrients such as nitrogen, potassium, phosphorus, calcium, magnesium, and sulfur, and also discovered concentrations that are satisfactory, although not optimal, for growing many plants. Knop's solution, reported about 1865, is given in Table 10-3, along with a more modern nutrient solution containing essential micronutrients not known to those workers. Some of these solutions are better adjusted to certain plants than to others, although it is interesting that the balance of nutrients optimal for one species of crop plant will usually be suitable, if not optimal, for others.

The science of botany advanced in the United States along with the development of other sciences, and American plant physiologists became interested in plant nutrition, especially in the years following 1900. Much work was performed at Rutgers University by John Shive and W. R. Robbins, and by D. R. Hoagland, Daniel Arnon, A. L. Somner, and Perry Stout in California. These men and others, such as E. J. Hewitt in England, improved the nutrient formulas given by Sachs and Knop and, in addition, discovered some of the other elements essential for plants. Many of their experiments were performed using the hydroponic technique.

Although the composition of the nutrient medium can best be defined with solution culture, there are certain disadvantages to this technique. The need for aeration has already been mentioned, and it is usually necessary to replace the solutions every few days, or sometimes even daily, because the composition changes as certain ions are more rapidly absorbed than others. This preferential uptake also causes changes in pH, as discussed in Chapter 8. For example, the rapid uptake of nitrate ions is commonly associated with a release by the plant of bicarbonate or hydroxyl ions, both of which cause an increase in pH of most unbuffered nutrient solutions. Such pH increases decrease the availability of certain ions, such as iron and zinc, and should be prevented. Hydroponic solutions must usually be kept dark to prevent growth of algae often present. Solutions also present a minor problem in plant support.

10.3.2 Sand Culture

To avoid some of the disadvantages of hydroponic solution cultures, many experimenters have used **washed quartz sand** or other supporting material, such as **perlite**, which is reasonably inert. These materials solve the problems of plant support, root aeration, and the need for darkness, but difficulties sometimes arise because both already contain some essential nutrients in low amounts. The use of sand is therefore sometimes unsatisfactory when micronutrients are to be studied. Perlite is probably far less inert than good grades of washed white quartz sand but can be used in certain macronutrient experiments. Nutrient solutions are simply poured on the top of these media at suitable intervals and in amounts that insure the leaching out of the old solution, or they are allowed to drip continuously onto the surface at a proper rate. With a proper system, solutions can be supplied automatically at suitable intervals by subirrigation.

10.3.3 Special Techniques Used in Micronutrient Studies

10.3.3A Purification of salts
Early mineral nutritionists like Sachs and Knop were not aware of most of the micronutrients needed by plants. This was probably because these elements were present as contaminants in the salts used to provide the macronutrients. Later, as commercial salts became more highly purified and as the investigators realized the need

Figure 10-1

One method of growing plants in solution culture. The jar or crock in which the roots are immersed should be large compared to the volume of roots so that the solution composition does not change too rapidly. Note aeration device to the right of roots. Before the photograph was taken, the glass jar had been wrapped with aluminum foil to exclude light. (Plant grown by B. W. Poovaiah. Photo by F. B. Salisbury.)

to purify them, other elements were found to be essential.

The concentration in ppm of micronutrients in the nutrient solution suitable for many plants grown hydroponically lie, depending upon the species, within the following ranges: Fe (0.5 to 5.0), Mn (0.1 to 0.5), B (0.1 to 1.0), Zn (0.02 to 0.2), Cu (0.01 to 0.05), and Mo (0.01 to 0.05). Higher concentrations of these are often toxic. The range for chloride has not been as well

TABLE 10-3

COMPOSITION OF KNOP'S NUTRIENT SOLUTION COMPARED TO THAT OF A MORE MODERN SOLUTION

Knop's solution		Evans's[a] modification of Shive's solution		
Salt	Molarity	Salt	Molarity	ppm
$Ca(NO_3) \cdot 4 H_2O$	0.003	$Ca(NO_3)_2 \cdot 4 H_2O$	0.005	
KNO_3	0.002	K_2SO_4	0.0025	
KH_2PO_4	0.0015	KH_2PO_4	0.0005	
$MgSO_4 \cdot 7 H_2O$	0.0008	$MgSO_4 \cdot 7 H_2O$	0.002	
$FePO_4$	trace	KCL		9.0 Cl
		Fe-versenate		0.5 Fe
		$MnSO_4$		0.25 Mn
		H_3BO_3		0.25 B
		$ZnSO_4$		0.25 Zn
		$CuSO_4$		0.02 Cu
		Na_2MoO_4		0.02 Mo

[a] From H. A. Evans and A. Nason, *Plant Physiology* 28:233–254, 1953.

established, but approximately 5 ppm are required for the tomato and are suitable for other plants, too. It is difficult to remove such traces of some of these elements from the necessary salts in which they are contaminants, but many techniques are partially successful. These include the preferential adsorption of micronutrient cations on insoluble materials such as calcium carbonate (from which the remaining soluble salts can be removed by filtration), the formation of compounds with the micronutrient ions and molecules such as diphenylthiocarbazone followed by removal of the compounds with solvents such as carbon tetrachloride or chloroform, and the selective precipitation of micronutrients with insoluble materials such as hydroxyquinoline.

10.3.3B Purification of water Once the salts are purified it is essential to dissolve them in water free of undesirable elements. It is necessary to distill ordinary tap water before use, and a glass still without exposed metal parts is usually necessary to prevent zinc and copper contamination. Ion-exchange resins are also often used, the

water being passed first through a resin that will adsorb cations and exchange hydrogen ions for these and then through an anion-exchange resin to remove contaminating anions, such as molybdate, borate, and chloride. Hydroxyl ions are exchanged for these anions.

10.3.3C Contamination by containers and by the atmosphere Most experiments can be safely conducted in containers made of ordinary borosilicate glass, but such containers provide amounts of boron which render them useless in many boron nutrition studies. In this case polyethylene beakers or buckets can be used, but in one experiment these were found to supply sufficient zinc for plant growth. Pyrex glass containers are usually suitable.

Atmospheric dust settling on the solutions or on the plants themselves contains certain elements and may preclude the appearance of deficiency symptoms. This occurred in the case of chloride and, with the contribution of chloride from the experimenter's fingers, was apparently sufficient to prevent recognition of its essential role until 1953.

10.3.3D Seed contamination Certain of such micronutrient elements as copper, molybdenum, and zinc cannot be demonstrated as essential for some plants because, even if these nutrients are not provided, the seeds from which the plants grow provide sufficient amounts for the entire growth and reproductive period. In these cases the deficiencies can be observed more easily if seeds taken from parents grown without the added elements are used. In general, plants having large seeds are able to supply elements in greater quantities to the developing seedlings than can those having small seeds.

10.3.4 Chelating Agents

10.3.4A Properties and absorption The micronutrient cations iron, zinc, and copper, are relatively insoluble in nutrient solutions when provided as common inorganic salts. This insolubility is especially marked if the *pH* is held above 5, since cations react with hydroxyl ions, precipitating out the hydrous metal oxides. An example in which the ferric form of iron yields the reddish-brown oxide (rust) is shown in reaction (R10-1).

$$2Fe^{+3} + 6OH^- \longrightarrow 2Fe(OH)_3$$
$$\longrightarrow Fe_2O_3 \cdot 3H_2O \quad (R10\text{-}1)$$

Because of these undesirable reactions, the metals, especially iron, are often added as metal **chelates** (from the Greek, clawlike). A chelate or **complex ion** is the rather stable product formed when certain atoms in an organic chelating agent (**ligand**) donate electrons to the metal cation. Negatively charged carboxyl groups and many nitrogen atoms possess available electrons that can be shared in this way. One of the best known synthetic ligands provides both carboxyl groups and nitrogen atoms. This is **ethylene-diamine-tetraacetic** acid, abbreviated **EDTA**. The structure of the zinc-EDTA chelate is shown in Fig. 10-2.

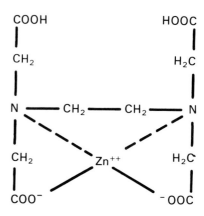

Figure 10-2
The zinc-EDTA chelate.

Ligands such as EDTA were first used in nutrition studies about 1951 and are now commonly used to prevent or correct deficiency symptoms of iron in many parts of the western United States where the high *pH* of the calcareous soils renders iron unavailable to some species. The same problem occurs in certain western areas with zinc, and studies indicate that chelating agents can often correct these deficiencies. In the acid soils of parts of the eastern United States, especially Florida, iron deficiency can result from the antagonistic effect of the high amount of copper sometimes present. Here, too, EDTA is added to prevent iron deficiencies in certain sensitive fruit trees and other crops.

Good chelating agents have at least two important properties. *First*, they should be resistant to microbial attack in the soil, and, *second*, they should form stable chelates with the micronutrient ions and not with more abundant competitive cations such as calcium or magnesium. EDTA has a high affinity for calcium ions and is thus a poor chelating agent for calcareous soils. Here it has been replaced with Fe-EDDHA, ethylenediamine di(*o*-

hydroxyphenyl acetic acid), a much better source of iron for calcareous soils. Several other synthetic ligands are used for certain purposes.

Naturally occurring chelates of micronutrient cations also exist in the soil, maintaining higher availability of these elements than would otherwise be the case. Although the chelating agents have not yet been identified, it is suspected that several compounds present in the organic matter are capable of this, including certain proteins, amino acids, organic acids, flavonoids, purines, and even riboflavin. Sometimes these chelating agents apparently exist in such high concentrations, and the element is held so firmly, that it is not released for uptake by the plant roots. Many such chelates are also insoluble. This is thought to be involved in the copper deficiencies commonly occurring in peat and muck soils, for example.

It is believed that chelating agents usually function as effective micronutrient sources simply by keeping the elements in solution, yet releasing part of them at or near the root surface. Occasionally the intact metal chelate is probably absorbed, as evidenced by the characteristic color of the chelate (often reddish) noted in the plant. The free ligand itself is usually colorless.

10.3.4B Chelates in the plant The absorption of naturally occurring or synthetic soil chelating agents is not necessary to maintain adequate solubility of micronutrient metals inside the plant. Instead, the plant contains ligands that prevent precipitation inside the xylem or in the vacuoles and cytoplasm of living cells. Amino acids, organic acids, or proteins are probably the predominant chelating agents, but little direct evidence of this is available. Lee Tiffin and John Brown at Beltsville, Maryland, found most of the iron in the xylem of soybeans to be present as chelates of malic acid and malonic acid, even though iron had been supplied to the roots as a synthetic chelate. In

tobacco xylem an unknown compound of higher molecular weight was complexed with the iron, indicating that plants may differ somewhat with respect to their natural ligands.

It is likely that all metal ions except the monovalent sodium and potassium are present to some extent as chelates inside plant cells. Monovalent cations do not form stable chelates, but even these are known to be present partially combined with proteins by electrostatic attraction. Iron and magnesium are important to plants partly because they are tightly chelated in the cytochrome pigments and photosynthetic chlorophyll pigments, respectively. In addition, both these and other essential divalent cations are necessary because of their ability to unite simultaneously with enzymes or substrates upon which enzymes act, allowing catalysis (see Chapter 11).

10.4 FACTORS AFFECTING NUTRIENT UPTAKE BY ROOTS

10.4.1 Temperature

The rate of salt absorption by plants increases with temperature from the melting point of water up to about 40°C, where it then begins to decrease (Fig. 10-3). The slow growth of plants in cold soils in the spring is partly due to the limited rate of ion uptake under these conditions. Increased absorption with rising temperatures results to some extent from the increased rate of diffusion of salts to the roots and also from the increased respiration of the plants at higher temperatures. The active absorption of elements requires cellular respiration, as discussed in Chapter 8.

Ion accumulation is reduced at temperatures above approximately 40°C. This is likely because such high temperatures interfere with respiration and perhaps also because the cell membranes become more permeable to the passive leakage of salts at high temperatures, so

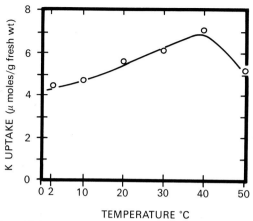

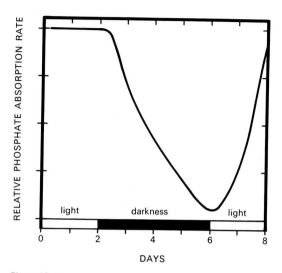

Figure 10-3

Influence of temperature upon potassium absorption by washed slices of carrot roots. Absorption periods were for 30 minutes at each temperature. The decrease at 50°C is probably due to enzyme inactivation. (From J. F. Sutcliffe, 1902, *Mineral Salts Absorption in Plants*, Pergamon Press, Oxford, London, New York, Paris, p. 48. Used by permission.)

Figure 10-4

Rates of absorption of phosphate by corn plants during successive periods of light and darkness. (Redrawn from T. Alberda, 1948, *Rec. Trav. Bot. Neer.* 41:541–601.)

that the net rate of accumulation then becomes less. It appears that temperature also affects the relative ratio of cations to anions absorbed. Various studies indicate that at low temperatures the uptake of anions is inhibited more than that of cations, although the reason for this is not clear.

10.4.2 Light

Although light striking roots has little direct effect on solute absorption, plants grown under high light intensities often absorb ions faster than those grown under weak light (Fig. 10-4). This is probably because photosynthesis provides sugars that are translocated to the roots, respired there, and the energy obtained used in active ion uptake. However, light also has a more direct effect on salt absorption by certain algae and other water plants. Here the energy from the light is converted into chemical forms, such as ATP, and these aid in ion uptake without the intervention of respiration.

10.4.3 Aeration

As first shown by Steward (1932), plant roots require oxygen in order to absorb appreciable quantities of salts. This is one reason that plant growth is slow in waterlogged or otherwise poorly aerated soils or in nonaerated nutrient solutions. In addition, it is likely that the accumulation of carbon dioxide (bicarbonate ions) in such soils is somewhat toxic to the roots, since it interferes with respiration and ion uptake.

Many studies relating salt uptake and oxygen content were performed with excised roots. The results indicate that the oxygen content of the soil need not be nearly as high as it is in the atmosphere surrounding the shoot (approximately 21 percent by volume) for rapid salt uptake to occur. Figure 10-5 shows that rice and barley roots absorbed potassium maximally when they were aerated with a gas stream containing only 2–3 percent oxygen. Lower concentrations affected the absorbing capacity of barley roots more than that of rice roots. This is to be expected, since rice commonly grows under almost anaerobic conditions.

10.4.4 pH

Plant growth is known to occur over at least the range of pH 4 to 9. Many species grow best when the pH of the soil or nutrient solution lies in the range 5 to 7, while others do very well at one of the extremes. Cranberries, for example, are almost always found in acid bogs, while certain desert species can compete favorably only if the soil pH is quite alkaline.

The pH affects salt absorption in various ways. At a low pH the hydrogen ions usually decrease the absorption of cations, while anion absorption may be stimulated. The apparent reason for this is that hydrogen ions compete with cations for uptake sites, while hydroxyl or bicarbonate ions present at a higher pH compete with anions such as nitrate, chloride, and phosphate. Such effects of pH on the absorption of potassium chloride are shown in Fig. 10-6.

The pH also strongly influences the uptake of phosphate because it influences the ionic charge. The predominant ionic forms are $H_2PO_4^-$ at low pH values, an equal mixture of $H_2PO_4^-$ and $HPO_4^=$ at pH 6.8, $HPO_4^=$ at values above but close to 6.8, and finally $PO_4^{\equiv}$ at higher pH values. As mentioned in Chapter 8, monovalent forms are usually absorbed more readily than divalent, and divalent faster than trivalent. This is certainly true for phosphate, and the inability of some plants to grow at a high pH may be due to a limited rate of phosphorus absorption. The poor availability of iron and certain other micronutrients is probably also involved in the slow growth of plants at a high pH.

10.4.5 The Nutrient Status of the Plant

Plant roots that already contain sufficient amounts of a particular element generally can-

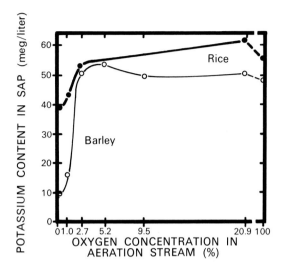

Figure 10-5

Influence of oxygen content in gas mixture used to aerate nutrient solutions upon potassium absorption by excised rice and barley roots. Plants were grown 4 weeks in a complete nutrient solution, and the roots were then excised and kept 24 hours in 5 mM KBr solutions aerated with various mixtures of oxygen and nitrogen. (Data of J. Vlamis, 1944, *Plant Physiol.* 19:38. Used by permission.)

not absorb this element as fast as can roots moderately deficient in it. This is true for several elements, and the explanation, when understood, will probably prove to be complex. Apparently, roots containing high amounts of salts do not simply let these leak out, reducing the observed net uptake. Rather, the effect is more directly on the active uptake mechanism.

Sometimes the abundance of one ion in the plant may influence the uptake of another. For example, plants already containing adequate amounts of nitrogen are subsequently able to absorb more phosphate and sulfate per unit weight of root tissue than are others. Similarly, plants relatively high in phosphate can more easily absorb nitrogen. These interactions may occur because nitrogen and phosphate and nitrogen and sulfate become essential parts of the same organic molecules inside plants, so that the one aids the absorption of another by allowing its more rapid incorporation into protoplasm.

10.4.6 Growth

Mature cells that have stopped growing are not able to accumulate ions as well as are rapidly dividing and growing cells. Young cells actively synthesizing protein create binding sites for such cations as magnesium, iron, calcium, and potassium; while such ions as phosphate, nitrate, and sulfate are rapidly changed into other compounds and also become a part of the increasing protoplasm. This difference is undoubtedly partly responsible for the relation of growth and solute uptake, although other factors may also be involved. It has been suggested, for example, that solute uptake into mature cells not synthesizing protein is decreased because the needed carrier molecules are not being synthesized.

10.5 ANATOMICAL RELATIONS OF NUTRIENT ABSORPTION AND THE INFLUENCE OF WATER ABSORPTION

Early experimenters tracing processes with radioactive elements found that the meristematic region of plant roots just back of the rootcap accumulated ions more effectively than did older regions where cell elongation and differentiation were occurring or were complete. The accumulation of salts near the root tips is probably due to a high respiratory activity in this region and to the absence of conducting xylem to transport the salts away.

Herman Wiebe and Paul Kramer of Duke University found, in 1954, that although the meristematic region absorbed salts, it had little ability to translocate them, so that they were retained there. Older regions, in which root hairs were present and in which the xylem was well differentiated, were far more effective in providing transportable ions (Fig. 10-7). This work has been confirmed using other ions, and

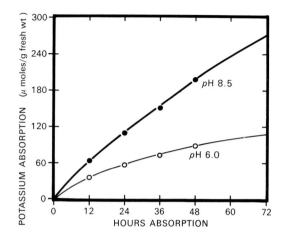

Figure 10-6
Progress of potassium absorption by slices of red beet roots at pH 8.5 and at pH 6.0. The slower rate at the lower pH might result from competition by hydrogen ions with potassium. (Redrawn from R. G. Hurd and J. F. Sutcliffe, 1957, *Nature* 180:233–235. Used by permission.)

so it seems that most salts are probably absorbed through regions of the root containing root hairs, and are then moved through the xylem to the upper parts of the plant. In addition, some transport from the root hair region toward the root tip occurs, probably through the phloem or through the apoplast. If salts were entirely absorbed into the apoplast of roots and taken into the xylem without having ever passed through a living cell, the rate at which they were absorbed should be directly related to the water uptake and to transpiration. If they were forced to pass through living tissue, a selective membrane could allow relatively more water than ions to penetrate, so that salt uptake would not be directly related to water movement through the plant. Many experiments have been performed to determine the extent to which salt and water absorption are related (Chapter 7). Different results and thus different conclusions have been obtained. The problem has recently been clarified to a large extent by the demonstration that the result depends upon the concentration

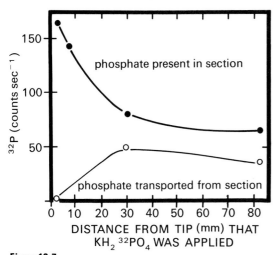

Figure 10-7

Ability of various regions of barley roots to accumulate phosphate and to translocate it to other parts of the plant. Phosphate containing ^{32}P was provided to 3 mm sections of the root at various distances from the apex for uptake periods of 6 hours. The plant was then harvested, and the treated section and other organs were analyzed for ^{32}P. (Drawn from data of H. Wiebe and P. Kramer, 1954, *Plant Physiol.* 29:342.)

10.6 FOLIAR NUTRITION OF PLANTS

Certain aquatic plants, such as species of *Elodea*, *Lemna*, and *Vallisneria*, absorb most nutrients through their submerged leaves. In these, neither is a cuticle formed nor are stomates present; absorption occurs directly into the cells. In terrestrial plants, a waxy cuticle is formed on the outer epidermal walls of the stems and leaves; yet they too can absorb salts applied to their leaf surfaces. Apparently the presence of stomates is often of little help in aiding salt uptake here, because the stomates are so small that the high surface tension of water prevents its flowing through.

The presence of cracks in the cuticle and the possible occurrence of plasmodesmata (**ectodesmata**) extending from the epidermal cells into the cuticular layer may explain the pathway for nutrient transport into the leaves. Regardless of the mechanism of entry, certain nutrients have been applied as foliar sprays to some crops with increasing frequency in recent years. Aerial sprays of iron, zinc, copper, and manganese are often used on fruit trees in preference to soil applications, from which uptake is poor because these elements are not highly soluble in the soil. For example, iron chelates sprayed on to correct iron deficiencies in fruit trees are often considerably more economical treatments than are soil applications. Nitrogen fertilization through the leaves is an effective mechanism for supplying this element, especially when it is added as urea, which penetrates rapidly. An estimated 80 percent of the nitrogen applied to pineapple fields in Hawaii is added in frequent sprays with iron and zinc. Leaf application of fertilizers has been used principally in cases requiring quick recovery from a nutrient deficiency.

If nutrients can be absorbed through the leaves, some should also be lost from leaves by leaching due to rainfall, and indeed some mineral salts, amino acids, and other organic com-

of salt used in the experiment. When the salt content supplied to the roots is high, sufficient ions are apparently absorbed so that water transport then becomes the limiting process for moving them into the xylem, and for allowing more to be absorbed. In this case salt uptake and transpiration are directly related.

If, however, experimental conditions include low external salt concentrations, the actual absorption process is limiting, and rapid transpiration does not increase mineral uptake. These observations are consistent with there being a barrier that forces salts to penetrate a selective membrane. They agree with the conclusion in Chapter 7 that ions must pass through living parts of the root, a conclusion based upon the observation that the nonliving (and thus nonaccumulating) xylem cells contain a higher concentration of salts than is present in the soil solution.

pounds are lost in this way. Potassium appears to be particularly easily lost by leaching, perhaps because of its high solubility and mobility in the plant.

10.7 FUNCTIONS OF MINERAL ELEMENTS AND SYMPTOMS OF DEFICIENCIES

Plants usually form characteristic symptoms in response to the lack of essential elements. Such visually observed symptoms often aid in determining the necessary functions of the element in the plant, and some symptoms are of real practical importance to farmers and agronomists in determining how and when to fertilize their crops. Several such symptoms are described below.

Most of the symptoms described appear on the shoot of the plant and are easily detected. The roots are, of course, also injured by the lack of these elements. Unless the plants are grown hydroponically, the condition of the roots cannot easily be seen without removing them from the soil, and root deficiency symptoms have been generally less well described.

10.7.1   Macronutrient Elements

10.7.1A   Nitrogen   Most soils are more commonly deficient in nitrogen than in any other element. Soil parent materials usually contain little or no nitrogen, and this element is rather easily lost through the leaching of nitrate ions or through its conversion to volatile N_2 by microorganisms. Nitrogen is essential to plants because it is a part of a large number of necessary organic compounds, including amino acids, proteins, coenzymes, nucleic acids, and chlorophyll. Plants developing without added nitrogen make almost no growth. Those containing enough to attain limited growth exhibit deficiency symptoms consisting of a general yellowing (**chlorosis**) from a lack of chlorophyll, especially in the older leaves. In severe cases,

these leaves become yellow and eventually fall off the plant. The younger leaves remain green longer, because soluble forms of nitrogen are transported to them from the older leaves. Some plants, including the tomato and certain varieties of corn, exhibit a purplish coloration in the stems, petioles, and lower leaf surfaces due to the accumulation of anthocyanin pigments (Chapter 18).

Plants grown with excessive amounts of nitrogen are usually dark green in color and show an abundance of foliage, usually with a poorly developed root system. Potato plants grown with superabundant nitrogen supplies show an excessive shoot growth but form only very small tubers. The reason for this is not yet known, but undoubtedly sugar translocation to the tubers or roots is affected in some way, and plant physiologists suspect that the normal hormonal relations of the plant are altered. Excess nitrogen also retards flowering and seed formation in several agricultural crops. However, flowering is not affected in some species, and still others, which flower only in favorable daylength conditions (especially short days), do so faster with abundant nitrogen (Chapter 26).

10.7.1B   Phosphorus   Phosphorus is absorbed by plants as a monovalent or divalent phosphate ion. Much phosphate is converted into organic forms upon entry into the root or after it has been transported through the xylem into the shoot. Molecules containing phosphate include sugar phosphates, nucleotides, nucleic acids, phospholipids, and certain coenzymes. Its presence as a part of sugar phosphates and coenzymes is very important, because here it allows the sugars to be metabolized by the plant and acts as an energy carrier. These functions will be discussed in later chapters.

Phosphorus-deficient plants appear stunted and, in contrast to those lacking nitrogen, are often a rather dark green in color. Anthocyanin pigments again sometimes accumulate. Maturity of the plants is often delayed, while those containing abundant phosphate usually mature rather early. A close interaction apparently exists between phosphorus and nitrogen in this respect.

Phosphate is easily redistributed in most plants from one organ to another and is lost from older leaves, accumulating in younger leaves and in developing flowers and seeds. As a result, deficiency symptoms occur first in more mature leaves.

10.7.1C Potassium

Like nitrogen and phosphorus, potassium is easily redistributed from mature to younger organs, and deficiency symptoms are first observable on the older, lower leaves. In dicots these leaves initially become somewhat chlorotic, but scattered, dark-colored necrotic lesions soon develop. In many monocots, such as the cereal crops, the cells at the tips and margins of the leaves die first, and this necrosis spreads basipetally toward the younger, lower parts of the leaf. Potassium-deficient corn and other cereal grains develop weak stalks and, in addition, the roots become more easily infected with root-rotting organisms. These abnormalities cause the plants to be rather easily bent to the ground (**lodged**) by wind or rain.

Unlike nitrogen and phosphorus, potassium does not form a stable structural part of any molecules inside plant cells, yet surprisingly large amounts of this element are needed for proper growth and development. It is almost surely essential because it acts as a coenzyme, or activator, for many enzymes. These enzymes cannot act as effective catalysts for necessary metabolic reactions in its absence. Protein synthesis is one process that requires high amounts of potassium, although the exact chemical reaction involved has not yet been pinpointed. This probably explains the long-known fact that potassium-deficient plants are usually low in protein content but high in amino-acid building blocks of proteins. One of the enzymes activated by potassium is a respiratory enzyme called pyruvate kinase. Here the element does become ionically, yet rather strongly, bound into the enzyme molecule, and causes it to attain a particular structure that can act catalytically, thus allowing normal carbohydrate breakdown to occur.

10.7.1D Sulfur

Sulfur is absorbed as the divalent sulfate ion. It is metabolized by roots only to the extent that they require it, and most of the absorbed sulfate is translocated unchanged to the shoots. Here it is incorporated into organic compounds by processes discussed in Chapter 16, the most abundant products being sulfur-containing amino acids. These are incorporated into the proteins, which are so essential for plant structure and function. Other important compounds containing sulfur include the respiratory compound coenzyme A and the vitamins thiamine and biotin (Chapter 11).

Sulfur-deficient plants are not often encountered in agriculture, since sufficient sulfate is present in most soils. The symptoms consist of a general yellowing throughout the affected leaves. Sulfur is not easily redistributed from mature tissues, and deficiencies are usually noted first in the younger leaves. This is sometimes not the case, however, and most of the leaves then become chlorotic at the same time.

10.7.1E Magnesium

This element seems to play at least two important roles in green plants. It is an essential part of the chlorophyll molecule (Chapter 13) and thus is essential to prevent the chlorosis that otherwise develops interveinally, first on the older leaves. Roots and microorganisms lacking chlorophyll also require magnesium, and here the principal function of the element is an activation of numerous essential enzymes. For example, many enzymes are known to utilize the energy in ATP. So far as is known, magnesium (or manganese) activates all of them. The magnesium probably combines strongly with the ATP and facilitates bond breakage. Examples of these enzymes and others requiring magnesium will be given in subsequent chapters. Proper amounts of magnesium are also essential to maintain the structure of ribosomes, small ribonucleoprotein bodies essential for protein synthesis (Chapters 8 and 17).

10.7.1F Calcium Much of this element is found in plants inside the vacuoles, where it often precipitates as crystals of calcium oxalate. Solid deposits of calcium oxalate and even calcium carbonate are sometimes found along the vascular bundles of leaves, and sulfate and phosphate ions probably also form insoluble calcium salts in some cases. Calcium is also found in the cell walls, where it is believed to form relatively insoluble salts by reacting with pectic acids in the middle lamella (Chapter 12). To remove the resulting pectate salts from the walls for investigation and analysis of the structural materials present, it is first necessary to add soluble oxalate salts that remove the calcium.

It is thought that calcium pectates of the middle lamella act to cement the adjacent primary walls together so that cells of a tissue remain bound to one another. If this is true, it may explain why calcium deficiency causes a marked inhibition of bud development and also causes death of root tips. Cell division is most active in these affected meristematic areas. The cell plate dividing two daughter cells becomes the middle lamella, and it is rich in pectic substances. Perhaps calcium performs an essential function in its synthesis and stability. Such a role for calcium is consistent with the observation that certain fungi and unicellular algae require only little, if any, of this element and do not possess a middle lamella. In higher plants, at least, calcium is needed in low concentrations in membranes to maintain their proper structure and differential permeability characteristics. Finally, calcium is an essential part of α-amylase, a starch-digesting enzyme.

Evidence obtained by Arthur Wallace of the University of California at Los Angeles indicates that calcium is needed *only* in trace amounts for higher plants. Bush beans grew very well when the calcium content of the leaves was only 210 ppm (0.021 percent) and that of the roots 350 ppm, each on a dry weight basis (compare Table 10-2). Healthy tobacco and corn plants were also grown with very low calcium contents. To obtain normal plants in the presence of very low amounts of calcium in the nutrient solutions, it was necessary to reduce levels of certain other cations such as magnesium, copper, and iron, since they were otherwise toxic. Evidence was obtained that magnesium was also required in smaller amounts than previously thought. The usual large quantities of calcium may primarily only detoxify other elements.

A few enzymes, such as amylase, seem to require calcium as an activator, but most of the observations indicate, on the contrary, that it usually has little stimulating effect and often interferes with magnesium in this respect.

10.7.2 Micronutrient Deficiencies

10.7.2A Iron Iron-deficient plants are characterized by development of a pronounced interveinal chlorosis similar to that caused by magnesium deficiency but on the younger leaves. Iron is very immobile in the plant, perhaps because it is precipitated as an insoluble oxide or in the form of inorganic or organic ferric phosphate compounds. Direct evidence that such precipitates form is weak; perhaps unknown but similarly insoluble compounds are produced. The entry of iron into the phloem transport stream may be prevented for other reasons. In any case, once it is taken into an organ from the soil through the xylem, its redistribution is extremely limited.

The reason that iron deficiency results in a rapid inhibition of chlorophyll formation is poorly known, even though this problem has been studied for more than 20 years. Many scientists now believe that iron is an essential activator for one or more enzymes catalyzing reactions involved in chlorophyll synthesis. Most of these reactions have not yet been investigated thoroughly, but once this is done, the site at which iron is involved should become apparent.

Iron is also required for other reasons in photosynthetic cells and is essential to organisms lacking chlorophyll. It forms a necessary part of certain pigment molecules, the cytochromes, which act as electron carriers in photosynthesis and in respiration. It also is an essential part of another photosynthetic electron carrier called ferredoxin and perhaps of nitrite reductase, one of the enzymes participating in the reduction of nitrate to ammonium ions. In the cytochromes and ferredoxin, the iron becomes alternately reduced and oxidized from the ferric to the ferrous state, and this may prove to be true in nitrite reductase. Iron is also an activator for certain other enzymes discussed in Chapter 15.

10.7.2B Chlorine Chlorine is absorbed from the soil as the chloride ion and probably remains in this form in the plant without becoming a structural part of organic molecules. Deficiency symptoms, discovered first in 1953, consist of wilted leaves, which then become chlorotic and necrotic, eventually attaining a bronze color. Roots become stunted in length but thickened, or club-shaped, near the tips.

The best known function for chlorine in plants is its stimulation of photosynthesis. It seems to act as an enzyme activator for one or more reactions in which water is split and oxygen released, but the mechanism of its action is not understood. The fact that roots also show deficiency symptoms suggests an additional role for chloride ions.

10.7.2C Manganese Manganese exists in various oxidation states in the soil but is probably absorbed largely as the divalent manganous ion. It is likely that the element in this state is most stable in the plant. Deficiencies of manganese are not common, although various disorders such as "gray speck" of oats, "marsh spot" of peas, and "speckled yellows" of sugar beets result from its lack. Initial symptoms are often an interveinal chlorosis on younger or older leaves, depending on the species, followed by, or associated with, necrotic lesions. Electron microscopy of chloroplasts from spinach leaves showed that the absence of manganese caused a disorganization of the lamellar membrane system extending through those bodies but had little effect on the structures of nuclei and mitochondria. This suggests that the element plays a structural role in the chloroplast membrane system.

Manganese is known to activate many enzymes, several of which are also activated by magnesium, and this is an important function in plants. For example, it activates one or more enzymes involved in fatty acid synthesis, those responsible for deoxyribonucleic acid and ribonucleic acid formation, and a respiratory enzyme of the Krebs cycle that decarboxylates and oxidizes isocitric acid. It is also directly involved in photosynthesis, participating in a reaction by which water is split and oxygen is released. Here it probably acts as an electron carrier. In addition, it may play a fairly direct role as a catalyst in an unknown reaction of chlorophyll formation, since a chlorosis results from its absence.

10.7.2D Boron Boron is probably largely absorbed from soils in the form of the soluble borate ion ($BO_3^=$), and it is not known to what extent the plant alters this ion. Deficiencies are not common in most areas, yet several disorders related to disintegration of internal tissues ("heart rot" of beets, "stem crack" of celery, "water core" of turnip, and "drought spot" of apples) result from its lack. Plants deficient in boron show a wide variety of symptoms, depending upon the species, but death of the stem and root apical meristems is observed in a large number. In several plants the root tips become swollen and discolored. The element is rather immobile, thus tending to be poorly re-distributed from one tissue or organ to another. In contrast to other essential elements, the function of boron in plants is not yet fully understood. A role in carbohydrate transloca-tion was suggested in 1953 by H. G. Gauch and W. M. Dugger, and it is well established that sugar transport through the phloem is indeed poor when boron is limited. It is likely, however, that the element has other essential functions.

10.7.2E Zinc Disorders arising from a lack of zinc include "little leaf" and "rosette" of apples, peaches, and pecans, resulting from a strong reduction in the size of the leaves and the length of the internodes. Leaf margins are often distorted and puckered in appearance. Inter-veinal chloroses often occur in the leaves of several fruit trees, suggesting that zinc somehow participates in chlorophyll formation. The re-tardation of stem growth in its absence probably results partly from the fact that zinc is needed to produce a hormone, indoleacetic acid. Indole-acetic acid is essential for the normal enlarge-ment of cells in the stems (Chapter 21). Zinc is also an essential part of certain enzymes whose functions are well understood. These include alcohol dehydrogenase, lactic acid dehydro-genase, glutamic acid dehydrogenase, and cer-tain peptidases such as carboxypeptidase. If the zinc is removed from these enzymes with zinc-chelating agents, they become inactive, and some even break down into smaller subunits.

10.7.2F Copper Plants are rarely deficient in this element. Symptoms of a lack of copper are largely known from nutrient solution studies in which it was not provided, since it is lacking in only a few soils. The young leaves often become dark green in color and are twisted or otherwise misshapen, often accompanied by necrotic spots. Citrus orchards are occasionally deficient, in which case the dying young leaves led to the name "die back" disease. Copper is largely absorbed as the divalent cupric or monovalent cuprous ion. It probably exists in plants primarily in the cupric form, although it under-goes alternate oxidation and reduction as it acts as an electron carrier and part of certain enzymes. It is a necessary part of plastocyanin, a compound forming part of the photosynthetic electron transport chain, of polyphenol oxidase, and perhaps of nitrite reductase. It may also play a catalytic role in nitrogen fixation, and it is involved in certain other chemical processes in the plant.

10.7.2G Molybdenum Molybdenum exists to a large extent in soils in the form of molybdate ($MoO_4^=$) salts and also as MoS_2. It is not known whether the element can be absorbed in both oxidation states. It is usually provided in nutrient solution studies as a molybdate salt. The compounds with which it reacts in plants are not known, except that it is active in the hexavalent state. Its best known function is as an electron carrier when present in certain enzymes necessary to convert nitrate to am-monium ions. However, it must also perform another role, since most plants grown with ammonium fertilizers still require it. It is also essential to the process of nitrogen fixation (Chapter 16).

Most plants require less molybdenum than any other element, yet molybdenum deficiencies are geographically widespread. Examples of dis-orders due to lack of this element include "whiptail" of cauliflower and broccoli, found in certain areas of the United States, Europe, Australia, and New Zealand, and "yellow spot" of citrus orchards in the United States. Symp-toms often consist of an interveinal chlorosis occurring first on the older or midstem leaves, then progressing to the youngest. Sometimes, as in the "whiptail" disease, the plants grown on an ammonium nitrogen source may not become chlorotic, but develop severely twisted young leaves, which eventually die.

Enzymes, Proteins, and Amino Acids

11.1 ENZYMES AND THEIR PROTEIN NATURE

An important characteristic of living organisms is the tremendous number of complex, yet beautifully coordinated, chemical reactions constantly occurring within the individual cells. In spite of the many different types of reactions taking place at any given time, there is not chaos. Instead, cells contain means for regulating the various processes. The compounds controlling this metabolism are called **enzymes**. Enzymes are proteins having catalytic activity. They control the rate at which chemical reactions take place. Because almost no reaction occurs in the cell in their absence, their over-all effect is actually to dictate what chemical processes can occur, that is, what **metabolic pathways** may proceed. For example, roots have no chlorophyll probably because the necessary enzymes for its synthesis are lacking. Similarly, broad variation in morphology in the plant kingdom arises from differences in the kinds, quantities, and activities of the enzymes plants contain.

The word enzyme, meaning *in yeast*, was apparently mentioned first in 1867 by Willy Kuhne, yet demonstration of enzyme effects became common as early as the late 1700s when interest in chemistry was developing. Among these demonstrations were the liquefaction of starch by water extracts of sprouted barley and the liquefaction of meat by gastric juices from birds. An understanding of the nature of enzymes began with James Sumner's preparation of **urease**, the enzyme that destroys urea, in 1926. Sumner obtained fairly pure crystals of urease from jack bean seeds and showed that urease, like all enzymes since discovered, is a protein.

Enzymes occur in all cells, but they are not uniformly mixed throughout. Thus, enzymes responsible for photosynthesis are concentrated in chloroplasts, those essential for respiration are divided among the mitochondria and the nonparticulate cytoplasm, and those necessary for nucleic acid synthesis and cell division occur mainly in the nuclei. Many of the intermediates in one process are members of some of the other metabolic pathways, so that this compartmentalization also aids in maintaining the integrity of each process without unnecessary competition from another. However, the membranes of each subcellular particle are somewhat permeable to most metabolites, allowing, for example, some compounds synthesized in photosynthesis to be acted upon later by enzymes of respiration.

11.2 PROPERTIES OF ENZYMES

11.2.1 Specificity and Nomenclature of Enzymes

One of the most important properties of these catalysts is their specificity. Each acts on only a single **substrate** (reactant) or group of closely related substrates. For example, one known enzyme called **hexokinase** catalyzes the addition of phosphate only to the aldehyde sugar glucose, but another, known in yeast, can add phosphate to the ketose sugar fructose, as well as to glucose. Usually when only partial specificity is exhibited, one substrate is still preferred and is converted to **products** at a faster rate.

In plants and animals combined, more than 1,000 different kinds of enzymes have been found, and a much larger number will probably be discovered in the future. Each enzyme studied has been named. In fact, some have been given more than one name, since various researchers studying the same reaction have not always agreed on the same name for the catalyst involved. The names are usually descriptive, indicating what type of compound (or substrate) is acted upon as well as the type of change caused. Enzyme names nearly always end with the suffix **-ase**. Thus, **cytochrome oxidase**, an important respiratory enzyme, oxidizes a cytochrome. **Malic acid dehydrogenase** removes hydrogen atoms from this common organic acid. At least four enzymes are known to act on glucose-6-phosphate, but since the products are different in all cases, the enzymes must be different, and they are named accordingly.

Several attempts have been made to classify enzymes according to the kinds of reactions they catalyze. One scheme established by an International Enzyme Commission is now widely recognized as superior to others. This scheme is listed in several modern biochemistry books.

11.2.2 Reversibility

Enzymes catalyze *the rate at which chemical equilibrium is established* among products and reactants. From the equilibrium standpoint, the assignment of the terms "reactants" and "products" is rather arbitrary and depends upon the point of view. Under normal physiological conditions, the enzyme has no influence on the relative quantities (ratios) of products to reactants that would otherwise eventually be reached, although such effects have been demonstrated *in vitro*, with unusually high enzyme concentrations.

The equilibrium constant depends upon the chemical potential of all compounds involved in the reaction [Chapter 3, equation (9)]. If the chemical potential of reactants is very high compared to the products, the reaction may proceed essentially only in one direction. Examples of such reactions are most of the decarboxylations, in which carbon dioxide is split out of a molecule. Because the CO_2 can escape, its concentration and, hence, its chemical potential, remain low. Hydrolytic reactions involving water such as the breakdown of starch by **amylases** and the splitting of phosphate from various molecules by **phosphatases**, are other almost irreversible processes. Other enzymes, using different substrates with higher energy levels, carry out starch synthesis and the addition of phosphate to molecules. In fact, observers commonly find that large molecules, such as fats, proteins, starch, nucleic acids, and even sugars, are synthesized by one series of reactions and broken down by another.

11.2.3 Chemical Composition

All enzymes thus far discovered are composed of a protein part, but some also contain an essential nonprotein organic portion called a **prosthetic group**. The prosthetic group is bound firmly to the protein portion and often remains with it even during the course of the complicated series of procedures needed to isolate the enzyme from the plant. Good examples of enzymes with prosthetic groups are certain of the **dehydrogenases** involved in respiration, fatty acid breakdown, and nucleic acid formation. Here a yellowish-colored pigment called a **flavin** is attached to the protein. The flavin is essential to catalytic activity because of its ability to undergo alternate oxidation and reduction as it transfers and accepts hydrogen atoms during the course of the reaction. Many enzymes without strongly bound prosthetic groups nevertheless require for activity the participation of another organic compound or a metal ion, or both. These are usually called **coenzymes**, although some refer to the metal ions only as **metal activators**. Coenzymes are generally not tightly held to the protein, but no sharp distinction between prosthetic groups and organic coenzymes is presently possible.

The molecular weights of enzymes are very large, many being in the neighborhood of 100,000. Urease, perhaps one of the largest, has a molecular weight of 438,000, while ribonuclease is much smaller at 12,700, and ferredoxin is one of the smallest known at 11,500.

A systematic investigation of the elemental composition of proteins was first begun in the 1830s by the Dutch chemist Gerardus Mulder, who studied such proteins as silk, egg white, and gelatin. Most proteins consist of about 50–55 percent carbon, 20–23 percent oxygen, 12–19 percent nitrogen, and 6–7 percent hydrogen. Many contain small amounts of sulfur (0.2–3 percent), and phosphorus is present in a few. It is often assumed that proteins contain 16 percent nitrogen, and the protein content of plants used for foodstuffs is thus estimated by determining the total nitrogen content, then multiplying by 6.25 (dividing by 0.16).

Proteins are made by the union of smaller molecules called **amino acids**. The composition and size of the protein depends upon the kind and number of its amino acid subunits. Commonly, around 19 or 20 different amino acids are present, but some proteins have slightly more or less than this number. Amino acids may be represented by the general formula

$$R-\underset{\underset{NH_2}{|}}{\overset{\overset{H}{|}}{C}}-\overset{\overset{O}{\diagup\!\diagup}}{C}\diagdown_{OH} \quad \text{or} \quad RCHNH_2COOH$$

The $-NH_2$ is the amino group, and the $-COOH$ is the carboxyl or acid group. The carbon atom adjacent to the carboxyl group, and to which the amino group is attached, is called the α carbon. The R represents the remainder of the molecule, and it is different for each amino acid.

Similar compounds called **amides** are sometimes found in proteins. Two important amides, **glutamine** and **asparagine**, are known. These are formed from the amino acids having carboxyl groups at either end of the molecules, **glutamic acid** and **aspartic acid**.

11.3 THE AMINO ACIDS AND AMIDES

A list of amino acids and amides occurring in proteins, along with their structures, is given in Table 11-1. They are classified on the basis of the R groups, which may contain **additional amino groups** (as in arginine and lysine), an **extra carboxyl group** (as in glutamic and aspartic acids), a **hydroxyl group** (as in serine and threonine), or a **sulfur atom** (as in cysteine, cystine, and methionine). Phenylalanine and tyrosine have **aromatic R groups**, while R **is heterocyclic** in tryptophan, histidine, proline, and hydroxyproline, since nitrogen, as well as carbon, exists in the rings. Tyrosine and hydroxyproline might also be classified with serine and threonine because they, too, possess hydroxyl groups. Although proteins sometimes contain phosphorus, this element is not found in any of the free amino acids. When phosphorus is present, it is usually attached in ester linkage with the hydroxyl group of serine or to a nitrogen atom in the heterocyclic ring of histidine.

11.3.1 Acid and Base Properties of Amino Acids

The carboxyl group of amino acids is responsible for their acidic properties, and, as expected, aspartic and glutamic acids, having two such carboxyls, are more acidic than the others. Amino acids can also behave as bases, since the

TABLE 11-1

AMINO ACIDS AND AMIDES DERIVED FROM PLANT PROTEINS

I. Aliphatic amino acids	II. Basic amino acids

I. Aliphatic amino acids

Glycine

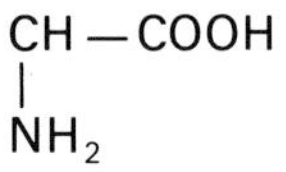

$$CH-COOH$$
$$|$$
$$NH_2$$

Alanine

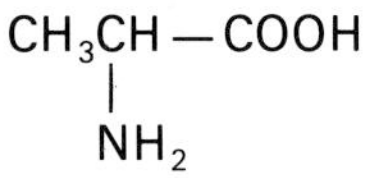

$$CH_3CH-COOH$$
$$|$$
$$NH_2$$

Valine

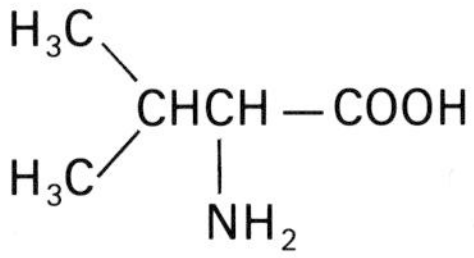

$$H_3C$$
$$\diagdown$$
$$CHCH-COOH$$
$$H_3C \diagup \quad | $$
$$NH_2$$

Leucine

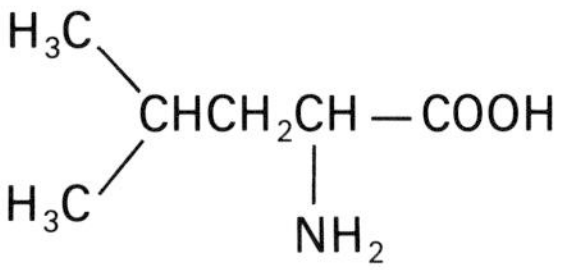

$$H_3C$$
$$\diagdown$$
$$CHCH_2CH-COOH$$
$$H_3C \diagup \qquad | $$
$$NH_2$$

Isoleucine

$$CH_3CH_2$$
$$\diagdown$$
$$CHCH-COOH$$
$$H_3C \diagup \quad | $$
$$NH_2$$

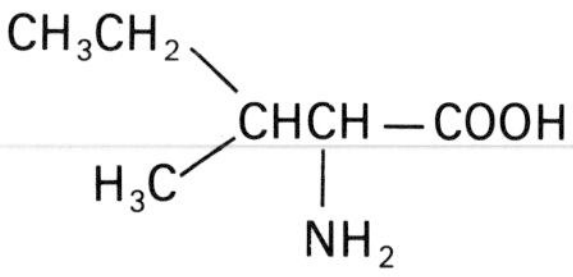

II. Basic amino acids

Arginine

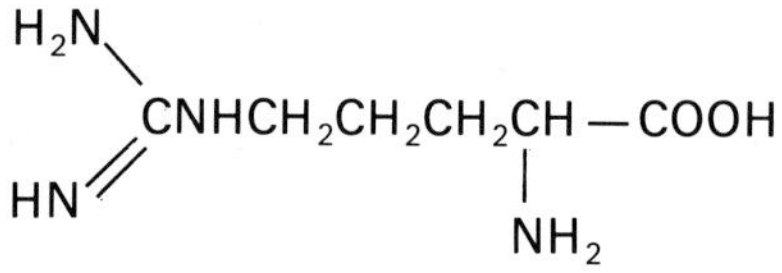

$$H_2N$$
$$\diagdown$$
$$CNHCH_2CH_2CH_2CH-COOH$$
$$HN \diagup\!\!\!/ \qquad\qquad\qquad | $$
$$NH_2$$

Lysine

$$H_2NCH_2CH_2CH_2CH_2CH-COOH$$
$$|$$
$$NH_2$$

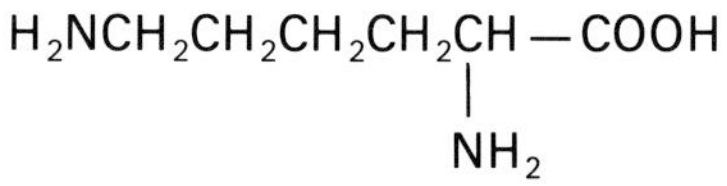

III. Acidic amino acids (and their amides)

Aspartic acid

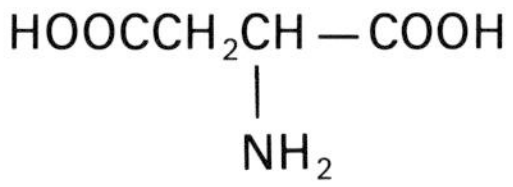

$$HOOCCH_2CH-COOH$$
$$|$$
$$NH_2$$

Glutamic acid

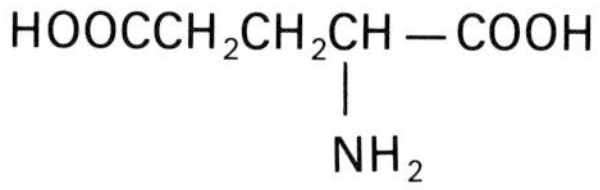

$$HOOCCH_2CH_2CH-COOH$$
$$|$$
$$NH_2$$

Asparagine

$$O$$
$$\diagdown\!\!\!\backslash$$
$$CCH_2CH-COOH$$
$$H_2N \diagup \quad | $$
$$NH_2$$

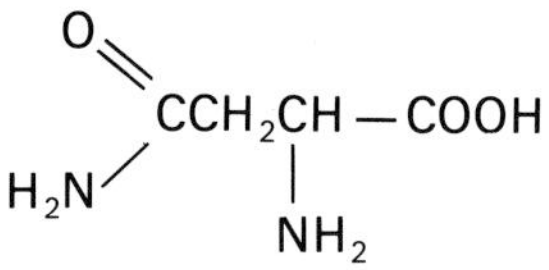

Glutamine

$$O$$
$$\|$$
$$CCH_2CH_2CH-COOH$$
$$H_2N \diagup \qquad | $$
$$NH_2$$

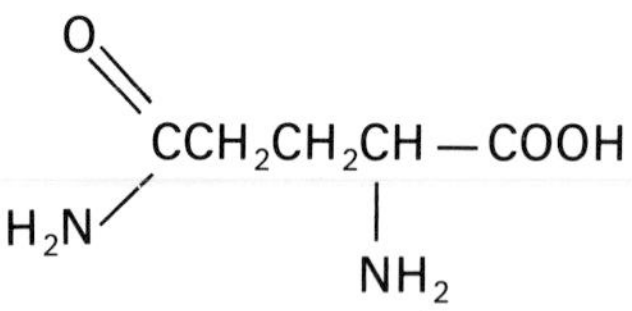

TABLE 11-1

AMINO ACIDS AND AMIDES DERIVED FROM PLANT PROTEINS

IV. Hydroxylated amino acids	VI. Heterocyclic amino acids continued

IV. Hydroxylated amino acids

Serine

$$HOCH_2CH-COOH$$
$$|$$
$$NH_2$$

Threonine

$$CH_3CHOHCH-COOH$$
$$|$$
$$NH_2$$

V. Aromatic amino acids

Phenylalanine

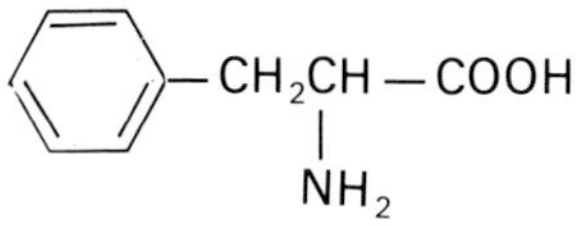

$$-CH_2CH-COOH$$
$$|$$
$$NH_2$$

Tyrosine

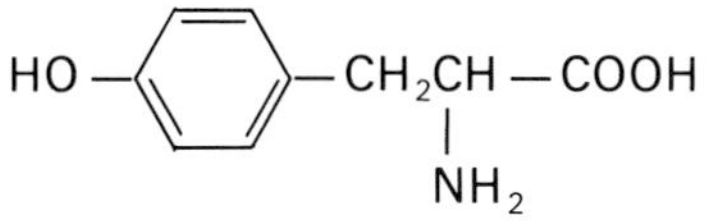

$$HO-\quad-CH_2CH-COOH$$
$$|$$
$$NH_2$$

VI. Heterocyclic amino acids

Proline

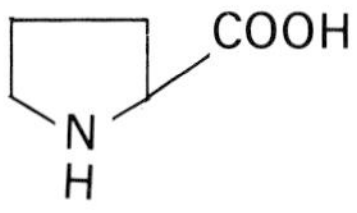

Hydroxyproline

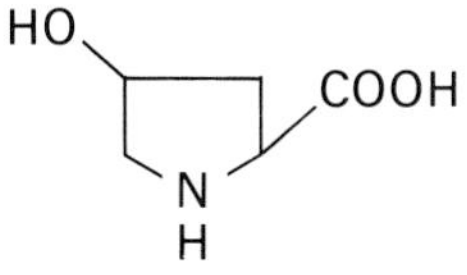

VI. Heterocyclic amino acids   continued

Tryptophan

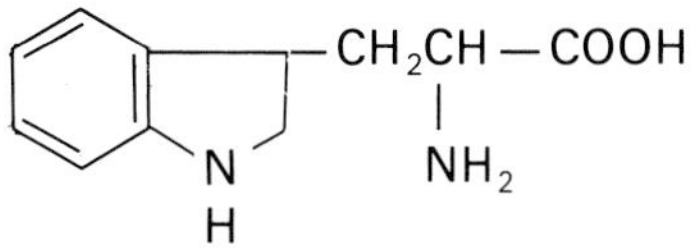

$$-CH_2CH-COOH$$
$$|$$
$$NH_2$$

Histidine

$$\begin{array}{cc} N-CH \\ \| \quad \| \\ HC \quad C-CH_2CH-COOH \\ \diagdown / \qquad | \\ N \qquad NH_2 \\ H \end{array}$$

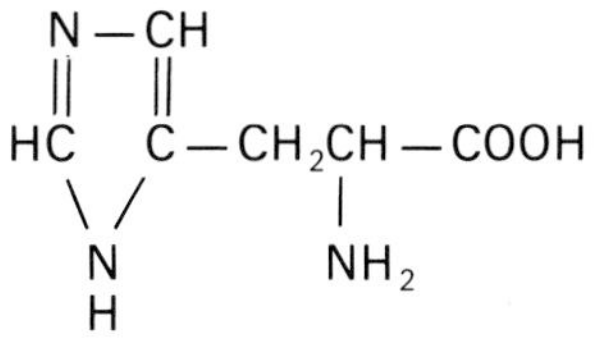

VII. Sulfur-containing amino acids

Cysteine

$$HSCH_2CH-COOH$$
$$|$$
$$NH_2$$

Cystine

$$SCH_2CHNH_2COOH$$
$$|$$
$$SCH_2CHNH_2COOH$$

Methionine

$$CH_3SCH_2CH_2CH-COOH$$
$$|$$
$$NH_2$$

nitrogen atom of the amino group possesses electrons that can be shared by hydrogen ions. Arginine, lysine, and histidine contain more than one such nitrogen atom and are more effective bases than any others. The remaining amino acids are considered neutral, because they have the same number of effective amino and carboxyl substituents.

The simplest of the neutral amino acids is glycine. A dilute solution of glycine has a pH of about 6. At this pH the carboxyl groups are almost completely dissociated, having a negative charge, but the amino groups have accepted hydrogen ions and are positively charged:

$$
\begin{array}{c}
H \quad\quad\quad O \\
\backslash \quad\quad\quad /\!/ \\
H-C-C \\
/ \quad\quad\quad \backslash \\
\oplus NH_3 \quad\quad O\ominus
\end{array}
$$

Such an ionized form is often called a **dipolar ion**, because of the separation of charges, or a **Zwitterion**, from the German word for hybrid or mongrel. This dipolar ion has no net charge and will not migrate in an electrical field toward either the cathode or anode.

Other forms of glycine can be produced by adjustment of the pH. If acid is added to the solution, the negatively charged carboxyl group will attract hydrogen ions, leaving only a plus charge on the molecule. Adding a base, such as NaOH, will cause removal of the hydrogen ion attached to the amino group, water will be formed, and the resulting form of glycine [shown in (R11-1)] will be negatively charged.

$$
\underset{\substack{H \\ | \\ R-C-COO\ominus \\ | \\ NH_2 \\ pH > 6}}{} \xleftarrow{+\,OH^-} \underset{\substack{H \\ | \\ R-C-COO\ominus \\ | \\ \oplus NH_3 \\ pH\ 5\text{-}6}}{} \xrightarrow{+H^+}
$$

$$
\underset{\substack{H \\ | \\ R-C-COOH \\ | \\ \oplus NH_3 \\ pH < 5}}{} \quad\quad \text{(R11-1)}
$$

The pH at which there is no net charge on the amino acid is called the **isoelectric point** (see Chapter 4), abbreviated pI. At most pH values, mixtures of the various ionic forms will be found, but one particular species will predominate.

The pI is considerably lower for the acidic aspartic and glutamic acids than for other amino acids, because more hydrogen ions must be added to solutions of these two acids to repress ionization of the additional carboxyl group they contain. For the basic amino acids, the pI is higher, since more hydroxyl ions are needed to remove the hydrogen ion from the extra nitrogen atom. The pI is between 5 and 6 for the neutral amino acids, near 3 for the acidic, and above 7.5 for the basic amino acids. The isoelectric point of proteins depends upon the kinds and relative amounts of amino acids they contain.

An understanding of the amphoteric properties of proteins and of the isoelectric point is important, because a careful control of the pH of amino acid and protein solutions can be used to facilitate their purification, as indicated in Chapter 4. The catalytic activity of enzymes also is controlled by pH, since attachment to the substrate and to coenzymes and metal activators often depends upon whether certain of their amino or carboxyl groups are charged. The solubilities of proteins and the viscosities of protein solutions are lowest at the isoelectric point.

11.3.2 Stereoisomerism

The α carbon of all amino acids except glycine is attached to four different groups. Hence, it is an **asymmetric carbon atom**, and amino acids containing such asymmetry are capable of rotating a beam of **plane polarized** light.

One characteristic almost always shared by the amino acids found in plants or animals is the arrangement of the amino group and H atom

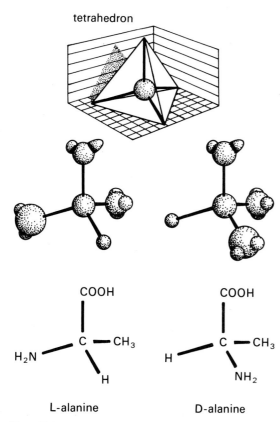

tetrahedron

COOH

$$H_2N \overset{\displaystyle |}{\underset{\displaystyle H}{C}} \!\!-\!\! CH_3$$

L-alanine

COOH

$$H \overset{\displaystyle |}{\underset{\displaystyle NH_2}{C}} \!\!-\!\! CH_3$$

D-alanine

Figure 11-1
Tetrahedral models representing nonsuperimposable forms of alanine. Figure at the top is an attempt to show a tetrahedron; middle figures are expanded molecular models; bottom figures indicate positions of the various atoms.

around the α carbon atom. This is usually shown on paper with the amino group to the left and the H to the right when the carboxyl is written above the other carbon atoms. This arrangement is indicated by a small capital L, and it has no consistent relation to the direction of rotation of plane polarized light, which is indicated by a lower case l (or −, levorotatory, to the left) or d (or +, dextrorotatory, to the right). Amino acids with the opposite arrangement of amino and H groups are called D-amino acids, because the H atom is on the right, as in the

compound arbitrarily called D-glyceraldehyde. Figure 11-1 shows the D- and L-forms of alanine.

D-amino acids are rarely encountered in living cells, although several antibiotics synthesized by bacteria contain certain of the D-forms. Because only the L-amino acids are usually encountered, this must mean that the enzymes synthesizing and utilizing them can somehow distinguish the two configurations. When they are produced in the absence of enzymes, equal amounts of the D- and L-forms ordinarily result. Because proteins are composed of amino acids, they also rotate plane polarized light. Since enzymes are proteins, this accounts for their ability to distinguish between D- and L-forms, not only of amino acids, upon which some act, but of most other substrates as well.

11.3.3 The Peptide Bond

In 1902 the chemists Emil Fischer and Franz Hofmeister each correctly suggested that in proteins the carboxyl group of one amino acid and the α-amino group of another are united, with the elimination of a water molecule, to produce an **amide bond**. This amide linkage joining two amino acids is termed a **peptide bond**. The linkage for aspartic acid and glycine is shown in (R11-2).

$$HOOC-CH_2-\overset{\overset{\displaystyle NH_2}{|}}{\underset{\underset{\displaystyle H}{|}}{C}}-CO\!\!\overbrace{OH \;\; H}\!\!N-\overset{\overset{\displaystyle H}{|}}{\underset{\underset{\displaystyle H}{|}}{C}}\overset{\displaystyle H}{}-COOH \longrightarrow$$

$$H_2O$$

$$HOOC-CH_2-\overset{\overset{\displaystyle NH_2 \downarrow H}{|}}{\underset{\underset{\displaystyle H \;\;\; O}{|}}{C}}-\overset{\displaystyle ||}{C}-N-CH_2-COOH + H_2O$$

(R11-2)

When aspartic and glutamic acids form peptide bonds with other amino acids, the carboxyl group nearer the amino group participates, while the other is free and conveys acid properties upon the protein. When arginine and lysine are united in this manner, the additional amino groups distal to the carboxyl groups are free, giving basic properties to the protein. These peptides are shown in Fig. 11-2.

11.4 THE SEPARATION OF ENZYMES FROM CELLS

To study how an individual enzyme functions, we must remove it from the heterogeneous mixture of compounds inside the cells. In this way we can analyze the complicated reactions involved in metabolism one by one. It is important that knowledge about the mechanism of each reaction be obtained. With this knowledge, understanding of (and perhaps control over) cellular processes and plant functions can eventually be realized.

The first step involves breaking the tissue in some way to obtain a crude solution of the enzyme. The cells may be crushed by grinding in a blender or even with quartz sand and a mortar and pestle. Two precautions are important at this and the following stages of purification: the enzyme must be kept cold and the solution should be buffered, usually at a pH near neutrality. In addition, many enzymes contain sulfhydryl groups, and these are easily oxidized during separation procedures unless protective reducing agents are added. Some common reducing agents include mercaptoethanol, glutathione, cysteine, and Cleland's reagent (dithiothreitol). Dithiothreitol is the most effective. For further purification of the enzyme, many of the principles introduced in Chapter 4 on colloids are applied.

An additional problem presented by many plant tissues is the presence of phenolic compounds (Chapter 18, 18.2). Proteins combine with phenolics reversibly by hydrogen bonding and irreversibly following oxidation of the phenols to quinones, resulting in a loss of enzyme activity. W. D. Loomis and J. Battaile, in Oregon, developed a method for removing phenolics with insoluble polyvinylpyrrolidone (PVP) at the time the tissue is disrupted. Apparently the protons of the phenolic hydroxyl groups combine very strongly with the oxygen of the peptide bonds in the PVP instead of with the enzyme peptide bonds. The resulting phenolic-PVP complex is centrifuged out of the enzyme solution, and in this way many enzymes can be shown to be active which were previously not known to be present in plants.

11.4.1 Dialysis

Smaller contaminating molecules and ions can be removed by the process called **dialysis**. The solution is placed inside a membrane (e.g., cellophane) that allows smaller substances to pass through into a surrounding large reservoir of cold water or buffer solution but is impermeable to the protein (Fig. 4-3).

11.4.2 Fractional Precipitation

We can remove the desired enzyme from others by taking advantage of the fact that not all proteins are equally soluble in organic solvents, such as acetone or alcohols, or in salt solutions. The salt most commonly used to precipitate proteins (a process called "salting out," Chapter 4, 4.2.4A) is ammonium sulfate, which is highly soluble in cold water (760 g/l at 0°C) and gives a pH near neutrality. After addition of salt or organic solvent, the solution is kept cold 15 minutes or so to allow precipitation, and then it is centrifuged. Although one cannot predict whether the enzyme to be studied will be more or less soluble than others, both the proteins precipitated by treatment and those remaining in solution may be tested for their ability to catalyze the reaction.

11.4.3 Molecular Sieve Chromatography

A three-dimensional polysaccharide network called **Sephadex**, and certain polyacrylamide

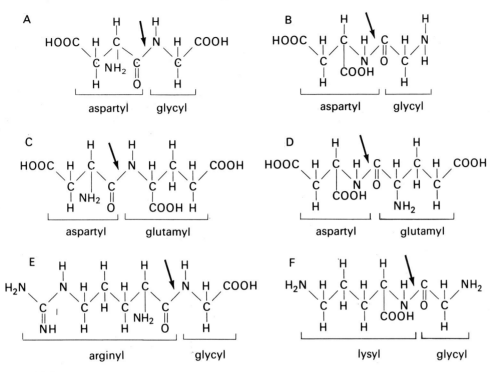

Figure 11-2
Examples of peptides formed between various amino acids. Either the α-amino or α-carboxyl group of each amino acid may participate in peptide bond formation. Two different peptides may thus be formed using any two different amino acids [compare A with B, and C with D]. Arrows indicate peptide bonds.

gels in the form of tiny beads, act as **molecular sieves** and are used to separate mixtures of proteins differing in size. These materials are packed into a glass column, and the crude protein mixture is then added at the top. As the proteins pass through, the smaller molecules penetrate and diffuse into the beads of the gel and are retained by them. The larger molecules, however, are sterically prevented from entering the beads and thus move more rapidly through the column (Fig. 11-3). Fractions collected at various times then contain different-sized molecules. This technique is also used extensively for separating salts and small molecules in cells from proteins.

11.4.4 Column Chromatography

A further step often involves the use of a technique called **chromatography**. A material having the ability to adsorb proteins is placed in a glass tube, forming a column similar to that of Fig. 11-3. Materials in common use include cellulose powders and certain forms of calcium phosphate. The celluloses are previously chemically treated to attach substituent groups with basic or acidic properties. Carboxymethyl cellulose is an example of a common negatively charged adsorbent, while DEAE (diethylaminoethyl) cellulose is an important positively charged ion exchanger.

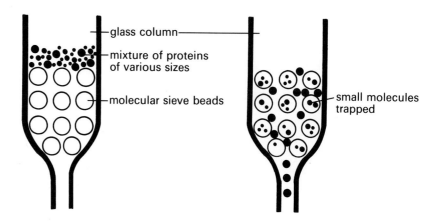

Figure 11-3
Schematic diagram of a molecular sieve column for separating proteins or other compounds differing in molecular weight. A solution of the mixture to be resolved is carefully layered by pipetting it onto the surface of the molecular sieve beads held in a glass column (bead size greatly enlarged relative to column). Buffer or water carries the larger molecules through to the bottom of the column, where they collect, while the smaller molecules are trapped and pass through more slowly, thus allowing a separation. Various molecular sieve materials can be chosen, depending upon the molecular weights of compounds in the mixture.

The adsorbent in the column is wetted with buffer, and the heterogeneous protein solution is poured on the top. Next, a buffer of different pH is added in a quantity sufficient to carry the proteins down through the adsorbent. Each different protein present will have a different net charge at the prevailing pH because of its different amino acid composition. If the adsorbent has a positive charge, any proteins charged similarly will be repelled and will pass rapidly through the column. Those with the greatest negative charge will be held most tightly on the column, and they can be removed only by decreasing the pH of the buffer solution passing through. In this manner the desired enzyme can be resolved from other very different proteins, although complete separation is usually not obtained where proteins with similar isoelectric points are present.

11.4.5 Electrophoresis

Another technique that takes advantage of differences in electrical charge as affected by pH is **electrophoresis** (Chapter 4, 4.2.5). The dialyzed protein mixture is placed in a U-tube, and a buffer solution is carefully layered above it. The pH is often kept slightly alkaline to maintain a net negative charge on most of the proteins. An electrode is placed in each arm of the tube, and the current is turned on. Proteins with the greatest negative charges will move most rapidly toward the anode, those with positive charges will move toward the cathode, and those whose pI just equals the pH of the buffer will not migrate. The position of the proteins may be monitored by an optical system that detects changes in the index of refraction of the liquid where proteins are concentrated. The current is turned off and various layers of the solution are carefully removed. Each may then be tested for the presence of the enzyme.

Electrophoresis can be carried out in agar gel, polyacrylamide gel, a layer of starch, or a strip of filter paper. The protein mixture is placed near the middle in a spot or a narrow band. Identical buffer solutions at each end keep the supporting material moist and at the desired pH. Electrodes are placed in the buffer solutions, and after suitable time the power is turned off to prevent movement of the proteins into the buffer.

11.4.6 Ultracentrifugation

With centrifuges capable of forces from 100,000 to 500,000 times gravity, many proteins are sedimented. The pH again must be carefully controlled, since solubility is dependent upon pH. The rate of sedimentation is dependent upon the size and shape of the protein; those of large molecular weights and compact shapes will move most rapidly.

Many molecular weight determinations have been made with the ultracentrifuge by calculating the rate of movement through the centrifugal field. Some inaccuracy is always present because of the unknown influence of the shape of the protein on its movement.

With the techniques described, and others, many proteins have been obtained in the form of rather pure crystals. Their mechanisms of action can then be studied intensively without interference from other contaminants. It is important for a final understanding of enzyme catalysis to know which amino acids are essential for activity, and which, if any, are dispensable. The complete determination of the amino acid sequence in some proteins has been accomplished, promising to add greatly to our knowledge of how they act. Sequence determinations on similar proteins from different species hold much promise in studies of evolution. Can we suppose that enzymes catalyzing identical reactions in plants and man have identical composition and sequence of amino acids? Let us first examine some methods by which answers to such questions can be obtained.

11.5 DETERMINATION OF AMINO ACID COMPOSITION AND SEQUENCE IN PROTEINS

11.5.1 Methods of Hydrolysis

All that is required to determine the composition is to split the protein, thus freeing the amino acid subunits, and then to measure those present and the concentration of each. Common techniques for splitting proteins include boiling for several hours in 6 N HCl, or, less often, in 2 N NaOH, but each method partially destroys one or more amino acids. Certain enzymes such as trypsin also hydrolyze peptide bonds, and these are often used to break down proteins. Sometimes digestion with enzymes is used in combination with HCl or NaOH treatment. The material produced by such hydrolysis is called the **protein hydrolysate**.

11.5.2 Chromatography

As late as 1941 there was no way of completely analyzing with accuracy the number and kinds of amino acids present in a mixture formed from protein hydrolysis. Thus, even composition studies were almost impossible. But in that year two English biochemists, A. J. P. Martin and R. L. M. Synge, developed the technique of **paper chromatography**. Separation of compounds by this technique is based on differences in their solubility in two liquid phases. One phase, usually an aqueous solution, is a polar solvent, whereas the other phase is a more nonpolar organic solvent. The two phases may or may not be miscible; in either case the principles of separation and the chromatographic procedure remain the same. A sample of the protein hydrolysate is placed in a small spot (the **origin**) on the corner of a sheet of filter paper, which is then placed in a container such as an airtight box or glass jar (Fig. 11-4). The two solvent phases are placed in the container so that the vapors saturate the enclosed atmosphere. The filter paper, spotted with the amino acids, is allowed to equilibrate with the vapors of the solvent until a water layer (**stationary liquid phase**) becomes adsorbed to the paper. Hydrogen bonding between the water and the cellulose fibers of the paper permits a stationary phase of water constituting from 15 to 20 percent of the weight of the paper. After equilibration, the nonpolar phase (or a solution of both the aqueous and the nonpolar phase if the two are miscible) is placed in direct contact with the paper, and the organic liquid begins to flow by capillarity along it. Care must be taken to insure that the sample spot is not submerged in the liquid. When the nonpolar organic phase (**mobile liquid phase**) reaches the sample, partitioning of the amino acids between the two phases begins. Those readily soluble in the mobile phase are carried along near the **solvent front**, while others more soluble in the stationary aqueous phase remain behind. Thus, a separation occurs, made possible because various amino acids have different solubilities in the two liquids. In addition, there is some adsorption of the compounds directly to the paper, the extent of adsorption differing among molecules, so that separation may also occur because of this. Molecules most tightly adsorbed remain closest to the origin.

This separation along one edge of the paper is usually not complete, so the paper is removed and dried, turned 90°, and a different water-organic mixture allowed to carry the amino acids along the paper toward another edge. In this way, compounds not resolved in the first direction are usually separated in the second.

Although the amino acids are colorless, they can be located on the paper by spraying with **ninhydrin**. A purple color soon develops, the intensity of which is nearly proportional to the amount of amino acid present. To decide which purple spot corresponds to each amino acid it is necessary to run the amino acids individually in the chromatography system, noting their movement in each of the two solvent systems. Under strictly defined conditions of temperature, etc., the ratio of the distance moved by an amino acid to the distance moved by the organic phase is constant from one experiment to the next. This ratio is called the R_f (meaning relative to the solvent front) and is always a fraction less than 1.0. R_f values are of great help in identifying unknown compounds, although other evidence is also required.

With paper chromatography, the kinds of amino acids present in a protein hydrolysate and their concentrations can be measured. This method is not always entirely quantitative, and **column chromatography** on ion-exchange resins has partially replaced it. Commercial instruments are now available, and, as amino acids come off the bottom of the column, ninhydrin is added, a color formed, and the intensity of the color measured electronically. The amino acids present and the concentration of each are plotted on a graph by the instrument.

A newer technique called **thin layer chromatography** is now in use for resolution of mixtures of amino acids or other compounds. A wet slurry of cellulose, silica gel, or another suitable substance is spread on a piece of glass in a thin layer. The amino acids are added in a spot and separated as on paper, except that much less time is needed for the separation.

11.5.3 Sequence Analysis

The procedures for determinations of amino acid arrangement or **sequence** in proteins are

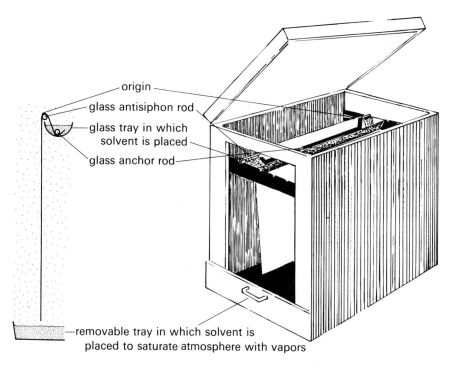

origin
glass antisiphon rod
glass tray in which solvent is placed
glass anchor rod
removable tray in which solvent is placed to saturate atmosphere with vapors

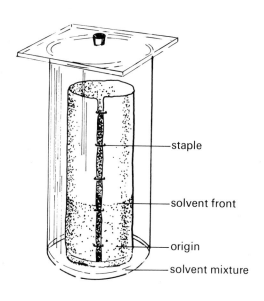

staple
solvent front
origin
solvent mixture

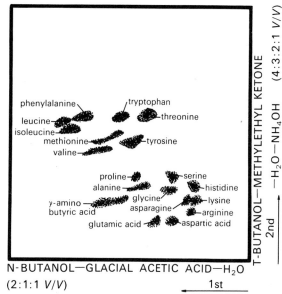

phenylalanine   tryptophan
leucine   threonine
isoleucine
methionine   tyrosine
valine

proline   serine
alanine   histidine
γ-amino   glycine   lysine
butyric acid   asparagine   arginine
glutamic acid   aspartic acid

T-BUTANOL—METHYLETHYL KETONE   (4:3:1 V/V)
—H$_2$O—NH$_4$OH

2nd

N-BUTANOL—GLACIAL ACETIC ACID—H$_2$O
(2:1:1 V/V)   1st

Figure 11-4

Apparatus used for paper chromatography. (top) An insulated, vapor-tight cabinet in which up to eight paper sheets (18×22 inches) can be descendingly chromatographed together. Chromatograms are then removed, allowed to dry, turned 90°, and run again in the second dimension using a different solvent system. Schematic drawing to the left illustrates how sheets are held by one glass rod, immersed in the trough of solvent and held there by another glass (anchor) rod, and hung above solvent, giving an atmosphere saturated with the solvent vapor. (lower left) A less expensive system often used for smaller papers in which chromatography is ascending. (lower right) Separation of amino acids obtained in a cabinet like that above. Amino acids are made visible (purple) on the paper by treatment with ninhydrin. (Unpublished data of J. Miller and C. Ross.)

long and tedious. The number of chains in the molecule is measured by analyzing the number of end groups present. The terminal acids must have either a free α-carboxyl group or a free α-amino group, the other reactive portion being united to the neighbor amino acid in a peptide bond. The terminal amino acids having free carboxyl groups are split off by a specific enzyme called **carboxypeptidase** and are then analyzed. The terminal α-amino groups react with **dinitro-fluorobenzene**, releasing HF, and producing a yellow combination product. When the protein is subsequently split, this product can be separated and the amino acid identified. Measuring the number of terminal amino acids by end-group analysis tells the number of chains present. Some proteins contain only one chain, while others contain as many as four.

Proteins often contain chains linked together by disulfide bridges (—S—S—). These result when the —SH groups of two cysteines come into contact and the hydrogens are removed by oxidation. Disulfide bonds can be broken by **performic acid oxidation**, and when the breaks occur, the apparent molecular weight of the protein decreases by an amount dependent upon the number of chains present. Furthermore, since the sulfur in the amino acids at the junction points is oxidized to $-SO_3^-$, subsequent detection of this group in an amino acid establishes its participation in a cross-link.

The next procedure is to destroy the peptide bonds holding the amino acids together. If this is not done judiciously, no more information of the amino acid sequence could be obtained than of the order of arrangement of bricks in a building destroyed by a bulldozer tractor. The first successful sequence analysis was completed in 1953 on the small protein **beef insulin** by the British biochemist Frederick Sanger. For this, he was awarded the 1958 Nobel prize in chemistry. Sanger broke insulin down, not into individual amino acids at first but into small units of a very few amino acids, or **peptides**.

These peptides were separated, and the amino acid sequence in each was determined by methods such as sequential hydrolysis and identification of the terminal amino acids. Much effort then went into deducing just how each peptide originally fit into the intact protein. By a "jigsaw-puzzle approach," it was possible to find overlapping sequences in the various peptides. Amino acid sequences have subsequently been determined for several other proteins in a similar manner.

11.5.4 Analysis of the Secondary and Tertiary Structures of Proteins

The peptide bonds holding the amino acids together in a particular sequence constitute the **primary structure** of proteins. Ultracentrifugation and other physical measurements indicate that many proteins have roughly spherical shapes, showing that the amino acids are not simply held in extended linear chains. More information about their structures can be obtained by **x-ray diffraction techniques**. In fact, the complete atomic maps of three crystalline proteins (myoglobin, lysozyme, and ribonuclease) have been deciphered with x-ray diffractometers. In this technique x-rays pass through the protein and are diffracted to a greater extent where atoms, especially heavy atoms, are concentrated. The x rays then strike a film, exposing it in some places but not in others, depending upon the arrangement of atoms in the molecules. Computers aid interpretation of the film patterns.

Portions of the peptide chains of some proteins prove to be twisted into a helix, a structure that is probably stabilized by hydrogen bonding from one amino acid to another in a turn below it (Fig. 11-5). Such a helical arrangement constitutes the **secondary structure** of these proteins.

The individual peptide chains are further extensively coiled into sphere-like shapes with

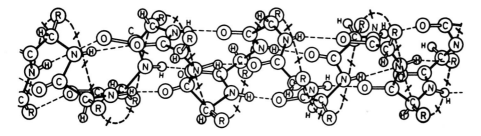

Figure 11-5

The α-helix arrangement of amino acids in a protein molecule. (From V. Kretovich, 1966, *Principles of Plant Biochemistry*, Pergamon Press, London, p. 27. Used by permission.)

hydrogen bonds between amino and carboxyl groups and various other kinds of bonds cross-linking one chain to another and stabilizing the **tertiary structure**. Some of these bonds are shown in Fig. 11-6. It is presumed that protein shape is almost completely determined by the kind and arrangement of amino acids present, because the coiling and folding must result when these come into proper contact at points where cross bonding can occur. The particular tertiary structure attained by an enzyme is of primary importance in determining whether or not it is catalytically active, and small changes in critical places are known to cause inactivation.

11.6 CONCLUSIONS FROM STUDIES OF INDIVIDUAL PROTEINS

Many plant proteins have been purified by methods outlined above, and the amino acid composition has been determined for some, especially seed proteins, which are of great nutritional importance. However, the amino acid sequence is known for only a very few, including the protein coat of the tobacco mosaic virus and **ferredoxin** from spinach and from the bacteria *Clostridium* and *Chromatium*. Ferredoxins are reddish brown, iron-containing proteins involved in photosynthesis and nitrogen

fixation in various organisms. The molecular weights of the bacterial ferredoxins are about 6,000 each, that from *Chromatium* containing three iron atoms per molecule and the *Clostridium* ferredoxin, seven per molecule. Spinach ferredoxin has a molecular weight of about 11,500 and contains two iron atoms per molecule. It contains 19 different amino acids, and a total of 97 are present. Arginine, histidine, methionine, and tryptophan occur only once per molecule, while the content of aspartic and glutamic acids is high.

Alfalfa ferredoxin is almost identical in composition to that of spinach ferredoxin. It differs in having only 18 different amino acids (methionine is absent) and in having a total of 101. Arginine, histidine, and tryptophan also occur only once per molecule here. The sequence of alfalfa ferredoxin has not yet been determined, but it is almost surely very similar to that of the spinach ferredoxin, which, in turn, is identical over some lengths to the bacterial proteins. The biological activity of these proteins from plants and bacteria is, at least in part, interchangeable. This indicates that their function does not depend upon the whole molecule, but rather upon a few amino acids in the identical sequences.

An enzyme called **papain** obtained from leaves of the papaya plant and used as a meat

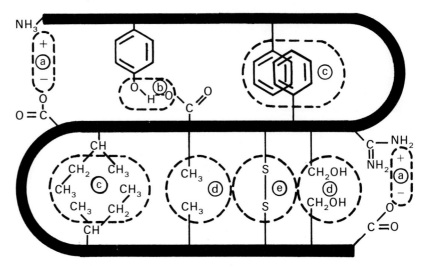

Figure 11-6
Probable types of bonding responsible for holding one polypeptide chain close to another.
(a) Electrostatic attraction, (b) hydrogen bonding, (c) interaction of nonpolar side chain groups
caused by repulsion of each by water, (d) van der Waals attractions, (e) disulfide bonding between
former −SH groups of cysteine molecules. (Modified after C. B. Anfinsen, 1959, *The Molecular
Basis of Evolution*, John Wiley & Sons, Inc., New York.)

tenderizer because of its ability to digest proteins has also been studied in some detail. Two-thirds of its amino acids can be removed without destroying its activity. It is clear that only a small part of a molecule so large as an enzyme can combine with the relatively small substrates upon which many act. The part essential for catalytic activity that combines with the substrate is referred to as the **active site**. In the case of papain, one-third of the molecule contains the active site. Just how many amino acids are required for activity is not known, but one cysteine and one aspartic acid are part of the active site of papain. That cysteine is essential for catalytic activity in many other enzymes is indicated by inhibition of their activity when compounds that destroy free sulfhydryl groups are added.

Much more research has been performed on the proteins of animals and man than on those of green plants, but many of the interpretations undoubtedly apply to plant proteins as well. Hemoglobin, the oxygen-carrying protein of the red blood cells, has a total of 574 amino acids divided among four protein subunits (polypeptide chains). The amino acid sequence for each chain has been determined. Two chains are identical "alpha chains" containing 141 amino acids, while the other two are identical "beta chains," each having 146 amino acids. Normal humans all contain the same alpha hemoglobin chains in their red blood cells. Occasionally, however, the amino acid valine is substituted for glutamic acid in one pair of chains. This inherited single change leads to a fatal disease called sickle cell anemia. It is clear that this glutamic acid is part of an active site of the normal hemoglobin. Another case is known where glycine may substitute for another glutamic acid near the first, with no harmful effect on the hemoglobin's properties. Whether or not a small change in amino acid sequence of a protein will cause a deleterious effect is thus difficult to predict and depends upon the type and position of such change.

Other animals also contain hemoglobins with alpha-type chains. Horse alpha hemoglobin contains 17 differences from human alpha hemoglobin in one chain of amino acids, while gorilla alpha hemoglobin differs from that of humans in only two amino acids.

The complete amino acid sequence of the protein cytochrome c has been determined in the case of humans, horses, pigs, rabbits, and chickens. Each cytochrome c molecule contains 104 amino acids. Two long amino acid sequences are identical among all five proteins, one (or both) of which likely contains an active site. Presumably the rest of the chain is necessary only to form a particular tertiary structure, and differences among the species studied were found here. In general, more closely related species have more nearly identical hemoglobin and cytochrome c proteins. Studies such as these are important in determining how enzymes are able to act as catalysts, and they also contribute to theories of evolution.

From the above discussion it may be seen that proteins can vary in at least three ways: *First*, in the total number of amino acids present; *second*, in the kinds of amino acids present and their abundance (composition); and *third*, in the arrangement or sequence of amino acids, which in turn apparently determines the way the chains are folded into the active tertiary structure. Even a small protein with a molecular weight of 12,500 could contain 100 amino acids with an average molecular weight of 125 each. Assuming the presence of 20 different amino acids, the number of theoretically possible ways to arrange these would be nearly 20^{100} (10^{130})! This staggering figure could never be approached in nature, although as many as ten thousand different proteins are thought by some experts to occur in certain plant cells. How various forms of life can be so different

should no longer be puzzling. The mystery lies more in how such great possible variety is limited. It is now known that a control mechanism exists in nucleic acid templates that restricts the number of different amino acid sequences actually formed in proteins (Chapter 17).

11.7 ISOZYMES

As mentioned earlier, hemoglobin is a protein containing more than a single polypeptide chain. Most other proteins having molecular weights greater than about 50,000 appear to be composed of two or more such chains, and these are said to possess a **quaternary structure**. (Each individual chain has its own primary, secondary, and tertiary structure.) The bonds holding the chains together are in some cases disulfide bonds, while others are not as strong as covalent bonds, and their exact types are not well understood. Hemoglobin is a good example of an enzyme with quaternary structure. Another, lactic acid dehydrogenase of various animals, is a tetramer consisting of four associated monomeric polypeptide chains, two of which may be different. These two different subunits are referred to as monomer *A* and monomer *B*. Five different forms of lactic acid dehydrogenase occur, each having a different number of each monomer, i.e., A^4B^0, A^3B^1, A^2B^2, A^1B^3, and A^0B^4. These different forms all catalyze the same reaction and are referred to as **isozymes** (or **isoenzymes**). Isozymes of various other enzymes are known. Leland Shannon and his colleagues at the University of California in Los Angeles studied the isozymes of peroxidase, an oxidizing enzyme especially abundant in horseradish roots. They purified seven isozymes from this source, using the techniques of ammonium sulfate precipitation, column chromatography on carboxymethyl and DEAE cellulose, and polyacrylamide gel electrophoresis, and were able to crystallize two of them.

Isozymes of aspartic acid—α-ketoglutaric acid transaminase, malic acid dehydrogenase and other enzymes are also known to exist in plants, and many more will surely be discovered. Several of these will likely prove to represent multiple forms resulting from different arrangements of subunit polypeptide chains. In some cases one isozyme is found in one subcellular organelle and a different one in another. For example, peas contain both a mitochondrial and a cytoplasmic malic acid dehydrogenase. In addition, several cases are known where one isozyme is abundant in one tissue or organ, while another is more important in a different tissue.

11.8 MECHANISM OF ACTION OF ENZYMES

As chemical reactions proceed, the most energetic molecules undergo change. Enzymes function by increasing the proportion of molecules having sufficient energy to react, thus speeding the rate of the process. They do this by *decreasing the energy required for reaction*, not by increasing the amount of energy in any molecule. This is illustrated in Fig. 11-7, which shows that as substrates are converted into products, an energy barrier must be overcome. This barrier is called the **energy of activation**. The presence of an enzyme greatly reduces this activation energy. For example, the energy of activation for the hydrolysis of sucrose to glucose and fructose is about 32,000 calories per mole, but the presence of the enzyme invertase lowers it to about 9,400 calories per mole.

Just how the activation energy is decreased by an enzyme is not certain. An **enzyme-substrate complex** is formed, although the bonds between the enzyme and substrate must be weak and short-lived, because such complexes are difficult to demonstrate experimentally. In the presence of the enzyme, the reactive electrons of the substrate apparently become oriented in such a manner as to allow bonds to be broken

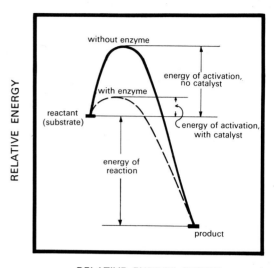

RELATIVE ENERGY STATES

Figure 11-7
Energy diagram for a metabolic reaction occurring in the presence and absence of an enzyme. Reacting substrate molecules must pass over an "energy hump" (accumulate activation energy) to allow formation of new chemical bonds present in the product, even though the product may be at a lower free energy level than the substrate. A catalyst, such as an enzyme, lowers the activation energy required, thus increasing the fraction of molecules that can react in a given time.

and reformed properly in an easier manner. There is evidence that a **three-point attachment** takes place between at least some enzymes and their substrates. This type of attachment explains how enzymes distinguish between D- and L-forms of various metabolites, as shown in Fig. 11-8. In this example, it is assumed that three functional groups of the enzyme are the —NH₂, the —COOH, and the —SH, and that these will unite only with the substrate groups as indicated on the left. The substrate on the right has the same groups, but in the wrong arrangement for combination. This union of enzyme and substrate is sometimes referred to as a lock-and-key process.

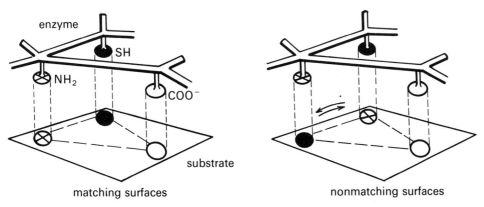

enzyme

SH

NH₂

COO⁻

substrate

matching surfaces

nonmatching surfaces

Figure 11-8
An illustration of how a part of an enzyme (branching structure at top with three "active groups")
might distinguish between D- and L-forms of substrates (lower rectangles with corresponding
but mirror image "reactive groups").

11.9 DENATURATION

Enzymes, unlike inorganic catalysts, are usually inactivated easily by temperatures much above those normally occurring in the cells. Above about 50°C, most, although not all, enzymes are rapidly converted into an inactive form. This inactivation is known as **denaturation**. In many cases denaturation is irreversible. Cold temperatures are nearly always used during the extraction and purification of enzymes to prevent heat denaturation. Surprisingly, a few are even sensitive to cold temperatures and must be kept well above the freezing point of water to prevent loss of activity.

Many agents other than temperature may also cause denaturation. These include strong acids or bases; heavy metals, such as silver, mercury, and lead; some detergents; oxidants; and ultraviolet and ionizing radiation. Sometimes the effects can be reversed by proper treatment. High concentrations of urea and guanidine cause denaturation, but their effects can easily be overcome by their removal or by dilution.

Denaturation is believed to result from changes in the spatial configuration of the amino acid chains (tertiary structure changes) in some proteins, and, in addition, to actual separation of the individual polypeptide chains in those having a quaternary structure. The hydrogen bonds of the tertiary structures can be easily broken by heat, which partly explains denaturation due to high temperatures. These factors also cause dissociation of some enzymes with a quaternary structure into their monomeric subunits. Oxidation may denature by causing disulfide bridges to be formed in the chains at points where SH groups of cysteine are present. Radiation can bring about this effect and probably others as well. The influence of heavy metals may result from their ability to unite with negatively charged carboxyl groups or with the sulfur of sulfhydryl groups. In all cases of denaturation the active site of the enzyme is altered so that catalytic activity is lost.

Because proteins unfold during denaturation, hydrophobic groups are exposed to the water, where formerly they were contained under more exposed hydrophilic portions of the molecules. Denatured proteins are thus much less soluble than the native forms. Sometimes this unfolding is accompanied by a measurable increase in volume. When this occurs, it has occasionally been possible to reverse the denaturation by the application of pressure to reduce the volume. Several cases of harmful effects of temperature on biological processes have been overcome by pressure.

Enzymes are often less sensitive to heat when they are inside the native cell environment than when they are in a solution alone or with only a few other protein types. The reasons for this are not understood, although there is evidence that they are protected by the substrates upon which they normally act and by other cellular constituents.

When enzymes are in a dry state, they are much less sensitive to heat denaturation than when water is abundant. This explains why dried seeds and the spores of fungi and bacteria are able to withstand temperatures as high as that of boiling water for short periods. The presence of steam in autoclaves used for sterilization increases the effectiveness of the treatment above that which would be obtained with only dry heat at the same temperature.

11.10   FACTORS INFLUENCING RATES OF ENZYMATIC REACTIONS

11.10.1   Enzyme and Substrate Concentrations

Catalysis is carried out only if the enzyme and substrate combine to form a transient complex. The rate of reaction is thus dependent upon the number of successful collisions of the two, which in turn is dependent upon the concentration of each. If sufficient substrate is present, doubling the enzyme concentration usually causes a two-fold increase in the rate of the reaction. The same is true for an increased substrate concentration in the presence of adequate amounts of

enzyme. Further addition of substrate eventually will cause no further rise in the reaction rate, because nearly all of the enzyme molecules are then combined with substrate. When this occurs, there are no more free enzyme active sites to cause catalysis. To increase the speed of reaction then requires addition of more enzyme.

Leonor Michaelis and Maude Menten reported, in 1913, a mathematical description of the kinetics of enzyme reactions, based on the assumption of a rapid formation of an enzyme-substrate complex (EnS). They arrived at an equation that relates the maximum possible velocity (V_{max}) of a reaction, observed initially when the substrate concentration is highest, and the velocity observed at a later time (v), to the substrate concentration (S) and to a property of the enzyme called the **Michaelis-Menten constant** (K_m). From the equation

$$v = \frac{V_{max}}{1 + \dfrac{K_m}{(S)}}$$

or the equivalent

$$\frac{1}{v} = \left[\frac{K_m}{V_{max}}\right]\left[\frac{1}{(S)}\right] + \frac{1}{V_{max}} \tag{43}$$

it can be seen that a plot of $1/v$ versus $1/(S)$ is equivalent to the expression

$$y = ax + b$$

where a is the slope and b the intercept of a straight line.

Figure 11-9 shows data obtained with an enzyme from bean leaves that catalyzes the conversion of orotic acid and 5-phosphoribosyl-1-pyrophosphate (PRPP) to orotidine monophosphate and pyrophosphate. This enzyme is essential to the synthesis of nucleic acids. In this reaction the rate of disappearance of orotic acid was measured in the presence of various concentrations of PRPP but with a constant amount of enzyme. The slope of the straight line usually obtained by plotting rates of

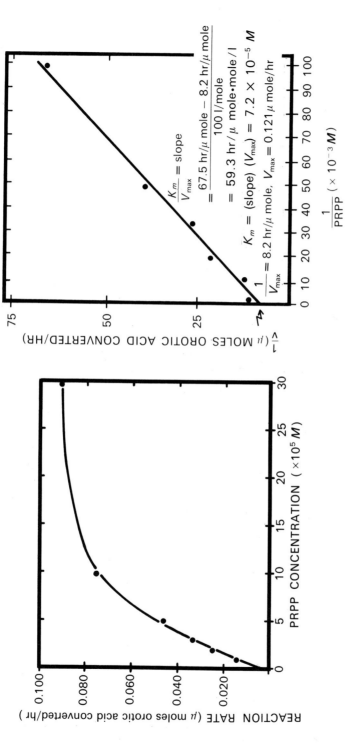

Figure 11-9

Relation of orotidine-5'-phosphate pyrophosphorylase activity to concentration of substrate (5-phosphoribosyl-1-pyrophosphate, PRPP). The enzyme (left) appears to be nearly saturated at a **PRPP** concentration of $30 \times 10^{-5} M$. The value ($\times 10^{5}$) on the abscissa indicates that molarities have been multiplied by 10^{5}. The reciprocal of enzyme activity (reaction rate) is plotted (right) against the reciprocal of PRPP concentration according to the method of H. Lineweaver and D. Burk, 1934, *J. Amer. Chem. Soc.* 56:658. From the resulting straight line, the K_m was calculated as shown. (Redrawn from data of J. Wolcott and C. Ross, 1967, *Plant Physiol.* 42:275. Used by permission.)

enzyme reactions in this way is equal to K_m/V_{max}. Since the intercept of the line with the ordinate is equal to $1/V_{max}$, K_m can be calculated. In the example of Fig. 11-9, K_m was found to be 7.2×10^{-5} moles/liter. Commonly, K_m values vary within a wide range, from about 10^{-1} to 10^{-6} M.

K_m is an important property of an enzyme, because once this value is obtained, the velocity of the reaction at any substrate concentration can be calculated. The K_m represents the (S) required for one-half the maximum reaction velocity. Furthermore, K_m is also an approximately inverse measure of the affinity of the enzyme for the substrate (the smaller the K_m, the greater the substrate affinity).

11.10.2 Temperature

A rise in temperature increases the kinetic energy of substrate and enzyme molecules, more frequent collisions occur, and the measured reaction rate becomes greater. Over the temperature ranges to which plants are most commonly exposed, the Q_{10} for diffusion of many substrates is between 1.2 and 1.4. However, the Q_{10} for many enzymatic reactions is above 2.0. The higher value indicates that temperature has an effect in addition to its influence on enzyme-substrate collisions. In 1889 the Swedish chemist Svante Arrhenius proposed a possible explanation for a two-fold or greater increase in the rate of a reaction when the temperature is raised 10°C.

Arrhenius pointed out that addition of heat to such a system increases the fraction of molecules having very high energies, energies sufficient to undergo reaction. This was illustrated in the Maxwell–Boltzmann curve of Fig. 3-1, which shows that a 10°C temperature rise caused only a small increase in the average kinetic energy of the molecules, but a doubling in the fraction having energies sufficient to react.

Temperatures much above 50°C rapidly denature most enzymes, so that the effect of further increases is difficult to measure. Another possible influence of temperature on measured reaction rates is upon the equilibrium constant. Sometimes the products may be thermodynamically favored at one temperature while the substrates are favored at a different temperature. The observed reaction rate is always a net rate, equal to the forward reaction minus the reverse reaction. Examples are known where a temperature rise causes a greater increase in the reverse reaction than in the direction in which it is being measured. Because of this and the different susceptibility of various enzymes to denaturation, concentrations of many cellular components vary with temperature.

11.10.3 Hydrogen Ion Concentration

The pH of the medium influences enzyme activity in various ways. Usually there is an optimum pH at which enzymes function, with decreases in activity at higher or lower pH values. Sometimes a plot of activity versus pH, as in Fig. 11-10, gives an almost bell-shaped curve, while with another enzyme the curve may be almost flat. The optimum pH is often between 6 and 8 but may be somewhat higher or lower. Extremes of the pH scale usually cause denaturation.

Apart from the denaturation effect, the pH can influence reaction rates in at least two ways. *First*, enzyme activity often depends upon the presence of free amino or carboxyl groups. These may be either charged or uncharged, but only one form is presumed effective in a given case. If an uncharged amino group is essential, the pH optimum will be relatively high, while a neutral carboxyl group requires a low pH. *Second*, the pH controls the ionization of many substrates, some of which must be ionized for the reaction to proceed.

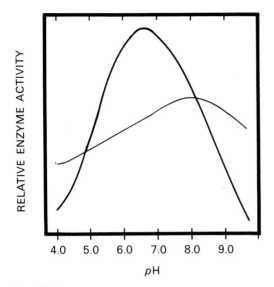

Figure 11-10
Influence of pH upon activity of two different enzymes. The pH optimum and shape of the curve vary greatly among enzymes and depend somewhat upon reaction conditions.

11.10.4 Reaction Products

The reaction rate may be determined by measuring the rate of disappearance of substrates or the rate of product accumulation. By either method the reaction is usually observed to proceed more slowly as time proceeds. Part of this rate decrease can be explained by the constant denaturation of enzyme, but another factor is often involved. As the products accumulate, their concentrations become high enough so that reversal becomes more likely.

11.10.5 Inhibitors

An enormous group of substances have been discovered to block the catalytic effects of enzymes. These may be either inorganic, such as many heavy metal cations, or they may be organic. Both groups are usually classified according to whether their effect is competitive or noncompetitive with the substrate.

Competitive inhibitors commonly have structures sufficiently similar to the substrate that they *compete* for the active site of the enzyme. When such a combination of enzyme and inhibitor is formed, the concentration of effective enzyme molecules is lowered, decreasing the reaction rate. The inhibitor may or may not itself undergo a change caused by the enzyme. Addition of more of the natural substrate overcomes the effect of a competitive inhibitor.

Noncompetitive inhibitors also appear to combine with the enzyme, but at a location different from where the substrate attaches. This effect is not overcome by simply raising the substrate concentration. Noncompetitive inhibitors generally show less structural resemblance to the substrate than do the competitive type. Toxic metal ions and compounds that destroy essential sulfhydryl groups often are noncompetitive inhibitors.

A difficulty with classifying inhibitors as competitive or noncompetitive is that they may inhibit more than one enzyme, but not in all cases be reversed by addition of substrate. For example, sometimes an essential sulfhydryl group is part of the molecule to which the substrate attaches, while with other enzymes it is only adjacent to this point. Certain compounds such as iodoacetic acid, potassium ferricyanide, p-chloromercuribenzoate, and iodine combine with or oxidize these —SH groups. Their effects are usually overcome by additional substrate only if they react with the active site.

Most poisons have an effect upon plants and animals because they inhibit enzymes. Certain of these will later be discussed in relation to the specific processes that are affected. Enzymes may also be inhibited by any protein denaturant, such as strong acids or bases, or by high concentrations of urea.

11.11 ALLOSTERIC PROTEINS

Z. Dische discovered in about 1940 a phenomenon that has recently been recognized as having considerable importance in regulation of enzyme activity. He found that the phosphorylation of glucose in erythrocytes was inhibited by phosphoglyceric acid, a molecule quite different from glucose in structure. Dische realized that this acid was neither a substrate nor a product of the phosphorylation and that it was thus not likely to be a competitive inhibitor of that reaction. The significance of his discovery was not appreciated until the mid-1950s when it was found that several amino acids in bacteria effectively and specifically inhibit their own syntheses by what has become known as **feedback inhibition**.

Inhibition of the formation of many products by a feedback mechanism occurs in various organisms, and in all cases it results from combination of the product with one of the early enzymes in the metabolic pathway responsible for its synthesis. This combination is not with the active site of the sensitive enzyme, but with another, or **allosteric site**. Proteins having two or more stereospecifically different and non-overlapping receptor sites are called **allosteric proteins**. Molecules that bind with allosteric sites are **allosteric effectors**. The formation of an enzyme-allosteric effector complex is assumed to bring about a reversible alteration of the molecular structure of the protein, referred to as an **allosteric transition**. Such transitions presumably modify the active site so that its ability to unite with the substrate is altered (Fig. 11-11). Although most of the allosteric transitions known lead to inhibition, some result in activation. Activation is assumed to be often caused by a greater affinity of the active site for the substrate after the allosteric transition. This view is supported by observations of lower K_m values for the substrate in the presence of some activating effectors. The important functions that feedback or allosteric inhibitions

and stimulations probably play in regulating metabolism and development of plants are discussed in Chapter 20.

Most allosteric enzymes are composed of subunits, such as occur in isozymes. With some of these, a reversible dissociation into monomers can take place, often accompanied by a loss in catalytic activity. This dissociation and the reassociation that can occur is influenced by concentration of the enzyme, pH, ionic strength, temperature, the presence or absence of certain cations, and by certain allosteric effectors. It is thus not surprising that activity of enzymes within the cell is easily influenced by environmental factors.

11.12 PROSTHETIC GROUPS, COENZYMES, AND VITAMINS

11.12.1 Hydrogen-carrying Coenzymes

The first coenzyme was discovered in a yeast extract by A. Harden and W. J. Young, in about 1904. They found that a dialyzable substance was necessary for fermentation by yeast enzymes, and they called this unknown compound cozymase. Since then it has been called coenzyme I or **diphosphopyridine nucleotide** (abbreviated **DPN**). Now it is more properly named **nicotinamide adenine dinucleotide** and is abbreviated **NAD**. This important molecule contains nicotinamide (an amide of nicotinic acid), adenylic acid (a nucleotide), and phosphate. Lack of nicotinic acid, also called **niacin** or vitamin B, in the diet of animals causes pellegra.

A second coenzyme, discovered in 1934, was originally named coenzyme II, later called **triphosphopyridine nucleotide (TPN)**, and is now called **nicotinamide adenine dinucleotide phosphate**, or **NADP**. The structure of NAD is shown in Fig. 11-12, and NADP is identical except that a third phosphate is attached to the position indicated by the asterisk.

NAD and NADP play vital roles in oxidation-reduction reactions in all cells. Hence they

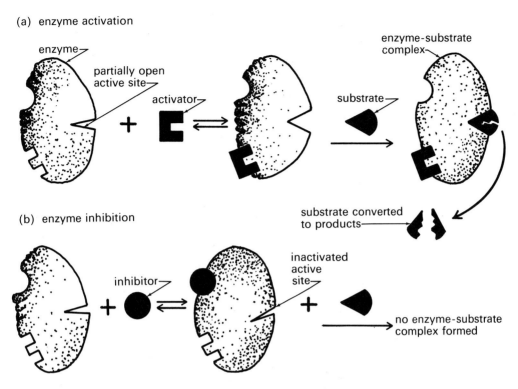

(a) enzyme activation

enzyme

partially open active site

activator

enzyme-substrate complex

substrate

substrate converted to products

(b) enzyme inhibition

inhibitor

inactivated active site

no enzyme-substrate complex formed

Figure 11-11
A hypothetical model illustrating how the presence of activators and repressors might influence allosteric enzymes, thus affecting reaction rates. In (a), attachment of the activator to the enzyme opens the active site, allowing it to combine with the substrate. In (b), attachment of the inhibitor closes the active site, preventing attachment of the substrate.

are essential for photosynthesis, respiration, fat metabolism, and many other physiological processes. The nicotinamide ring has the ability to accept two electrons from several reduced hydrogen donors (denoted AH_2 in the reaction below), thus becoming reduced. The **reduced forms** are called **NADH** and **NADPH**. The added hydrogen atom accounts for one electron, while a second electron is accepted with the expulsion of the proton:

$$NAD \text{ or } NADP + AH_2 \rightleftharpoons NADH$$
$$\text{or} \quad NADPH + H^+ + A$$

NAD and NADP are coenzymes for several of the **dehydrogenases**. These enzymes remove hydrogens from various substrates, determined by the specificity of the enzyme involved, and transfer them to either NAD or NADP. From NADH or NADPH the electrons are passed to some other substrate, regenerating the oxidized forms of the coenzymes. From this standpoint, NAD and NADP act catalytically and are not changed by the reactions. Actually, however, there is often an appreciable lag between the time they accept and donate the electrons, and NADH and NADPH then accumulate. In this respect they are more properly defined as substrates of the reaction than as coenzymes, and in practice there is no rigorous distinction between substrates and coenzymes like these.

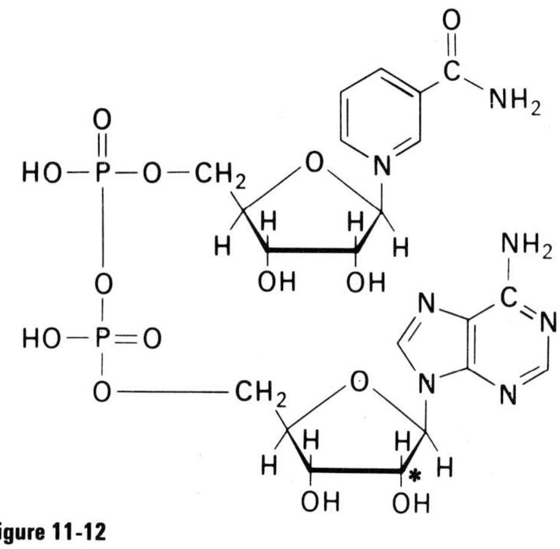

Figure 11-12

The structure of nicotinamide adenine dinucleotide (NAD). NADP is identical to NAD except that it has a phosphate esterified at C-2 of ribose in the position indicated by an asterisk. The nicotinamide ring that can undergo reduction is shown in the upper right of the figure.

The concentrations of these coenzymes, as well as others, are very low in plants and vary with the plant age and the tissue examined. The total content of NAD, NADH, NADP, and NADPH in most tissues was estimated to be less than 0.1 mg per gram fresh weight. The amount of NADH is usually least of all, perhaps because it is quickly oxidized to NAD.

A second group of compounds undergoing alternate oxidation and reduction also exists. These are yellowish substances called **flavins**. The most common is called **flavin adenine dinucleotide** (abbreviated **FAD**), while a second lacks the adenine part and is named **flavin mononucleotide**, or **FMN**. The reduced forms are **FADH$_2$** and **FMNH$_2$**. The yellow component is **riboflavin**, or **vitamin B$_2$**. Their functions are similar to those of NAD and NADP except that they react with different substrates. The flavins are usually rather tightly held to the enzymes, many of which are dehydrogenases. Sometimes as many as four molecules of flavin occur per molecule of enzyme. Usually the enzyme con-

cerned contains either FMN or FAD, but at least one case is known where both are attached to the same protein.

11.12.2 Coenzymes of Phosphate Transfer

Coenzymes are known for which the primary function is to accept and transfer a phosphate group. The predominant member of this group is **adenosine triphosphate**, universally abbreviated **ATP** (Fig. 11-13). ATP contains three phosphates connected to the sugar ribose, which in turn is connected to a heterocyclic ring structure called adenine. The combination of such a nitrogen-containing ring with a sugar and one or more phosphate groups is a **nucleotide**. Nucleotides in general are very important in metabolism and play vital roles in hereditary properties because of their presence in nucleic acids. NAD and NADP, mentioned above, consist partially of nucleotides.

ATP functions as an energy carrier throughout the cell. The energy is stored in the two phosphate groups farthest from the ribose (most commonly, the terminal phosphate). The bonds holding these two phosphates together are **pyrophosphate bonds**. These are **anhydride bonds**, formed when two phosphoric acid groups are united in a water-releasing reaction. These bonds are different from those of ordinary phosphate esters, which are formed between a hydroxyl group of an alcohol and a phosphoric acid group. Pyrophosphate bonds, as in ATP and other closely related nucleotides, directly or indirectly provide the energy to drive many of the processes of life that need an energy source. When either of the two pyrophosphate bonds is split off from one mole of ATP with the addition of water, as is easily done in acid or alkaline solutions, approximately 10,000 calories of free energy are released. This contrasts to the free energy change of about 2,000 or 3,000 calories per mole accompanying the hydrolysis of such ordinary phosphate ester bonds as the

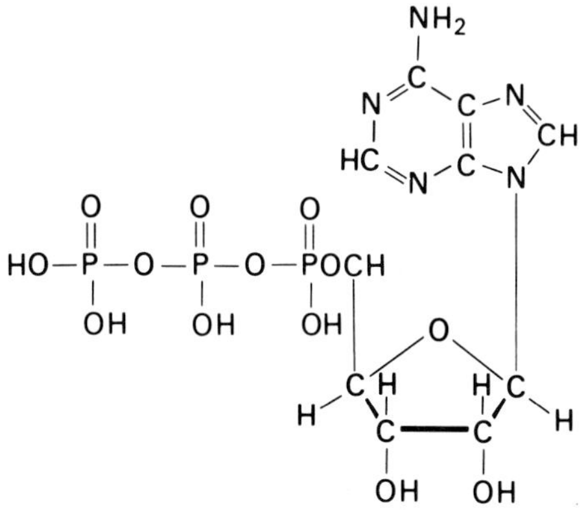

Figure 11-13
The structure of adenosine triphosphate (ATP).

one between ribose and the adjacent phosphate in ATP. The pyrophosphate bonds are thus much more easily hydrolyzed, or are more **labile**, than ordinary phosphate ester bonds. From this standpoint, they are not strong bonds in the same sense that chemists express the energies in most covalent bonds. Instead, pyrophosphate bonds are recognized as being energy-rich because the energy released when they are split can be used to drive other reactions. The energy that would ordinarily be released and lost as heat is trapped in the bonds of a new compound, the product of the reaction.

Two examples of the type of reactions driven by ATP will illustrate the importance of energy rich pyrophosphate bonds. The utilization of glucose by nearly all cells, plant or animal, requires an initial **phosphorylation**. That is, phosphate must be combined with glucose in order for this sugar to provide cells with energy. Even though the proper enzyme is present, a suitable supply of phosphate is essential for the reaction to occur at a measurable rate. Only a pyrophosphate as in ATP can provide phosphate at an energy potential sufficient to transfer it to glucose [see (R11-3)].

Glucose + ATP $\longrightarrow$ glucose-6-phosphate

+ adenosine diphosphate (R11-3)

Note that **adenosine diphosphate (ADP)** is also a product. Similar transfer reactions are very common, and for this reason the terminal phosphate of ATP is often said to have a **high transfer potential**.

A second type of process requiring the split of ATP is one in which another reactant accepts the energy of the pyrophosphate bond but does not combine with the phosphate. The formation of glutamine from glutamic acid [shown in (R11-4)] is a good example:

NH_4^+ + glutamic acid + ATP $\longrightarrow$

glutamine + ADP + H_3PO_4 (R11-4)

Here inorganic orthophosphate, often abbreviated **Pi**, is also a product. All, or nearly all, enzymatic reactions involving ATP require a divalent cation (most commonly magnesium, but often manganese, and occasionally zinc or calcium), and in some cases it is fairly well established that this is because the metal becomes attached to the ATP to yield an active complex. The metal is probably bound to two negatively charged oxygen atoms of adjacent ionized phosphate groups, forming a bridge between them and facilitating bond breakage or formation in the terminal or subterminal phosphate group. Several enzymes requiring such divalent cations act upon molecules that do not contain phosphate, or upon phosphate-containing substances other than ATP. In some of these cases the metal reacts with the enzyme itself, inducing conformational (structural) changes that increase catalytic ability.

Subsequent chapters will show how energy released in respiration or provided by light energy during photosynthesis is trapped in the terminal phosphate of ATP. Other important molecules having a terminal phosphate of high transfer potential include triphosphates of the nucleosides **uridine, guanosine,** and **cytidine (UTP, GTP,** and **CTP)**. Their functions will be described later.

11.12.3 Sugar-Transferring Coenzymes

Coenzymes having the ability to transfer sugar units to acceptor molecules are present in plants. They participate in the formation of substances that make up a large part of the weight of a plant, including cellulose, starch, hemicelluloses, and sucrose. These coenzymes are combinations of a sugar, most commonly glucose, with a phosphate group of a nucleotide. Examples are **uridine diphosphoglucose, adenosine diphosphoglucose, cytidine diphosphoglucose,** and **guanosine diphosphoglucose,** abbreviated **UDPG, ADPG, CDPG,** and **GDPG,** respectively. Their functions and structures will be more fully described in the following chapter.

11.12.4 Coenzymes Transferring One or a Few Carbons

Two coenzymes are known whose function is concerned with the addition of CO_2 **(carboxylation)** or loss of CO_2 **(decarboxylation)** from certain metabolites. The first is a pyrophosphate form of **thiamine (vitamin B_1)**, called **thiamine pyrophosphate**, which is essential for enzymes decarboxylating the respiratory substrates pyruvic acid and α-ketoglutaric acid. It is also necessary for the enzyme transketolase, whose function is to transfer a two-carbon unit from one molecule to another. Transketolase is important in both respiration and photosynthesis. The second coenzyme in this category is **biotin (vitamin H)**, which is needed in a key carboxylation reaction of fat synthesis.

In 1953, Fritz Lipmann discovered a compound referred to as **coenzyme A,** abbreviated **CoA.** CoA is now known to explain the requirement of animals for the vitamin **pantothenic**

acid. The function of CoA is to transfer acyl groups such as acetyl or succinyl from one compound to another in respiration and in fat metabolism. CoA possesses the ability to do this partly because of a sulfhydryl group at one end of the molecule. The sulfur on the —SH group unites with the carboxyl group of organic acids such as acetic or succinic acid, forming a **thiol ester,** as in the combination of coenzyme A and acetate:

$$CH_3-\underset{\underset{O}{\|}}{C}-S-CoA$$

Coenzymes transferring one-carbon units include **folic acid** and **S-adenosyl methionine.** Folic acid, or its derivatives, transfers formate $(HCOO^-)$ or formaldehyde (HCHO) units during the synthesis of certain nucleotides and in the formation of serine from glycine. *S*-adenosyl methionine is a combination of the amino acid methionine and the nucleoside adenosine (adenine-ribose):

$$Adenosine-\underset{\underset{CH_3}{|}}{\overset{+}{S}}-CH_2-CH_2-\underset{\underset{NH_2}{|}}{CH}-COOH$$

The presence of adenosine facilitates the transfer of the methyl group from the sulfur atom to a variety of other cellular compounds such as lignins and pectins.

11.12.5 Pyridoxal Phosphate

The amino group of many amino acids can be transferred to an α-keto acid, forming a new amino acid and a different α-keto acid. These transamination reactions, which will be discussed in Chapter 16, and several others involve the coenzyme **pyridoxal phosphate,** which is derived from **pyridoxin, vitamin B_6**

11.12.6 Porphyrin Compounds

Finally, the metalloporphyrin prosthetic groups should be mentioned. These are groups of

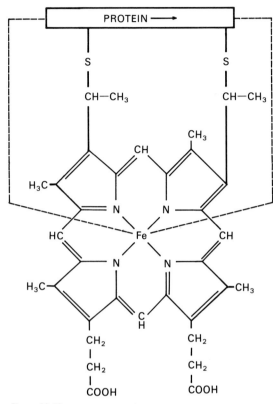

Figure 11-14

The heme structure of cytochrome *c* according to H. Theorell, 1947, *Adv. in Enzymol.* 7:265. The pigment is believed to be bound to the protein through the sulfur atoms of two cysteine residues and also through association of the iron atom with nitrogen atoms in histidine residues of the protein.

pigments usually attached to proteins and containing either iron or magnesium chelated to each of four **pyrrole** units. Some of these are iron-containing heme proteins called **cytochromes**. Cytochromes participate in respiration and photosynthesis, because they can shuttle electrons from one compound to another. The structure of the heme portion of one of these, cytochrome *c*, is illustrated in Fig. 11-14. The iron is bound both to the nitrogen atom of each of the four pyrrole units and also to the nitrogen atoms of two histidines in the protein.

Iron is essential for cytochrome function, since it is reversibly reduced and oxidized from the ferric to the ferrous state as respiration or photosynthesis proceeds. Cytochromes were first described in 1886 by C. A. MacMunn, a Scottish physician, who suggested that they function in respiration. Unfortunately, few scientists accepted his beliefs, and it was not until 1925 that D. Keilin verified and extended his results and named these pigments cytochromes. Keilin recognized at least three different cytochromes, and he named these by adding small subscript letters, such as *a*, *b*, or *c*, after the word cytochrome. They are distinguished most easily by the fact that the ferrous form of each absorbs slightly different wavelengths of visible light. Similar pigments with only slightly different absorption bands from the above three were discovered, and these were named by attaching subscript numbers to the letters, i.e., cytochromes b_6, a_1, a_3, etc.

In the **chlorophylls**, pyrrole molecules surround magnesium, and the side-chains differ, but otherwise the structures of the chlorophylls and the nonprotein, pigment portions of the cytochromes are basically similar. Chlorophyll structures are given in Chapter 13. Their function, of course, is in photosynthesis.

11.13 THE RELATIONSHIP BETWEEN COENZYMES AND VITAMINS

It may be noted that many of the prosthetic groups or coenzymes described are similar or identical to several vitamins. It has become increasingly apparent that most, although perhaps not all, vitamins act as coenzymes in animals. Their function in plants is usually identical, but animals require an exogenous supply of vitamins, while plants possess the enzymes to synthesize their own. We shall later see (Chapters 20 and 21) that some coenzymes are translocated within the plant, performing the function of hormones.

Carbohydrates and Related Compounds

12.1 CARBOHYDRATES IN THE PLANT

Carbohydrates are of special significance in plants, since they represent important food reserves and are part of the structural framework of each cell. They comprise 50–80 percent of the total dry weight of most species. Many compounds (such as lignin) can be considered carbohydrate derivatives, and they, too, are very important in the structure and metabolism of the plant. Of course, all the carbohydrates are ultimately produced from the products of photosynthesis. Metabolism of a plant is, to a large extent, concerned with changing such photosynthetic products into the derivatives that constitute the plant. To understand cellular structure, metabolism, and growth, it is essential to investigate the chemistry of some of the carbohydrates and related compounds.

12.2 CHEMISTRY OF THE CARBOHYDRATES

Carbohydrates are molecules composed of carbon, hydrogen, and oxygen corresponding to or approximating the empirical formula $(CH_2O)_n$. Many compounds contain, in addition, such other elements as phosphorus and nitrogen. Some carbohydrates are important components of the cell wall, while others are found only in the cytoplasm or vacuole.

12.2.1 Simple Sugars

The most fundamental group of carbohydrates consists of **monosaccharides**, which do not yield simpler compounds upon hydrolysis. The number of carbon atoms in the monosaccharides found in most plants varies from three to eight, while the most common contain five and six carbons. Present in all of these is either of two functional groups, an **aldehyde**

in the **aldoses**, or a **ketone**

$$-\underset{\underset{O}{\|}}{C}-R$$

in the **ketoses**. These groups will reduce the cupric ion to the cuprous form, and hence sugars that contain these groups are known as **reducing sugars**.

The chemical structures of the monosaccharides having more than four carbon atoms may be written in various ways. Perhaps the simplest method is to show them as a straight chain,[1] as indicated below for **glucose**, an aldose; and **ribulose**, a ketose.

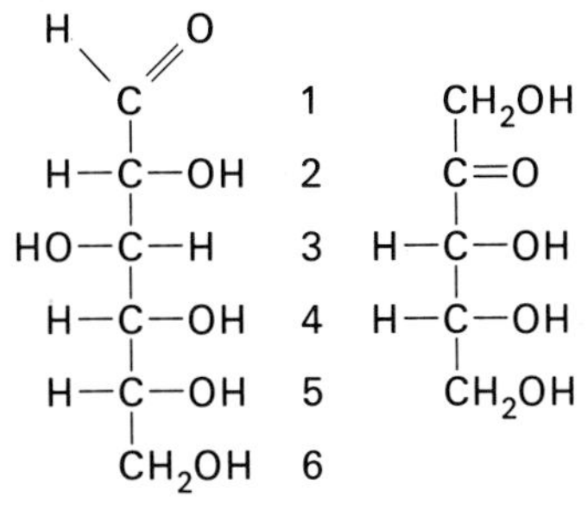

D-glucose   D-ribulose

Note that these molecules contain asymmetric carbon atoms, glucose having four of these, and ribulose two. When the hydroxyl group of the asymmetric carbon farthest from the aldehyde or ketone group (carbon-5 of glucose or carbon-4 of ribulose) is shown on the right, the sugar is of the D-form. If this hydroxyl is on the left, and the hydrogens and hydroxyls on the other asymmetric carbons are also reversed in such a way that a mirror image is produced, the corresponding L- sugar results. D- sugars are by far the most common in living organisms, and only a very few of the L-form have ever been found.

Most monosaccharides behave as if they exist in a ring structure rather than in an open chain. The most common rings are those containing six members, the **pyranoses**, or five members, the **furanoses**. Most sugars having six or more carbons are more stable in the pyranose form, but fructose, a very common six-carbon sugar, and those with only five carbons, exist as furanoses. In each case the ring contains the oxygen of the hydroxyl group from the asymmetric carbon atom farthest from the aldehyde or ketone group. The

---

[1] In reality, a chain of carbon atoms must always zigzag or form a ring, since the tetrahedral bonds are never separated by 180°.

functional aldehyde or ketone reacts with this hydroxyl, yielding a ring, as is shown in (R12-1) for D-glucose:

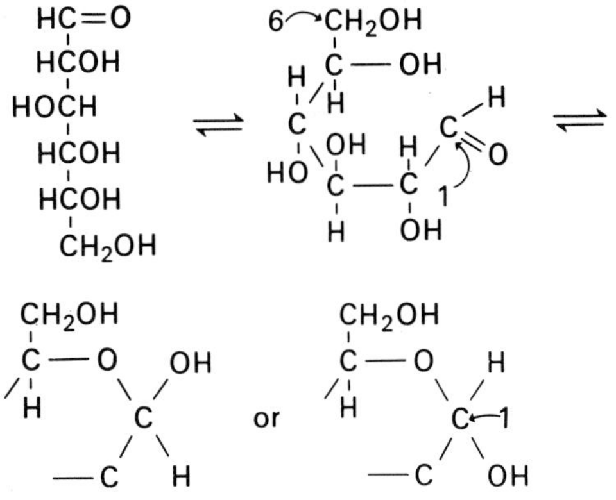

(R12-1)

When the ring closes, the oxygen atom formerly a part of the aldehyde group but now a part of the new hydroxyl group is arranged in a manner that may be written either above or below the carbon to which it is bonded. The structure in which the hydroxyl is written above, nearer the oxygen of the ring, is called **the beta form**, and when below, it is called **the alpha form**. Starch is a polymer composed of α-D-glucose units, while cellulose is made up of β-D-glucose units.

From the above convention for writing the structures, it might be implied that all of the members of the ring lie in the same plane and the other groups lie above or below this plane. This is not the case, however, since four groups arranged around a carbon atom tend to form a tetrahedron, and for six-membered rings this results in two of the members lying in a plane different from the other four. Such a ring can exist in either the **chair** or the **boat** form (Fig. 12-1). The free sugars are much more stable in the chair form, although the boat form of glucose apparently exists in starch.

12.3 SUGAR DERIVATIVES

Many derivatives of the monosaccharides exist in plants, and most of these are present in

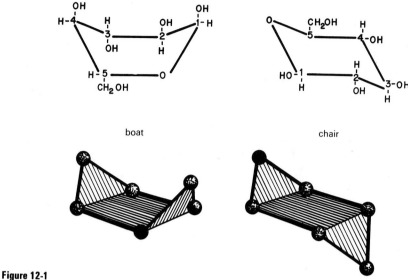

boat   chair

Figure 12-1
Boat and chair forms of a hexose ring sugar molecule like glucose.

amounts even greater than the corresponding sugar from which they are formed. The structures of some of these are presented in Fig. 12-2. Perhaps the most important group consists of compounds in which one or two of the hydroxyl groups are combined with phosphoric acid. The addition of phosphate to a sugar is called phosphorylation and is a necessary step before the many sugar transformations of metabolism can occur. Few reactions in the plant are known in which sugars participate except in a phosphorylated form. Most of these phosphate compounds are true esters formed between the hydroxyl groups of the sugar and phosphoric acid. Some, however, are anhydrides produced by reactions between phosphate and the carboxyl groups of certain sugar acids.

Other compounds that can arise from sugars are the **sugar acids**. These acids are formed when either the aldehyde or the terminal —CH_2OH is oxidized to a carboxyl group. Examples of the latter type of oxidation are **glucuronic acid** and **galacturonic acid**, formed from the sugars glu-

cose and **galactose**. Each is a component of cell walls. **Gluconic acid** is formed from glucose by oxidation of the aldehyde group. In plants, gluconic acid exists in the phosphorylated form, the phosphate being attached by an ester linkage at carbon-6. This compound, **6-phosphogluconic acid**, is an important respiratory intermediate (Fig. 12-2).

The cell walls of fungi (but not of higher plants) contain a polysaccharide called **chitin**. Chitin is a polymer of **acetyl glucosamine**. Glucosamine itself is formed by replacement of the hydroxyl group on carbon-2 of glucose with an amino group. Chitin also occurs in the exoskeletons of arthropods (insects, spiders, crustaceans, etc.).

A final type of sugar derivative includes the **sugar alcohols**. Here the aldehyde group is reduced to a primary alcohol. Two common examples are **sorbitol** and **mannitol**, often found in appreciable concentrations in woody species and fungi. Sorbitol is an important carbohydrate translocated in the bark of apple trees,

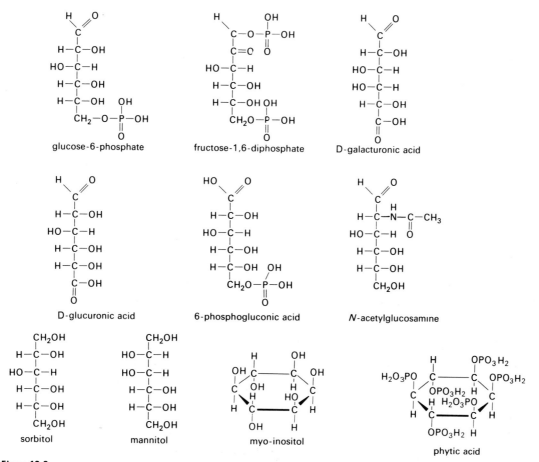

Figure 12-2
Molecular structures of some sugar derivatives.

along with sucrose. Sorbitol also occurs in particularly high concentrations in fruits of pears, apricots, cherries, and apples, and other members of the Rosaceae family. Another sugar alcohol, consisting of six carbons connected in a ring, is **myo-inositol**, formerly called *meso*-inositol. This compound is most abundant in certain seeds, where the hydroxyl groups are phosphorylated to produce **phytic acid** (Fig. 12-2). Phytic acid and its calcium and magnesium salts (phytates) act as storage forms of phosphorus needed by the germinating seed.

Myo-inositol also forms a part of certain phospholipids and is thus important in membrane structure.

12.4 CLASSIFICATION OF IMPORTANT PLANT CARBOHYDRATES

12.4.1 Monosaccharides

Of the many different sugars capable of synthesis by the organic chemists, only a few are common in plants. They may be classified first according to their number of carbon atoms.

12.4.1A Trioses

The **trioses** have three carbons, and the two common ones both exist as phosphate esters. These are D-**glyceraldehyde-3-phosphate** and **dihydroxyacetone phosphate**, both essential respiratory intermediates (Chapter 15):

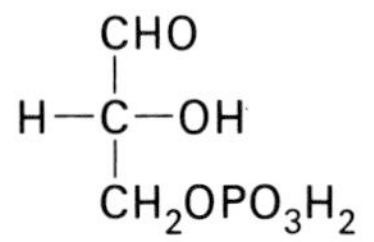

$$
\begin{array}{c}
CHO \\
| \\
H-C-OH \\
| \\
CH_2OPO_3H_2
\end{array}
$$

D-glyceraldehyde-3-phosphate

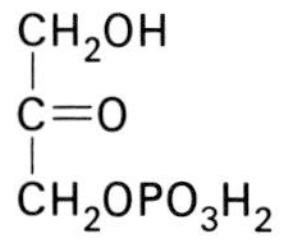

$$
\begin{array}{c}
CH_2OH \\
| \\
C=O \\
| \\
CH_2OPO_3H_2
\end{array}
$$

dihydroxyacetone phosphate

12.4.1B Tetroses

A four-carbon **tetrose, erythrose,** may exist in plants as D-erythrose-4-phosphate:

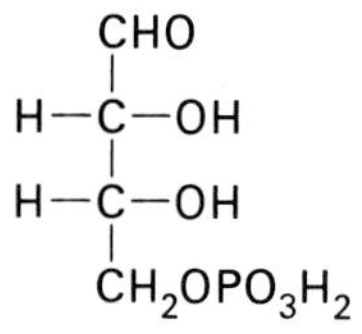

$$
\begin{array}{c}
CHO \\
| \\
H-C-OH \\
| \\
H-C-OH \\
| \\
CH_2OPO_3H_2
\end{array}
$$

This compound is believed to be involved in respiration and in synthesis of certain aromatic compounds (including the amino acids phenylalanine and tyrosine); of lignin (a cell wall material); and of the blue, purple, or pink anthocyanin pigments.

12.4.1C Pentoses

Several **pentoses** (five-carbon sugars) are important. These may be divided into the **aldopentoses**, having an aldehyde group, and the **ketopentoses**, having a ketone group. They are shown in Fig. 12-3.

L-**arabinose** is one of a few L-configuration sugars commonly encountered in plants. Both arabinose and **xylose** apparently rarely occur free but instead are often found as part of polymers in cell walls, the **arabans** and **xylans**, respectively. **Ribose** and its derivative, **deoxyribose**, also usually exist only in combined form. Ribose has already been encountered in Chapter 11 in the nucleotide coenzymes such as ATP, NAD, NADP, FAD, and coenzyme A. In a similar nucleotide form it occurs as part of **ribonucleic acid, RNA.** Deoxyribose is found exclusively as part of the nucleotides making up the hereditary material **deoxyribonucleic acid, DNA.** In these cases, both ribose and deoxyribose exist in furanose ring forms, in which the oxygen of carbon-4 is also united to carbon-1.

Two phosphorylated forms of ribose have been found. One of these, **ribose-5-phosphate**, is involved in respiration, photosynthesis, and nucleic acid synthesis. The second, **5-phosphoribosyl-1-pyrophosphate**, is necessary for nucleic acid synthesis and is probably the form of ribose used for synthesis of all nucleotides:

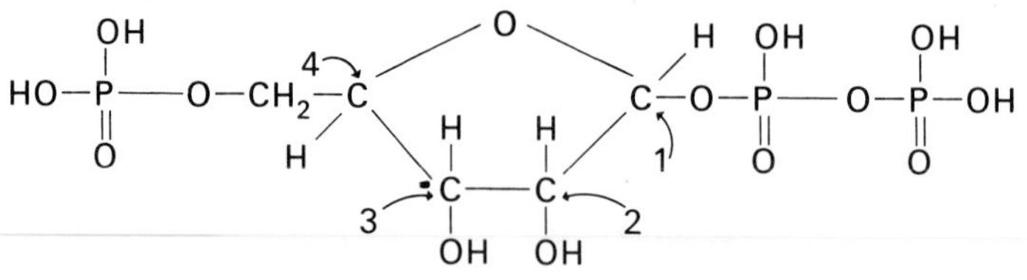

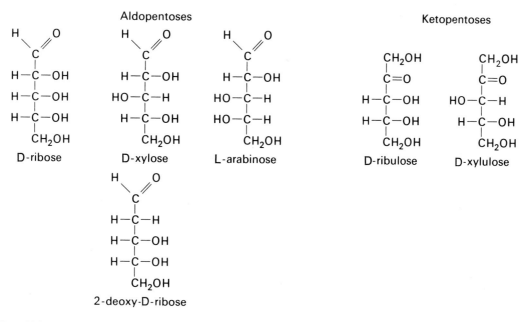

Figure 12-3
Molecular structures of some pentose sugars.

Apparently the pyrophosphate group of this molecule provides the energy necessary to transfer the remaining ribose-5-phosphate portion to a suitable acceptor, since pyrophosphate is split away from ribose when nucleotides are formed.

The ketopentoses **xylulose** and **ribulose** also occur almost exclusively as phosphate esters. **Xylulose-5-phosphate** and **ribulose-5-phosphate** are respiratory compounds. **Ribulose-1,5-diphosphate** is the usual compound with which carbon dioxide reacts in photosynthesis (Chapter 14).

12.4.1D Hexoses The common **hexoses** (six-carbon sugars) may be classified into the aldohexoses, D-**glucose**, D-**galactose**, and D-**mannose**, and the ketohexose D-**fructose** (Fig. 12-4). D-glucose is also variously known as dextrose,

corn sugar, and grape sugar. It usually occurs both free and in the phosphorylated esters, **glucose-1-phosphate** and **glucose-6-phosphate**. In addition, starch and cellulose are both polymers of glucose. Galactose and mannose are found only in traces in uncombined form but both are common in larger molecules.

The sugar alcohol **mannitol** is formed metabolically from fructose and is common in fungi but probably exists only in small amounts in most higher plants. (It has been used in osmotic studies—Chapter 5.) **Agar**, a cell wall constituent present in certain marine algae, is made up largely of galactose. In addition, both galactose and mannose may be polymerized to yield the **galactans** and **mannans**. These, like the arabans and xylans, are of wide occurrence in secondary cell walls of wood, straw, and seeds.

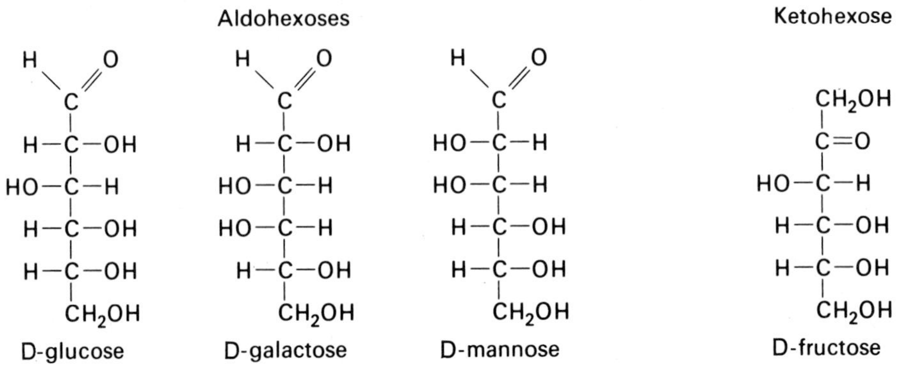

Figure 12-4
Molecular structures of some hexose sugars.

Fructose, also called levulose or fruit sugar, is found in appreciable amounts in fruit juices, in the nectar from plant glands, and in honey. Condensation of many fructose units yields the **fructosans**, storage forms of carbohydrate found in some plants. Two phosphorylated derivatives of fructose are important in respiration. These are **fructose-6-phosphate** and **fructose-1,6-diphosphate**. Both fructose and glucose exist in sucrose, the common table sugar.

12.4.1E Heptose One seven-carbon sugar is believed to be important. This is **sedoheptulose**, which is present in the free state primarily in leaves of *Sedum* and other succulents. **Sedoheptulose-7-phosphate**, however, is a respiratory and photosynthetic intermediate presumably occurring in all plants.

12.4.2 Disaccharides, Trisaccharides, and Tetrasaccharides

The union of two monosaccharides yields the **disaccharides**. Of these, **sucrose** is the most significant because of its wide distribution, its relatively high concentration in most cells, and its metabolic importance. Sucrose contains one molecule each of glucose and fructose (except

that one H_2O is split out between them). It was long known that sucrose is not a reducing sugar, suggesting that both the C-1 aldehyde of glucose and the C-2 ketone of fructose must somehow be masked. Yet it was not until 1927 that the complete structure of sucrose was worked out by W. N. Haworth and his co-workers. Glucose and fructose are combined through their reactive aldehyde and ketone groups in sucrose as follows:

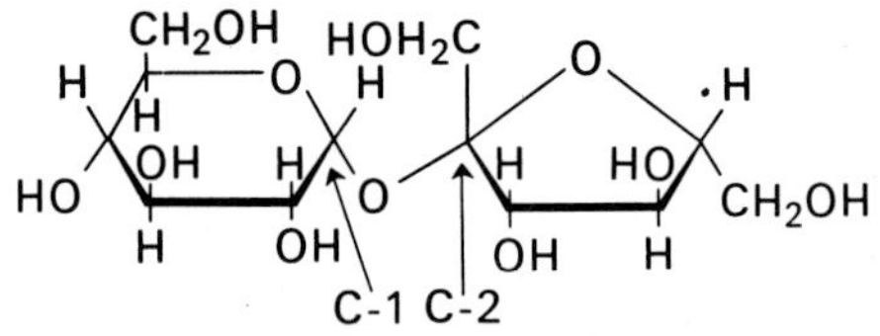

Sucrose is believed to represent the principal form in which carbohydrates are translocated in most, although not all, plants. Along with starch, it is a major reserve carbohydrate in plants. Sugar beets and sugar cane plants are grown for the high concentrations of sucrose found in the beet roots and cane stalks.

A second disaccharide is **maltose**, a combination of two glucose molecules in α-linkage. These are united through the aldehyde group of one and the hydroxyl at C-4 of the second, leaving one aldehyde unmasked. As a result of the free aldehyde group, maltose is a reducing sugar. It is usually found in detectable amounts only in tissues breaking down starch, such as germinating seeds.

A nonreducing **trisaccharide** sugar, **raffinose**, is a compound of widespread occurrence in higher plants. It is often present in greater quantities when plants are grown in relatively cold temperatures or at high altitudes. It is an important translocatable sugar in white ash (*Fraxinus americana*) and lilac (*Syringa vulgaris*) and probably in many other species. The three sugar subunits are galactose-glucose-fructose. A nonreducing **tetrasaccharide**, **stachyose** (galactose–galactose–glucose–fructose), was found to be the primary carbohydrate translocated in straight-necked squash, and it also plays an important translocation role in other species. It is not normally found in detectable concentrations except in the phloem and in various seeds.

12.4.3 Polysaccharides

These are a group of carbohydrates made up by the polymerization of a large number of monosaccharides. Sometimes more than one type of sugar is present, as, for example, in the gums and mucilages produced by some species. In other cases, such as in starch and cellulose, only one kind of sugar occurs. Due to their high molecular weights, most of the polysaccharides are not very water soluble, although some dissolve in hot water. They are found principally in cell walls or in plastids.

12.4.3A The pentosans and hexosans The **pentosans** are pentose polymers and include the xylans and arabans. These are found in the cell walls. Xylans are especially common in hardwoods, coniferous woods, corncobs, and grass straws. Several marine algae also contain xylans as important cell wall components. The **hexosans** include the mannans (major cell wall constituents in certain algae and in the xylem of the conifers); the galactans (further components of secondary cell walls); and cellulose, starch, and inulin.

12.4.3B Cellulose Cellulose is found in the walls of all plant cells, both in the young primary walls and in greater amounts in thickened secondary walls. This molecule is probably the most abundant compound in plants. It was estimated that about half of the weight of lumber and of paper is cellulose, while 90 percent of the cotton in clothing is this molecule. Because of its commercial importance, a large amount of industrial research has been devoted to this polysaccharide.

Cellulose molecules are exceptionally long and are built up of glucose units that are believed to be in the chair form. The number of glucose units present varies greatly, but it is often between 3,000 and 10,000. These are attached between C-1 of one molecule and C-4 of the next. The linkage is of the β type, as illustrated in Fig. 12-5.

The chainlike cellulose molecules are insoluble in water and in organic solvents, but when exposed to concentrated acids they are hydrolyzed into β-D-glucose. Enzymes capable of hydrolyzing cellulose, the **cellulases**, are found in many microorganisms but are not present in effective amounts in most higher plants. Once cellulose is synthesized into cell walls, it is thus quite resistant to degradation. Man lacks the ability to digest cellulose; otherwise, the world's food supply would be much less of a problem.

12.4.3C Starch The major storage form of carbohydrate in most plant cells is **starch**. It is found inside plastids, where it is formed by photosynthesis in leaf chloroplasts, or in leucoplasts (amyloplasts) of storage organs where it is synthesized following sugar translocation to

these regions. Two types of starch are present in most plastids, amylose and amylopectin, both of which are composed of α-D-glucose units connected in 1,4-linkages (Fig. 12-5). The glucose units are believed to exist in a boat form. The α-1,4 linkages cause the chains to coil into a helix (Fig. 12-6).

Amylopectin consists of branched molecules, the branches occurring between C-6 of a glucose in the main chain and C-1 of the first glucose in the branch chain. The number of glucose units present in various amylopectins is believed to range from 2,000 upward to 200,000. Amylose molecules are smaller and contain perhaps 200 to 1,000 sugar units. This probably explains the greater water solubility of amylose than amylopectin. Amylose, and to a small extent, amylopectin, become purple or blue when stained with iodine–potassium iodide solution. This test is often used to determine the presence of starch in cells.

The percentage of amylose in starch from most species varies from zero to about 40 percent. Potato tubers are a rich source of starch, containing about 22 percent amylose and 78 percent amylopectin in their starch granules. These ratios are similar for starches of banana fruits and the seeds of wheat, rice, and field corn. The amylose content is genetically controlled, and some waxy varieties of cereal grains have only amylopectin in their starch. The inheritance of waxy grains is controlled by a recessive gene, and only those homozygous for the gene produce amylose-free starch. In a few other plants the starch is composed almost entirely of amylose (e.g., wrinkled peas).

The deposition of starch in the plastids occurs in a different pattern for many species, resulting in the formation of starch grains of size and shape somewhat characteristic of the species (Fig. 12-7). The grains of potato are relatively large, while those of rice are among the smallest yet observed. Microscopic observation of starch grains reveals a visible layering

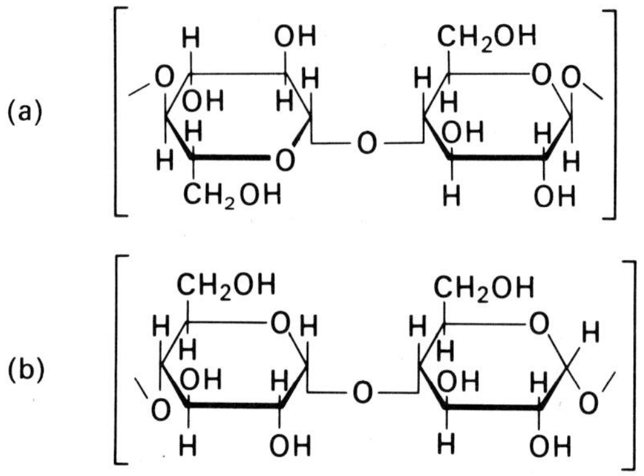

Figure 12-5

(a) The beta (β) linkage between glucose residues as in cellulose. (b) The alpha (α) linkage between glucose residues as in starch.

pattern. This is in part due to the alternation of night and day, a more dense starch with a higher index of refraction being deposited during daylight. Starch grains from endosperm of wheat and barley seeds grown under continuous illumination do not show such layering patterns, but the grains of potato tubers and of *Pellionia* and tobacco leaves do. It has been proposed that an endogenous diurnal rhythm is involved.

(1) *Starch breakdown.* At least three known enzymes can break down starch into sugars or sugar derivatives usable by plants. These include an α- and a **β-amylase**, and **starch phosphorylase**. Alpha amylase is a Ca^{++}-requiring enzyme which initially degrades both forms of starch into fragments containing about ten glucose units, the **dextrins**, and eventually to maltose and glucose. It appears to attack at random points throughout the starch molecules. Beta amylase hydrolyzes starch into maltose, starting only from one end. Its breakdown of amylose is nearly complete, but amylopectin breakdown is only about half complete because the branch linkages are not attacked. Activity of both

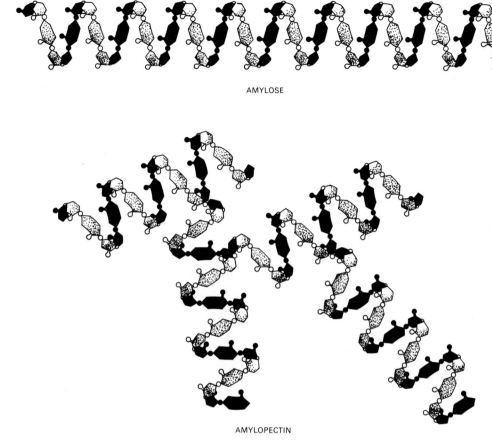

AMYLOSE

AMYLOPECTIN

Figure 12-6
A schematic representation of starch molecules. Amylose and amylopectin are similar, except that amylopectin is branched.

enzymes involves the uptake of one water molecule for each bond cleaved. The reactions are not reversible, and no starch synthesis by the amylases can be detected. These enzymes are widespread in various plant tissues but are most active in germinating seeds high in starch, such as those of the cereal grains. Although β-amylase is already present in the seed, most of the α-amylase is produced as germination proceeds. The discovery of an amylase by A. Payen and J. Persov in 1833 was probably the first clear recognition of the existence of an enzyme. They called this substance **diastase**.

(2) *Starch phosphorylase and other starch-to-sugar transformations.* **Starch phosphorylase** breaks down starch, not by incorporating water into the products as the amylases do but by incorporating phosphate [see (R12-2)].

$$\text{starch} + H_2PO_4^- \rightleftharpoons \text{glucose-1-phosphate}$$

$$(R12\text{-}2)$$

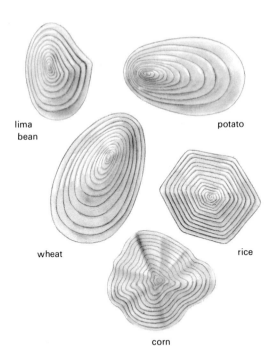

lima bean

potato

wheat

rice

corn

Figure 12-7
Magnified starch grains from several species. (Modified from Figure 9-2, p. 195, in *Principles of Plant Physiology*, by James Bonner and Arthur W. Galston, W. H. Freeman and Company. Copyright © 1952.)

Amylopectin is only partially degraded by this enzyme, the reaction proceeding only to within two or three glucose residues of the α-1,6 branch linkages. Starch phosphorylase is widespread in plants, but its concentration is particularly high in potato tubers, from which it has been obtained in crystalline form. It was found to contain two molecules of pyridoxal phosphate as firmly bound prosthetic groups. In leaves it appears to reside primarily in the chloroplasts, and its presence in chloroplasts of guard cells may be important in the opening and closing of stomates.

The reaction catalyzed by starch phosphorylase is freely reversible and may even be important in starch synthesis, as well as in its deg-

radation, since the equilibrium actually favors formation of the polymer. However, current evidence indicates that starch is primarily synthesized by other reactions described later.

An interesting effect of temperature on the ratio of starch to sugars has been discovered in several plant tissues. In the potato tuber, for example, storage at temperatures only slightly above freezing causes an accumulation of reducing sugars, such as glucose and fructose, and of sucrose, with an accompanying loss of 1–5 percent of the starch. This explains the sweet taste of potatoes stored at low temperatures. On rewarming the tubers to above 10°C, the sugars are reconverted back to starch. Research of Russell Pressey and Roy Shaw at the Red River Valley Potato Processing Laboratory in Minnesota indicates that the accumulation of reducing sugars comes from an accompanying increase in the enzyme invertase. They found an excellent correlation between the buildup of reducing sugars and of invertase in the tubers. Similar effects of temperature on the starch-to-sugar ratios have been observed in acorns, in sweet potato roots, and in banana fruits, although the critical temperatures for starch breakdown vary with the tissues involved. The mechanism of such an effect in these organs has not been well explained. It is probable that temperature affects several reactions involving starch and the various sugars and sugar phosphates, not just a single reversible reaction. Because sugars are important substrates for respiration, the amount available, as influenced by temperature, affects the rates of respiration and of other metabolic processes.

12.4.3D Fructosans A further group of polysaccharides includes the fructose polymers, the **fructosans**. These compounds, like starch, act as food reserves in many plants, but they are especially common in the Graminae (grass) and Compositae families. The number of fructose units varies from about ten or twelve in the grass leaves up to about 35 in members of the Compositae. Thus, none of the fructosans are nearly as large as starch molecules, and as a result they are much more water soluble. Some are branched, while others are not. Many contain fructoses connected by β-links between C-1 of one molecule and C-2 of another. These are often collectively called **inulins**. The inulins generally contain 25 to 35 fructose units and one glucose at the end of the chain, suggesting that they have been formed by the successive addition of fructoses to a terminal sucrose molecule.

Most fructosans of grasses are connected by β-links between the C-2 and C-6 carbons of adjacent fructoses, although those of the inulin type are also present. One such fructosan occurs in abundance in roots of timothy (*Phleum pratense*), and is called **phlein**. Similar molecules in the grasses are often also referred to as phleins.

Inulins are often found only in roots or underground systems and tubers. They are accumulated in dandelion roots, Jerusalem artichoke tubers, *Iris* bulbs, *Dahlia* tubers, and in roots and shoots of guayule. Starch in some of these plants forms in the aerial parts, although starch is absent in guayule. Grasses contain mainly sucrose and fructosans in the leaves as carbohydrate storage products, and there is usually little starch present. Small fructosans are common in the cereal stems, but only starch is deposited in the developing seeds. Such variation among species and tissues in the type of polysaccharide produced is undoubtedly due to differences in the kinds or amounts of enzymes present.

When Jerusalem artichoke tubers are stored at low temperatures, the high-molecular-weight inulin compounds disappear, with an accompanying increase in sucrose and small polymers of fructose. Various hydrolytic enzymes acting on inulin have been found in this plant, but their relation to the temperature effect is not clear.

12.4.3E Pectic substances Polymers containing primarily galacturonic acid, the **pectic substances**, are polysaccharide-like compounds primarily important in cell walls. At least three types of these polymers are recognized in citrus fruits (where pectic substances are abundant), and a distinction among them may be possible in some other kinds of cells, too. The simplest type is **pectic acid**, found in the middle lamella between primary walls of adjacent cells. It is an unbranched chain of α-1,4 linked D-galacturonic acid units. These units are believed to be present in a chair form with 100 or less present per molecule of pectic acid. Pectic acid itself is water soluble, but many of the carboxyl groups in the middle lamella at C-6 are combined with calcium or magnesium, thus forming insoluble salts. These salts will, however, dissolve in ammonium oxalate solutions (which remove the calcium), and this method is often used to remove the pectates from cell walls for further analyses.

The **pectins** are a second type of pectic substance found in plants. These are also formed from galacturonic acid, but most of the carboxyl groups have been esterified by addition of methyl groups, as indicated in (R12-3). The pectins are larger molecules than

(K12-3)

the pectic acids, possessing 200 or more residues per chain. Nevertheless, they are quite soluble in hot water. Pectins are found inside the middle lamella, in the primary wall, and even in the cytoplasm or vacuole. These compounds occur in greatest amounts in various fruits.

The third class of pectic compounds includes the **protopectins**. These substances have even higher molecular weights than pectic acids and pectins, and they are probably intermediate between these in the degree of methylation of carboxyl groups. Protopectins are found mostly in the primary walls of various cells, and their content is especially high in such fruits as apples and oranges. They are not soluble in hot water, although hot dilute acids readily dissolve them.

Ripening of fruits involves important changes in the pectic substances, as in other chemical substances. In the apple, for example, ripening is accompanied by a loss of protopectin and an accumulation of pectin with little change in calcium pectate. Further storage leading to overripening causes still further decreases in protopectin and even in calcium pectate. At this time the cells are held together only loosely, probably because of losses of pectates and pectins from the middle lamellae. It is likely that hydrolytic enzymes such as various **protopectinases**, **pectinases**, and **pectases** become active during maturation and senescence, thus accounting for loss of the pectic compounds.

Many microorganisms possess pectinase enzymes, the **polygalacturonases**, which attack plant tissues and dissolve the middle lamellae. This is responsible for the softening of many fruits and vegetables invaded by saprophytic organisms. Some of these enzymes have recently been purified from certain fungi and applied to potato tuber tissue, causing maceration of the cells. Such results give important evidence that the pectins and pectates in the middle lamella do act in some way to bind cells together,

although the mechanism for this cementing action has not yet been discovered.

Although pectins, protopectins, and pectic acids of citrus and perhaps apple fruits consist primarily of galacturonic acid, other sugar-like units, including galactose, arabinose, xylose, and others, are present in the pectic substances of many plant cells. Also, more recent investigations indicate that there is no clear-cut distinction between any of the pectic substances, but that a gradual transition from one to another occurs.

12.4.3F The hemicelluloses The **hemicelluloses** represent a final recognized group of polysaccharides also found in the cell wall. These compounds consist of a wide variety of cell wall polysaccharides not classified as cellulose or pectic substances. They are a heterogeneous and complicated group of compounds that we now recognize as including xylans, arabans, galactans, mannans, combinations of these in the same chain, and combinations of the xylans or arabans with glucuronic or galacturonic acid. Most of the chains are branched, and the total number of sugar subunits varies from about 40 to 200. Once formed, these compounds are usually metabolized very slowly, and, like cellulose, do not represent important energy sources for the plant. The hemicelluloses are not water soluble but can be removed from the cell walls for analysis by treatment with dilute alkali.

12.5 STRUCTURE OF THE CELL WALL

12.5.1 Cell Wall Composition

As we have seen, the cell walls of higher plants that have not undergone extensive thickening contain cellulose, pectic substances, and hemicelluloses. In the secondary walls of woody cells, the pectic compounds are not important. These secondary walls contain higher concentrations of cellulose and, in addition, large amounts of **lignin**, a large polymeric type of compound made up of aromatic subunits. The chemistry of lignin is discussed in Chapter 18.

Most of the information available concerning the composition, structure, and development of cell walls deals with the primary wall. There are major differences in primary walls of various cell types, but all possess important similarities. Cellulose typically accounts for 25–40 percent of the dry weight, hemicelluloses usually make up slightly more, and the pectic substances vary widely in importance.

Proteins have also recently been found to occur in primary walls, when careful analyses have been made to determine their presence. These proteins are an unusual type, possessing a very high content of hydroxyproline. In this respect they are similar to **collagen**, a structural protein of mammals. **Lipids** are also found in small amounts in preparations of some cell walls. These probably occur in the layer of **cutin** that often surrounds the walls at the intercellular spaces.

12.5.2 Cell Wall Structure and Growth

The arrangement of all these compounds to produce the highly organized primary wall is a problem which has been attacked by techniques of x-ray diffraction, electron microscopy, and polarizing microscopy. The results obtained collectively show that many cellulose chains are packed together along their long axes to form **microfibrils**. These microfibrils exist as a complex network as shown in Fig. 12-8. The arrangement of microfibrils in the wall is closely related to the final shape attained by the cells. Some cells grow considerably more in length than in width, including those of the vascular cambium, phloem sieve tube elements, cortex cells of root and stem, and the parenchyma cells of elongating grass coleoptiles. In these elongating cells many of the microfibrils are oriented in a direction

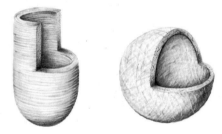

Figure 12-8

Arrangement of long-chain cellulose molecules in the primary walls of two types of cells. Left, transverse orientation as in an elongating cell. Right, random orientation as in a cell expanding more-or-less uniformly. (Modified from p. 206, *Principles of Plant Physiology* by James Bonner and Arthur W. Galston, W. H. Freeman and Company. Copyright © 1952.)

nearly perpendicular to the long axis of the cell, while fewer are oriented parallel to this axis. As these cells grow longer, there is some sliding of the microfibrils past each other, as shown in Fig. 12-9. This causes some reorientation of the microfibrils, so that they become more nearly parallel to the direction of growth. Meanwhile, as growth occurs, more are deposited transversely on the inner surface of the wall by the protoplast. Thus the microfibrils that were laid down earliest have stretched most and are oriented more nearly parallel with the long axis of the cell, while the youngest look somewhat like hoops in a barrel.

In cells that grow more or less uniformly in all directions, such as parenchyma cells in fleshy fruits, there is a random orientation of microfibrils on the surface of the walls. It is probable that the direction in which these cellulose microfibrils are formed actually determines the direction in which the cell can expand. Expansion in a direction parallel to the microfibrils cannot readily occur because the cellulose chains do not stretch easily. A problem in understanding plant form, then, is to understand what controls the orientation of deposition of cellulose material. Recently discovered cyto-

Figure 12-9
Reorientation of cellulose microfibrils in the outer part of the primary wall of latex tubes of *Euphorbia splendens*. (top) Wall before cell expansion, (middle) wall after some cellular expansion. Microfibrils have become statistically oriented in the direction of cell growth. (bottom) Mature primary wall with microfibrils on the outer wall longitudinally oriented in the direction that cell growth occurred. Enlarged about 38,000 diameters. (From H. Moor, 1959, *J. Ultrastructure Research* 2:393. Used by permission.)

plasmic **microtubules** (Fig. 12-10) adjacent to growing walls are arranged in a definite manner, and these may be responsible for synthesizing cellulose in a characteristic microfibril pattern. What controls the arrangement of these microtubules remains an equally important question.

Since each microfibril is actually formed of many cellulose chains, somewhat like the arrangement of wires in a steel cable, great strength results. This strength is necessary to prevent the cells' bursting from the high pressures built up inside them through the action of osmosis. These pressures actually support a herbaceous plant without the need of a rigid skeleton. It is not known precisely how the hemicelluloses, pectic materials, and protein are arranged in the cell wall. They seem to form an amorphous matrix in which the cellulose microfibrils are embedded.

The primary wall is thought not to be a serious obstacle for the passage of water and most dissolved solutes into and out of the cell. There are many holes in the network through which these can pass. Nevertheless, the negative charges of the ionized carboxyl groups of galacturonic acid present in the pectic substances and hemicelluloses do bind cations. It has been observed, in fact, that the cation-binding capacity (Donnan effect, section 4.2.4D) of oat coleoptile cells can be completely accounted for in this way.

12.6 SYNTHESIS OF POLYSACCHARIDES

Photosynthesis produces the sugars and sugar phosphates used in the production of polysaccharides. As will be shown later, the hexose phosphates arising from photosynthesis in the shoot are rapidly converted into other carbohydrate forms, especially sucrose, which then are accumulated, translocated, or changed into polysaccharides. Roots, fruits, and even seeds must synthesize their own polysaccharides,

and sucrose is the most common sugar source provided them by the green leaves. Let us follow the transformations of hexose phosphates such as glucose-6-phosphate, glucose-1-phosphate, and fructose-6-phosphate into sucrose and the larger polysaccharides.

12.6.1 Glucose Activation (UDPG and ADPG Formation)

Before these sugar units are combined into larger compounds, they must first be converted to an active form that the polymerizing enzymes can utilize. These more active forms are combinations of the sugar with a nucleotide. The role of nucleotide-sugars in polysaccharide synthesis has been known only since about 1953, and more information is still needed to clarify the mechanisms involved. The first nucleotide-sugar to be discovered in higher plants was **uridine diphosphoglucose**, abbreviated **UDPG**. Since then, **adenosine diphosphoglucose (ADPG)** and a few others have been detected, and the ability of plants to form still others has been demonstrated. The structures of UDPG and ADPG are shown in Fig. 12-11.

The synthesis of UDPG can take place from glucose-1-phosphate and **uridine triphosphate (UTP)**. UTP is a compound having two phosphate groups at a high transfer potential similar to those in ATP, but united to uridine monophosphate rather than to adenosine monophosphate (**AMP**) as in ATP. UDPG formation involves the splitting of these two phosphates from UTP, and the formation of a bond between the remaining phosphate and that on glucose-1-phosphate, as shown in (R12-4).

Glucose-1-phosphate + UTP $\rightleftharpoons$

$$UDPG + HO\!-\!\overset{\displaystyle O}{\overset{\|}{P}}\!-\!O\!-\!\overset{\displaystyle O}{\overset{\|}{P}}\!-\!OH \qquad \text{(R12-4)}$$
$$\qquad\qquad\underset{OH}{|}\qquad\underset{OH}{|}$$

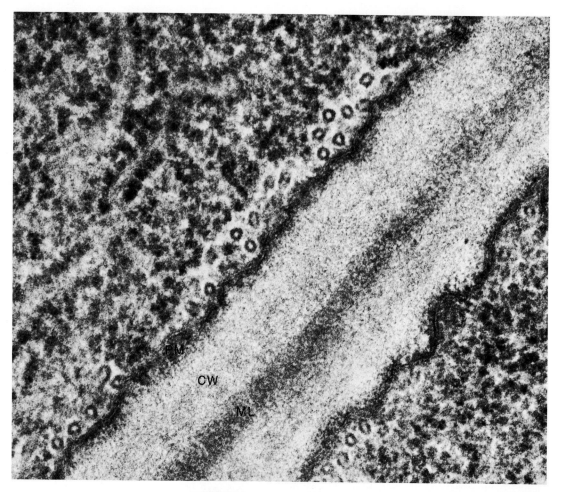
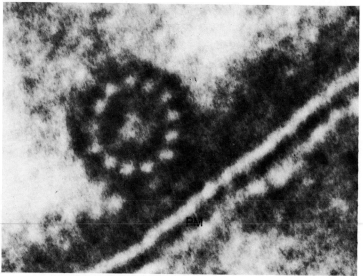

ADPG is formed by a similar reaction involving ATP instead of UTP. The enzyme involved is called **ADPG pyrophosphorylase**.

12.6.2 Sucrose Synthesis

UDPG transfers its glucose to fructose-6-phosphate or to free fructose [see (R12-5a and b)]

(a) UDPG + fructose-6-phosphate
$\rightleftharpoons$ sucrose-phosphate + UDP   (R12-5)

(b) UDPG + fructose $\rightleftharpoons$ sucrose + UDP

Both reactions can account for sucrose synthesis in most plants, and the relative importance of each probably varies among different plants and tissues. Both are probably physiologically reversible, but reaction (a), especially, greatly favors disaccharide formation. Sucrose-phosphate, rather than sucrose, is the immediate product. However, enzymes capable of splitting off the phosphate from sucrose-phosphate and, in fact, from many other phosphorylated compounds, are known to be present in plants. These are called **phosphatases**. Phosphatase action on sucrose-phosphate would then account for sucrose formation. This enzyme is apparently very active, since sucrose-phosphate is never found in quantities equal to free sucrose. The fructose required in the second reaction could arise from the prior action of a phosphatase on fructose-6-phosphate, or it could be formed by splitting previously synthesized sucrose molecules into the subunits glucose and fructose.

It should be noted that since these reactions are reversible it is also possible to form UDPG by their reversal. In fact, there is considerable evidence that both UDPG and ADPG are produced in developing cereal grain seeds by reaction of sucrose transported to these sites with UDP and ADP, respectively. The glucose of UDPG and ADPG can then be converted into starch and other polysaccharides in the seeds as described further below.

12.6.3 Sucrose Hydrolysis

Sucrose breakdown can occur by action of an enzyme called **invertase**, or **sucrase**. Invertase simply hydrolyzes sucrose irreversibly into glucose and fructose [see (R12-6)] with the loss of significant amounts of heat energy ($\Delta G = -6,600$ cal/mole).

sucrose + $H_2O \longrightarrow$ glucose + fructose   (R12-6)

12.6.4 Further Synthesis Reactions

The glucose in UDPG is converted into many other compounds besides sucrose. It can serve as the glucose for starch synthesis and can undergo reactions leading to glucuronic acid, xylose, and arabinose, as well. However, UDPG is probably not the most important glucose source for starch formation, since ADPG is an

---

Figure 12-10

(top) Electron micrograph of part of a meristematic cell from a *Juniperus chinensis* root tip showing microtubules (small circles) adjacent to the plasmalemma (PM). The primary cell wall (CW) and its middle lammella (ML) are also shown ($\times 51,000$). The microtubules are most abundant in a zone about 0.1 μ (1,000 Å) thick adjacent to the plasmalemma, and are arranged in meristematic cells of root tips circumferentially around the cells, much as hoops around a barrel. Along both the side and end walls of these cells the arrangement of these microtubules is very similar to that of the cellulose *microfibrils* in the adjacent wall. (bottom) Higher magnification of a microtubule from *Juniperus chinensis*. The microtubules appear to be made of a wall about 70 Å thick enclosing a lumen some 100 Å in diameter. The wall is composed of 13 subunits. (Electron micrographs courtesy of M. Ledbetter, Harvard University. See *J. Agric. and Food Chem.* 13:405, 1965. Copyright 1965 by the American Chemical Society. Reprinted by permission of the copyright owner.)

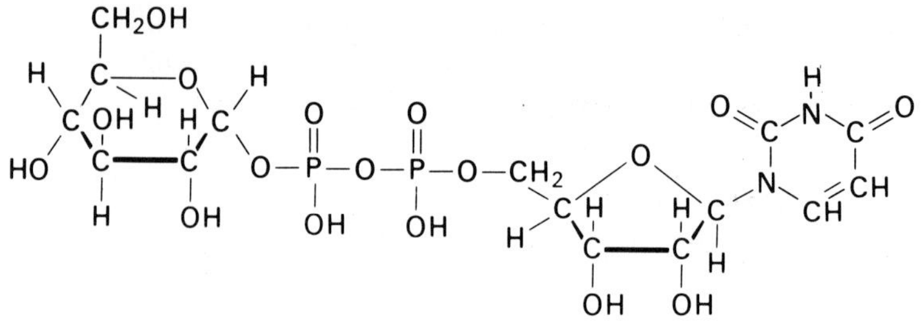

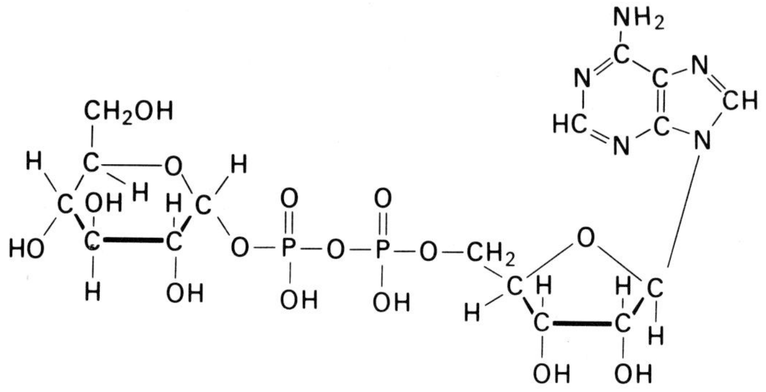

Figure 12-11
(top) The structure of uridine diphosphate glucose (UDPG). (bottom) Adenosine diphosphate glucose (ADPG).

even better glucose donor for this process in all plant parts so far investigated, including leaves, developing seeds, and potato tubers. The enzyme transferring glucose from ADPG to a growing starch chain is called **ADPG-starch transglucosylase**. It forms the 1–4 linkages between adjacent glucoses in amylose or amylopectin, but another branching enzyme, the **Q enzyme**, is essential to synthesize the 1–6 bonds at the branch points in amylopectin.

It appears that UDP-galacturonic acid is the immediate precursor of the pectic compounds. The complete formation of pectins and protopectins requires a methyl donor to methylate some of the free carboxyl groups of the galacturonic acid residues. It is believed that these methyl groups arise indirectly from methionine, through the intermediary coenzyme S-adenosyl methionine.

The reactions leading to fructosan synthesis have not yet been discovered. It seems certain that fructose units are added to sucrose, since sucrose is found at the end of the chain in most fructosans. Based on analogy with the other polysaccharides where nucleotide sugars participate, it is suspected that a uridine diphosphofructose is necessary. There is evidence that this compound is present in *Dahlia* tubers, where inulin accumulates, and it has also recently been found in Jerusalem artichoke tubers.

In the fungi, **chitin** is a principal cell wall component. Here the repeating subunit is acetyl glucosamine, donated by another nucleotide-sugar, **uridine diphosphoacetyl glucosamine**.

12.6.5 Cellulose Synthesis

Previous to 1964 the synthesis of cellulose had been studied almost entirely in a cellulose-forming microorganism, and little was known of the manner in which higher plants form so much of this compound. In that year, George Barber, A. D. Elbein, and W. Z. Hassid, of the University of California, found that **guanosine diphosphoglucose (GDPG)** acts as the glucose donor for cellulose synthesis in a variety of plants. GDPG is very similar in structure to ADPG and can be synthesized in plants by reaction of guanosine triphosphate (GTP) with glucose-1-phosphate, analogous to the way in which UDPG and ADPG are formed from glucose-1-phosphate with UTP and ATP. Previous unsuccessful attempts to obtain enzymes synthesizing cellulose had involved the addition of UDPG, ADPG, or other glucose donors.

12.7 THE ORGANIC ACIDS OF PLANTS

Plant cells contain a large number of organic aliphatic acids dissolved in their cytoplasm and vacuoles. Of these, the best known (because of their primary roles in respiration) contain from two to six carbon atoms. Their structures are given in Fig. 12-12. Many other acids also exist in plants, but these will not be discussed here. Several of the plant acids accumulate in vacuoles and cause the vacuolar sap to be slightly acid, usually in the range of pH 5.5 to 6.5, although more acid values are common in vacuoles of many fruits.

Three two-carbon acids are found in most plants. These are **glycolic**, **glyoxylic**, and **oxalic** acids. They differ only in the extent of oxidation of the α-carbon atom, which varies from an alcohol in glycolic to an aldehyde in glyoxylic acid, and finally to a carboxylic acid in oxalic acid. Glycolic and glyoxylic acids are found in

leaves, mainly in chloroplasts, while oxalic acid usually exists as insoluble crystals of calcium oxalate in vacuoles. While the first two probably have important functions in respiration and in photosynthesis, oxalic acid should probably be considered a by-product, the role of which is nonexistent or unknown. In some plants oxalic acid is absent, while in *Oxalis*, rhubarb, spinach, and buckwheat, its concentration is very high. In the desert species *Halogeton glomeratus*, sufficient soluble oxalates accumulate sometimes to poison livestock. Apparently the animals suffer from calcium deficiency caused by oxalate precipitation of bloodstream calcium. Glycolic and glyoxylic acids exist in only relatively low amounts, but their distribution is probably much wider than that of oxalic acid.

Three acids with three carbons are known. These are **pyruvic**, an α-keto acid, D-**glyceric**, a dihydroxy acid, and **malonic**, a dicarboxylic acid especially abundant in legumes. The first two exist in only small quantities in most plants. Malonic acid has not been found in a large number of species, but where it does exist its concentration is often as high as that of several other organic acids. It is thought to be present primarily in vacuoles. Pyruvate is believed to occur in all living cells, since it is an essential respiratory intermediate. The role of glyceric acid is not clear. It is formed in the chloroplasts during photosynthesis.

Five acids having four carbons have been found in plants. The first of these, L-**tartaric acid**, is present in many plants, but is best known in grapes. Its physiological role is unknown, but it has historical interest in that it was one of the compounds Pasteur studied most carefully in his research on the rotation by crystals of plane polarized light.

Succinic, **fumaric**, L-**malic**, and **oxaloacetic** acids all have two carboxyl groups. These are listed in increasing order of oxidation. They are

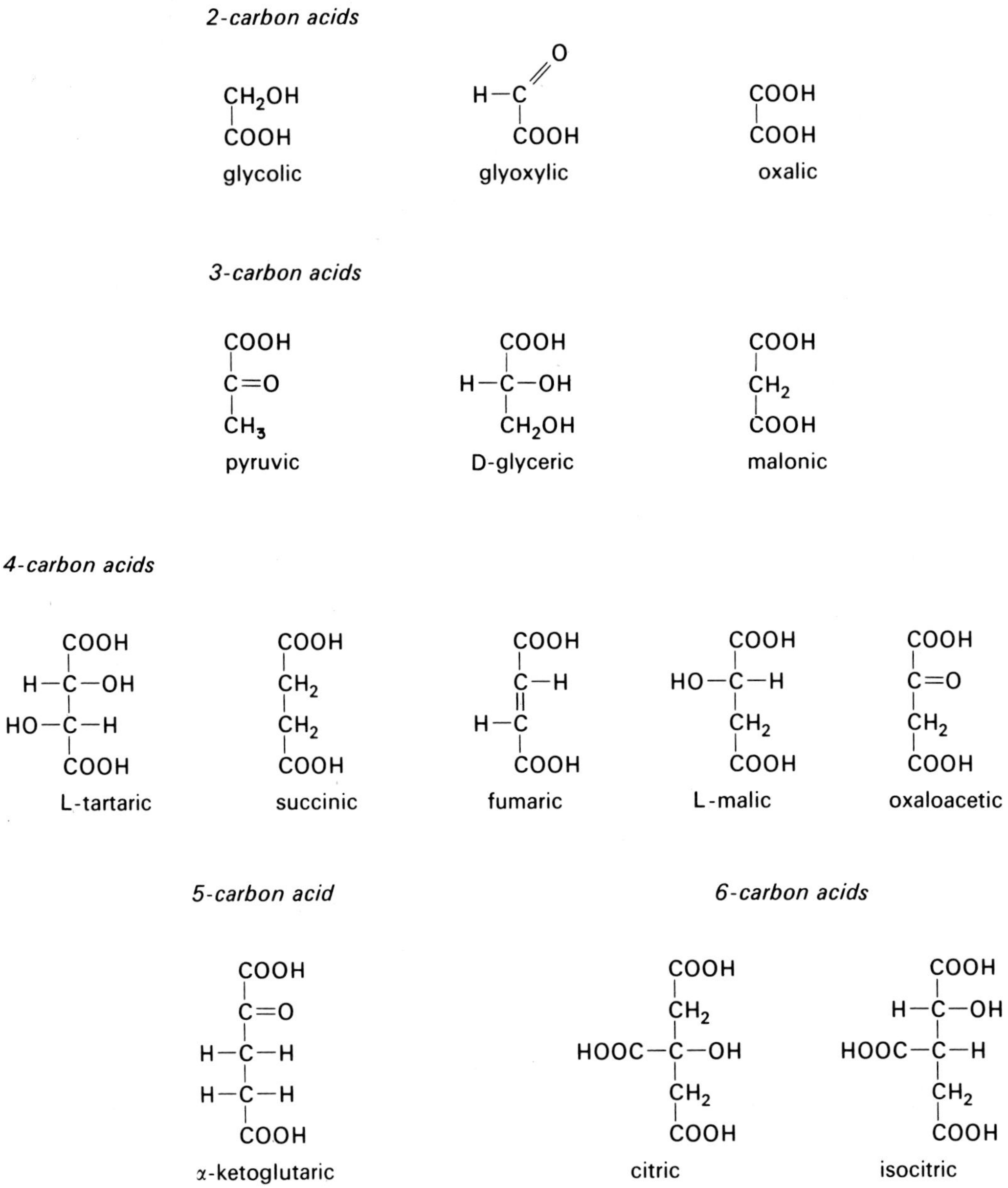

2-carbon acids

<pre>
CH₂OH   H—C⟍O   COOH
| \ |
COOH   COOH   COOH
glycolic   glyoxylic   oxalic
</pre>

$$\begin{array}{ccc}
\text{CH}_2\text{OH} & \text{H-C}^{\nearrow\text{O}} & \text{COOH}\\
| & | & |\\
\text{COOH} & \text{COOH} & \text{COOH}\\
\text{glycolic} & \text{glyoxylic} & \text{oxalic}
\end{array}$$

3-carbon acids

$$\begin{array}{ccc}
\text{COOH} & \text{COOH} & \text{COOH}\\
| & | & |\\
\text{C=O} & \text{H-C-OH} & \text{CH}_2\\
| & | & |\\
\text{CH}_3 & \text{CH}_2\text{OH} & \text{COOH}\\
\text{pyruvic} & \text{D-glyceric} & \text{malonic}
\end{array}$$

4-carbon acids

$$\begin{array}{ccccc}
\text{COOH} & \text{COOH} & \text{COOH} & \text{COOH} & \text{COOH}\\
| & | & | & | & |\\
\text{H-C-OH} & \text{CH}_2 & \text{C-H} & \text{HO-C-H} & \text{C=O}\\
| & | & \| & | & |\\
\text{HO-C-H} & \text{CH}_2 & \text{H-C} & \text{CH}_2 & \text{CH}_2\\
| & | & | & | & |\\
\text{COOH} & \text{COOH} & \text{COOH} & \text{COOH} & \text{COOH}\\
\text{L-tartaric} & \text{succinic} & \text{fumaric} & \text{L-malic} & \text{oxaloacetic}
\end{array}$$

5-carbon acid   *6-carbon acids*

$$\begin{array}{ccc}
\text{COOH} & \text{COOH} & \text{COOH}\\
| & | & |\\
\text{C=O} & \text{CH}_2 & \text{H-C-OH}\\
| & | & |\\
\text{H-C-H} & \text{HOOC-C-OH} & \text{HOOC-C-H}\\
| & | & |\\
\text{H-C-H} & \text{CH}_2 & \text{CH}_2\\
| & | & |\\
\text{COOH} & \text{COOH} & \text{COOH}\\
\alpha\text{-ketoglutaric} & \text{citric} & \text{isocitric}
\end{array}$$

Figure 12-12
Molecular structures of some organic acids common in plant cells.

believed to be present in all cells of higher plants, and they are essential respiratory compounds. However, only malic acid usually accumulates in appreciably high concentrations. It is often found in levels as high as 0.01 M, especially in cells of such fruits as the apple.

One organic acid having five carbons is well known. This is **α-ketoglutaric acid**, which, like oxaloacetic, possesses an α-keto group adjacent to one of the two carboxyl groups. Both α-ketoglutaric and oxaloacetic acids are usually present only in trace amounts, probably because their high reactivity allows their rapid conversion to other compounds. They are, however, believed to be essential metabolites for cells of all higher plants.

Two acids with similar structures having six carbons are found in all plants. These are **citric** and **isocitric** acids.[2] Citric acid accumulates in large amounts in citrus fruits, causing their acidity and sour taste. Citric acid is a symmetrical molecule, while isocitric has two asymmetrical carbons. Isocitric acid is rarely found in concentrations as high as those of citric, although it is the principal organic acid of blackberry fruits and of leaves of the succulent *Bryophyllum* species.

---

[2] Isocitric acid has two asymmetric carbon atoms and is properly described as *threo*-D_s-isocitric acid. The subscript s refers to the fact that the uppermost asymmetric carbon has the D-configuration.

13

Photosynthesis

Previous to the time of Stephen Hales in the early 18th century, it was believed that plants obtained all of their elements from the soil. Hales suggested, in 1727, that part of their nourishment came from the atmosphere, and even that light participated somehow in this process. It was not known then that air contained several different gaseous elements. Joseph Priestly, an English clergyman and chemist, implicated oxygen in 1771 when he found that green plants could renew air made bad by the breathing of animals. Then a Dutch physician Jan Ingenhousz, while in London in 1779, demonstrated that light was necessary for this purification of air. He found that plants, too, made bad air in darkness. This caused him to recommend (unnecessarily) that plants be removed from houses during the night to avoid the possibility of poisoning the occupants.

In 1782, Jean Senebier showed that the presence of the noxious gas produced by animals and plants in darkness (carbon dioxide) stimulated oxygen release by plants in the light. So by this time the participation of both carbon dioxide and oxygen in photosynthesis had been demonstrated. Water was implicated by Nicholas Th. de Saussure when, in 1804, he made the first quantitative measurements of photosynthesis. He found that plants gained more weight during photosynthesis than could be accounted for by the amount by which the weight of carbon dioxide absorbed exceeded the weight of oxygen released. He attributed the difference to an uptake of water. He also noted that approximately equal volumes of carbon dioxide and oxygen were exchanged during photosynthesis.

The other product of photosynthesis, organic matter, was demonstrated by Julius Sachs in 1864 when he observed the growth of starch grains in illuminated chloroplasts. The starch is detected only in areas of the leaf exposed to light. Thus the over-all reaction of photosynthesis was demonstrated to be as shown in (R13-1).

$$CO_2 + H_2O \xrightarrow[\text{green plant}]{\text{light energy}} (CH_2O) + O_2 \qquad (R13\text{-}1)$$

A further important discovery was that of C. B. van Niel, who, in the early 1930s, pointed out the similarity between the over-all photosynthetic process in green plants and that in certain bacteria. Various bacteria were known to reduce carbon dioxide using light energy and an electron source different from water. Some of these use organic acids such as acetic or succinic acid as electron sources, while those to which van Niel gave primary attention use H_2S and deposit sulfur as a by-product. The

TABLE 13-1

PROPERTIES OF PHOTOSYNTHETIC PIGMENTS

Pigment	Color	Principal visible absorption peaks (mμ)[a]	Solubility
chlorophyll a	blue-green	430 (blue violet), 660 (red)	acetone, ether, alcohols; insoluble in water
chlorophyll b	yellow-green	455 (blue), 640 (orange-red)	same as chl. a, but aldehyde group makes it more sol. in polar solvents
phycocyanins	blue	560 to 660 (yellow to orange-red)	dilute acids, alkalies, chloroform, alcohols, ether. When attached to proteins, soluble in water
phycoerythrins	red	500 to 570 (green to yellow)	same as phycocyanins
carotenoids	yellow, orange-red	430 to 490 (violet to blue-green)	benzene, petroleum ether, ethyl ether, alcohols, chloroform, acetone; insoluble in water

[a] Data given for the extracted pigments. When in the plant, the absorption may differ somewhat (see text). Various phycobilins and carotenoids are known, and properties vary among them.

over-all photosynthetic equation in these bacteria was believed to occur as shown in (R13-2).

$$CO_2 + 2H_2S \longrightarrow (CH_2O) + H_2O + 2S \quad (R13\text{-}2)$$

When (R13-2) is compared to (R13-1), an analogy can be seen between the role of H_2S and H_2O, and of O_2 and sulfur. This strongly suggested to van Niel that the oxygen released in plants is derived from water, not from carbon dioxide. More convincing evidence that this is true came in 1941 from results of Samuel Ruben, an American biochemist, and his associates. They supplied the green alga *Chlorella* with water containing ^{18}O, a heavy, nonradioactive isotope of oxygen that can be detected with a mass spectrometer. The O_2 produced in photosynthesis was labeled with ^{18}O, thus confirming the prediction of van Niel. It is thus necessary to modify the summary photosynthetic equation for green plants (R13-1) to include two water molecules as reactants [see (R13-3)].

$$CO_2 + 2H_2O^* \xrightarrow[\text{green plant}]{\text{light energy}} (CH_2O) + O_2^* + H_2O$$

$$(R13\text{-}3)$$

13.1 CHEMISTRY, PROPERTIES, AND SYNTHESIS OF PHOTOSYNTHETIC PIGMENTS

All algae and higher plants require **chlorophyll *a*** to photosynthesize, except for the photosynthetic bacteria, which possess similar pigments. Nevertheless, other forms of chlorophyll exist in plants. Higher plants and green algae contain chlorophylls *a* and *b*, while chlorophyll *a* is the only chlorophyll found in blue-green and some red algae. Still other red algae have chlorophyll *a* and small amounts of chlorophyll *d*, and the brown algae and diatoms contain both chlorophylls *a* and *c*. In addition, pigments such as the **carotenoids** and, in the red and blue-green algae, the **phycobilin pigments** (**phycoerythrin** and **phycocyanin**) participate in photosynthesis. Table 13-1 lists the pigments present in various photosynthesizing organisms, their colors, some of the principal wavelengths absorbed by each, and some of their solubility characteristics. Representative chemical structures are shown in Fig. 13-1.

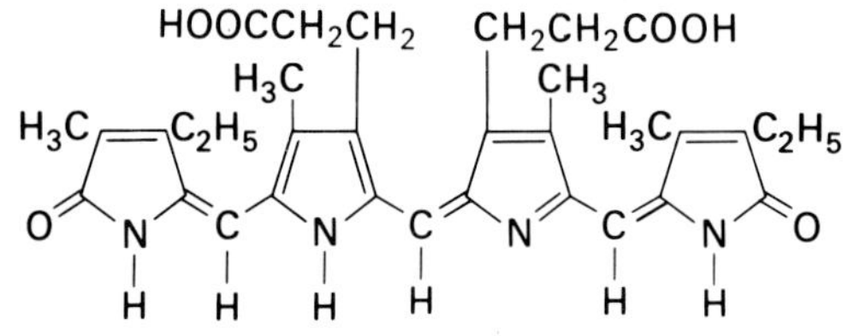

(a) a phycocyanin chromophore

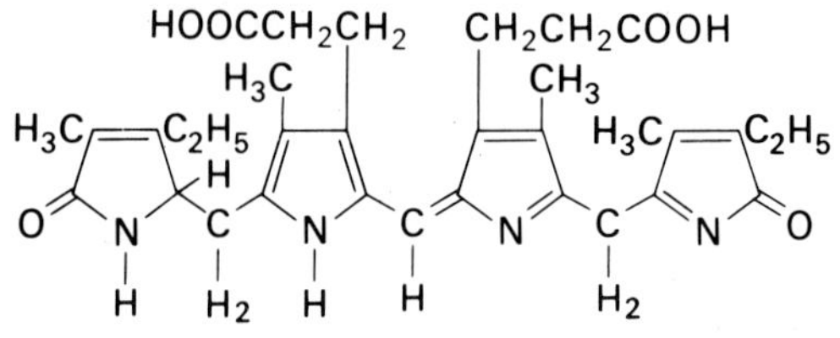

(b) a phycoerythrin chromophore

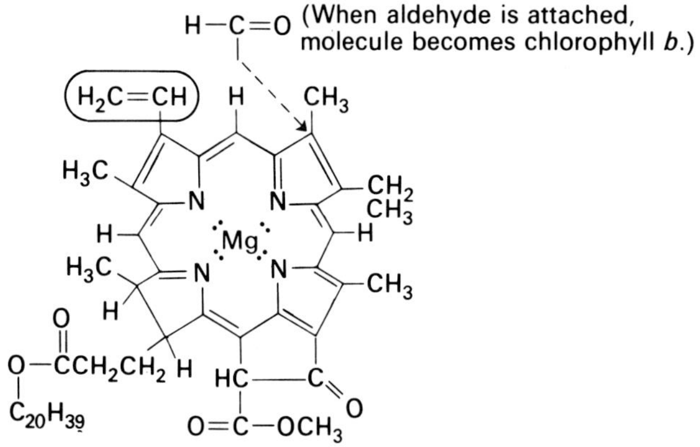

(c) chlorophyll *a*

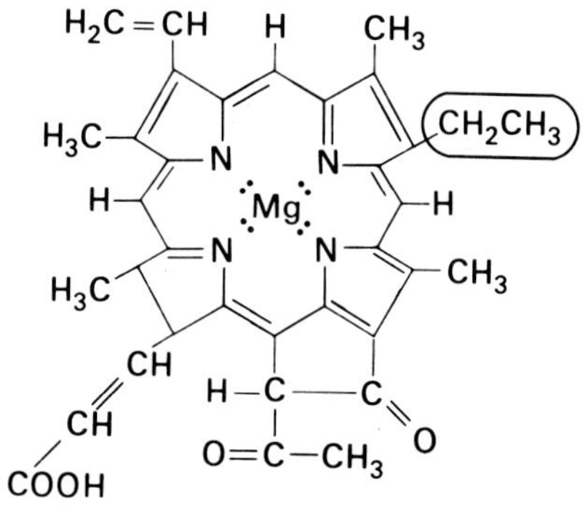

(d) chlorophyll *c*

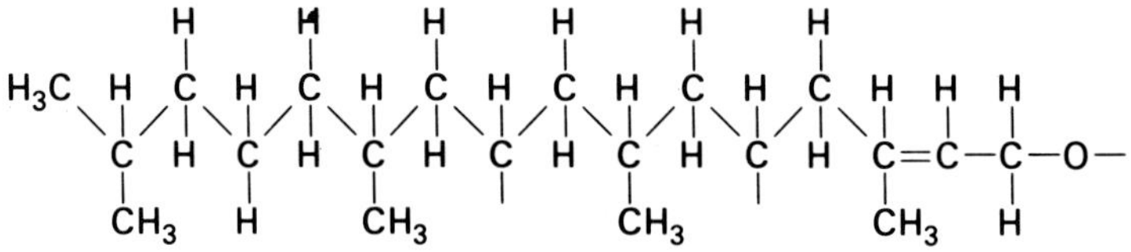

(e) phytol tail of chlorophyll

Figure 13-1

Structures of phycobilin chromophores, chlorophylls, and carotenoids. The phycobilins shown in (a) and (b) exist in the plant attached to proteins. In chlorophyll *a* (c) replacement of the methyl group with a —CHO group as indicated gives chlorophyll *b*. Replacement of the circled ethylene group with a —CHO group gives chlorophyll *d*. Chlorophyll *c*, shown in (d) from the marine diatom *Nitzschia closterium*, seems to exist in two forms, one of which has an ethyl group in the position circled, while the other has an ethylene group here instead. Note that chlorophyll *c* contains no phytol tail. The structure of the phytol tail is shown in (e). (Data of R. C. Dougherty et al., 1966, *J. Amer. Chem. Soc.* 88:5037.)

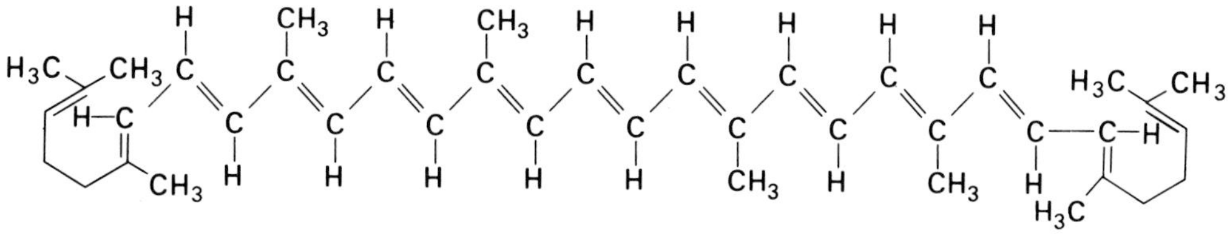

(f) lycopene

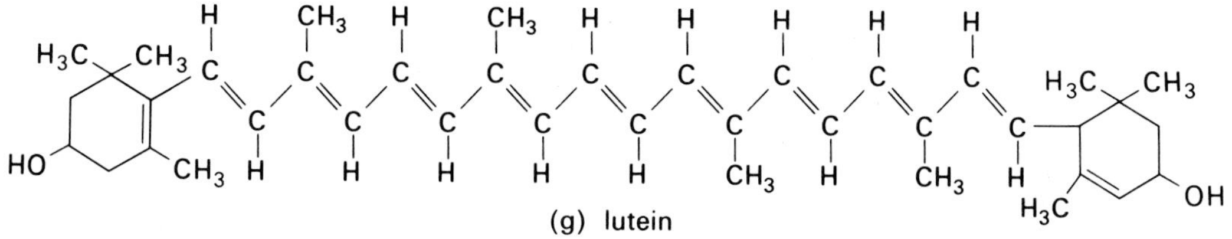

(g) lutein

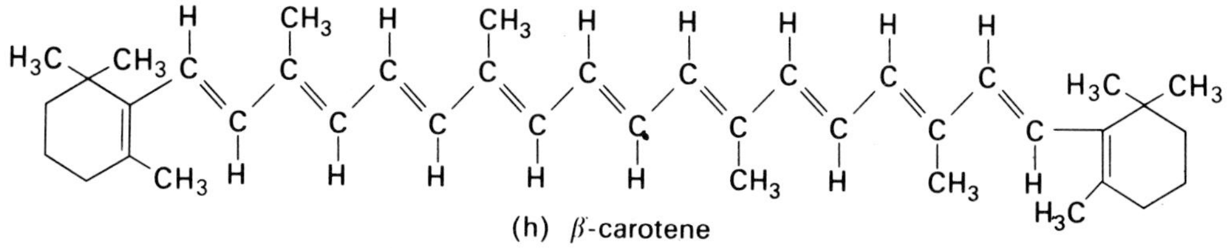

(h) β-carotene

Figure 13-1

(*continued*). The carotenoids β-carotene (h) and lutein (g) are very abundant in photosynthetic tissues (in chloroplast membranes), while lycopene (f) is the pigment giving the reddish color to tomato fruits.

13.1.1 Chemistry of Chlorophyll

All forms of chlorophyll contain the same **porphyrin** structure, in which four **pyrrole** rings are united by their nitrogen atoms to magnesium. Each chlorophyll further has a fifth ring containing only carbon atoms, and the long chain **phytol alcohol** is also common to most chlorophylls, chlorophyll *c* being an exception. The chlorophylls vary in the structures of side chains attached to the pyrrole rings. Chlorophylls *a* and *b* differ in that chlorophyll *a* has a methyl group on ring 3, while chlorophyll *b* has an aldehyde instead. The aldehyde group makes chlorophyll *b* slightly more hydrophylic (it is soluble in 92 percent methyl alcohol) than chlorophyll *a* (more soluble in ether). Most plants contain two or three times more chlorophyll *a* than *b*. The molecular structures were largely solved in the early part of this century by the Germans R. Wilstätter and A. Stoll and by the famous organic chemist Hans Fischer. In 1960, Robert Woodward, also an organic chemist, was able to synthesize chlorophyll *a*. For this and other brilliant work, he was given a Nobel prize in chemistry in 1965.

The wavelengths of light absorbed by chlorophylls *a* and *b* after extraction are shown in Fig. 13-2. Both pigments absorb primarily blue-

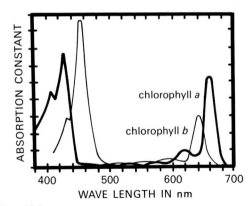

Figure 13-2

Absorption spectra of chlorophylls *a* and *b* dissolved in diethyl ether. The absorption constant used here is equal to the absorbance (optical density) given by a solution at a concentration of 1 g/l with a thickness (light path length) of 1 cm. (From F. Zscheile and C. Comar, 1941, *Botan. Gazette* 102:463.)

violet and red light and very little of the green wavelengths. Chlorophyll *a* has a maximum in the violet region at a shorter wavelength than does chlorophyll *b*, while in the red region its maximum occurs at a longer wavelength. The exact position of the peaks depends upon the solvent in which the pigments are dissolved; that is, upon the type of molecules with which they are associated. For example, in the living plant a major absorbance peak in the red for chlorophyll *a* is shifted to about 683 mμ from the 660 mμ peak observed in diethyl ether. Another chlorophyll *a* peak is also found at 672 mμ, which may represent the effect of a slightly different environment.

Such plots of light absorbance at various wavelengths are called **absorption spectra**. An absorption spectrum is measured by use of a **spectrophotometer**, an instrument that contains a light source emitting all the desired wavelengths, a prism or diffraction grating to separate these, mirrors to reflect the selected wavelength through the sample, and a detector to detect the amount of light absorbed by the sample (Fig. 13-3).

In solution, chlorophyll is highly fluorescent, emitting a deep red color when illuminated. In the living plant, most of this energy responsible for fluorescence is used in photosynthesis, and hence intact plants do not fluoresce appreciably.

13.1.2 Chlorophyll Formation

The synthesis of chlorophyll is affected by various factors, including hereditary characteristics, light, and the supply of certain mineral elements. In certain varieties of corn and sunflower, some of the germinating seeds produce seedlings lacking chlorophyll. This is an inherited recessive trait, and these "**albino**" seedlings die as soon as their food supply in the seed is exhausted. Such plants have been grown nearly to maturity, however, by providing them with sugars as an energy source.

Light is required for chlorophyll formation in nearly all angiosperms, although the conifers, mosses, some ferns, and most algae can form this pigment in darkness. Dark-grown angiosperms produce small quantities of a greenish pigment similar to chlorophyll, yet not enough of it accumulates to cause the plants to appear green. Upon illumination, this pigment disappears, and chlorophyll *a* appears in increasing amounts with time. The disappearing pigment has, therefore, been named **protochlorophyll**. Chemically it differs from chlorophyll *a* only in lacking two hydrogen atoms. It also absorbs blue and red light, with peaks near 450 and 650 mμ, and these wavelengths are most effective in causing its transformation to chlorophyll *a*. The origin of chlorophyll *b* has not yet been discovered.

Several mineral elements seem to be rather directly involved in chlorophyll synthesis, because in their absence a bleaching, or **chlorosis**, results. The pyrrole rings of chlorophyll arise after prior combination of the amino acid glycine and succinic acid. Several enzymatic

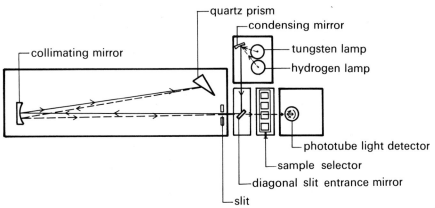

Figure 13-3
Diagram of the Beckman model DU spectrophotometer. By use of the sample selector, any of four cuvettes containing solutions under investigation may be positioned in front of the light path. Usually one cuvette (called the blank) contains only the solvent, while any of the other three cuvettes contains a pigment dissolved in the same solvent. The blank is set in front of the light beam, and the meter (not shown) is adjusted to read zero absorbance. A sample is then positioned, and the absorbance due only to the pigment is measured. Since the blank cuvette absorbs somewhat differently at each wavelength, selected by adjusting the angle of the prism, it is necessary to adjust the meter to zero at each wavelength when determining an absorption spectrum. The tungsten lamp is used as a source of visible light for colored solutions, such as chlorophyll, while the hydrogen lamp is a source of ultraviolet radiation absorbed by many colorless solutions, such as those of nucleic acids, nucleotides, or phenolic compounds.

steps occur between the union of these two molecules and the production of the final, more complex chlorophyll compound. The reaction between glycine and succinyl coenzyme A require iron as a coenzyme, and iron deficiency rapidly causes a chlorosis of the young developing leaves. Manganese, potassium, zinc, and copper deficiencies also lead to chloroses, but their roles are not understood. Perhaps they, too, activate enzymes necessary for certain of the reactions along the pathway of chlorophyll synthesis. Manganese deficiency leads to a disorganization of the internal lamellar (membrane) system of chloroplasts, which might result from a lack of chlorophyll to stabilize these membranes.

The lack of nitrogen and magnesium also causes a yellowing of plants. Their functions are clear, since each is an essential structural element in chlorophyll. Other more indirect roles are not, however, eliminated, and magnesium probably acts as a coenzyme (activator) for one or more of the steps forming chlorophyll.

13.1.3 Chemistry and Formation of the Carotenoid Pigments

The **carotenoid pigments** are a group of pigments which, in higher plants, are usually red, orange, yellow, or brown and are associated with chlorophyll in the chloroplast. Sometimes they also occur in other plastids, as in the chromoplasts of carrot roots, the red fruit of tomatoes, and in many yellow flowers. Their yellow colors are evident in dark-grown angiosperms in which chlorophyll is absent (showing that light is not essential for their accumulation) and in many autumn leaves from which the chlorophyll has disappeared. Actually, they may have colors other than those listed above, such as the green of an avocado fruit, the pink of a shrimp, or the nearly black ink of a squid. They occur in all major groups of plants and animals, but we are primarily concerned with their occurrence with chlorophyll in chloroplasts.

The carotenoids are divided into two chemical groups, the **carotenes** and the **xanthophylls**. Several distinct types of each group occur. All have 40 carbon atoms. The carotenes themselves, of which **β-carotene** is the most important example, are pure hydrocarbons (Fig. 13-1). The xanthophylls, such as **lutein** and **zeaxanthin**, possess oxygen atoms united to the terminal rings. Both the xanthophylls and carotenes are synthesized from an activated form of acetate, **acetyl coenzyme A**, through the mevalonic acid pathway (Chapter 18).

Almost no carotenoids dissolve in water, but they dissolve in many organic solvents such as acetone or ether. The xanthophylls, because of the oxygen atoms, are more hydrophylic than the carotenes. When in solution, most carotenoids absorb primarily violet and blue light between 400 and 500 mμ (Fig. 13-4). The absorption spectrum depends upon the unsaturation present, yet in the intact chloroplast the spectra can be somewhat different. There is evidence that the absorption maxima for some carotenoids may shift from about 500 mμ in the cell to about 450 mμ when removed by an organic solvent.

13.1.4   Functions of the Carotenoids

The carotenoids are probably important to photosynthesis for two reasons. *First*, the carotenes appear to prevent a destruction of chlorophyll in the presence of light and oxygen. Such a destructive phenomenon is called **photo-oxidation** (Chapter 14). It is readily observed that an alcoholic solution of chlorophyll is bleached by light, and oxygen is consumed in this process. Apparently a similar reaction would normally occur in the plant were it not for the protection of carotenoids. Evidence from this

is best seen in certain bacterial mutants that lack carotenoids and in which photo-oxidation occurs readily. In addition, an example is known of white albino sunflower mutants that lack the ability to synthesize carotenoids but can form trace amounts of chlorophyll. Increasing the light intensity in this case simply causes additional photo-oxidation of the chlorophyll as rapidly as it is formed. The mechanism by which carotenoids afford this protection to chlorophylls is not certain, but it is assumed by some that the carotenoids themselves are photo-oxidized by light that would otherwise destroy chlorophyll.

The *second* probable function of carotenoids, perhaps particularly the xanthophylls, is a role in absorption of light active in photosynthesis. The evidence is excellent that carotenoids such as **fucoxanthin** (also called fucoxanthol) of the brown algae (e.g., kelps) participate actively in photosynthesis. This evidence was obtained by comparing the absorption spectrum of the pigment in question with the so-called **action spectrum** for photosynthesis by the organisms. An action spectrum is simply a graph of the magnitude of the response, in this case photosynthesis, plotted as a function of the wavelength of light causing the reaction[1] (Fig. 13-5). In the green algae and higher plants it also appears that certain of the carotenoids absorb light, causing photosynthesis. In these cases the action spectra show maxima in the red and blue where the chlorophylls absorb best, but photosynthesis is still appreciable in the blue-green regions where certain of the carotenoids are thought to be active.

The best evidence that carotenoids are functional in photosynthesis is their ability to transfer excitation energy, when illuminated,

---

[1] The light energy of any wavelength applied cannot be such that the response is saturated. That is, the experimenter must choose energies that affect the response in a linear manner.

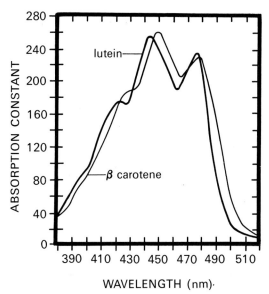

Figure 13-4

Absorption spectra of β-carotene in hexane, and of lutein (a xanthophyll) in ethanol. The absorption constant used is the same as that described in Fig. 13-2. (Data are from F. Zscheile et al., 1942, *Plant Physiol.* 17:331. Used by permission.)

directly to chlorophyll *a*. Thus when a plant is exposed to wavelengths of light absorbed almost exclusively by the carotenoids, a red fluorescence of chlorophyll *a* can be observed. It is believed that the excitation energy sometimes thus released as fluorescence is more commonly used to drive photosynthesis.

13.1.5 The Phycobilins

The **phycobilins** are a final group of photosynthetic pigments occurring in blue-green and red algae. These are classified into two types, the red **phycoerythrin**, and the blue **phycocyanin**. Like chlorophyll, these compounds are tetrapyrroles. However, the phycobilins are open pyrroles and contain neither magnesium nor a phytol chain. They are attached to proteins in the living cell, and they are water soluble. Both

types absorb light, causing photosynthesis, and, in the red algae, the highest efficiency is in the green region where phycoerythrin absorbs maximally and where chlorophyll absorbs least. As with the carotenoids, the phycobilins transfer excitation energy to chlorophyll *a* and can cause the latter to fluoresce. That such an energy transfer occurs indicates that the phycobilins are effective in photosynthesis by gathering photons, the energy of which is normally utilized by chlorophyll *a* to drive photosynthesis. Such pigments as carotenoids and phycobilins, which transfer energy to an absorption sink like chlorophyll *a*, are often called **accessory.pigments**. Chlorophylls *b*, *c*, and *d* are also often considered accessory pigments because they, too, harvest light energy, which can be transferred to chlorophyll *a*.

13.2 THE STRUCTURE OF THE CHLOROPLAST

The entire photosynthetic process occurs in the chloroplasts. R. Jensen and J. Bassham at the University of California found that isolated chloroplast material from spinach leaves could fix CO_2 about two-thirds as rapidly as could the leaves themselves, when compared on a weight of chlorophyll basis (155 micromoles CO_2/hr/mg chlorophyll). To understand the process of organic matter production completely, we must realize not only the types of machinery present in this factory, but also the way in which these are assembled.

Figure 13-6 shows an electron micrograph of a leaf chloroplast. Chloroplasts are easily seen with the light microscope, but their fine structure requires higher magnification. They are found in higher plants, mosses, ferns, and green algae, although in green algae their shapes are usually much different from the typical higher plant chloroplast. True chloroplasts are missing in other algae and in photosynthetic bacteria. In these organisms the photo-

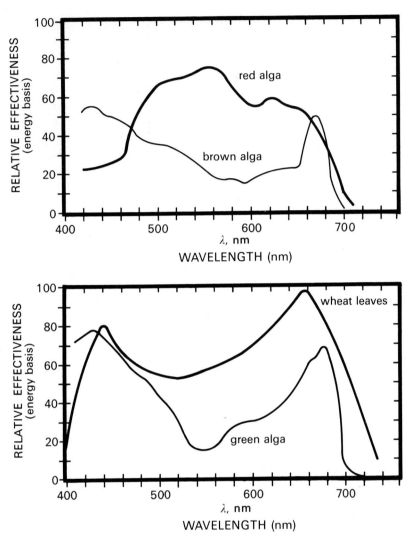

Figure 13-5
Photosynthesis action spectra for various organisms. [Data for wheat leaves are from W. H. Hoover, 1937, *Smithsonian Inst. Misc. Coll.* 95:11. Data for red alga (*Porphyra*), brown alga (*Coilodesme*), and green alga (*Ulva*) are from F. T. Haxo and L. R. Blinks, 1950, *J. Gen. Physiol.* 33:414.]

synthetic factories are of somewhat different structural types.

The chloroplasts of higher plants are disc-shaped objects, typically near $5\,\mu$ long by $2\,\mu$ wide and 1 or $2\,\mu$ thick, but their sizes and shapes change somewhat in light and darkness and with their activities. They are surrounded by a double membrane, the inner membrane extending in several places across the plastid to form a lamellar system. At various points these extensions unite with a stack of nearly identical membranes. Each such stack is called a **granum** (plural, **grana**). There are usually 40 to 60 grana per mature chloroplast, and 20 to 100 chloroplasts are usually found in each photosynthetic leaf cell. The chlorophyll and carotenoids are in close association in the membranes of the grana, allowing the efficient transfer of light energy from the carotenoids to chlorophyll *a*. It is postulated that chlorophyll exists in a monomolecular layer sandwiched between proteins and carotenoids or galactolipids. It has been thought that the chlorophylls and carotenoids occur only in the grana membranes, and the green color of the chlorophylls is certainly most easy to detect there. However, electron microscope investigations by Roderic Park at the University of California indicate that chlorophyll, at least, also occurs in the membranes outside the grana.

Most of the remainder of the chloroplast appears to consist of enzymes involved in the fixation of carbon dioxide and its conversion to other carbohydrates, such as sucrose, starch, fats, and proteins. This proteinaceous matrix is called the **stroma**. In addition to enzymes, the stroma also contains some DNA as well as granules called **ribosomes**, which consist of RNA combined with protein. The functions of ribosomes and DNA will be discussed in detail in Chapter 17. It appears that the presence of DNA allows some chloroplasts to be capable of reproducing themselves somewhat independently of the nucleus, and that ribosomes permit the synthesis of chloroplast proteins here.

13.3 PARTICIPATION OF CHLOROPHYLL IN PHOTOSYNTHESIS

If light is to be effective in a process, it must first be absorbed. Hence, if the chlorophylls participate actively in photosynthesis, the wavelengths of light they absorb should be very effective in causing this process. Figure 13-5 shows the action spectrum for photosynthesis in leaves. Two major peaks are found, one in the red and one in the blue. The exact wavelengths most effective may be expected to differ somewhat among various green plants. Nevertheless, the action spectrum always more closely resembles the absorption spectrum of the chlorophylls than of any other pigment found in chloroplasts. This is excellent evidence that the chlorophylls are indeed the pigments that absorb the light energy driving photosynthesis.

The green and yellow wavelengths are surprisingly effective in causing photosynthesis compared to their absorption by chlorophylls in organic solvents. It has been suggested that this is because of the absorption of these wavelengths by carotenoids. However, most of the carotenoids known absorb only in the blue or blue-green regions. Perhaps other, unknown carotenoids or other pigments exist in leaves, which absorb green light and transfer the energy to chlorophyll *a*, or perhaps the chlorophylls or the carotenoids absorb green and yellow wavelengths more efficiently when in the intact chloroplasts than they do after extraction.

The first action spectrum for photosynthesis was cleverly obtained in 1883 by a German physiologist, T. W. Englemann, who worked with various algae. He placed a strand of filamentous alga (*Spirogyra*) on a microscope slide and illuminated it from below with light that had passed through a prism to separate it into the various component colors. Each color thus struck a different segment of the alga. Bacteria that required oxygen for motility were also placed on the microscope slide. Englemann found that these bacteria collected along the portion of the alga where most oxygen was being released in photosynthesis. For the green algae this was near the regions absorbing red and blue light. Other algae photosynthesized best in light of the color approximately complementary to their own cells, red algae in green

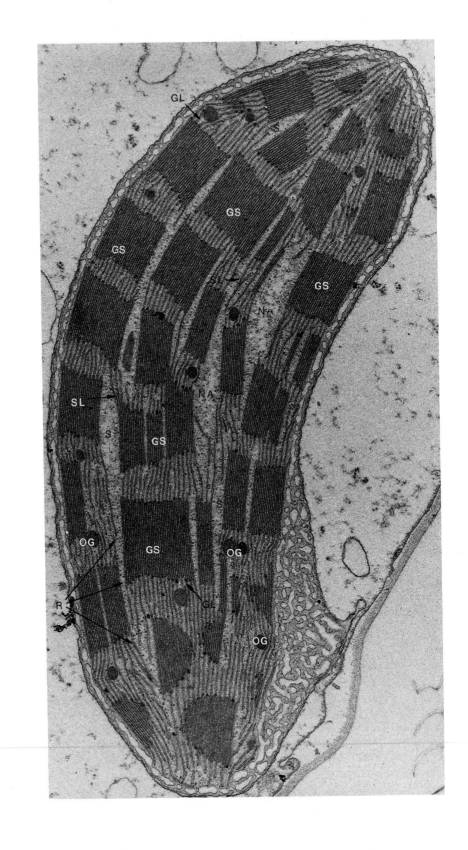

light, and brown algae in blue light. The blue-green algae have an action spectrum peak in yellow or orange light.

In general, a comparison of the action spectrum for the reaction with the absorption spectrum of suspected known pigments is one of the first experiments to be performed by researchers seeking the cause for responses brought about by light. Several other examples of plant physiological processes caused by light are discussed in Chapter 23.

13.4 SUMMARY REACTIONS OF PHOTOSYNTHESIS

Photosynthesis may be divided into three general reactions, two of which occur only in light, and one that does not require light. The two **light reactions** can occur even in isolated grana. They provide reduced pyridine nucleotide (NADPH) and ATP. The third reaction, the fixation and reduction of carbon dioxide, could then occur even in darkness, since the enzymes of the stroma do not require light but only the ATP and NADPH provided by the grana.

13.4.1 The Hill Reaction

The splitting of water by illuminated isolated chloroplasts to form a reduced electron acceptor was first demonstrated by Robin Hill and R. Scarisbrick, in England, about 1940. Oxygen is released in this process, now called the **Hill reaction**. In the early studies of the Hill reaction

only compounds not normally found in plants were reduced by the electrons of water, but in 1951 it was found that NADP could also be reduced [see (R13-4)] by isolated chloroplasts.

$$\text{light} + H_2O + NADP \longrightarrow$$

$$\frac{1}{2}O_2 + NADPH + H^+ \quad \text{(R13-4)}$$

The discovery that NADP served as a Hill reagent was exciting, because the ability of NADPH to reduce various plant metabolites was well known. It was immediately suspected that NADPH is used to reduce CO_2, and this proved correct. Thus the Hill reaction accounts for the use of water as a source of electrons for CO_2 fixation and the elimination of oxygen as a by-product during photosynthesis.

13.4.2 Photosynthetic Phosphorylation

A second function of the grana is to form ATP. The energy of the terminal phosphate bond of ATP is, along with NADPH, later used to convert carbon dioxide into more complex products of photosynthesis. The light-driven formation of ATP from ADP and inorganic phosphate (Pi) was demonstrated at the University of California in the laboratory of Daniel Arnon, about 1954. Arnon first showed that carefully prepared chloroplasts could carry out the entire photosynthetic process. Later, he and his coworkers found that if these chloroplasts were provided ADP, Pi, and NADP, in the

Figure 13-6

Thin section of gluteraldehyde-osmium fixed corn leaf tissue showing a chloroplast in cross section. The internal membrane system contains chlorophyll and is the site of the light reactions and associated electron transport reactions of photosynthesis. This continuous membrane system can be divided into two morphological groupings: those membranes occurring only in grana stacks (GS) are called grana lamellae (GL) or small thylakoids, while those membranes connecting and traversing various grana stacks are called stroma lamellae (SL) or large thylakoids. The embedding matrix is called stroma (S) and contains the photosynthetic carbon cycle enzymes, ribosomes, and perhaps the DNA of the chloroplast. Ribosomes (R), osmiophilic granules (OG), and DNA containing areas (NA) may also be seen in this micrograph ($\times 67,200$). (Photograph courtesy of L. K. Shumway, Washington State University. From W. A. Jensen and R. B. Park, 1967, *Cell Ultrastructure*. © 1967 by Wadsworth Publishing Company, Inc., Belmont, California. Used by permission.)

presence of light but in the absence of CO_2, then ATP as well as NADPH accumulated.

13.4.3 Dark Fixation

They next turned off the lights and added CO_2, with a resulting utilization of ATP and NADPH accompanied by the conversion of CO_2 to carbohydrates. Hence they clearly separated the Hill reaction and photosynthetic phosphorylation from the so-called **dark reactions** of CO_2 fixation and reduction, although it was fully realized that all normally occur together in the light. These reactions are summarized in (R13-5) and (R13-6).

light reactions

$$\text{chloroplasts} + H_2O + ADP + Pi + NADP \xrightarrow[\text{no } CO_2]{\text{light}}$$

$$\tfrac{1}{2}O_2 + ATP + NADPH \quad \text{(R13-5)}$$

dark reactions

$$\text{chloroplasts} + CO_2 + ATP + NADPH \xrightarrow{\text{darkness}}$$

$$ADP + Pi + NADP + \text{sugars and starch} \quad \text{(R13-6)}$$

Before it was known that NADPH and ATP are formed in light reactions, the real mystery of photosynthesis was the way in which light energy could be converted to the chemical energy of carbohydrate compounds. Now a concerted attack is being made to discover how the light energy is, instead, more immediately converted to the chemical energy of NADPH and ATP. This problem has been partially solved.

13.5 ENERGY RELATIONS OF PHOTOSYNTHESIS

Using water to reduce one mole of CO_2 to its level of reduction when found in carbohydrate (CH_2O) requires about 118 kcal. When the energy present in one einstein of red light of 660 mμ is calculated (see Chapter 3, Example 3-1), a value of about 43 kcal is obtained. This

is only about 43/118, or one-third, of the amount required to convert one mole of CO_2 to (CH_2O). At least three photons would be required. Although the energy present in a photon of blue light is greater than that in red, it is still too low to reduce one CO_2 molecule. Experimental measurements of the actual number of photons required commonly give values of about eight to ten for either blue or red light. This number is referred to as the **quantum requirement** for photosynthesis.

Such a high quantum requirement compared to that theoretically needed means that there is considerable waste in photosynthesis. Calculations show that under ideal experimental conditions in algae the process is only about 22 percent efficient, the remainder of the light energy being wasted as heat. Blue is more wasteful than red, since the quantum requirement for blue light is just as high as that for red light,[2] and there is more energy per quantum in the blue.

Some interesting computations were made to discover whether one chlorophyll molecule could absorb eight to ten photons and store this energy to form sufficient ATP and NADPH later. It was calculated that in a suspension of the alga *Chlorella*, exposed to light of an intensity that saturates the photosynthetic process, each chlorophyll molecule would absorb a photon only about every eight minutes. If each molecule needed to absorb eight such photons before causing a reaction, it would require an hour before photosynthesis could occur after turning on the lights. Nevertheless, the process

---

[2] In a photochemical reaction, the photons act as individual units. They enter into the reaction in a stoichiometric relationship to other reactants. To act, a photon must have *enough* energy to excite the absorbing pigment, but any additional energy is wasted. Blue light activates electrons in chlorophyll molecules to a higher energy state than does red light, but this excess energy is rapidly lost as heat as the electrons fall back to the same energy level to which they are excited by red radiation.

was known to start almost immediately after illumination began. Furthermore, the lifetime of excited chlorophyll molecules is always less than 0.01 second, and may be as low as 10^{-8} second. So how could as many as eight or ten quanta be collected by a single molecule to participate jointly and cause photosynthesis? The answer is apparently that the energy of photons absorbed by many chlorophyll molecules or other photosynthetic pigments is quickly transferred to a common reaction center where this energy can be accumulated, so that oxygen release occurs without a lag. One reaction center is believed to be a chlorophyll with a red absorption peak at 700 mμ called **P700**, which is probably a special form of chlorophyll *a* in an environment favorable for energy transfer to other molecules. One P700 molecule is present for approximately each 400 other chlorophylls in chloroplasts.

The functional group of a few hundred chlorophyll molecules around a reaction center is referred to as a **photosynthetic unit**. Small protuberances on the grana that can contain about 240 chlorophyll molecules have been discovered through electron micrographs. These tiny structures are called **quantasomes** (Fig. 13-7). The photosynthetic unit was suggested to exist within a single quantasome, but evidence of Stephen Howell and E. N. Moudrianakis at Johns Hopkins University indicates that this is not correct.

13.6 THE EMERSON ENHANCEMENT EFFECT

At the University of Illinois in 1957, Robert Emerson made a discovery that has proved to be of great importance in explaining how several quanta might cooperate to split a molecule of water. Emerson found that the quantum requirement increases greatly at wavelengths longer than 680 mμ, even though these wavelengths are still absorbed by chlorophyll *a*. That is, the

photosynthetic efficiency of these long wavelengths is poor. Emerson and his coworkers found that when light of shorter wavelengths was provided at the same time as the longer, inefficient wavelengths, the rate of photosynthesis was even greater than could be expected from adding the rates found when either color was provided alone. This suggested that two separate light reactions normally cooperate in photosynthesis. When the short wavelengths were further investigated to determine which were most effective in causing enhancement, the resulting action spectrum for the Emerson effect in green algae resembled the absorption spectrum for chlorophyll *b*. In algae possessing phycobilins instead of chlorophyll *b*, these accessory pigments also cause enhancement.

It thus appears that photosynthesis is cooperatively driven by light absorption by two pigment systems. System I proves to contain the long-red-wavelength (683 mμ) absorbing form of chlorophyll *a*, with P700 as the energy-collecting pigment, and the photosynthetically active carotenoids. System II contains chlorophyll *b* and the short-red-wavelength (672 mμ) absorbing form of chlorophyll *a* in higher plants and green algae, or phycobilins and other chlorophylls in the blue-green and red algae.

13.7 FURTHER COMPOUNDS PARTICIPATING IN PHOTOSYNTHESIS

The chlorophylls and carotenoids alone cannot cause photosynthesis in green plants, and other essential compounds in chloroplasts have been identified. These possess the ability to undergo alternate oxidation and reduction. Although many of them are colored, they do not absorb photosynthetically active light themselves. They instead participate in an electron transport chain, helping transfer electrons from water to NADP where they can be stored and eventually

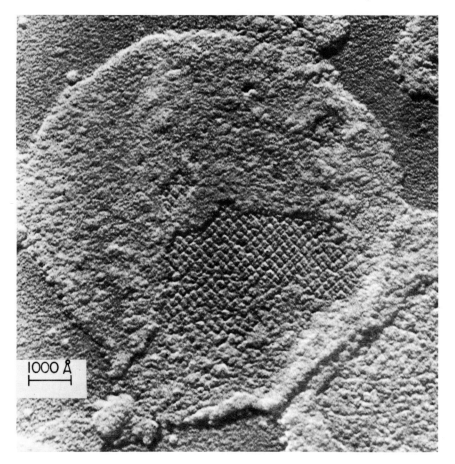

Figure 13-7
Surface view electron micrograph of part of a granum from spinach chloroplasts. Quantasomes
are the tiny beadlike objects giving the rough appearance to the lower portion of the photograph.
(From R. B. Park and J. Biggins, 1964, *Science* 144:1009. Used by permission.)

used in various reductive processes, especially
the conversion of CO_2 to carbohydrates.

13.7.1 Cytochromes

One group of such compounds includes the
cytochrome pigments. The structure of the
heme portion of a typical cytochrome, cytochrome *c*, was given in Chapter 11 (Fig. 11-14).

Cytochrome *c* itself is not present in chloroplasts, although a similar cytochrome, **cytochrome *f***, is present; and, like P700, it occurs
in the ratio of about one molecule per 400
chlorophyll molecules. Chloroplasts also contain a second cytochrome named **cytochrome b_6**,
which is about four times as abundant as
cytochrome *f*. The complete structures of these
are not yet known, but the ability of each to be

reduced or oxidized comes from the conversion of the iron they contain from the ferric to the ferrous form and vice versa as shown in (R13-7).

$$\text{cytochrome (Fe}^{+3}\text{)} \underset{-1e}{\overset{+1e}{\rightleftharpoons}} \text{cytochrome (Fe}^{+2}\text{)}$$

$$\text{(R13-7)}$$

13.7.2 Plastoquinone

A compound called **plastoquinone** also shows redox changes during photosynthesis [see (R13-8)].

As contrasted to the cytochromes, plastoquinone does not appear to be attached to any protein in the chloroplast. Other closely related quinones also occur and may function in the same way that the plastoquinone in (R13-8) does. Some of these are chemically very similar to the plastoquinone shown in (R13-8) and are themselves referred to as plastoquinones. In addition, **tocopherylquinones** and **naphthoquinones** (vitamin K) are present. Spinach chloroplasts contain at least four closely related plastoquinones, two naphthoquinones (vitamin K_1 and another naphthoquinone), and three tocopherylquinones. About one-tenth as many quinones as chlorophylls are found in chloroplasts, but the photosynthetically active percentage of these is unknown.

13.7.3 Ferredoxin

Ferredoxin is another iron-containing protein essential to photosynthesis. The nature of this molecule was discussed in Chapter 11. One of the two iron atoms present may be oxidized or reduced, the electrons needed for its reduction coming ultimately from water. The iron is not bound in a heme structure as it is in the cytochromes, but instead it is bound to sulfur atoms. Ferredoxin is the most difficult to reduce of all the known compounds participating in electron transport in the chloroplasts. This means that it is also the most easily oxidized, and as a result it passes electrons readily to NADP [reaction (R13-9b) below], producing NADPH and oxidized ferredoxin. Since NADP can accept two electrons, while ferredoxin can donate only one, it requires two molecules of reduced ferredoxin to reduce each NADP [see (R13-9)].

(a) $\text{ferredoxin (Fe}^{+3}\text{)} \underset{-1e}{\overset{+1e}{\rightleftharpoons}} \text{ferredoxin (Fe}^{+2}\text{)}$

(b) $2 \text{ ferredoxin (Fe}^{+2}\text{)} + \text{NADP} + \text{H}^+ \rightleftharpoons$

$$2 \text{ ferredoxin (Fe}^{+3}\text{)} + \text{NADPH}$$

$$\text{(R13-9)}$$

13.7.4 Plastocyanin

In addition to the iron-containing cytochromes and ferredoxin, a blue protein containing two atoms of copper called **plastocyanin** is apparently also a member of the photosynthetic electron transport chain. Thus, both iron and copper perform specific, essential roles in photosynthesis. Plastocyanin is present only in chloroplasts, where it occurs in the ratio of about one molecule for every 600 chlorophyll molecules.

During photosynthesis, long wavelengths of red light (about 690 mμ) absorbed primarily by chlorophyll *a* cause oxidation of plastocyanin, while shorter wavelengths absorbed by both chlorophylls *a* and *b* sometimes even cause its reduction. The interpretation of these observations is presently that excitation of chlorophyll *a* by the long red wavelengths leads to its oxidation, the excited electron being transferred to another acceptor molecule. Chlorophyll *a* is then quickly reduced to its original condition by obtaining an electron from plastocyanin, causing the observed oxidation of the latter. Plastocyanin remains oxidized until reduced by an electron derived from water, this process being driven by the shorter wavelengths of red light absorbed by chlorophyll *b*. Apparently only one of the two copper atoms present undergoes redox changes [see (R13-10)].

$$\text{plastocyanin (Cu}^{++}) \underset{-1e}{\overset{+1e}{\rightleftharpoons}} \text{plastocyanin (Cu}^{+})$$

(R13-10)

13.8 A MODEL FOR THE LIGHT REACTIONS OF PHOTOSYNTHESIS

The exact arrangement of the components involved in the transfer of electrons from water to NADPH is not yet clear. Nevertheless, a very tentative and incomplete model (Fig. 13-8) of the series flow type has been proposed that shows the likely role for these components and the way in which light energy is used to drive the electrons from water to ferredoxin. NADP normally accepts electrons from ferredoxin, as described above for use in CO_2 fixation, but the same electrons may also provide the energy for nitrogen fixation in certain organisms (Chapter 16) or for other reductive processes requiring energy (Chapter 14).

In the scheme of Fig. 13-8, a photon of light is used to excite an electron in chlorophyll *b* or other accessory pigment of system II. The energy of two such excited electrons is then accepted by one oxidized plastoquinone, producing fully reduced plastoquinone and electron-deficient chlorophyll *b*. In some unclear manner, chlorophyll *b* then accepts an electron from a water molecule. This latter step requires both manganese and chloride

ions and is an important reason why these elements are essential to plants. Manganese appears to undergo reduction and oxidation, but little else is known about its function or about the role of chloride. The net result is that water loses electrons, producing oxygen as the by-product of photosynthesis and yielding reduced plastoquinone.

Plastoquinone then donates the electrons, one at a time, to an acceptor compound, probably cytochrome *f*. From cytochrome *f* the electron may fall to plastocyanin and then to P700, provided the latter can accept it. P700 can accept an electron only if it has just lost one of its own when excited by the energy in a second photon of light collected by one of the pigments of system I. It is assumed that ferredoxin is the direct acceptor of the electron lost by the excited P700 molecule.

When electrons fall from plastoquinone through cytochrome *f* and plastocyanin to P700, some energy is released. This energy is not entirely lost as heat, but instead a part is somehow used to form ATP from ADP and Pi (photosynthetic phosphorylation). The enzymes essential for this phosphorylation are closely associated with the chlorophyll and cytochrome molecules of the grana. Best estimates are that one or perhaps two molecules of ATP are produced for each two electrons transferred.

This part of the scheme explains how two photons cooperate in driving an electron from water to NADPH (**Emerson enhancement**) and explains the observed oxidation and reduction of cytochrome *f*, plastocyanin, and of plastoquinone in light. The fact that excitation of system II by light not absorbed by system I is effective in photosynthesis is accounted for by the fact that excitation energy is readily transferred from system II to system I, but not in the reverse direction. The scheme also accounts for at least part of the ATP needed for later CO_2 fixation, and it incorporates the processes of

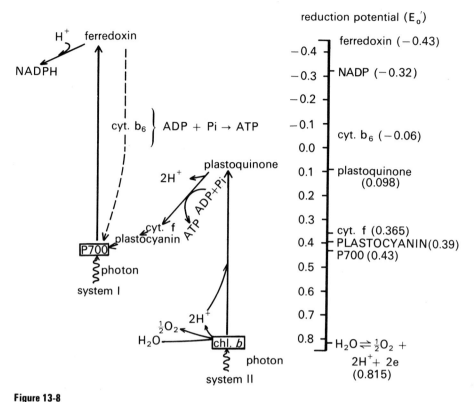

reduction potential $(E_o{}')$

Figure 13-8

Proposed model explaining electron flow from water through chlorophylls to NADP, with suggested associated photosynthetic phosphorylation sites. ATP production between plastoquinone and cytochrome f is often called noncyclic photophosphorylation. Cyclic photophosphorylation occurs, but the electron-return mechanism associated with the dashed line is only speculative, and the role of cytochrome b_6 is not established. The more positive the reduction potential indicated, the more easily the reduction process occurs, so ferredoxin is the most difficult to reduce, and water is the most difficult to oxidize. Thus, light energy is essential for electron flow.

water splitting and of oxygen release, as well. However, if only one ATP molecule is made for each two electrons transferred (i.e., for each water molecule split), not enough ATP is accounted for. As indicated in the next chapter, three molecules of ATP are probably required to fix one molecule of CO_2 or to release one molecule of oxygen. It has been suggested that electrons from ferredoxin can sometimes fall back to P700 through the other cytochrome found in chloroplasts, cytochrome b_6. In this case an additional ATP could be formed for each two electrons transferred by a type of **cyclic photophosphorylation**. This would account for all of the ATP needed, but to ensure that sufficient NADPH would still be produced, two additional photons would be needed to excite system I. Calculations show that this would require ten quanta to form three molecules of ATP and two molecules of NADPH per molecule of O_2 released. A quantum requirement of ten is very consistent with most of the measurements made by many plant physiologists.

Nevertheless, the scheme described will be modified by further research. Other compounds have already been discovered that may soon be incorporated into the proposed pathway of electron transport from water to NADPH. In addition, changes in the order of components in the electron transport chain may be made as better evidence accumulates. Much remains to be discovered about the way in which electrons are removed from the water molecule and the role of chlorophyll, manganese, and chloride in this process. Answers to these problems must await further research.

Carbon Dioxide Fixation and Photosynthesis in Nature

14.1 EARLY IDEAS

In the early part of this century it was assumed that the fixation of carbon dioxide by green plants required its direct combination with the chlorophyll molecule, and that the oxygen released in photosynthesis came from carbon dioxide. The erroneous belief was prevalent that CO_2 was reduced to formaldehyde (CH_2O), and that these molecules somehow condensed to form a sugar with the same empirical formula. G. Paechnatz showed, however, in 1928, that formaldehyde is toxic to plants and that it could not be converted to sugars by photosynthesis.

Considerable progress concerning the mechanism of CO_2 fixation was made after discoveries of H. Wood and C. H. Werkman during the period of 1936–1940. These scientists found that certain bacteria had the ability, using CO_2, to carboxylate pyruvic acid to oxaloacetate and reduce this to malic acid as in (R14-1).

$$CO_2 + CH_3-\overset{\displaystyle O}{\underset{\displaystyle \|}{C}}-COOH \underset{-2H}{\overset{+2H}{\rightleftharpoons}}$$

$$HOOC-CH_2-\underset{\displaystyle |}{\underset{\displaystyle OH}{CH}}-COOH \quad (R14\text{-}1)$$

Soon, a similar fixation and reduction of carbon dioxide was demonstrated in rat liver. These reactions suggested, in principle, that such processes might occur in any living cell. The possible application of these observations to the problem of photosynthesis was soon recognized by plant physiologists, but the sequence of reactions leading from CO_2 to the more complex organic products was solved only after radioactive carbon-14 became available following World War II. Carbon dioxide containing ^{14}C was then prepared, and all molecules produced from it during photosynthetic experiments were labeled. Paper chromatography was developed at about the same time, making separation of many of the photosynthetic compounds practical.

Labeled molecules present on the chromatograms were detected by autoradiography (Chapter 9). In this technique, x-ray film is placed in tight contact with the paper chromatograms in darkness for a few days to a few months (depending upon the amount of radioactivity present), while the radioactivity exposes the film. Upon development of the films, dark spots are seen which indicate the locations of the radioactive compounds. The identity of the compounds and the amount of radioactivity present in each can be determined by cutting out the areas of paper that correspond to the dark spots on the film. Geiger-Müller tubes or the more sensitive **liquid scintillation counters** are used to measure radioactivity, while direct chemical analyses and rechromatography of unknown substances with known compounds (**cochromatography**) are used to identify radioactive photosynthetic products.

14.2   PRODUCTS OF CARBON DIOXIDE FIXATION

14.2.1   The First Product

These techniques were applied to the problem of photosynthesis by A. Benson and M. Calvin and their colleagues at the University of California in Berkeley, in 1949. They allowed green algae such as *Chlorella* to attain a steady rate of photosynthesis, then introduced radioactive $^{14}CO_2$ into the solution in which the algae were growing. By opening the container at various times after introduction of the isotope, the algae were dropped into boiling 80 percent ethanol to kill them instantly and to extract any metabolites containing ^{14}C (Fig. 14-1). This extract was chromatographed and autoradiograms were made.

It was found that even after photosynthesizing only seven seconds in the presence of $^{14}CO_2$ the algae had formed as many as twelve radioactive compounds. After 60 seconds many dark spots on the film were detected, as shown in Fig. 14-2. By this time, both amino acids and organic acids had become radioactive. The compounds containing most of the ^{14}C were phosphorylated sugars, shown at the lower right of the figure. It was desirable to identify the first product formed from CO_2; so the time periods were shortened even below five seconds. When this was done, most of the ^{14}C was found in a phosphorylated three-carbon acid called **3-phosphoglyceric acid**, abbreviated **PGA**. PGA,

then, was the first detectable product of photosynthetic carbon dioxide fixation in these algae. Similar results were found with these techniques using leaves of higher plants or chloroplasts isolated from them.

14.2.2   The Compound Combining with CO_2

The search next began for a two-carbon substance with which CO_2 could react to form PGA. Such a two-carbon unit was not found. When $^{14}CO_2$ was fed to the algae for some time and then suddenly removed, it was expected that the compound with which it normally combines would accumulate. The substance which did accumulate was found to be a five-carbon sugar, phosphorylated at each end of the molecule, **ribulose-1,5-diphosphate**. At the same time, there was a rapid drop in the level of labeled PGA. This suggested that ribulose diphosphate is the normal substrate to which carbon dioxide is added, leading to the formation of PGA.

14.2.3   The Reaction of CO_2 Fixation

Soon an enzyme was found that catalyzes the combination of carbon dioxide with ribulose diphosphate to form two molecules of PGA. Some evidence indicates that an unstable intermediate product is formed [shown in brackets in (R14-2)] that may either split into two PGA molecules with the addition of water [as in reaction (R14-2a)] or may be reduced, perhaps by ferredoxin, and subsequently split into one molecule of PGA and one of 3-phosphoglyceraldehyde [reaction (R14-2b)].

Light has no effect on the rate at which PGA is formed, as long as sufficient ribulose diphosphate is available. In fact, the enzyme involved, named **carboxydismutase** (also referred to as **ribulose diphosphate carboxylase**), has even been found in various microorganisms that do not require light for growth. Furthermore, when the lights were turned out above photosynthesiz-

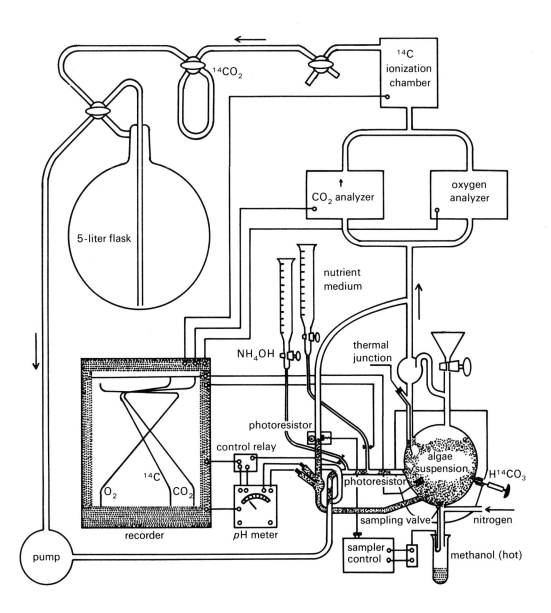

Figure 14-1
University of California system used to expose algae to $^{14}CO_2$ for short time periods under steady state photosynthetic conditions. Total CO_2, oxygen, and $^{14}CO_2$ were analyzed and recorded as a function of time. ^{14}C was injected into the algae suspension with a syringe (lower right) as $NaH^{14}CO_3$. After short periods of ^{14}C fixation, some of the algae were dropped into boiling methanol to kill them and to extract labeled compounds. (From J. Bassham, 1962, "The Path of Carbon in Photosynthesis," *Sci. Amer.* 206:88. Copyright © 1962 by Scientific American, Inc. All rights reserved.)

ing *Chlorella* cells, PGA accumulated and ribulose diphosphate disappeared. This suggests that the role of light in photosynthesis is to provide energy for conversion of PGA to ribulose diphosphate and other products, and that it has nothing more directly to do with the fixation of CO_2.

CO_2 fixation into PGA is not reversible, and most of the CO_2 absorbed by the majority of plants is thought to be combined with ribulose diphosphate rather than with other known CO_2 acceptors. However, other carboxylations do occur, such as the Wood–Werkman reaction, but in most of these reactions, either the enzymes have a low attraction for CO_2 or the process is not energetically favorable, or both. Nevertheless, some CO_2 is undoubtedly fixed by other processes, and direct support for this will be presented later in this chapter (14.4.1).

14.3 THE CALVIN–BENSON CYCLE

Further investigations by Calvin, Benson, and J. A. Bassham of radioactive compounds formed from $^{14}CO_2$ and found on chromatograms from extracts of photosynthesizing plants showed that other sugar phosphates containing five, six, and even seven carbon atoms were produced. These compounds included the pentose phosphates ribose-5-phosphate, xylulose-5-phosphate, and ribulose-5-phosphate; the hexose phosphates fructose-6-phosphate, fructose-1,6-diphosphate, and glucose-6-phosphate; and the heptose phosphates sedoheptulose-7-phosphate and sedoheptulose-1,7-diphosphate. By noting time sequences in which these became labeled from $^{14}CO_2$ and by degrading the molecules to determine which atoms contained the ^{14}C, it was possible to predict a metabolic pathway relating them.

When PGA was degraded, most of the radioactivity proved to be in the carboxyl carbon, as shown by asterisks in reactions (R14-2a and b) (14.2.3), but the alpha and beta carbons were also labeled. This suggested that the latter two carbons were not derived from $^{14}CO_2$ directly, but rather that they were formed from the carboxyl carbon atom of PGA by some cyclic process. A cycle was soon found that uses the PGA to form the other sugar phosphates mentioned, and that also converts some of the carbon atoms back to PGA via ribulose diphosphate. These reactions have collectively been named the **Calvin–Benson cycle**, in honor of the scientists who discovered them. Calvin was awarded a Nobel Prize in 1961 for this work.

The Calvin–Benson cycle consists of four parts:

1. Carbon dioxide is added to ribulose diphosphate to form two molecules of PGA, or perhaps one PGA and one phosphoglyceraldehyde.

2. PGA is reduced to phosphoglyceraldehyde, probably by NADPH. ATP is also essential in the process, and both the NADPH and ATP

ribulose diphosphate   PGA   phosphoglyceraldehyde   (R14-2)

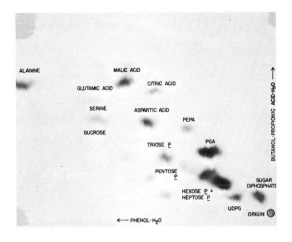

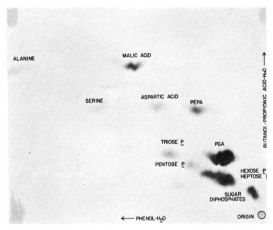

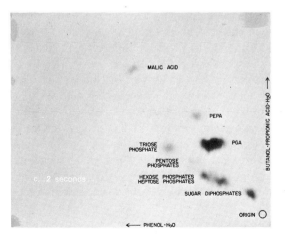

are produced in the light reactions of photosynthesis.

3. Some of the phosphoglyceraldehyde molecules are converted to fructose diphosphate, part of which is then converted to xylulose-5-phosphate. Other phosphoglyceraldehyde molecules unite with sedoheptulose-7-phosphate, yielding ribose-5-phosphate and xylulose-5-phosphate. Ribulose-5-phosphate is produced directly from either of these two pentose phosphates.

4. Ribulose-5-phosphate is phosphorylated by ATP to form ribulose diphosphate, which can then accept CO_2 to continue the cycle.

The cycle accounts for regeneration of ribulose diphosphate and also allows for the net storage of carbohydrate molecules, since some of the fructose-diphosphate is used for the synthesis of sucrose, starch, cellulose, pectins, etc., instead of being entirely converted to ribulose-5-phosphate. These relationships are summarized in Fig. 14-3.

The individual reactions of the cycle and the names of the enzymes participating are shown in Fig. 14-4. Note that all of the sugars are phosphorylated at one or at both ends of the molecules. No free sugars are involved, and sucrose is typically the first nonphosphorylated sugar formed in photosynthesis. Erythrose-4-phosphate is shown in brackets because it is probably usually bound tightly by an enzyme.

The enzyme called **transketolase** reacts with fructose-6-phosphate or with sedoheptulose-7-

Figure 14-2
Autoradiograms showing the products of photosynthesis in the alga *Chlorella pyrenoidosa* after various times of exposure to $^{14}CO_2$. (top) Sixty seconds, (middle) seven seconds, (bottom) two seconds. Note the increasing importance of PGA and other sugar phosphates as the exposure time is shortened. (From J. A. Bassham, 1965. In *Plant Biochemistry*, J. Bonner and J. E. Varner (eds.), Academic Press, New York, pp. 883–884. Used by permission.)

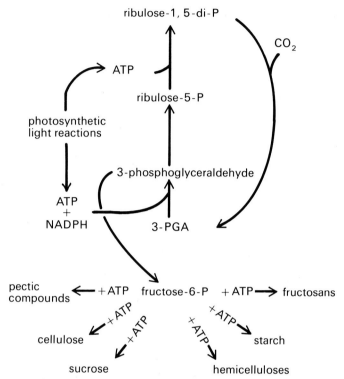

Figure 14-3

A summary of the Calvin–Benson photosynthetic cycle. NADPH and ATP are products of light reactions summarized in Fig. 13-8. Sucrose and higher polysaccharides formed from fructose-6-phosphate are products of the cycle, and their biosynthesis requires additional ATP.

phosphate, in each case combining with the keto group and removing two carbons. Transketolase requires thiamine (vitamin B_1) in the form of thiamine pyrophosphate (TPP) as a coenzyme in this process. The two-carbon unit removed is, in fact, combined directly with TPP. This unit can be added to phosphoglyceraldehyde, which accounts for the production of the pentose phosphates. It is also suspected that the vitamin can be split off, releasing **glycolic acid**.[1] Glycolic

acid can, in turn, be used in the synthesis of **glyoxylic acid**, glycine, and serine (Chapter 16).

Some of the products formed from fructose-6-phosphate, such as sucrose and starch, arise directly inside the chloroplasts themselves. The use of electron microscopes has shown that starch grains begin to grow very close to the grana, and that their growth eventually disrupts the organization of the grana and stroma membranes. Finally, the chloroplast pigments disappear and the entire cavity is filled with one or more starch grains. Four or five starch grains often develop in a single chloroplast of the potato leaf. The formation of cellulose and

---

[1] A phosphorylated form, phosphoglycolate, may actually be the compound initially produced.

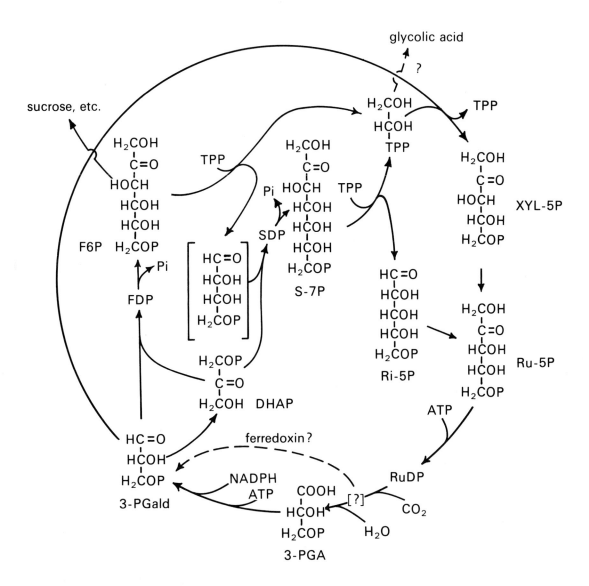

Figure 14-4

The Calvin–Benson CO_2 reduction cycle. Abbreviations: P, PO_3H_2; TPP, thiamine pyrophosphate; PGA, phosphoglyceric acid; 3-PGald, phosphoglyceraldehyde; DHAP, dihydroxyacetonephosphate; FDP, fructose-1, 6-diphosphate; F6P, fructose-6-phosphate; SDP, sedoheptulose-1,7-diphosphate; S-7P, sedoheptulose-7-phosphate; Ri-5P, ribose-5-phosphate; xyl-5P, xylulose-5-phosphate; Ru-5P, ribulose-5-phosphate. The reaction involving ferredoxin indicated near the bottom of the cycle is hypothetical. The origin of glycolic acid (upper right) is also still under active investigation. Most of the reactions of the cycle are reversible. (After J. Bassham, 1964, *Ann. Rev. Plant Physiol.* 15:104. Used by permission.)

pectins, however, takes place outside the chloroplasts. Here it is likely that sucrose and other photosynthetic products are transported out into the surrounding cytoplasm, where they are then converted into cell wall components and into many other compounds as well.

14.4 OTHER PHOTOSYNTHETIC REACTIONS

14.4.1 An Alternative Carbon Dioxide Fixation Mechanism

It has been known since the purification of ribulose diphosphate carboxylase was accomplished that this enzyme has a high K_m for bicarbonate ions (about $2.2 \times 10^{-2} M$), which indicates a poor affinity for this molecule. This is somewhat surprising, since it is well known that many plants can photosynthesize under very low CO_2 partial pressures. It has been suggested that the unusually high concentrations of this enzyme in leaves (about 16 percent of the total protein in spinach leaves, for example) would allow rapid photosynthesis even when the CO_2 level is low. It is also possible that affinity of the enzyme for CO_2 is much higher in the chloroplasts than it is when extracted from them for K_m determinations. These suggestions may explain the difference between the rate of CO_2 fixation in the living leaf and in the isolated reaction, but they have nevertheless stimulated investigations to discover whether alternate fixation reactions may also occur.

In Hawaii, Hugo Kortschak, Constance Hartt, and George Burr discovered in 1965 that sugarcane leaves (in which photosynthesis is very efficient) fix most CO_2 into carbon-4 of malic and aspartic acids. After approximately one second of photosynthesis in $^{14}CO_2$, 80 percent of the ^{14}C recovered from labeled compounds was present in these two acids, and only 10 percent was found in PGA, indicating that in this plant PGA is not the first product of photosynthesis. These results were confirmed by

M. D. Hatch and C. R. Slack in Australia, who found that some tropical species of the Graminae (grass) family and corn (*Zea mays*) displayed similar labeling patterns after fixing $^{14}CO_2$. Other grasses such as wheat, oat, rice, and bamboo, not closely related taxonomically to most of the others, and sugar beet and eight other dicots showed PGA as the predominant fixation product. It is thus clear that the primary carboxylation reaction of some species is different from that involving ribulose diphosphate.

The most likely reaction scheme by which CO_2 is converted into carbon-4 of malic and aspartic acids is through an initial addition to phosphoenolpyruvic acid to form oxaloacetic acid and Pi. (Oxaloacetic acid is not usually a detectable product of photosynthesis, but it was found when special precautions were taken to prevent its destruction in the isolation and chromatography procedures.) This reaction, along with that catalyzed by ribulose diphosphate carboxylase, is one of the few carboxylations occurring in plants that is thermodynamically feasible. The estimated ΔG is about minus 5.7 kcal/mole under physiological conditions. **Phosphoenolpyruvate carboxylase**, an enzyme widely distributed in plants, is the catalyst involved. Reactions converting oxaloacetate to both malate and aspartate are also well known in plants (Chapter 15), and these probably account for the observed labeling patterns (Fig. 14-5). The mechanism by which sugars and sugar phosphates are formed and by which the phosphoenolpyruvate is regenerated to keep the fixation process going in these plants is not yet understood. It is almost certain that ATP and NADPH or other electron donors are needed to carry out these reactions.

14.4.2 Alternate Uses of ATP and Electron Donors in Photosynthesis

The reactions of the Calvin–Benson cycle show that light is required in photosynthesis of most

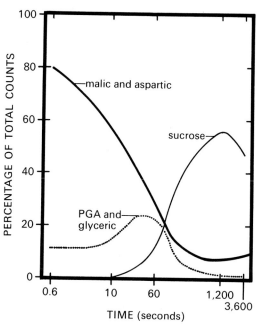

Figure 14-5

Incorporation of $^{14}CO_2$ into various products by photosynthesizing sugar cane leaves. The abscissa represents time of exposure of the leaves to ^{14}C before killing. Note the predominant early incorporation into malic and aspartic acids rather than into PGA. (From H. Kortschak et al., 1965, *Plant Physiol.* 40:209. Used by permission.)

plants only to provide the ATP and NADPH needed to reduce PGA to phosphoglyceraldehyde and to supply the ATP essential for maintaining an adequate supply of ribulose diphosphate. The rate of CO_2 fixation will depend upon the concentrations of these compounds and hence the intensity of light.

Carbon dioxide is not the only compound in the atmosphere that can be fixed by plants in the light. Certain photosynthetic bacteria and blue-green algae can, with the aid of light, reduce atmospheric nitrogen to ammonia (Chapter 16). The ammonia so formed is then incorporated into amino acids and finally into proteins. This nitrogen fixation seems also to require ATP as an energy source. The ATP can be formed in these organisms by photosynthetic phosphory-

lation; and the electrons needed for the reduction process come from ferredoxin. This process, too, is a photosynthesis, since amino acids are synthesized with the energy of light.

Still other light-stimulated reactions are known to occur in plant leaves, such as the reduction of nitrate ions to ammonia, reduction of sulfate to sulfide, formation of fats and other lipids, and the ATP-dependent conversion of amino acids to protein (Table 14-1). In all cases, light is believed to supply either ATP or available electrons, or both. Reduced ferredoxin may sometimes act in place of NADPH as the electron donor. When nitrate is reduced, flavin nucleotides ($FADH_2$ or $FMNH_2$) apparently participate. In green plants the needed electrons ultimately come from water split in the Hill reaction.

Because of these observations, several experts now wish to refer to photosynthesis basically as the conversion of light energy into chemical energy in the form of ATP and NADPH or reduced ferredoxin. The subsequent utilization of these compounds in such secondary reactions as those in Table 14-1 can go on even in organisms devoid of chlorophyll.

14.5 MEASURING PHOTOSYNTHETIC RATES

Photosynthetic rates theoretically could be measured by determining the rate of appearance of either of the usual products (oxygen and carbohydrates) or by the loss of either reactant (carbon dioxide or water). The difficulty of measuring decreases in water content is obvious, but all of the other measurements have given useful quantitative information.

Since carbon dioxide and oxygen are both gases, changes in their amounts may be analyzed conveniently by increases or decreases in either volume or pressure in a closed system surrounding the plants. Because respiration is also constantly occurring, observed variations in these gases are actually due to a combination of photosynthesis and respiration. The rate of

TABLE 14-1

USE OF ELECTRONS ARISING FROM WATER IN LIGHT-STIMULATED PROCESSES

Process	Probable Electron Donor	Plant or Organ
1. $CO_2 \longrightarrow (CH_2O)_n$	NADPH or ferredoxin?	Higher plants, algae
2. $SO_4^= \longrightarrow SO_3^=$	?	Leaves
3. $SO_3^= \longrightarrow S^=$	Ferredoxin?	Leaves
4. $NO_3^- \longrightarrow NO_2^-$	Reduced flavins or NADPH	Leaves, green algae
5. $NO_2^- \longrightarrow NH_4^+$	Ferredoxin or NADPH	Leaves, green algae
6. $N_2 \longrightarrow NH_4^+$	Ferredoxin?	Blue-green algae
7. Fatty acid formation	NADPH	Leaves, algae

respiration must, therefore, be measured in darkness, and the resulting changes in carbon dioxide or oxygen taken into account to obtain true photosynthetic rates.

14.5.1   Volume Change

Suppose a leaf, for example, is placed in a closed glass container with known amounts of oxygen and carbon dioxide, and is then illuminated for a measured period of time. Now the atmosphere of the container is passed through an alkaline solution of KOH. The carbon dioxide is completely removed by reaction with the KOH, forming potassium carbonate. The amount of carbon dioxide used can be calculated from the decrease in volume of the atmospheric gases not absorbed by KOH.

The gases may now be passed through an oxygen-absorbing solution of alkaline pyrogallol, the consequent volume decrease giving the oxygen content of the atmosphere. Since the contents of both gases were known before the photosynthetic period, differences in each due to photosynthesis can be calculated. It is usually found that the uptake of carbon dioxide closely balances the oxygen released. This method is advantageous in that intact plants, as well as excised plant parts, can be studied. However, it is relatively slow and not very sensitive. Most

measurements of gas exchange, especially for excised tissues, are now made by other methods.

14.5.2   Pressure Changes

An improved, sensitive, and popular technique to measure changes in photosynthetic gases is by determining the pressure changes that occur in a closed system during the process. This is called the **manometric method**.

Manometric techniques were developed and used extensively in the 1920s by a famous German biochemist, Otto Warburg, although he was not the first to use this method. An apparatus used for measuring photosynthesis manometrically is called the **Warburg apparatus** and is shown in Fig. 14-6. This technique is usually limited to the use of pieces of plant tissue or to suspensions of algae, because the flasks are commonly small.

14.5.3   Electrical and Other Methods

A sensitive technique for measuring concentrations of oxygen electrically has been developed. This is an example of **polarography**, the theory of which is described in physical chemistry textbooks and in certain textbooks of quantitative chemical analysis. The main advantages of

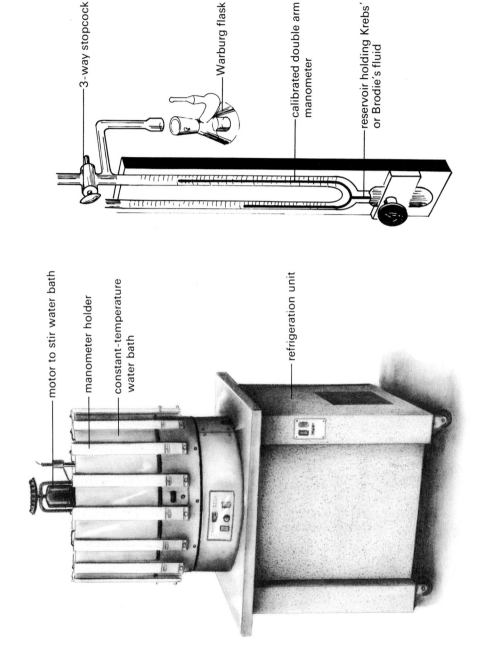

3-way stopcock

Warburg flask

calibrated double arm manometer

reservoir holding Krebs' or Brodie's fluid

motor to stir water bath

manometer holder

constant-temperature water bath

refrigeration unit

Figure 14-6

(left) Warburg apparatus capable of holding several manometers. Photoflood lights (not shown) may be attached just under a transparent plastic bottom of the constant temperature bath. (right) Manometer attached to holder, with flask in which plant tissue is placed. When manometers are placed on apparatus shown at left, the flask is immersed in water of desired temperature and is illuminated from below. After temperature equilibrium is reached, stopcock is closed and photosynthetic gas exchange causes pressure changes measured by a difference in height of fluid in the two arms of the manometer. Volume is maintained constant by adjusting screw knob on the reservoir of Krebs' or Brodie's fluid.

polarographic oxygen measurements are their rapidity, accuracy, and sensitivity.

It is also possible to measure decreases in carbon dioxide by direct chemical methods. An atmospheric sample may be passed through solutions of calcium hydroxide or barium hydroxide. This lowers the pH, since the bases are partially converted into calcium or barium carbonates. The amount of neutralization occurring may then be measured by titration with a suitable acid in the presence of an indicator. Alternatively, the pH may be measured with a pH meter, and these values converted into carbon dioxide changes by proper calculations.

A further method for measuring carbon dioxide changes involves an **infrared spectrophotometer**. Carbon dioxide absorbs infrared radiation; and, as photosynthesis occurs, less infrared is absorbed by the atmosphere around the plant. Portable spectrophotometers capable of field measurements are now in use. These make it possible to attain photosynthetic measurements with less disturbance of the plant than with most of the other techniques.

14.5.4 Measurements of Increase in Dry Matter

In this method increases in the dry weight of the leaves during photosynthesis are used as measurements of the production of organic matter. The technique is widely used because of its simplicity. It is, however, only semi-quantitative, because decreases in dry weight may result from translocation of carbohydrates out of the leaves, and because transport of minerals into the leaves may also occur. It is necessary to correct for losses in dry weight due to respiration over the same experimental period. This method is especially valuable for estimates of net photosynthesis of entire agricultural fields or plant communities.

14.6 PHOTOSYNTHESIS IN NATURE

Many scientists believe that before green plants became prevalent on the earth, all life was necessarily anaerobic. With the evolutionary developments of the photosynthetic apparatus for splitting water, vast quantities of oxygen were released into the atmosphere. Some of this oxygen was converted into ozone, which absorbs much of the sun's damaging ultraviolet radiation before it reaches the earth. Presumably when oxygen became available, aerobic organisms (including animals) evolved.

The amount of photosynthesis estimated to occur on the entire surface of the earth provides a staggering figure. Approximately 200 billion tons of carbon are fixed per year, about 90 percent of this fixation taking place in the oceans. This occurs in spite of the fact that the average CO_2 concentration in the atmosphere is only about 0.033 percent by volume, an amount considerably less than that of the inert gas argon.

The amount of atmospheric CO_2 has not changed much during the past hundred years, showing its return closely balances its use in photosynthesis. Important return agencies are the respiration of plants, microorganisms, and animals, and the activity of volcanoes, factories, and automobiles (Fig. 14-7). Perhaps even more important in maintaining a constant atmospheric CO_2 level are the oceans. Here the dissolved carbonates are in equilibrium with CO_2, a change in one quickly affecting the other. It has been found, however, that the CO_2 content may fall appreciably below 0.03 percent during daylight hours around the growing plants in a corn field, for example, while the content is higher than this during darkness, when respiration predominates.

Although the CO_2 composition of the atmosphere does not change much at increasing elevations on the earth's surface, the rate at which it diffuses into a plant depends upon its total pressure, rather than upon its concentration relative to other gases. At an elevation of 11,000 feet, for example, approximately timberline in the central Rocky Mountains of the United States, the CO_2 pressure is only about 0.2 millibars (mb), compared to 0.3 mb at sea

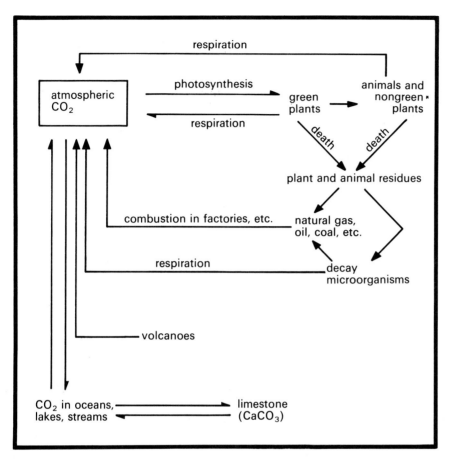

Figure 14-7
The carbon cycle in nature.

level. This gradient of CO_2 with altitude could be one of the factors that controls the distribution of species at various elevations.

14.7 ENVIRONMENTAL FACTORS INFLUENCING PHOTOSYNTHESIS

Several environmental factors are known to influence the rate of photosynthesis. These include the CO_2 pressure surrounding the photosynthetic cells, light intensity and its quality, temperature, and water availability. Besides these factors, certain internal properties of the plants themselves affect photosynthetic rates. These include the chlorophyll content, age of the photosynthetic cells, and certain less-understood biochemical or anatomical features found in various species.

14.7.1 The Availability of CO_2

14.7.1A The path of CO_2 to the chloroplast
Figure 6-4 shows a section of a leaf of a typical dicotyledon. Photosynthesis occurs primarily in the palisade parenchyma cells and the spongy mesophyll cells, although the guard cells also

contain chloroplasts and are capable of photosynthesis (Chapter 6). How does carbon dioxide get from the atmosphere to the chloroplasts within the active cells?

For a century and a quarter, plant physiologists have discussed this problem, particularly the relative importance of CO_2 penetration into the leaf via the cuticle or via the stomates. Early studies seemed to imply that the cuticle was the primary pathway of entry of CO_2. (CO_2 was thought to be highly soluble in the materials constituting the cuticle.) Then work during the two or three decades before and after the turn of the century seemed clearly to indicate that CO_2 would penetrate the leaf almost exclusively through open stomates. Most of the evidence was based upon the observation that rates of photosynthesis were at least roughly correlated with the number of stomates on the top of the leaf when those on the bottom were plugged with vaseline or some such material, as compared to the number and the rates when those on top were plugged. Correlations of photosynthesis with the degree of stomatal opening were also observed. In this context, as well as in relation to the movement of water vapor through the stomates in transpiration, several workers contributed to our understanding of the physics of diffusion of gases through small pores, a topic we have already discussed (Chapter 6).

There were several cases, however, even in the early literature, in which photosynthetic rates could not be accounted for on the basis of stomatal aperture, and cuticular penetration seemed to be implicated. More recently, the experimental approach to the problem has been greatly simplified by the availability of $^{14}CO_2$. Using a porometer to monitor stomatal aperture, penetration of CO_2 via the cuticle or the stomates can be readily determined. As might be expected, the emerging picture is complicated, and the role of the two modes of penetration is strongly dependent upon the species. In some cases, as F. F. Blackman in England suggested, stomatal penetration is almost the only means of entry of CO_2 into the leaf. Penetration through the cuticle constitutes only zero to 10 percent of the total when stomates are open (e.g., in the rubber plant: *Ficus elastica*). Yet with different species (e.g., avocado: *Persea sp., Begonia*), cuticular penetration may be as high as 70 percent of the total even with open stomates.

Thus the entry of CO_2 through the cuticle appears to be considerably more important than has been thought. This could be of interest in terms of heat transfer between the plant and its environment, as discussed in Chapter 6. If CO_2 penetration is primarily cuticular, then photosynthesis is not completely dependent upon stomatal aperture, and photosynthesis and transpiration are not absolutely coupled to each other. The stomatal mechanism then becomes somewhat more important in transpiration (and heat transfer) than in photosynthesis.

Whether CO_2 penetrates through the cuticle or through the stomates, the leaf is extremely efficient at removing it from the atmosphere. It has been estimated that a leaf is about half as effective at CO_2 absorption from the atmosphere as an equivalent surface of concentrated sodium or potassium hydroxide solution.

While penetration into the leaf is relatively rapid, the pathway of CO_2 from the intercellular space into a chloroplast appears to be much more tortuous. As a molecule strikes a wet cell wall, its diffusion rate is markedly decreased, the diffusion of CO_2 through water being 10,000 times slower than diffusion through air. Thus even though the total distance from the cell wall into the chloroplast is very small, this seems to be the limiting factor in the supply of CO_2 from the atmosphere to the reaction site. In submerged water plants, no stomates are present, and the epidermis lacks any cuticle development. Diffusion here proceeds rather slowly into the epidermis and then into the photosynthesizing cells entirely through an aqueous medium.

Although large amounts of CO_2 exist in water as the dissolved gas, some is present as bicarbonate ions. These ions are able to penetrate plant membranes only at slow rates, much slower than for CO_2 or nonionized carbonic acid (H_2CO_3). The doubly charged carbonate anions are taken up even more slowly than the monovalent bicarbonate. It is probable, therefore, that CO_2 actually is taken into cells largely in the form of molecular CO_2.

14.7.1B Quantitative relations During the summer growing season, it appears that a lack of CO_2 is a common cause of suboptimal photosynthetic rates. That is, the photosynthetic apparatus in plants is so constructed as to be able to fix much more CO_2 than is usually available in the chloroplasts. There are, of course, conditions under which the light intensity is the limiting factor, such as with plants growing in deep shade or during cloudy days. Nevertheless, experiments show that artificially increasing the CO_2 content around many plants stimulates the rate of photosynthesis. Figure 14-8 exemplifies this condition, showing the results of experiments in which both CO_2 and light intensity were varied.

Note that the greatest increases due to added CO_2 were obtained when the light intensity was greatest. At the highest light intensity, CO_2 limited the rate until its atmospheric concentration reached 0.16 percent, a value about five times higher than is normally found in air. Further additions of CO_2 did not continue to promote photosynthesis, because light intensity was now the limiting factor. In the regions of the curves where photosynthesis was increasing, the light intensity was presumably sufficient to provide adequate amounts of reduced ferredoxin and NADPH, and sufficient ATP, but these compounds lacked the molecules resulting from CO_2 fixation with which they react in the Calvin–Benson cycle. It seems probable, therefore, that as ATP and NADPH accumulate they

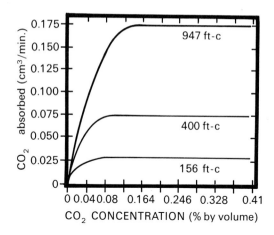

Figure 14-8
Effect of carbon dioxide concentration upon photosynthetic rate in wheat at various light intensities. (Data of W. Hoover et al., 1933, *Smithsonian Inst. Misc. Coll.* 87:16. Used by permission.)

somehow prevent the further splitting of water, thus decreasing their own formation.

In the flat region of the curves, adequate CO_2 is present, but it is not fixed because of the lack of reducing agents and ATP to act on the fixation products. Higher light intensities would now cause more water to be split, oxygen released, ferredoxin reduced, ATP formed, and thus more CO_2 to be reduced. The observed close relationship between light intensity, CO_2 content, and photosynthesis in nature can thus be appreciated at the biochemical level.

The fact that CO_2 appears commonly to be the limiting factor in photosynthesis has resulted in fertilization of the atmosphere of greenhouses with this gas to obtain increased growth of various greenhouse crops. Results of several such experiments in Europe were published as early as the period 1920–1930, and studies in Holland and other areas are continuing. Recent work with ornamental flowers has been performed at Colorado State University by Robert Holley and Kenneth Goldsberry. During the winter when greenhouses are normally kept closed, the CO_2 concentration in the air often drops as low as 0.0125 percent (125 ppm). Increased yields of carnations and chrysanthemums can then be obtained by artificially raising the level to 0.05 percent. With roses, 0.1 percent concentrations appear to be commercially economical.

Wind can sometimes also stimulate photosynthetic rates. This occurs because increased air movement reduces the thickness of the boundary layer, in which the CO_2 has been depleted, resulting in a steeper gradient and hence more rapid diffusion into the leaf. The effect is more pronounced with plants having broad leaves than with those having smaller or finely divided leaves, around which the boundary layer is normally thin anyway (Chapter 6).

Some species appear to be better able to photosynthesize under lower CO_2 conditions than do others. For example, a two-fold increased CO_2 content stimulated the growth of tomato much less than it did that of cucumber, while wheat growth was increased most of all. Furthermore, there are definite limits within which added CO_2 stimulates photosynthesis and growth. A tenfold increase in the atmospheric CO_2 content caused a harmful effect on the growth of tomato within about two weeks.

14.7.2 Light Intensity and Quality

14.7.2A Intensity effects upon various species

In the absence of light, there is no net uptake of CO_2, though the use of $^{14}CO_2$ demonstrates that some of this gas is being fixed. Even in dim light the CO_2 released by respiration may overbalance the small amounts being fixed by photosynthesis. Further increases in light intensity will eventually allow fixation to compensate exactly for the loss by respiration. The intensity at which this occurs is called the **compensation point** (see Fig. 14-9). At this intensity, there is no net exchange of oxygen, either. The com-

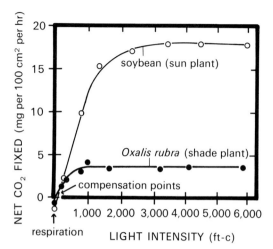

Figure 14-9

Photosynthetic rates of typical sun and shade plants as affected by light intensity. Single leaves from the plants were placed in a transparent plexiglass chamber through which 0.0288 percent CO_2 flowed (as in Fig. 6-1B). Changes in CO_2 concentration were measured by an infrared gas analyzer. Light was filtered through a water layer to prevent overheating the leaf, and the intensity was varied with cheesecloth screens. Several plants behaved like the soybean, including tomato, tobacco (white burley), castor bean, sunflower, cotton, and bean (black valentine). These plants were not light saturated at the given CO_2 level until about 2,500 ft-c light intensity was reached; they had compensation points at 100 to 150 ft-c. Plants behaving as shade plants and responding as did *Oxalis* were *Saintpaulia ionantha* (African violet), *Philodendron cordatum*, and two ferns, including *Nephrolepis exaltata* and a *Dryopteris* sp. Photosynthesis rates of these were usually saturated at 1,000 ft-c, and the compensation points were near 50 ft-c. (Data of R. Böhning and C. Burnside, 1956, *Amer. J. Bot.* 43:557.)

pensation point varies somewhat for different species but is commonly within the range of 50 to 200 foot-candles (ft-c).[1] These values are only a small fraction of the intensity normally found under the summer sun. Light intensity, even in a cloudless sky, varies in nature with the time of day and with elevation, but noontime values of about 8,000 ft-c at sea level to 11,000 ft-c

---

[1] A 100-watt incandescent bulb produces approximately 19 ft-c on a surface one meter distant.

at an elevation of 5,000 feet on an early summer day are common.

Plants may be approximately classified into two categories, based on the normal amount of light required to saturate their photosynthetic rates. **Sun plants** are saturated by intensities roughly one-fifth those of full sunlight or more, while **shade plants** may be saturated at intensities lower than one-tenth those of full sunlight. Shade plants are thus better able to compete under conditions of weak light and are often found growing in the shade of taller species. Most crop species are examples of sun plants, while *Oxalis*, which often grows beneath greenhouse benches, is a good example of a shade plant. Figure 14-9 indicates how increasing the light intensity at constant CO_2 concentrations and approximately constant temperature affected the photosynthetic rate of soybean and *Oxalis*. *Oxalis* was fully light saturated with this amount of CO_2 by 1,000 ft-c, while the soybean required over 2,000 ft-c to reach the maximum rate. Also illustrated is the typical observation that shade plants have lower compensation points and that they have lower maximum rates than sun plants. Because of a low compensation point, shade plants are thus able to grow, although weakly, at a light intensity under which the dry weight of sun plants would decrease. On the other hand, the high maximum rates of sun plants allow them to serve as effective crop plants. Individual leaves from a high-yielding corn variety were found not to be saturated by light intensities even up to those of full sunlight.

Various trees also differ markedly in response to light intensity. Comparisons were made between Eastern red oak, a shade-tolerant species, and Loblolly pine, an intolerant species. The oak was saturated by 3,000 ft-c, but Loblolly pine showed a small but steady increase in photosynthesis even up to 8,000 ft-c. Under these conditions, it is probable that the needles on the upper and outer parts of the Loblolly pine were saturated by lower intensities, but further increases of light caused more of the needles on the lower, shaded parts of the tree to receive additional light, thus increasing the rate for the tree as a whole. Such a shading effect could probably be found over some intensity range in red oak and in all species having more than one layer of leaves, and such diverse plants as alfalfa and apple trees grow better at high light intensities because the shaded leaves then receive more light. Herbaceous plants or trees grown under high light intensities also often develop an additional layer of leaves compared to those grown under lower intensities, so that light saturation for some of the leaves is never reached.

It is also interesting that shade leaves (those from shade species or the shaded side of a given plant) usually contain more chlorophyll per unit weight (more or larger chloroplasts) than do sun leaves. Thus, their relatively low photosynthetic ability at light saturation compared to sun leaves is not due to a lack of sufficient chlorophyll to catalyze the reaction. Some other factor is undoubtedly involved.

Inspection of Fig. 14-9 shows that in experiments representing the flat part of the curves, much of the light intensity was wasted. The rates were then clearly limited by something else. On bright, clear days the photosynthetic rate of most plants is similarly restricted. The factor required in the warm days of summer is typically CO_2, while in winter the evergreens are limited by cold temperatures and certain internal factors.

If the light intensity is raised even farther than indicated in Fig. 14-9, abnormal photochemical reactions occur which eventually oxidize many of the cellular components, including chlorophyll. This destructive process is considerably more pronounced in the presence of oxygen. There is then actually a net uptake of oxygen and release of CO_2. The process has been named **photo-oxidation**, although it is also sometimes called **solarization**. Certain of the carotenoids have a protective action against photo-oxidation by acting as anti-oxidants, at least in some plants (Chapter 13).

14.7.2B Effects of light on chloroplast arrangement

Light has an interesting effect upon the arrangement of chloroplasts in the cells of many plants. This effect has been studied mostly in water plants, such as the water weed, *Elodea*, the moss, *Funaria*, the duck weed, *Lemna*, the lycopod, *Selaginella*, and certain algae. In all cases, of course, the chloroplasts are found in the cytoplasm and not in the vacuole, although they sometimes occur in cytoplasmic strands that extend across and through the vacuole. When light intensity is strong, as in full sunlight, these plastids are aligned along the radial walls, becoming shaded against damage by strong illumination (Fig. 14-10). In weak light, or sometimes in darkness, they are separated into two groups distributed along the cell walls nearest to and farthest from the light source. More of the low-intensity light is then absorbed. In darkness, they are also often scattered between the two positions mentioned.

The colors of light most effective in causing chloroplast movement differ with the plant involved. Blue light is by far the most effective in many species, but in others red is also effective. The photoreceptors involved are not yet known, although a yellow pigment, perhaps a flavin, absorbs the blue light. The red wavelengths are believed to be absorbed by a pigment called **phytochrome** (Chapter 23).

Just how the absorption of light by a chloroplast could cause it to move through the cytoplasm has not been explained either, but the cause may be similar to that allowing amoeba to move by sending out small protuberances of protoplasm. In some cases, the chloroplasts are distributed by light because light affects cytoplasmic streaming, although this is not always the reason. Light hitting the chloroplasts themselves also has an effect. Regardless of the mechanism, the position of the chloroplasts

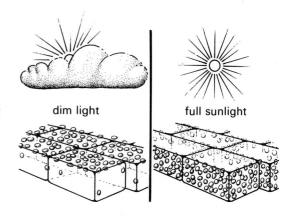

Figure 14-10

Influence of light intensity upon position of chloroplasts in a moss, *Funaria*. In weak light, the plastids are distributed along the wall perpendicular to the light source, while in strong light they line the walls in such a way that some are shaded by others. The cells are purely schematic. (See J. Zurzycki, 1953, *Acta Soc. Botan. Polon.* 22:299.)

in the cells will greatly affect the amount of light capable of causing photosynthesis. Leaves may appear slightly darker green in dim than in bright light because the chloroplasts are then oriented closer to the leaf surfaces.

14.7.2C Morphological and physiological adaptations

Leaves have the ability to adapt, morphologically as well as physiologically, to the light intensities present during their growth. If plants are grown under weak light they possess the common properties of shade plants, such as (1) a low compensation point, (2) a short range over which increased light intensity stimulates photosynthesis, and (3) a lower photosynthetic rate at a saturating intensity. They commonly possess more chlorophyll per unit weight than similar plants grown under high intensities. Shade leaves are often thinner than leaves developed in a strong light, because high intensities stimulate the formation of a second or third layer of palisade parenchyma in the leaves. These palisade cells are also often longer in

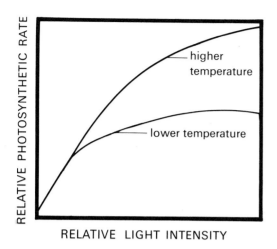

Figure 14-11
Effect of light intensity upon photosynthesis at two different temperatures. At low intensities, temperature has little or no influence, but at higher intensities promotions by the higher temperature are observed.

leaves exposed to high illumination, while the spongy mesophyll is less well-developed.

Algae also show adaptation to light. Species that normally develop at greater water depths are light saturated at lower intensities and are more susceptible to photo-oxidation at high intensities. Some marine algae are even fully light saturated at intensities as low as 100 ft-c.

14.7.2D Light quality The quality or color of light also varies somewhat in nature and may be expected to influence photosynthetic rates. Light quality changes appreciably with depth in the ocean, and those species growing at greater depths are exposed to light relatively rich in the blue and green portions of the spectrum and relatively weak in the orange and red. The red algae, which utilize the blue and green portions of the spectrum, are thus typically found at the greatest ocean depths. At high altitudes, land plants are exposed to light relatively richer in blue and ultraviolet wavelengths than are those growing near sea level, since increased thickness of the atmosphere preferentially filters out these

wavelengths. Nevertheless, no effects on the distribution of plants in nature due to color variation with altitude have been demonstrated.

Plants growing under a thick forest canopy are exposed to light containing a relative abundance of green wavelengths but limited in the blue and red colors, which are absorbed by the taller trees above. This almost surely decreases the ability of these short herbs and shrubs to carry out maximum photosynthesis. The reduced intensity of blue and red wavelengths also allows increases of height (via stem elongation) of many plants, apart from any direct influence on photosynthesis (Chapter 23).

14.7.3 Temperature

The temperature range over which plants can photosynthesize is surprisingly large. Certain bacteria and blue-green algae photosynthesize at temperatures as high as 70°C, while many conifers can apparently maintain this process, although weakly, at air temperatures as low as −6°C. In many species exposed to bright sunlight on a hot day of summer, the leaf temperatures probably often reach 40°C, with photosynthesis continuing. The optimum temperatures for photosynthesis probably fall within 20° to 35°C for most species of temperate regions. It is often observed that maximum photosynthesis occurs at temperatures a few degrees lower than those for most rapid respiration.

The influence of temperature on photosynthesis depends on both the light intensity and the CO_2 availability (Fig. 14-11). If these two factors are adequate, photosynthesis will occur faster at moderately higher temperatures. Temperature has little influence on the light-driven splitting of water, which is primarily a photochemical process. The light-absorbing chlorophyll molecules are excited so much by absorption of a photon that any heat-caused excitation is small in comparison. Q_{10} values for the light reaction of photosynthesis are, as a result, usually 1.0 or very slightly higher. The over-all process is much more temperature sensitive, however, since use of the reductants produced in the light reaction requires molecules that can be excited only by heat. All of the reactions of the Calvin–Benson cycle are temperature dependent, and a low rate of any one might slow the entire process of CO_2 fixation. The Q_{10} for processes like these is typically between 2.0 to 3.0.

Finally, the rate of diffusion of CO_2 to the chloroplasts will be increased by a higher temperature. The Q_{10} for diffusion of solutes through water is usually between 1.2 and 1.4. It is not surprising, therefore, that the entire photosynthetic process has been found to have Q_{10} values between 1.0 and 2.7, depending on the other environmental conditions of light intensity and CO_2 concentration.

14.7.4 Water Availability

Although the fixation of CO_2 requires electrons obtained from water, it appears that a primary effect of reduced water availability on photosynthesis is on the closing of stomates. Under summertime conditions, when CO_2 availability so often limits the rate, photosynthesis in many plants will be approximately proportional to the size of the stomatal openings. In wilted leaves, of course, the stomates are usually closed.

14.7.5 Leaf Age

As individual leaves on a plant grow and develop, their ability to photosynthesize increases for a time and then, often upon reaching maturation, begins to decrease. An example of this is illustrated for the primary leaves of the pea plant in Fig. 14-12. Old, senescent leaves eventually become yellow and are unable to photosynthesize due to a breakdown of chlorophyll and a loss of functional chloroplasts.

14.7.6 Chlorophyll Content

It might be suspected that the more chlorophyll a plant contains, the more rapidly it should photosynthesize. However, many studies with various kinds of plants (and with leaves of the same plant containing different amounts of chlorophyll) indicate that there is little such correlation. Willstätter and Stoll, for example, in 1918, compared the rates of photosynthesis in elm leaves varying more than ten-fold in chlorophyll contents. The chlorotic leaves photosynthesized almost as rapidly as the normal leaves. The ability of sun leaves to photosynthesize more rapidly in bright light than do shade leaves, which usually contain more chlorophyll, also shows the complexity of the problem. Perhaps the leaves with high chlorophyll content do not photosynthesize more rapidly because they lack the enzymes or coenzymes to use the products of the light reactions to reduce available CO_2.

14.7.7 Endogenous Rhythms

Apart from environmental factors and chlorophyll content, certain internal properties of plants influence their photosynthesis. Some of these internal properties vary in a rhythmic fashion in a daily and even seasonal manner (see Chapter 24). The single-celled dinoflagellate *Gonyaulax polyhedra* photosynthesizes best near noon, even though it is removed from the ocean and kept under continuous light of constant intensity. In this case, the content of the enzyme ribulose diphosphate carboxylase was found to increase and decrease in the cells according to the peaks and minima of the photosynthesis curves. Whatever controls the rhythm in this plant apparently does so, at least partly, by affecting the synthesis or destruction of the carboxylase.

A periodic photosynthetic behavior also occurs in certain evergreens. These are only

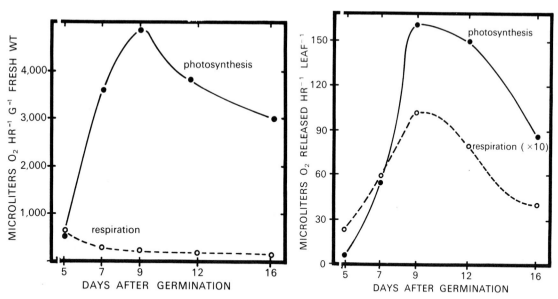

Figure 14-12

(left) Changes in the photosynthetic and respiratory rates of pea leaves with age (weight basis). (right) Changes in the photosynthetic and respiratory rates of pea leaves with age (per-leaf basis). (Redrawn from data of R. Smillie, 1962, *Plant Physiol.* 37:716. Used by permission.)

weakly capable of photosynthesis during the winter when the buds are dormant, but a maximum capability occurs during the summer. For these measurements, the plants are brought into the greenhouse and all measurements are made under approximately constant conditions. This seasonal rhythm is probably controlled by the previous environmental conditions to which the plants were exposed and may not continue under a constant environment. It thus may not be persistent in the same way that the daily rhythm of *Gonyaulax* is. Nevertheless, it is clear that some internal or endogenous conditions even here determine the ability of such plants to photosynthesize and thus to grow.

14.8 MAGNITUDE OF PHOTOSYNTHESIS

It is clear that many external and internal factors influence photosynthesis, and photosynthetic rates thus vary greatly among plants in nature. The maximum rate of photosynthesis in a sunflower plant exposed to bright light is about 25 mg of CO_2 per hour per 100 cm^2 of leaf surface. Such a rate would correspond to a gain of about 5 percent of the original dry weight of the leaf in a single hour. In general, the magnitude for most plants exposed to good environmental conditions falls between 8 and 80 mg CO_2 per hour per 100 cm^2 leaf area.

When various species from different habitats are compared, it appears that those living in places where the growing season is short have relatively high abilities to photosynthesize, thus partially compensating for their limited growth period. For example, various alpine and arctic plants photosynthesize surprisingly rapidly when conditions are favorable (Chapter 29).

Figure 14-13 illustrates the course of CO_2 fixation and release during daylight and dark-

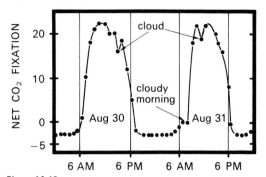

Figure 14-13
Photosynthesis in an alfalfa plot over a two-day period in late summer. The effect of periods of cloud cover can be noted. Negative CO_2 fixation values during hours of darkness indicate the respiration rates. (Reproduced by permission from the data of M. Thomas and G. Hill, as they appear in *Photosynthesis in Plants*, James Franck and Walter E. Loomis (eds.), © 1949 by the Iowa State University Press, p. 35.)

ness for alfalfa. The maximum rate of photosynthesis occurs near noon, and here the amount of CO_2 fixed exceeds that released by respiration in darkness by a factor of about eight. Sometimes this ratio in nature is even higher, and values of ten to thirty times as much photosynthesis as respiration have been reported when suitable temperatures and light intensities were available.

14.9 EFFICIENCY OF PHOTOSYNTHESIS

Some interesting measurements and theoretical calculations have been made to determine the efficiency of conversion of light energy into chemical energy by plants. The problem is important, since this efficiency could determine the maximum human population attainable on earth. Much information indicates that many crops, including forest trees and herbaceous species, convert about 1–2 percent of the total visible energy striking the field during their growing season into chemical energy in the form of plant material. Efficiencies of conversion of light striking individual leaves is approximately 15 percent, and values as high as 19 percent have been measured for leaves of sugar beets. The discrepancy between the 2 percent and 15 percent values is partly due to the low leaf area of plants during the early part of the growing season, and the consequent low absorption of the incoming radiation. In addition, when the light intensity is high, much of the energy is wasted by leaves closest to the sun, causing the values for the whole crop over the entire growing season to be much lower than the 15 percent values that can be obtained when the light intensity is lower and more effectively utilized.

15

Respiration

15.1 RESPIRATORY METABOLISM

All living cells respire continuously, usually absorbing oxygen and releasing carbon dioxide —often in nearly the same volumes. The over-all process of respiration is an oxidation-reduction in which substrates are oxidized to CO_2 and the O_2 absorbed is reduced to form water. Starch, sucrose or other sugars, fats, organic acids, and proteins, under certain conditions, can all serve as respiratory substrates, sources of the carbon dioxide. The common oxidation of sucrose, for example, can be written as in (R15-1).

$$C_{12}H_{22}O_{11} + 12O_2 \longrightarrow 12CO_2 + 11H_2O$$

(R15-1)

Much of the considerable energy released during respiration is lost in the form of heat. However, the cells are able to trap significant amounts of this energy in chemical forms that can be used later for many essential processes of life, such as those involved in growth and ion accumulation.

The above equation is misleading in a way, because respiration is not a single reaction; it is rather a complex of many component reactions, each catalyzed by a different enzyme.

This breakdown of large molecules by many steps provides a means for trapping energy. Furthermore, as the breakdown proceeds, the carbon skeletons are provided for a large number of other essential plant products. These include amino acids for proteins, nucleotides for nucleic acids, and carbon precursors for porphyrin pigments (such as chlorophyll and cytochromes), fats, sterols, carotenoids, anthocyanins, and certain other aromatic compounds. Of course, when these are formed, conversion of the original substrates to CO_2 and water is not complete. Usually only some of the respiratory substrates are fully oxidized. The energy trapped from the oxidized molecules can then be used to synthesize the above compounds required for growth. When plants are growing rapidly, most of the disappearing sugars are diverted into such synthetic reactions and never appear as CO_2.

15.2 MEASURING AND EXPRESSING RESPIRATION RATES

In general, gas exchange techniques similar to those used to measure rates of photosynthesis can be applied to respiration. Either the rate of oxygen utilization or the rate of carbon dioxide

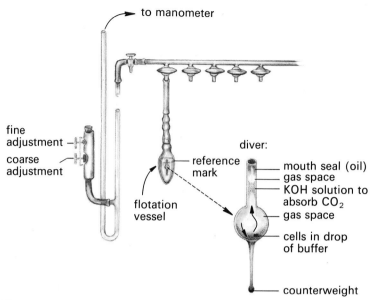

Figure 15-1

Cartesian diver assembly. The diver itself is only about 1.5 cm long. Just before measurements are made, the top of the diver is adjusted exactly to the reference mark in the flotation vessel by means of the screw adjustments at the left of the figure. These screws alter the pressure in the entire system, changing the volume and thus the density of gases in the diver, so that it rises or sinks. The alteration in pressure that this adjustment has made is then measured on a manometer (not shown). For details of construction and operation, see W. A. Jensen, *Botanical Histochemistry* (San Francisco and London: W. H. Freeman and Company, 1962), p. 307.

production is usually determined. Most of our knowledge about respiration of various parts of plants has been obtained with the Warburg apparatus mentioned in Chapter 14. Respiration must occur in darkness when this instrument is used, so that photosynthesis does not reverse the respiratory reactions.

For very small amounts of tissue, an extremely sensitive device called the **Cartesian diver** is often used (Fig. 15-1). Oxygen is consumed by the cells, but the carbon dioxide released is absorbed by a basic solution such as KOH, which is separated from the cells by a tiny air bubble. The diver is immersed in a liquid, and as oxygen inside is utilized the buoyancy decreases, causing the diver to sink. Some Cartesian divers can measure the rate

of oxygen absorption even from single cells. The sensitivity of many such instruments is as low as 10^{-5} microliters (abbreviated μl and equal to mm^3), compared to about $1.0\,\mu$l or more for the Warburg apparatus.

The rate at which starch or sugars are lost from plant cells has also been used to indicate respiration rates. This requires a direct chemical analysis of the plants and is, therefore, not commonly done. However, it is essential for some purposes to know how fast these substrates are being utilized. Furthermore, by making such analyses it is possible to determine just what compounds are being oxidized during respiration. The rate of CO_2 release or O_2 uptake alone gives no indication of the type of respiratory substrates used.

To compare respiration rates of various plants or parts of the same plant, it is necessary to express the rate in similar units. The most common units where O_2 and CO_2 changes are measured are μl per hour per gram of tissue. This is called the Q_{O_2} or Q_{CO_2}. Since the volumes of gases depend upon the temperature and pressure, they are commonly corrected to 20°C and 1 atm. Results are often given for either fresh- or oven-dry weights of the tissue. Expression of data in terms of dry weight removes error due to differences in water content of the cells. The dry weight includes much inert organic matter, such as cell wall material, yet respiration is more closely related to the amount of protoplasm present. It is often desirable, then, to express respiration in terms of the total protein or nitrogen content of the tissue.

15.3 THE RESPIRATORY QUOTIENT

If such carbohydrates as sucrose or starch are serving as respiratory substrates, and if they are completely oxidized, the volume of O_2 taken up exactly balances the CO_2 released from the cells. Often this ratio of CO_2/O_2, called the **respiratory quotient**, or **R.Q.**, is very near unity. For example, the R.Q. obtained from leaves of many different species averaged about 1.05. Germinating seeds of the cereal grains, which primarily utilize stored starch, also exhibit R.Q.s of approximately 1.0. Seeds from many other species, however, contain considerable amounts of fats. When these are oxidized during germination, the R.Q. is often as low as 0.7. Consider the breakdown of a common fatty acid, oleic acid indicated in (R15-2).

$$C_{18}H_{34}O_2 + 25.5O_2 \longrightarrow 18CO_2 + 17H_2O$$

$$(R15-2)$$

The R.Q. for this reaction is $18/25.5 = 0.71$. By measuring the R.Q. for various seeds or other plant parts, information can be obtained about the type of compounds being oxidized. The problem is complicated, because at any time several different types of substances may be respired. Thus, the measured R.Q. really is only an average value, dependent upon the respiratory contribution of each substrate and its relative content of carbon, hydrogen, and oxygen.

15.4 THE CHEMISTRY OF RESPIRATION

As noted above, the complete oxidation of any respiratory substrate consists of a stepwise degradation. Most of these steps do not involve the direct participation of oxygen. At certain steps, however, especially in the final stages of breakdown, hydrogen atoms are removed and ultimately combined with oxygen to form water. Other steps may be thought of as preparatory reactions, in which the molecules are changed into forms more susceptible to oxidation.

Respiration of starch or sugars may conveniently be divided into three important parts (Fig. 15-2). The first consists of a series of steps in which sugars are broken down into the three-carbon acid pyruvic acid. This process can take place even without oxygen. It apparently occurs in the cytoplasm separate from the various known subcellular particles, such as chloroplasts, nuclei, and mitochondria, although recent evidence indicates that in yeast and red blood cells, at least, it may occur in subunits of the plasmalemma. The second part involves the further breakdown of pyruvic acid into carbon dioxide. Although oxygen does not participate directly, it must be available for this second part to proceed. This, then, is an aerobic process and occurs in the mitochondria. Several organic acids are essential participants in this phase of respiration. Closely allied with this second part is a third process in which hydrogen atoms are removed from the organic acids and, after a series of oxidation-

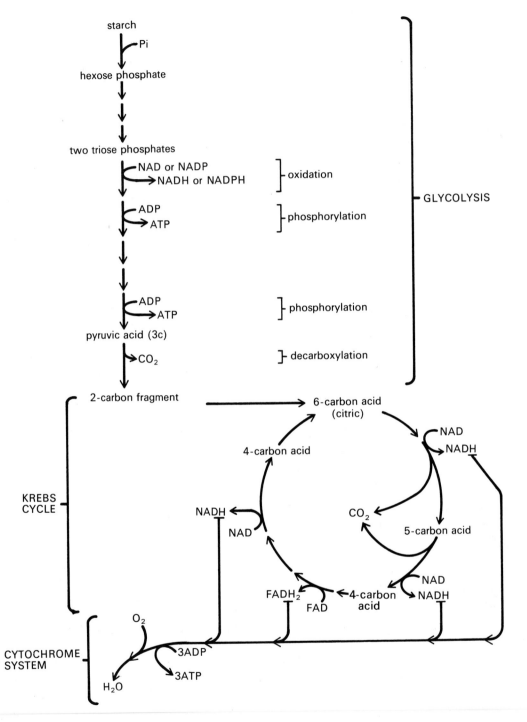

Figure 15-2
Simplified diagram illustrating the relationships of glycolysis, the Krebs cycle, and the cytochrome electron transport system.

reduction steps, they unite with O_2, yielding water. It is here that the major portion of energy released in respiration is trapped in utilizable form.

Let us examine these three interesting processes in greater detail.

15.4.1 Glycolysis and Fermentation

The process by which starch is broken down into pyruvic acid is commonly called **glycolysis**. It was named after a very similar series of reactions occurring in muscle to convert glycogen (animal starch) into the three-carbon lactic acid. It is now known that most of these steps also occur during **fermentation**, the production of ethyl alcohol and carbon dioxide from sugars.

Historically, many of the individual reactions of this phase of respiration, now. believed to occur universally in all plants and animals, were first discovered by scientists interested in the production of alcohol by yeast. E. Buchner made one of the first important contributions in 1897, while attempting to preserve an extract from yeast cells. He added high concentrations of sugar as a preservative, as in the process of making jellies, and he found unexpectedly that the sugar was fermented. This was probably the first demonstration that any metabolic process could occur completely apart from any living cells. Of course, Buchner's extract contained the essential enzymes necessary for fermentation.[1]

---

[1] Although various kinds of yeasts can ferment several different sugars, most are not capable of fermenting starch, because they lack the necessary amylase enzymes to hydrolyze starch to maltose. For this reason the brewing industry uses germinated barley seedlings (called malt) rather than the dry, starch-containing seeds, since starch is converted to sugars by the enzymes of the seeds during germination and especially in the subsequent mashing process.

The reactions of glycolysis or fermentation may occur anaerobically, and the term **anaerobic respiration** has also been used to describe these reactions. In certain conditions when oxygen cannot readily enter plant cells or is not available, respiration may be largely restricted to the anaerobic phase. Poor entry of oxygen is common in the initial stages of germination of seeds, such as those of peas, corn, and probably many others, where the seed coats prevent adequate gas diffusion. In waterlogged soils the oxygen content and especially its rate of diffusion are reduced, so that aerobic respiration in roots is often inhibited in these soils. In such situations pyruvic acid is not oxidized but instead is usually decarboxylated to form acetaldehyde and CO_2. The acetaldehyde is then reduced directly to ethyl alcohol, which accumulates. Alternatively, pyruvate itself may be reduced, forming lactic acid. Lactic acid formation is less common but does occur in many higher plants and in some algae.

Provision of oxygen prevents accumulation of either alcohol or lactic acid, since the pyruvate is then rapidly oxidized. The reactions of glycolysis leading to pyruvic acid occur normally in plant tissues fully exposed to air, so that we may think of glycolysis as being only *potentially* anaerobic. Furthermore, as we shall see below, hydrogen atoms removed at one step in glycolysis may combine with oxygen if it is available, in which case the process is truly aerobic. To avoid ambiguity in relation to oxygen requirements, many biochemists call the conversion of sugars to pyruvate the **Embden–Meyerhof–Parnas (EMP) pathway**, in honor of G. Embden, O. Meyerhof, and J. K. Parnas, three workers who, publishing in the German biochemical journals from about 1912 to the early 1930s, formulated the scheme of glycolysis as it seemed to apply in muscle tissue.

Glucose-1-phosphate, formed from starch by starch phosphorylase action, is catabolized to pyruvic acid according to the sequence of

Fig. 15-3, which should be referred to frequently during the following discussion. Before glucose can undergo these reactions it too must be phosphorylated. Addition of Pi to free glucose is a much more difficult process, as far as energy is concerned, than is addition of Pi to glucose present in starch. Thus, cells containing glucose in uncombined form must supply ATP as an energy source to carry out the necessary phosphorylation. The necessary enzyme is a **glucokinase** often called **hexokinase** (Chapter 11). Glucose-6-phosphate and ADP are the products. An apparently identical reaction occurs in animals fed glucose, before its chemical energy can be converted to muscular or heat energy.

Sugar diphosphates do not seem to leak out of the chloroplasts where they are primarily synthesized in leaves, and it may be that only sucrose, PGA, or the hexose monophosphates serve as the primary respiratory substrates.

Glucose-6-phosphate can be formed from glucose-1-phosphate by a transfer of phosphate from the first to the sixth carbon atom. Next, glucose-6-phosphate is changed into the structural isomer fructose-6-phosphate in the presence of an isomerase enzyme, **phosphohexoseisomerase**. When free fructose occurs in plant cells, as from invertase action on sucrose or release from sucrose in the presence of UDP or ADP (Chapter 12) it can be converted directly to fructose-6-phosphate by action of **fructokinase**. The reaction is analogous to that catalyzed by the glucokinase acting on glucose, and it also requires ATP. Regardless of its origin, whether from glucose, starch, or sucrose, fructose-6-phosphate can be further metabolized to fructose-1,6-diphosphate. The source

of phosphate on carbon-1 is again from ATP, and still another kinase enzyme is necessary.

In the next step, fructose-1,6-diphosphate is split by an **aldolase** enzyme into two 3-carbon molecules, dihydroxyacetone phosphate and 3-phosphoglyceraldehyde. Dihydroxyacetone phosphate may suffer either of two fates. *First*, it may be reduced, forming alpha-glycerolphosphate, which is an important source of the glycerol present in fats. This reaction is likely to occur in developing seeds of many species. *Second*, it may be changed into 3-phosphoglyceraldehyde by **triose phosphate isomerase**.

The phosphoglyceraldehyde is the first compound to be *oxidized* in the respiration pathway. Two hydrogen atoms are removed and are accepted by NAD (or perhaps NADP), forming NADH (or NADPH). The other product of this important reaction is 1,3-diphosphoglyceric acid. The enzyme required is named **3-phosphoglyceraldehyde dehydrogenase**. Note that two phosphate groups are present in 1,3-diphosphoglycerate. The additional phosphate arises from inorganic phosphate. This reaction explains the observation made by A. Harden and W. Young in 1908 that Pi was essential for fermentation by yeast. Recent evidence indicates that this reaction is responsible for phosphate absorption in anaerobic yeast cells, coupling respiration to the uptake mechanism.

The two phosphates of diphosphoglyceric acid are quite different in energy or transfer potential. The phosphate linkage of carbon-1 is an anhydride type and has a considerably higher transfer potential than does the simple ester phosphate of carbon-3. In the next reaction of glycolysis this phosphate from carbon-1 is

Figure 15-3

The glycolytic or Embden–Meyerhof–Parnas metabolic pathway. Dotted lines (lower left) show that, in the absence of oxygen, the NADH accumulating in the oxidation of 3-phosphoglyceraldehyde may be used to reduce acetaldehyde to ethanol (fermentation) or pyruvate to lactate. If oxygen is plentiful, however, the NADH is itself oxidized and is not available for formation of ethanol or lactate. Pyruvate is then metabolized according to the cycle of Fig. 15-4.

GLYCOLYSIS

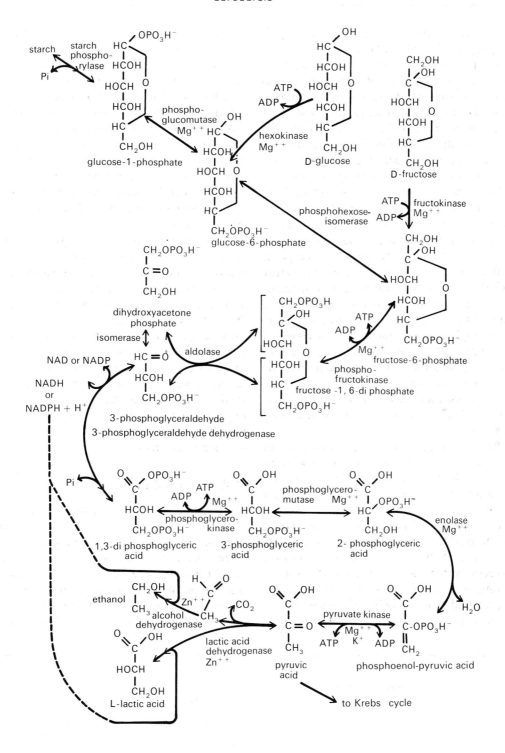

transferred to ADP, producing ATP and 3-phosphoglyceric acid (3-PGA).

The phosphate of 3-PGA is converted from carbon-3 to carbon-2 by **phosphoglyceric acid mutase**, forming 2-PGA. Next, water is removed from 2-PGA by the enzyme **enolase**, and phosphoenolpyruvic acid (PEPA) is produced. This reaction is inhibited by fluoride ions, and this is an important reason why high concentrations of fluoride are poisonous to living organisms.

Next, there is a transfer of phosphate from PEPA to ADP, again synthesizing ATP. Pyruvic acid is also produced. This phosphate transfer, catalyzed by **pyruvic acid kinase**, apparently can readily occur only because energy is obtained from conversion of the enol structure in PEPA to the keto group present in pyruvate. This energy, plus that present in the phosphate group of PEPA, is sufficient to allow formation of the high transfer potential phosphate in ATP. Some of the PEPA not converted to pyruvate is used for synthesis of such aromatic compounds as lignin and the anthocyanin pigments. **Shikimic acid**, an important intermediate in these syntheses, will be discussed in Chapter 18.

The above reactions, then, constitute all those necessary to change starch or glucose to pyruvic acid. Only one step involves oxidation-reduction, one involves a change in the number of carbons, and none requires oxygen. If oxygen is present, the NADH (or NADPH) may be oxidized to form water, and much of the pyruvate will be completely broken down by reactions to be described below. If oxygen is limiting, however, the NADH formed during the oxidation of phosphoglyceraldehyde is available to reduce pyruvate to lactic acid. A zinc-

dependent enzyme called **lactic acid dehydrogenase** catalyzes this reaction. If, instead, pyruvate is decarboxylated, yielding carbon dioxide and acetaldehyde, the acetaldehyde is reduced by **alcohol dehydrogenase** and NADH. Alcohol dehydrogenase also contains zinc. The over-all process of formation of lactate or alcohol from glucose is shown in (R15-3). Note that two ATP molecules are used in the process but four arise from it. Hence the net production of the energy-rich ATP in fermentation is two molecules for each initial molecule of free glucose.

A further possible fate of pyruvate is its conversion to the amino acid alanine. This reaction would be expected to be most important in cells actively synthesizing protein, such as those of young, rapidly growing plants. Pyruvate is thus a key compound that can provide carbon skeletons for several other important compounds, depending upon the kinds of enzymes present. Not necessarily all of these reactions involving pyruvate will occur in the same cells at the same time, for they depend upon the kind of plant, its age, and probably upon the type of cells and their location in the plant.

15.4.2 The Krebs Cycle

In contrast to glycolysis, the further breakdown of pyruvate occurs inside mitochondria. Many of these reactions probably take place directly on the surface of the extensive inner membranes of these bodies (Fig. 8-6). These steps collectively make up what is usually called the **Krebs cycle**, in honor of the English biochemist H. A. Krebs, who, in 1937, proposed a cycle of reactions to

$$\text{glucose} + 2\text{ATP} + 2\text{Pi} + 2\text{ADP} \longrightarrow \begin{cases} 2 \text{ lactate} + 4\text{ATP} \\ 2 \text{ ethanol} + 2\text{CO}_2 + 4\text{ATP} \end{cases} \qquad \text{(R15-3)}$$

explain how pyruvate breakdown took place in the breast muscle of pigeons. He called his proposed pathway the **citric acid cycle**, because citric acid is an important intermediate. Another common name for the same group of reactions is the **tricarboxylic acid** (or **TCA**) **cycle**, a term used because some of the acids involved have three carboxyl groups. It was not until the early 1950s that mitochondria capable of carrying out this cycle were isolated from plant cells. This work was accomplished almost simultaneously in the United States and England.

The Krebs cycle is outlined in Fig. 15-4. The initial step, first worked out in detail by various workers in the early 1950s, involves loss of CO_2 from pyruvate and combination of the resulting 2-carbon acetate unit with the sulfur-containing compound, coenzyme A (abbreviated CoA, see Chapter 11), forming acetyl CoA. This reaction normally proceeds only in the forward direction. The sulfur atom in CoA bonds directly with the acetyl group. This is an important reason why sulfur is an essential element for plants and animals. The enzyme catalyzing pyruvate decarboxylation also requires a phosphorylated form of thiamine (vitamin B_1) as a prosthetic group. Participation of thiamine in this reaction partially explains the essential function of vitamin B_1 in plants and animals. Two hydrogen atoms are also lost from pyruvic acid during the formation of acetyl CoA. The enzyme catalyzing the complete reaction is called **pyruvic acid dehydrogenase**, but it is probably actually a complex of three or four enzymes. The hydrogen atoms are accepted by NAD, yielding NADH.

Acetyl CoA is a very reactive compound, and it combines with the four-carbon acid, oxaloacetic acid, producing the six-carbon citric acid. The necessary enzyme is commonly referred to simply as the **condensing enzyme**. Citric acid is changed to isocitric acid, which is then dehydrogenated and decarboxylated by **isocitric acid dehydrogenase**, forming the five-carbon α-ketoglutaric acid. The hydrogens from isocitric acid are accepted by NAD, while the CO_2 usually escapes out of the mitochondria, out of the cell, and finally out of the plant into the surrounding atmosphere.

Next, α-ketoglutarate undergoes a reaction similar to that described above in which pyruvate lost both hydrogen and CO_2. It, too, is an irreversible reaction under conditions normally occurring in plant cells. CoA and vitamin B_1 are again involved, and the product is a four-carbon molecule named succinyl CoA. The enzyme is **α-ketoglutaric acid dehydrogenase**, and, like pyruvic acid dehydrogenase, it is probably a complex of enzymes. Some of the α-ketoglutarate is not changed to succinyl CoA, but is diverted into glutamic acid when ammonia is available. Thus, formation of proteins is dependent upon reactions of the Krebs cycle.

Succinyl CoA is split by **succinic acid thiokinase**, yielding succinic acid and regenerating CoA. In this reaction considerable energy is released, much of which is somehow trapped in ATP. The mechanism of this energy trapping is not completely understood, but one molecule of Pi is added to ADP for each succinyl CoA split. If it is not converted into succinic acid, succinyl CoA can be used to form larger compounds. The porphyrin pigments, such as the chlorophylls and cytochromes, and the phycobilin pigments derive many of their carbons from succinyl CoA.

Next, two hydrogens are removed from succinic acid and are accepted not by NAD, but this time by a riboflavin-containing molecule, FAD (Chapter 11). Riboflavin is also known as vitamin B_2, and this reaction constitutes one important reason that this vitamin is required by living organisms. The FAD is bound tightly to an iron-containing enzyme

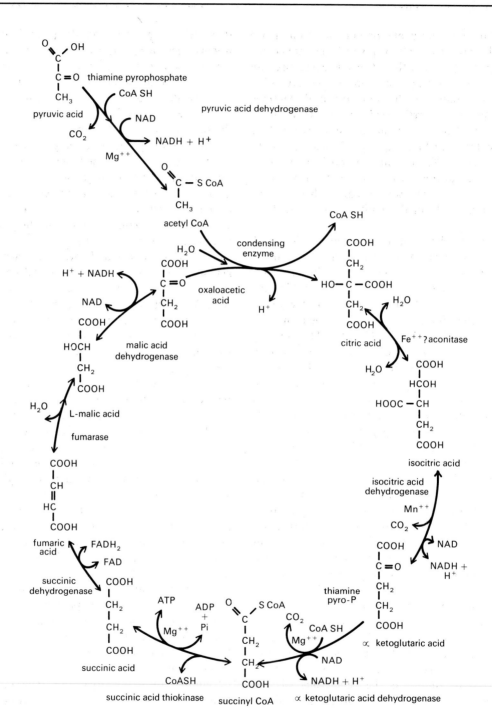

catalyzing this reaction, **succinic acid dehydrogenase**. The product is the unsaturated acid fumaric acid.

An enzyme named **fumarase** now adds water to fumaric acid, and malic acid results. Dehydrogenation of malic acid by **malic acid dehydrogenase** with NAD produces oxaloacetic acid. Oxaloacetate is now able to react with acetyl CoA, starting another turn around the cycle. Like α-ketoglutarate, oxaloacetate performs a dual role, because it is also an amino acid precursor. Oxaloacetate is converted to aspartic acid in the presence of a suitable amino donor and a suitable enzyme.

Let us now summarize the reactions of glycolysis and the Krebs cycle, observing what has been accomplished. Production of two molecules of pyruvate per molecule of glucose used in glycolysis did not yield any CO_2, but two NADH molecules were produced by oxidation of two phosphoglyceraldehydes. As we shall see, the hydrogens of NADH are later combined with oxygen to form water. For every molecule of pyruvate used in one turn of the Krebs cycle, three carbon dioxide molecules are released and five electron pairs are made available. Four of these pairs are in the form of NADH, and one pair (that from succinate) is in reduced FAD, $FADH_2$. Since two pyruvates are produced from each glucose used, a total of twelve electron pairs arise when glucose is completely oxidized.

The student may note that although twelve electron pairs arise in glucose oxidation, this molecule does not contain 24 hydrogen atoms. The additional twelve electrons needed arise from the hydrogen atoms of water, which are added at various steps in the Krebs cycle.

15.4.3 The Electron Transport (Cytochrome) System and Energy Trapping

The NADH produced in glycolysis and the Krebs cycle cannot combine directly with oxygen to form water. Rather, the electrons are transferred via several intermediate compounds, comparable to a bucket brigade, before water is made. The transfer proceeds from compounds with low reduction potentials to those with higher reduction potentials (a greater tendency to accept electrons, thus becoming reduced). Oxygen has the greatest tendency to accept electrons, and so, ultimately oxygen accepts them. Apparently, each enzyme in the chain is specific in that it can accept electrons only from the previous member of the chain, and hence none of the steps can be bypassed. Like the Krebs cycle reactions, these also occur in mitochondria, probably in tiny, yet highly organized particles **(oxysomes)** attached to the inner membrane (Fig. 8-10).

Figure 15-5 shows the possible sequence of reactions by which electrons are passed from various substrates finally to oxygen. These essential compounds constitute what is known as the **electron transport system** or **cytochrome system**.

NADH loses the electrons it received from such substrates as phosphoglyceraldehyde, pyruvate, isocitrate, α-ketoglutarate, or malate by transfer to a flavoprotein such as FAD. NAD is then again free to remove electrons

Figure 15-4

The Krebs, tricarboxylic acid, or citric acid cycle. In each turn of the cycle, one molecule of pyruvate is completely broken down to CO_2 and NADH (or $FADH_2$). Although pyruvic acid has only four hydrogens, five electron pairs (equivalent to ten H atoms) are released as NADH and $FADH_2$. The additional hydrogens needed arise from H_2O or $H_2PO_4^-$ ions (Pi) entering in the reactions as indicated. NADH and $FADH_2$ are oxidized according to the electron transport system in Fig. 15–5.

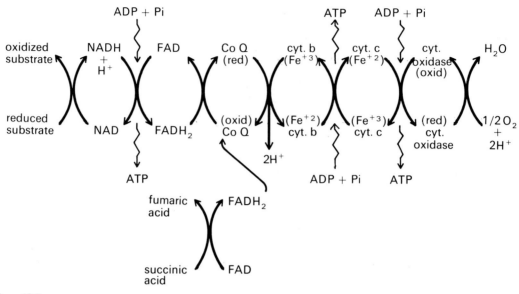

Figure 15-5

Tentative model of the mitochondrial electron transport or cytochrome system. Sites of ATP production are not well established, especially the second one. Except for CoQ (the function of which is tentative) and perhaps NAD (and NADH), the participants are tightly bound to proteins associated with the mitochondrial membranes. Electrons can be driven in the reverse direction if ATP is added.

with the aid of various dehydrogenase enzymes. When $FADH_2$ is formed from FAD and NADH, an additional hydrogen ion is removed from the cell solution, which, with the hydrogen atom and the extra electron from NADH, accounts for an addition of two hydrogen atoms to FAD. When hydrogens are removed from succinate, they are received by FAD directly, without intervention of NAD. From $FADH_2$ the electrons are possibly taken by a quinone compound, called **coenzyme Q (CoQ)**, also known as **ubiquinone**. This compound is similar to the plastoquinones involved in photosynthesis, but the latter are found in chloroplasts, while CoQ exists mainly in mitochondria. It transfers electrons to one of the iron-containing cytochromes. As indicated in Fig. 15-5, the order of electron transfer is probably from CoQ to one of three **cytochromes b**

present in plant mitochondria, then to a cytochrome c, then to **cytochrome oxidase**, and from there to oxygen. Since only one electron can be accepted by the cytochromes, two molecules of one of the b cytochromes probably react with one coenzyme Q.

Cytochrome oxidase contains copper, which undergoes reduction and oxidation from the cuprous to the cupric state as oxygen is absorbed. Both iron and copper are likely necessary at this step. If so, this would account for another essential function of copper in plants. It is interesting that carbon monoxide and hydrogen cyanide (**prussic acid**) are poisonous to some plants because of their ability to combine with the iron of cytochrome oxidase, thus preventing oxygen from acting as an electron acceptor. According to research by Walter Bonner at the University of Pennsylvania, plant mitochondria contain, in small concentration, a different cytochrome of the *a* type that can transfer electrons to oxygen in a reaction not so sensitive to carbon monoxide or cyanide. This may explain the mechanism by which some tissues are able to respire quite well even in the presence of these inhibitors.

15.4.4   Oxidative Phosphorylation

The electron transport system is very important, because closely associated with it is the mechanism by which much of the energy released in respiration is trapped in a chemical form usable by the cells. ATP is again the important compound in which the energy is stored. This process of synthesizing ATP from ADP and Pi in conjunction with oxygen uptake is called **oxidative phosphorylation**. In contrast, the glycolytic reactions and the succinyl CoA-to-succinate reaction of the Krebs cycle, whereby some ATP is also made, are examples of **substrate phosphorylations**.

The energy necessary to form ATP in oxidative phosphorylation comes from the drop in electrochemical potential as electrons are transferred from one compound to another having a greater tendency to accept them. Exactly how this formation is coupled to electron transfer is only now being clarified, and several problems still await further study. Evidence exists that high-energy phosphorylated proteins are formed upon electron transport, and these transfer phosphate to ADP. An alternative viewpoint, initially proposed by Peter Mitchell in 1961, is that high-energy phosphorylated proteins do not exist and that ATP is synthesized in mitochondrial membranes (and grana membranes of chloroplasts) by another process. This revolutionary theory, which is receiving increasing support, indicates that the known secretion of hydrogen ions out of mitochondria and accumulation of hydroxyl ions inside these bodies creates a dehydration effect

in the membranes themselves. Since the conversion of ADP + Pi to ATP + H_2O is a dehydration reaction, the removal of water would allow the reaction to proceed toward ATP synthesis.

Regardless of the mechanism, it is known that if electrons are received from one NADH, as many as three ATP molecules can be made. However, if succinate is the source, no more than two ATPs are synthesized per oxygen atom absorbed. This indicates that one ATP is made in a reaction between NADH and FAD. Another likely occurs between cytochromes *b* and *c* or perhaps between CoQ and cytochrome *b*, and the third between cytochrome *c* and cytochrome oxidase (Fig. 15-5).

Mitochondria can be separated from cells, and oxidative phosphorylation can then be studied in the test tube. In fact, most of what we know about the electron transport sequence has been learned in this way. One of the limiting factors in oxygen uptake (and electron transfer) is the abundance of ADP and Pi. If they are limiting, ATP production and oxygen uptake soon cease. This indicates that the processes of oxidative phosphorylation and electron transport are closely coupled. It appears that in the living plant the same thing is true, because experimentally imposing a "work load" on it, such as by providing an abundance of nutrient ions to be actively absorbed, increases the oxygen uptake rate. This increased respiration is known as **salt respiration**. Salt respiration almost surely results from the increase in ADP and Pi formed when the energy in the terminal phosphate bond of ATP is utilized in ion transport.

Another way of stimulating respiration of plants is by adding proper concentrations of **dinitrophenol**, a compound sometimes used as an herbicide. Dinitrophenol acts by causing ATP to be split as rapidly as it is formed, producing ADP and Pi, which are then again available to unite temporarily in a reaction coupled to electron transport. Dinitrophenol thus acts as an uncoupler of respiration and phosphorylation in mitochondria, because a net production of ATP does not occur in its presence, even though respiration continues. Some naturally occurring substituted phenolic compounds also act as uncouplers and thereby may inhibit the development of certain plant pathogens. In addition, an antibiotic of microbial origin, **chloramphenicol (chloromycetin)**, acts as an uncoupler, although its primary mode of action upon bacteria is an inhibition of protein synthesis. Another antibiotic, **oligomycin**, inhibits both ATP formation and oxygen uptake in mitochondria. Dinitrophenol and both antibiotics potently inhibit ion uptake. John Hanson, C. Stoner, and T. Hodges at the University of Illinois suggested a tentative scheme that partially explains the mechanism of oxidative phosphorylation in plant mitochondria and its relation to the uptake of calcium and phosphate ions, as well as the influence of dinitrophenol, oligomycin, and chloramphenicol on both processes. Their model is explained in Fig. 15-6.

Calculations of the total amount of ATP synthesized during oxidation of one molecule of glucose indicate that about 38 such high transfer potential bonds are made. If one mole of these has an energy of about 10,000 calories, 380,000 calories will be saved for further uses of the cell for every mole of glucose completely burned in respiration. From this figure we can calculate the efficiency of respiration, since it is known that there are about 710,000 calories potentially available ($\Delta G = 710$ kcal) when a mole of glucose is respired. The efficiency is equal to output/input, or 380,000/710,000, which is approximately 54 percent. The other 46 percent of the energy escapes as heat and can serve no useful function except to warm the plant. Nevertheless, the trapping of even 54 percent of the energy released in respiration is a notable

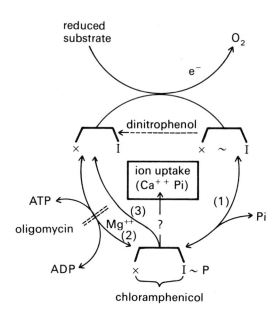

Figure 15-6

A tentative model to explain the relationship of respiration to ion uptake into plant mitochondria. As reduced substrates (i.e., Krebs cycle acids) are oxidized by the electron transport system, low-energy intermediates ($\times$ I) are converted into a high energy state ($\times \sim$ I) by the drop in oxidation-reduction potential between two proper participants of the system. This would occur at the sites of ATP production in Fig. 15-5. Pi is then activated to form a phosphorylated protein intermediate ($\times$ I $\sim$ P) which is susceptible to destruction by chloramphenicol. This intermediate may either react with ADP to form ATP, as in the oligomycin-sensitive reaction (2), or may be converted back to $\times$ I accompanied by transport of ions into the mitochondria (reaction 3). Since reaction (2) is reversible, ATP itself may form the phosphorylated protein intermediate, thus driving ion uptake. Dinitrophenol discharges $\times \sim$ I, thus reversing reactions (1) and (2). Consequences are the breaking down of ATP into ADP and Pi and the regenerating of $\times$ I, thus blocking ion uptake but stimulating respiration. Salt respiration presumably would arise from the utilization of $\times$ I $\sim$ P in ion accumulation, thus regenerating $\times$ I needed for electron transport to oxygen. The way in which chloramphenicol might destroy $\times$ I $\sim$ P is not known. (From T. Hodges and J. Hanson, 1965, *Plant Physiol.* 40:101. Used by permission.)

achievement for living cells. Steam engines, for example, have efficiencies of less than 10 percent.

15.4.5 Molecules Derived from Respiration Used for Synthetic Purposes

Near the beginning of this chapter it was emphasized that respiration is also important to cells because many compounds are formed that can be diverted into other substances needed for growth. Many of these are large molecules, including lipids, proteins, and nucleic acids. To form these, the aid of the high transfer potential in the terminal ATP bond is needed. Protein and nucleic acid synthesis will be described in more detail in Chapter 17, while lipid synthesis is discussed in Chapter 18. In addition to ATP, the subunits from which other large molecules can be assembled are derived from the intermediates of respiration. Several of these interesting relationships are summarized in Fig. 15-7.

The ability of dihydroxyacetone phosphate to provide the glycerol needed for fat formation has already been mentioned. Another function of the three-carbon sugars of glycolysis appears to be their conversion to the amino acid serine, although serine is probably principally formed from glycine by a different route (Chapter 16) during photosynthesis.

Phosphoenolpyruvic acid may be utilized for synthesis of shikimic acid, after condensation with the four-carbon compound **erythrose-4-phosphate**. Shikimic acid then provides many of the carbon substances for phenolic compounds, including lignin and the anthocyanin pigments. A further very important function of PEPA in plants is its direct conversion to oxaloacetate by PEPA carboxylase (Chapter 14). In this reaction carbon dioxide is added while Pi is split out of PEPA. In fact, one enzyme is known that even causes the Pi to be added to ADP, thus forming an ATP.

As discussed in Chapter 12, malic and citric acids (and sometimes isocitric acid) are often found in rather high concentrations in the vacuoles of some plant cells, while other acids are present in smaller amounts. Reactions of the Krebs cycle do not allow the accumulation of any acid, because for every molecule of each formed, one molecule must also be used to continue the cycle. The major way in which organic acids are accumulated is probably through oxaloacetate formation from PEPA. Both malic and citric acids arise rather directly from oxaloacetic acid. In the leaves of most plants the CO_2 level is often kept low during daylight hours because of its photosynthetic combination with ribulose diphosphate. During darkness, the CO_2 content surrounding the cells will be higher, and fixation into oxaloacetate appears to be more favorable. In fact, certain succulent plants of the *Crassulaceae* family such as *Bryophyllum crenatum* synthesize organic acids such as malic, citric, and isocitric in their leaves almost entirely in the dark. Their stomata, unlike those of most species, are open at night and closed in daylight. Some succulents live in dry climates, and stomatal closure during daylight conserves water. It also interferes with CO_2 absorption, of course, but not with light reception. Thus the plants apparently produce NADPH and ATP in the light and use these to convert organic acids (formed the night before) into sugars. The use of radioactive CO_2 to label the organic acids showed that fixation by this means is common in darkened leaves, in stems, and even in roots of most plants.

Finally, the two-carbon compound acetyl CoA has several important functions other than its role in the Krebs cycle. Most of the fatty acids are derived entirely from this compound, so that there is a close relationship of respiration to fat metabolism. Isoprenoid compounds and part of the anthocyanin mole-

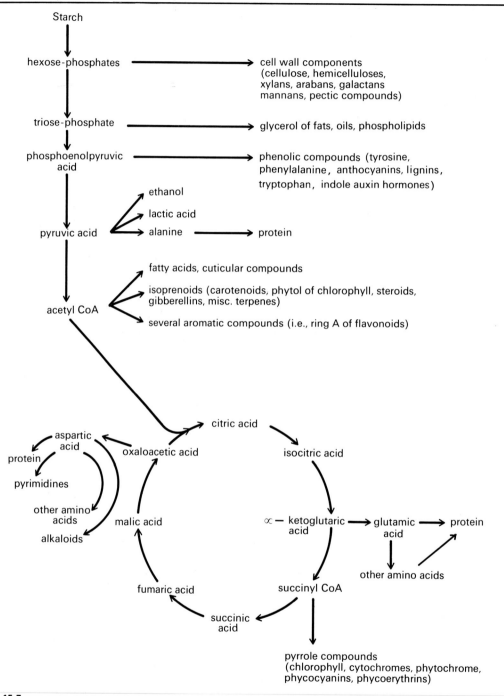

Figure 15-7
Relation of glycolytic and Krebs cycle reactions to production of compounds involved in growth.

cules are also synthesized from acetyl CoA (Chapter 18).

15.5 METHODS OF INVESTIGATING METABOLIC PATHWAYS IN PLANTS

The figures summarizing glycolysis, the Krebs cycle, and the cytochrome system include about 50 known individual metabolic steps. How could such a complex system of pathways be worked out? Solution of the puzzle of respiration was one of the most challenging achievements of 20th century biology. The two or three decades required for the work were an exciting time for the various teams of workers who were exploring leads as they became apparent. Much highly original and creative thought was required, and this was subsequently recognized through a number of Nobel Prizes. As we shall see in Chapter 18, one of the current, equally rewarding areas of study in the life sciences is the study of molecular genetics.

The general approach was to postulate a given step, perhaps adding a new idea to knowledge about compounds or reactions known by organic chemists, and then to search for evidence that would either support or disprove the suspected step. Then as evidence for certain reactions became more convincing, attempts were made to study the manner in which a number of steps might fit together. Several methods were devised, and, when possible, many were applied to a single problem. Certain of these procedures are described in the paragraphs below, and many challenging problems of plant metabolism still await their application.

Most of the original work on glycolysis was performed in the 1920s and 1930s with microorganisms or with animal tissues. Building upon this foundation, studies of the respiratory pathways in higher plants were then initiated

in the 1940s. Even now it is not certain that the same reactions take place in all plants, but a considerable body of evidence from the plants so far investigated is in favor of this conclusion.

15.5.1 The Intermediate Compounds Must Be Present in the Cells

If all of the reactions of the Krebs cycle occur in plants, it should be possible to isolate the member organic acids. In fact, all of these have been found. Of course, their presence alone does not indicate their order of formation, and other techniques must be used to determine this. It is possible that the concentrations of some essential intermediates are extremely low, so low as to escape detection. This is a common complication, because some compounds apparently react almost as quickly as they are formed. In this case, we say that their **pool size** is small and their **turnover rate** is large. When a small pool size is suspected, some trapping agent is often added, that is, some compound with which the intermediate will react and accumulate. An early example of this technique was the addition of lime to yeast cells, which caused formation of calcium pyruvate in detectable amounts. Otherwise, even pyruvate, important as it is, could not easily be found. A more recent technique used to trap pyruvate and other α-keto acids (glyoxylate, oxaloacetate, and α-ketoglutarate) is to add a hydrazine derivative such as 2,4-dinitrophenylhydrazine to cell extracts. These acids are converted to 2,4-dinitrophenylhydrazones, which are stable and can be chromatographed.

15.5.2 The Enzymes Necessary to Catalyze the Reactions Can Be Demonstrated in Cell Extracts

The demonstration that enzymes exist that are capable of catalyzing suspected reactions is extremely important in defining metabolic pathways. In some cases 'these enzymes can be highly purified by the techniques described in Chapter 11, and their properties can then be studied. However, the mere presence of an enzyme capable of catalyzing a certain reaction does not always prove that the reaction is quantitatively important in the plant, although it is certainly very useful suggestive evidence.

Sometimes, even though enzymes are present in certain tissues, they are difficult to demonstrate, because natural inhibitors of their action are released when the cells are disrupted. These inhibitors may usually be removed by methods of protein purification described in Chapter 11.

15.5.3 Addition of a Specific Enzyme Inhibitor, by Blocking a Given Reaction, May Allow Accumulation of a Suspected Reactant

The reaction from 2-phosphoglyceric acid to phosphoenolpyruvic acid in glycolysis is catalyzed by the enzyme enolase. As mentioned before, this enzyme is inhibited by fluoride ions. Adding fluoride should then provide a tool for determining whether this reaction is important in the sequence, for 2-phosphoglycerate should accumulate behind the block. This is nearly what happens. Actually, 3-phosphoglycerate is the main substance accumulating. This occurs because the 2-phospho compound is converted back to the 3-phospho form, the equilibrium between these two being more favorable for the latter. Accumulation of the 3-phosphoglycerate in the presence of fluoride was originally a clue to discovery of certain reactions of glycolysis.

Other good examples of the use of enzyme inhibitors to break a reaction sequence are known. Many such inhibitors have structures similar to the natural substrates. For example, the poison

malonic acid,[2] $HOOC-CH_2-COOH$, differs from succinic acid,

$$HOOC-CH_2-CH_2-COOH,$$

only in one CH_2 group. Added malonic acid combines with succinic dehydrogenase, thus preventing normal fumaric acid formation from succinic acid. In this case, small increases in succinate levels in the cells are noted, additional evidence that succinate is the precursor of fumarate in plants.

Compounds with structures similar to a given metabolite and able to compete with it for the active site on a necessary enzyme are called **antimetabolites**. Many are now known. For example, certain anticancer agents similar to normal metabolites have been synthesized, but they differ slightly, in that a hydrogen atom may be replaced by a fluorine. One such substance contains a molecule of 5-fluorouracil, which is so similar to uracil that certain of the enzymes are "fooled" into combining with it, and they are thus not available for the essential reactions of nucleic acid synthesis. Because of a lack of nucleic acids, growth of the cancer cells is slowed.

15.5.4 After Addition of Suspected Intermediates to the Tissues, It Can Often Be Found That They Are Metabolized

Glucose or fructose almost always disappear when they are added to plants. In some cases, oxygen uptake and carbon dioxide release are stimulated by these sugars, indicating they are being respired. There is some uncertainty to experiments like these, since it is possible that

---

[2] Malonic acid occurs naturally in the leaves of some plants (especially legumes such as beans), and it is probably formed primarily by a decarboxylation of oxaloacetate. It apparently does not poison respiration in the cells in which it exists, because it is kept in the vacuoles and does not come into contact with the mitochondria.

the cells could metabolize an added compound, even though the compound might normally be absent or unimportant.

15.5.5 The Use of Isotopic Tracers Has Provided a Vast Amount of Information about Reaction Pathways

Usually the isotope is radioactive, although suitable radioactive forms of oxygen or nitrogen are not available. The heavy isotopes ^{15}N and ^{18}O are employed, but their detection is more difficult because an expensive mass spectrograph must be used. Radioactive compounds can easily be detected with a geiger counter or liquid scintillation counter.

Metabolites containing ^{14}C have been used in many experiments other than those of photosynthesis mentioned in the last chapter. An example of the kind of results obtainable can be seen in a study in which ^{14}C-labeled glucose was fed to corn root tips by the Purdue University plant biochemist, Harry Beevers. Only the aldehyde carbon (carbon-1) of the added glucose contained radioactivity. The roots absorbed the sugar and metabolized it to ethanol and CO_2. These products were collected, and radioactivity was measured with a geiger counter. It was found that the CO_2 was not labeled, but that the ethanol was. By further chemically degrading the ethanol, it became apparent that only the methyl group contained ^{14}C. Inspection of the glycolytic reactions of Fig. 15-3 indicates that if the glucose were converted to ethanol by this pathway, the fate of ^{14}C would have been just as was observed in the actual experiment. When glucose containing ^{14}C in other positions was fed to similar groups of roots, the distribution of radioactivity in ethanol and CO_2 was also as predicted. Thus, these experiments gave added evidence that glycolysis proceeds as outlined.

15.6 THE PENTOSE PHOSPHATE PATHWAY

After about 1950, plant physiologists gradually became aware that glycolysis and the Krebs cycle were not the only reactions by which plants could obtain energy from the breakdown of sugars into carbon dioxide and water. Otto Warburg and W. Christian had discovered in the 1930s that glucose-6-phosphate could be oxidized in yeast by reactions different from those of glycolysis, and that NADP rather than NAD was an essential coenzyme. Further research by F. Dickens and F. Lipmann established that 6-phosphogluconic acid is an intermediate in these other reactions. Then, in the 1950s, E. Racker and B. L. Horecker discovered additional reactions in the new pathway for breakdown of glucose-6-phosphate, and demonstrated that pentose phosphates and heptose phosphates participate. Much of the research indicating that a similar pathway occurs in plants was performed in the 1950s by Martin Gibbs at Cornell University and by Bernard Axelrod and Harry Beevers at Purdue University. Because five-carbon sugar phosphates are intermediates, this series of reactions is often called the **pentose phosphate pathway**, sometimes abbreviated **PPP**.[3] With the exception of the use of inhibitors, all of the other techniques listed above have contributed much information to the role of this pathway in plants. The intermediate compounds were found, the enzymes were shown to be present, the pentose and seven-carbon sugars fed to plants were rapidly broken down, and, finally, radioactive glucose labeled in various carbon atoms was converted to intermediates containing ^{14}C in the positions predicted by the pathway.

---

[3] This pathway has also often been called the direct oxidation pathway, the Warburg–Dickens pathway, and the hexose monophosphate shunt.

Several of the compounds of the PPP were previously described in the Calvin–Benson photosynthetic cycle, in which sugar phosphates were synthesized in chloroplasts. But in the pentose phosphate respiratory pathway, the reactions are believed to occur in the cytoplasm, outside any subcellular particles, and sugar phosphates are degraded, rather than synthesized. In these two respects, the reactions of the PPP are similar to those of glycolysis. In addition, glycolysis and the PPP have certain reactants in common, so that they are probably interwoven to some extent. One important difference is that in the PPP, NADP always accepts the electrons from the sugar phosphates, whereas in glycolysis, NAD is the more common acceptor.

15.6.1   Reactions of the Pathway

Reactions of the PPP are outlined in Fig. 15-8. The first reaction involves glucose-6-phosphate, which may arise from starch breakdown followed by the initial reactions of glycolysis, from the addition of the terminal phosphate of ATP to glucose, or directly from photosynthetic reactions. It is immediately oxidized by **glucose-6-phosphate dehydrogenase** to 6-phosphogluconic acid. This is a case of oxidation of an aldehyde to an acid, and NADP is reduced in the process. The 6-phosphogluconate doesn't accumulate, for it is then both dehydrogenated and decarboxylated by **6-phosphogluconic acid dehydrogenase**, yielding the five-carbon compound ribulose 5-phosphate. This reaction is not reversible and, as in the first step, NADP rather than NAD is reduced.

These two steps represent the only oxidations in the PPP, and this CO_2 is the only one released

in the entire pathway. The main function of the subsequent reactions is to cycle the ribulose-5-phosphate back into glucose-6-phosphate molecules, which can undergo dehydrogenation and decarboxylation. This begins by the conversion of ribulose-5-phosphate to xylulose-5-phosphate, while reaction four (Fig. 15-8) produces the aldehyde, ribose-5-phosphate. In reaction five the thiamine-requiring enzyme transketolase catalyzes the transfer of the two-carbon ketol group of xylulose-5-phosphate to ribose-5-phosphate, thus forming a seven-carbon aldehyde, sedoheptulose-7-phosphate. Phosphoglyceraldehyde accounts for the other three carbons of the xylulose-5-phosphate.

Now sedoheptulose-7-phosphate is attacked by an enzyme called **transaldolase**, which transfers the upper three carbons of sedoheptulose to 3-phosphoglyceraldehyde (reaction six). The resulting products are fructose-6-phosphate and the four-carbon compound erythrose-4-phosphate. Erythrose-4-phosphate can accept a ketol group, and transketolase thus adds to it two carbons from xylulose-5-phosphate, yielding another fructose-6-phosphate and phosphoglyceraldehyde (reaction seven).

The fructose-6-phosphate from reactions six and seven is directly changed to glucose-6-phosphate in step eight, and the oxidations then may start again. Of course, some of the phosphoglyceraldehyde and hexose phosphates would also be broken down by enzymes of glycolysis, and the two processes are closely interwoven, at least in some tissues.

15.6.2   Control of PPP Activity

It was interesting to discover the factors that determined which pathway would predominate

Figure 15-8

The pentose phosphate respiratory pathway. The thiamine pyrophosphate-bound glycolaldehyde group shown in brackets at the center of the figure is hypothetical and probably exists bound to an enzyme.

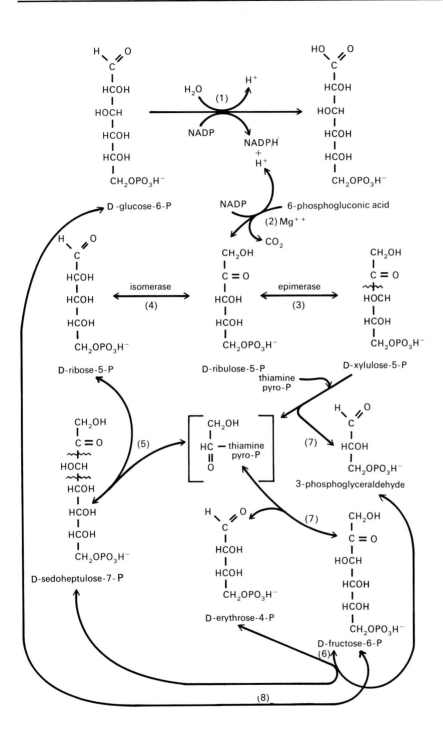

in the utilization of glucose-6-phosphate. Certainly the enzymes present and their activities will ultimately decide whether glucose-6-phosphate is catabolized via glycolysis or by direct oxidation in the PPP. There is, however, considerable evidence indicating that the particular electron acceptor, NAD or NADP, has great importance in controlling the pathway. The PPP is entirely dependent on NADP, while the glycolytic dehydrogenase enzyme and mitochondrial enzymes of the Krebs cycle rely mainly on NAD to accept electrons. Therefore, if NADP is at a high concentration in the cells relative to NAD, the PPP is favored. Various other reactions influence the concentrations of these coenzymes. For example, if oxygen is readily available, NADH is probably rapidly used by the mitochondrial electron transport pathway, keeping the NAD at a high level and thus favoring glycolysis.

A high oxygen level should also allow rapid oxidation of NADPH produced by PPP reactions, but it appears that NADPH is not easily oxidized by the cytochrome system. However, other oxidative reactions that do convert NADPH to NADP are known. In addition, many synthetic reactions require NADPH rather than NADH as a source of electrons. Conversion of acetyl CoA to fatty acids and sterols requires additional electrons, and NADPH appears to be the primary source of these. Similarly, certain aromatic syntheses seem to utilize NADPH instead of NADH. Synthetic reactions like these probably indirectly influence the pathway of glucose-6-phosphate breakdown by their effect on the cellular concentrations of the necessary pyridine nucleotides, NAD and NADP.

15.6.3 Significance of the PPP

The PPP is important because it acts as a mechanism for glucose breakdown, because it provides reduced NADPH for synthetic reactions, because it provides the ribose-5-phosphate for nucleic acid synthesis (except in chloroplasts), and, as will be seen in Chapter 18, because the erythrose-4-phosphate needed in synthesis of lignin and other aromatic compounds arises from this pathway. Doubt now exists that ATP is a major product of the PPP, since the mitochondrial cytochrome system apparently cannot use the NADPH effectively, and no oxidative phosphorylation can then result. Furthermore, exclusive breakdown of glucose-6-phosphate by PPP reactions would not allow for the formation of pyruvate and Krebs cycle acids, which provide the essential carbon skeletons for several amino acids. It appears, therefore, that the Krebs cycle is essential for normal plant functions. In most plant parts so far investigated, both the PPP and glycolysis with the associated Krebs cycle operate. In leaves, stems, and the various underground storage tissues (such as carrot roots), estimates indicate that about one-fourth to one-half of the CO_2 is released through the PPP, while in embryonic tissues (seedlings) and some fruits the PPP is less important.

15.7 OTHER OXIDATIVE SYSTEMS

Although the cytochrome system probably accepts most of the electrons removed from glycolytic or Krebs cycle intermediates, other enzymes have long been known which can, potentially at least, transfer electrons to oxygen.

15.7.1 Phenol Oxidases

One such group of related enzymes consists of the **phenol** or **polyphenol oxidases**. When many plant tissues, such as apple fruits or potato tubers, are injured, the surfaces soon become brown. This browning reaction occurs because of the activity of these oxidase enzymes. Upon injury the enzymes apparently can then contact certain phenolics such as catechol, chlorogenic acid, gallic acid, caffeic acid, or anthocyanins. The hydroxyl groups on these phenolics are oxidized to quinone structures. Oxygen is absorbed in the process and is combined with the removed hydrogens to form water as in (R15-4). The quinones can be further oxidized and polymerized, producing the complex colored substances that are actually responsible for the dark pigments often observed.

There is some evidence that when reduced NADPH is present, the quinones are reduced instead of being converted to colored products. Should this occur there could exist a continuous transfer of electrons from respiratory intermediate to NADP to quinone to oxygen as shown in (R15-5). Such a process probably accounts

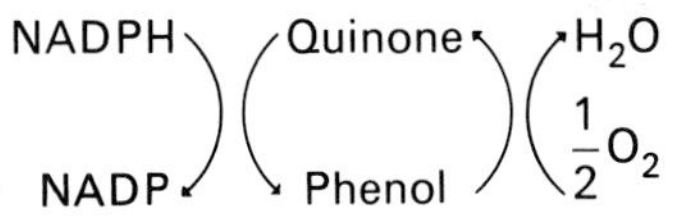

$$\text{NADPH} \diagdown \quad \diagup \text{Quinone} \diagdown \quad \diagup \text{H}_2\text{O}$$
$$\text{NADP} \diagup \quad \diagdown \text{Phenol} \diagup \quad \diagdown \tfrac{1}{2}\text{O}_2 \qquad \text{(R15-5)}$$

for very little oxygen uptake under the usual situations in most plants. In fact, the polyphenol oxidase system appears to be absent from some plant parts. It is interesting that this enzyme system contains copper and is dependent upon it for catalytic activity.

15.7.2 Glycolic Acid Oxidase

Another enzyme that directly uses molecular oxygen in an oxidation process is **glycolic acid oxidase**. This oxidase is not found in roots but is present in green leaves and stems. It oxidizes glycolic acid to glyoxylic acid [see (R15-6)].

$$\text{CH}_2\text{OH}-\text{COOH} + \text{O}_2 \longrightarrow \text{CHO}-\text{COOH} + \text{H}_2\text{O}_2$$

glycolic acid $\qquad\qquad\qquad$ glyoxylic acid

(R15-6)

Hydrogen peroxide is a product of the reaction, and, if not removed, it causes a further oxidation of glyoxylic acid to formic acid and CO_2. Enzymes are present, however, that normally destroy the peroxide, as will be described later. Glyoxylic acid can also be converted to oxalic acid, although oxalic acid appears normally to be formed from oxaloacetic acid.

Glycolic acid oxidase is a flavoprotein enzyme. The flavin is FMN, as contrasted to the FAD-containing enzymes essential to the electron transport pathway of mitochondria. The role of glycolic acid oxidase in plant respiration is not yet entirely clear. There is evidence that it is active in leaf respiration, especially in the light when glycolic acid is being formed. Glycolic acid is apparently produced in photosynthesis by activity of transketolase in the Calvin-Benson cycle (see Chapter 14).

Different enzymes, **glyoxylic acid reductases**, capable of reducing glyoxylate back to glycolate are also present in plants. These require specifically either NADH or NADPH as a source of electrons. Thus, another possible pathway

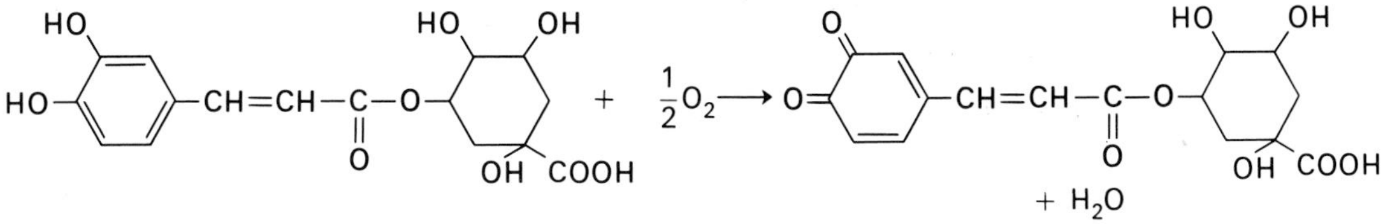

chlorogenic acid

(R15-4)

[shown in (R15-7)] for electron transfer from respiratory substrate to oxygen exists.

Certain other oxidases have also been discovered by plant physiologists, but their importance is even more obscure. It should be noted that except for substrate level phosphorylations, ATP synthesis has so far been demonstrated only in connection with the cytochrome system. This system therefore appears to be of primary significance in plant respiration.

15.7.3 Peroxidase and Catalase

Hydrogen peroxide is produced not only by glycolic acid oxidase activity but also by certain other metabolic reactions. Its removal is essential to prevent destructive oxidations from occurring. Two enzymes are known to be capable of performing this function. The first, called **peroxidase**, requires the presence of another substrate, which is oxidized by the peroxide, as illustrated in (R15-8) for hydroquinone.

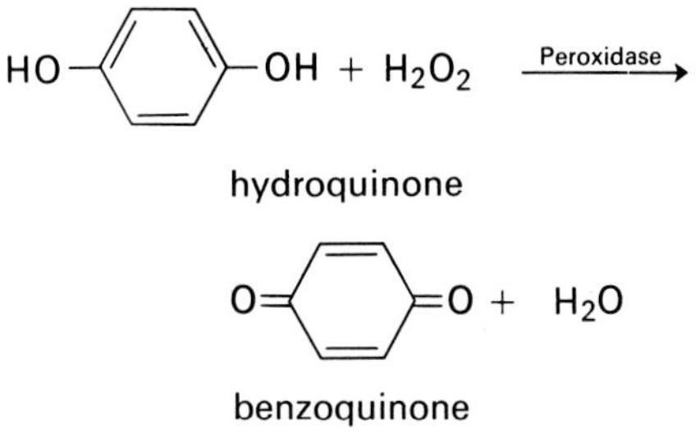

hydroquinone

$$O = = O + H_2O \qquad (R15\text{-}8)$$

benzoquinone

The second enzyme, **catalase**, usually breaks down the H_2O_2 directly to H_2O and O_2 [see (R15-9)].

$$H_2O_2 \xrightarrow{\text{catalase}} H_2O + \frac{1}{2}O_2 \qquad (R15\text{-}9)$$

Both peroxidase and catalase are iron-containing enzymes, the iron being bound to a porphyrin group. In each case, only the ferric form of iron occurs. These enzymes are very common in plants. Horseradish roots contain large amounts of peroxidase, and it has been obtained in crystalline form from this source.

15.8 METAL REQUIREMENTS FOR RESPIRATION

The important function of iron in the cytochromes, in catalase, and in peroxidase; the role of copper for polyphenoloxidase and cytochrome oxidase activity; and the essentiality of zinc for reduction of pyruvate to either lactate or ethanol have already been mentioned. In addition, several enzymes of glycolysis, the PPP, and the Krebs cycle are stimulated by metal ions, including magnesium, manganese, or potassium. Both a divalent and a monovalent cation are essential for maximum activity of certain respiratory enzymes. Magnesium ap-

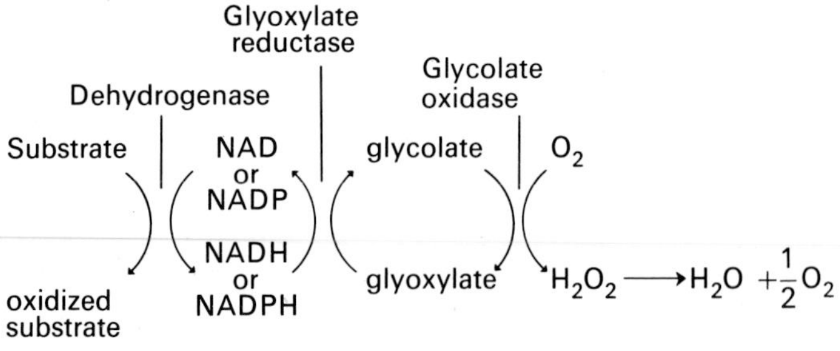

$$(R15\text{-}7)$$

pears to have the most important catalytic role, since all of the steps involving ADP or ATP proceed effectively only if this ion (or manganese) is present. Thus the reactions of respiration explain at least in part why these metals are essential for normal plant growth.

15.9 FACTORS AFFECTING RESPIRATION

It has long been known that many environmental factors influence the respiratory activity. An appreciation of the individual reactions involved should allow a more adequate understanding of how these and other factors affect the over-all rate.

15.9.1 Starvation

Any respiration depends upon the presence of a substrate, and it is evident that starved plants having low starch or sugar reserves respire at relatively poor rates. Plants deficient in sugars often respire noticeably faster when sugars are added. Sugars may be provided by immersing the petioles of excised leaves directly in suitable solutions, as shown in Fig. 15-9.

If starvation becomes extensive, even the proteins can be oxidized. These proteins are hydrolyzed into their amino acid subunits, which are then probably catabolized by glycolytic and Krebs cycle reactions. In the case of glutamic and aspartic acids, at least, the relation to the Krebs cycle is clear, because of their conversion to α-ketoglutaric and oxaloacetic acids, respectively. Similarly, alanine is probably oxidized via pyruvic acid. As leaves become senescent and yellow, most of the protein and other nitrogenous compounds in the chloroplasts are broken down. Resulting ammonium ions are primarily combined in glutamine and asparagine during this process, and this prevents ammonium toxicity.

15.9.2 Available Oxygen

The O_2 supply also markedly influences respiration, but the magnitude of its influence differs greatly with various plant species and probably even with different organs of the same plant. It is likely that normal variations in O_2 content of the air have little influence on the respiratory rate of most leaves and stems, since the penetration rate is probably sufficient to maintain normal O_2 uptake levels.

One might suspect that in such tissues as carrot roots, potato tubers, and other storage organs, the rate of O_2 penetration would be so low as to cause the respiration inside to be primarily anaerobic. Quantitative data on gas penetration into such organs is rather meager, but the measurements at hand show that rate of O_2 movement is certainly much less than in air. In pure water, oxygen diffusion is nearly 300,000 times slower than in air. However, the French physiologist Devaux showed, in 1890, that central regions of bulky plant tissues do respire aerobically. He demonstrated the importance of intercellular spaces for gaseous diffusion. We now know that these spaces may represent significant amounts of the total tissue volume. For example, in potato tubers approximately 1 percent of the tissue volume is occupied by air spaces. In these organs the oxygen was calculated to penetrate 430 times as fast as through water.

The influence of oxygen on respiration also depends upon the way in which the rate is measured. Of course, if no O_2 is present, as when nitrogen is used to replace it, none can be absorbed. Under this condition the rates of sugar loss and CO_2 output are, however, not reduced to zero. In fact, they often increase. This surprising result shows that oxygen can actually inhibit the utilization of sugars in respiration. The effect is on glycolysis and is known as the **Pasteur effect**, after Louis Pasteur, who first recorded the phenomenon in his studies with microorganisms.

Figure 15-9

A method by which compounds may be fed to plant leaves. Absorption is usually much better by this technique than by spreading solutions directly upon the leaf surfaces. (Photograph by F. B. Salisbury.)

Figure 15-10 shows an example of how CO_2 release can change with varying oxygen concentrations. As O_2 is reduced, the CO_2 production gradually decreases but then begins to increase again. This increase results when the oxygen level is so low that it no longer interferes with glycolysis (fermentation). Respiration is then anaerobic, and alcohol usually accumulates.

A convincing explanation of the Pasteur effect is still lacking, but various suggestions have received experimental support. One states that oxygen has a destructive effect on one or more glycolytic enzymes, probably by oxidizing active sulfhydryl groups required for enzyme activity. Another possible explanation is that with adequate oxygen the electron transport pathway involving cytochromes proceeds rapidly, thus converting Pi and ADP into ATP by oxidative phosphorylation. Both Pi and ADP are required for glycolysis, and their concentrations might become limiting for this process if oxygen allowed their extensive conversion to ATP. Perhaps a more likely explanation is that phosphofructokinase, the glycolytic enzyme converting fructose-6-phosphate to fructose-1,6-diphosphate, is inhibited by citric acid or ATP, which are formed by oxygen-dependent reactions of the Krebs cycle or the mitochondrial electron transport system, respectively. ATP is, of course, necessary for phosphofructokinase to form fructose diphosphate, and so it plays both an essential and an inhibitory role. This surprising result is accounted for by the fact that phosphofructokinase is an allosteric enzyme (Chapter 11), and ATP can combine with both the active site and an allosteric site. The active site has the greatest affinity for ATP, while the allosteric site binds ATP only when its concentration becomes high. The inhibition by ATP is partially overcome in plants by Pi, and in other organisms also by ADP. Thus, the rate of sugar utilization by glycolysis can be modulated by oxygen through its influence upon aerobic reactions regulating the intracellular levels of citrate, ATP, ADP, and Pi.

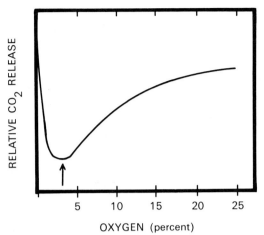

Figure 15-10

The influence of atmospheric oxygen concentration upon CO_2 production in plant tissue. On the right side of the arrow, increasing oxygen supply increases respiration because of stimulated Krebs cycle activity, yet anaerobic CO_2 release from pyruvate and accompanying ethanol release become insignificant in this region of the curve due to indirect inhibition effects of oxygen on glycolysis. At the left of the arrow, oxygen concentration is low enough to allow a very rapid breakdown of sugars to ethanol and CO_2.

A recognition of the Pasteur effect has some practical importance in fruit storage, especially with apples. Here the object in storage is to prevent extensive sugar loss during over-ripening. This is done by carefully decreasing the oxygen to the point (often 3–5 percent O_2) where aerobic respiration is at a minimum, but where sugar breakdown by anaerobic processes is not stimulated. Additional carbon dioxide is also added to the air, and the temperature is lowered, which further prevent over-ripening. As discussed in Chapter 21, carbon dioxide inhibits action of a fruit-ripening hormone, ethylene, and this seems to be at least one explanation for its effectiveness.

15.9.3 Temperature

For most plant species and even for individual tissues, the Q_{10} for respiration between 5° and 25°C, is usually near 2.0 to 2.5. With further increase in temperature up to 30° and 35°C, the respiration rate increases, but less rapidly, so that the Q_{10} begins to decrease. A possible explanation for the decrease is that the rate of O_2 penetration into the tissue begins to limit respiration at these higher temperatures where chemical reactions could otherwise still proceed rapidly. Diffusion of O_2 and CO_2 are also stimulated by increased temperature, but the Q_{10} for these physical processes is less than for the chemical reactions of respiration.

With further rise in temperature, respiration is actually decreased, especially if the plants are maintained under such conditions for long periods. Apparently the required enzymes begin to be denatured at a rapid rate, thus preventing a continued stimulation of metabolism. With pea seedlings it was found that, although increasing the temperature from 25° to 45°C initially caused a much more rapid respiration, within about two hours the rate was less than before. Perhaps some time was required to decrease the amounts of active enzymes below the necessary levels.

A further complicating effect of temperature is on the equilibrium between starch and sugars. As noted in Chapter 12, cooling potato tubers to just above freezing converts some of their starch to sugar. With acorns, a similar conversion of fats to sugars occurs. This effect allows a greater respiration under cool conditions than would be expected, since the high sugar content causes a more rapid CO_2 release.

The actual range of temperature at which respiration occurs in various plants is surprisingly large. For example, some thermophilic bacteria and algae exist in hot springs at temperatures of 60°C and above. Even at atmospheric pressures, the upper limit for active growth of such organisms is not known, since bacteria were found growing at the boiling point (above 90°C) in hot springs in Yellowstone National Park. At high pressures, growth has been observed at temperatures above 100°C. Certain bacteria apparently grow, although slowly, in ice cream at − 10°C, while respiration in conifer needles probably continues slowly under even colder conditions. We shall return to this topic in Chapter 28.

15.9.4 Injury, Mechanical Effects, and Disease

Wounding of plants usually causes a faster respiration, but the reason for this is not known. Even simply rubbing or bending leaves of several plants causes increases in their respiration, the increase varying from about 20 percent up to 180 percent. Severe wilting of leaves often also causes a more rapid respiration, although the effect is similarly unexplained. It was recently shown by Merrill Ross at Colorado State University that a wide variety of herbicides caused a rapid rise in respiration which decreased only as the plants approached death. In most cases the increased respiration ·was accompanied by increases in ATP, although, as expected, dinitrophenol caused decreased ATP levels. Again, their effects remain unexplained, but the results agree with the generalization that injury increases respiration.

Infection of plants by pathogens often increases respiration in and near the infected areas. For example, in wheat leaves infected by the rust-causing fungus *Puccinia graminis*, the rate was nearly three times as large as in uninfected leaves. In this and certain other cases there is an accompanying stimulation of growth and dry-matter production. It was suggested that a more rapid utilization of ATP in growth processes caused larger amounts of available ADP for electron transport reactions, thus stimulating O_2 absorption. There is evidence that the pentose phosphate pathway is more active in certain diseased plants, which would probably account for at least part of the increased respiration. Exactly how the pathogens involved are able to cause such alterations in metabolism is not understood.

15.9.5 Light

In green tissues light sometimes influences respiration. Inhibitory effects on the oxidation of pyruvate have been noted by various researchers, suggesting that where light interferes with respiration the effect might be due to decreased Krebs cycle activity. Other researchers, however, have found that light·did not interfere with the Krebs cycle, so the mechanism is still uncertain.

Occasionally, stimulations by light have been noted. At least some of these results may be indirect, due to increased sugar levels caused by photosynthesis. In addition, light appears to cause increases in glycolic acid formation in chloroplasts. A more rapid oxidation of this compound was reported to increase CO_2 release and oxygen absorption.

In any case, if light influences respiration, accurate measurement of photosynthesis becomes very difficult, since in photosynthesis measurements, values of gas exchange are usually corrected by subtracting respiration values measured in the dark. This is based on the assumption that light does *not* influence respiration, an assumption that has long troubled plant physiologists.

15.9.6 Type and Age of Plant

Because there are large morphological differences among members of the plant kingdom, it is to be expected that differences in metabolism also exist. In general, bacteria and fungi respire considerably more rapidly than do higher plants. Various organs or tissues of higher plants also exhibit large variations in rates. Table 15-1 lists some of the measurements obtained for several species and plant parts. One reason that bacteria and fungi have so much higher Q_{O_2}

TABLE 15-1

RESPIRATION RATES OF VARIOUS ORGANISMS

Organism	Temp (°C)	$\mu l\ O_2$/g dry wt/hr
Azotobacter chröococcum	22	2,000,000
Escherichia coli	40	200,000
Micrococcus luteus	35	15,000
Chlorella pyrenoidosa	25	350 to 1,500
Ulva lactuca	25	810
Neurospora crassa (mycelium)	30	24,000 to 43,000
bakers yeast	28	400 to 800
Neurospora tetrasperma (dormant spores)	25	250 to 590
barley *(Hordeum vulgare)* (dry grain)	22	0.05
barley *(Hordeum vulgare)* (roots)	20	4,840 to 7,400
Arum maculatum (spadix)	30	15,600 to 31,800

		$\mu l\ O_2$/g fresh wt/hr
barley *(Hordeum vulgare)* (roots)	20	960 to 1,480
barley *(Hordeum vulgare)* (leaves)	23	266
carrot *(Daucus carota)* (root)	25	25 to 30
carrot *(Daucus carota)* (young leaves)	25?	1,133
carrot *(Daucus carota)* (mature leaves)	25?	439
Verbascum thapsus (leaves)	23	382
Verbascum thapsus (sepals)	23	747
Verbascum thapsus (petals)	23	177
Verbascum thapsus (stamens)	23	761
Verbascum thapsus (pistils)	23	815
Xanthium strumarium (cocklebur) (half grown leaves)	28	350

Data for *Xanthium* leaves are from unpublished experiments of C. Ross. *Verbascum* data were compiled by W. Stiles and W. Leach, *Respiration in Plants*, Methuen and Co., London, 4th edition, 1960, p. 38. Other data were compiled by D. Goddard and W. Bonner, in *Plant Physiology*, F. Steward, ed. Academic Press, New York, Vol. 1A, 1960, p. 213.

values than higher plants, based on dry weight, is that they contain only small amounts of stored food reserves and have no nonmetabolic woody cells. Similarly, root tips and other regions containing meristematic cells with large protoplasm contents have high respiratory rates expressed on a dry weight basis. If comparisons are made on a protein basis, these differences are smaller. Dormant seeds and spores have the lowest rates, but here the effect is not entirely due to low protoplasmic contents. Rather, certain changes in the protoplasm, such as desiccation, limit the metabolism.

Several interesting studies have been made to determine the respiration of various cells in young roots. Such roots have provided good material for measurements of activity in very young meristematic cells, in growing and differentiating cells, and in mature cells. Several small sections, perhaps only one millimeter in length, are cut, starting at the tip. Respiration rates are measured on groups of sections, sometimes with a Cartesian diver, and the values are plotted as a function of distance from the tip, as in Fig. 15-11. Many such measurements were made by W. A. Jensen at the University of California, and the results were then related to data from careful chemical analyses and microscopical observations of the tissues involved (Chapter 22).

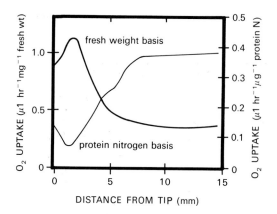

Figure 15-11

Respiration of corn roots at various distances from the root tips. Mitoses occurred between 0.7 and 2.2 mm; elongation was maximal at 4 to 5 mm and ceased at 9 mm. (Data of D. Goddard and W. Bonner, 1960. In F. C. Steward (ed.), *Plant Physiology*, Vol. 1A, Academic Press, New York, pp. 214–215. Used by permission.)

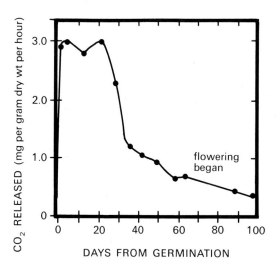

Figure 15-12

Respiration of whole sunflower plants from germination until maturity. The rate gradually declined after the twenty-second day, even though the rate for individual parts, such as inflorescences, increased for a time after that. (Drawn from data of F. Kidd et al., 1921, *Proc. Roy. Soc. Lond. B.* 92:368.)

When oxygen consumption was expressed as a function of fresh weight (heavier line) a maximum was seen in the region of most active cell division close to the apex. However, when comparisons were made on the basis of O_2 uptake per amount of protein, quite the reverse picture occurred. A minimum was found where meristematic activity was highest, followed by a rise to the point near which cell elongation ceased. The explanation for this is apparently that in the youngest cells the mitochondria are not well developed, although the cells are high in protein. As mitochondria become functional in the growing cells, the respiratory rate increases and finally reaches a maximum as the cells reach their final size. Here, therefore, is a clear-cut example of respiration being partly independent of protein content, because the mitochondria are not entirely functional in the youngest cells. It is also quite likely that the rate of synthetic reactions which require ATP in the growing cells influences respiration, because the turnover of ATP to ADP and Pi during energy-dependent growth processes should facilitate mitochondrial electron transport and oxygen uptake.

The age of intact plants influences their respiration to a large degree. As the plant becomes older the rate per unit weight decreases. Figure 15-12 shows how the Q_{CO_2} changed in sunflower plants from germination until after flowering. The curve is extrapolated from zero time to show the common initial large burst in respiratory activity as the dry seed germinates.

Changes in respiration also occur during the development of ripening fruits. In all fruits the respiration rate is very high when they are young, while the cells are still rapidly dividing. The rate then gradually declines, even if the fruits are picked. In many species, however, of which the apple is a good example, the gradual decrease in respiration is reversed by a sharp increase, known as the **climacteric rise**. The

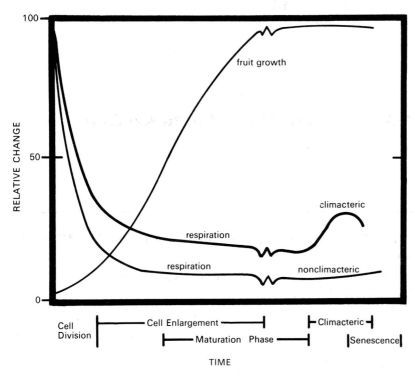

Figure 15-13

Stages in development and maturation of fruits that undergo the climacteric respiration increase and of those that do not. Discontinuities in the lines indicate that the time scale was changed to show differences in development rates of different fruits. The growth pattern may be single or double sigmoid (see Chapter 19). (From J. Biale, 1964, "Growth, maturation and senescence in fruits," *Science* 146:880. Used by permission. Copyright 1964 by the American Association for the Advancement of Science.)

climacteric usually coincides with full ripeness and flavor of the fruits, and its appearance is hastened by traces of ethylene, known to stimulate fruit ripening. Further storage is accompanied by senescence and decreases in respiration, which would approach zero in the absence of attack by microorganisms.

Some fruits do not show the climacteric rise, including the citrus fruits, grapes, pineapple, and strawberry. Grapefruits, oranges, and lemons are allowed to ripen·on the trees, and, if removed sooner, their respiration simply continues at a gradually decreasing rate. Figure 15-13 illustrates the respiration changes in species showing the climacteric rise and in those in which it is absent, in relation to their growth and development.

The chemical basis for the climacteric respiratory rise is not yet clear, but it is currently being actively investigated.

16

Metabolism and Functions of Nitrogen and Sulfur

It gradually became apparent in the first half of the 19th century that most plants obtained their nitrogen from the soil, rather than from the atmosphere. The work of T. DeSaussure and the French scientific farmer J. Boussingault did most to further this correct concept. Their ideas eventually prevailed over those of the famous German chemist J. von Liebig, who thought there was sufficient ammonia in the air to support plant growth. Since then, advances in chemistry have explained the important roles of nitrogen in plants. The forms of nitrogen available to plants have been discovered, and great progress has been made regarding the kinds of nitrogen compounds present in plants, their functions, and the way in which they are synthesized and broken down.

Although many plants contain only 1 or 2 percent nitrogen on a dry weight basis (Chapter 10), this element is found in amounts exceeded only by carbon, oxygen, and hydrogen. Most of the nitrogen exists in proteins and amino acids, which themselves usually contain 12–19 percent nitrogen, but the element is also present in a vast number of other plant constituents. The functions and metabolism of nitrogen compounds will be discussed in the present chapter. Because of the importance of the sulfur-containing amino acids in proteins, sulfur metabolism will also be emphasized here.

16.1 AVAILABLE SOURCES OF NITROGEN

16.1.1 Geochemistry of Nitrogen

The nitrogen molecule, N_2, is believed to contain a triple bond. It might be expected that because of this the gas would be rather reactive, but instead, nitrogen molecules are quite stable. Most of the earth's nitrogen is in the atmosphere, where it accounts for 78 percent of the molecules present, yet it is energetically difficult for living organisms to obtain it directly for their use. Although nitrogen is absorbed along with CO_2 through stomates, enzymes are present to reduce only the CO_2. The soil itself contains only small amounts of nitrogen, and most of this is present as part of organic compounds produced from decaying organisms. Sedimentary rocks often contain nitrogen, much of which is held in the lattice structure of the silicate minerals as ammonium ions, but the amounts of nitrogen present are very small. Igneous rock contains even less nitrogen.

At the Rothamstead Agriculture Experiment Station, in England, where careful records have been kept for many years, it was found that rain carries about 2.6 lb per acre per year of nitrogen as nitrate and ammonia into the soil. The amount precipitated is closely related to the annual rainfall in various locations, being considerably less in desert regions. Atmospheric nitrate is believed to arise from a combination of gaseous nitrogen and oxygen caused by lightning or by ultraviolet radiation. Atmospheric ammonia arises from volcanic activity, from the industrial burning of organic matter, especially coal, and from forest fires.

Traces of nitrogen compounds may be carried to the land from ocean sprays by wind. It has been clearly demonstrated that significant amounts of chloride are transported hundreds of miles inland in this way. However, although the oceans contain dissolved nitrogen compounds, most of these are in deep water, while the plankton keep most of the surface nitrogen assimilated. The actual importance of wind acting on ocean sprays to provide nitrogen for growing crops is thus believed to be much less than other effects.

16.1.2 Nitrogen Compounds of the Soil

Most of the soil nitrogen occurs as decaying microbial, plant, and animal matter, but the majority of it is insoluble and, therefore, not immediately available for plant use. Several soils contain small but detectable amounts of various amino acids, the origin of which is probably from the action of microorganisms on decaying organic matter and from excretion by living roots. Many studies have been performed to determine if such amino acids can be absorbed and metabolized by plants. The results seem to vary among different plant species, but perhaps a general conclusion is that all plants can absorb amino acids to some extent. Amino acids are usually less effective nitrogen sources than are inorganic forms.

The first organic nitrogen compound to be studied as a nitrogen source for higher plants was probably urea:

$$H_2N-\underset{\underset{O}{\|}}{C}-NH_2$$

This compound is usually rapidly absorbed and metabolized, and at least some plants can use it as the sole source of nitrogen. Urea is widely and successfully used as an agricultural fertilizer.

The absorption and utilization of more complex organic nitrogen compounds, such as the pyrimidines, purines, and even soluble proteins, have been demonstrated. However, the importance of these compounds to plant nutrition is almost certainly minor and, in fact, the dissolved amounts in soils are largely unknown.

By far the most effective nitrogen sources for most plants are the inorganic ions nitrate and ammonium. Most plants absorb both ions rapidly, but nitrate is usually the preferred source. Exceptions that grow better on ammonium salts are known, including the potato, pineapple, *Chenopodium album* (lambs-quarter), and young cereals such as rice, wheat, corn, oats, and rye. Surprisingly, however, as the cereals studied became older, their ability to use nitrate increased so that, when mature, they often responded better to this ion than to ammonium.

One complication encountered when comparing the ability of plants to utilize nitrate and ammonium ions is the effect of pH. Various researchers found sugar beets to prefer ammonium salts to nitrate, while another reported that although this was true at a nutrient solution pH of 7, the reverse occurred at pH 5. Many workers have concluded that plants use ammonium better under neutral or slightly alkaline conditions than at lower pH values, while nitrates are taken up fastest from slightly acid media.

16.2 UTILIZATION OF ATMOSPHERIC NITROGEN

Certain nitrogen deficient plants absorb ammonia from an atmosphere containing low concentrations of this gas, their yellow-green leaves soon becoming a healthy darker green color. In fact, Liebig used his great prestige to convince other scientists that atmospheric ammonia was the main source of nitrogen for plants. However, the atmosphere contains only traces of ammonia, and the relatively few species of plants able to obtain nitrogen from the air must thus depend on N_2.

The conversion of atmospheric nitrogen into organic compounds by living organisms is called **nitrogen fixation**. This process is carried out by microorganisms, including the free-living bacteria, the blue-green algae, and bacteria associated in a symbiotic condition with plant roots, especially legumes.

The over-all equation for nitrogen fixation may be represented as in (R16-1).

$$N_2 + 8 H^+ + 6 \text{ electrons} \longrightarrow 2 NH_4^+ \quad (R16\text{-}1)$$

Although the ammonium ions are usually rapidly converted to organic forms of nitrogen, they represent the first important stable product of the fixation process.

16.2.1 Classification of Nitrogen Fixing Organisms

16.2.1A Free-living bacteria Free-living bacteria fixing nitrogen may be classified according to the source of energy they require, and they may be either aerobic or anaerobic.

Heterotrophic forms require an external supply of reduced carbon, which they then oxidize, using the electrons obtained to reduce nitrogen. The first organism conclusively shown to fix nitrogen was the anaerobe *Clostridium pasteurianum*. The work was carried out by S. Winogradsky, in 1893. Since then, several other species of *Clostridium* were found to do this. These species are almost universally distributed in soil, grow rapidly, and are probably among the most important nitrogen fixing bacteria known. Well-known aerobic heterotrophic nitrogen fixers include members of the genus *Azotobacter*.

Autotrophic bacteria usually obtain the necessary electrons photosynthetically. In fact, all photosynthetic bacteria examined can fix nitrogen. A well-studied example is *Rhodospirillum rubrum*, in which the electrons arise directly from reduced ferredoxin. Here the energy of light is used to raise the electrons, not from water but from certain organic acids, to their energy level in reduced ferredoxin.[1]

16.2.1B Blue-green algae The blue-green algae are the most important organisms in maintaining an adequate nitrogen supply in rice fields of Asiatic countries. At least nine genera include nitrogen fixers, the best known being members of the genera *Anabaena*, *Nostoc*, and *Oscillatoria*. These organisms usually are free-living but sometimes form symbiotic associations with fungi to produce a plant structure unlike either partner, a **lichen**. Although many lichens are associations between fungi and the green algae, blue-green algae also participate, and some of these fix nitrogen. It is probable that, in all blue-green algae, light acting on the photosynthetic pigments provides the necessary energy to split water, the electrons then being used to reduce either CO_2 or N_2.

16.2.1C Bacteria in root nodules Root nodules capable of nitrogen fixation are well known in the legume family and also occur in species of at least ten other genera. About 10 percent of the 12,000 or more species in the Leguminosae have been examined for nitrogen fixation, and approximately 90 percent of these were found to possess this ability. The non-legumes of importance are primarily trees and shrubs, and include members of the genera *Alnus* (alder), *Myrica* (such as *M. gale*, the bog myrtle),

---

[1] In photosynthetic bacteria, molecular hydrogen is released in the light, especially if nitrogen is not being fixed. In the absence of sufficient nitrogen, the electrons from ferredoxin are united with hydrogen ions to form molecular hydrogen, a reaction catalyzed by a hydrogenase enzyme.

Shepherdia, Coriaria, Hippophae, Ceanothus, Elaeagnus, and *Casaurina.*

It was recognized at least 2,000 years ago that legume crops fertilized the soil if plowed under as a green manure, but it was not until 1888 that the German chemists H. Hellriegel and H. Wilfarth stated that root nodules were induced by bacteria, and that these nodules were the active centers of nitrogen fixation. A specific bacterial species, a member of the genus *Rhizobium,* is usually effective only on one species of legume, and sometimes only on a particular variety of a species. They are aerobic organisms that can persist saprophytically in the soil until they infect a root hair or a damaged epidermal cell. Within the root hair the bacteria are surrounded by a thread-like structure produced by the plant called the **infection thread** (Fig. 16-1). The infection thread has, by electron microscopy, proved to consist, in part, of the greatly infolded plasmalemma of the cell being invaded. The bacteria multiply extensively inside the thread. The infection thread extends inwardly and penetrates into the cortex and, less commonly, even to the pericycle. Here the bacteria are released into the cytoplasm and apparently produce a stimulus causing some of the cortex or pericyle cells (especially tetraploid cells) to divide. These divisions lead to a proliferation of tissues, eventually forming a mature nodule made up of tetraploid cells filled with bacteria and extending outside the root, as shown in Fig. 16-1. The bacteria usually occur in the cytoplasm in groups, each group being present together inside a membrane sheath. The enlarged, nonmotile bacteria in the membranes are referred to as **bacteroids.**

Nitrogen fixation occurs near the center of the nodule in cells largely filled with bacteroids. The legume provides the bacteria with carbohydrate materials they can oxidize, the electrons obtained being used by the bacteria to reduce nitrogen to ammonium ions. The latter can then be converted into other nitrogenous compounds, part of which are absorbed by the surrounding plant cells and translocated to other regions of the plant. Thus, the plant benefits from the nitrogen provided by the bacteria, while the bacteria require the supply of carbohydrate and probably also other unknown compounds from the plant. Part of the nitrogen-containing compounds are excreted into the soil where they are often beneficial to surrounding plants of other species.

16.2.2 The Mechanism of Nitrogen Fixation

Healthy legume nodules are usually pink or reddish. H. Kubo showed, in 1939, that the color is due to the presence of a hemoglobin, one of a group of pigments previously believed to occur only in animals. Later, A. Virtanen and coworkers named this compound **leghemoglobin** to distinguish it from other hemoglobins. Similar compounds are found in several non-legumes but are not present in bacteria and blue-green algae capable of fixing nitrogen.

The function of hemoglobin in nitrogen fixation is unknown. It is not a part of the necessary bacterial cells, but it is believed by some to participate actively in the electron transport process. Iron is essential for fixation, and it occurs in hemoglobin. A role for this pigment could then account for the iron requirement. It has been suggested that N_2 combines directly with the hemoglobin as the first step in the reduction process, but of course this cannot occur in the free-living bacteria and algae where hemoglobin is absent.

Molybdenum and cobalt are also essential micronutrients needed for nitrogen fixation. Cobalt is necessary because it is an essential part of **vitamin B_{12}**, a compound possibly involved in the production of leghemoglobin in root nodules. Cobalt is not essential to legumes given nitrate or ammonium forms of nitrogen. The function of molybdenum has not been clarified, but it probably exists as a co-

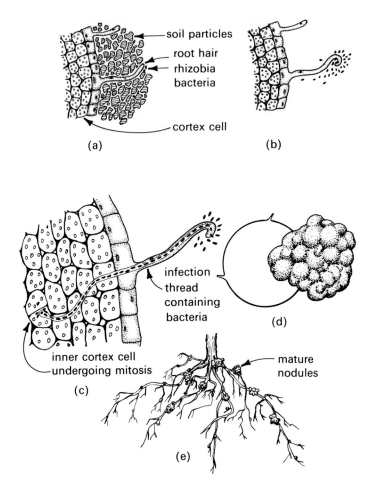

Figure 16-1

Stages in the formation of a root nodule on legumes. Substances are presumably released from root hairs which stimulate *Rhizobia* to divide (a to b). Bacteria somehow enter root hairs and cause the plasmalemma to infold and extend intracellularly and intercellularly across the cortex, accompanied by further bacterial multiplication inside the infection thread thus formed (c). Bacteria are released by a process involving pinching off the end of the infection thread (D. Goodchild and F. Bergersen, 1966, *J. Bacteriol.* 92:204) and stimulate tetraploid cortical or pericycle cells to divide rapidly. An extensive hyperplasia occurs (cross section of root in (d) is indicated by a line), resulting in formation of mature nodules (e).

enzyme and undergoes alternate oxidation and reduction as electrons are carried from some donor to nitrogen, eventually forming ammonia.

The intermediate reactions and compounds involved in nitrogen fixation have not all been determined. The best information available at present is from studies of the anaerobic bacterium *Clostridium pasteurianum*, where even cell extracts can rapidly carry out the process if fortified with certain compounds. An electron donor, such as pyruvic acid, must be present. Ferredoxin and ATP are also essential, although

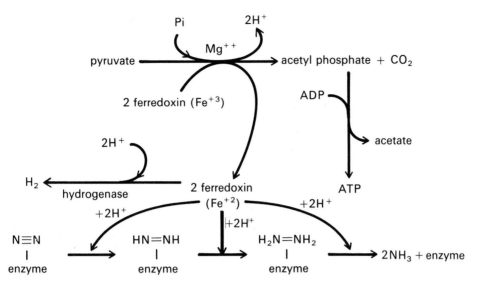

Figure 16-2

A postulated sequence for electron transfer during nitrogen fixation in *Clostridium pasteurianum*. (Modified after R. Burris, 1965. In J. Bonner and J. Varner (eds.), *Plant Biochemistry*, Academic Press, New York, p. 978.) The role of ATP is still uncertain. It might aid in the function of the nitrogenase enzyme or in the formation of acetyl phosphate.

the role of ATP is probably indirect. Oxidation of pyruvate by this bacterium provides ATP, and in addition, electrons that are transferred to ferredoxin. From ferredoxin, electrons are added to the nitrogen-reducing enzyme, **nitrogenase**, and then to nitrogen, finally producing ammonium ions. The electrons can also be added to hydrogen ions, thus accounting for some of the hydrogen gas released from anaerobic soils.

For other nitrogen-fixing organisms, the electron source may be different from ferredoxin, and we do not yet know whether this protein is always involved. Until 1965 no fixation could be observed in cell-free extracts prepared from root nodules, but this has now been accomplished by F. J. Bergersen in Australia and by Burton Koch, Harold Evans, and Sterling Russell at Oregon State University, using soybeans. Bacteroids appear to be the active fixing agents in the extracts. A tentative scheme

for fixation in the absence of hemoglobin proposed by R. H. Burris and his colleagues at the University of Wisconsin is outlined in a modified form in Fig. 16-2.

16.3 ASSIMILATION OF NITRATE AND AMMONIA

16.3.1 Reduction of Nitrate Ions

After nitrate is absorbed by plant roots, it may be directly transported to the shoot, moving along with the transpiration stream through the xylem. Often, however, only small quantities of nitrates are detected in the xylem exudate collected from excised stems. Only traces of ammonium ions also occur. Instead, most of the nitrogen provided to the shoots by the roots is present in an organic form. A great variety of amino acids, including several not present in proteins, has been reported in the many plants investigated. Aspartic and glutamic acids, and their amides, asparagine and glutamine, are often the most abundant forms.

There are certain plants, however, including cotton and various grasses and woody species, that do have appreciable amounts of nitrates in the xylem stream. Even plants that normally do not translocate much nitrate do so if provided with excessive amounts in the soil, or if the roots are kept cold. Under these conditions the reduction of nitrate in the roots cannot keep pace with the transport process. Reduction will then occur in the leaves and stems, taking place at rapid rates under high light intensities and warm temperatures.

16.3.1A The reduction process

The general form of the reaction may be described as in (R16-2).

$$HNO_3 + 8 \text{ electrons} + 9H^+ \longrightarrow$$
$$NH_4^+ + 3H_2O \quad (R16\text{-}2)$$

The oxidation number of nitrogen changes from $+5$ to -3, the electrons being provided from reducing agents found in the cells. Since most of the oxidation and reduction changes occurring in living organisms proceed by an addition of one or two electrons at a time, this suggests that nitrate reduction occurs by a number of separate reactions, most likely four.

16.3.1B Enzymes of nitrate reduction

A well-known enzyme from microorganisms called **nitrate reductase** catalyzes the formation of nitrite ions from nitrate, an addition of two electrons to the nitrogen atom. This enzyme is a flavoprotein, containing FAD as a tightly bound prosthetic group. In plant roots the same or a similar enzyme reacts with NADH, or less often, with NADPH, the FAD of the enzyme becoming converted to $FADH_2$. The $FADH_2$ is then probably oxidized by transfer of electrons to molybdenum ions, which are also an essential part of the enzyme, and from molybdenum they are finally transported to nitrate, as shown in (R16-3).

Many plants grown entirely with ammonium salts or with organic forms of nitrogen lack any detectable nitrate reductase. When nitrate is provided, however, they then rapidly produce this enzyme and utilize nitrate. This is an example of an **adaptive** or **induced enzyme**, one which is synthesized only when its normal substrate is provided. These enzymes are numerous in microorganisms, and others are also known in higher plants (Chapter 20).

The nitrite ions are next reduced by nitrite reductases, flavoprotein enzymes that can use reduced ferredoxin, NADH, or NADPH as electron donors. Ferredoxin is the most important direct source of electrons for nitrite reduction in leaves, but the occurrence and importance of this enzyme in roots is not yet clear. Nitrite reductases do not require molybdenum but may contain copper and iron. The copper probably undergoes alternate reduction and oxidation and is believed by some to transfer electrons from the flavin to nitrite. There is evidence that nitrite reduction requires ATP, but the reason for this is not yet known.

The immediate product of nitrite reductase action is presently in doubt. It is certainly a very reactive compound that is quickly reduced further, and it probably remains bound to an enzyme. Thus, it is difficult to isolate, and the

$$\begin{array}{ccccc} \text{NADH or NADPH} + H^+ \\ \text{NAD or NADP} \end{array} \Big) \quad \Big(\begin{array}{c} \text{FAD} \\ \text{FADH}_2 \end{array} \Big) \quad \Big| \begin{array}{c} 2 \uparrow H^+ \\ 2Mo^{+5} \\ 2Mo^{+6} \end{array} \Big(\begin{array}{c} 2H^+ + NO_3^- \\ NO_2^- + H_2O \end{array} \qquad (R16\text{-}3)$$

further steps leading to ammonium formation remain to be clarified. It was formerly thought that free hydroxylamine (NH_2OH) was the immediate precursor of ammonium, but more recent evidence indicates that all intermediates between nitrite and ammonium are enzyme bound.

Some plants appear to have very little nitrite reductase activity; so the uptake of nitrate from the soil leads to an accumulation both of nitrate and, to a lesser extent, of nitrite. Although nitrate is not toxic to plants, nitrite is injurious to both plants and animals. Livestock eating vegetation high in nitrite are occasionally poisoned, apparently because this ion interferes with the oxygen-transporting ability of hemoglobin.

16.3.1C Relation to respiration and photosynthesis

A close relationship exists between plant respiration and the reduction of nitrate and nitrite, probably because respiration normally provides the NADH or NADPH needed for ammonia synthesis—perhaps also because the ATP believed necessary for nitrite reduction is formed as plants respire. When respiration occurs in the dark, reduction of nitrates sometimes stimulates CO_2 production. This is probably because the reduction process quickly converts the reduced pyridine nucleotides back to the oxidized forms, and they can then again participate in respiration, causing a greater release of CO_2.

Production of ammonium ions from nitrate is greatly stimulated by light in green leaves and stems. As described in Chapter 13, this is because light causes the chlorophyll-dependent formation of $FADH_2$, NADPH (or perhaps NADH), and reduced ferredoxin, using electrons from water. A "**photosynthetic nitrite reductase**" that uses the electrons from reduced ferredoxin occurs in various plants, while a "**photosynthetic nitrate reductase**" system that transfers electrons from NADH or NADPH to FMN via ferredoxin, and from the resulting $FMNH_2$ to nitrate exists in leaves of spinach and probably in other species. Figure 16-3 summarizes the relationship of nitrate reduction to respiration and photosynthesis.

16.3.2 Conversion of Ammonia into Organic Compounds

Whether ammonium ions are absorbed from the soil or are produced in roots, leaves, or stems from nitrate, they do not accumulate in the plant. Ammonium is, in fact, somewhat toxic to plants, perhaps because it inhibits the production of ATP in the mitochondrial and photosynthetic electron transport systems. There appear to be three major ports of entry for conversion of ammonium into organic compounds.

16.3.2A Formation of glutamic acid

The principal use of ammonium is probably in a reaction synthesizing glutamic acid from α-ketoglutaric acid, as in (R16-4).

The reaction is reversible and is physiologically important in respiration of amino acids formed during protein breakdown. The necessary enzyme is named **glutamic acid dehydrogenase**.

$$\begin{array}{c} COOH \\ | \\ C{=}O \\ | \\ CH_2 \\ | \\ CH_2 \\ | \\ COOH \end{array} + NH_4{}^+ + NADH \rightleftharpoons \begin{array}{c} COOH \\ | \\ H{-}C{-}NH_2 \\ | \\ CH_2 \\ | \\ CH_2 \\ | \\ COOH \end{array} + NAD^+ + H_2O \qquad (R16\text{-}4)$$

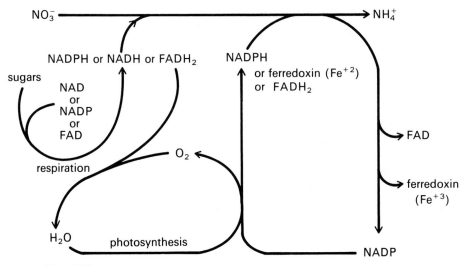

Figure 16-3

Dependence of nitrate reduction upon photosynthesis or respiration. Reduction in chloroplasts can proceed using reducing power supplied only by photosynthesis, while reduction elsewhere in cells probably proceeds using reducing power arising mainly from respiration.

It seems to occur primarily in the mitochondria where a supply of NADH and α-ketoglutaric acid allows its effectiveness. Glutamic dehydrogenase of animals and microorganisms contains zinc in a rather firmly bound form, and we may presume that the plant enzyme also depends upon this element for catalytic activity.

16.3.2B Glutamine synthesis In this reaction, previously mentioned in Chapter 11, glutamic acid and ammonium ions are combined to form glutamine. The reaction is dependent on ATP and, therefore, also upon magnesium or manganese ions. The necessary enzyme is called **glutamine synthetase** [see (R16-5)].

Glutamine is an important storage form of nitrogen in plants; storage organs, such as potato tubers and the roots of beet, carrot, radish, and turnip, are especially rich in this amide. In old leaves, glutamine is often formed as proteins are broken down and ammonium ions are released. Glutamine formation here probably performs an important function in keeping toxic levels of ammonium from accumulating. Asparagine probably plays a similar role, and an enzyme converting aspartic acid

$$
\begin{array}{l}
\text{COOH} \\
\mid \\
\text{H}-\text{C}-\text{NH}_2 + \text{NH}_4{}^+ + \text{ATP} \overset{Mg^{++}}{\rightleftharpoons} \\
\mid \\
\text{CH}_2 \\
\mid \\
\text{CH}_2 \\
\mid \\
\text{COOH}
\end{array}
$$

$$
\begin{array}{l}
\text{COOH} \\
\mid \\
\text{H}-\text{C}-\text{NH}_2 + \text{ADP} + \text{Pi} + \text{H}^+ \\
\mid \\
\text{CH}_2 \\
\mid \\
\text{CH}_2 \\
\mid \\
\text{C}-\text{NH}_2 \\
\parallel \\
\text{O} \qquad \text{glutamine}
\end{array}
$$

(R16-5)

and ammonium ions to asparagine (similar to glutamine synthetase) has been sought, but without success. It is possible that plants might synthesize asparagine from aspartic acid using glutamine as the amide nitrogen donor, similar to a reaction discovered in 1966 in chick embryos.

The amide group of glutamine and asparagine can also be utilized via transfer reactions in the synthesis of purines and of the amino group of cytosine. In addition, since the reaction above catalyzed by glutamine synthetase is reversible, it probably allows some ATP synthesis from ADP and Pi.

16.3.2C Carbamyl phosphate synthesis

An essential process for all living organisms is the formation of nucleic acids. Present in nucleic acids are nucleotides, some of which contain the pyrimidines **cytosine**, **uracil**, and **thymine**. The importance of uracil was also evident in Chapter 12, where functions of uridine triphosphate and uridine diphosphoglucose were discussed. The initial step in pyrimidine formation is the synthesis of carbamyl phosphate as indicated in (R16-6).

$$NH_4^+ + CO_2 + ATP \rightleftharpoons$$

$$H_2N-\underset{\underset{O}{\|}}{C}-OPO_3H_2 + ADP + H^+ \quad (R16\text{-}6)$$

Carbamyl phosphate is also essential to the formation of the amino acid arginine.

Three different enzymes catalyzing carbamyl phosphate synthesis are known to exist in various organisms. One of these was found in mung bean seedlings, and a different one occurs in mushrooms,[2] but which enzyme is most important in higher plants is unknown.

---

[2] The mushroom enzyme utilizes the amide nitrogen of glutamine as the source of the amino group of carbamyl phosphate.

A few other reactions are also known in nature that require ammonium ions. Most of these have not yet been studied in plants, and their importance is surely less than that of the three processes above.

16.4 SYNTHESIS OF OTHER AMINO ACIDS

When ammonium ions containing isotopic ^{15}N are fed to plants or excised plant parts, both glutamic and aspartic acids become rapidly labeled, as detected with a mass spectrograph. It might be suspected that a reaction exists for synthesis of aspartic acid similar to that for glutamate mentioned above, but this is not true. It appears that the amino group of aspartate, and perhaps of all other amino acids, arises ultimately from glutamate. In the following discussion of amino acid synthesis, the reader should refer frequently to the structures of the amino acids shown in Chapter 11, Table 11-1.

16.4.1 Transamination Reactions

Glutamate transfers its amino group directly to a variety of α-keto acids in **transamination** reactions. The best known example of transamination occurs between glutamate and oxaloacetate, producing α-ketoglutarate and aspartate as in (R16-7).

This transamination is reversible. Similar reversible reactions are known, and several amino acids other than glutamate transfer their amino groups to other α-keto acids. In one series of experiments glutamate provided the amino group for the production of 17 different amino acids.

Transaminase enzymes require **pyridoxal phosphate** as a coenzyme. Pyridoxal phosphate is a derivative of vitamin B_6, one form of which is pyridoxal itself. Since transaminase reactions probably occur in all living cells, this explains a primary function for this vitamin in animals. In plants, pyridoxal phosphate is also a coenzyme in a further reaction of glutamic acid, its de-carboxylation to **γ-amino butyric acid**. The latter is an amino acid of common occurrence in plants, although it is not found in proteins.

16.4.2 Further Reactions of Glutamate

Besides its direct role in glutamine synthesis and its importance in donating the amino group for several amino acids, glutamate provides the carbon skeletons for the amino acids proline, hydroxyproline, and **ornithine**. Although tentative pathways for forming these amino acids have been proposed and some reactions clearly demonstrated in microorganisms, more research is needed with higher plants to confirm these.

Ornithine is an amino acid not found in proteins, although it is probably of universal occurrence in plants. It reacts with carbamyl phosphate to produce another nonprotein amino acid, **citrulline**, which is then indirectly converted to arginine [see (R16-8)].

These same reactions occur in animals in the synthesis of urea and arginine, but plants form urea only in trace amounts and not as a waste product of nitrogen metabolism.

16.4.3 Synthesis of Glycine and Serine

It is believed that glycolic acid synthesized in the Calvin–Benson photosynthetic cycle is oxidized to glyoxylic acid (Chapter 15) and that glycine arises from the glyoxylate by transamination as in (R16-9).

$$CH_2OH-COOH \xrightarrow[-H_2O_2]{+O_2} CHO-COOH \xrightarrow{\text{transamination}}$$

$$H_2NCH_2-COOH \quad\quad (R16\text{-}9)$$

Synthesis of serine in higher plants occurs primarily from glycine, but an additional carbon atom is needed. Extensive work at the University of Alberta in Canada by E. A. Cossins and S. K. Sinha indicates that this carbon arises directly

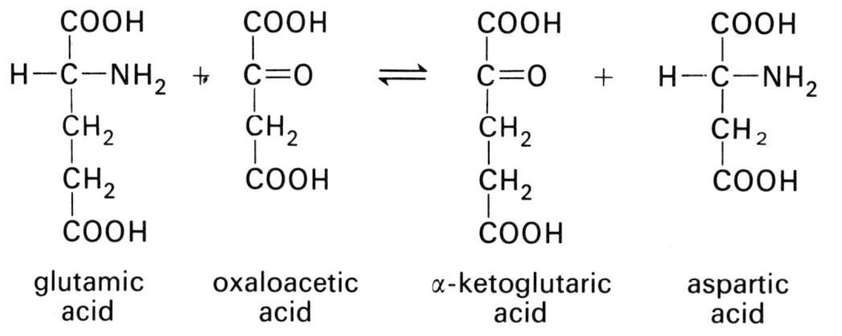

(R16-7)

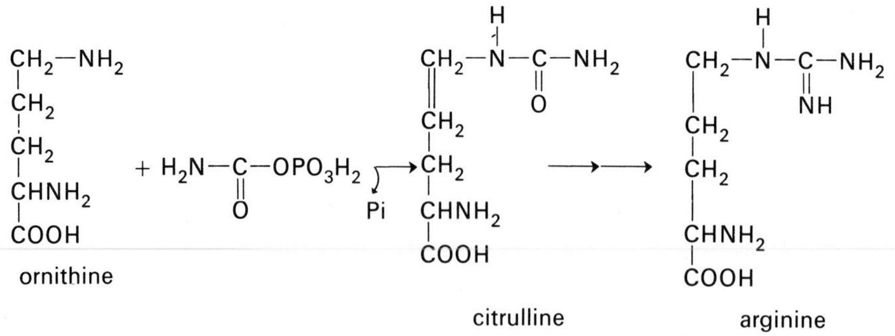

(R16-8)

from a formaldehyde group of a **tetrahydrofolic acid (THFA) coenzyme**, which in turn derives the formaldehyde from glyoxylic acid. The reactions shown in (R16-10) may then account for serine synthesis.

Enzymes that convert phosphoglyceric acid to glycerate, glycerate to hydroxypyruvate, and hydroxypyruvate to serine by transamination occur in higher plants and in green algae, but this pathway for serine production appears to be important only in the algae.

16.4.4 Amino Acids Derived from Aspartate

Tracer studies indicate that aspartic acid gives rise to two other amino acids, **homoserine** and threonine. A suspicion exists, based on work with bacteria, fungi, and algae, that lysine generally arises from aspartic acid and pyruvic acid, but the complete reaction sequence has not yet been definitely established.

16.4.5 Alanine Synthesis

A wide variety of amino acids transfer their amino groups to pyruvic acid, forming alanine. Glutamic acid is probably one of the most important of these.

16.4.6 Formation of Aromatic and Other Amino Acids

The way in which tyrosine and phenylalanine are synthesized will be discussed in Chapter 18. Erythrose-4-phosphate and phosphoenolpyruvate appear to provide the necessary carbon atoms. With the exception of leucine and perhaps the sulfur-containing amino acids, pathways of formation have not been well established for most other amino acids in plants.

16.4.7 Sulfur-containing Amino Acids

Sulfur is probably first converted into organic combination by incorporation into cysteine. A pyridoxal phosphate-dependent enzyme capable of synthesizing cysteine from serine and H_2S occurs in microorganisms and in spinach leaves, and there is evidence for its presence in beet roots. Microbes also contain an enzyme catalyzing a similar reaction converting homoserine and H_2S to **homocysteine** as in (R16-11).

Hydrogen sulfide itself is not a suitable source of inorganic sulfur for plants. Instead, the absorbed sulfate ions must be reduced to the sulfide level of oxidation, as described later.

Methionine is likely produced from homocysteine and the methyl group of a folic acid

$$\text{glycolate} \longrightarrow \text{glyoxylate} \longrightarrow \text{glycine} \rightleftarrows \underset{\text{serine}}{HOCH_2-\underset{\underset{NH_2}{|}}{CH}-COOH} \qquad \text{(R16-10)}$$

$$\searrow \rightarrow THFA-CH_2OH$$
$$CO_2$$

(a) $H_2S + HOCH_2-\underset{\underset{NH_2}{|}}{CH}-COOH \longrightarrow HS-CH_2-\underset{\underset{NH_2}{|}}{CH}-COOH + H_2O$
serine   cysteine   (R16-11)

(b) $H_2S + HOCH_2-CH_2-\underset{\underset{NH_2}{|}}{CH}-COOH \longrightarrow HS-CH_2-CH_2-\underset{\underset{NH_2}{|}}{CH}-COOH + H_2O$
homoserine   homocysteine

coenzyme. Homocysteine itself may arise either as described above or by another known reaction [see (R16-12)] involving sulfhydryl transfer from cysteine.

16.5 REDUCTION OF SULFATE IONS

Except for traces of sulfur dioxide absorbed by plants growing near industrial smokestacks, sulfate ions absorbed by the roots provide the necessary sulfur for plant growth. Just as the reduction of nitrate and carbon dioxide are energy-dependent reduction processes, so is the conversion [shown in (R16-13)] of sulfate to sulfide.

$$SO_4^= + 8 \text{ electrons} + 8H^+ \longrightarrow$$
$$S^= + 4H_2O \qquad (R16\text{-}13)$$

Although roots apparently have the ability to reduce sufficient sulfate to provide the sulfide for their own needs, they do not translocate appreciable amounts of reduced sulfur forms to the shoots. (This is in contrast to the reduction of nitrate, which occurs readily in the roots of some species and less readily in their

shoots.) Almost no information has yet appeared regarding the chemical reactions of sulfate absorption and reduction in roots. A few studies of the process have been performed with leaves, in which light stimulates the rate of sulfate reduction, apparently by providing electrons taken from water (Chapter 14). Most of our information about sulfate reduction has come from experiments with microorganisms, especially yeast and bacteria. The limited information available suggests that the mechanism is similar in higher plants.

The first reaction occurring after absorption of sulfate is its reaction with ATP, producing **adenosine-5′-phosphosulfate**[3] and pyrophosphate as in (R16-14).

The pyrophosphate is probably rapidly split into $H_2PO_4^-$ by a pyrophosphatase enzyme, while adenosine phosphosulfate then reacts with another molecule of ATP. The

---

[3] The prime signs in compounds of this type refer to the numbering of the ribose unit rather than to the adenine ring, which may also be numbered.

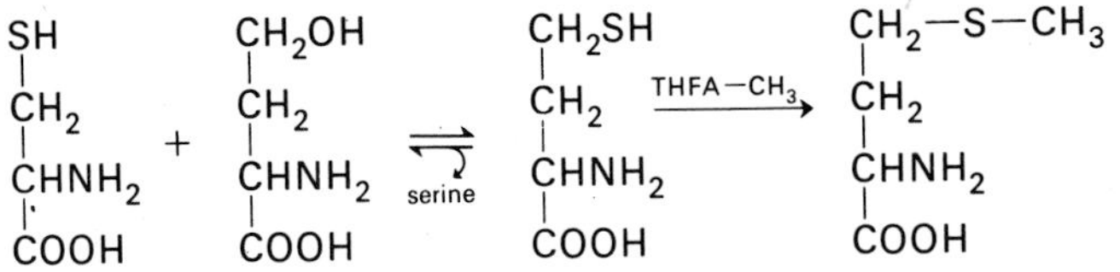

$$(R16\text{-}12)$$

cysteine   homoserine   homocysteine   methionine

$$ATP + SO_4^= \rightleftharpoons$$

$$(R16\text{-}14)$$

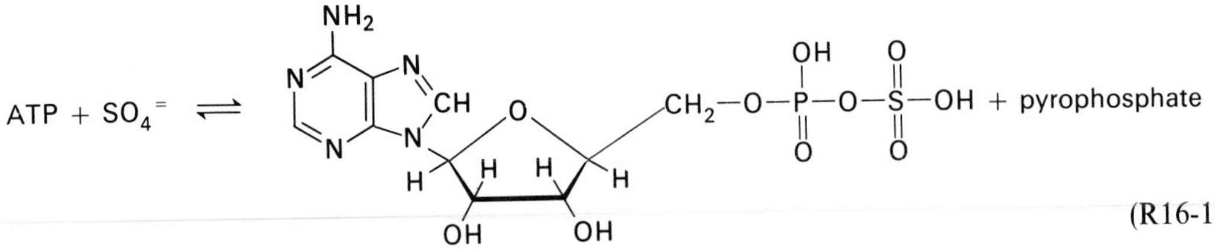

adenosine-5′-phosphosulfate

products are now ADP and **3'-phosphoadenosine-5'-phosphosulfate** (abbreviated **PAPS**) [see (R16-15)].

The sulfate in the PAPS molecule may be considered to be in an activated form, and reduction can now occur. The source of the electrons in illuminated green leaves is still in doubt. Neither NADH nor NADPH are direct electron donors in spinach chloroplasts. Perhaps either reduced ferredoxin or a reduced flavin nucleotide plays this role. In any case, the stimulation of sulfate reduction in leaves by light indicates that the ultimate source of electrons is water. Perhaps NADH or NADPH participate in the sulfate metabolism of roots.

Upon reduction of PAPS, sulfite ions ($SO_3^=$) may be split out of the molecule. The leaves and stems of several plants contain small amounts of sulfite, and chloroplasts possess enzymes capable of reducing sulfite directly to sulfide. However, evidence of R. Bandurski and his colleagues at Michigan State University indicates that free sulfite may never be a product of sulfate reduction. Instead, it is probably bound to an enzyme upon which it is reduced, and all sulfur intermediates between sulfite and sulfide are apparently similarly bound. It may be remembered that all intermediates of nitrite reduction are probably also held to enzymes until ammonium ions are finally released. The electron donor for conversion of sulfite to

sulfide has not been established. The resulting sulfide reacts with serine to form cysteine, as described above, and perhaps with homoserine to produce homocysteine. Figure 16-4 briefly summarizes probable reactions converting the sulfur of sulfate into cysteine and methionine.

16.6 MISCELLANEOUS NITROGEN AND SULFUR COMPOUNDS

16.6.1 The Alkaloids

Many plants, especially members of the Solanaceae family, contain compounds that appear to have no important function in those species producing them. These compounds are organic molecules containing nitrogen, which is usually present in a heterocyclic ring, and are called **alkaloids**. The nitrogen present will act as a base, since it has the ability to accept hydrogen ions, just as it does in amino acids. Thus, most solutions of alkaloids are usually slightly basic, as their name indicates. Most alkaloids are white crystalline compounds and are only slightly water soluble.

Approximately 3,000 alkaloids have been found in some 4,000 species of plants; many plants apparently do not produce most of these molecules. The first alkaloid to be isolated and crystallized was the drug **morphine**, found over 150 years ago in the opium poppy, *Papaver*

adenosine-5'-phosphosulfate + ATP $\longrightarrow$ ADP +

(R16-15)

3'- phosphoadenosine-5'-phosphosulfate

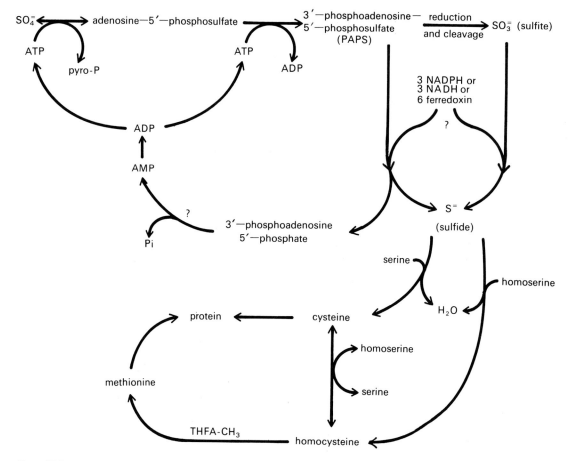

Figure 16-4

A tentative pathway for conversion of sulfate to cysteine and methionine. The sulfur in PAPS presumably can be reduced directly to sulfide in a series of reactions involving a still uncertain electron donor. It can also be reduced to sulfite, after which the latter is split out and itself reduced to sulfide. The sulfide can be converted either to cysteine or to homocysteine, which then accepts a methyl group from a tetrahydrofolic acid coenzyme to produce methionine.

somniferum. Other well-known alkaloids include **nicotine**, present in cultivated varieties of tobacco (*Nicotiana tabacum*); **anabasine**, the principal alkaloid of wild tobacco (*Nicotiana glauca*); **quinine**, from cuprea bark; **caffeine**, from coffee beans and tea leaves; **strychnine**, from the seeds of *Strychnos nuxvomica*; **theobromine**, from cocoa beans; **atropine**, from the poisonous black nightshade (*Atropa belladonna*); and **colchicine**, from *Colchicum byzantinum*. The structures of several alkaloids are shown in Fig. 16-5.

Many other alkaloids have far more complex chemical structures than either nicotine or caffeine. They are often synthesized only in plant shoots, but nicotine appears to be produced only in the roots of tobacco. The chemical reactions involved in formation of alkaloids are largely unknown, although the precursor com-

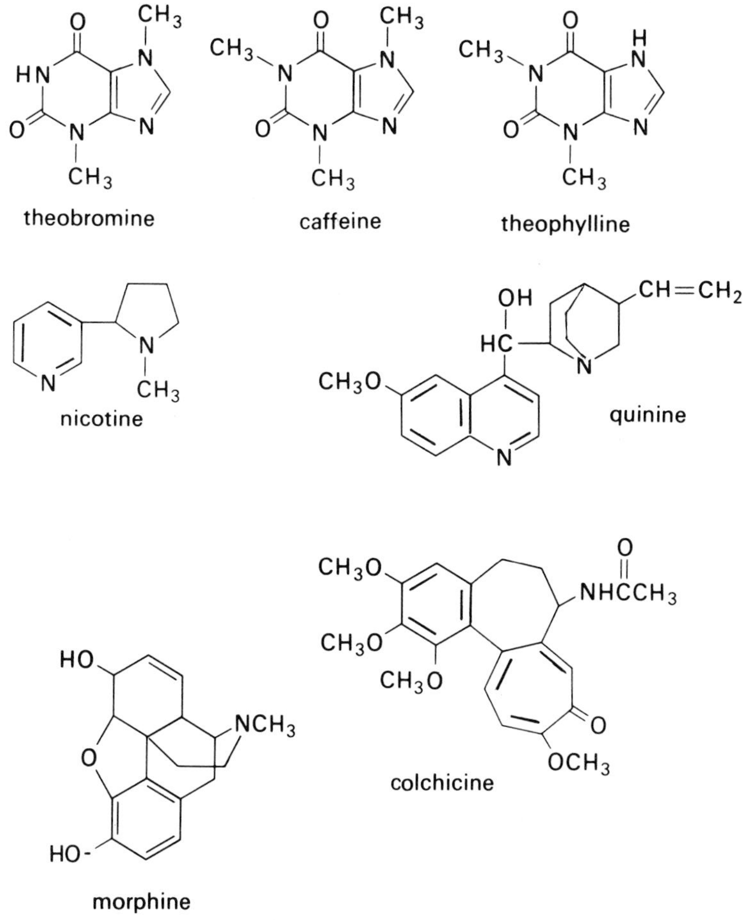

Figure 16-5
Alkaloid structures.

pounds providing the carbon skeletons and nitrogen atoms of a few have been established. Synthesis of nicotine has received greatest attention, probably because of its commercial importance. Nicotinic acid (niacin), present in NAD and NADP molecules, is a precursor of nicotine. The nitrogen and carbon atoms of nicotinic acid, in turn, arise from a product obtained when aspartic acid and 3-phospho-glyceraldehyde are combined. Other amino acids are precursors of various alkaloids, tryptophan probably providing several of the atoms of quinine; phenylalanine, of colchicine; lysine, of anabasine; and tryrosine, of morphine. Very few of the thousands of enzymes that must be necessary for production of the various alkaloids have been demonstrated in the plant kingdom. Furthermore, one author recently speculated that there are tens of thousands of new alkaloids yet to be discovered in plants.

The physiological role of most alkaloids is unknown, and it has been suggested that they perform no important metabolic function, being merely by-products of other, more important pathways. Yet it is conceivable that they could be of ecological importance, providing some survival value to the plant. Plants containing such toxic substances might be avoided by grazing animals and leaf-feeding insects, for example.

16.6.2 Urea and Ureides

Although animals excrete excess nitrogen compounds largely in the form of urea, plants are much more conservative with their nitrogen. It is true that certain amino acids and other small nitrogenous molecules leak out of plant roots, but urea probably does not. In fact, urea is only occasionally found in plants, and then only in trace quantities.

Urea can be readily metabolized by plants, however, and it is not only an important soil-applied fertilizer, but it is also becoming important as a foliage spray for certain crops. The manner in which plants metabolize urea is not certain, although it is probably hydrolyzed by the enzyme **urease** to two molecules of ammonia and one molecule of carbon dioxide. The ammonia could then be metabolized according to previously discussed reactions.

Certain compounds containing a urea unit, the **ureides**, exist in plants. Citrulline, mentioned previously, is an excellent example of a common plant ureide, and it is an important form in which nitrogen is translocated in certain woody plants, especially members of the birch (Betulaceae) family. **Allantoin**, another ureide, and the closely related **allantoic** acid, are major transportable compounds of nitrogen in various maple (*Acer*) and other species.

Two other ureides should be mentioned, because they are essential intermediates in the pathways of breakdown of the pyrimidines thymine and uracil found in the nucleic acids (to be discussed further). These are **β-ureidoisobutyric acid** and **β-ureidopropionic acid**, formed from thymine and uracil, respectively. It is suspected that allantoin and allantoic acid are formed during the breakdown of adenine. The structures of these ureides are given in Fig. 16-6.

16.6.3 Nitriles or Organic Cyanides

Nitriles are organic compounds containing a —CN group. Such compounds are usually present in small amounts, but they are widely distributed in the plant kingdom. Most nitriles are **glycosides**, in which a sugar (usually glucose) is combined to the remaining nonsugar portion of the molecule. The structure of **prunasin**, found in various species of the genus *Prunus*, is typical of plant nitriles:

prunasin

The products of enzymatic hydrolysis of the glycosidic nitriles are an aldehyde (benzaldehyde, with prunasin), a sugar, and HCN. HCN is not usually found in plants, but cyanide poisoning of livestock sometimes occurs when the animals eat leaves of plants such as chokecherry (*Prunus virginiana*). HCN is probably formed as the leaves are chewed, the consequent injury to the plant cells releasing the enzymes capable of breaking down nitriles.

16.6.4 Miscellaneous Sulfur Compounds

Some plants contain appreciable amounts of sulfur in compounds other than the sulfur

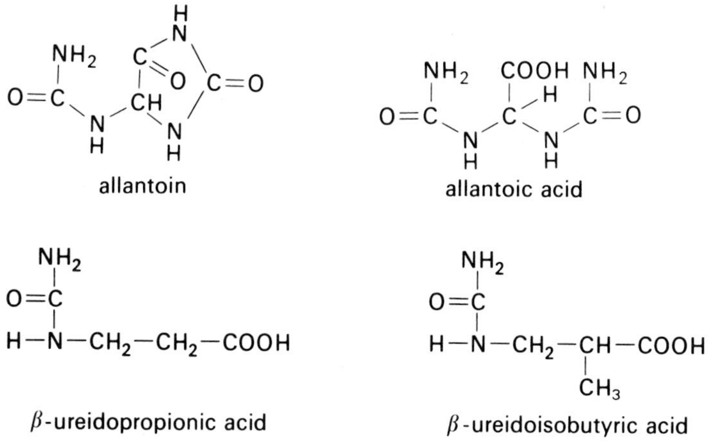

Figure 16-6

Structures of ureides found in plants.

amino acids and the coenzymes thiamine, biotin, and coenzyme *A*. Most of these compounds are volatile and have offensive odors. The structures include the simple **mercaptans** such as methyl mercaptan

$$CH_3—SH$$

found in radish roots and *n*-propylmercaptan of onions; **sulfides**

$$R—S—R$$

and **disulfides**

$$R—S—S—R$$

produced by onions; **polysulfides**

$$RS_nR$$

present in garlic oil; **sulfoxides**

$$R—\underset{\underset{O}{\|}}{S}—R$$

also found in garlic oil; and **methyl sulfoniun compounds**

$$(CH_3)_2—\overset{+}{S}—R$$

Many of the sulfides and disulfides produced by onions do not normally occur in the tissues but are enzymatically produced from other molecules when the cells are injured.

Important sulfonium compounds include **S-methyl methionine** and **S-adenosyl methionine**. The sulfonium compounds are positively charged, analogous to ammonium compounds. Their primary function is in the transfer of their methyl groups to other compounds, including various alkaloids, the lignins, and the pectins.

16.6.5 The Purines and Pyrimidines

Molecules containing **purines** and **pyrimidines** have previously been encountered in this book. ATP, ADP, AMP, ADPG, NAD, NADP, and *S*-adenosyl methionine, all important nucleotides, contain the purine adenine. A second purine-containing molecule, GDPG, was also mentioned previously as a glucose donor in cellulose synthesis. Uridine triphosphate (UTP),

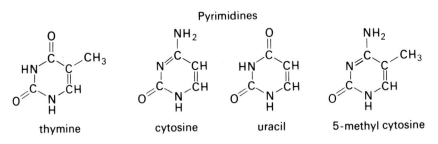

Figure 16-7

Structures of the most common purines and pyrimidines found in nucleic acids.

UDP, and UDPG are important pyrimidine-containing nucleotides previously mentioned.

In addition, three other pyrimidines are essential to plants because of their presence in nucleic acids. These are **cytosine**, **5-methyl cytosine**, and **thymine**. The structures of the more important plant purines and pyrimidines are indicated in Fig. 16-7.

Thymine and uracil can exist in either of two forms, the keto structure shown in Fig. 16-7, or with the hydrogen atoms formerly present on the nitrogen atoms shifted to the keto oxygens, forming hydroxyl groups, as indicated in (R16-16) for uracil. The keto form on the left

in (R16-16) is considered more stable but does not always predominate.

(R16-16)

The purines and pyrimidines are probably present in greatest quantities in the form of nucleotides bound as nucleic acids, ribonucleic acid (RNA) and deoxyribonucleic acid (DNA). The chemistry and functions of these compounds will be discussed in the next chapter.

17

Nucleic Acids, Proteins, and the Genetic Code

For many years biologists have been aware that hereditary characteristics are ultimately determined by chromosomes in the nucleus. As the functions and properties of enzymes were discovered, it became evident that these compounds play an important role in controlling cellular properties, and thus the activities, of organisms. It was not apparent, though, how chromosomes were able to influence the kinds or amounts of enzymes synthesized by the cell. This problem was of sufficient interest and importance that it was attacked by a large number of geneticists, physiologists, microbiologists, and biochemists, with the very rewarding results to be discussed in this chapter. The key to understanding the expression of hereditary properties was the discovery of the nature and function of various kinds of nucleic acids found in all living cells.

17.1 THE NUCLEIC ACIDS

Regardless of their names, the nucleic acids are not found exclusively in the nucleus. Both **ribonucleic acid (RNA)** and **deoxyribonucleic acid (DNA)** are distributed in nuclei, chloroplasts, and mitochondria, but not in the vacuoles.

DNA does occur principally in the nucleus, and although RNA is also present there and in chloroplasts and mitochondria, most of it occurs outside these organelles in the ground cytoplasm and attached to the endoplasmic reticulum.

Nuclear DNA is present in the chromosomes, associated with particular arginine- and lysine-rich proteins, the **histones**. DNA makes up the active part of the genes, the functional units controlling hereditary characteristics. Hereditary properties are determined by the kinds and activities of enzymes present, and these are dictated by "information" contained in the DNA held in the nucleus, but most of the cellular enzymes are synthesized and function completely outside the nucleus. Almost all of what is known about how the nucleus controls activities in the parts of the cell surrounding it has been obtained since 1960. A type of RNA has been discovered which carries the "genetic message" to other parts of the cell, where, with the help of two other kinds of RNA, it specifies the type of proteins to be synthesized. To understand how genetic information is stored and used to form the specific enzymes controlling cellular activities, it is first necessary to learn what nucleic acids are composed of and how they are formed.

17.1.1 Properties of the Nucleic Acids

Both DNA and RNA are made up of nucleotides containing the purines and pyrimidines listed below:

$$
\text{DNA} \left\{ \begin{array}{l} \text{adenine} \\ \text{guanine} \\ \text{thymine} \\ \text{cytosine} \\ \text{5-methyl cytosine} \end{array} \right. \qquad \text{RNA} \left\{ \begin{array}{l} \text{adenine} \\ \text{guanine} \\ \text{uracil} \\ \text{cytosine} \end{array} \right.
$$

DNA contains no uracil but does contain thymine and 5-methyl cytosine, which RNA lacks. A second difference between RNA and DNA is the sugar unit of the nucleotide; 2-deoxyribose is present in DNA, while ribose occurs in RNA.

Both nucleic acids contain phosphate attached to the sugar unit. In fact, each phosphate is esterified to two sugars, at the hydroxyl group of C-5 of one molecule and C-3 of the next. In this way, long chains of nucleotides are built up, the purine and pyrimidines not becoming part of the chains, but extending approximately at right angles to them, as shown in Fig. 17-1.

17.1.1A DNA
In the DNA of all organisms, except for a few bacterial viruses, the molecules exist in two chains, one attached to the other. These chains are held together by hydrogen bonds between the **bases** (the purines and pyrimidines). Figure 17-2 illustrates a model for part of the DNA molecule as it normally exists in a cell.

Each chain is coiled around the same long axis, while the bases of both chains lie in a plane perpendicular to this axis. The entire helix is nearly 20 Å in diameter, and, because the purines are larger than the pyrimidines, this diameter is thought to be always attained by hydrogen bonding between a purine of one chain and a pyrimidine of the other. Furthermore, because of differences in chemical struc-

tures, adenine can form stable hydrogen bonds only with thymine, while guanine must bond with cytosine or 5-methyl cytosine. The pairing of these bases is shown in Fig. 17-3. Note that guanine and cytosine are held by three hydrogen bonds, while adenine and thymine are held by only two. DNA molecules richer in guanine and cytosine are thus held together more strongly than those in which adenine and thymine are more abundant.

The helical structure of DNA shown in Fig. 17-2 was first suggested in 1953 by James Watson and Francis Crick. They were able to propose such a model because of three primary facts. *First*, many analyses had shown that the content of guanine in DNA is equal to the cytosine, while the content of adenine is equal to that of thymine. These analytical results are required by the proposed structure. Table 17-1 shows base composition data of DNA from a number of higher plants. Since they contain 5-methyl cytosine, which is genetically equivalent to cytosine, the guanine content is equal to the sum of these two. *Second*, x-ray diffraction studies of crystals of the sodium salt of DNA had been made by M. Wilkens, so Watson and Crick were able to interpret the resulting patterns of exposure on the films to construct their hypothetical model. *Third*, when DNA was titrated with bases or acids, the titration curves indicated that the amino groups of guanine, cytosine, and adenine were masked and were not able to accept a hydrogen ion. The interpretation is that hydrogen atoms of the amino groups are united to the keto oxygens, as shown in Fig. 17-3. For their brilliant work, Watson, Crick, and Wilkens shared the 1962 Nobel Prize in medicine and physiology.

The bases in any one chain may theoretically be arranged in many different ways. For example, three adenines may occur in succession, or an adenine, guanine, and cytosine, etc. Of course, once a given base occurs in a certain

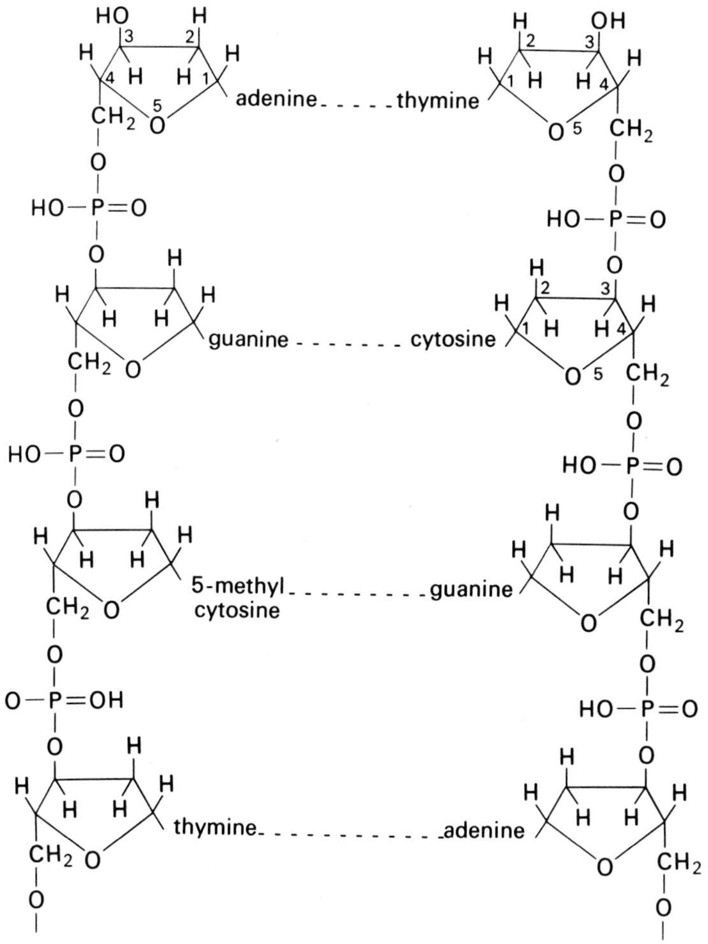

Figure 17-1

DNA chains built up of 2-deoxyribose and phosphate with purines and pyrimidines attached at right angles to the chain axes. Dotted lines indicate hydrogen bonds between purines and pyrimidines holding the two chains together.

position of one chain, the base in the complementary chain is determined because of the adenine-thymine, guanine-cytosine rules. The **genetic code** is contained in the **base sequence** of the DNA. As we shall see, there is evidence that three successive bases of DNA (a **triplet**) are a coding unit (**codon**) for an individual amino acid.

The amino acid sequence in a part of a protein containing 100 amino acids would be determined by a part of the DNA molecule containing 300 nucleotides (100 triplets).

The amount of DNA in individual cells of the same plant varies with the number of chromosomes present. Although many of the cells are

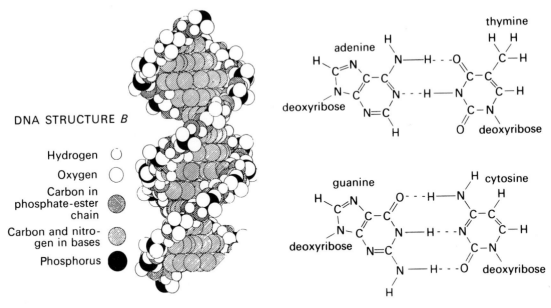

DNA STRUCTURE *B*

Hydrogen

Oxygen

Carbon in
phosphate-ester
chain

Carbon and nitro-
gen in bases

Phosphorus

Figure 17-2

Molecular model of part of a DNA molecule based on the
Watson–Crick theory. (From M. Feughelman et al., 1955,
Nature 175:834. Used by permission.)

Figure 17-3

Hydrogen bonding between purines and pyrimidines. Note
that the guanine-cytosine pair is held together by three such
bonds, while adenine and thymine are held by only two.

diploid, as expected, and have equal quantities of
DNA, **endomitosis** (doubling of chromosomes
without separation) is common in some species,
and the resulting polyploid cells have proportionally more DNA than do the diploid. There
are rather large differences among species in the
amount of DNA per cell. Table 17-2 lists
analyses of DNA and RNA in root tip cells of
several different species. Values between 10
and 100 picograms of DNA (1 picogram is equal
to 10^{-12} grams) per cell are usually observed,
and there is no consistent relation between
amount and chromosome number. For example, *Vicia faba* (12 chromosomes) has nearly
ten times as much DNA per cell as *Lupinus
albus* (48 chromosomes), and both are in the
Leguminosae family. That the major portion of
the DNA of many cells exists in the nucleus is
indicated by the fact that the mitochondria so

far investigated have only about 10^{-4} picograms
of DNA each, and chloroplasts about 5×10^{-3}
picograms.

The RNA contents of the root tip cells of the
species listed in Table 17-2 were generally two
to six times as high as the DNA contents, and
ratios at least as high as ten to one occur in cells
of certain other tissues of the plant.

17.1.1B RNA Three types of RNA involved
in protein synthesis are currently known to
exist, and a more recently discovered fourth
type may participate. One of these is a relatively small nucleic acid called **soluble RNA**
(abbreviated **sRNA**), because when biochemists
ground tissues in buffers and centrifuged the
homogenates this type of RNA was not centri-

TABLE 17-1

BASE COMPOSITION OF DNA FROM VARIOUS PLANTS

Plant	Mole percent				
	A	T	G	C	5-Methyl-C
Pisum sativum[a] (pea)	30.8	30.5	19.2	13.5	5.0
Pinus sibirica[b] (pine)	29.2	30.5	20.8	14.6	4.9
Glycine max[c] (soybean)	25.6	26.0	23.8	18.2	6.4
Phaseolus vulgaris[b] (bean)	29.7	29.6	20.6	14.9	5.2
Arachis hypogea[b] (peanut)	29.3	29.8	20.3	14.4	6.1
Triticum vulgare[b] (wheat)	25.6	26.0	23.8	18.2	6.4
Gossypium hirsutum[d] (cotton)	32.8	33.0	17.0	12.7	4.6
Nicotiana tabacum[e] (tobacco)	29.6	30.7	19.8	14.0	5.6

[a] Unpublished results of J. Rho, quoted by J. Bonner, in *Plant Biochemistry*, J. Bonner and J. Varner, eds. Academic Press, New York, 1965, p. 46.
[b] S. Uryson and A. Belozerski, *Dokl. Biochem. Sect.* (English Translation) 125:116, 1959.
[c] J. Ingle et al., *J. Mol. Biol.* 11:730, 1965.
[d] D. Ergle et al., *Plant Physiol.* 39:145, 1964, data for 12 other species of *Gossypium* are also given.
[e] J. Lyttleton and G. Peterson, *Biochim. Biophys. Acta* 80:391, 1964.

fuged out, but remained with other small soluble molecules of the supernatant liquid. Soluble RNA has more recently been called **transfer RNA**, since the majority of such molecules are now known to combine with and transfer amino acids to their proper positions during protein synthesis.

Transfer RNA molecules contain about 75 nucleotides and have molecular weights of about 25,000 to 30,000. At least 20 different kinds of transfer RNA molecules exist, one (or more) for each different amino acid occurring in proteins. In 1965, R. W. Holley and coworkers Cornell University, reported the complete sequence of nucleotides in an alanine transfer RNA from yeast. The nucleotide sequence of a few other transfer RNA molecules has been reported since, but those of other RNA and DNA molecules have not yet been established. The alanine transfer RNA, like other transfer RNA molecules, is partially double stranded as shown in Fig. 17-4, the single strand present being folded back upon itself.

A second type of RNA, **ribosomal RNA**, is closely associated with protein in small bodies called **ribosomes**. Ribosomes from pea stems are oblate spheroids, approximately 250 Å long and 160 Å wide. They are visible only in electron micrographs and are commonly attached to the endoplasmic reticulum, although they also exist in the cytoplasm unattached to any membranes (Fig. 17-5), especially in younger cells. They have also been seen in electron micrographs of nuclei and chloroplasts, and similar or identical bodies also exist in mitochondria. Roughly 80 percent of the total cellular RNA is contained in the ribosomes. In the pea stems, approximately 6,000 nucleotides are present in each ribosome, giving an RNA molecular weight of nearly two million. Plant ribosomes consist of about 40 percent RNA and 60 percent protein. They contain two subunits, each of which is made of both RNA and protein, and these subunits separate when the magnesium concentration is less than about $1 \times 10^{-3} M$. One subunit is about twice as large as the other. In fact, if the

TABLE 17-2

SPECIES MEANS FOR DNA, RNA, FRESH WEIGHT, AND NUCLEOLAR VOLUME OF CELLS FROM ROOT TIPS OF VARIOUS PLANTS[a]

Species	DNA per cell $(g \times 10^{-12})$	RNA per cell $(g \times 10^{-12})$	Fresh weight per cell $(g \times 10^{-9})$	Nucleolar volume (μ^3)
Allium cepa	65.6	131.1	21.1	21.3
Tulipa gesneriana	100.7	182.7	32.9	34.6
Scilla campanulata	89.9	139.2	31.0	16.7
Narcissus pseudonarcissus	64.9	117.6	24.8	26.9
Galtonia candicans	40.0	145.4	20.9	42.4
Agave attenuata	14.4	69.1	14.1	12.8
Lilium longiflorum	141.1	339.5	41.0	51.9
Phalaris minor	33.4	166.2	13.4	32.9
Phalaris coerulescens	21.4	134.2	10.0	21.4
Phalaris hybrid	32.0	195.6	15.0	31.0
Zea mays	30.2	181.5	16.1	29.4
Vicia faba	56.2	132.9	13.4	23.4

[a] From P. Martin, *Exptl. Cell Res.* 44:84, 1966.

magnesium level is lowered still further by chelating it with EDTA, each of these subunits is further broken down into still smaller particles. It is not certain how magnesium cements ribosomal subunits together, but such action is apparently an essential function of the element, since the intact but not the fragmented ribosomes are active in protein synthesis.

Ribosomes from many different organisms appear to be similar, although bacterial and chloroplast ribosomes (which appear to be extremely similar or perhaps even identical) are smaller than cytoplasmic ribosomes from plant or mammalian cells. When ribosomes function in protein synthesis, several are often agglomerated to form a structure called a **polysome** (Fig. 17-6). The RNA in ribosomes is apparently largely single stranded.

There is evidence that the factor holding individual ribosomes together in the polysome is a third type of RNA, **messenger RNA**. A messenger RNA molecule is a long, single-stranded one that carries the genetic message for synthesis of a particular enzyme from the gene

to the site of synthesis. The lengths of these molecules apparently depend upon the size of the protein, or occasionally upon the number of proteins, for which they contain genetic information.

The existence of messenger RNA molecules is not easy to prove. They have been most clearly established in microorganisms, and, less often, in animal tissues. Some direct evidence also exists that they are formed in plants. From other well-known similarities in the metabolism of widely different creatures, we feel confident that plant messenger RNA molecules indeed exist. Two properties usually found in messenger RNA have been demonstrated in plant RNA molecules separated by column chromatography or by ultracentrifugation. One of these is the characteristic of rapid synthesis and rapid breakdown, that is, a fast **turnover**. A rapid turnover rate is not an essential property of messenger RNA, however.

A second common property of messenger RNA is a base composition similar to the DNA of the organism in which it exists, with the

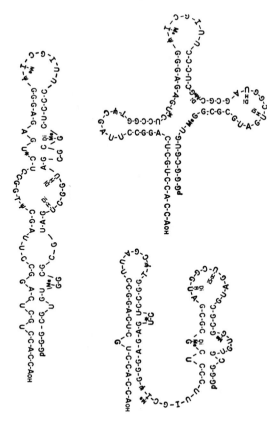

Figure 17-4

Proposed possible structures for alanine transfer RNA from yeast. Abbreviations: G = guanosine-3'-P; U = uridine-3'-P; A = adenosine-3'-P; C = cytidine-3'-P; ψ = pseudo-uridine-3'-P; DiHU = 5,6-dihydrouridine-3'-P; DiMeG = N²-dimethylguanosine-3'-P; I = inosine-3'-P; MeG = 1-methylguanosine-3'-P; MeI = 1-methylinosine-3'-P; T = thymine-ribose-3'-P; U* = mixture of U and DiHU. (From R. Holley et al., 1965, "Structure of a ribonucleic acid," *Science* 147 (March 19):1462. Copyright 1965 by the American Association for the Advancement of Science. Used by permission.)

exception that the content of RNA-uracil is close to that of the DNA-thymine. This similarity of composition is expected of a group of messenger RNA molecules which are synthesized by using statistically large amounts of the DNA of the genes as templates, and, as we shall see later, that is what occurs. To discover

whether cells have a type of RNA that satisfies this criterion, it is necessary to separate the various kinds of RNA present. This can be done (although not as completely as is desirable) by subjecting a nucleic acid mixture to chromatography upon a column of methylated albumin-kieselguhr or by polyacrylamide gel electrophoresis.

Figure 17-7 illustrates a separation of nucleic acids from soybean hypocotyls as performed at Purdue University by Joe Key and his colleagues. The nucleic acids in the eluates from the column are detected by measuring their absorbence (optical density) in a spectrophotometer at 260 nm, at which wavelength they absorb very strongly. The nucleic acids in each fraction are then degraded into their constituent nucleotides, and these are separated chromatographically and the amount of each is measured spectrophotometrically. In this way the base composition of all of the nucleic acids separated is determined. Only the fraction into which radioactive phosphate is incorporated most rapidly (the fraction synthesized fastest) has a base composition similar to that of the DNA. This fraction is shown in Fig. 17-7 only partly resolved from the heavy ribosomes. If it could be shown that these molecules indeed contain genetic information, as believed, their messenger function would be proved. To do this, it will be necessary to isolate from the cells enough of these hypothetical messengers so that they can be used to synthesize proteins in the absence of cells (*in vitro*). This has often been done using artificial, commercially synthesized RNA molecules, but not often with those from living cells.

A fourth type of RNA existing in pea seeds was discovered by James Bonner and his colleagues at the California Institute of Technology, in 1965. This RNA is a smaller molecule containing perhaps only 40 nucleotides. It has not yet been named, and has so far been found only in nuclei, where it is attached at one end by a covalent bond to the histone. This RNA-histone

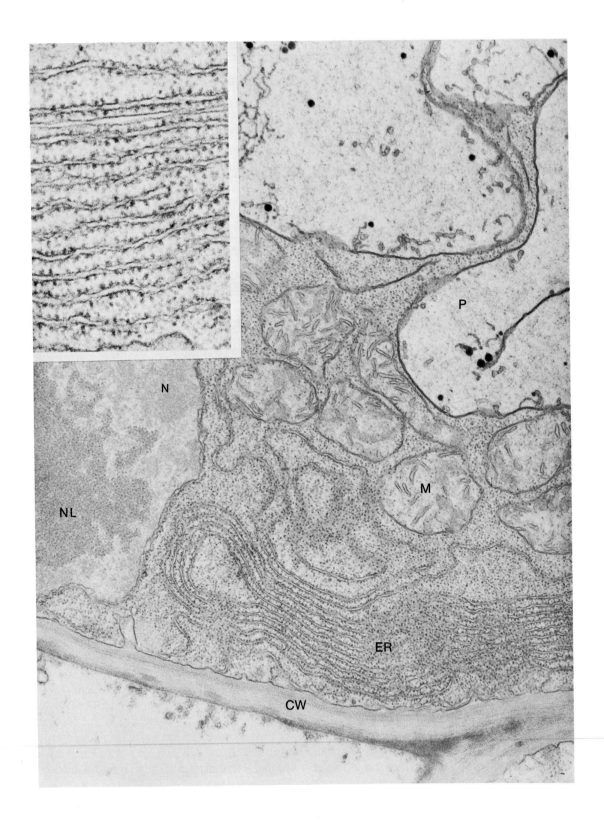

compound may control whether or not genes are able to express themselves, probably by combining with the DNA and preventing its acting as a template for messenger RNA synthesis. This topic of gene control will be further discussed in Chapter 20.

17.1.2 Synthesis of Nucleic Acids

17.1.2A DNA Just before mitosis, during interphase and early prophase, the DNA content is doubled. (The histone is at least approximately doubled at this time, too, apparently in the nucleolus, followed by its transfer to the DNA.) Enzymes capable of synthesizing DNA have been found in microorganisms, animal cells, and plant cells. All of these require the deoxynucleotide triphosphates of adenine, thymine, guanine, and cytosine (or 5-methyl-cytosine), magnesium or manganese ions, and a portion of a DNA molecule to act as a template. When these materials are mixed with the enzymes *in vitro*, appreciable amounts of DNA are synthesized. Pyrophosphate is split out of each added nucleotide as in (R 17-1).

$$\text{4 deoxynucleotide triphosphates} \xrightarrow[\text{DNA template}]{\text{Enzyme, Mg}^{++}}$$

$$\text{DNA} + \text{4 pyrophosphate } (P_2O_7^{-4}) \quad \text{(R17-1)}$$

The necessary enzymes are called DNA polymerases, and the first of these was discovered by Arthur Kornberg of Stanford University, in 1956. For this and other biochemical contributions, Kornberg shared the 1959 Nobel Prize in medicine and physiology with Severo Ochoa. Ochoa, in 1955, had found an enzyme capable of synthesizing RNA, as discussed

further below. The reaction catalyzed by DNA polymerase is reversible; yet we know that DNA of the chromosomes does not undergo a rapid turnover. It is assumed that DNA synthesis is made irreversible by a phosphatase that destroys pyrophosphate as rapidly as it is produced.

The DNA resulting from DNA polymerase action has a base composition similar or identical to the DNA template molecule added to initiate the reaction. This suggests a mechanism for replication, because such results would be obtained if each new DNA strand were built up on one of the two original template strands, and if new hydrogen-bonded base pairs were formed between an adenine of the template strand and thymine of the new strand, etc. This process is illustrated in Fig. 17-8.

17.1.2B RNA synthesis At least two enzymes capable of forming RNA are known. The first is Ochoa's **polynucleotide phosphorylase**, which uses the nucleotide diphosphates of adenine, uracil, cytosine, and guanine, splitting out inorganic orthophosphate, Pi. A molecule of either DNA or RNA "primes" the reaction but does not act as a template, for the RNA product has a composition not dependent upon the composition of the "primer," but upon the relative concentrations of ADP, CDP, GDP, and UDP added. The reaction is easily reversible, so that in the presence of Pi the enzyme will degrade RNA.

Because polynucleotide phosphorylase does not form template-directed RNA molecules, and since the reaction is easily reversible, it is thought not to be important in RNA synthesis in cells. Instead, another more recently discovered enzyme, called **RNA polymerase**, has the desired

---

Figure 17-5

Electron micrograph of a pea root meristematic cell showing nucleus (N), nucleolus (NL), mitochondria (M), proplastid (P), cell wall (CW), endoplasmic reticulum (ER) with attached ribosomes, and free ribosomes scattered throughout the ground cytoplasm. Insert shows higher magnification of part of the endoplasmic reticulum to illustrate ribosomes in greater clarity. (Reprinted by permission of The Rockefeller University Press from G. B. Bouck, 1963, *J. Cell Biol.* 18:441).

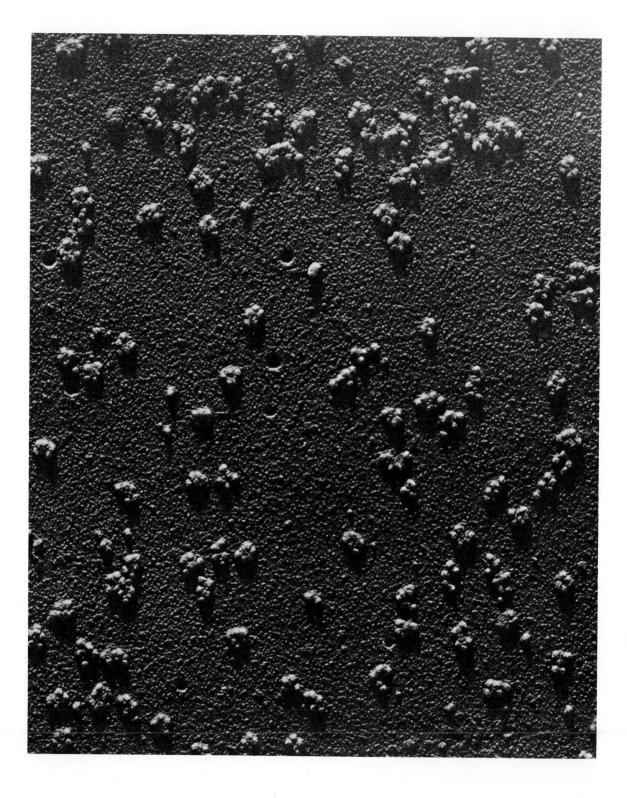

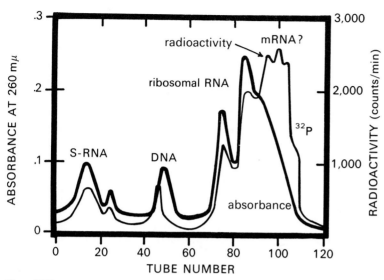

Figure 17-7

Separation of nucleic acids from soybean hypocotyls by chromatography of a methylated albumin-kieselguhr (MAK) column. The solid heavy line represents absorbance and is a measure of nucleic acids present in the various fractions (tubes), while the light line indicates ^{32}P present in each fraction. The fraction at the right, believed to be messenger RNA, is highly radioactive, although little RNA is present (low absorbance), indicating a rapid metabolic turnover. In addition, this fraction also has a base composition similar to that of the DNA of this plant. The DNA fraction probably also contains small amounts of RNA. (From J. Key, 1966, *Plant Physiol.* 41:1257. Used by permission.)

qualities. This enzyme catalyzes a synthesis of RNA using the nucleotide triphosphates (ATP, UTP, CTP, and GTP). A priming template of DNA is required, and the RNA product reflects its base composition, the RNA uracil being equal to DNA-adenine, adenine equal to thymine, cytosine to guanine, and guanine to cytosine (or 5-methyl-cytosine) of the DNA [see (R 17-2)].

$$4 \text{ nucleotide triphosphates} \xrightarrow[\text{DNA template}]{\text{enzyme, Mg}^{++} \text{ or Mn}^{++}}$$

$$\text{RNA} + 4 \text{ pyrophosphate} \quad (R17\text{-}2)$$

It is likely that all types of RNA are formed in this way, using the DNA of the genes (and probably also chloroplast and mitochondrial DNA) as the templates. Most of the RNA synthesis occurring at any given instant, however, is of the messenger variety. Messenger RNA formation is very rapid, but because these molecules are usually also degraded rapidly, they never reach a high concentration in the cells. Ribosomal and transfer RNA molecules are also formed using small segments of the long strands of chromosomal DNA as templates, and their base compositions are not as similar to that of

Figure 17-6

Polysomes (polyribosomes) from rabbit reticulocytes (magnified 100,000 diameters). (From A. Rich, 1963, *Scientific American* 209 (December):44–53. Used by permission.)

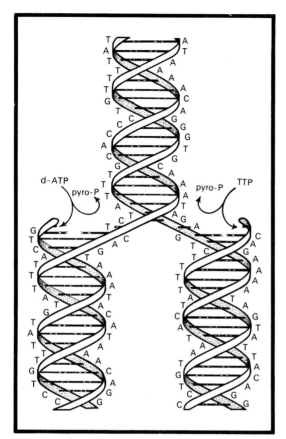

Figure 17-8

Model illustrating a way in which DNA replication might occur. Hydrogen bonds presumably break between complementary bases of opposite DNA strands. At the same time, DNA polymerase adds a new nucleotide from available deoxynucleotide triphosphates (d-ATP and TTP above) onto new growing strands. Pyrophosphate (pyro-P) is split out from the triphosphate. Each new nucleotide added must contain a base (A = adenine, T = thymine, C = cytosine, G = guanine) complementary to the base in the parent strand to form a new, stable double helix. By this method of replication, two helices identical to the original are formed.

Only one strand of the DNA helix is used as a coding template for messenger RNA synthesis in microorganisms. This is probably true for all cells; otherwise there could exist two messenger RNA molecules that would themselves be complementary and able to form hydrogen bonds and stable double helices. Figure 17-9 outlines a suggested way in which the DNA might temporarily uncoil, allowing an RNA strand to be produced on one of the separated DNA strands. The conversion of genetic information present in a sequence of bases in DNA to a sequence of bases in RNA constitutes what is commonly called **transcription** of the genetic code.

RNA synthesis is potently inhibited by the antibiotic, **actinomycin D**. This compound appears to act primarily by combining with guanine in the DNA, preventing its action as a template for RNA polymerase, but not for DNA polymerase. Because of this inhibition, actinomycin D has been important in studies relating **differentiation** of plant tissues to RNA synthesis (see later chapters).

17.1.3 Breakdown of Nucleic Acids

A few enzymes have been found in plants that degrade nucleic acids into nucleotides by hydrolytic reactions. These include the **nucleases**, and both **deoxyribonucleases (DNases)** and **ribonucleases (RNases)** are known. Polynucleotide phosphorylase (Ochoa's enzyme) might also catalyze the breakdown of RNA if Pi is readily available.

17.2 PROTEIN SYNTHESIS AND BREAKDOWN

As was mentioned in Chapter 11, a staggering number of different kinds of proteins could be formed from only 20 different amino acids; yet most cells probably synthesize only a few thousand of these types during their lifetime. The number of different kinds of proteins that

DNA as is the composition of messenger RNA. (Ribosomal protein is apparently synthesized in the nucleolus, along with histones and other nuclear proteins. A primary function of the nucleolus is thus to synthesize proteins.)

cells are capable of forming is believed to be predetermined by the amount of DNA that they contain and the arrangement of bases in these molecules. Let us investigate the mechanism of protein synthesis and determine how nucleic acids can so intimately participate in this process.

17.2.1 Amino Acid Activation and the Role of Transfer RNA

Protein formation entails several separate reactions. As with the synthesis of starch, cellulose, hemicelluloses, and pectic substances, a prior activation of the small compound to be incorporated is essential. For the amino acids, ATP performs this function. A separate enzyme is thought to be required for each amino acid activated [see (R 17-3)].

amino acid + ATP $\xrightarrow[\text{Mg}^{++}]{\text{enzyme}}$

   amino acid-AMP + pyrophosphate (R17-3)

The amino acid is linked through its carboxyl group to the phosphate of the AMP.

In the next step, transfer RNA participates. The amino acid is transferred from AMP to a particular transfer RNA, in a reaction probably catalyzed by the same enzyme used in the step described above. Apparently the enzyme has active sites by which it "**recognizes**" both the amino acid and the transfer RNA molecule [see (R 17-4)].

amino acid-AMP + transfer RNA $\rightleftharpoons$

   RNA-amino acid + AMP   (R17-4)

A different kind of transfer RNA is thought to be required for each different amino acid accepted. The resulting bond is an ester, involving the amino acid carboxyl group and one of the free hydroxyl groups of ribose present at the end of the RNA chain (probably the 3'-hydroxyl group).

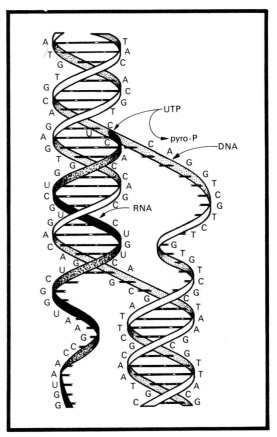

Figure 17-9

Synthesis of RNA using one of the strands of DNA as a template (transcription). According to this model, the DNA helix is temporarily uncoiled as RNA synthesis progresses along it. RNA polymerase molecules presumably become bound to the DNA and attach nucleotides from triphosphates such at UTP to the growing RNA chain. Pyrophosphate (pyro-P) is a by-product. The RNA thus would have a composition identical to the DNA strand not acting as a template, except that U (uracil) is present in the RNA and T (thymine) in the DNA, and the DNA contains some 5-methylcytosine (not shown), while the RNA has essentially only cytosine in this position. (See H. Jehle, 1965, *Proc. Natl. Acad. Sci.* 53:1451.)

17.2.2 Function of Ribosomes and Messenger RNA—Translation of Genetic Information

The next step is the transfer of the amino acid to a ribosome and the formation of a peptide bond. In this process the genetic information is **translated** from a nucleotide code to an amino acid code. The end of a messenger RNA molecule evidently becomes attached in an unknown manner to a ribosome before peptide bond formation can begin. The transfer RNA then becomes bound to the same end of the messenger RNA, perhaps by hydrogen bonds between a particular three bases in each RNA molecule; adenine to uracil, cytosine to guanine, uracil to adenine, etc. For example, suppose a given transfer RNA carries the amino acid lysine. Three uracil molecules of this RNA form base-pairs with three adenines of the messenger RNA, because the RNA codeword or **codon** for lysine proves to be three successive adenines. The DNA codon for this amino acid would then necessarily be three successive thymines. The three receptive bases of the messenger RNA with which the transfer RNA unites are collectively referred to as a **messenger codon,** and the complementary triplet in the transfer RNA, as an **anticodon.**

Now, it is hypothesized that the messenger molecule moves along the ribosome (or vice versa) a distance of three more bases. As this occurs, a new transfer RNA with its amino acid diffuses into position. Base pairing occurs with this second transfer RNA and three new bases of the messenger molecule. During this time, an enzyme thought to be potassium dependent catalyzes the formation of the first peptide bond between the carboxyl group of the initial amino acid and the amino group of the second. The first transfer RNA molecule, originally held to the amino acid carboxyl group, is displaced as the peptide bond is formed. The terminal phosphate of guanosine triphosphate (GTP) somehow participates in peptide bond synthesis, but the mechanism of this is not yet clearly understood.

Further movement of the messenger along the same ribosome allows a new codon to form hydrogen bonds with the anticodon of still another transfer RNA, and a third amino acid is attached to the free carboxyl group of the second. A long chain of amino acids is rapidly built up in this way. Each time a new transfer RNA with its amino acid arrives at the ribosome site, the preceding transfer molecule is released. The released molecule may then unite with another identical amino acid, and as soon as the messenger RNA again presents the three bases with which it may pair, the amino acid may again be inserted into the growing chain.[1]

Soon, part of the messenger RNA molecule where protein synthesis began is free to attach to a second ribosome, and eventually a third, fourth, and fifth, creating the polysomes seen in electron micrographs. The longer the messenger RNA molecule, the longer the protein synthesized will be, and the more ribosomes will be present in each such polysome. Each ribosome in the polysome unit helps synthesize a separate molecule of the same kind of protein, as dictated by the sequence of bases in the messenger RNA. Of course, each cell is constantly forming several different kinds of proteins, using different messenger RNA molecules coded by separate genes. Figure 17-10 illustrates the postulated role of nucleic acids in protein formation.

17.2.3 The Genetic Code

It appears, then, that the ultimate seat of genetic information rests within the DNA molecules. This information is converted (transcribed) into specific messenger RNA molecules, which then

---

[1] Other antibiotics, **puromycin** and **cycloheximide** (or **actidione**) are inhibitors of protein synthesis. Puromycin contains an amino group and has a structure similar to that of an amino acid-transfer RNA complex. It appears to act by forming a peptide bond with the carboxyl group of the last amino acid added to the unfinished polypeptide chain. This often causes the chain to be prematurely released from the ribosome. Cycloheximide seems also to act at the ribosome stage, since it does not prevent combination of amino acids with transfer RNA molecules, but it does prevent their conversion into proteins.

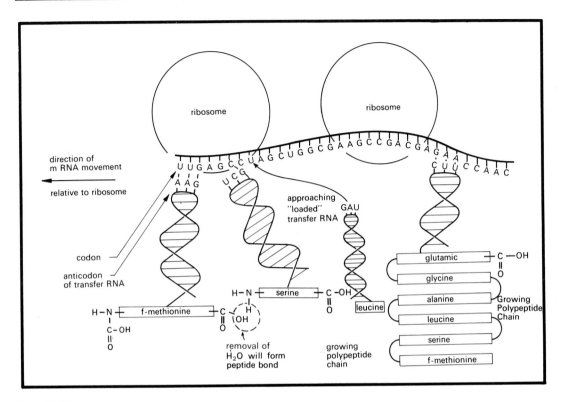

Figure 17-10

Hypothetical model illustrating protein synthesis upon a messenger RNA template, that is, translation of the genetic code. A long strand of mRNA containing genetic information for one protein begins to move across the surface of ribosomes. The ribosome at the left is involved in initiation of its first peptide bond, while the one at the right participated in bond formation between several amino acids as the mRNA moved across it. The mRNA may be attached to several ribosomes (forming a polysome), each of which helps synthesize identical proteins. Protein synthesis always begins with peptide bond formation between the carboxyl group of the terminal amino acid and the amino group of the second. The mRNA is probably read beginning from the end having a free 5'-ribose group (i.e., from the nucleotide having its 3'-ribose group bridged to the second nucleotide by phosphate). The positions of anticodons in most transfer RNA molecules are still not established, and the transfer RNA molecules are oversimplified as shown (see Fig. 17-4).

penetrate the bilayer nuclear membrane and diffuse into the cytoplasm where their genetic information is translated into specific proteins. We do not have evidence that individual ribosomes contain genetic information, and most ribosomes are probably much alike, although chloroplast ribosomes differ in both size and base composition from cytoplasmic ribosomes of the same cells. Transfer RNA molecules apparently vary in base sequence (certainly in

the anticodon portion) sufficiently so that they can be recognized by various enzymes, which, in turn, attach only certain amino acids.

17.2.3A The triplet nature of the code It was indicated above that base pairing between DNA and RNA, and between messenger RNA and transfer RNA, involves three bases, so that the genetic code is a **triplet** code. Why should it be assumed that a triplet code exists, rather than a

TABLE 17-3

NUCLEOTIDE COMBINATIONS FOR SINGLET, DOUBLET, AND TRIPLET CODES

			Singlets (4)				
		A	G	C	U		

			Doublets (16)				
AA	AC	GA	GC	CA	CC	UA	UC
AG	AU	GG	GU	CG	CU	UG	UU

			Triplets (64)				
AAA	ACA	GAA	GCA	CAA	CCA	UAA	UCA
AAG	ACG	GAG	GCG	CAG	CCG	UAG	UCG
AAC	ACC	GAC	GCC	CAC	CCC	UAC	UCC
AAU	ACU	GAU	GCU	CAU	CCU	UAU	UCU
AGA	AUA	GGA	GUA	CGA	CUA	UGA	UUA
AGG	AUG	GGG	GUG	CGG	CUG	UGG	UUG
AGC	AUC	GGC	GUC	CGC	CUC	UGC	UUC
AGU	AUU	GGU	GUU	CGU	CUU	UGU	UUU

singlet or a doublet code? *First,* we must remember that there are only four different coding bases in DNA,[2] yet at least twenty different amino acids must be accounted for. If a singlet code existed, each base in DNA would contain the information for only one amino acid, so that proteins could contain only four different amino acids. If two bases represented the genetic information for each amino acid, $4^2 = 16$ amino acids could be accommodated. Three different bases arranged in all possible ways would account for $4^3 = 64$ different amino acids, more than occurs in any protein. The various nucleotide combinations for singlet, doublet, and triplet codes are listed in Table 17-3.

Second, there is now *direct* evidence that for synthesis of certain proteins, three bases are used to code for each amino acid present. Such evidence has been obtained only for specialized cells that synthesize only one or a few proteins at a given time, such as the hemoglobin-producing

reticulocytes of mammals. In these cases, both the messenger RNA molecules and the protein were isolated, and the number of nucleotides present in this type of RNA was then compared with the number of amino acids in the protein. A ratio of approximately three was obtained. Additional evidence for a triplet code is given further below.

17.2.3B Triplet compositions and base sequences Even before the existence of the triplet code was proved, attempts were being made to determine which bases are the codons for each amino acid. An important breakthrough was made in 1961 by Marshall Nirenberg and J. Heinrich Matthaei of the National Institute of Health in Bethesda, Maryland. They took advantage of Ochoa's RNA-synthesizing enzyme, polynucleotide phosphorylase, to synthesize artificial messenger RNA. This enzyme catalyzes the synthesis of an RNA containing only one nucleotide if only a single kind of nucleotide diphosphate is provided. For ex-

---

[2] 5-methyl cytosine codes as cytosine.

ample, polyuridylic acid was formed when only UDP was present. The polyuridylic acid was then incubated with several amino acids, a mixture of cellular enzymes and transfer RNA molecules, ATP, GTP, and ribosomes. Magnesium ions and relatively large concentrations of potassium ions are also essential for protein synthesis and were provided. Only phenylalanine was incorporated into protein by this system, producing a polyphenylalanine "protein." Clearly, therefore, the RNA codon for phenylalanine can contain only uracil, and was correctly believed to be UUU.

By mixing various nucleotide diphosphates with polynucleotide phosphorylase, more complex RNA molecules of known compositions were prepared in the laboratories of both Ochoa and Nirenberg. By statistically comparing the composition of these nucleic acids with their ability to direct various amino acids into protein, the triplet groups of bases coding for all the amino acids was then established. The *sequence* of bases within this triplet codon, however, cannot be determined in this way. Base-sequence analyses have been obtained indirectly from certain studies of virus mutations but are more directly determined by mixing small trinucleotides (nucleotides containing only three bases[3]) with various amino acids attached to their transfer RNA molecules. When provided with the necessary ribosomes, enzymes, etc., each of these short trinucleotides attaches to ribosomes and binds a specific transfer RNA molecule attached to its amino acid. Dinucleotides do not bind transfer RNA-amino acid molecules in this way, indicating that trinucleotides are sufficient. This is further direct evidence that the genetic code indeed exists in triplets. The sequence of bases in a trinucleotide

---

[3] The trinucleotides can be obtained by partially degrading RNA molecules with RNase. The products include the trinucleotides, which are then separated chromatographically and used in the described studies.

is easily determined, and so the codon for each amino acid will probably soon be completely specified in this manner. The genetic code will then be "cracked!"

The presently assigned codon sequences for several amino acids are listed in Table 17-4. Note that two or more different codons are effective for most of the amino acids. For example, serine is probably coded by both UCU and UCC, where U stands for uracil and C for cytosine. Because the information for a single amino acid is represented by two or more different triplets, the genetic code is said to be **degenerate**. This does not mean that the same triplet sequence will code for two different amino acids.

17.2.3C Other properties of the code

Another important feature of the genetic code is that it is **nonoverlapping,** meaning that in the messenger RNA a mechanism of some type must exist to prevent transfer RNA molecules from forming base pairs with purines or pyrimidines in two adjacent codons. Similarly, formation of messenger RNA molecules on the DNA templates must somehow start and end only at specified points. These observations present stimulating problems to be explained by future research.

Finally, it appears that the code is **universal,** the same codons representing the same amino acids in all organisms, from algae to elephants. This, of course, will never be rigorously proved, since there are too many living species for scientists to examine completely. Nevertheless, the limited information obtained thus far from studies with viruses, bacteria, and some animal cells indicates universality.

17.2.3D The one-gene, one-enzyme theory

In the 1940s, George Beadle and Edward Tatum performed several genetic experiments with the red breadmold fungus, *Neurospora crassa,* which led them to suggest that each gene produced

TABLE 17-4

BASE SEQUENCES IN RNA CODONS AS DETERMINED FOR *ESCHERICHIA COLI*[a]

1st Base	2nd Base				3rd Base
	U	C	A	G	
U	phenylalanine phenylalanine leucine? leucine, f-methionine[b]	serine serine serine serine	tyrosine tyrosine termination termination?	cysteine cysteine cysteine? tryptophan	U C A G
C	leucine leucine leucine leucine	proline proline proline proline	histidine histidine glutamine glutamine	arginine arginine arginine arginine	U C A G
A	isoleucine isoleucine isoleucine methionine f-methionine[b]	threonine threonine threonine threonine	asparagine asparagine lysine lysine	serine serine arginine arginine	U C A G
G	valine valine valine valine, f-meth.	alanine alanine alanine alanine	aspartic aspartic glutamic glutamic	glycine glycine glycine glycine	U C A G

[a] Data compiled by M. Nirenberg et al., *Cold Spring Harbor Symposium on Quantitative Biology*, XXXI, pp. 11–24, 1966.

[b] f-methionine = N-formyl methionine, thought to be an important initiator of protein synthesis in *E. coli* and perhaps of all organisms. Thus, methionine is a principal amino acid found in the N-terminal positions of *E. coli* proteins.

only one enzyme. This idea became known as the **one-gene, one-enzyme,** theory. Further evidence supported their theory, and Beadle and Tatum received a share of the 1958 Nobel Prize in medicine and physiology. We now realize that this theory requires slight modification. For example, the hemoglobin proteins of blood contain different "alpha" and "beta" polypeptide chains, coded by different genes. In fact, many proteins are composed of two or more different chains (Chapter 11). Because of this, scientists now prefer to speak of a **one-gene, one-polypeptide-chain** theory.

17.2.4 Sites of Protein Synthesis

Protein synthesis occurs fastest in rapidly growing organs, such as young roots, stems, leaves, and flowers and in developing seeds. However, all plant tissues are probably able to synthesize their own proteins, since these molecules are not usually translocated intact from one organ to another.

Within individual cells, protein synthesis is carried out in nuclei, mitochondria, and chloroplasts, as well as in the cytoplasm surrounding them. Nuclei synthesize the histones, ribosome proteins, and probably certain of their other proteins, too. The types of proteins formed by mitochondria and chloroplasts have not been determined, but these are likely to be both enzymatic and structural. Whether chloroplast ribosomes, which differ in base composition and are smaller than cytoplasmic ribosomes, are formed in the plastids themselves or in the nucleolus is an unsolved question. It is more likely that they are formed inside the plastids.

In leaf cells, more than half of the total protein is found inside the chloroplasts, which are themselves composed of 40–50 percent protein on a dry weight basis. It is very likely, since chloroplasts are capable of reproduction (division), that their RNA and protein molecules are produced according to specifications of DNA present in the plastids rather than of DNA in the nuclei. Light greatly stimulates the protein synthesis occurring in chloroplasts, whether the process is measured by incorporation of $^{14}CO_2$ or of ^{14}C-labeled amino acids. It is believed that one of the beneficial agents is ATP, supplied by photosynthetic phosphorylation.

17.2.5 Protein Breakdown

Early workers in biochemistry and plant physiology suggested that proteins are continuously being broken down and reformed in living organisms. In 1924, A. C. Chibnall observed a decrease in the protein content of the leaves of runner bean plants (*Phaseolus multiflorus*) during the night, followed by a rise again during the daylight. Such diurnal alterations have been observed in several plants since then. Chibnall suggested that these fluctuations were due to changes in the relative rates of synthesis and degradation, both occurring continuously. Direct demonstrations that these processes both occurred together were finally made in the early 1940s by various scientists who used isotopic ^{15}N-labeled compounds as tracers.

It is possible that protein catabolism could occur by reversal of reactions of protein synthesis. This would represent a conservation of energy, since ATP would be formed. However, large molecules are usually synthesized by cells according to one pathway, and degraded by another. It is more likely that proteins are degraded by a hydrolytic cleavage of the peptide bonds, a process catalyzed by **proteolytic enzymes**, the **proteases**, which act on intact proteins, and the **peptidases**, which can split only the smaller peptides or polypeptides. Papain, mentioned in Chapter 11, and **bromelin**, a similar enzyme found in pineapple fruits, are well-known proteases. Germinating seedlings also contain active proteases, and they are probably found in varying amounts in most, if not all, plant cells.

There appear to be several different peptidases that vary in the type of peptide bonds they can split, depending upon the kind of amino acids forming the bond. Furthermore, certain peptidases will function only on a peptide bond at the end of the polypeptide chain, and this often depends on whether the terminal amino acid has a free carboxyl group or a free amino group. The function of peptidases is not entirely clear, although they almost surely participate in protein breakdown, particularly during the utilization of stored protein during seed germination.

17.3 CHANGES IN NITROGEN COMPOUNDS DURING ONTOGENY

17.3.1 Nitrogen Metabolism in Germinating Seeds

The dormant seed is a specialized organ, basically containing the **embryo** that develops into a new plant, a **seed coat**, and **storage tissues**. The cotyledons are specialized leaves present in all seeds. In some, such as the dicotyledonous pea, bean, and peanut, they constitute the

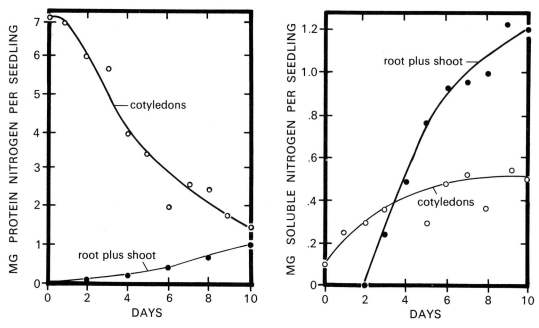

Figure 17-11

Changes in protein and soluble nitrogen compounds (amino acids plus amides) during germination of pea seedlings in darkness. The decrease in protein content of the cotyledons is accompanied by an appearance of soluble nitrogen compounds in the growing seedling axis (root plus shoot) and in the cotyledons. These are utilized in the axis for production of proteins, which increase with time. (Data of L. Larson and H. Beevers, 1965, *Plant Physiol.* 40:424. Used by permission.)

principal storage tissue. In others, such as the monocotyledonous grasses or cereals, storage is provided by **endosperm**, a special tissue initially present in all seeds but finally predominant only in some.

The absorption of water by a dry seed sets off a variety of reactions that convert stored materials in the endosperm or cotyledons into soluble compounds that can be metabolized by the growing embryo. Various nitrogen compounds are among those metabolized. For many years it has been known that seed germination involves the breakdown of storage proteins and their conversion into smaller, more soluble nitrogenous compounds, such as amides and amino acids. This is followed by the translocation of the smaller compounds to the embryo

and their use in synthetic processes. These changes occurring in pea seedlings germinated in darkness are illustrated in Fig. 17-11.

In corn seeds, the endosperm was found to undergo decreases in dry weight, total nitrogen, fats, etc., but the nucleic acid content remained relatively constant during a five-day germination period. Although nucleic acids are usually found in only low amounts in storage tissues, they do often undergo breakdown in seeds other than corn. It is assumed that this is due to activation of the nucleases, RNase and DNase, or perhaps of polynucleotide phosphorylase, and that the resulting nucleotides (or nucleosides) are later transported to the embryo and converted into its nucleic acids. More experiments are needed to determine if this is true.

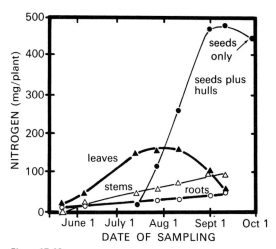

Figure 17-12

Changes in nitrogen content of various organs of the broad bean *Vicia faba* during growth. The extensive accumulation of nitrogen compounds in the fruits (seeds plus hulls) was accompanied by a loss from the leaves and a large uptake from the soil. (Data of A. Emmerling, 1880, *Landw. Versuchsstat.* 24:113.)

There are claims that in one plant (*Vigna sesquipedalis*) certain intact ribonucleic acids are transported from the cotyledons to the developing embryo.

In many seeds the presence of the embryo is required for, or at least increases, the breakdown of products in the storage tissues, suggesting that some stimulating factor is normally supplied by the embryo. A plant hormone, gibberellic acid, is translocated from the embryos of barley and other cereal grain seeds to the living aleurone layers of the endosperm, where it stimulates the synthesis of certain hydrolytic enzymes, including α-amylase, a protease, and a ribonuclease (Chapter 21). There is evidence that this hormone activates the formation of messenger RNA molecules, which then code for the synthesis of these new digestive enzymes, since both actinomycin D (which inhibits RNA synthesis) and puromycin (which blocks protein formation) inhibit the action of gibberellic acid.

It also appears that synthesis of new messenger RNA occurs in storage organs of seeds of peanuts and wheat during germination, and the same is probably true of most species. With this RNA, the enzymes necessary for mobilization of various storage products are produced.

17.3.2 Nitrogen Metabolism in Growing Plants

As the embryo develops into a seedling with active leaves and roots, these organs develop somewhat characteristic properties of nitrogen transformations. For example, leaves synthesize many proteins that roots do not produce, and seeds form certain proteins that neither leaves nor roots are able to synthesize. Roots usually supply the leaves primarily with organic forms of nitrogen; yet it is the photosynthetic organs that provide roots with the sugars needed to synthesize the carbon skeletons necessary for amino acid formation. Leaves of different ages vary in their abilities to synthesize certain amino acids, young leaves usually producing more amino acids and at a faster rate than older ones.

Young, growing leaves usually contain more nitrogen per unit dry weight than do older leaves. This is also reflected in their chlorophyll contents, the lower mature leaves eventually becoming yellow and low in chlorophyll, protein and nucleic acids. As maturity occurs, various nitrogenous materials (and many other compounds and mineral ions) are translocated to regions of the plant that are still developing. The nitrogen content of certain plant organs was studied by A. Emmerling as early as 1900. Figure 17-12 shows the changes he found in total nitrogen in various parts of the broad bean plant, *Vicia faba*, during its growth. It is apparent that the large accumulation of nitrogen compounds in the seeds is accompanied by a loss in the leaves.

Functions and Metabolism of Plant Lipids and Aromatic Compounds

It was emphasized in Chapter 15 that reactions of glycolysis and the Krebs cycle provide the carbon skeletons needed for the formation of a large number of other compounds present in the plant. The importance of some of these compounds to plant functions and the manner in which they are metabolized will be discussed in the present chapter. We will emphasize primarily the lipids, a heterogeneous group of compounds characterized by their solubility properties, and the aromatics or phenolic compounds, molecules or their derivatives containing one or more benzene rings.

18.1 THE LIPIDS

The **lipids** are a group of fatty-like substances, rich in carbon and hydrogen, that dissolve in such organic solvents as acetone, alcohols, ethers, and benzene but do not dissolve in water. Some of these compounds are important as reserve food materials (the **fats** and **oils**), others contribute to the structure of membranes (the **phospholipids** and **glycolipids**), while another group (the **waxes**) provides a protective coating, the cuticle, over much of the plant.

18.1.1 Fats and Oils

18.1.1A Kinds of fats and oils and their properties
The fats and oils are chemically very similar compounds, distinguished only by the fats being solids at room temperatures while the oils are liquids. Both compounds are composed of long-chain **fatty acids** esterified by their single carboxyl group to a hydroxyl of the 3-carbon alcohol **glycerol**. In fats and oils all three hydroxyl groups of glycerol are esterified, and so these compounds are often called **triglycerides**. The general formula for a triglyceride is given in (R18-1), where R^1, R^2, and R^3 represent the carbon chains of the different fatty acids.

The physical properties (such as the melting points) of fats and oils are determined by the kinds of fatty acids they contain. A given fat or oil usually contains three different fatty acids, although molecules occasionally are found to contain two or, less often, three identical fatty acids. These acids almost always have an even number of carbon atoms, commonly from 12 to 18, and they may or may not be unsaturated (contain double bonds). The melting point increases with the length of the fatty acid and with the extent of its saturation, so that the solid fats usually have saturated acids containing 16 or 18 carbon atoms. The oils also have acids with 16 or 18 carbons, but these commonly contain from one to three double bonds. Examples of commercially important plant oils are those from the seeds of cotton, corn, peanuts, and soybeans. All of these oils principally contain fatty acids with 18 carbon atoms, including **oleic acid**, with one double bond, and **linoleic acid**, with two double bonds. In fact, these two acids, in the order named, are believed to be the most abundant fatty acids existing in seeds, while **linolenic acid,** an 18-carbon acid with three double bonds, is the most abundant fatty acid of leaves.

Table 18-1 contains a list of some of the important fatty acids occurring in plants with their number of carbon atoms, structures, and degree of unsaturation, and the position of double bonds, where present.

The most abundant saturated fatty acids are **palmitic acid**, with 16 carbons, and **stearic acid**, with 18 carbon atoms. These acids are important constituents of fats from both plants and animals. Coconut fat is also a rich source of **lauric acid**, a saturated acid with 12 carbon atoms. Both plant and animal fats often contain saturated fatty acids at the terminal 1- and 3-positions of glycerol, and an unsaturated acid attached to the central, secondary alcohol position.

The seeds of many plants contain a high percentage of fatty acids not important in fats of their vegetative organs. Castor beans (*Ricinus communis*), for example, contain **ricinoleic acid** (12-hydroxyoleic acid), which makes up between 80 and 90 percent of the fatty acids in castor oil, but which is absent from castor bean leaves and is only rarely found in other species.

18.1.1B Distribution and importance of plant fats and oils
Fats and oils are found in small amounts in leaves, stems, and roots, where they may make up approximately 0.5–2 percent of the dry weight of the organ. In fact, *Mentha aquatica* (peppermint) leaves reportedly consist of 5.0 percent fat. Because of their insolubility in water, fats are usually found as small droplets (emulsions) present in the cytoplasm of the cells. Seeds usually contain much higher concentrations of fats and oils, and these usually occur in far greatest abundance in the endosperm or cotyledon storage tissues. In fact, most seeds contain fats or oils as the principal reserve food. As contrasted to carbohydrates, these molecules contain large amounts of carbon and hydrogen compared to oxygen, and when they are broken down relatively large amounts of oxygen are utilized. As a result, considerable ATP is formed, and thus far greater amounts of chemical energy can be stored in a small volume as fats or oils than as carbohydrates. Perhaps because of this, small

triglyceride

glycerol

fatty acid

(R18-1)

TABLE 18-1

FATTY ACIDS ABUNDANT OR COMMON IN VARIOUS PLANTS

Name	No. carbons: no. double bonds	Structure
lauric	12:0	$CH_3(CH_2)_{10}COOH$
myristic	14:0	$CH_3(CH_2)_{12}COOH$
palmitic	16:0	$CH_3(CH_2)_{14}COOH$
stearic	18:0	$CH_3(CH_2)_{16}COOH$
oleic	18:1 at C-9,10	$CH_3(CH_2)_7 \overset{H}{C}{=}\overset{H}{C}{-}(CH_2)_7 COOH$ (10 9)
linoleic	18:2 at C-9,10;12,13	$CH_3(CH_2)_4 \overset{H}{C}{=}\overset{H}{C}{-}CH_2 \overset{H}{C}{=}\overset{H}{C}{-}(CH_2)_7 COOH$ (13 12 10 9)
linolenic	18:3 at C-9,10;12,13;15,16	$CH_3CH_2\overset{H}{C}{=}\overset{H}{C}{-}CH_2\overset{H}{C}{=}\overset{H}{C}{-}CH_2\overset{H}{C}{=}\overset{H}{C}{-}(CH_2)_7{-}COOH$

seeds nearly always contain fats or oils as the primary storage materials. When these are respired, sufficient amounts of energy are released to allow establishment of the seedling, and yet the fact that the seeds are light often allows them to be scattered effectively by wind. Larger seeds, such as those of peas and the cereal grains, contain only small amounts of fats and oils, and the principal reserve food is starch.

The plant oils are important in commerce. One major use is in foods. In the preparation of butter substitutes and cooking oils, the oils are often **hydrogenated**, a process in which hydrogen gas is bubbled through the oil containing a suspension of finely divided nickel as a catalyst. During hydrogenation, the double bonds of oleic, linoleic, and linolenic acids are saturated, and more solid mixtures can be produced as desired. Oils are also used in the production of paints. Drying oils, such as linseed oil, from seeds of *Linum usitatissimum* (flax), containing such fatty acids as linolenic with two or more double bonds, absorb oxygen when exposed in thin layers to the air, forming peroxides that spontaneously polymerize and become solid, tough, and protective.

18.1.1C Synthesis of fats and oils

Fat and oil accumulation has been studied primarily in seeds of fruits that accumulate large quantities of these substances. It has been suspected for many years that the fats of developing seeds are formed at the expense of sugars translocated to these tissues, and that intact fats and the fatty acids themselves are not translocated. As early as 1896, L. du Sublon found that when fats were accumulating in almond and walnut seeds, sugars in those seeds were disappearing. Data for the almond are presented in Fig. 18-1.

In many plants the content of carbohydrates in the seed may decrease, but not by an amount nearly large enough to account for the fats that are accumulated. Here the fats arise from sugars translocated into the seeds from the leaves, so that a large amount of fat may build up with

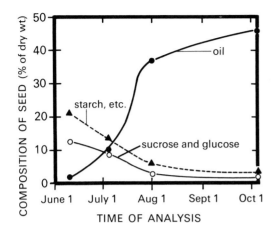

Figure 18-1

Changes in carbohydrate and fat (oil) content of almond seeds during ripening. (Drawn from data of L. du Sablon, 1897, *Rev. gén.botan.* 9:313, as tabulated in J. Bonner, 1950, *Plant Biochemistry*, Academic Press, New York, p. 369.)

little detectable change in the seed carbohydrate content.

A discussion of the biogenesis of fats and oils may conveniently be divided into three parts: *the formation of glycerol, the synthesis of the fatty acids*, and *their union in the finished product*.

(1) *Glycerol formation.* Little evidence as to the origin of glycerol has been obtained with plants. It is assumed that, as in animals, the glycerol arises from an intermediate of glycolysis, dihydroxyacetone phosphate. This compound is reduced by NADH as shown in (R18-2) to form L-α-glycerophosphate.

It is α-glycerophosphate that provides the glycerol unit present in the fats and oils and certain other lipids to be discussed later.

(2) *Synthesis of fatty acids.* The fact that nearly all long-chain fatty acids contain an even number of carbon atoms suggests that these are built up by the repeated addition of a two-carbon unit. It was found that ^{14}C-labeled acetate was converted into the fatty acids of microorganisms, animals, and plants, and that if both carbon atoms of acetate were labeled, all of the carbons of the fatty acid molecules contained ^{14}C. Acetate is thus established as the necessary two-carbon unit, but the reactions of its incorporation are more complex than might be suspected. For example, free acetate does not usually exist in plants in detectable quantities, even though they can absorb and metabolize this compound. Instead, the activated form of acetate, acetyl CoA, provides the necessary carbon atoms for fatty acid synthesis. The origin of acetyl CoA from carbohydrates during respiration was discussed in Chapter 15.

It was discovered in 1957 by H. Klein that carbon dioxide greatly stimulates the process of fatty acid synthesis in yeast cells. This important discovery was soon verified for plants and animals in the laboratories of P. K. Stumpf and Salih Wakil, respectively, who have since contributed greatly to our knowledge about fat synthesis. It was then found that carbon dioxide is a necessary reactant, although it is not finally incorporated into any fatty acid. Carbon dioxide reacts with acetyl CoA, as in (R18-3), yielding an activated three-carbon compound, **malonyl CoA.**

$$
\begin{array}{ccc}
\text{CH}_2\text{OH} & & \text{CH}_2\text{OH} \\
| & & | \\
\text{C}=\text{O} \quad + \text{NADH} + \text{H}^+ \rightleftharpoons & \text{HO}-\text{C}-\text{H} & + \text{NAD} \\
| & & | \\
\text{CH}_2\text{OPO}_3\text{H}_2 & & \text{CH}_2\text{OPO}_3\text{H}_2
\end{array}
$$

dihydroxyacetone phosphate   L-α-glycerophosphate   (R18-2)

$$CH_3-\underset{\underset{O}{\|}}{C}-SCoA + CO_2 + ATP \xrightarrow[\text{carboxylase}]{\text{biotin, Mn}^{++}}$$

acetyl CoA

$$HOOC-CH_2-\underset{\underset{O}{\|}}{C}-SCoA + ADP + Pi$$

malonyl CoA   (R18-3)

This reaction requires the vitamin biotin, is greatly stimulated by manganese ions, and requires the energy in the terminal phosphate of ATP. The carboxylase enzyme responsible is stimulated by certain Krebs cycle acids. On the other hand, palmitic acid, one of the most common end products of fatty acid synthesis, inhibits the enzyme and may serve through feedback inhibition at this point to control the process of fat production.

Further reactions involve the repeated use of malonyl CoA, as it condenses first with acetyl CoA and later with other fatty acid **acyl CoA** compounds that result from prior condensations. Each time malonyl CoA undergoes condensation, the previously incorporated CO_2 molecule is split out. The product of each condensation must be reduced before it, in turn, can combine with another malonyl CoA. This reduction requires NADPH, and NADH is not effective. The over-all process of the synthesis of the 16-carbon palmitic acid is summarized in (R18-4).

The mechanisms of the condensing reactions are more fully understood as a result of recent experiments of P. Roy Vagelos and Wakil, where the requirement of a small, heat-stable protein (mol. wt. 9,500) for the synthetase system of the bacteria *Escherichia coli* and *Clostridium kluyveri* was shown. Synthesis of fatty acids

takes place only in the presence of the heat-stable protein and, furthermore, only in the presence of enzymes capable of transferring the acetyl and malonyl groups (**acyl groups**) from CoA to the new carrier protein. The acyl carrier proteins (ACP) contain as a prosthetic group, **4′phosphorylpantetheine**, which attaches by a thioester bond to the acyl groups. Phosphorylpantetheine also forms a part of CoA, and the acyl groups involved in fatty acid synthesis become attached to its sulfur atom in the same way in both cases. Once transferred to ACP, the acetyl and malonyl groups are condensed to form the fatty acids as indicated in Fig. 18-2.

The presence of ACP in plant systems has now been demonstrated by Paul Stumpf and his coworkers at the University of California at Davis, and by others. A comparison of the ACP from bacterial and plant systems reveals that they contain the same number of amino acids but that a few residues of the bacterial ACP have been replaced by other amino acids in plant ACP.

Fatty acids of intermediate chain lengths do not accumulate but are quickly converted into the final products, which are usually palmitic and oleic acids. There is evidence that the rate-limiting reaction in fatty acid formation is the carboxylation of acetyl CoA to malonyl CoA, the succeeding reactions then occurring very rapidly. It is known, too, that the acyl-ACP intermediates are bound to enzymes and do not occur free in detectable amounts. The rapidity of the reactions suggests that a highly organized system may be responsible for fatty acid formation, and, in fact, in yeast, one large-protein complex has been found (molecular weight, 2.3 million) that contains all of the enzymes necessary for the synthesis of fatty acids.

---

acetyl CoA + 7 malonyl CoA + 14NADPH + 14H$^+$ ⟶

        palmitic acid + 7CO$_2$ + 8CoA + 14NADP + 6H$_2$O

                                 (R18-4)

While bacteria and yeasts synthesize both saturated and unsaturated fatty acids, the reactions of Fig. 18-2 do not account for the formation of unsaturated acids, such as oleic acid in plants. Instead, only saturated fatty acids are initially produced in this cycle. Konrad Bloch at Harvard University showed that unsaturated fatty acids in several higher plants arise by desaturation of stearyl-ACP in the presence of oxygen and oxidized ferredoxin. The synthesis of oleic acid and polyunsaturated fatty acids can tentatively be summarized as in Fig. 18-3.

It is interesting that higher animals cannot synthesize certain unsaturated fatty acids, such as linoleic and linolenic acids, and thus depend upon the ability of plants to do this.

Some efforts have been made to determine the parts of individual cells responsible for fat synthesis in plants. In avocado fruit, palmitic and stearic acids are probably formed by the reactions involving malonyl CoA and biotin described in Fig. 18-2. These reactions can occur in the mitochondria, where the necessary ATP is constantly being formed, but they can also take place somewhere in the surrounding cytoplasm, perhaps in the endoplasmic reticulum. Mitochondria can, in addition, form oleic acid. In leaves, chloroplasts appear to be the major site for synthesis of fatty acids and other lipids, and light greatly stimulates the process. Light energy probably provides both ATP and NADPH, each of which is essential to lipid synthesis.

(3) *Combination of glycerol and fatty acids to produce triglycerides.* As fatty acids are synthesized in the above-described reactions, they do not accumulate, but rapidly react with α-glycerol phosphate to form the fats and oils that are deposited in the cells. The union of the alcohol groups of glycerol with the carboxylic acid groups of the fatty acids produces esters. It is likely that the reason free fatty acids do not accumulate in large amounts is that they react with glycerol phosphate while still attached to the acyl carrier proteins or to CoA. If this is true, ACP or CoA would be split off only as the glycerol-fatty acid esters are formed. The phosphate of glycerol phosphate must also be removed, since three fatty acids are esterified.

18.1.1D Breakdown of fats and oils The catabolism of fats and oils begins with the action of the **lipases**, which can break the ester bonds. The lipases catalyze hydrolytic reactions, shown in (R18-5), in which water is taken up and glycerol and the three fatty acids are released. The reactions are reversible but do not seem to be important in the synthesis of fats.

(1) *Glycerol breakdown.* The glycerol resulting from lipase action is converted by reaction with ATP to α-glycerophosphate, and the α-glycerophosphate is then oxidized by NAD to dihydroxyacetone phosphate. Dihydroxyacetone phosphate is either broken down by glycolytic and Krebs cycle reactions, or it can also be converted to sucrose under certain conditions.

(2) *Catabolism of fatty acids.* The fatty acids resulting from the action of lipase upon triglycerides can be broken down to CO_2 and H_2O, accompanied by the production of large amounts of ATP and NADH. The fat stored in most seeds provides an energy supply needed for germination, and thus for survival of the

$$R^2-\underset{\underset{O}{\parallel}}{C}-O-\underset{\underset{CH_2O-\underset{\underset{O}{\parallel}}{C}-R^3}{|}}{\overset{\overset{CH_2O-\underset{\underset{O}{\parallel}}{C}-R^1}{|}}{C}}-H \;\; + 3H_2O \;\; \underset{}{\overset{lipase}{\rightleftharpoons}} \;\; HO-\underset{\underset{CH_2OH}{|}}{\overset{\overset{CH_2OH}{|}}{C}}-H \;\; + R^1-\underset{\underset{O}{\parallel}}{C}-OH \;\; + R^2-\underset{\underset{O}{\parallel}}{C}-OH \;\; + R^3-\underset{\underset{O}{\parallel}}{C}-OH$$

$$(R18\text{-}5)$$

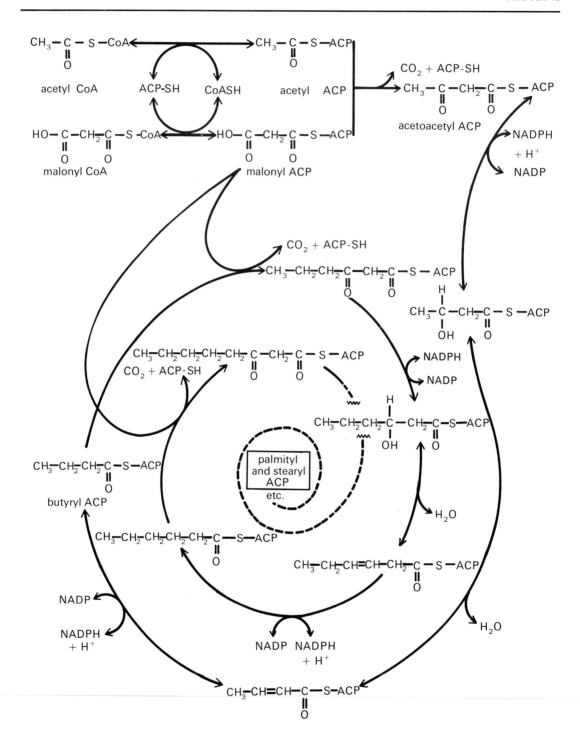

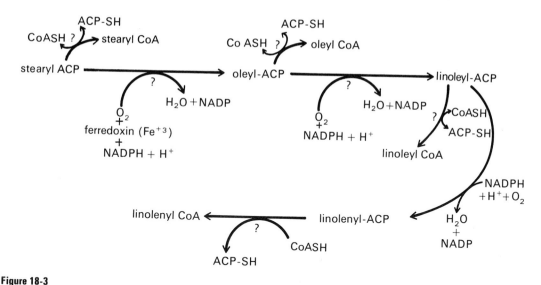

Figure 18-3

Outline of tentative reactions involved in conversion of stearyl ACP to unsaturated fatty acid derivatives. Introduction of double bonds occurs in chloroplasts and is greatly facilitated by light. The fatty acids of the ACP derivatives are presumably rapidly esterified with glycerol to form fats and oils, or perhaps are first converted to CoA derivatives and then esterified. The roles of O_2, NADPH, and ferredoxin in introduction of double bonds are not yet established.

species. Although the oxidation of glycerol also releases significant energy, by far the most arises when the fatty acids are oxidized.

Two mechanisms are known to exist in plants for the oxidation of fatty acids. The basis of the first mechanism was suggested as early as 1904 by F. Knoop, who studied the breakdown of fatty acids fed to dogs. Knoop correctly suggested that two carbons were removed at a time, following the oxidation of the β-carbon from a $-CH_2-$ group to a keto group. Finally, in the 1950s, these reactions were completely clarified by animal biochemists working in Madison, Wisconsin, and Munich, Germany.

It also became apparent at this time that similar reactions occurred in plant cells. This group of reactions is called the **β-oxidation pathway**, because the β-carbon (numbering from the carboxyl group) is attacked and oxidized first. The β-oxidation pathway for a saturated fatty acid is outlined in Fig. 18-4.

The first step necessary before β-oxidation can proceed is the activation of the fatty acid through its combination with CoA. This is an ATP-dependent reaction, and it is necessary before the fatty acid can be attacked by oxidative enzymes. Subsequent reactions involve first a removal of two hydrogen atoms by a

Figure 18-2

Synthesis of palmitic and stearic acids. Acyl groups such as an acetyl, butyryl, and successively longer even-numbered acyl carrier protein (ACP) derivatives are condensed with malonyl ACP, accompanied by the loss of CO_2 from the β-carbon of the malonyl group. With each turn of the cycle, a saturated acyl ACP containing two more carbons is thus synthesized until palmityl and stearyl ACP molecules are formed. In chloroplasts, elongation usually ends here, and desaturation of stearyl ACP begins as outlined in Fig. 18-3. In membranes associated with the cytoplasm (endoplasmic reticulum?), however, an elongation system seems to be present which allows formation of molecules containing 30 or more carbons such as exist in cuticular waxes.

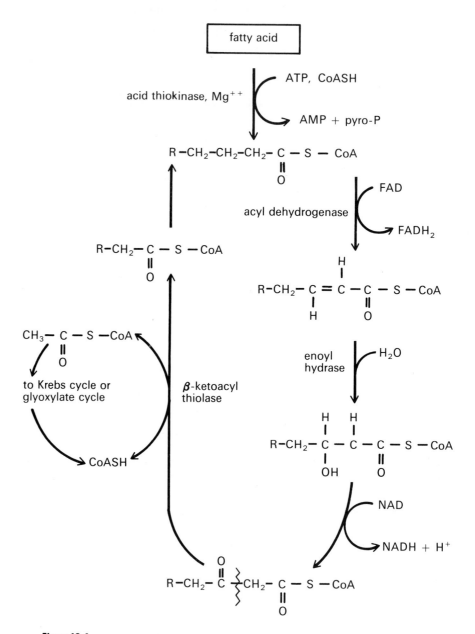

Figure 18-4
The β-oxidation pathway for conversion of fatty acids to acetyl coenzyme A.

flavin-enzyme, thus creating unsaturation between the α- and β-carbons, then the addition of water to form an —OH group on the β-carbon, and then the oxidation of this —OH to a keto group with NAD as the electron acceptor. Finally, the two terminal carbon atoms are removed as acetyl CoA, and the β-keto group of the partially oxidized fatty acid is combined with a new CoA molecule. This new combination product of CoA and the shortened fatty acid molecule can then undergo the reactions of the cycle until two more carbon atoms are split out as acetyl CoA. In this way, the long-chain fatty acid is eventually totally degraded to acetyl CoA molecules, the fate of which will be discussed further below.

In the seeds of peanuts and castor beans where these reactions have been studied most extensively, β-oxidation occurs primarily outside such cellular particles as chloroplasts and mitochondria, apparently taking place in the nonparticulate cytoplasm.

A second mechanism for fatty acid breakdown also exists in some plants but is apparently not important in animals. This is an **α-oxidation pathway**, which begins by the oxidation of the α-carbon. In this pathway, it is not necessary that the acids be esterified with CoA. The reactions of α-oxidation are summarized in Fig. 18-5. The fatty acid is first oxidized at the α-carbon atom by a **fatty acid peroxidase**, and, at the same time, the carboxyl carbon is removed as carbon dioxide. The oxidizing agent in this step is believed to be hydrogen peroxide, which is produced by another reaction such as the oxidation of glycolic acid by glycolic acid oxidase [see Chapter 15 (R15-6)]. The product of the first step in α-oxidation is a long-chain aldehyde having one less carbon than the original fatty acid. This aldehyde is then directly oxidized with NAD by a **fatty aldehyde dehydrogenase**, yielding NADH and a fatty acid with an uneven number of carbon atoms. This fatty acid may then enter the cycle again,

whereby further reactions lead to the removal of more carbon atoms as carbon dioxide and also to the formation of NADH.

The significance of the α-oxidation system is not yet clear. It is probably of less importance than the β-oxidation pathway for fatty acid breakdown, and in the fat-rich seeds of castor bean no evidence for α-oxidation was found. The pathway may account for the occasional appearance in various plant tissues of long-chain fatty acids with an uneven number of carbon atoms.

(3) *Conversion of fats to sucrose: The glyoxylate cycle.* During the germination of seeds that store fats or oils as the important storage material, these molecules disappear and sugars, especially sucrose, accumulate. These sugars arise directly from the fats, but the mechanism of this conversion was long in doubt. Even after it was learned that fatty acids are broken down into acetyl CoA, problems of understanding still existed, because it was known that acetyl CoA cannot be converted back to pyruvic acid and then into sugars by a reversal of glycolysis. Such a conversion cannot occur because the respiratory reaction normally producing acetyl CoA and carbon dioxide from pyruvic acid is irreversible[1] (see Chapter 15).

This problem was solved in the late 1950s and early 1960s largely by Harry Beevers at Purdue University through his demonstrations that the **glyoxylate cycle** functioned in germinating seeds. This cycle had previously been found by H. L. Kornberg and H. A. Krebs to exist in certain microorganisms that can exist on acetate as the only source of carbon. These microorganisms derive all their energy from the breakdown of acetate to CO_2 and water via

---

[1] Certain photosynthetic bacteria possess an enzyme that can add CO_2 to acetyl CoA, thus producing pyruvate, but only in the presence of reduced ferredoxin. This seems to be a significant photosynthetic reaction in these organisms, although fixation into 3-phosphoglyceric acid also occurs.

acetyl CoA, and they also convert acetyl CoA to sugars and all other cellular materials required for their growth and functions.

The glyoxylate cycle as shown in Fig. 18-6 is basically a modified Krebs cycle. Acetyl CoA is converted to citric and isocitric acids as usual, but then an enzyme called **isocitritase** splits isocitric acid into succinate and glyoxylate, so that the enzymes isocitric dehydrogenase and α-ketoglutarate dehydrogenase of the Krebs cycle are bypassed. The succinate is converted into fumarate, the fumarate to malate, and the malate to oxaloacetate according to the Krebs cycle. The glyoxylate, however, combines with another acetyl CoA formed by β-oxidation, producing malate. This condensation is catalyzed by the enzyme **malate synthetase**. The resulting malate is also converted to oxaloacetate, which could again start the cycle by combining with another acetyl CoA. However, much of this oxaloacetate is instead decarboxylated.

This decarboxylation of oxaloacetate is an ATP-dependent reaction, which produces phosphoenolpyruvic acid. Phosphoenolpyruvate can then be converted to sugars by a reversal of the reactions of glycolysis. Sucrose is the predominant sugar accumulating from operation of the glyoxylate cycle. The energy required to convert oxaloacetate via phosphoenolpyruvate to sucrose by reversing glycolysis presumably arises as follows: *First*, the NADH essential to convert 3-phosphoglyceric acid to 3-phosphoglyceraldehyde (see Chapter 15) is formed indirectly in the glyoxylate cycle when malate is oxidized to oxaloacetate. NADH also arises at various steps in the β-oxidation process leading to acetyl CoA formation. *Second*, some of these NADH molecules are apparently oxidized by the mitochondria, which produces ATP by oxidative phosphorylation. These ATP molecules are presumably available for driving oxaloacetate to phosphoenolpyruvate, phosphoglyceric acid to phosphoglyceraldehyde,

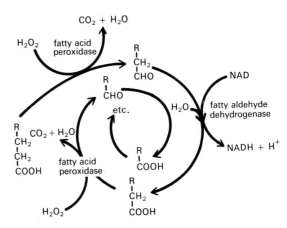

Figure 18-5

The α-oxidation mechanism for breakdown of fatty acids to CO_2 and NADH.

and phosphoglyceraldehyde via the hexose phosphates and UDPG to sucrose. A final factor causing reactions of glycolysis to be reversed is probably that of mass action. As the glyoxylate pathway continues to utilize acetyl CoA units, the concentrations of phosphoenolpyruvate and other intermediates probably build up, thus helping to make sucrose formation thermodynamically feasible. Sucrose can then be translocated from the storage tissues of the seed in which the above reactions operate into the developing embryo. There it is used as a source of energy and of carbon skeletons for growth of the seedling. The glyoxylate cycle is thus important to seeds by providing a mechanism for conversion of fats, which cannot be transported to the embryo, into sucrose, which can be (Fig. 18-7).

18.1.2 Plant Waxes

Waxes have been physically defined as substances with a waxy feel and with a melting point above body temperature and below the boiling point of water. Chemically, the waxes include a variety of long-chain carbon com-

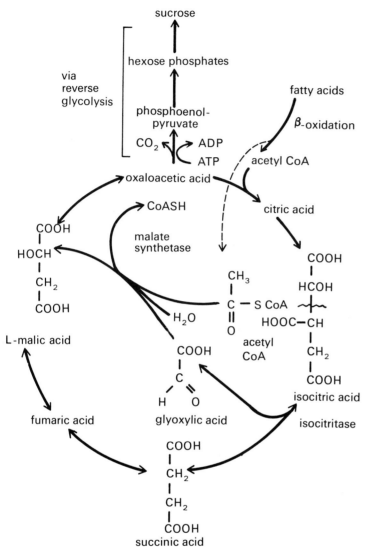

Figure 18-6

Conversion of fatty acids to sucrose through the glyoxylate cycle.

pounds rich in hydrogen and poor in oxygen. The composition of plant waxes varies widely among different species. Many contain fatty acids esterified with long-chain monohydric alcohols. Plant waxes also contain free long-chain alcohols, aldehydes and ketones ranging from 22 to 32 carbon atoms long, and even hydrocarbons containing up to 37 carbon atoms, and thus with high melting points. Most of the pure hydrocarbons and secondary

peanut seed

cotyledon

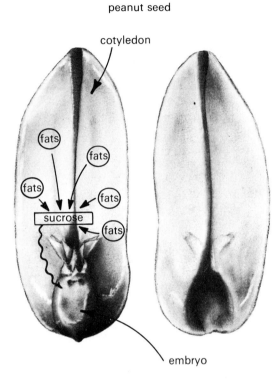

embryo

Figure 18-7
Fats and oils stored in the cytoplasm of cells such as those of the cotyledons of peanut seeds are broken down to acetyl CoA by β-oxidation, and the acetyl CoA is converted to sucrose through the glyoxylate cycle and reverse glycolysis. The sucrose can be transported from cell to cell (perhaps through plasmodesmata), while the larger, insoluble fat molecules are not transportable.

anical damage and some plant pathogens. It may allow penetration of certain molecules, including CO_2. A cuticle is usually absent from roots. The waxes seem to originate in the epidermal cells as oily droplets, which then move into the outer cell walls through plasmodesmata and crystallize on the epidermal surfaces.

18.1.3 The Phospholipids and Glycolipids

18.1.3A Phospholipids   Phospholipids are lipids containing phosphate, as well as fatty acids, esterified with glycerol. The structures of phospholipids are exemplified by a **phosphatidic acid**, shown below.

$$CH_2O-\overset{\overset{\displaystyle O}{\|}}{C}-\text{fatty acid}$$

fatty acid$-\overset{\overset{\displaystyle}{}}{\underset{\overset{\displaystyle \|}{O}}{C}}-O-\overset{\overset{\displaystyle}{}}{\underset{}{C}}-H$

$$CH_2O-\overset{}{\underset{\overset{\displaystyle \|}{O}}{P}}\overset{OH}{\underset{}{-}}OH$$

phosphatidic acid

Phosphatidic acids do not commonly accumulate in plants but are intermediates in formation of other similar compounds, including **lecithin**, in which the phosphate is esterified to **choline**, $HO-CH_2-CH_2-N^+(CH_3)_3$; **cephalins**, in which the phosphate is esterified to the hydroxyl group of **ethanolamine**, $HO-CH_2-CH_2-NH_2$ (or serine); **phosphatidyl glycerol**, in which an additional glycerol is esterified with the phosphate; and **phosphatidyl inositol**, which contains an ester linkage between the phosphate and the sugar alcohol inositol.

The phospholipids contain both a water-insoluble portion (the fatty acids) and a hydrophilic water-soluble portion (choline, ethanolamine, serine, inositol, glycerol). They are important constituents of various membranes, such as those of the chloroplast, mitochondria,

alcohols have an odd number of carbon atoms, while the primary alcohols, aldehydes and carboxylic acids are even numbered.

Little is known of their metabolism, although acetyl CoA is a probable source of most of the atoms they contain. Waxes are important because they form a protective coating (the cuticle) over leaves, stems, flowers, fruits, and seeds. The cuticle slows water loss from the aerial parts of plants, thus providing protection against desiccation and perhaps against mech-

and apparently the nuclear membrane, tonoplast, plasmalemma, and endoplasmic reticulum.

18.1.3B The glycolipids

The **glycolipids** are lipids in which a terminal hydroxyl group of glycerol is attached by a glycosidic bond to a sugar, most commonly galactose or glucose. Glycolipids are especially important in green leaves, and their concentration there greatly exceeds that of the phospholipids. Chloroplast membranes are especially rich in glycolipids, although these compounds do not appear to be significant components of mitochondria.

Three important glycolipids are known. One of these contains galactose linked to a terminal hydroxyl group of glycerol; another contains two connected galactose residues attached to this position; and the third contains 6-deoxyglucose. The deoxyglucose-containing glycolipid also contains sulfur. This sulfur is present as a sulfate group attached directly to the free C-6 deoxy group of the sugar by a carbon–sulfur bond. The structures of these compounds have been primarily worked out by A. A. Benson in the United States and by scientists in Japan.

18.1.3C Metabolism of the phospholipids and glycolipids

It is probable that plant phospholipids are synthesized by a pathway similar to that established for animals, but direct evidence that this is the case has thus far been found primarily only in the case of spinach leaves. The proposed reactions for synthesizing some of the phospholipids are summarized in Fig. 18-8.

The first reaction in lecithin and cephalin synthesis is an activation by ATP of choline, or ethanolamine. Phosphoryl choline and phosphoryl ethanolamine are formed, and ADP is the other product of this reaction. Next, the phosphoryl choline and phosphoryl ethanolamine are further activated by reaction with cytidine triphosphate (CTP), forming cytidine diphosphate choline, etc. The **cytidine diphosphate choline** then reacts with a molecule of glycerol to which two fatty acids are already attached (a diglyceride). A finished phospholipid is the product of this reaction, and cytidine-5'-phosphate (CMP) is released.

CTP is also thought to be necessary for synthesizing phosphatidyl glycerol and phosphatidyl inositol, but here it is the diglyceride that is probably activated by CTP. This activated CDP-diglyceride then likely reacts with either an inositol-phosphate or with an α-glycerophosphate to produce phosphatidyl inositol or phosphatidyl glycerol.

Little is known of the formation or breakdown of the glycolipids or of the breakdown of the phospholipids in plants.

18.1.4 The Isoprenoid Compounds

A diverse group of plant products including compounds such as the **steroids**, **carotenoids**, **turpentine**, and **rubber** have some of the general properties of lipids. The functions of many of these compounds are unknown, and many simply appear to be metabolic by-products, similar to the alkaloids discussed in Chapter 16. Important functions for some of these, however, such as the carotenoids, are known, and it is likely that roles for others will eventually be discovered. Many of these are of interest because of their commercial uses and because they illustrate the ability of plants to synthesize a vast complex of compounds not usually formed by animals.

Most of the isoprenoids may be considered to be polymers of **isoprene units**, in which these are joined in a head-to-tail fashion:

$$\text{(head)} \quad -CH=\overset{\overset{\displaystyle CH_3}{|}}{C}-CH=CH- \quad \text{(tail)}$$

isoprene unit

A description of a few of the isoprenoids and a brief description of what is known about the way in which they are formed will follow.

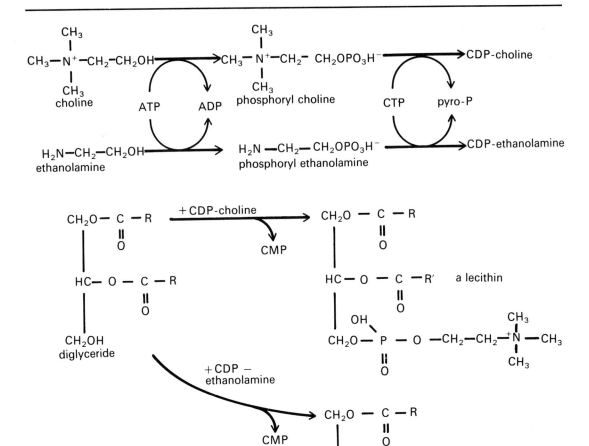

Figure 18-8
Reactions involved in synthesis of some lecithins and cephalins.

18.1.4A Steroids The best known steroids include **stigmasterol**, **β-sitosterol**, **ergosterol**, and **cholesterol**. Cholesterol was thought to be present only in animals until 1958. It was then discovered in red algae, and in 1963 it was found in *Solanum tuberosum* (potato) and in *Dioscorea spiculiflora* plants. It has since then been observed in small quantities in other species. Certain fungi, including yeasts and *Neurospora*, the red bread mold fungus, contain

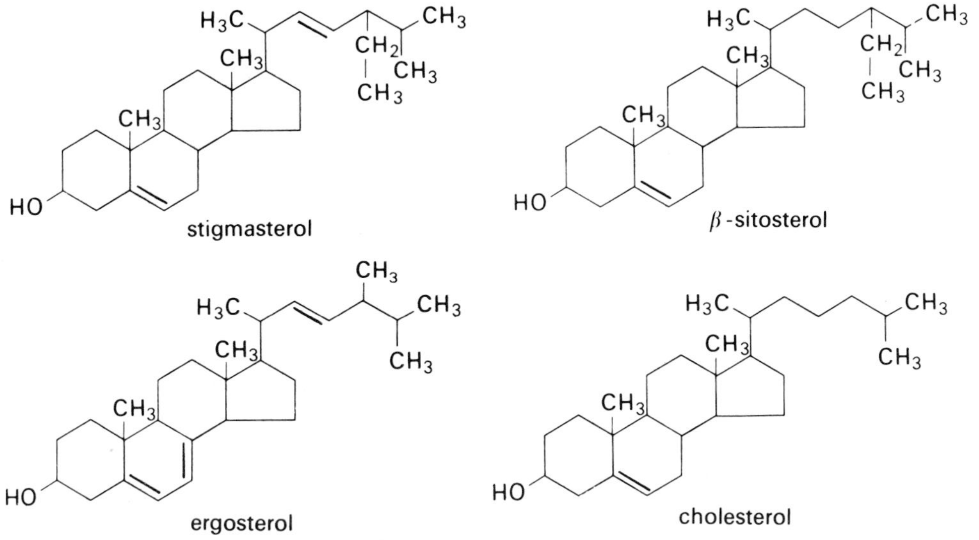

Figure 18-9

Structures of some important sterols. Note that each has one hydroxyl group through which it may be attached to sugars (glycosidic linkage) or to organic acids (ester linkages).

appreciable amounts of **ergosterol**, although this compound is less abundant in higher plants.

The structures of these steroids are given in Fig. 18-9. Most contain 27 to 29 carbon atoms. Because each possesses a hydroxyl group, such steroids are usually called sterols. Sterols exist in the plant in the free form but are also present as glycosides, in which various sugars are attached to the hydroxyl groups or as esters.

Sterols appear to be widely distributed in the plant kingdom but are believed to be absent in most blue-green algae and bacteria. Their function in plants is not known, although many of them are identical to compounds that are of considerable physiological importance in animals. They are of additional importance to man because of their use as starting materials for the chemical synthesis of certain synthetic animal hormones, including the male sex hormone, **androsterone**, and the female ovarian hormone, **progesterone.** In addition, ergosterol is of im-

portance because it is converted by ultraviolet radiation to vitamin D_2 (calciferol).

Similar although generally larger molecules occurring in certain plants, such as **digitalin** from *Digitalis purpurea*, are used in heart therapy. Certain related compounds such as **digitoxigenin** have been used since prehistoric times as arrow poisons.

18.1.4B The carotenoids The carotenoids were discussed in Chapter 13 in relation to their functions in photosynthesis. Both the **carotenes**, which are pure hydrocarbons, and the **xanthophylls**, which contain in addition small quantities of oxygen, are isoprenoids. The carotenoids are a group of yellow, orange, or red pigments existing in various kinds of plastids in roots, stems, leaves, flowers, and fruits of various plants. They are not water soluble but do dissolve readily in petroleum ether, 80 percent acetone, and certain other organic solvents.

About eighty different carotenoids are known in the plant kingdom, although not all are found in any given plant. Most of the carotenoids contain forty carbon atoms. **β-carotene** is the most abundant carotenoid found in higher plants and is the compound imparting the orange color to carrot roots. **Lutein**, an example of the oxygen-containing xanthophylls, is believed to be present in all plants and is probably the predominant xanthophyll of leaves. The structures of both β-carotene and lutein shown in Chapter 13 (Fig. 13-1) are typical of several other carotenoids found in various plants. **Lycopene**, a similar carotenoid, is the compound giving the reddish color to tomato fruits.

The functions of the carotenoids are still not completely clear. As discussed in Chapter 13, there is evidence that they participate in photosynthesis, especially in the brown algae, and that they prevent photooxidation of chlorophylls. They may also act as photoreceptors for light causing **phototropism**, a plant bending phenomenon discussed in Chapter 21. It has been postulated that carotenoids present in flowers might benefit certain plants by attracting insects necessary for pollination of some species.

18.1.4C Miscellaneous isoprenoids and essential oils

A large number of miscellaneous isoprenoid compounds are present in various amounts among certain members of the plant kingdom. In these the isoprene unit is condensed into ring compounds containing ten, fifteen, twenty, thirty, and even more carbon atoms. Many of the isoprenoids containing ten or fifteen carbons are present in **essential oils**. The "essential" does not derive from any known essential function the oils perform in plants, but because they are volatile and contribute to the odor, or essence, of certain species.

One of the best known essential oils is **turpentine**, present in certain specialized cells of members of the genus *Pinus*. The turpentine

of some species consists largely of *n*-heptane, although ten-carbon isoprenoids are also present. The essential oils sometimes contain hydroxyl groups or are chemically modified in other ways. The structures of two such compounds, **menthol** and **menthone**, both components of mint oils, are as follows:

menthol   menthone

Essential oils often contain compounds other than isoprenoids. The essential oils of orange and jasmine flowers, for example, contain **indole**, a nitrogen-containing compound structurally related to the amino acid tryptophan.

Certain compounds containing twenty or thirty carbon atoms make up the **resins**, which are common in gymnosperms. Resins and related materials are formed in conifer leaves by specialized cells that line the so-called **resin ducts** (Fig. 6-4) and are then secreted inside the ducts where they accumulate. Similar resin ducts also occur in the vascular tissues of other organs of these species (e.g., in wood, Fig. 18-10).

Finally, it should be mentioned that the phytol alcohol esterified to the chlorophyll molecule is an isoprenoid compound. This compound contains twenty carbon atoms and is thus a product of four isoprene units. Reduction has occurred so that only one double bond remains in the phytol group.

18.1.4D Rubber

Rubber is also an isoprenoid compound. It contains some 3,000 to 6,000 isoprene units linked together in very long, unbranched chains (Fig. 18-11). Most natural rubber is commercially obtained from the

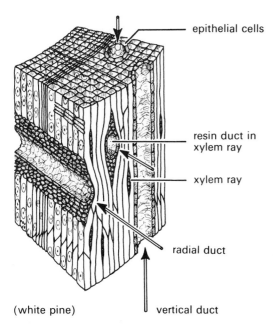

(white pine)

Figure 18-10

A three-dimensional schematic drawing of a piece of pine wood (highly magnified), drawn to show vertical and horizontal (radial) resin ducts with their lining of epithelial cells.

tropical plant *Hevea brasiliensis*, a member of the Euphorbiaceae family. It has been reported, however, that over 2,000 plant species form rubber in varying amounts. Various *Taraxacum* (dandelion) species are among the most well known North American species possessing this ability.

18.1.4E The gibberellins A final group of isoprenoid compounds of great importance in plant physiology are the **gibberellins**. At least twenty-four such compounds have been reported to occur in various plant species (including fungi), each differing from the others in only a minor way. The gibberellins possess carboxyl groups and are commonly called **gibberellic acids,** the various types being distinguished by adding subscript numbers. The structure of one of these, GA_3, is as follows:

The gibberellins are important plant hormones controlling growth and several important functions discussed especially in Chapter 21.

18.1.4F Metabolism of the isoprenoid compounds The initial reactions leading to the synthesis of the isoprenoids are presently thought to be common to all of these compounds. Eventually, however, branches in the pathway occur, and a great deal of variation in reactions leading to the final formation of the large number of such compounds must exist. No attempts have yet been made to study most of these reactions. Research on the biosynthesis of certain of these compounds, especially the carotenoids, suggests that the initial reactions are similar or identical to those leading to cholesterol synthesis in animals.

Several of the known and suspected steps leading to the formation of isoprenoid compounds are outlined in Fig. 18-12. These reactions will be only briefly summarized here. A more complete description can be found in various modern biochemistry books. As with other lipids such as the fatty acids, nearly all of the carbon atoms of the isoprenoids arise from acetyl CoA molecules produced from the partial breakdown of products of photosynthesis. Many of the intermediate compounds formed from acetyl CoA are covalently bound to sulfur atoms of proteins and never occur free, which is also a feature common to the formation of fatty acids, as mentioned earlier.

When the various isoprenoids are being built, the acetoacetate-protein compound reacts with another molecule of acetyl CoA, yielding a six-carbon molecule, **hydroxymethyl glutaric acid**. This is then reduced by NADPH, forming

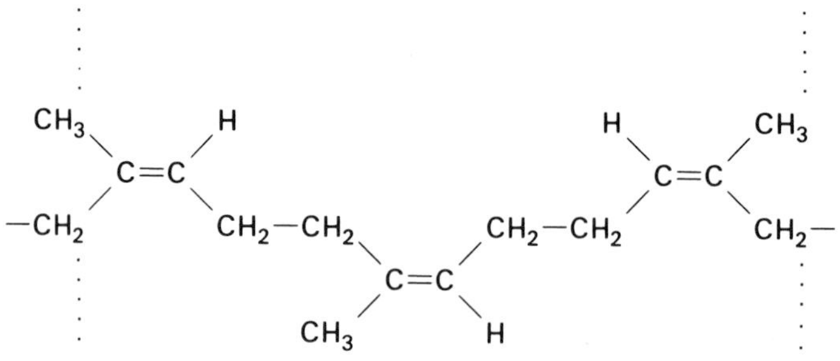

Figure 18-11

Three isoprene units of a molecular chain in rubber.

a key intermediate, **mevalonic acid**. Many of the plant isoprenoids are readily formed from ^{14}C-labeled mevalonic acid, even though most of the necessary intermediate reactions are not well established.

ATP participates in isoprenoid formation in three reactions: Mevalonic acid is first converted to **5-phosphomevalonate**, a reaction in which the terminal alcohol group is phosphorylated by ATP. Then a second molecule of ATP is used to convert 5-phosphomevalonate to **mevalonic acid diphosphate**, a molecule with two phosphate units attached in a pyrophosphate bond just as in ADP, UDP, etc. The third molecule of ATP participates in a reaction that now removes the carboxyl and the hydroxyl groups of mevalonic acid diphosphate, forming CO_2, Pi, ADP, and the five-carbon, isoprene-like compound, **isopentenyl pyrophosphate**. Isopentenyl pyrophosphate is an active form of an isoprene unit and is also the immediate precursor of another such unit, **dimethylallyl pyrophosphate**. The structures of these two very reactive compounds are as follows:

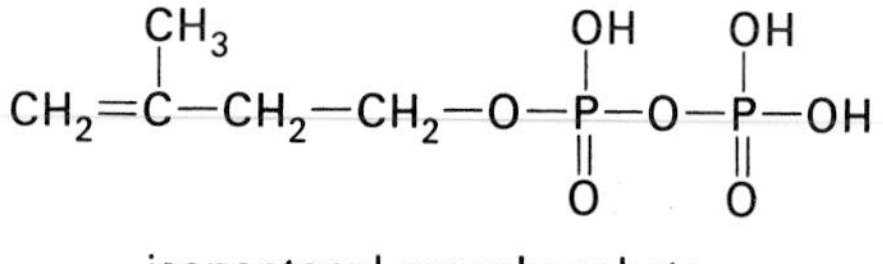

isopentenyl pyrophosphate

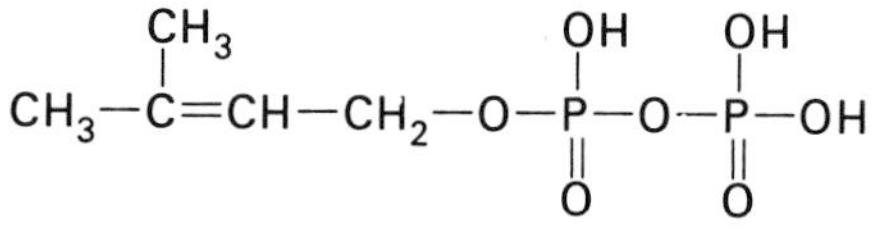

dimethylallyl pyrophosphate

Various isoprenoid compounds containing multiples of five-carbon atoms arise by suitable combinations of the two molecules above and pyrophosphate-containing products of their combination as outlined in Fig. 18-12. Occasionally, single carbon atoms may be removed, as in the gibberellins, or they may be added from *S*-adenosyl methionine, as is the case with some of the sterols. In this way the plant is able to build up a large number of different yet related products from the activated isoprene groups, undoubtedly including many compounds that have not yet been discovered.

Essentially nothing is known of the breakdown of isoprenoids, or even whether they are degraded at significant rates. It is interesting, though, that in the animal body the cleavage of β-carotene at the double bond in the center of the molecule, followed by the conversion of the two resulting terminal carbon atoms to hydroxyl groups, results in two molecules of **vitamin A**.

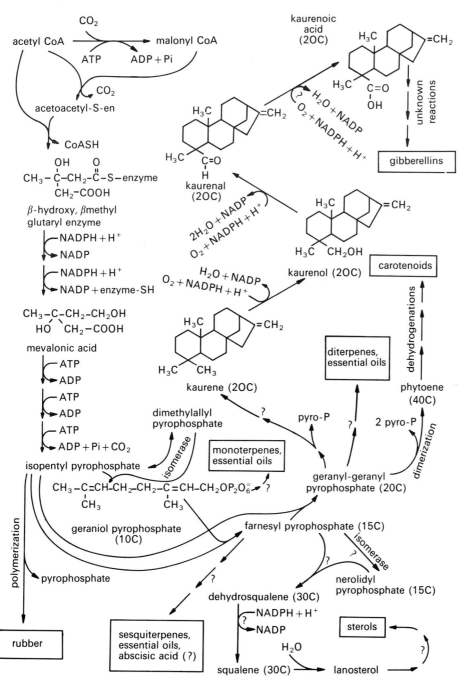

Figure 18-12

A summary of some known and postulated reactions in the metabolism of isoprenoids.

18.2 PHENOLIC AND RELATED COMPOUNDS

Flowering plants, ferns, mosses, liverworts, and many microorganisms contain various kinds and amounts of **phenolic compounds**. With certain important exceptions, the functions of most of these substances are obscure, and many appear at present to be simply by-products of metabolism.

All of the compounds to be discussed are called **aromatic compounds** because they possess a benzene ring. This ring contains various attached substituent groups, such as hydroxyl, carboxyl, and methoxyl ($-O-CH_3$) groups, and often other nonaromatic ring structures. The phenolic compounds themselves always contain at least one hydroxyl group on the benzene ring. The phenolics differ from the lipids in being generally soluble in water and less soluble in nonpolar organic solvents such as benzene. Some, however, are rather soluble in ether, especially when the pH is low enough to prevent ionization of the carboxyl and hydroxyl groups that are often present.

18.2.1 The Aromatic Amino Acids

Phenylalanine, tyrosine, and tryptophan are aromatic amino acids formed by a route common to many of the phenolic compounds. The structures and importance of these amino acids were discussed in Chapter 11.

The pathway of biosynthesis of phenylalanine and tyrosine was first determined in bacteria in the 1950s. Their formation in flowering plants is presently thought to occur by the same reactions, but the mechanism of tryptophan formation has not been studied extensively in higher plants. Two respiratory intermediates appear to be the basic precursors of the aromatic amino acids and of many other phenolic compounds as well. These are phosphoenolpyruvic acid from the glycolytic pathway, and erythrose-4-phosphate from the pentose phosphate respiratory pathway. These two molecules combine, producing a seven-carbon compound that forms a ring structure similar to that of the hexose, pentose, and heptose sugars in solution (Chapter 12). This is then converted by several reactions into a more stable compound called **shikimic acid**. These steps make up what has come to be known as the **shikimic acid pathway**. Shikimic acid is converted into a key intermediate, **prephenic acid**, with the help of ATP, by combination with another molecule of phosphoenolpyruvate. Phenylalanine and tyrosine then arise by separate reaction sequences from prephenic acid (Fig. 18-13). The structures of shikimic and prephenic acids are shown below:

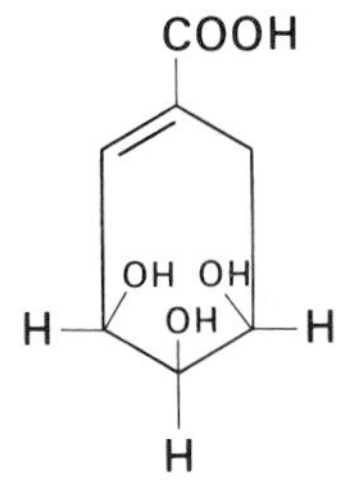

shikimic acid

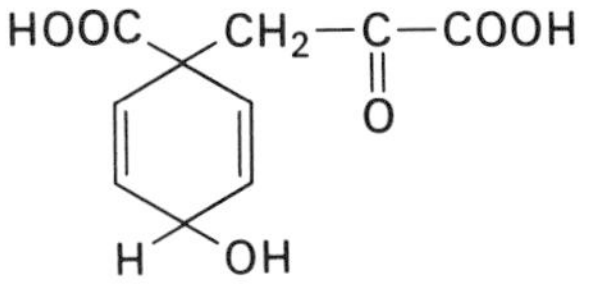

prephenic acid

In the formation of phenylalanine, prephenic acid is converted to **phenylpyruvic acid**

$$C_6H_6-CH_2-\underset{\underset{O}{\|}}{C}-COOH$$

another important α-keto acid. Phenylpyruvate is converted directly to phenylalanine by the addition of an amino group from another amino acid, such as glutamate in a transamination reaction (Chapter 16). Tyrosine, however, arises from prephenic acid by a slightly different route, involving no loss of the hydroxyl group

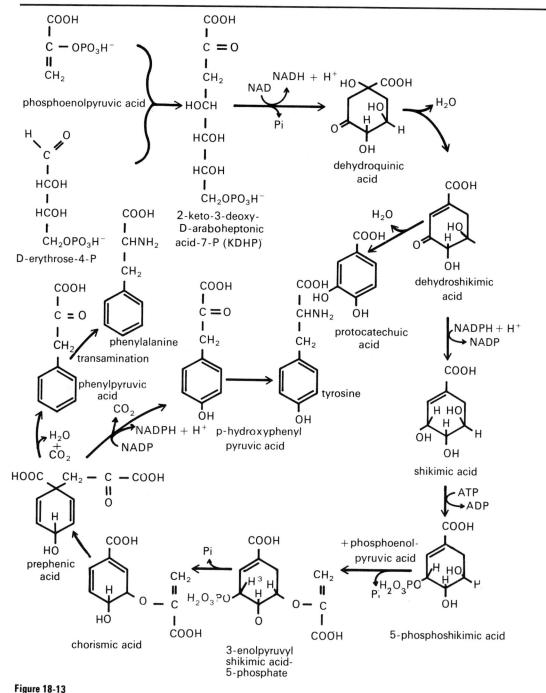

Figure 18-13

Biosynthesis of phenylalanine and tyrosine from respiratory intermediates. All of the carbon atoms seem to arise from phosphoenolpyruvate (two molecules) and from erythrose-4-phosphate (one molecule). ATP is required as an energy source, but there is no net utilization of reducing power (NADH or NADPH).

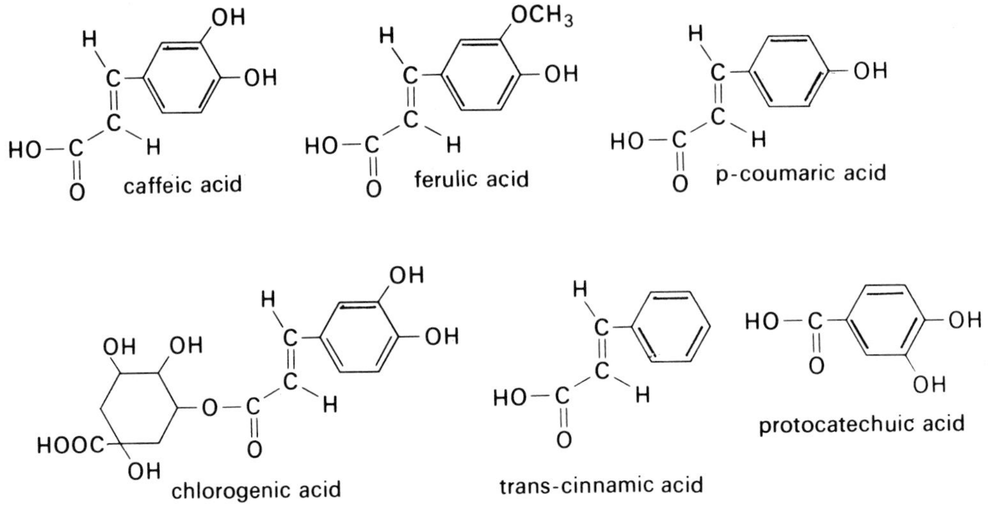

Figure 18-14

Structures of phenolic acids often found in plants. Chlorogenic acid is an ester formed from caffeic and quinic acids.

present in prephenate. As with phenylalanine, the amino group of tyrosine is thought to be donated by another amino acid in a transamination reaction. Phenylalanine and tyrosine are not interconvertible to any important extent in plants, and each arises only by separate reactions from a common precursor. Recent research by Deborah Delmer and S. E. Mills in California indicates that tryptophan is formed in plants (as in microorganisms) from products of the shikimic acid pathway.

18.2.2 Miscellaneous Simple Phenols and Related Compounds

An extensive number of other relatively simple compounds also arise from the shikimic acid pathway and subsequent reactions. Among these are the acids **trans-cinnamic, *p*-coumaric, caffeic, ferulic, protocatechuic,** and **chlorogenic**. The structures of these are presented in Fig. 18-14.

Except for the last two, all of these acids arise directly from either phenylalanine or tyrosine. In grasses, both tyrosine and phenylalanine can be **deaminated**, a reaction in which ammonia is split out, producing *p*-coumaric acid from tyrosine, and trans-cinnamic acid from phenylalanine. Dicots do not deaminate tyrosine readily, but they do form trans-cinnamic acid directly from phenylalanine. Dicots further have the ability to add hydroxyl groups to trans-cinnamic acid, forming *p*-coumaric and caffeic acids. It is believed that the methoxyl group of ferulic acid arises by addition of a methyl group from *S*-adenosyl methionine to caffeic acid.

Trans-cinnamic, caffeic, and *p*-coumaric acids do not commonly occur free in plants but are usually combined with sugars, most commonly glucose, through either their hydroxyl groups or their carboxyl groups, forming glycosides or esters, respectively.

Chlorogenic acid is an example of an ester of caffeic acid, except that it is esterified to another phenolic acid, D-**quinic acid**, instead of to glucose. Both quinic acid and protocatechuic acid also seem to be formed from intermediates of the shikimic acid pathway.

The functions of trans-cinnamic, caffeic, and ferulic acids in plants are not entirely clear, even though these compounds are widely distributed throughout the plant kingdom. However, they seem to be important in the formation of lignin, since if they are tagged with ^{14}C and fed to plants the lignin is readily labeled, and because, as will be shown later, lignin contains subunit molecules similar to these acids.

Present work indicates that protocatechuic and chlorogenic acids may have special functions in disease resistance of certain plants. It appears definite that protocatechuic acid is one of the compounds preventing smudge in certain colored varieties of onions, a disease caused by the fungus *Colletotrichum circinans.* This acid occurs in the scales of the neck of colored onions that are resistant to the pathogen, but it is absent from susceptible white varieties. When extracted from these onions it is found to inhibit strongly the growth of the smudge fungus and other fungi.

There is some indirect evidence that high amounts of chlorogenic acid may similarly prevent certain diseases, such as the scabs of potato tubers and of apple leaves of resistant varieties. Chlorogenic acid is widely distributed in various parts of many plants and usually occurs in easily detectable quantities. It is formed in relatively high amounts in many potato tubers, and its oxidation followed by polymerization causes the darkening of freshly cut tubers, as mentioned in Chapter 15. It is thought that chlorogenic acid and certain other compounds can be readily formed and oxidized into potent fungistatic quinones by certain disease resistant varieties, but less readily by

susceptible ones. In this way the infection is well localized in the resistant plants. Chlorogenic acid and certain other phenolic compounds that are easily oxidized by specific oxidase enzymes increase the rate of formation and the thickness of periderm (cork) produced when potato tubers and certain other tissues are cut. They thus further aid in protecting these plants from the invasion of microorganisms.

A group of compounds closely related to the phenolic acids and also believed to be products of the shikimic acid pathway are the **coumarins**. Approximately 50 coumarins are known, although only a few are usually found in any particular plant family. The structures of two coumarins, **scopoletin** and **coumarin** itself, are as follows:

scopoletin   coumarin

Coumarin is a volatile compound and is present in especially significant amounts in alfalfa and sweet clover, where it causes the characteristic odor of recently mown hay. Certain sweet clover strains have been developed that contain low amounts of coumarin and others that contain it in a bound form. These are of economic importance, because free coumarin forms a toxic product, **dicumarol**, if the clover becomes spoiled during storage. Dicumarol is a hemorrhagic and anticoagulant agent responsible for sweet-clover disease in ruminant animals that are fed plants containing it.

Scopoletin is a toxic compound widespread in plants and is often found in seed coats. In some of these seeds there is evidence that scopoletin prevents germination, causing a dormancy that exists until the chemical is leached out of the seed. It may thus function as a natural inhibitor of seed germination. It appears to be formed from coumarin, which, in turn, arises from phenylalanine and trans-cinnamic acid. Apparently a hydroxyl group is added in the ortho position of trans-cinnamate that then reacts intramolecularly with the carboxyl group, splitting out water, and forming the **lactone rings** present in coumarins. These are unsaturated lactones, because the side chain of trans-cinnamic acid contains a double bond.

Certain toxic coumarin derivatives are synthesized in response to parasite invasion and may prove to play a role in disease resistance. Since about 1960, various other antifungal compounds have been discovered that also appear to be synthesized by the plant only when it is infected by certain fungi. These compounds act, in a way, comparably to the antibodies of animal cells. They are collectively referred to as **phytoalexins** (from the Greek, *phyton*, or plant, and *alexin*, a warding-off substance). Compounds that act as phytoalexins include **pisatin**, in pea pods and **phaseollin**, in bean pods. Others that apparently are produced only when the plant is invaded and thus seem to be phytoalexins include **orchinol**, from orchid tubers, **trifolirhizin**, from red clover roots, and an **isocoumarin**, from carrot roots. It appears that nonpathogenic fungi often induce large, toxic levels of phytoalexins in the host, and this prevents their establishment, while pathogenic fungi are successful parasites because they induce phytoalexin levels not toxic to themselves. How these compounds can prevent fungal growth without injuring the host cells in which they are produced is an interesting question.

18.2.3 Lignin

Lignin is a strengthening material that occurs together with cellulose, hemicellulose, and other sugar polymers in the cell walls of higher plants. It occurs in largest amounts in woody plants,

where it accumulates in the secondary walls of the xylem elements. Here the lignin is found between the cellulose microfibrils where it serves to resist compression forces. Resistance to tension is primarily a function of the cellulose. Lignin may easily be detected by the bright red color it gives when stained with a mixture of phloroglucinol and hydrochloric acid. It is normally a brown, amorphous solid.

Lignin is not readily soluble in most solvents, primarily because it, like cellulose, has a high molecular weight (probably more than 10,000), and because in the native state it is chemically united to the cellulose at various points by ether linkages through the cellulose hydroxyl groups. It is possible to remove lignin from wood by dissolving it in sodium bisulfite, which, however, breaks it down into small water-soluble sulfite derivatives. The treatment with sodium bisulfite is used in the paper industry to remove lignin from wood. The presence of lignin otherwise causes the paper to become yellow. Lignins remain almost entirely a waste product in the pulp and paper industry. Canadian industries alone were estimated to discard over 3 million tons annually.

Because of the difficulty in dissolving lignin without destroying it and some of its subunits, it has been impossible to ascertain its exact chemical structure. Much of what is known about lignin structure has been determined by analyzing several large molecules that are intermediates in its synthesis. This is contrasted with our knowledge of polysaccharides, proteins, and nucleic acids, the structures of which were largely determined by analyzing degradation products. It is currently not possible to state the exact structure of any lignin, and, in fact, lignins from the conifers, angiosperms, and mosses differ in the amounts of subunits they contain. Nevertheless, lignins from all these plants primarily contain three aromatic alcohols, including **coniferyl alcohol** (which predominates in the conifers), **sinapyl alcohol**, and *p*-coumaryl alcohol. The structure of these compounds are given in Fig. 18-15, along with a proposed model showing the way they may be connected in lignin.

Note the close relationship of these alcohols to the phenolic acids presented in Fig. 18-14. In fact, several acids such as shikimic acid, ferulic acid, *p*-coumaric acid, and phenylalanine are easily converted by plant tissue into lignin, as shown by the Canadian scientists, Stewart Brown and A. C. Neish. Much of what we know about the reactions by which coniferyl alcohol, sinapyl alcohol, and *p*-coumaryl alcohol are converted into lignin was determined in the laboratory of Karl Freudenberg in Germany. There is considerable indirect evidence that peroxidase enzymes act as catalysts in the initial reaction of lignification, but no proof of this yet exists. They are believed to remove hydrogen atoms from hydroxyl groups of the phenolic alcohols, combining these with hydrogen peroxide to produce H_2O (see Chapter 15). The phenolic alcohols presumably attain free radical structures as a result of hydrogen loss and then polymerize spontaneously in various ways. In any case, it is now clear that lignin is a product of the shikimic acid pathway, and that tyrosine (in grasses and certain members of the Compositae family) and phenylalanine are important for lignin biosynthesis, as well as being essential components of proteins. Just how the aromatic alcohols present in lignin are attached to each other and to the cellulose molecules of the cell walls remains to be seen.

18.2.4 The Flavonoids

The **flavonoids** are fifteen-carbon compounds that are generally distributed throughout the plant kingdom. The most common basic flavonoid skeleton, shown below, is usually modified in such a way that more double bonds are present, causing the compounds to absorb visible light and thus giving them color. The two carbon rings at the left and right ends of the molecule are designated the *A* and *B* rings, respectively.

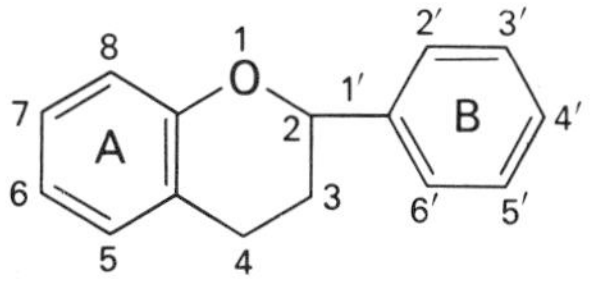

Hydroxyl groups are usually present in the flavonoids, making them sufficiently water soluble so that they often accumulate in the cell vacuoles. Furthermore, one of the hydroxyl groups is often combined to a sugar in a typical glycosidic unit, which makes the molecules even more water soluble. Without hydroxyl groups they are often soluble in certain organic solvents, such as ethyl ether and ethyl acetate. All flavonoids, whether containing added sugar units or not, are readily soluble in methanol or ethanol, and these solvents are commonly used to remove them from the cells.

Three groups of flavonoids are of particular interest in plant physiology. These are the **anthocyanins**, the **flavonols**, and the **flavones**.

18.2.4A The anthocyanins

The **anthocyanins** (from the Greek *anthos*, a flower, and *kyanos*, dark-blue) are colored pigments most commonly seen in the red, purple, and blue flowers. They are also present in various other plant parts, such as certain fruits, stems, leaves, and even roots. Most fruits and many flowers owe their colors to anthocyanins, although some, such as tomato fruits and several yellow flowers, are colored by carotenoids. Anthocyanins are thought to be generally absent in the liverworts, algae, and other lower plants, although certain anthocyanins and other flavonoids were recently clearly demonstrated in certain mosses. They have only rarely been demonstrated in gymnosperms. Several different anthocyanins exist in angiosperms, and often more than one is

(a)

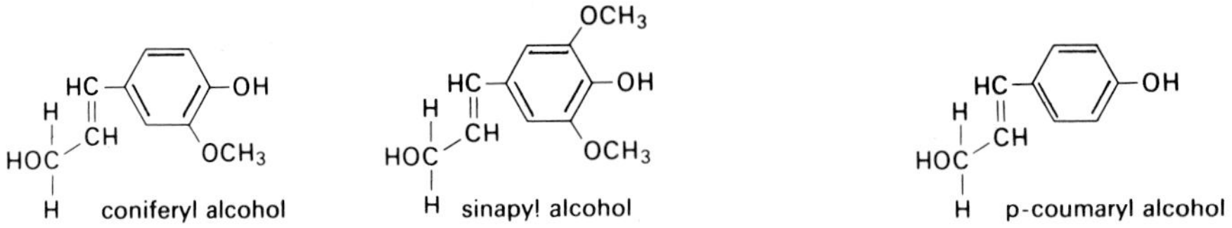

coniferyl alcohol   sinapyl alcohol   p-coumaryl alcohol

(b)

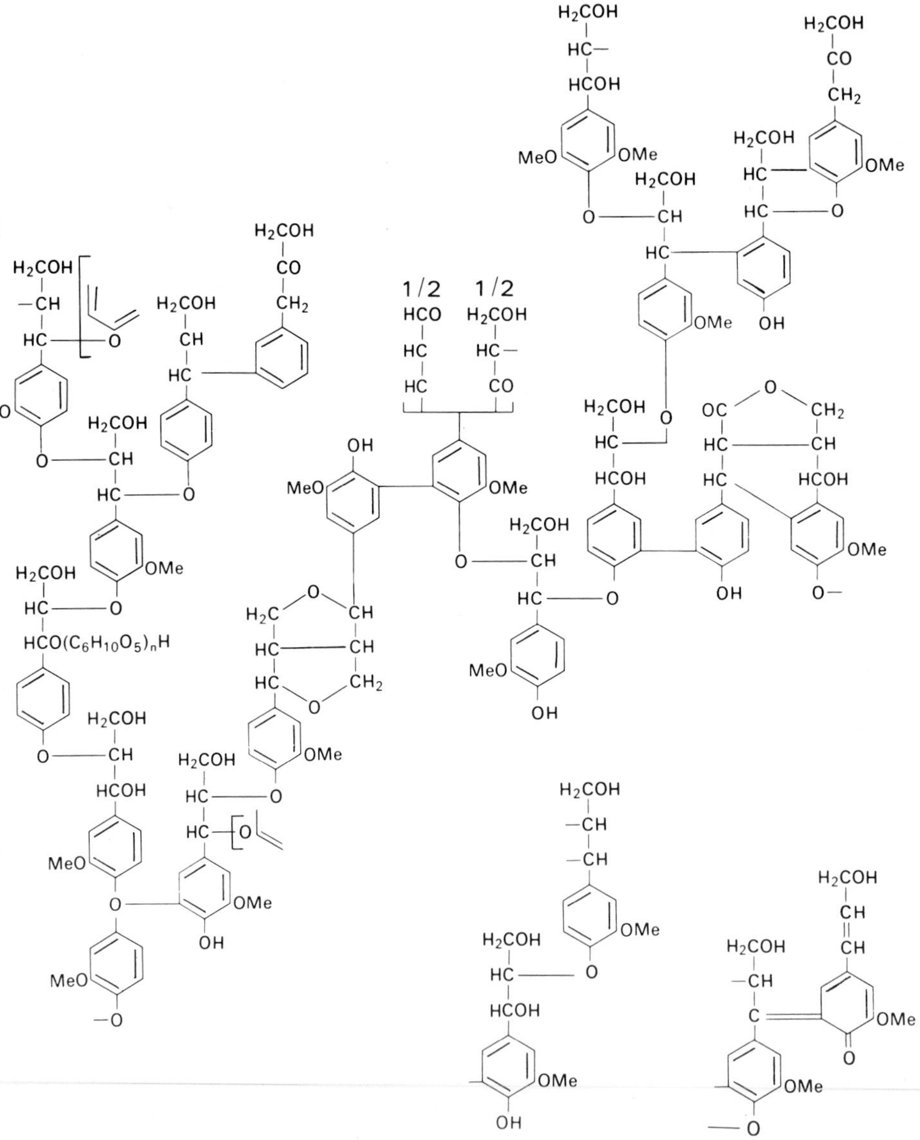

present in a particular flower or other tissue. They are always present as glycosides, containing most commonly one or two glucose or galactose units attached to one of their hydroxyl groups. When the sugars are removed, the remaining parts of the molecules, which are still colored, are called **anthocyanidins**. These compounds are usually named after the particular plant from which they were first obtained.

The most common anthocyanidin is **cyanidin**, which was first isolated from the blue cornflower, *Centaurea cyanus*. Another, **pelargonidin**, was named after a bright red geranium of the genus *Pelargonium*. A third anthocyanidin, **delphinidin**, obtained its name from the genus *Delphinium* (blue larkspur). These molecules differ only in the number of hydroxyl groups attached to the *B* ring of the basic flavonoid structure. Other important anthocyanidins include the reddish **peonidin** (present in peonies), the purple **petunidin** (in petunias), and the mauve-colored (purplish) pigment **malvidin**, which was first found in a member of the Malvaceae, the mallow family.

Figure 18-16 gives the basic anthocyanin structure and shows the differences in the *B* rings occurring in the various anthocyanidins. Also included are the sugar units attached to the anthocyanidin portions of the molecules. Note that the oxygen atom present in the ring between the *A* and *B* rings is written as possessing a double bond and containing a positive charge. The anthocyanins are thus associated with an inorganic anion, such as chloride, sulfate, or phosphate, or with an organic acid anion.

The exact color of the anthocyanins depends first upon the substituent groups present on the *B* ring. When methyl groups are present, for example, as in peonidin, they cause a reddening effect. Secondly, the anthocyanins are sometimes associated with other phenolic types of compounds, and this seems to cause them to become more blue. Finally, the pH of the cell sap has a strong controlling influence upon their color. Most anthocyanins are reddish in acid solution but become purple and blue as the pH is raised. In fact, those isolated from red cabbage become green and finally yellow as the pH is made even more alkaline. These changes are fully reversible. Because of these properties and the common presence of more than one anthocyanin, there is wide variation in the hues of flower colors in higher plants.

The functions anthocyanins perform have presented interesting topics for discussion ever since their discovery. One of their useful functions to certain species is the attraction of birds and insects that carry pollen from one plant to another, thus facilitating pollination. It has also been suggested that they may play a role in disease resistance, although the evidence for this is rather weak. Like other phenolic compounds and the alkaloids, it presently appears that many of the anthocyanins are just interesting by-products of plant metabolism. They are of particular interest to many plant geneticists, because it is possible to correlate phenotypic differences among closely related species in a particular genus, for example, with changes in the type of anthocyanins or other flavonoids they contain. A knowledge of the flavonoid pigments present in related species of the same genus gives information that can be used by biosystematists to determine the lines of evolution of these plants.

Figure 18-15

(a) Common phenolic subunits found in lignins. (b) Constitutional model of spruce lignin, showing possible mechanisms by which alcohol subunits may be connected. The ratio of alcohols in this lignin is about 14 coumaryl:80 coniferyl:6 sinapyl. Beechwood, a typical hardwood lignin, may have ratios about 5:49:46. Methyl groups are represented as Me. (From K. Freudenberg, 1965, *Science* 148:595. Copyright 1965 by the American Association for the Advancement of Science. Used by permission.)

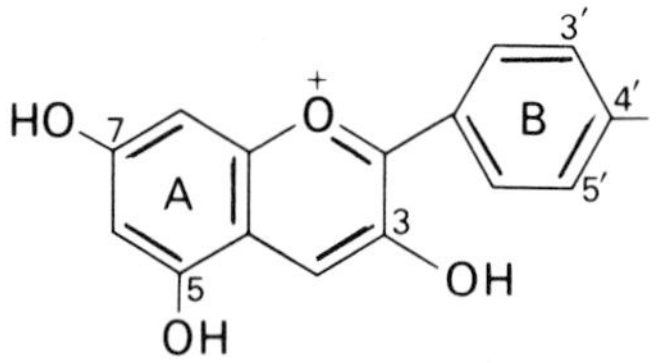

POSITION SUGAR ATTACHED

3   This position is always glycosylated, commonly by glucose, galactose, rhamnose, xylose-glucose, rhamnose-glucose, or glucose-glucose

5   Sometimes glyco-sylated; if so, by glucose

7   Almost never glyco-sylated; if so, by glucose

basic anthocyanidin   structure

(*a*) Hydroxylated Anthocyanidins

pelargonidin (scarlet)   cyanidin (crimson)

delphinidin (blue-violet)

(*b*) Methylated Anthocyanidins

peonidin (rosy red)   petunidin (purple)   malvidin (mauve)

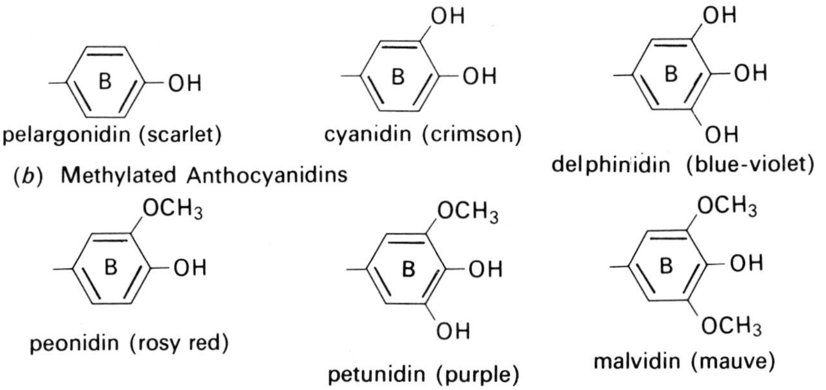

Figure 18-16
The basic anthocyanidin ring, showing variations of *B* ring by hydroxylation and methylation to produce various anthocyanidins. Anthocyanins are produced by attachment of sugars (glycosylation) to the 3 hydroxyl position of the anthocyanidin, and sometimes also to the 5 or 7 position.

18.2.4B The flavonols and flavones The **flavonols** and **flavones** are closely related to the anthocyanins, except that they differ in the central oxygen-containing ring structure, as follows:

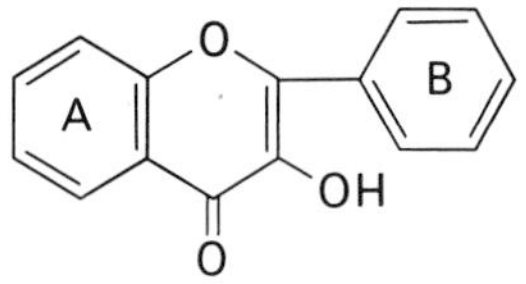

flavonols

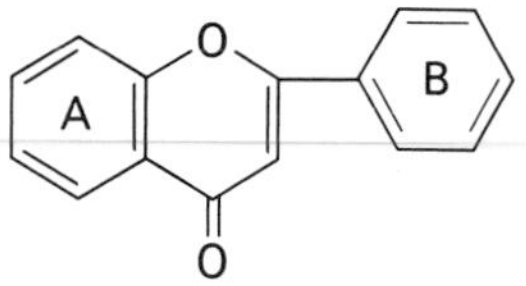

flavones

Most of the flavones and flavonols are yellowish or ivory colored pigments and, like the anthocyanins, they often contribute to the color of flowers. Sometimes they do not appear colored to the human eye, but they are apparent to bees or other insects that are attracted to flowers containing them. This is because the eyes of the insects are sensitive to ultraviolet wavelengths that give these compounds their colors.

Naturally occurring flavonols and flavones are hydroxylated in various positions on both the *A* and *B* rings. Two important flavonols that are very widespread in the plant kingdom are **quercetin** and **kaempferol**. These compounds are present in the flowers, fruits, and leaves of a large number of plants. Like the anthocyanidins, quercetin and kaempferol are usually present in the form of glycosides, with various sugars attached to the hydroxyl group in the central ring. The flavones also occur primarily as glycosides, but since no hydroxyl group is present in the central ring, the sugars are connected on one of the two hydroxyls usually present on the *A* ring.

18.2.4C Synthesis of flavonoids

(1) *The pathway.* Flavonoids are partially products of the shikimic acid pathway. Ring *B* and the carbon atoms of the central ring are formed from shikimic acid and thus from phenylalanine or tyrosine. The difference in the number of hydroxyl groups on ring *B* may be due to the extent of hydroxylation that compounds like trans-cinnamic and *p*-coumaric acids undergo before they are combined with ring *A*. It is more likely, however, that trans-cinnamic acid itself is first combined with ring *A*, and that hydroxyl groups are introduced only later.

Ring *A* does not arise from the shikimic acid pathway, but ^{14}C labeling studies indicate that it is instead produced from head-to-tail condensations of acetate units. It has been suggested that acetyl CoA is converted to malonyl CoA, as in fatty acid formation, and that three such malonyl CoA molecules condense with each other and with a CoA derivative of a phenolic acid, such as *p*-coumaric, forming the basic flavonoid structure. A CO_2 molecule would be released from each malonyl CoA used in the process, thus accounting for the observed labeling patterns. This tentative proposal is diagrammed in Fig. 18-17. It is not yet known how flavonoids are broken down, or even if this occurs readily.

(2) *Environmental influences on flavonoid formation.* It is interesting that light stimulates the formation of flavonoids in many, although not all, plants. The anthocyanins have been studied most in this respect. It has undoubtedly been known for years that the reddest apples are found on the sunny side of the tree. This is due to an accumulation of anthocyanin in these fruits, a process increased by light. The most effective wavelengths are blue and red. The pigment or pigments involved will be more fully discussed in Chapter 23. It is not yet known whether light is stimulatory because of an effect on the formation of ring *A* or ring *B*, or both. Evidence has been obtained for influences on each ring in various tissues.

The nutritional status of a plant also affects its production of anthocyanins. A deficiency of nitrogen, phosphorus, or sulfur leads to accumulations of anthocyanins in certain plants. Low temperatures also increase anthocyanin formation in some species. These effects will be discussed further in subsequent chapters.

18.3 BETACYANINS

The red pigment of beets is an example of a **betacyanin**, one of a group of pigments long thought to be related to the anthocyanins, even though they contain nitrogen. It is now known that they are not at all structurally related to the anthocyanins, and the two types of pigments do not occur together in the same plant. Betacyanins are restricted to eight plant families so far as is known, all of which are members of the order Centrospermae, including the Chenopodiaceae, Amaranthaceae, Nyctaginaceae, Phytolaaccaceae, Cactaceae, Portulacaceae, Basellaceae, and Ficoidaceae. The Caryophyllaceae family, also classified in this order, contains no betacyanins but does contain anthocyanins. Betacyanins do not undergo the characteristic extensive changes in color with *p*H that the anthocyanins do.

Like the anthocyanins and most other flavonoids, these pigments can be hydrolyzed into a sugar and a remaining colored portion. The most extensively studied member of this group is **betanin**, which has been crystallized

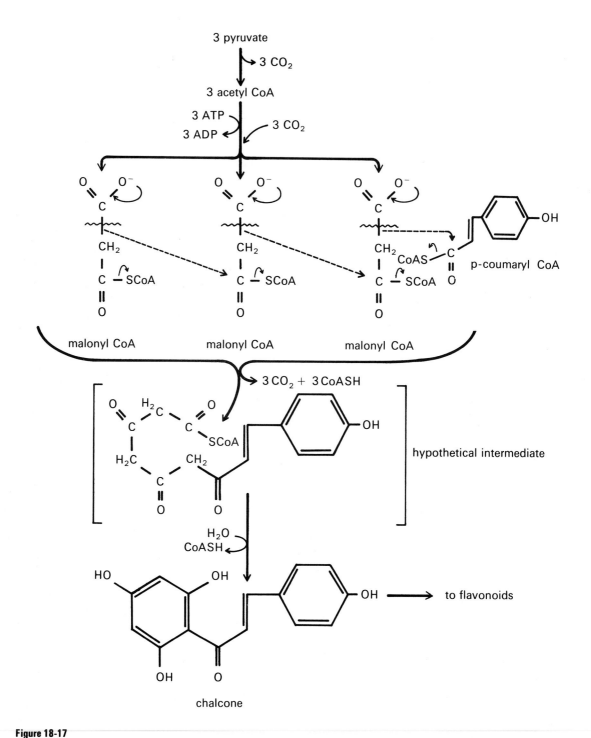

Figure 18-17

Hypothetical conversion of malonyl CoA and *p*-coumaryl CoA to flavonoids via a chalcone. (After H. Grisebach, 1965. In T. W. Goodwin (ed.), *Chemistry and Biochemistry of Plant Pigments*, Academic Press, London, p. 284.)

from red beet roots. Betanin is hydrolyzed into glucose and **betanidin**, a reddish pigment with the following structure:

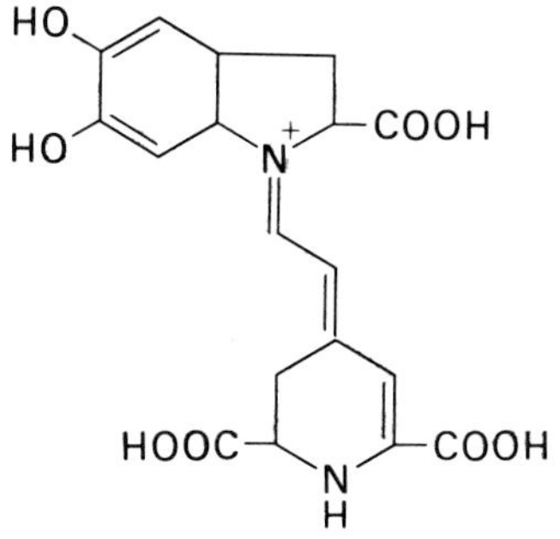

betanidin

Little is yet known of the metabolism or functions of betacyanins.

18.4 SUMMARY OF PLANT METABOLISM

As we can now describe a relatively complete and satisfying picture of the physical functions within the living plant, so it has also become possible in recent years to outline the chemical aspects of plant function. It is obvious that much remains to be learned in both areas, but it should be clear from the nine chapters constituting this section that much is now known about the metabolism of plants. Some high points are summarized in the following paragraphs.

The problem of plant composition has been largely solved. We recognize the importance of carbon, hydrogen, oxygen, and nitrogen in primary plant structure, and we also understand the necessity for relatively large quantities of other so-called major elements, phosphorus, sulfur, potassium, calcium, and magnesium. Intermediate quantities of iron and chlorine are essential, while only trace amounts of the minor elements, molybdenum, manganese, zinc, boron, and copper are required. We are becoming convinced that a few other elements such as sodium, selenium, cobalt, aluminum, and silicon might also be important, particularly for certain species. We recognize that the quantitative relationships among these various elements in the plant differ considerably from those in the earth's crust, atmosphere, and hydrosphere, and we are beginning to understand the mechanisms by which plants selectively accumulate those elements required for life, even though they may be present in the environment only in very small quantities. Perhaps the chemical processing of the atmosphere to obtain the carbon dioxide essential in photosynthesis is the most striking example of this selectivity. We have long recognized the symptoms of the deficiency of any given essential element in the plant, and in more recent years we have been able to understand these symptoms in terms of the roles played by the different elements in plant biochemistry. Recognition that the mineral elements often act as coenzymes or enzyme activators has been especially important in this understanding, but the significant biochemical functions of nitrogen, phosphorus, and sulfur are also impressive.

The enzymes are the key to metabolism. Thousands of different kinds may exist in a single cell, and a highly developed science devoted to their study has come into existence. We have learned how to extract, purify, and examine the activity of enzymes, understanding at least some of this activity at the molecular level. We know that enzymes are proteins exhibiting a high degree of specificity as determined partially by the order of arrangement of amino acids held together in long chains by peptide bonds; by the secondary and tertiary structures of these proteins; and by their dual acid-base nature. Altering enzyme structure often leads to denaturation. We can speak of the enzyme-substrate complex with participation of coenzymes or prosthetic groups, and the resultant lowering of an energy barrier leading to a more rapid attainment of equilibrium in the catalyzed reaction. In these terms, we understand the factors that influence the rate of enzymatically controlled reactions and how this rate relates to metabolism. The picture is being further sketched by our growing understanding of isozymes, allosteric proteins, and the relationship between vitamins, coenzymes, and hormones. Clearly the enzymes open the door to an understanding of metabolism.

The most recent triumph of modern biological science has been the deciphering of the process of protein synthesis. This has opened to our comprehension much of the very nature of life itself, including knowledge about enzyme specificity and the preservation of this specificity from generation to generation. The breakthrough came with the solution of the problem of nucleic acid structure. Knowing this structure provided two extremely important principles: *First*, it was recognized that the arrangement of nucleotides in the nucleic acid chains might constitute the information in control of enzyme specificity. This led to the concept of the genetic code. It became clear that nucleotide triplet groups could act as codons for individual amino acids in the peptide chains of proteins. *Second*, complementary bonding between nucleic acid strands allows for the transfer of this information. This occurs in the replication of DNA, indicating how the highly specific structural characteristics of life can be transmitted through cell divisions and thus through the generations. Complementary bonding of DNA to the RNA strands being built upon it transfers the information to the messenger RNA. Recognition by complementary bonding also makes possible the attachment of a specific amino acid at a proper point in a protein chain by attachment of transfer RNA to messenger RNA on the ribosome. The over-all picture is the preservation of life by preservation of genetic information and application of this

information in the synthesis of enzymes, some of which will, in turn, provide for the duplication and replication of the DNA.

Much of the metabolism controlled by enzymes is concerned with the transformations of carbohydrates. Movement of chemical energy within the plant is primarily the movement of soluble sugars, in most plants, sucrose. These soluble sugars also constitute the primary substrates for respiration, although other compounds may also be oxidized in this process. The monosaccharides are first converted to nucleotide diphosphate sugars (UDPG, ADPG, GDPG, etc.) and are then polymerized to produce starch and related compounds for structural material. The cell wall, consisting largely of polymerized monosaccharides, is highly characteristic of plants and extremely important to their functions.

The carbohydrates are formed by the process of photosynthesis. In this process the one source continuing to provide available energy to the surface of our planet, namely, the sun, provides light that is captured and transformed into chemical bond energy. Chlorophyll and other pigments are important in this energy transformation, and the entire process is dependent upon the well-organized structure of the chloroplast, with its resulting ability to collect a number of photons to be used in the reduction of a single molecule of carbon dioxide. The carbon dioxide is not reduced directly by light, but ATP and NADPH are the first rather stable products of the photoreaction. The manner in which excited electrons in the chlorophyll molecule may be transferred through a series of intermediate steps producing the ATP and NADPH is becoming understood. The manner in which reduced NADPH and ATP are used in the fixation of carbon dioxide has been discovered, at least for most species. This energy is not used in the first step but only in further transformations of the immediate product of carbon dioxide fixation. Phosphoglyceric acid, formed by addition of carbon dioxide to ribulose diphosphate and subsequent splitting of this molecule, appears to be the first product of photosynthesis in most species. In other plants the first product may be oxalo-acetic acid, and, as usual, we find that specific details vary among different species. In any case, it appears that cyclic transformations utilizing the chemical energy made available by the photoreaction and beginning with the first products of carbon dioxide fixation result, not only in the carbohydrates, amino acids, and other possible products of photosynthesis, but also in a continuing supply of the acceptor molecules that originally combined with the carbon dioxide.

The carbohydrates, as well as fats and various amino acids, are oxidized by the processes of respiration, releasing energy essential to other metabolic steps. The usable energy produced by respiration also occurs as reduced pyridine nucleotides and as ATP. Respiration is an involved process, consisting of at least fifty enzymatically controlled steps. Part of the process (glycolysis) can be anaerobic, while an alternative pathway involving pentose phosphates is oxygen dependent. Another part of respiration (the Krebs cycle) is cyclic and dependent upon oxygen. The cytochrome system, which transfers electrons ultimately to oxygen, may obtain these electrons (usually a pair of hydrogen atoms) from various intermediates of the Krebs cycle and from one intermediate in glycolysis. In all of this, many intermediate carbon skeletons are produced that may be further metabolized to produce fats, amino acids, and a myriad of other metabolic products. Phosphate esters are important in respiration, particularly in the steps of glycolysis or the pentose phosphate pathway. A number of coenzymes, some of them containing sulfur, are also essential at several points in the respiratory pathway. (Those involving coenzyme A seem to be especially central.) Our first real insights into the complexity of metabolism were gained from the initial understanding of respiration, and this has now developed into a very comprehensive and detailed picture.

For example, respiration can be directly related to the metabolism of nitrogen in the plant. The energy for the reduction of nitrate to ammonium often comes from respiration, and the ammonium can then be incorporated into amino acids by combining with the Krebs cycle intermediate α-ketoglutaric acid, forming the amino acid glutamic acid. Other amino acids are formed by transamination from glutamic acid to other α-keto acids, some of them also intermediates in the respiratory pathways. We are also learning many details about the biosynthesis of many amino acids, the carbon atoms of which arise from various respiratory intermediates. We have discovered the presence of many compounds, such as the alkaloids and isoprenoids, the functions of which are not understood. There are many branches and tributaries of plant metabolism. We are learning how sulfur enters into some of these steps, and we are gaining insight into the metabolism of the fats. Glycerol comes from a glycolytic intermediate, and fatty acids themselves arise from a fairly complex system involving malonyl CoA which itself is produced from acetyl CoA and CO_2. The acetyl portion is incorporated into the fatty acid, and the CO_2 molecule is split out. Interesting acyl carrier proteins are essential to the process of fatty acid synthesis. The breakdown and respiration of fats and their interconversions to carbohydrate are also becoming understood. Along these branches and tributaries of the metabolic stream flow a host of other compounds such as the phospholipids, isoprenoids, lignin, anthocyanins, and flavones discussed in this chapter.

It is apparent that we have learned much about the basic principles of plant metabolism: the importance of enzymes, their synthesis, and the processes of photosynthesis and respiration in which energy is preserved and transformed and carbon skeletons are constructed and rearranged. On the other hand, we see many plant products about which far too little is known. We have become quite knowledgeable during the past century and a half about the molecular activities of plants, but much remains for the future.

SECTION THREE

Morphogenesis

Growth and the Problems of Morphogenesis

19.1 INTRODUCTION

Man is confronted with the phenomenon of life, a phenomenon of which he is a part. In his attempts to fathom it, he dissects it and analyzes it in intricate detail, as we have done in the previous chapters. Yet there is one aspect, perhaps most representative of life, that is not as readily dissected. This is the phenomenon of morphogenesis, the topic of this third section. Morphogenesis undoubtedly consists of all of the biochemistry we have discussed (and more), as well as many of the physical activities we considered in the first section. Yet it is a process that involves the entire organism and cannot, therefore, be readily considered apart from the entire organism. Ultimately an understanding of morphogenesis must involve a complete synthesis of all of the individual details of plant function.

In everyday usage, the term *growth* may come closest to bringing to mind the concept the scientist calls **morphogenesis**. It is the origin of form, as is evident from its roots (*morpho*, form; *genesis*, beginning or origin). A standard dictionary definition of growth is "the process whereby plants and animals increase in size by taking in food." Although we will restrict the use of the term growth, this dictionary definition conveys the meaning of morphogenesis. Plants

and animals begin as zygotes and become mature organisms. Our assignment is to understand how.

Morphogenesis may be thought of as consisting of two primary functions: **growth** and **differentiation** (or **development**). We shall consider definitions of growth in more detail later. For the moment, we may think of growth primarily as an increase in *size* (a more restricted definition than the dictionary one given above), whereas differentiation may be thought of as an increase in *complexity*. These two processes operating together produce a multicellular organism from a single cell. Indeed, even in single-celled organisms we can see aspects of increase in size (the daughter cells following division must grow to the size of the parent cell) and of differentiation (e.g., development of the "hat" in the alga *Acetabularia*, see section 24.6). In this chapter we will consider first the nature of growth and some of the problems concerned with it, and then we will introduce the problems of morphogenesis, including both growth and differentiation.

19.2 GROWTH

Growth in its simplest context is still somewhat complex. We haven't even a truly satisfactory definition as yet, and while the mathematical descriptions are interesting and even enlightening, they are not really satisfying.

19.2.1 The Definitions of Growth

In addition to the dictionary definition given above, biologists have considered at least four definitions of the term growth. Each has some merits for certain applications, but none is entirely satisfactory for all situations.

19.2.1A An increase in dry weight

Workers who are concerned with applications of plant physiology to agriculture may find this definition a particularly valuable one. Crop production is usually more accurately given by measurement of dry matter than by measurement of the fresh weight, which could be strongly influenced by the moisture conditions prevailing at the moment. An increase in dry weight is a widely used definition, but in the theoretical sense it is hardly a satisfactory one. A seed may germinate and "grow" in the dark into a seedling many times the size of the original seed, and this will occur with a *loss* in dry weight. The germinating seed may absorb only water from its environment, utilizing its stored foodstuffs to grow; these are not replenished until its photosynthetic organs have become functional.

19.2.1B Duplication of protoplasm

Some physiologists have suggested that the best definition of growth is the self-multiplication of living material, the protoplasm itself. As the seedling grows, it converts much of its stored carbohydrates, fats, and proteins into more functional compounds within the protoplasm of the growing and newly formed cells. This is an appealing theoretical definition, but it is not a very practical one. How can we measure the functional protoplasm in a plant? No single activity such as respiration would be truly indicative. It is a concept worth keeping in mind but hardly one we can apply.

19.2.1C Cell multiplication

Perhaps if we sampled the organism, counted cells, and tried to estimate the rate of cellular increase, we would come close to meeting the objections to the above two definitions. It would not be an easy process, but it probably could be accomplished easier than measuring the quantity of protoplasm itself. Of course this would not account for growth of a single cell, and there are other instances in which cell multiplication does not seem to be a good indication of growth. At one point, for example, the developing female gametophyte in the ovary of a flowering plant has become a relatively large cell with a number of nuclei. At some signal, these nuclei begin to be partitioned off by the formation of cell walls. Cell division is taking place. Yet there is no increase in size of the female gametophyte itself. Is this growth, or not? It would be, according to this definition, but a definition of growth omitting an increase in size seems faulty. The process just described is differentiation.

19.2.1D A permanent increase in volume

Measurement of a permanent increase in volume is feasible. While there are some problems,[1] this is probably the best definition from the standpoint of morphogenesis.

19.2.2 The Kinetics of Growth

Many investigators have measured the size of an organism and have plotted the results as a function of time. Julius Sachs in Germany pioneered these measurements in the 19th century. An immediate result is the observation that the curve of size versus time is very similar for a wide variety of organisms and even parts of organisms. The S-shaped curve of Fig. 19-1 may be observed when one measures growth of

---

[1] The volume of a turgid leaf is not really permanent. The leaf may wilt. To use even this definition, we must simply ignore such problems (arbitrarily use turgid material).

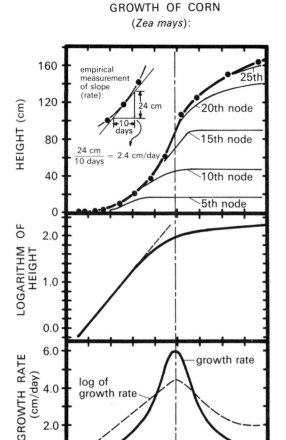

GROWTH OF CORN
(*Zea mays*):

empirical
measurement
of slope
(rate):

24 cm

←10→
days

$\frac{24 \text{ cm}}{10 \text{ days}} = 2.4 \text{ cm/day}$

25th

20th node

15th node

10th node

5th node

log of
growth rate

growth rate

DAYS AFTER PLANTING

Figure 19-1

Growth curves for a corn plant expressed in different ways, as discussed in the text. Slope may be measured empirically by laying a ruler tangent to the point on the curve in question, as illustrated in the upper left part of the figure. It is interesting to consider growth of the individual nodes as well as the plant as a whole. Elongation is occurring below the tenth node, for example, until at least the time the twentieth node has become apparent. At that time elongation is occurring in more than the upper half of the stem, about the upper 50 cm. Compare this figure with Fig. 19-2. (Data were reworked from W. G. Whaley, 1961, "Growth as a general process," *Encyc. of Plant Physiology*, W. Ruhland (ed.), Springer-Verlag, Berlin, 14: 71–112.)

plants or animals, or even leaves, fruits, internodes, or root tips.

19.2.2A Ways of expressing the curve The **size-versus-time plot** is the most direct way of handling growth data. We may also plot the logarithm of the size as a function of time (also shown in Fig. 19-1). Sachs was interested in the **growth rate**; that is, the increment of growth occurring per unit interval of time throughout the life of an organism. In the *size* plot, the units are length, volume, or weight, but in the *rate* curve the units are length, volume, or weight *per unit time*. The microbiologist measures the number of cells (size of population) and the change in the number of cells per unit time.

The growth curves plotted in any one of the three ways have two clearly distinguishable phases. The first is a rapid increase during which the rate curve as well as the size curve is increasing. In the last phase, the size continues to increase, but more slowly, so that the rate decreases. The first phase has been called the **logarithmic** or **exponential phase**, and the last is referred to as **senescence**, although this term is not always applicable in its usual sense (old age), especially in animals. In many examples of the growth curve, another phase is also clearly evident. This is a **phase of maximum growth rate** or the **linear phase** (called by Sachs the **grand phase**), and it lies between the logarithmic phase and the senescence phase. In the example of Fig. 19-1, this phase is at best only barely discernable. In many other plant examples, however, this is an extremely important period during growth (see Fig. 19-3).

19.2.2B The exponential or compound-interest phase The first phase has long been of interest to mathematicians. One reason for this is evident in the fact that this phase appears as a straight line when the logarithm of size is plotted as a function of time. This implies that the rate curve has the same function as the size curve.

In the calculus there is one function, the derivative of which is the same as the function. This is the function:

$$y = e^x \qquad (44)$$

where x and y are variables, and e is the base of natural logarithms. When it is plotted, the curve expressing its slope has the same shape as the original curve. This is evident in Fig. 19-1. In terms of the log plot, the log of the size is a straight line when plotted as a function of time, and the log of the growth rate is also a straight line when plotted as a function of time.

The implication of this part of the curve is that the larger the organism, the faster it is able to grow. This is reasonable, since we can understand that the more available protoplasm, the more new protoplasm can be produced by it. If there is more leaf area for photosynthesis, then more food can be produced to make more leaves. In a culture of single cells, if each cell divides at a constant rate, we would expect to have more cells produced per unit time if there were more cells available to produce them.

The mathematics expressing these ideas are identical to the computation of compound interest, which is as follows:

$$G = G_0 e^{rt} \qquad (45)$$

where:

G = the amount of money at any given time (or the number of cells or the size of the organism—growth)
G_0 = the initial amount of money (or initial size of organism or number of cells)
r = the rate of compounding of interest, or of increasing growth
t = time
e = the base of natural logarithms (2.71828)

19.2.2C Analogy to an autocatalytic reaction

The shape of the growth curve often closely resembles the curve for an autocatalytic reaction in which the amount of product is plotted as a function of time. In such a reaction, the product catalyzes its own formation, and consequently the initial part of the curve has a slope equal to the curve; i.e., the rate of increase is exponential: the more product available, the more product is formed. After a time, however, substrate begins to become limiting, and product cannot be formed as rapidly. Eventually the rate will drop to zero as the substrate becomes completely exhausted. The rate of the reaction is proportional both to substrate and to product:

Reaction: Rate of reaction:

$$S \xrightarrow{P} P \qquad \frac{dP}{dt} = kSP \qquad (46)$$

where:

S = substrate
P = product
k = a constant
$\frac{dP}{dt}$ = an increment of product produced in an increment of time (reaction rate)

If this situation is considered in terms of growth, we might say that rate of increase in size is initially proportional to size, but that rate of increase decreases as the maximum size (genetically and environmentally determined) is approached. In the above example, the quantity of substrate at any point in time will be equal to the quantity of final product (P_{max}) minus the amount of product already formed at that time ($S = P_{max} - P$). The rate will be:

$$\frac{dP}{dt} = kP(P_{max} - P) \qquad (47)$$

In the case of growth, we might say that rate of growth would be proportional to final size minus the size at any given point in time ($G_{max} - G$). We can then write the equation for rate of growth as follows:

$$\frac{dG}{dt} = kG(G_{max} - G) \qquad (48)$$

The equation in this form is instructive from the standpoint of our understanding of the growth rate curve. If it really describes the growth process, then we can easily see why the curve increases rapidly at first when G is small [and $(G_{max} - G)$ is consequently nearly constant] and less rapidly as the maximum size is approached [when $(G_{max} - G)$ begins to approach zero]. The equation written in that form, however, cannot be used to plot a curve as a function of time.

Time is not one of the variables. Equation (48) is the first derivative of the equation for growth in which size is a function of time. In the calculus, the method of integration is used to obtain an original equation from its first derivative. With equation (48), this is not a simple procedure, but the following equation can be so obtained:

$$\frac{1}{G_{max}} \ln \frac{G}{G_{max} - G} = k(t - t_{1/2}) \quad (49)$$

In the process of integration, a constant must be added. This is $t_{1/2}$, which proves to be the **half time**, that time at which half of the maximum size (G_{max}) is reached, or when half of the auto-catalytic reaction is complete.

Use of the equation can be simplified by combining the constants k and G_{max} and including the factor that converts common logarithms to natural logarithms:

$$k' = \frac{G_{max}k}{2.31} \quad (50)$$

Now the equation becomes:

$$\log \frac{G}{G_{max} - G} = k'(t - t_{1/2}) \quad (51)$$

Figure 19-2 shows theoretical curves for size as a function of time and for growth rate as a function of time, each plotted from the above equation. This approach, incidentally, was taken as early as 1923 by T. B. Robertson who suggested that growth was indeed under the control

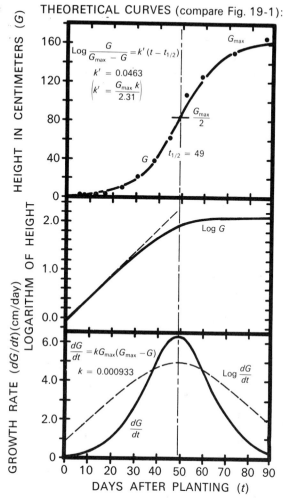

THEORETICAL CURVES (compare Fig. 19-1):

Figure 19-2

Curves drawn according to the equations discussed in the text. Constants have been chosen so that the curves match as closely as possible those shown in Fig. 19-1. The points in the upper part of this figure are the same as those shown in Fig. 19-1. The fit of the theoretical curve is quite good, although some deviation occurs at about 15 days and again between 50 and 60 days. When the logarithm of height is plotted as a function of time, deviation from a straight line occurs somewhat sooner than in Fig. 19-1. Furthermore, the log of the growth rate is never a straight line in this figure, but seems to be straight for almost 50 days in Fig. 19-1. Actually, the data of Fig. 19-1 are not good enough during the early days of growth to allow highly accurate plotting of the logarithms of height and rate.

of autocatalytic reactions that were substrate limited.

19.2.2D Some problems Unfortunately, such a straightforward explanation of growth fails upon close examination. There are at least four reasons why this is so.

First, as is evident in Fig. 19-2, when the logarithm of size is plotted as a function of time using the curve for an autocatalytic reaction, a straight line does not result, but rather a convex curve. That is, in the case of growth, rate of growth is truly proportional to size during the first phase, but in an autocatalytic reaction, rate of increase in product (size in terms of growth) is proportional not only to product (size) but also to substrate (final size minus size) right from the beginning. No equation yet devised that expresses a continuous function can satisfactorily describe the change from the truly logarithmic rate of growth to the senescence phase. Equations expressing discontinuous functions could, however, easily describe the curves (an equation for each part).

Second, the equations given above always predict a bell-shaped rate curve. In many and perhaps most cases of plant growth, however, the maximum or grand phase of growth is maintained over a long interval of time. In such a case the rate curve is not bell-shaped but flat on top, as indicated in Fig. 19-3. For many species of plants this is the rule rather than the exception, and consequently it would hardly be appropriate to apply the above mathematics in such cases.

Third, there are many instances in which the typical *S*-shaped curve is not even approximated. Figure 19-4 indicates a few examples. In these cases, growth may level off for a period of time (a double *S*-shaped curve) or it may start out from the seed at the maximum rate, never going through the first logarithmic phase. Other aberrations may occur. The growth curve for a

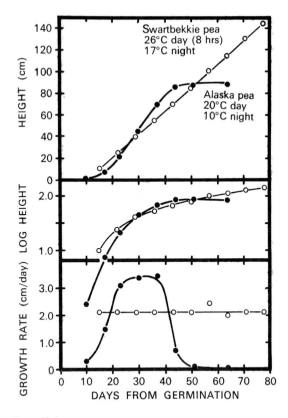

Figure 19-3

Two examples of plant growth curves that deviate rather strongly from the ideals illustrated in Figs. 19-1 and 19-2. The data for the Swartbekkie pea indicate a constant growth rate over a period exceeding 60 days. The curve for Alaska pea more closely resembles those of Figs. 19-1 and 19-2, but again the growth rate is nearly constant from about 22 to 37 days. These data never yield a straight line when the logarithm of height is plotted. (Data are from F. W. Went, 1957, *The Experimental Control of Plant Growth.* Copyright © 1957, The Ronald Press Company, New York. Used by permission.)

human being is a good example of one that deviates strongly from the usual sigmoid curve.

Fourth, equation (48) seems to imply that final size (G_{max}) is always influencing growth rate. It has been suggested that such a teleological striving for a predetermined end result is not in keeping with our mechanistic concepts of

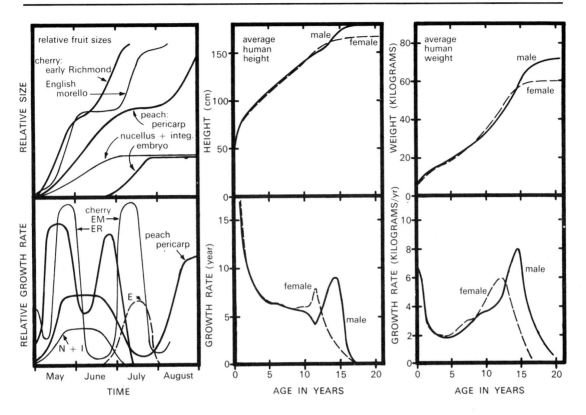

Figure 19-4

Some growth curves that deviate markedly from the ideals indicated in Figs. 19-1 and 19-2. The left figures show sizes and rates for fruit development in cherry and peach. The rate with double peaks exhibited by cherry and peach pericarps are especially striking. (Data modified from H. B. Tukey, 1933, *Botan. Gaz.* 94:433 and 1934, *Proc. Amer. Soc. Hort. Sci.* 31:125.) The human growth curve is especially interesting. Curves are similar when either height or weight are plotted as a function of age, but even here important differences are apparent. The extremely rapid rate of growth immediately following birth is rather typical of mammals, but atypical of other organisms. The sharp increases in growth rates at puberty are also of special interest, as is the early maturing of the female. For a few years (about ten to thirteen) the average height of girls exceeds that of boys, and weight is greater for girls from about ages 7 to 14. The curves represent the "average individual," as determined by measurements of several hundred children in California. (Data modified from Leona M. Bayer and Nancy Bayley, 1959, *Growth Diagnosis*, University of Chicago Press.)

plant growth. Alternatively, the mathematics may imply that growth is always limited by substrates, and this is especially so as final size is approached. If this is the case, then there should be *no* limit to the final size produced, providing only that all conceivable substrates are always provided at optimum levels. Sizes and yields can often be increased by providing optimum conditions, but there appears to be an internally (genetically) controlled upper limit (a mechanistic explanation for the apparent teleology?). Senescence factors apparently exist, although they are rather poorly understood (Chapter 27). Regardless of conditions, for example, small alpine species will never reach the size of redwoods!

19.2.2E Plant growth as an open system[2]

Most of the formulations described above are derived from models of various types of chemical reactions occurring in **closed systems**. These are thermodynamic systems studied under conditions such that no matter enters or leaves the system. One studies the rates at which these systems go to equilibrium, as in the autocatalytic system described above. **Open systems** are studied under conditions in which both matter and energy may enter and leave the system.

It should be evident that the principles of the kinetics of open systems apply to plant growth, and indeed to most of the ecological and energy relationships of biological systems. Energy continuously enters the plant system in the form of light, and matter continuously enters as CO_2, minerals, and water. Energy may leave the system by radiation, convection, or transpiration, and both matter and energy may leave the system in the form of gases and volatile organic compounds, which may also contain some of the energy that entered the system as radiation. Furthermore, plant growth is an irreversible process, another frequent characteristic of open systems.

This may be outlined as:

Radiant energy $+$ CO_2, etc.

↓

Plant system

↓

Chemical products,
Chemical energy,
Heat.

It should be possible to develop simplified mathematical models to analyze the growth process, based upon the principles of open systems, rather than simply to test known mathematical formulations that seem to have some of the properties observed in growth curves, as has been done in the past.

Unfortunately, few models of plant growth based upon open systems have as yet been devised, but generalized biological models based on these principles have been developed. These formulations have been found to have some surprisingly interesting and complex properties.

L. von Bertalanffy, a leading figure in theoretical biology, has applied open-system kinetics to biological systems somewhat as follows. If we let Q_i be a measure of the ith element of the system, e.g., a concentration or energy in a system described by a set of simultaneous equations, its variation with time ($\partial Q_i/\partial t$) may be expressed by:

$$\frac{\partial Q_i}{\partial t} = T_i + P_i \tag{52}$$

where T_i is the rate of transport of Q_i (in or out), and P_i is the rate of its production (or destruction), at a certain point in space. A system defined by such a set of equations may, in principle, have three kinds of solutions: There may be an unlimited increase in the Qs; there may be periodic solutions (variations that follow a repeating cycle); or a time-independent steady state may be reached.

A **steady-state system** is defined as an open system in which the concentrations of all elements remain constant. If products are formed that are insoluble or are transported out of the system, they are no longer elements of the system. A steady-state system is one in which, for all *is*:

$$\frac{\partial Q_i}{\partial t} = 0 \tag{53}$$

More generally and from equation (52), if $\partial Q_i/\partial t = 0$ for all components, then $T_i + P_i = 0$ for all components, or $T_i = P_i$. Thus, a steady state requires that the rate of inward production and transport be equal to the rate of outward conversion and transport.

---

[2] This section (modified somewhat) was kindly supplied by Dr. James Lockhart.

It should be noted that the *size* of the system is not defined. Thus, the organism could, in principle, grow indefinitely and, as long as the *concentrations* remain constant, steady-state growth would continue (the linear phase of growth).

As von Bertalanffy has demonstrated, one of the outstanding characteristics shown by even simple models of steady-state, open systems is their tendency to **homeostasis**, in which there is a strong inclination to maintain constant ratios of intermediates regardless of changes in the concentrations of the inputs. These ratios depend only upon the rate constants of the system. Thus, if this model represented a growing system, it would have a general tendency to maintain constant proportions and form regardless of the relative levels of nutrients available. The nutrient supplies would affect the rate of *growth* but would have little effect on *development*—as is commonly observed in plant morphogenesis.

If the plant shares these properties of the simple model, then no special mechanisms will be required to account for the general constancy of form under different environmental conditions. Furthermore, major modifications of development could be brought about by any treatment that would change one or more of the rate constants of the system. This could be done, for example, by changing the quantity or activity of an important enzyme in the system. In subsequent chapters we will consider several environmental effects that could act in this way.

19.2.2F Determinate and indeterminate growth

In our considerations of growth, it is important to distinguish between determinate and indeterminate structures. A **determinate structure** grows to a certain size and then stops, ultimately reaching senescence and death. Leaves, flowers, and fruits are excellent examples of determinate structures, and the great majority of animals also grow in a determinate way. On the other hand, the vegetative stem and the root are **indeterminate structures**. They grow by **meri-stems**, which continually replenish themselves, remaining youthful. A foxtail pine that has been growing for 4,000 years could yield a cutting that would form roots at its base, producing another tree that might live for another 4,000 years. At the end of that time another cutting might be taken, and so on, potentially forever. Although a meristem may be killed, in one sense it is immortal, while a determinate structure is subject to senescence and death.

Studies have shown that indeterminate structures grow larger if their growth rate is faster. Heterozygous (hybrid) corn seems to be an excellent example. These plants do not grow for longer periods of time than their more homozygous counterparts, but while they are growing, they do so faster and consequently reach larger sizes. Final size of determinate structures such as fruits, on the other hand, may depend more upon the *duration* of growth than upon the *rate*. In certain studies it was shown that growth rates of various cucurbit fruits were essentially identical, but that those fruits having long periods of growth naturally reached larger sizes.

19.2.2G Distribution of growth

Growth in the plant is not evenly distributed throughout the entire organism but is restricted to certain areas. A century ago, Sachs studied the distribution of growth in a root by marking it at equal intervals with India ink (Fig. 19-5). Observations several hours or days later indicated the regions that had grown the most. In the case of the root, only a very restricted region approximately 2 mm behind the tip exhibited any significant elongation. If elongation occurred at distances farther back, the growing cells could not force the tip through the soil. In the case of the stem, elongation does continue for considerably greater distances below the tip (see Fig. 19-1), but again a distance was reached beyond which no stem elongation occurs. Thus, growth in the trunk of a tree occurs only laterally and not longitudinally.

Expansion of dicot leaves is relatively uniform in all directions, although some distortion occurs. Grass leaves grow primarily only at the base due to the location of the intercalary meristem. It is also interesting that growth of the internodes is not uniform either. These tissues may grow more in one location than another.

19.3 THE APPROACHES TO MORPHOGENESIS

In the above discussion it became apparent that no simple mathematical expression could properly account for the observed rates of growth of living organisms. The process is obviously an extremely complex one, being intricately intertwined with the many processes of differentiation and being influenced strongly not only by the internal genetic constitution of the organism but also by a host of environmental factors frequently interacting with each other. It is our task in the chapters of this section to try to survey this complex process.

It becomes apparent to the teacher or author that the task of organizing our present state of knowledge relating to morphogenesis is an extremely difficult one. There are at least three reasons for this, and some discussion of these will help the student to understand some of the challenges he faces (as well as the organization followed in the chapters of this section).

19.3.1 Knowledge Is Extensive but Incomplete

People have been actively studying the problems of morphogenesis since early in the 19th century. One of the most detailed books on the topic was written by Hermann Vöchting in 1878. One German journal devoted almost exclusively to the problems of morphogenesis (*Archiv für Entwicklungsmechanik der Organismen*) now occupies over 16 feet of library shelf! In recent

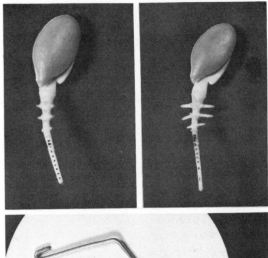

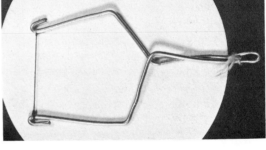

Figure 19-5

A method for measuring rate of growth in a seedling root (here a germinating squash seedling). The root may be marked at equal intervals (here about 1 mm) and examined some time later (12 hours in this case). It is apparent that expansion has occurred only close to the tip. India ink was applied to the thread of the tool at the bottom of the picture to conveniently mark the root. (Photographs by F. B. Salisbury.)

years there has been an upsurge of activity in this area, and by now there must be tens of thousands of papers devoted primarily to the problems of morphogenesis. Any such mass of published material would be virtually impossible for an author to read himself, let alone summarize in a limited space. In this case the problem is further compounded by the fact that much of this material describes the unsolved problems in the area without contributing much

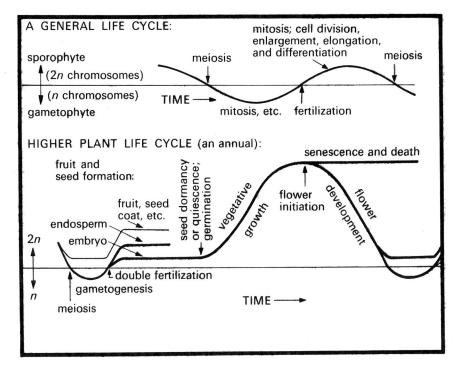

Figure 19-6
One way of illustrating life cycles for living organisms in general (top) and for a higher plant,
an annual (bottom).

to their solution. We are faced, then, with a mass of information, much of it only a careful statement of the kinds of information that are needed!

19.3.2 Facts in the Field Are Mostly Observational

In some areas of modern science, large quantities of information are unified through some general theory. For example, the immense quantity of taxonomic data falls fairly well into place in light of evolutionary theory. In morphogenesis we have no such truly unifying concept, or if such a concept exists it is only presently developing. Possibly our recent advances in the area of molecular biology may ultimately provide this

unifying concept. We will make every attempt in this section to consider the problems of morphogenesis in these terms. But for a few years this will have to be rather tentative.

19.3.3 The Problems of Morphogenesis Are Multidimensional

As we considered the possible approaches that might be taken in the discussion of morphogenesis, at least three excellent possibilities became apparent. The problems of plant morphogenesis might easily be discussed from the standpoint of *life cycle*. Figure 19-6 is a generalized life-cycle diagram indicating a number of the problems of morphogenesis, each of which involves physical and chemical processes discussed in previous chapters. The diagram could be discussed essentially in chronological order beginning at some logical point in the life cycle, such as formation of the zygote. The life cycle might also be thought of as a progressive increase in complexity from the single cell to the multicellular adult, as in the discussion of organization levels in Chapter 1.

On the other hand, one might consider the problems of morphogenesis from the standpoint of the *environment*. Certain morphogenetic processes are strongly influenced by daylength, for example. The response is referred to as photoperiodism, and it would be possible to discuss this, considering several aspects of plant growth that are influenced by photoperiodism even though they occur at widely separate points in the life cycle (germination, dormancy, and flowering, for example).

In our attempts to gain unity by the establishment of fairly general theories, we are beginning to recognize certain systems within the plant that exercise morphogenetic control, again frequently at various points in the life cycle and sometimes in response to several different environmental factors. It would be of interest, then, to discuss *response systems* as such, rather than life-cycle steps or environmental factors as they relate to morphogenesis. The phytochrome system, a pigment sensitive to certain wavelengths of light and influencing a great many morphogenetic responses, is an excellent case in point.

We have utilized all of these approaches in the chapters of this section, even though this introduces certain difficulties. It should at least illustrate the multidimensional nature of morphogenesis.

19.4 THE PROBLEMS OF MORPHOGENESIS

We have summarized in Table 19-1 all of the topics of plant morphogenesis of which we are

aware, following the three main approaches or dimensions discussed above. In the remainder of this chapter we shall consider this table as an introduction to the remaining chapters of this section. In a few cases, the discussion of a given topic here will be its only discussion in this textbook.

19.4.1A Cellular level The growth and development of plants is ultimately the growth and development of plant cells. Fundamentally, we can think of cellular growth as consisting of five phases, and by seeking proper examples it is possible to separate each of these phases from the others.

19.4.1 Processes of Plant Growth and Morphogenesis (Life Cycle)

The following topics follow the outline of organizational levels of complexity as introduced in Chapter 1 which only roughly matches a true life-cycle approach.

The daughter cells following division are small and must **enlarge**. To begin with, they usually enlarge in all directions, but in the plant it is very common for the cell to grow more in one dimension than in the others, resulting in **elongation**. The auxins and gibberellins, special growth-regulating chemicals, often promote cell enlargement and elongation.

Of course, growth of the higher plant would soon cease if it were restricted to cell enlargement and elongation. New cells must be formed by the processes of **nuclear division** and **cell-wall formation**. The auxins, gibberellins, and the cytokinins are important chemical regulators of these processes. There are instances in which nuclear division will take place without cell-wall formation (e.g., maturation of the female gametophyte), and there are also instances in which cell-wall formation will occur without nuclear division (e.g., maturation of the megaspore mother cell).

It is important to recognize that growth of the plant is strongly a function of cell-wall formation. Animal cells will often slide over each other as the organism assumes its mature form, but plant cells do not do this nearly as readily if at all. To achieve a certain form, the walls usually must grow at various rates, always such that adjoining walls grow at the same rate. The plane in which the cell wall is laid down following nuclear division is of considerable importance. If this occurs in a plane parallel to the surface of the stem, increase in stem girth may occur. If walls form in the plane of cross section, increase in length may occur.

The final step in cellular development is that of **specialization** or **differentiation**, the topic of Chapter 22. The plant anatomist describes a vast number of details of cell-wall differentiation, plastid formation, pigmentation, formation of vacuoles, chloroplast and mitochondria development, and others. These processes result in specialized tissues throughout the plant and consequently determine the final form of the plant body. These things are typically considered at levels above that of the cell, and yet their origin is obviously at the cellular level. Figure 19-7 illustrates schematically the five processes of cellular growth and development.

We can describe these steps in detail, and indeed the process of nuclear division may be the most extensively described event in all of biology. The physiologist interested in morphogenesis, however, seeks more than a description. He would like to understand the causal mechanisms underlying each step. He is making progress, but actually little is known about this most important aspect of the problem. As we shall see, most of our successes in this area have been limited to the discovery of chemical factors that might influence the processes (Chapters 20 and 21). How these factors work, we are only now beginning to learn.

It is obvious that final growth in the organism is dependent upon growth of its cells. Is it possible that the converse might also be true? Do the cells act as individuals, all contributing to the growth of the mature organism? Or does the organism control the growth of the cells?

Let us consider two examples. There are certain slime molds (Chapter 22) that, at one stage of their life cycle, consist of individual amoeboid cells. In response to some signal (apparently chemical), these cells aggregate together into a small mass, which then begins to act as an organism. A fruiting body is constructed. Each cell, depending upon its location in the slug, has a certain role to play in erection of the stipe, anchoring organ, and fruiting body. Here the cells clearly make the organism, but there is just as clearly some sort of organismal control exercised over the cells. Each cell, originally like all the others, assumes an identity dependent upon its positional relationship to all the other cells. This is also true in higher plants.

Edmund W. Sinnott, recently deceased, spent most of a lifetime considering the problems of morphogenesis. He studied extensively the growth of cucurbit fruits and was concerned at one point with the question of whether fruit size is determined by cell number or by cell size. He carefully measured the growth rates and found the logarithm of size to form a straight line when plotted against time over a period of several weeks before senescence became apparent (Fig. 19-8). During this period of constantly increasing growth rate (logarithmically increasing size), average cell size remained constant for the first half of the time interval involved. Then cell divisions began to slow down and finally ceased, although the logarithmic growth curve continued uninterrupted. Cells were enlarging now at a rate just sufficient to maintain the logarithmic growth phase originally dependent upon cell division! It could have been coincidence, but this switchover from cell division to cell enlargement without any apparent break in the over-all progress of growth would seem to argue in favor of the organism controlling the growth of the cells rather than the reverse. Such a situation would be difficult to envisage in terms

TABLE 19-1

THE TOPICS OF PLANT MORPHOGENESIS

Processes of Plant Growth and Morphogenesis
(life cycle)
Cellular Level

Cell enlargement
Cell elongation
Nuclear division (mitosis)
Cell division (cytokinesis)
Cell differentiation

Organ Level

Organ formation and growth (including regeneration)
Embryo growth and development
Root initiation
Root growth
Stem (bud) initiation
Stem growth
Leaf initiation
Leaf growth
Flower initiation
Flower development
Fruit development (and post-harvest physiology)
Special organ (e.g., tubers, rhizomes, bulbs, corms, plantlets, etc.) initiation
Special organ growth and development
Organ abscission (primarily fruits and leaves)
Organ movements
Environmentally controlled
Geotropism
Phototropism
Hydrotropism
Thigmatropism
Nastic movements (relation to environment not clear)
Time-related, endogenously controlled movements (may be phased or set by *changes* in the environment: leaves and petals, various plant parts)

Whole Plant Level

Space correlation (form of the plant)
Polarity
Correlation of plant mass
Stimulatory growth
Inhibitory growth
Compensatory growth
Allometric growth and other size correlations (e.g., the root/shoot ratio)
Symmetry: radial, spiral, bilateral, and dorsiventral

Time correlations
Germination
Juvenility
Vegetative growth rates
Reproductive transformation
Dormancy
Senescence

Environmental *Factors*

Time (any of the factors below may vary with time)
Temperature (ultimately want to know plant temperature itself)
Air temperature
Soil temperature
Radiation (primarily ultraviolet, visible, and infrared light)
Intensity
Quality (wavelength or frequency
Time related (duration, in the simplest case)
Atmosphere
Composition (O_2, CO_2, H_2O—humidity, even precipitation)
Pressure
Velocity (time)
(Temperature, but listed above)
Soil
Composition of solids and solutes (nutrients, pH, etc.)
Water
Soil atmosphere
Texture and structure
Organisms
(Temperature, but listed above)
Force fields
Gravity (accelerational)
Magnetic
Electric
Vibrations (e.g., sound—pressure changes in gaseous, liquid, or solid media)
Other living organisms and their influence on all the above factors

Plant Response *Mechanisms*

The genetic material
The enzymes
The pigments
Energy is absorbed and directly converted to chemical energy
Chlorophyll and photosynthesis
Conversion of protochlorophyll to chlorophyll

TABLE 19-1 continued

THE TOPICS OF PLANT MORPHOGENESIS

Synthesis of anthocyanins and other pigments (parts of the process, at least)
Energy absorption results in a switching-type process control
    Phototropism pigment
    Phytochrome (the red-far-red pigment system)
    High Energy Reaction pigment (if it exists)
Special sensors such as statoliths, the thigmatropic response system
Hormones and growth regulators (may be made by enzymes, etc.)
    Auxins
    Gibberellins
    Cytokinins (cell-division factors)
    Root growth hormones
    Wound hormones
    Organ formers
        Flowers (florigens)
        Tubers
        (Roots, leaves and other organs postulated)
Inhibitors of most of the above compounds
Integrated, as yet only partially understood processes consisting of various aspects of these charts (e.g., photoperiodism, vernalization, thermoperiodism, scarification, germination, stratification, etc.)

of the mechanisms we shall discuss in ensuing chapters, but it is certainly an interesting concept, and we should keep it in mind.

19.4.1B Organ level One can study both the **initiation** and the **growth** of the various plant organs, including roots, stems, leaves, flowers, fruits, and the special organs such as tubers, rhizomes, bulbs, corms, and plantlets. We might also begin by studying the formation, growth, and development of the embryo in the seed. An added complication is the **abscission** (falling off) of certain organs, particularly fruits and leaves, but also flowers and flower petals, depending always upon the species. Within the approximately 200,000 species of angiosperms, there is

a wide but not surprising variety of manifestation in organ formation and growth.

In our studies of these phenomena we have also been particularly concerned with the action of certain chemicals, including again the auxins, gibberellins, and cytokinins. All of these will be discussed to some extent in the next two chapters. Various aspects of the problems of organ formation and growth will also be discussed in the special chapter on differentiation.

An interesting aspect of morphogenesis at the organ level is that of movement of specific plant parts. We can think of these plant movements as consisting fundamentally of three types. *First*, are the **tropisms**, in which plant roots, stems, leaves, and other parts respond to certain directional fluxes or gradients in environmental factors. **Geotropism** is a response of plant parts to the directional flux of gravity. **Phototropism** is a response to the direction of light rays. **Hydrotropism** and **chemotropism** are responses to gradients in water potential or certain chemicals. **Thigmotropism** is a response to touch, perhaps to be considered as a gradient in pressure. The tropistic responses are said to be positive if movement occurs in the direction of the emanating force field (gravity or light) or the higher concentration in the gradient (water, chemicals, or pressure).

Second, plants exhibit **nastic movements**, in which the causative stimulus affects all parts of the organism or growing organ equally, and the response is not dependent upon direction of origin of the stimulus. They also exhibit **nutation** in which the stem or tendril tip may be seen to move in a roughly periodical, circular way if it is observed over a period of time (particularly with time-lapse photography). A rotation of the stem tip may require from one to four hours for completion. Apparently the motion is caused by varying growth rates on different sides of the stem.

Third, other plant movements seem to be related to some **endogenously-controlled time-**

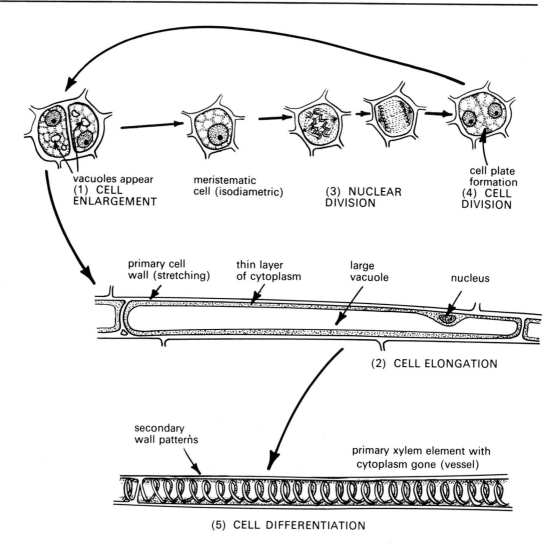

vacuoles appear
(1) CELL
ENLARGEMENT

meristematic
cell (isodiametric)

(3) NUCLEAR
DIVISION

cell plate
formation
(4) CELL
DIVISION

primary cell
wall (stretching)

thin layer
of cytoplasm

large
vacuole

nucleus

(2) CELL ELONGATION

secondary
wall patterns

primary xylem element with
cytoplasm gone (vessel)

(5) CELL DIFFERENTIATION

Figure 19-7
A schematic representation of the processes of cellular growth and differentiation discussed in the text.

measuring system within the plant. These include movements of leaves, petals, and various other parts, and they continue to occur with a predictable time relationship even though plants are placed under conditions of nonvarying gravity, light, temperature, moisture, chemicals, and pressure. A cycle approximating 24 hours is common. If certain of these factors are varied (particularly light), the phase of the cycle may be reset, and consequently even these movements bear a relationship to the environment, but not in the same sense as the tropisms dis-

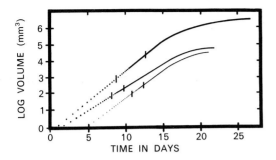

Figure 19-8

The relationship between cell division and cell enlargement in the growth process. The logarithm of ovary volume is plotted as a function of time for three races of *Cucurbita* differing in fruit size. The dotted parts of the curve indicate growth by cell division, and the solid parts show growth by cell enlargement. The vertical bars indicate more exactly the change from predominant cell division to predominant cell enlargement. Note that growth rate remains constant in spite of this change. (From E. W. Sinnott, 1960, *Plant Morphogenesis*, McGraw-Hill Book Company, New York. Used by permission.)

cussed above. We will devote Chapter 24 to a discussion of a biological clock that seems to control these responses.

19.4.1C Whole-plant level Morphogenesis at the whole-plant level is based upon growth and development at the cellular and the organ level. Yet there are some interesting phenomena that seem to transcend in complexity the morphogenetic problems of these two lower levels. These are **correlative effects**, and for the most part they may be thought of as the effect of one part of the plant on another. They influence the form of the plant both in space and in time.

The **space correlations**, which may be thought of as determining the form of the plant at any stage, have long intrigued natural historians. These problems were studied and described by many workers in the 19th century and during the early years of this century. Yet these are the

problems about which we know the least in terms of causal mechanisms.

Consider, for example, the phenomenon of **polarity**. From the moment of fertilization of the egg by the sperm, polarity seems to be established. After a single division of the zygote, it is usually possible to distinguish which cell will give rise to the root and which to the shoot. Furthermore, this polarity seems to permeate to the level of the individual cells. The auxin hormones, for example, pass primarily only in a direction from the shoot tip toward the root when moving through living stem tissue. A segment of a willow stem when inverted and hung in a moist atmosphere (Chapters 20 and 22) still produces roots at the top (the basal end) and shoots at the bottom (the apical end). We must have a long way to go in our understanding of molecular biology before we will be able to say anything conclusive about the manner in which the genes within the nucleus can enable the cell to distinguish one end from the other.

There are also many fascinating correlations of plant mass that we will not be able to discuss in detail in this book. Early morphogeneticists described **stimulatory growth, inhibitory growth, compensatory growth, allometric growth**, and other size correlations. **Allometry** is an especially interesting example in which growth rate of one part of a plant may be closely related to growth rate of another part. Even though the individual rates are themselves quite different, the ratio of the rates remains constant. We are also fascinated by the problems of **symmetry** (Chapter 22).

During the plant's life cycle, certain morphogenetic events may be thought of as **correlations in time**. **Germination** typically occurs at a season favorable for growth of the seedling. Certain plants exhibit special characteristics termed "**juvenile**," and in many cases the shift from the juvenile form to the **adult** form may be induced by certain environmental factors and thus may occur at a certain time during a season. In many other cases this shift seems to be quite independent of the usual environmental factors.

The **rates of vegetative growth** discussed in the first sections of this chapter may be thought of as examples of whole-plant correlations in time. The **initiation of flowers** is typically discussed as a single problem in plant physiology, but we will consider two mechanisms that are often in control of it: one induced by low temperatures in the environment (**vernalization**, Chapter 25), and the other induced by day-length and apparently related to the biological clock mentioned above (**photoperiodism**, Chapter 26).

In many temperate-zone plants, changes occur at a certain time during the season, as though they were in preparation for the coming winter. These are examples of the problem of **dormancy** (rest), and since it is also often induced in response to temperature and daylength, we shall discuss it in relation to vernalization and photoperiodism. A separate problem of considerable practical importance to the agriculturist is that of **senescence** (Chapter 27).

19.4.2 Environmental Factors

In Table 19-1 we listed some 19 separate environmental factors, and it would probably be possible to find examples in which each of these has some morphogenetic effect upon a growing plant. A true conception of the environment is itself difficult to formulate, and factors of the environment are difficult to outline or classify. Some workers have considered the concept of the "**operational environment**," limiting this to those factors known to influence plant or animal growth or other responses. Radio waves, for example, while part of the environment in the broadest sense, are probably not part of the operational environment (although some workers think they may influence some plants). Examination of the outline will also show the difficulty of overlap. Temperature is frequently considered separately as a factor influencing plant growth, but air temperature, soil temperature, and ultimately the temperature of the plant itself must be considered.

Since the many factors of the environment do have morphogenetic effects, it would be possible to consider the problems of morphogenesis from the environmental standpoint. Chapter 23, a discussion of photobiology, takes this approach, but we will save most of the environmental approach for Chapter 29.

19.4.3 Plant Response Mechanisms

The mechanisms bear the most promise for our study of morphogenesis. If only we knew enough, we might proceed entirely by this approach, outlining and discussing the various mechanisms whereby a plant may progress from the fertilized egg to the senescent organism, following the plan (the program) laid out by its genetic material and acting along the way in response to the various factors of the environment. If enough were known, each of the above problems and topics could be channeled into such an approach.

Unfortunately, not enough is known. We can discuss a number of extremely important mechanisms, such as those indicated in Table 19-1, but many of the problems of morphogenesis remain only as descriptive observations with no real understanding of their functional nature. We hope, however, to emphasize what is known about mechanisms in the ensuing chapters, and consequently the chapter following this one is a further introduction to plant response mechanisms, while in Chapter 22 we will introduce the concept of morphogenetic programming.

Mechanisms and Problems of Developmental Control

It was emphasized in Chapter 11 that enzymes, by virtue of their specific catalytic activities, determine the functions of cells. In Chapter 17 the mechanism by which genes control hereditary characteristics by determining the kinds of enzymes produced was explored. It seems that the flow of genetic information proceeds as follows:

$$DNA \longrightarrow Messenger\ RNA \longrightarrow Enzymes$$

The length and sequence of nucleotides in a part of a DNA molecule determines the length and sequence of nucleotides in the messenger RNA that finally controls the length, composition, and amino acid sequence of a particular enzyme or enzymes. Cellular activity, and apparently cellular form as well, are direct products of the genes and of the enzymes produced under their control. Cellular activity and form constitute the activity and form of the organism.

The principal question of this section on morphogenesis is how cells in the same organism can have different shapes and perform different functions. For example, most epidermal cells differ considerably from the specialized guard cells surrounding the stomatal openings in leaves; phloem cells and xylem cells perform quite different roles in the plant and are morphologically distinct; leaf palisade parenchyma cells with their well-developed chloroplasts clearly carry out functions different from those of root endodermal cells. When we remember that all of these cells resulted from mitoses subsequent to the initial division of the diploid fertilized egg, and thus that all have identical genes (except for rare mutations in some), a problem appears. How can cells with identical genes, and therefore with identical DNA molecules, be so different in appearance and behavior if our above propositions about the transfer of genetic information are correct? Why do not all cells with the same genetic constitution possess identical amounts of identical enzymes at all times?

20.1 EVIDENCES FOR A FULL COMPLEMENT OF DNA IN EACH CELL

To begin with, how do we know that various unlike cells in a mature plant really do contain the same genetic information? Two lines of evidence and reasoning based upon it lead to this conclusion.

20.1.1 Totipotency

It has long been known that virtually any plant cell is capable of reproducing an entire plant

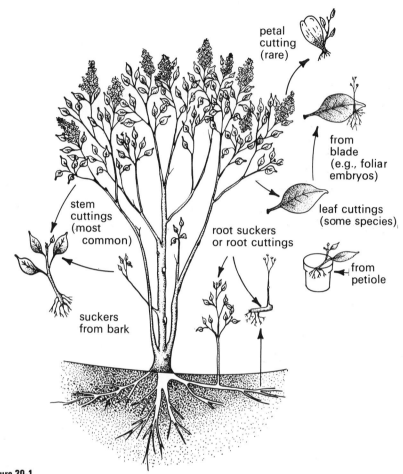

petal
cutting
(rare)

from
blade
(e.g., foliar
embryos)

stem
cuttings
(most
common)

leaf cuttings
(some species)

root suckers
or root cuttings

from
petiole

suckers
from bark

Figure 20-1

A schematic drawing illustrating the ways in which new plants may be vegetatively regenerated from an already existing plant. The plant illustrated is a lilac, but cultivation of petal or leaf cuttings from this plant would be unusual.

(Fig. 20-1). A root parenchyma cell, for example, may begin to divide, producing an adventitious bud and finally a mature shoot. This shoot might then be removed and roots induced at the base to form a mature plant completely descended from the initial cell which gave rise to the adventitious bud. Adventitious buds and roots will form on many tissues, including stems and leaves as well as roots. In each case, one or a few cells can give rise to an entire plant.

It is possible to obtain cultures of individual plant cells, particularly carrot root phloem tissue. Following proper treatment, many of these single cells will divide and grow to produce a plant. These experiments are to be discussed in more detail in Chapter 22. They clearly imply that each cell in the plant contains all of the hereditary information required to produce all of the cells in an entire plant. In view of this, the cell is said to be **totipotent.**

20.1.2 Implications from Molecular Biology

One of the most striking things about mitosis is the duplication of the chromosomes. If, as has long been assumed, they bear the hereditary information, it would appear that the daughter cells following a division always contain the full complement of genes possessed by the mother cell. By the beginning of the 1950s, a great body of observational data from the science of genetics supported this concept.

The development of molecular genetics was in response to the question of how the genetic material might be duplicated at the molecular level. The results of these studies make it clear why the daughter cells must have identical genes. During DNA replication, there is a strict requirement that the DNA polymerase must form two new double-stranded DNA molecules, one of which is complementary to one chain, and one to the other chain. This complementarity arises from the specific hydrogen bonding occurring between the nucleotide bases; adenine must always be added to a growing DNA chain opposite thymine, thymine opposite adenine, cytosine opposite guanine, and guanine opposite cytosine (or 5-methyl cytosine). This copying process is remarkably accurate, and only rarely can errors arise that result in **mutations**. Two identical double-stranded DNA molecules thus result from mitosis. In fact, all diploid cells in a given plant contain very nearly the same amount of DNA.

Many cells in the plant body do not simply possess the diploid ($2n$) number of chromosomes but instead contain tetraploid ($4n$) and far higher ploidy numbers (Chapter 22). Such polyploid cells result from chromosome duplication (**mitosis**) without the formation of a new cell plate cross wall, and thus without cell division (**cytokinesis**). Nevertheless, even polyploid cells presumably contain exactly the same *kinds* of genes and differ only in the number of times each gene is represented. Diploid and polyploid cells should therefore carry out the same activities, and, in fact, polyploidy is not thought to be an important factor leading to differentiation in plants, although polyploid cells are usually larger than diploid cells.

20.2 FUNCTIONAL AND NONFUNCTIONAL GENES

It is clear that much of the genetic information present in the cells of the carrot root phloem, for example, is not fully used at any given time, since these cells do not carry out all of the functions that other carrot cells perform. For example, they do not photosynthesize. Mechanisms must therefore exist for determining which genes function at particular times throughout the life of a cell. An analogy might be made between genes and the keys of a piano. If individual keys are played only at the proper times, a beautiful piece of music may result, just as genes functioning only at the proper times and in the correct places in a plant lead to proper coordination of its activities.

A limited amount of direct evidence exists showing that new genes do begin to function during differentiation, and that this results in the production of different messenger RNA and protein molecules. Techniques for detecting different kinds of messenger RNA during plant development are complicated because it has not been possible to separate these numerous and similar molecules. One new method with considerable promise takes advantage of the ability of a particular messenger RNA to combine by base pairing with the specific part of the DNA molecule upon which it was originally constructed[1] (Fig. 20-2). The DNA and messenger RNA molecules are removed separately from the cells, taking care to prevent their destruction by nuclease enzymes. The double-stranded

[1] As the molecular biologist says: "It takes one to know one."

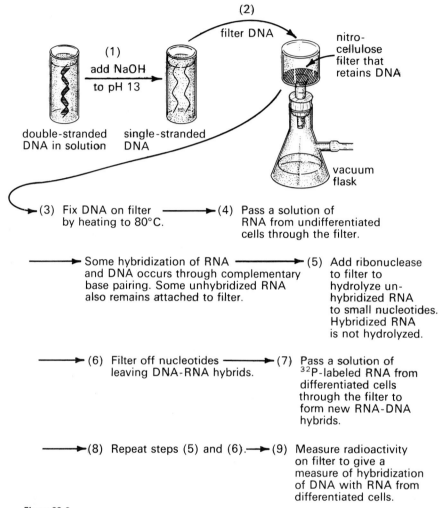

Figure 20-2

Techniques to demonstrate that differentiated cells contain kinds of RNA molecules different from those in undifferentiated cells. Differentiated cells are grown in the presence of ^{32}P so that their RNA thus labeled can be distinguished after hybridization with DNA from unlabeled RNA of undifferentiated cells.

DNA is heated, breaking the hydrogen bonds between strands and allowing them to uncoil and separate. The DNA strands are then attached to a small ion-exchange column or to a substance like nitrocellulose. A solution containing messenger RNA molecules from *undif-* *ferentiated cells* is then passed through the DNA, and these bind to parts of the DNA identical to those upon which they were originally synthesized, becoming united with all of the DNA of the genes that were active in the undifferentiated cells. Now if a messenger RNA fraction from an identical group of *differentiated* cells is passed through the DNA-messenger RNA hybrids, some new RNA molecules are also bound to the DNA, producing different hybrids and indicating that new genes have become active. It is clear that the second group of hybrids contains messenger RNA molecules unlike those in the undifferentiated cells, since they have combined specifically with DNA to which the messenger RNA of the undifferentiated cells could not unite. We shall later discuss theories about what prevents some of the genes in the undifferentiated cells from being active in messenger RNA synthesis.

That differentiation also leads to specialized proteins (enzymes) is more easily shown, since methods for separating proteins are better developed. The best technique presently employed is to use electrophoresis in polyacrylamide gels to separate a group of proteins from differentiating plant tissues. The resolved proteins are stained by such compounds as coomassie blue or amido black, which form chemical derivatives with them. The resulting patterns from the different tissues are then compared. Figure 20-3 shows the protein bands separated from various portions of pea seedlings and the differences between them. Each band probably contains many different proteins, the enzymatic functions of which are as yet unknown. More complete separations would be desirable.

In any case, gene regulation must be a key aspect of cellular control, but the problem of development must be considered in a broader context.

20.3   POSSIBLE REGULATORY MECHANISMS

Let us consider possible ways in which cellular activity and development of the organism might be controlled. An over-all problem concerns the manner in which the mature organism develops from the zygote. In this case the control might

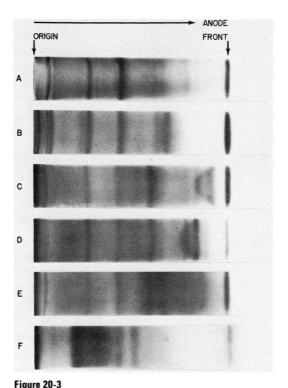

Figure 20-3

Electrophoretic separations of soluble proteins present in various parts of three-day-old pea seedlings. (A) A 1 mm segment from root tip, (B) 1 mm taken between 5 and 6 mm from root tip, (C) hypocotyl, (D) epicotyl, (E) plumule, and (F) cotyledons. (From F. C. Steward and D. J. Durzan, 1965. In F. C. Steward (ed.), *Plant Physiology*, Vol. IVA, Academic Press, New York, p. 546. Used by permission.)

be primarily internal, a programmed sequence of events brought about by information within the zygote. In other cases the response is caused by external changes in the environment. The mechanisms discussed in this section might play a role in the internally controlled development or in response to the environment, since an environmental response must always occur within the limits of the genetic potential. Most of the mechanisms discussed below have been demonstrated to exist in one or more kinds of living cells, but their importance and interrelationships in plants often remain to be established.

There are two basic ways in which a cell can control its production of a given substance, and both involve influences upon rates of enzyme-catalyzed reactions: *First*, a cell may change the effectiveness by which given enzymes can act or, *second*, it may alter the number of molecules of enzyme present to catalyze these reactions.

20.3.1 Control of Enzymatic Reactions by Environmental Factors and Principles of Mass Action

Apparently the products of enzymatic reactions are important in the development and differentiation of cells and tissues. Hence any variable that will influence enzymatic reaction rates could be of importance in development. In Chapter 11, factors influencing metabolic reaction rates were summarized. These included temperature, pH, and the presence of various kinds of inhibitors. All of these factors might, in certain situations, influence development by their effects upon rates of metabolism. Metabolic reaction rates are also functions of the concentrations of the reactants and the enzymes. In addition, most reactions appear to be somewhat reversible, so that the buildup in the products of a particular reaction should slow the rate of their formation. This is frequently indicated in enzymatic reactions carried out in the test tube by the decrease in the measured net rate of substrate utilization or product formation with time (Chapter 11). In the living cells, however, most enzymatic reactions are followed by others that convert the products even further, so that products often do not accumulate and thus cannot inhibit their own formation in reversible reactions.

Temperature changes could sometimes conceivably influence plant development through mass action effects, since some reactions are influenced more by temperature than are others. Consider an example in which a compound, *A*, undergoes competing reactions leading to two different final products. Suppose reaction number 1 is strongly promoted at high temperatures, while reaction number 2 is less influenced by temperature, or perhaps the equilibrium favors reversal under warm conditions. (Temperature does affect the equilibrium constant of many chemical reactions by influencing the free energy of products and reactants to a different extent.) High temperatures would then cause the conversion of compound *A* through the pathway initiated by reaction number 1, and the reverse might occur at low temperatures.

External changes in carbon dioxide concentrations and in mineral nutrient supplies probably also affect the metabolic pathway by which certain compounds are utilized. Spore formation, for example, in certain microorganisms is influenced by the carbon dioxide level or by nutrients available in the medium in which they exist. Flowering in some higher plants is also affected by the mineral nutrients available, especially nitrogen.

20.3.2 Feedback Inhibition and Stimulation

In 1954, it was discovered that if the amino acid tryptophan was fed to the bacterium *Escherichia coli*, the synthesis of a compound normally converted into tryptophan was inhibited. Subsequent work by H. E. Umbarger and others studying microorganisms showed that many compounds similarly inhibit an early reaction in the pathway leading to their synthesis by **feedback (allosteric) inhibitions** (Chapter 11). The process is also sometimes called **endproduct inhibition**, because the inhibitory compound is usually a product of several prior reactions.

Feedback inhibition usually results from the ability of the compound to combine with an early enzyme in the reaction sequence at an allosteric site, as contrasted with the case in simple mass action inhibition. Cases are also known in which an allosteric enzyme is even stimulated by the product of its activity or, more often, the product of another enzyme. As more enzymes are purified and studied carefully, more are found to possess allosteric sites, and the importance of the general phenomenon may be even greater than is presently thought.

Feedback inhibition also occurs in plants. A few examples will illustrate this. The reactions leading from carbamyl phosphate synthesis to the formation of pyrimidine nucleotides is outlined in Fig. 20-4. Certain of the compounds formed late in the reaction sequence, such as cytidine diphosphate, inhibit reaction number one by combining with the enzyme **aspartic acid transcarbamylase**. Starch breakdown by α-amylase is also subject to feedback inhibition. This enzyme is inhibited by a product of its action, maltose, and this is thought to be an operative control in starch hydrolysis in the endosperm of germinating seeds. Still another example is the regulation of glycolysis by products of the Krebs cycle and mitochondrial electron transport system. As discussed in Chapter 15, phosphofructokinase, the glycolytic enzyme converting fructose-6-phosphate to fructose-1,6-diphosphate, is inhibited by citric acid and by ATP.

Ann Oaks, at Purdue University, discovered that, as in bacteria, synthesis of various amino acids in plants is subject to feedback inhibition. She found that in germinating corn seeds the synthesis of leucine in the embryos is inhibited by leucine already present. This preformed leucine is presumably transported into the embryo from the endosperm, where it is released by protease action upon storage proteins. The inhibiting effect results from interference by the amino acid with an early enzyme in the leucine synthesis pathway, one which condenses α-**ketoisovaleric acid** with acetyl CoA. Oaks also found evidence that syntheses of threonine, valine, leucine, lysine, arginine, and proline in the tips of corn roots are inhibited by the presence of these amino acids, which are apparently normally transported to the tips from older, more basipetal cells. These feedback inhibitions appear to be advantageous to plants, because the sugars needed for energy release and production of cell wall components are not wasted in the formation of amino acids already present. For the sake of economy, metabolites should be produced by cells in amounts approximating those that can be utilized.

In all of the above cases, the control is *negative*. Several cases of *positive* feedback control involving activation of enzymes by metabolites have also been discovered. One of the most interesting examples is the stimulation of starch formation by 3-phosphoglyceric acid as observed by Jack Preiss and H. P. Ghosh at the University of California at Davis. It may be remembered from Chapter 12 that starch is synthesized principally by glucose units transferred from ADPG. Phosphoglyceric acid has no direct effect on this reaction, but it does strongly activate **ADPG pyrophosphorylase**, the enzyme forming ADPG from glucose-1-phosphate and ATP. It thus appears that starch formation is increased during photosynthesis not only by formation of sugars and a resulting mass action effect but also by an important control upon activity of an enzyme essential to starch production (Fig. 20-5).

Although much more evidence is needed, it is probable that feedback inhibitions and activations of this type represent important control mechanisms in all cells, maintaining proper concentrations of cellular components.

Such regulatory mechanisms clearly affect the ability of genes to express themselves, since their expression is observed only by noting the products of the enzymes they control. Such mechanisms do not, however, affect the rate at which genetic information is converted into messenger RNA nor the rate at which the corresponding enzymes are produced. The enzyme molecules continue to be synthesized as rapidly as ever, and only their function is affected.

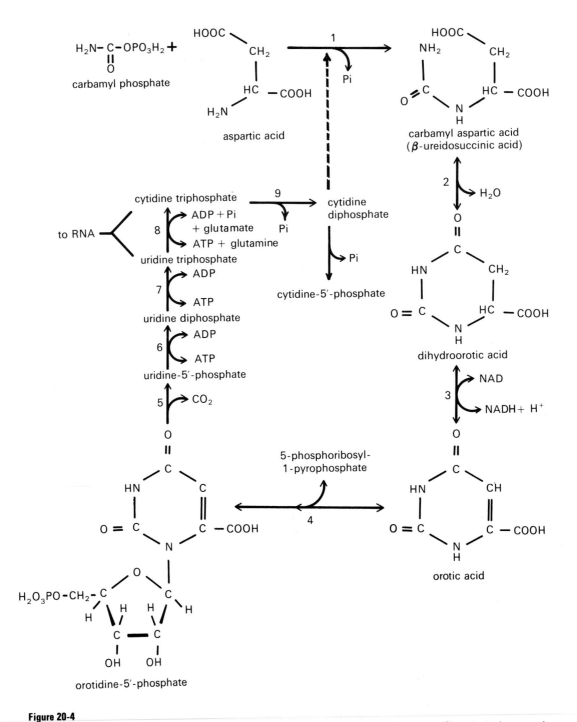

Figure 20-4

Synthesis of pyrimidine nucleotides from carbamyl phosphate and aspartic acid. Reactions (8) and (9) have not been directly demonstrated to occur in higher plants, although they occur in other organisms, and indirect evidence for their existence in plants has been obtained. Broken line with arrow indicates negative feedback inhibition of reaction number one by cytidine diphosphate.

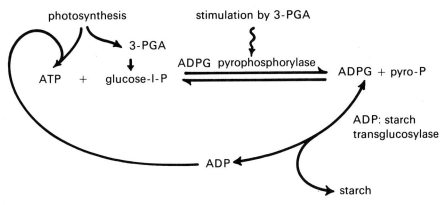

Figure 20-5

Positive feedback control of starch synthesis in spinach chloroplasts. Photosynthesis forms ATP, glucose-1-phosphate, and also 3-phosphoglyceric acid (3-PGA). Glucose-1-phosphate provides the glucose needed in starch synthesis (after its conversion to adenosine diphosphoglucose, ADPG). ATP formed in photosynthetic phosphorylation provides the energy needed to drive ADPG synthesis, and, through ·feedback stimulation, 3-PGA activates the enzyme synthesizing ADPG. *Negative* feedback has been discussed more often in this text than has the *positive* feedback illustrated here.

20.3.3 Control of Enzyme Synthesis: The Operon

Although some temporary control of cellular enzymatic activities through mass action and feedback effects likely occurs in most cells, it is thought that the more permanent changes occurring in differentiating cells are caused by other phenomena. Such phenomena were first discovered in yeast and bacterial cells and, indeed, most of what we presently know about the processes has come from research upon microorganisms.

20.3.3A Enzyme repression When the bacterium *Escherichia coli* was grown on a nutrient medium containing glucose as a carbon source but also containing some arginine, it was found, using radioactive tracers, that arginine incorporated into the cellular proteins arose entirely from the added arginine and not from the glucose. If arginine were not provided, glucose was easily converted into arginine of the proteins, as well as to all of the other necessary carbon-containing compounds of the cell. It appeared that when arginine was provided, the enzymes that normally form this amino acid from glucose either were absent or were not functioning.

This proved not to be just another case of feedback inhibition, in which the arginine simply blocks an enzyme involved in its synthesis from glucose. It was found that several of the enzymes for producing arginine were actually *not present* under these conditions, their synthesis being prevented when arginine was provided. This is an example of **enzyme repression**, and because the formation of several enzymes all participating in the same biochemical pathway is repressed, it is recognized as a special case of repression known as **coordinate repression**. Many other examples of enzyme repression are known in *E. coli* and other organisms.

20.3.3B Enzyme induction Even before enzyme repression was discovered, the phenomenon of **enzyme induction** was observed. One of the earliest and best studied enzymes whose synthesis was shown to be induced is **β-galactosidase**. This enzyme hydrolyzes certain disaccharides such as lactose (milk sugar: glucose-galactose) into monosaccharides. The *E. coli* cells normally grown on glucose or other simple sugars as a carbon source contain no β-galactosidase and thus cannot hydrolyze and utilize lactose. Now, if lactose is provided to the bacteria, it is rapidly utilized after a short lag period (Fig. 20-6).

Two new enzymes were found to be synthesized during the lag period, one a **galactoside permease** that participates in the carrier system transporting lactose into the cells, and the other the β-galactosidase that forms free galactose and glucose from lactose. It is interesting that, in this and other cases of enzyme induction, geneticists have found that the genes controlling functionally related enzymes (those that are members of a common biosynthetic or catabolic pathway) are often adjacent to one another on the chromosome. In cases where the formation of one or more enzymes is simultaneously induced by a single **inducer substance**, the process is referred to as **coordinate induction**. Many such examples of coordinate induction have been demonstrated in various microorganisms. So far, only a few enzymes in higher plants are known to be inducible. These include nitrate reductase by nitrate ions, indoleacetylaspartate synthetase by indoleacetic acid (a plant hormone), glycolic acid oxidase by glycolic acid or FMN, and α-amylase and invertase by gibberellic acid (another plant hormone). The specific case of α-amylase induction in cereal grain seeds by gibberellin is discussed in Chapter 21. It is suspected that enzyme induction will prove to be of considerable importance in differentiation of all organisms.

20.3.3C Mechanisms of induction and repression

Enzyme induction and repression are reversible effects, controlled by the presence or

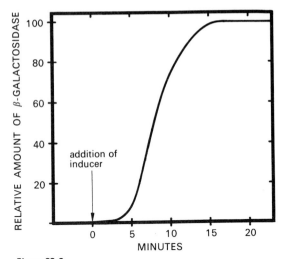

Figure 20-6

Induction of β-galactosidase in *Escherichia coli*. Addition of the inducer can stimulate production of the enzyme from a level of about three molecules per cell up to 3,000 molecules.

absence of inducing or repressing substances. This shows that the changes are really physiological changes, rather than permanent changes in genetic constitution. Clever genetic experiments with bacteria indicate that induction and repression can be explained by assuming that three kinds of genes exist. This idea was first suggested in 1961 by Francois Jacob and Jacques Monod of the Pasteur Institute in Paris, and it has received considerable support by others since. These men and Andre Lwoff, also at that institute, shared a Nobel prize in 1965 for their research and ideas.

Their general model for the control of enzyme synthesis is shown in Fig. 20-7. It is assumed that **structural genes** (SG_1 and SG_2, etc.) exist and that each codes for the structure of a particular messenger RNA molecule, which, in turn, and with the cooperation of ribosomes and transfer RNA molecules attached to amino acids, codes for the structure of a particular enzyme (as described in Chapter 17). These

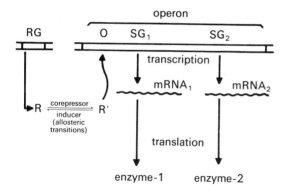

Figure 20-7

Jacob–Monod model of the regulation of protein synthesis. For explanation, see text. (After F. Jacob and J. Monod, 1961. In "Cellular regulatory mechanisms," *Cold Spring Harbor Symposia on Quantitative Biology* 26:193. Used by permission.)

structural genes can form messenger RNA molecules (mRNA) only when an adjacent DNA part of the chromosome called the **operator gene** (*O*) is in the functional (open) state. As long as this operator region (thought to be the starting point for RNA production) is open, all of the structural genes controlled by this operator can synthesize messenger RNA. If the operator is closed, none of these structural genes can function. The operator region and the structural genes dependent upon it are said to belong to the same **operon**.

Now whether or not the operator is open or closed depends upon still another type of gene called a **regulator gene** (RG). The regulator gene in its active condition nearly always acts negatively; that is, it closes the operator so that all of the structural genes present in that operon are nonfunctional. The·regulator gene inhibits the action of the operator by forming a **repressor molecule** (*R*) apparently an allosteric protein, which, in its active form (*R'*), is thought to somehow combine with the operator region, thus preventing the initiation of messenger RNA formation in that operon.

In the case of enzyme **induction** it is assumed that the **inducer molecule** which, when added, causes induction (for example, lactose in the case of the induction of β-galactosidase) by combining with the repressor and preventing it from repressing the operator (preventing its conversion to *R'*). This combination between repressors and small metabolites causing enzyme induction is currently thought to cause allosteric transitions (see Fig. 11-12) in the repressors, leading to a loss in their activity. As soon as this happens the entire operon begins to synthesize messenger RNA molecules, and the corresponding enzymes are then produced for the first time (coordinate induction). These enzymes will then metabolize the inducer substance added, but as long as this inducer is present in the medium in which the bacteria are growing, induction is not reversed. Although it was first proposed by Jacob and Monod that each structural gene synthesizes one special messenger RNA molecule, more recent evidence indicates that often a large messenger RNA is produced as a result of copying the DNA of an entire operon. In this case the long messenger would contain genetic information for perhaps several protein molecules.

When enzyme **repression** occurs, it is believed that the added metabolite causing repression (the **corepressor**, as arginine in our example above) also acts by combining with the repressor and causing an allosteric transition. In this case it is assumed that the previously inactive repressor becomes activated by such a transition. In its active condition (*R'*), the repressor then blocks a particular operon by combining with its operator. In the arginine example, this completely prevents the formation of enzymes necessary to synthesize arginine. This is probably advantageous to the cells, since there is no need to expend energy forming arginine when it is already present in the growth medium. In effect, then, enzyme repression leads to results similar to those caused by feedback inhibition, but the mechanisms differ in that enzyme production is decreased in the case of repression, while activity of enzymes is decreased in feedback inhibition.

V. G. Allfrey and A. E. Mirsky, both of the Rockefeller Institute in New York City, and Ru-chih Huang and James Bonner at the California Institute of Technology, obtained evidence that the histone proteins present in higher animals and plants (but absent from bacteria) could act as repressors. Thus, when histones were removed from DNA isolated from the nuclei of calf thymus glands or from pea seedlings, this DNA acted as a template for the production of RNA molecules in the presence of RNA polymerase. If, however, the histones remained attached to the DNA, RNA polymerase could synthesize little or no RNA (Table 20-1). Evidence therefore exists that histones may be natural repressor molecules, controlling differentiation by covering certain genes.

The histones are a rather simple group of proteins, rich in lysine or arginine, or both. They are attracted to the DNA molecules because the additional amino groups present in lysine and arginine attract hydrogen ions and become positively charged. The DNA molecules possess a net negative charge because of the phosphate groups that ionize by losing a hydrogen ion. The positively charged amino groups in the histone molecules are then ionically bound to the negatively charged phosphate groups of DNA. It is difficult to explain how histone molecules could possess much selectivity in their union with DNA, and it is likely that they would simply combine with any gene. Yet we know that in the normal development of organisms, specific genes must be repressed and de-repressed in a coordinated and specific fashion, making it doubtful that histones alone could be responsible.

In 1965, a new type of RNA from pea seedlings that exists covalently connected to the end of a histone protein was discovered in the laboratory of James Bonner (Chapter 17). A similar RNA-histone compound was also found in the nuclei of rat liver by scientists at Columbia University. Perhaps RNA of these molecules gives some specificity to repression by uniting only with a particular part of the DNA with which it could form complementary base pairs. The histone to which it is attached might then act as an allosteric protein, being activated or deactivated by various metabolites, thus influencing the operator region and controlling messenger RNA synthesis.

Certainly much of the information described relating to the mechanisms of induction and repression is still rather speculative, although the two phenomena themselves are well-established occurrences in microorganisms, and several cases of induction in higher plants are known. In addition, cases with corn and *Oenothera* have been described where the activity of one gene is controlled by another, suggesting that regulator genes exist in plants. There is reason to believe, then, that differentiation in plants is partially controlled by careful control of gene functions through enzyme induction and repression.

20.4 CONTROL OF MITOSIS AND CELL DIVISION

DNA molecules act not only as templates for messenger RNA formation, but when cell division occurs they must also act as a template for synthesis of more DNA. The enzyme DNA polymerase synthesizes DNA prior to mitosis, but at other times RNA polymerase is apparently attached to the active genes, allowing their expression and apparently inhibiting the action of DNA polymerase. The synthesis of DNA and RNA must be properly separated in time to allow normal cell development.

At least three possible factors could determine whether a cell would be able to undergo mitosis. *First*, the supply of deoxyribonucleo-

TABLE 20-1

INHIBITION OF DNA-DIRECTED RNA SYNTHESIS BY HISTONES[a]

Addition to reaction mixture	Relative RNA synthesis
50 micrograms pea embryo DNA	2,030
50 micrograms pea embryo DNA attached to histone	190
50 micrograms pea embryo DNA + 50 micrograms DNA attached to histone	1,910

[a] Data of J. Bonner and R. C. Huang, *J. Mol. Biol.* 6:169, 1963.

tide triphosphates could be limiting; *second*, the enzyme DNA polymerase might not be available; and *third*, DNA polymerase might be present but unable to function because the DNA was masked or otherwise prevented from acting as a suitable template. Evidence so far obtained indicates that the third factor is the one controlling DNA synthesis. In fact, Jacob and Monod have suggested that a part of the chromosomal DNA, when activated, produces a substance, an **initiator**, which then puts the remainder of the DNA in a state suitable for mitotic template activity. Direct evidence has been obtained that for cell division to occur in mammalian cells and in certain microorganisms, DNA must be able to act as a template for messenger RNA synthesis and that new enzymes needed for mitosis are then produced. Perhaps the same thing is true with plant cells. Little is known about the way in which DNA could be masked to prevent DNA polymerase from acting until the proper time.

Mitosis (nuclear division) is sometimes distinguished from **cytokinesis** (the production of a cross wall dividing the mother cell into two daughter cells). Although mitosis and cytokinesis usually occur in close sequence, different chemical reactions are involved, and they can sometimes be experimentally separated. Cyto-

kinesis occurs by the formation of a cell plate rich in pectic substances and making up the middle lamella of the new dividing wall. It might be expected that synthesis of this cell plate could be controlled by factors different from those affecting DNA synthesis and nuclear division, and this appears to be true. Although mitosis must occur for cytokinesis to take place, mitosis sometimes occurs without subsequent cell division. An example is the stimulation of nuclear division by certain plant hormones (auxins) without cytokinesis in tobacco pith cells grown by tissue culture techniques. Another hormone (a cytokinin) is required here to stimulate normal cell division. These processes, like others in the plant, are controlled by the interaction of the genetic potentialities of the plant with the environment in which it is growing.

20.5 PLANT HORMONES AND GROWTH REGULATORS

Growth and development of plants are thus processes that strongly depend upon the formation of enzymes and nucleic acids controlling the production of enzymes. One of the ways in which enzyme activity is correlated in multicellular organisms such as higher plants is by chemical messengers, or hormones. Hormone production is under partial environmental control, and this is one of the ways by which the environment affects plant growth. As we shall see in Chapter 21, the mechanism of hormone action is not understood, but they probably act either by controlling enzyme production or enzyme activity, or both.

A **hormone** has been defined as an organic substance synthesized in one part of an organism and *translocated* to another part, where it has a controlling or regulatory effect: it causes a physiological response. Hormones are active in very small amounts, which excludes sugars. Mineral nutrients are excluded because they are not organic. To merit the term hormone, the substance must be translocated, but sometimes a compound normally a hormone in this sense is active in the same cells in which it is synthesized. Since hormones may be synthesized in response to some environmental stimulus, and since they are translocated, they are clearly important in morphogenesis, especially in correlation phenomena where one organ influences the development of another. Current thought suggests that they may interact indirectly with the genetic material or act as inducer or corepressor molecules, thus affecting gene action through allosteric transitions in repressor proteins.

Compounds exist that influence plant growth and development in a manner similar or identical to that of the hormones. These agents, which need not be natural plant components and are not necessarily translocated within the plant, are called **plant growth regulators**. This broad term includes the true plant hormones. It also includes synthetic growth regulators that act much like hormones (e.g., naphthalenacetic acid, and the herbicide 2,4-*D*, both of which are auxins; see Chapter 22). These are often referred to as being "hormone-like."

20.6 MECHANISMS THROUGH WHICH PLANTS RESPOND TO THE ENVIRONMENT

According to the above discussion, the form and function of plants are dependent upon their genetic makeup and the ability of genes to express themselves through enzymatic action, as controlled by the rate of enzyme synthesis and activity. The environment in which a plant exists influences its growth and differentiation by controlling expression of its genetic makeup. The environment affects both enzyme synthesis and enzyme activity. How does the plant detect the environment and how are such detection systems able to control plant functions? Several detection systems have been identified, and a limited amount of information is now available

concerning the way in which they influence plant responses.

20.6.1 Response to Temperature

At least three aspects of temperature are important to plant development. These are its magnitude, duration, and periodicity. Organisms usually respond to increases in temperature by increased rates of metabolism, because of the resulting greater free energy of the molecules. However, a few dramatic effects of temperature are known that subsequently result in permanent developmental (morphological) changes even when the treatment is applied for relatively short periods. These are examples of **inductive changes**, those that develop and persist long after the environmental stimulus is removed.

An example of an inductive change caused by low temperatures is vernalization (see Chapter 25), classically shown in winter cereal grains and certain biennials. The grains are planted in late summer or autumn, but the biennials germinate in the spring. The cereals spend the winter as moist seeds or seedlings, while the biennials typically winter as rosette plants with a tap root. In either case, exposure to the low temperatures of winter results in flowering the next spring or summer. Plants not exposed to the low temperatures (e.g., in a greenhouse) remain vegetative or are significantly delayed in their flowering. The low temperatures are apparently detected by the meristematic cells themselves, and these respond by becoming induced to flower.

Other interesting responses to low temperatures include the breaking of dormancy in certain buds (particularly of deciduous trees) and various seeds, and the formation of tubers or other underground storage organs. These effects largely appear to be inductive phenomena, the temperatures being too cold to allow expression of the response immediately. Perhaps some inhibiting corepressor substance is removed during cold treatment, which then allows previously repressed genes to function and cause the various developmental responses that are observed. Alternatively, the formation of inducer substances could be encouraged by cold temperatures. In either case an inductive effect would result, but further research is needed to specify the existing mechanisms. Plant hormones might prove to be among the corepressors or inducer molecules involved, although there is as yet no good evidence that hormones act exactly in this way.

20.6.2   Response to Light

Intensity, quality (color), changes in these factors with time (duration, periodicity), and interactions among these three are aspects of light that influence plant development. Light sometimes produces **immediate** or **direct results**. Two well-known examples are photosynthesis and the formation of chlorophyll *a* from protochlorophyll. Here light causes chemical responses which, in the presence of substances other than the absorbing pigments, lead to rapid chemical reactions.

Most other effects of light can be observed only after a certain **lag period**. A few examples include the tropistic bending of plant stems toward unilaterally applied light (**phototropism**), inhibition of stem elongation, promotion of leaf growth in dicots, breaking dormancy of certain seeds, and stimulation of anthocyanin formation in certain plant organs by light. Here there is an interaction among intensity, quality, and duration of the light treatment. Other plant morphogenetic responses result from alternations in the light-dark cycles (photoperiodic responses), such as the initiation of dormancy, senescence, or of flower or tuber formation in some plants, and the breaking of seed or bud dormancy in some others. In all of these examples the final response requires much more

energy than is provided by the light itself, so than an **amplification** is involved. Sometimes the final result, though amplified, is nearly proportional to the energy of the initial light stimulus. In other cases light acts more like an on–off switch than a modulated (quantitative) control.

It is tempting to believe that some substances, perhaps growth hormones, are produced in the cells when light is absorbed by the particular pigment involved, and that these substances then activate genes necessary to code for the enzymes responsible for the particular response. In the case of anthocyanin formation and seed germination, there is evidence that messenger RNA and enzyme formation must be capable of occurring if light is to stimulate the process (Chapter 23). Whether this is also true for the other inductive effects caused by light remains to be seen. In phototropism it is clear that a growth hormone (an auxin) becomes more concentrated on the shaded than on the lighted side of the stem, but the mechanism by which this occurs has not been determined.

20.6.3   Response to Gravity

Everyone who has ever planted a seed and watched it sprout knows that normally oriented seedlings develop regardless of the way the seed is oriented in the soil. This is true because the shoot of a germinating seed always grows upward and the roots grow downward into the soil. As shown by experiments with seedlings in centrifuges, these are geotropic (gravitational) responses, or **geotropisms**. Roots are said to be positively geotropic, since they grow toward the direction of the gravitational stimulus (downward), while the shoots are said to be negatively geotropic, since they grow in a direction 180° away from the direction of the gravitational stimulus (upward). Geotropism is also an inductive effect, since the actual bending·process can be separated in time from the period during which the gravitational treatment is imposed.

Plant physiologists have long attempted to discover the mechanism by which plant organs detect the gravitational force and to determine how shoots and roots can behave oppositely. Since colloidal particles remain in suspension due to Brownian movement and hence do not settle in response to gravity, only particles or objects larger than these can act as gravity-detection sensors. The hypothetical sensors are called **statoliths**. Microscopical examination shows that mitochondria, chloroplasts, starch grains, and the nucleus are all displaced somewhat toward the bottom of a cell in response to gravity.

For some time it was thought that the gravitational displacement of starch grains against the plasmalemma on the lower side of a cell somehow stimulated an auxin-like hormone to be transported from cell to cell and to accumulate on the lowermost cells of the horizontally oriented root or stem. Using methods of detection described in the next chapter, some experimenters were indeed able to demonstrate accumulation of an auxin on the lower side of certain plant stems. This auxin then causes the cells to expand faster on the lower side, leading to an upward bending of the shoot. For roots, which respond oppositely, it was assumed that accumulation of auxin in the lowermost cells causes an inhibition of growth. The uppermost cells, then depleted of auxin, presumably grow faster than those on the lower side, and this causes a downward bending. Except at very low concentrations, the growth of root cells is inhibited by auxins, while the growth of shoots is usually stimulated, facts consistent with the theory. No large differences in auxin concentrations across horizontally placed roots have been detected, however, and other modern research suggests that unknown factors are responsible for geotropism in roots.

Starch grains are probably not the statolith-detecting sensors in either roots or stems, since coleoptiles depleted of starch (by treatment with gibberellin—see next chapter) still respond to gravity. The way in which gravity causes an unequal auxin distribution in stems leading to the geotropic response thus remains to be solved, but some progress is being made in understanding the general nature of the gravity response. R. R. Dedolph and other workers at the Argonne National Laboratory near Chicago have recently studied the distribution of cellular particles in plants rotated with the stem axis in a vertical or a horizontal position, or at various angles between the vertical and the horizontal. The device for rotating plants in this manner is called a **clinostat**, and it has been used for many years in studies on geotropism (Fig. 20-8). In horizontally rotated plants, gravity is compensated if the rate of rotation is faster than the time of response of the gravity receptors (and not so fast as to introduce centrifugal forces). **Such a plant is in a simulated zero g or weight**less environment. The vertical plant, even though rotated, would be exposed to the normal **downward gravitational forces of 1 g.** (Rotation would serve as a control indicating effects due to rotation and not due to gravity.)

Dedolph and his coworkers confirmed an increased rate of metabolism and increased growth, particularly in roots, of oat seedlings on the horizontal clinostat. Intermediate angles from the horizontal with their intermediate **simulated g levels produced intermediate levels** of growth and metabolism. Randomness of particle (amyloplasts and other cellular particles) distribution was closely correlated with this; as distribution of particles within the cell became more random (beginning at simulated g levels less than 0.14 g), metabolism and growth increased proportionally. These workers suggest that, since many of these particles are metabolically active, when they are concentrated in one part of the cell (at the bottom), molecular substrates distributed within the cell by thermal diffusion become somewhat depleted in the vicinity of the particles. Random dis-

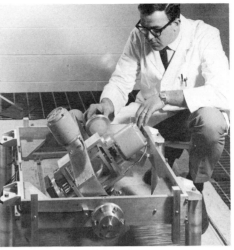

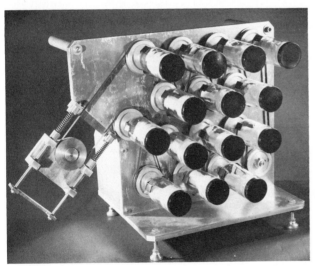

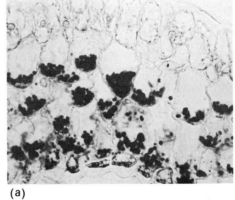

(a)

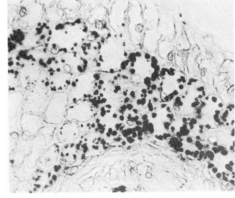

(b)

Figure 20-8

Clinostats and results, illustrating work done at the Argonne National Laboratory, Argonne, Illinois. (upper left) A 2-pi (two-axis) clinostat which can impose centrifugal force on samples in the bottles, while they are slowly tumbled to compensate for earth gravity. (Jane Shen-Miller and S. A. Gordon). (upper right) A 4-pi clinostat for the nullification of the directional components of earth fields (R. Hinchman). (lower left) A "serpentine" 1-pi clinostat, used to study interaction of ionizing radiation and gravity compensation. (lower right) Amyloplast distribution in the cells of the tip of the *Avena* coleoptile: (a), controls rotated on a single-axis, 1-pi clinostat with organ oriented *vertically*, axis of rotation vertical (rotation, but no gravity compensation); (b), seedling grown in multiple-axis (4-pi) clinostat by R. Hinchman and S. Gordon. (Photographs courtesy of S. Gordon and the Argonne Laboratories.)

tribution of particles due to rotation or zero *g* (as in an orbiting artificial satellite) thus results in more metabolism and consequent growth. The picture is complex, however, since some plants grow *less* on a horizontal clinostat, apparently due to a decreased rate of auxin translocation.

Distribution of cellular particles may influence metabolism but have little or nothing to do with auxin transport from cell to cell. Thus workers in this area, such as Kenneth V. Thimann and Solon Gordon, are beginning to wonder about the relative distributions in the cell of cytoplasm and vacuole. If the vacuole is less dense, it may tend to "float" in the cytoplasm, the result being a thinner layer of cytoplasm on the top of the cell than on the bottom. If thicker cytoplasm secretes more auxin into its neighboring cell than thinner cytoplasm, then a mechanism would be available to explain increased auxin on the bottom of a horizontal stem. This proposal must be experimentally tested.

20.6.4 Response to Touch or Injury

Several plant organs including petioles and stems, but especially tendrils, respond to contact with a solid object by differential growth. If the response is a normal function as occurs when tendrils of climbing plants become anchored to an object, it is called **thigmotropism**; if due to injury, it is called **traumatotropism** (a stem wounded on one side will often bend toward that side). If the organ bends toward or around an object or a wound, the response is said to be positive; if away from the object, negative.

In the case of tendrils, the response is sometimes extremely rapid. The tendril may wrap around a support in just a few minutes, or even in less than a minute in some species. Cells touching the support may shrink slightly, and those on the other side of the tendril elongate rapidly. These changes are permanent, and the

tendril is strengthened by secondary wall formation. It is interesting to note that the response will occur even if the tendril is touched only very lightly by an object such as a thread. If contact is made with a perfectly smooth surface, however, or with a liquid such as a drop of water or even a drop of mercury (much heavier than the thread), no response occurs. The mechanisms of these responses are not understood.

20.6.5 Chemotropism and Chemotaxis

As early as the late 1800s several botanists in Germany became curious about the way in which a plant sperm cell finds the female egg it fertilizes. The rather difficult pathway followed by the pollen tube carrying the sperm of higher plants is diagramed in Fig. 20-9. Both Julius Sachs and W. Pfeffer suggested that the growth of the pollen tube down through the style, through the micropyle, and into the embryo sac might be chemically directed.

In the 1890s H. Molisch demonstrated that the direction and extent of growth of pollen tubes can be controlled by chemical substances; i.e., that a **chemotropism** exists. Molisch placed pollen grains about a millimeter away from various test substances on the surface of nutrient agar upon which the pollen would germinate (produce a tube). Since his experiments were completed, pollen grains from over 100 species have been studied in experiments of this kind. Most grow toward various gynecial parts (ovary, ovules, and even stigma and style) whether these parts are from plants of the same species or not. This indicates that the compound involved has little specificity for pollen of the same plant. Various unsuccessful attempts have been made to identify the chemotropically active substances. The results do indicate, however, that the molecules are small enough to penetrate a dialyzing membrane, that they are water soluble, and that they are heat stable. More recent work, performed in the laboratory of Leonard Machlis at the University of Cali-

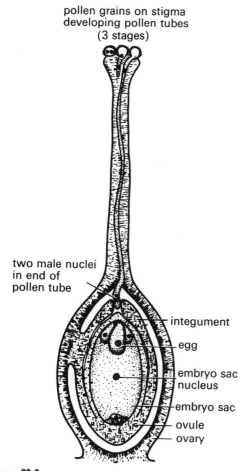

pollen grains on stigma
developing pollen tubes
(3 stages)

two male nuclei
in end of
pollen tube

integument

egg

embryo sac
nucleus

embryo sac

ovule

ovary

Figure 20-9

Growth of the pollen tube through the style and into the embryo sac, where fertilization occurs. Pollen grains are exaggerated in size. (After F. C. Steward, 1964, *Plants at Work*, Addison-Wesley Publishing Company, Reading, Mass., p. 150. Used by permission.)

fornia in Berkeley, indicates that calcium ions cause the chemotropic response in pollen of three species studied. A strong response due to calcium not given by other cations was found, and it was also observed that the concentration of calcium in snapdragon (*Antirrhinum majus*) is highest in the ovules, to which the pollen tube is attracted.

Calcium ions fit the observed properties of heat stability, dialyzability, and water solubility, and their presence in all plants would explain the lack of specificity involved. Further research is needed, however, to determine whether calcium is indeed the active substance in most plants or whether other, more specific chemicals are involved.

Successful fertilization in many of the lower plants, such as certain fungi, algae, and ferns, appears also to be directed by chemicals released from the female gametes or from the structures in which these gametes are produced. For example, in those algae in which eggs are not released from the oogonia, the chance entrance of a sperm would seem to be unlikely, without which sexual reproduction would fail. Much evidence indicates that rather specific compounds attract the motile sperm in many of these cases. Such movement toward a particular chemical is called **chemotaxis** and is often distinguished from chemotropism, in which growth, not motility, is involved. Several chemotactic agents have been identified, including various sugars, organic acids, inorganic ions, and even proteins. Whether these are indeed the important substances involved in the phenomena remains to be established. Leonard Machlis and coworkers, in 1966, found a very potent agent apparently responsible for the attraction of sperm by female gametes of one member of the genus *Allomyces* (water molds). This compound, called **sirenin**[2], is an oxygen-containing liquid terpene with an empirical formula of $C_{15}H_{24}O_2$ and a molecular weight of 236. Its mechanism of action is as yet unknown.

---

[2] The sirens of Greek and Roman mythology were nymphs who lured sailors to their destruction on rocks.

21

Plant Hormones and Growth Regulators

Participation of the growth hormones in phototropism and geotropism represents but two of the many hormone-mediated responses of plants. It is, in fact, likely that all developmental processes are influenced to some degree by one or more kinds of hormones. They have already been implicated in the growth and development of stems, roots, and leaves, formation of adventitious buds and roots, tubers, flowers, and in fruit development and maturation, senescence, dormancy of buds and seeds, germination of seeds, and other phenomena. In this chapter known natural growth regulators and hormones will be listed, along with an introduction to the effects they cause. Further details of their influence upon specific morphogenetic processes will be described in subsequent chapters.

Plant hormones have been classified upon the basis of the kinds of response they influence. The famous German botanist, Julius Sachs, spoke of the possibility of specific organ-forming hormones, supposing that one kind of hormone caused stem growth; another, leaf growth; another, flower development; and so on. This explanation has proved much too simple, and although various kinds of hormones do exist, the growth and development of most plant organs seem to depend upon the interaction of several of these. In addition, inhibitors exist in plants, and these accumulate under certain conditions and modify responses to the promotive hormones. By influencing growth after being translocated, they may also fit the definition of a hormone. They are clearly growth regulators, since they do affect plant growth. Synthetic growth regulators often mimic the effects of naturally occurring growth regulators (including hormones) or interfere with their actions.

21.1 THE AUXINS

21.1.1 Discovery

Several rather simple but ingenious experiments led to the discovery of the growth hormone called auxin (Fig. 21-1). Charles Darwin, in the 1890s, had found that grass coleoptiles exhibited phototropism in response to that light absorbed by the tip. Later (1914–1919), Paal of Hungary suggested that the correlative effect between the tip, which absorbed the light, and the more basal section, which responded by bending, arose from changes in the movement of some substance due to unilateral light. He showed that removal of the coleoptile tip in the dark stopped growth; replacing it caused elongation to be resumed, and replacing it on one side caused curvature. P. Boysen-Jensen of Denmark was also a pioneer in this field (1910–1913). Among other things, Boysen-Jensen showed that phototropism would

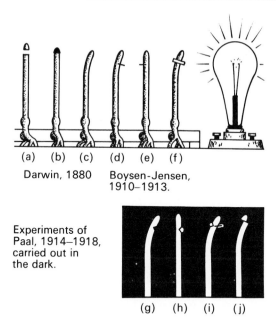

(a) (b) (c) (d) (e) (f)

Darwin, 1880   Boysen-Jensen, 1910–1913.

Experiments of Paal, 1914–1918, carried out in the dark.

(g) (h) (i) (j)

Figure 21-1

Some experiments preliminary to the discovery of auxin. When Darwin removed an *Avena* coleoptile tip (a) or covered it (b), the coleoptile failed to bend toward the light, as an intact coleoptile will (c). Boysen-Jensen observed bending when a sheet of mica was inserted into the light side of the coleoptile (d), but not when it was inserted into the dark side (e). He could also observe bending when the tip was separated from the coleoptile below by a small layer of gelatin (f). Went was especially influenced in his experiments by those of Paal, who observed bending in the dark when a portion of coleoptile tissue was removed from one side (g), but not when it was replaced or when the hole was filled with gelatin (h). Removing the tip and then replacing it with gelatin on one side and mica on the other side (i) caused bending, as did replacing the tip on one side of the coleoptile (j).

occur even if the tip was separated from the rest of the coleoptile by a small block of gelatin. He also found that phototropism would fail when flow of material down through the cells on the dark side was interrupted by a small piece of mica, but not when the mica was placed on the light side, indicating the presence of a growth *promotor*, rather than an *inhibitor*.

Building upon these experiments, Frits Went, a graduate student (1926) working in his father's plant laboratory at Utrecht, Holland, found that

such a growth-promoting chemical did exist. He cut off the tips of oat (*Avena sativa*) coleoptiles, placed these in darkness upon a block of agar, and after a period of time, placed the agar back upon one side of a properly prepared coleoptile stump (Fig. 21-2). The detipped coleoptile grew faster on the side to which the agar block was added, bending in the opposite direction. This demonstrated that a growth substance in the gelatin block could exist independent of the coleoptile tip. Existence of such a substance substantiated the proposed explanation for phototropism. Went showed that more of this substance would diffuse into a block placed below the dark side of a coleoptile tip than into one placed below the light side. He named the substance that must exist in the gelatin block **auxin**. The term is now used in a generic sense for all compounds (natural or synthetic) that are active in causing coleoptile curvature when applied unilaterally as in Went's experiment.

A few years later (1934) F. Kögl and his associates in Holland isolated from urine a compound which, when incorporated into the agar blocks, caused the decapitated coleoptile to bend in Went's curvature test. This proved to be **indoleacetic acid** (IAA),[1] a substance that had been isolated from urine and whose molecular structure (Fig. 21-3) had been determined toward the end of the 19th century. Kögl's group (1934) and K. V. Thimann (1935) also soon found IAA in plant tissues, and it has since been identified or at least implicated in a large number of plants. Went's auxin is believed by most workers to be IAA, but coleoptiles are now also known to contain other compounds that cause

[1] Kögl and his coworkers first found compounds they called auxin-*A* and auxin-*B*, but these compounds are probably identical with IAA and an ester of IAA. The controversy over this identity has continued for years, and some workers still point to differences between the properties of auxin-*A* and IAA. In the original structure determination of auxin-*A*, for example, no nitrogen was included, although this is an important part of IAA. The proposed structure of auxin-*A* was complex and unlike any familiar metabolites.

the bending response and are therefore defined as auxins. No auxin has yet been crystallized from coleoptile tips. It has been calculated that 20,000 tons of coleoptile tips would be required to produce one gram of pure IAA, indicating that auxins are active in extremely small amounts.

21.1.2 Synthesis and Degradations of IAA

IAA is structurally similar to tryptophan and, in fact, seems to be synthesized from this amino acid. Two possible mechanisms for synthesis exist (Fig. 21-3), both of which result in the loss of the amino group and the carboxyl group of tryptophan and the formation of the new terminal carboxyl group. One mechanism involves the amine **tryptamine** as an intermediate metabolite, while the other involves **indolepyruvic** acid, but both presumably lead to **indoleacetaldehyde**, and then to IAA. Which pathway is most important is still not established. Some plants may depend on one pathway, while different ones may depend upon the other.

The enzymes necessary for tryptophan conversion to IAA are most active in young developing tissues, such as meristems and young leaves, fruits, and roots. It is here that the auxin activity is usually found to be highest. The formation of IAA requires zinc ions in some plants, and the stems of certain fruit trees deficient in this element fail to elongate properly. This is believed to be because IAA is needed for normal cell elongation in such tissues, but it cannot be formed in the absence of zinc.

The concentration of IAA normally existing in plants is affected by processes that cause its destruction (Fig. 21-4) as well as its synthesis. One destructive process involves its oxidation and results in the uptake of oxygen and release of carbon dioxide. The enzyme involved is called **IAA oxidase**, and the products of oxidation appear to differ with various plants. IAA oxidase is inhibited by caffeic acid, quercetin, chloro-

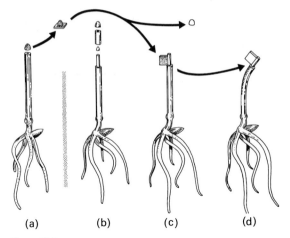

(a)	(b)	(c)	(d)

Figure 21-2

The demonstration by Went of auxin in the *Avena* coleoptile tip. Auxin is indicated by stippling. The tip was removed and placed on a block of gelatin (a). Another seedling was prepared by removing the tip, waiting a period of time, and removing the tip again (a new "physiological tip" sometimes forms) (b). The leaf inside the coleoptile was pulled out, and the gelatin block containing the auxin was placed against it (c). Auxin moved into the coleoptile on one side, causing it to bend (d). (From F. B. Salisbury and R. V. Parke, 1964, *Vascular Plants: Form and Function*, Wadsworth Publishing Company, Inc., Belmont, Calif. Used by permission.)

genic acid and certain other natural phenolic compounds with two hydroxyl groups on positions ortho to each other on an aromatic ring, but it is promoted by some having only one hydroxyl group (e.g., *p*-coumaric acid compounds). The orthodiphenols stimulate growth of coleoptile and stem sections in the presence of IAA, while the monophenols are inhibitory. This is at least partly due to their opposite effects on IAA oxidase. Other known mechanisms by which IAA levels in the plant are reduced include its conversion to derivatives by combination with aspartic acid, glutamic acid, myoinositol, or glucose. The enzyme combining aspartic acid and IAA is called IAA-aspartate synthetase and is an example of an enzyme in higher plants that seems to be induced by adding large amounts of one of its substrates

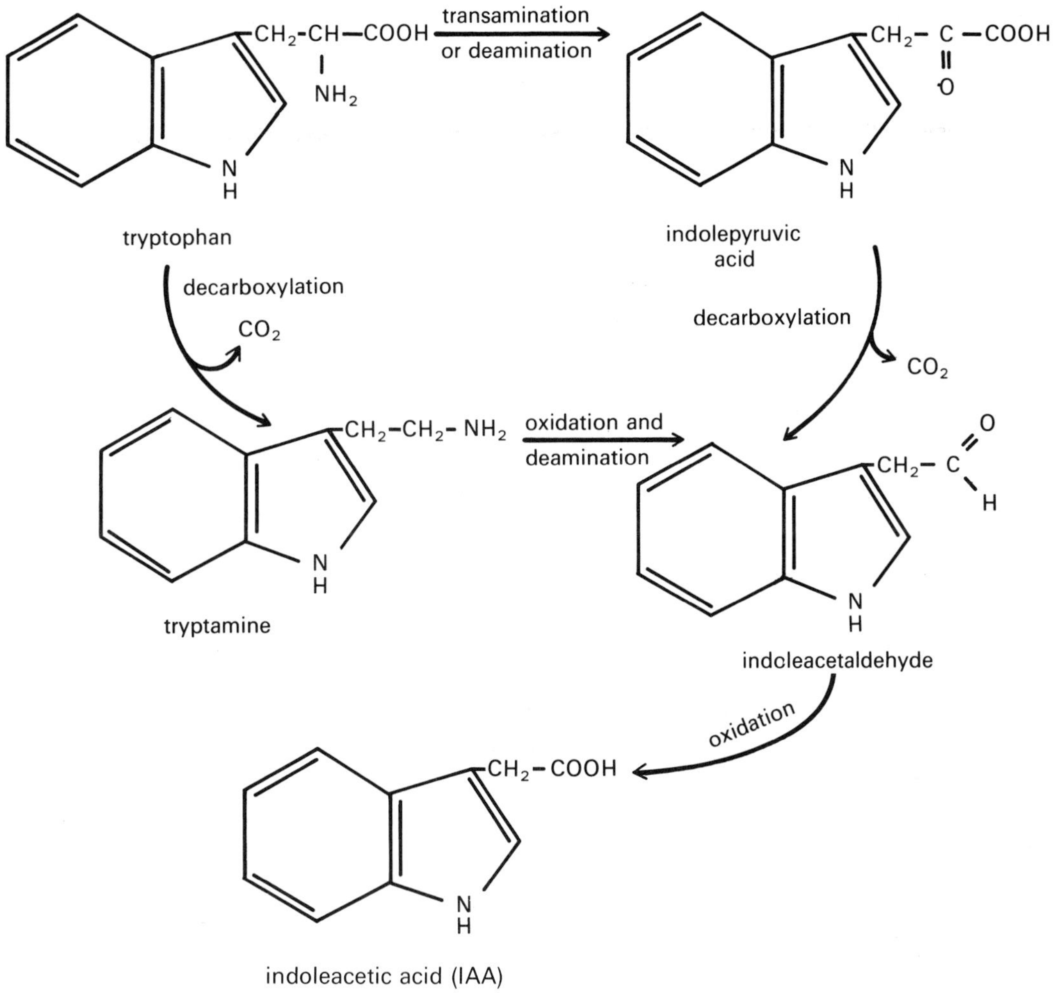

Figure 21-3
Possible mechanisms of formation of IAA in plant tissues.

(IAA). IAA can also be attached to some proteins, which sometimes renders it inactive. Such derivatives are often referred to as forms of "bound" auxin.

21.1.3   Extraction and Identification of Auxins

21.1.3A Techniques used   Following the identification of IAA in plants by Kögl and by Thimann, many physiologists began the search for this or other auxins in a number of species. Success depended upon the development of satisfactory methods for extraction of auxins from the tissues and for measuring the amounts extracted. Several techniques for removing auxins from the cells are used. Some of these involve cold ethyl ether, ethanol, or chloroform as an extracting solvent. The ether extract is

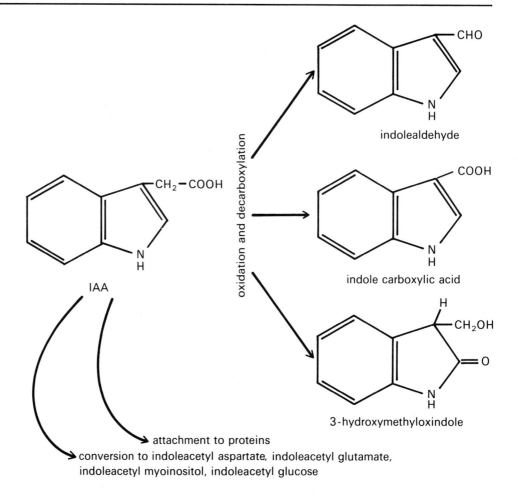

oxidation and decarboxylation

indolealdehyde

indole carboxylic acid

3-hydroxymethyloxindole

IAA

attachment to proteins

conversion to indoleacetyl aspartate, indoleacetyl glutamate, indoleacetyl myoinositol, indoleacetyl glucose

Figure 21-4

Mechanisms by which free IAA may be altered in plant cells.

concentrated by evaporation and may then be incorporated into a block of agar. In other techniques, agar blocks are simply placed in contact with the plant organ of interest, and the auxin diffuses out of the cells into the agar where it is collected, as in Went's original experiments with the *Avena* coleoptile tips. This auxin is called **diffusible auxin**, and some plant physiologists feel that since it is clearly capable of moving from the cells, it is more likely to

represent an important transportable auxin than auxins obtained by extracting the tissue. In **the *Avena* curvature test**, the auxin-containing agar block is placed on one side of a decapitated stump of an oat coleoptile. The auxin diffuses down through the coleoptile directly below the agar block and causes the cells there to grow more rapidly, which soon results in bending of the coleoptile stump toward the opposite side. Degree of bending is measured, usually on

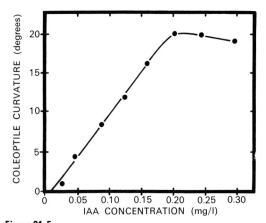

Figure 21-5

Curvature of decapitated oat coleoptiles caused by unilateral application of various amounts of IAA upon the cut stump. (From F. Went and K. V. Thimann, 1937, *Phytohormones*, Macmillan Company, New York, p. 41. Used by permission.)

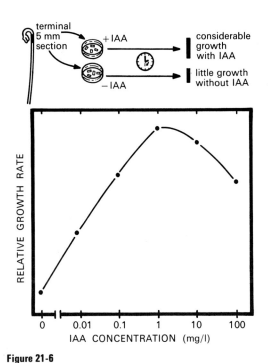

Figure 21-6

(top) Technique used in auxin bioassay using apical sections from etiolated pea stems (epicotyls). Sections are placed in petri dishes containing sucrose and certain mineral salts. Growth is often measured 12 to 24 hours later. (bottom) Influence of the IAA concentration upon growth rate of pea stem sections. Note that auxin concentrations are plotted logarithmically, and that an optimum concentration is reached which, when exceeded, results in less growth. (After Arthur W. Galston, 1964, *The Life of the Green Plant*, 2nd ed., Prentice-Hall, Inc., Englewood Cliffs, N.J., p. 75, © 1969. Used by permission.)

shadographs made by placing several coleoptiles in a holder in front of a sheet of photographic paper, exposing, and developing the paper.

When IAA is applied to the coleoptile stump, the degree of bending is closely proportional to the concentration used up to 0.2 mg/liter (Fig. 21-5). Unknown auxins removed from a plant can then be compared quantitatively with commercially synthesized IAA in their ability to cause bending. This is an example of a **bioassay**, an assay using biological material to measure the amount or activity of a particular unknown substance. The *Avena* curvature test is very sensitive, a response being elicited by as little as one-billionth of a gram applied to a coleoptile.

Another bioassay is often used to determine the presence of auxins in various plants. This method, called the **straight growth test**, also takes advantage of the ability of auxins to cause coleoptile or stem cells to elongate rapidly. Dark-grown coleoptiles are decapitated to remove the endogenous source of auxin, and sections of the remaining stump are placed in solutions containing an extract thought to con-

tain an auxin. Alternatively, sections of dark-grown stems of pea seedlings are used. (The growth of pea stems from plants grown in the light is less stimulated by added auxins.) The growth of such sections increases with auxin concentration of the solution (Fig. 21-6). By comparing the growth increase due to the plant extract with results obtained using known amounts of IAA, quantitative estimations of the activity of the auxin present can be obtained. Results can be expressed in units of IAA equivalents.

The straight growth test, like the coleoptile bending test, is a very sensitive bioassay and is usually even more convenient to perform. It is, however, less specific than is the bending test, since several other compounds that are present in plants are not active in the curvature test but sometimes cause responses in the straight growth test.

Neither auxin bioassay gives information about the chemical identity of the unknown auxin isolated from the plant. Rigorous identification of all of the compounds with auxin activity existing in such trace amounts in plants has so far not been feasible, but an indication of the identity of auxins can be obtained by first subjecting the plant extract to paper chromatography. After the partial chromatographic separations of the various compounds, several sections of the paper are cut out and the compounds present in each are dissolved in a suitable solvent. The resulting solutions are then used in a bioassay, and by this means any auxins present in the original plant extract may be detected (Fig. 21-7). By measuring the chromatographic movement (R_f) of an auxin in various solvent systems, clues as to its chemical nature are obtained. When such tests are performed, many plant extracts are found to contain a compound with auxin activity that chromatographs in the same position as IAA, but other compounds are also usually detected. Inhibitory substances are also observed. If these inhibitors should chromatograph in the same region as an auxin, growth promotion due to the auxin may be masked.

21.1.3B Auxins other than IAA present in plants

In certain plants, compounds occur that have auxin activity probably only because they are rapidly converted to IAA by the bioassay tissue. These are **indoleacetaldehyde, indole-ethanol**, and **indoleacetonitrile** (Fig. 21-8). Indoleacetaldehyde is probably present in all higher plants, while indoleacetonitrile is more

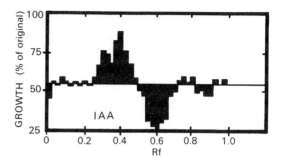

Figure 21-7

Influence of compounds present in black currant fruits upon elongation of wheat coleoptiles. An acidic extract of the fruits was made, and this was chromatographed in an isobutanol-NH_2OH-H_2O solvent. Strips were cut from the chromatogram, extracted, and the extract used in the wheat coleoptile assay. One compound promoting growth has an R_f value identical to that of IAA, suggesting the presence of this auxin in the berries. An area of the chromatogram containing substance(s) inhibitory to growth ($R_f = 0.6$) was also found. (From A. C. Leopold, 1964, *Plant Growth and Development*, McGraw-Hill, New York, p. 86. Data of S. T. Wright, 1956, *J. Hort. Sci.* 31:196. Used by permission.)

limited, being especially abundant in such plants as cabbage and other members of the Cruciferae family. Indole-ethanol has so far apparently been found only in cucumbers, but it probably also occurs in many other species. Some plants cannot convert indoleacetonitrile to IAA, although coleoptiles are able to do this. The conversion of indole-ethanol to IAA has also been demonstrated recently.

Other auxins that do not possess an indole structure have also been found by use of the chromatographic technique or by other separation methods, but these have not yet been clearly identified. One of these was first extracted from orange fruits in 1963 and was named **citrus auxin**. It also occurs in other citrus fruits and in several other plant families. At least eight auxins were found in apple seeds, two (other than IAA and different from those of the apple) in black currant fruits, and seven in strawberry fruits (achenes). In addition, there is evidence that certain unidentified steroids from *Coleus*

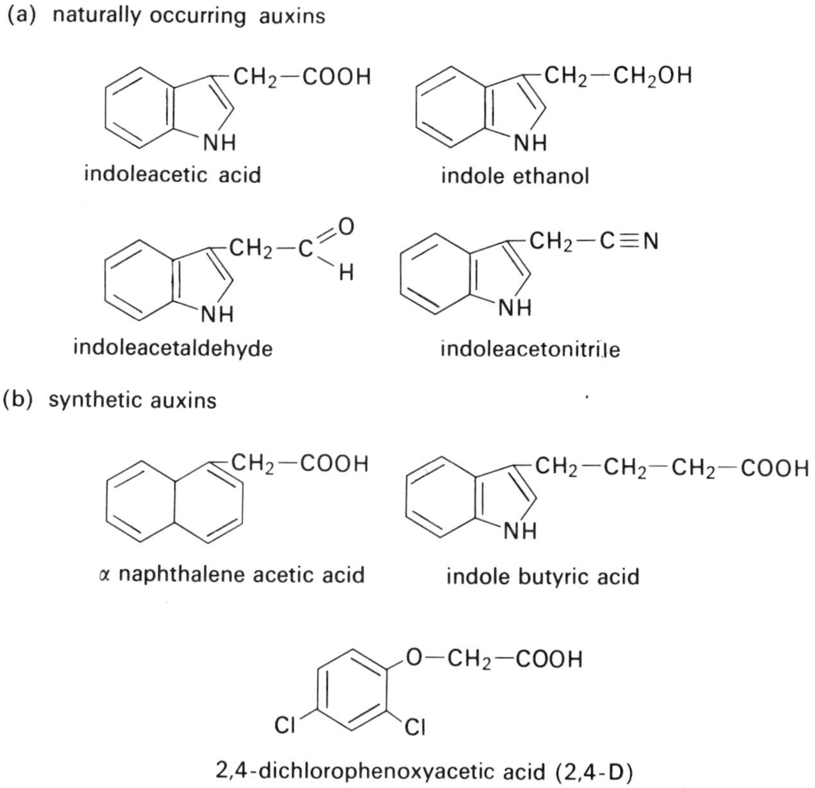

(a) naturally occurring auxins

indoleacetic acid

indole ethanol

indoleacetaldehyde

indoleacetonitrile

(b) synthetic auxins

α naphthalene acetic acid

indole butyric acid

2,4-dichlorophenoxyacetic acid (2,4-D)

Figure 21-8

Structures of some naturally occurring indole compounds having auxin activity (a), and of other compounds which are only synthetic auxins (b).

plants have auxin activity. Thus, many auxins other than IAA probably exist in the plant kingdom.

21.1.4 Synthetic Auxins

Along with the establishment of IAA as a plant hormone in the 1930s, work by P. W. Zimmerman and A. E. Hitchcock at the Boyce Thompson Institute in New York and by others established that synthetic substances like naphthaleneacetic acid (NAA) and certain phenoxyacetic acids also have auxin activity. The structures of several natural and synthetic auxins, including NAA, indole butyric acid, and one of the most active and widely used phenoxyacetic acids, 2,4-dichlorophenoxyacetic acid (2,4-D), are given in Fig. 21-8. Research with these compounds was performed under great secrecy during World War II because of their potential use as biological warfare agents.

The compound 2,4-D is active at very low concentrations in most auxin bioassays[2] and is

---

[2] 2,4-D is very active in the *Avena* straight growth test but nearly inactive in the *Avena* curvature test. This is probably because the polar transport of 2,4-D is rather weak, and it moves rather rapidly to *both* sides of a vertical coleoptile.

a very potent herbicide (Chapter 28). It kills most dicotyledonous (broad-leaved) plants, but has little effect upon members of the grass family when applied at proper concentrations and stages of crop development. It is widely used to kill broad-leaved weeds in cereal grain crops because of this selective action, and sales have increased tremendously since it became commercially available after World War II.

21.1.5 Other Effects of Auxins on Plant Development

The 1930s and 1940s were years in which plant scientists applied IAA or synthetic auxins to many different plants and plant parts to study their effects on various physiological processes. A large number of responses were noted, indicating that native plant auxins probably participate in many normal functions.

21.1.5A Growth of various plant parts Auxins seem to play a normal role in causing the elongation of stems and grass coleoptiles, and perhaps of roots, leaves, and flowers of most higher plants. The primary influence upon stem elongation is an increase in the elongation of the cells. Went stated that "without auxin there is no growth," and this idea has not yet been disproved.

21.1.5B Meristematic activity When auxins are mixed with lanolin and applied to the cut surface of a stem, a large swelling or callus is usually formed. The callus tissue results from the meristematic activity of cortex or pith cells which somehow become **dedifferentiated** as they attain the capacity to undergo mitosis. Cell division produces poorly organized cells with irregular shapes which make up the callus. Such callus may be cut off the plant and grown in nutrient culture, provided that an auxin is present in the growth medium (Fig. 21-9).

The ability of native auxins to increase cell division is believed to be of great importance in perennial woody plants. In temperate zones the vascular cambium becomes inactive in late summer and remains so during the winter months. It was suggested as early as 1893 by L. Jost that the cambium is reactivated during the spring by a hormonal substance produced by buds and the upper young leaves. R. Snow in 1933 obtained evidence that the substance involved might be an auxin when he demonstrated that IAA effectively stimulated normal cell division in the cambium. Auxins thus apparently perform important functions in meristematic activity, although, as will be described later, other growth-regulating substances interact.

21.1.5C Lateral bud development Some plants grow considerably more in height than in breadth, while in other species the difference is considerably less, depending upon the extent of branching. Branching results from the development of lateral or axillary buds (those present in the leaf axils). In many species the apical bud exerts an inhibitory influence (**apical dominance**) upon the lateral buds, preventing their development. It has long been known to gardeners that if the apical bud is removed, the lateral buds usually develop (see Chapter 22). It was found that if auxins are applied to the remaining cut stump, lateral bud development is again retarded in some plants (Fig. 21-10). This suggests that the active substance normally produced by the apical bud is an auxin, and that these hormones therefore control branching in plants. In addition, auxins retard tillering (branching) of grasses to some extent. However, in some species such as the cocklebur (*Xanthium strumarium*), lateral bud growth is not influenced by auxins added to the decapitated stump, and other substances seem to be involved. In various plants the cytokinins have also been implicated, in addition to auxins and gibberellins (see 21.4.3C). In flax and perhaps in other plants,

Figure 21-9

Callus formation on stems in response to applied auxin. (right) The cocklebur stem on the left has had the tip removed and auxin (1 percent NAA) in lanolin placed on the stump. Callus formation is very local. The other two plants with leaves had the leaves dipped in a relatively concentrated NAA solution ($1 \times 10^{-3}\ M$), and callus has subsequently formed on the stems below. The other two stems, showing heavy callus, were wounded and then treated with the auxin paste. (left) The tomato plant shows extreme callus formation.

too, a competition between the apical and lateral buds for nutrients seems to be primarily responsible for apical dominance.

21.1.5D Initiation of root primordia

Auxins have realized an important use in propagation of plants by stem cuttings. In many horticultural and other crops (e.g., fruits and ornamentals), it is important to maintain genetic purity of specially adapted hybrids by asexual reproduction. The practice is to propagate plants from excised stem sections. Marketable size is often reached faster by plants produced from cuttings than from those arising from seeds. The success of the technique depends upon the initiation of new roots at the base of the cutting. These roots usually arise from cells produced following division of an outer layer of phloem. Julius Sachs

(1880s) and Van der Lek (1925) obtained evidence that the existence of active buds or young leaves above the cut somehow stimulated root initiation, and they suggested that these supply a hormone to the place where new roots originate. In 1935, Went and Thimann showed that IAA would stimulate root initiation, suggesting that it or a similar hormone is the substance normally supplied by the growing leaves or buds. Synthetic auxins such as indole butyric acid and NAA are especially effective, and they are used commercially for this purpose. The use of auxins to stimulate rooting in cuttings was the first practical application of hormones in horticulture.

With some species, the formation of adventitious roots on a cutting always occurs at the physiological base, as first shown with willow by

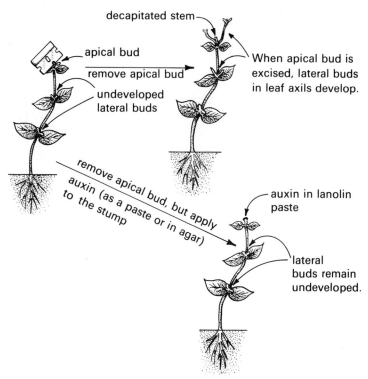

Figure 21-10

Experiment showing that removal of the apical bud allows lateral bud development, and that auxins replace this role of the apical bud in some plants.

H. Vöchting in 1878. Thus, whether the stem section is placed upside down or is oriented normally, the roots always form at the position which was the more basal when the section was intact, and buds always form at the end which was nearer the shoot apex[3] (Fig. 21-11). Transport of most auxins in stems is similarly polarized and nearly always occurs predominantly in a basipetal direction, presumably through parenchyma cells outside the vascular bundles. The velocity of its movement is about 0.5 to 1.5 centimeters per hour. This **polar movement** depends upon respiration and probably upon the ATP produced therein, since it is prevented by the lack of oxygen and the presence of respiratory poisons. A. Carl Leopold and co-workers at Purdue University showed that the much larger basipetal than acropetal (apex seeking) movement could arise from the passage of auxins through many cells even though there was only a small preferential secretion out of the basal end of each individual cell. For example, with the help of a computer they calculated that if 52.5 percent of the auxin secreted by a file of 100 cells were to come out of the basal end of each cell, over 10,000 times as much auxin would be found at the basal end of the tissue than at the acropetal end!

---

[3] In a few species, such as *Hibiscus*, roots form at the bottom of the stem whether it is the physiological base or the apex. In this case, gravity is apparently more important than polarity.

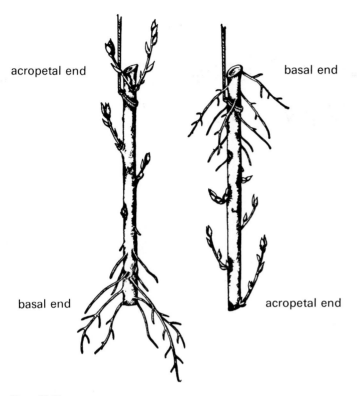

Figure 21-11

Polarity of root and bud formation in willow shoots suspended in moist air. (From E. W. Sinnott, 1960, *Plant Morphogenesis,* McGraw-Hill, New York, p. 120. Used by permission.)

A number of woody species, especially certain gymnosperms and fruit trees (e.g., apples, pears) do not readily form adventitious roots, even with auxin treatment, and other unknown substances seem to be involved. Went (1938) named these unknown compounds **rhizocalines**. Considerable indirect evidence that rhizocalines do exist and that they act in conjunction with auxin has been obtained (Fig. 21-12), but still none has been identified.

Normal branch roots are initiated in the pericycle and, like the formation of adventitious roots, they appear to depend upon the ability of auxin to initiate division in cells that had previously been well differentiated. The role of auxins in root *initiation* is to be contrasted with

their subsequent effects upon root *growth.* As mentioned in relation to geotropism, root growth is almost always inhibited by adding auxins, the tentative explanation being that the roots already contain sufficient amounts of endogenous auxins. Another more recent and likely suggestion is that the ethylene produced when excess auxins are present (see 21.8) is the real inhibitor of root growth.

21.1.5E   Other influences of auxins upon plant development   Auxins are known to have several other interesting effects upon plant development. They play a role in the enlargement of ovaries and their development into mature fruits, in the falling of leaves, flowers, and fruits (**abscission**),

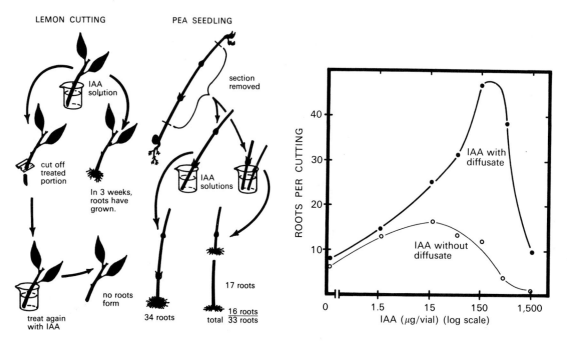

Figure 21-12

Experiments demonstrating that substances other than auxins (rhizocalines) may be involved in root initiation. (left) Once roots have formed on a lemon cutting, they will not form a second time even when treated with IAA, indicating, perhaps, that rhizocalines have been depleted. Furthermore, the number of roots which can be induced to form on a segment of pea stem is proportional to the length of the stem, as though rhizocaline existed at some constant concentration in stem tissue. (right) In addition, there is a synergistic effect of IAA and a diffusate from willow (*Salix alba*) cuttings on formation of adventitious roots in mung bean (*Phaseolus aureus*) stem cuttings. The diffusate was prepared by centrifuging willow stem sections basipetally (basal ends down), while the sections were immersed in 10 ml of water. The material diffusing from the sections into the water promoted root development in willow or mung bean cuttings, especially if IAA were present. The diffusate consisted of at least four heat-stable, active components. (Data of M. Kawase, 1964, *Physiol. Plantarum* 17:855. Used by permission.)

and in the initiation of flowering in some plants. These effects will be discussed in subsequent chapters.

21.2 THE GIBBERELLINS

A second group of hormonal substances that promotes the elongation of stems also occurs in plants. These were first discovered in Japan in connection with a disease of rice. It was noticed that diseased plants grew excessively tall. These usually could not support themselves and

eventually died from combined weakness and parasite damage. As early as the 1890s, the Japanese called this the bakanae (foolish seedling) disease. It is caused by the fungus *Gibberella fujikuroi*. E. Kurosawa, in 1926, found that extracts of the fungus applied to the rice plants caused the same symptoms, demonstrating the action of a definite chemical substance. In the 1930s, T. Yabuta and T. Hayashi were able to isolate and identify an active compound, which they named **gibberellin**. The existence of the gibberellins with their unique ability to cause intact plants to grow tall was actually discovered at about the same time as was the first auxin, yet because of preoccupation with the auxins, lack of contact, and then World War II, the western hemisphere did not become interested in them until the 1950s when J. E. Mitchell in the United States and P. W. Brian in England became aware of the gibberellins, obtained samples of the fungus from Japan, and began to investigate the unusual properties of these substances.

The Japanese first discovered that several gibberellins actually exist in fungi, all of which are acidic and so are often called gibberellic acids. These are usually abbreviated GA, with an accompanying subscript number to distinguish them. The structures of several of these are indicated in Fig. 21-13. One of the first good indications that gibberellins exist in higher plants was reported in 1956 by Charles A. West and Bernard O. Phinney at the University of California at Los Angeles. They found that an ether extract of wild cucumber seeds contained substances that promoted plant growth in the same way the gibberellins do. At the same time, Marion Radley, in England, found a substance in pea shoots that had the same R_f value on chromatograms as gibberellic acid and that increased the growth of wheat leaf sheaths. Since that time other gibberellins have been found in fungi and in higher plants, and at the present at least twenty-four identified have been given numbers, the majority of which may be considered hormones of higher plants. Gibberellins or similar compounds with gibberellin activity have thus far been found in gymnosperms, angiosperms, ferns, and algae, as well as fungi, but they probably do not exist in bacteria. Seeds of several angiosperms are particularly rich sources.

21.2.1 Bioassays of the Gibberellins

The promotion of the growth of rice plants led to one of several bioassays to allow their detection and quantitative measurement. Small rice seedlings are placed in a dish with a solution suspected of containing a gibberellin. After approximately a week, the growth promotion of the next leaf to expand is measured. Concentrations of some of the gibberellins as low as 10^{-6} M cause a detectable response.

It was discovered that if gibberellins were applied to dwarf mutants of several plants such as corn, peas, cucumbers, and beans, these dwarfs would become as tall as the normal varieties. Dwarf meteor peas are sensitive to as little as one-billionth of a gram of GA_3, and so this plant is used as the basis of another bioassay. Five different dwarf mutants of corn are known that are also caused to grow normally by proper gibberellin application (Fig. 21-14), although at least two are known that do not respond. Each of these responding dwarfs contains a mutation on a single different gene. It has been suggested that each mutation controls a different enzyme needed in the pathway of gibberellic acid synthesis. The growth of normal varieties of corn is not appreciably stimulated by gibberellins, as shown in Fig. 21-14. We cannot conclude, however, that all dwarfs are deficient in gibberellins. In addition to the fact that some dwarf corn mutants do not respond to added gibberellins, dwarf *Pharbitis nil* and pea, which grow tall when treated with exogenous gibberellins, seem to have as much gibberellin as their normal counterparts, although there is no assurance that the gibberellins found in them are in active forms. Dwarfing could also be due to low auxin contents or to an inability to *respond* to endogenous gibberellins or auxins.

There are considerable differences among responses to the various kinds of gibberellins. One gibberellin may be active in causing a particular response where another is much less effective. For example, dwarf and normal varieties of peas both contain nearly equal amounts of GA_1 and GA_5, yet when the plants are grown as usual in the light, the dwarfs seem

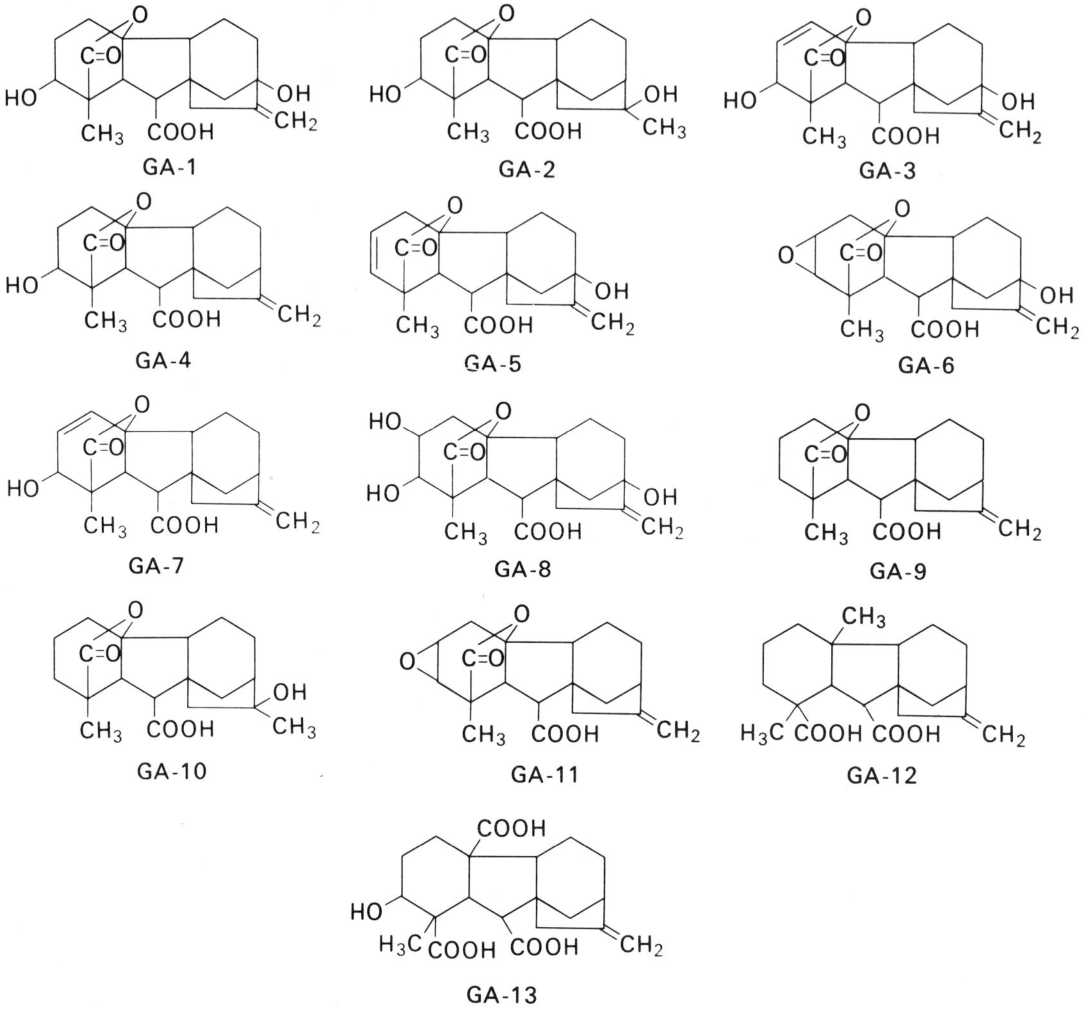

Figure 21-13

Structures of 13 naturally occurring gibberellins. (After L. G. Paleg, 1965, *Ann. Rev. Plant Physiol.* 16:291.)

not to be able to respond to their GA$_5$, and growth is retarded. If grown in darkness, both varieties reach the same height before their food supply is exhausted. Both endogenous gibberellins are apparently active in this condition. It thus seems that light prevents certain gibberellins from fully stimulating plant growth and also interferes with the synthesis of some of these hormones.

Another bioassay that is even more sensitive and reliable than the two above is based upon an interesting ability of the gibberellins to stimulate synthesis of α-amylase in cereal grain seeds. It is discussed in section 21.10.2.

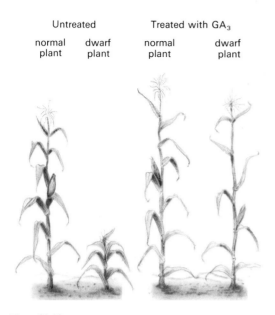

Untreated

normal   dwarf
plant   plant

Treated with GA₃

normal   dwarf
plant   plant

Figure 21-14

Influence of GA₃ on a normal corn plant and on a dwarf mutant. GA₃ had little effect upon the normal plant but caused the dwarf to grow as tall as the normal. (Redrawn from B. O. Phinney and C. A. West, 1963. In D. Rudnick (ed.), *Developing Cell Systems and Their Control*, Ronald Press, New York, p. 71. Used by permission.)

21.2.2 Physiological Effects of Gibberellins

The most striking effect resulting from application of gibberellins to most growing plants is the increase in length of the stems, as observed with rice. Here the primary cause of stem elongation is an increased length of the cells, rather than an increased number of cells. Some species, such as normal varieties of corn (Fig. 21-14), do not markedly respond to gibberellins. Most species of conifers are also not caused to elongate appreciably by these hormones, although the stems of loblolly pines (*Pinus taeda*) become both longer and thicker upon treatment. The stems of most other plants are affected, and this is due in many to a stimulation of cell division, often accompanied by an increase in cell size, particularly length. We may conclude

then that these hormones can, depending upon the plant, increase either cell division, elongation, or both. Several other effects of gibberellins are known:

21.2.2A Breaking of dormancy
As we shall discuss in Chapter 25, the buds of deciduous trees and evergreens growing in temperate zones usually become dormant in late summer or early fall. Certain desert species also become dormant prior to long dry periods. In the dormant condition these buds are protected against the cold winters or drought. Many seeds also exhibit a dormancy, and in this condition, adequate moisture, temperature, and oxygen will not cause the sprouting of buds or seeds. The dormancy of buds or seeds is often broken in nature by their exposure to long periods of cold temperatures. In buds and moist seeds the dormancy may sometimes also be overcome by exposure to light or to long-day conditions. Gibberellic acid sometimes overcomes both types of dormancy, in the one case acting in the same manner as a cold treatment, and in the other, as a light treatment. Several other examples are known where gibberellins interact with light or temperature treatments, modifying certain developmental effects.

21.2.2B Flowering
As we shall see in Chapters 24, 25, and 26, the time at which plants form flowers is dependent upon several factors, including their age and certain properties of the environment. For example, the relative lengths of light and darkness have key controlling influences upon several plants. Some plants flower only if the light period exceeds a critical length, while others flower only if this period is shorter than some critical length. Gibberellins can substitute for the long-day requirement in some species, again showing an interaction with light.

Gibberellins also overcome the need some species have for an inductive cold period to

flower (vernalization). It appears that the formation of flowers due either to long days or to cold
periods might normally depend upon the build-
up of endogenous gibberellins during these
periods, because the gibberellin content of some
affected plants has been found to increase
following these treatments.

21.2.2C Other effects of gibberellins

Gibberellins influence the geotropic responses of certain
plants. For example, several clover species
attain a more normal upright position when
treated with gibberellins. Like auxins, these
compounds also seem to stimulate cambial
activity of several plants, including apricot, begonia, bean, sycamore, poplar, ash, and potato.
Gibberellins act in the same manner as auxins
to prevent the development of lateral buds when
applied to decapitated shoots of several species.
Another property in common with auxins is the
formation of seedless (parthenocarpic) fruits in
some species. They are not classified as auxins,
because for one thing they do not cause significant bending when applied unilaterally to decapitated coleoptiles (Went's bioassay). This is
probably because they are not polarly transported like many auxins. Furthermore, they do
not promote root initiation or induce callus
formation, as do auxins. On the other hand, they
do promote the growth of intact plants, germination of many seeds, breaking of dormancy,
and flowering of some species, responses which
can seldom be caused by adding an auxin.

21.2.3 Commercial Uses of Gibberellins

During the 1950s, when GA_3 became available
in Western countries, many experiments were
performed to determine if this compound had
any practical commercial uses. It was thought
that the influence upon stem elongation might
lead to increased yields of dry matter in several
forage crops, but experiments proved that the
increases in growth were usually entirely due to

an increased water content. Celery plants, which
are valued for the length and crispness of their
stalks, were found to respond with desirable
increases in fresh weight, but side effects such as
poor storage qualities prevented the widespread
use of gibberellins in the celery industry.

These hormones do have certain profitable
agricultural uses, which are discussed in Chapter
28. For example, they increase the yield of
Thompson seedless grapes, and they are sometimes used in the brewing industry because they
stimulate the rate of germination of the barley
seeds used for the malt.

21.2.4 Antigibberellins

Certain synthetic compounds inhibit the growth
of plants in a manner suggesting that the
synthesis or action of the gibberellins within the
plant is being inhibited. These include **Amo-1618**
(2-isopropyl-4-dimethylamino-5-methylphenyl-
1-piperidene-carboxylate methyl chloride), **CCC**
or **cycocel** ([2-chloroethyl]trimethylammonium
chloride) and **phosphon D** (2,4-dichlorobenzyl-
tributylphosphonium chloride). They also inhibit flowering in several plants. Their inhibitory action upon both growth and flowering
is often partially or entirely overcome by adding
gibberellins, and they have thus been called
antigibberellins. They have been found to interfere with one or more enzymes synthesizing
gibberellin, and to decrease the production of
these hormones in *Pharbitis* seeds, which are
otherwise rich in them. Naturally occurring
antigibberellins not yet identified also exist in
plants.·

21.3 HORMONES REQUIRED BY ROOTS

It was discovered in 1922 by W. J. Robbins in
the United States and by W. Kotte in Germany
that roots of some species could be excised and
grown in isolated culture for periods of months.
Extracts of dried brewers yeast were found to

improve the growth of tomato roots and to extend the time that the roots could be kept alive. In 1938, Robbins and coworkers found that thiamine was probably one of the active substances present in the yeast extract.

Subsequent research showed that tomato roots and roots of other species required thiamine and pyridoxin, and Jimson weed (*Datura stramonium*) also required niacin (Fig. 21-15). James Bonner found that roots still attached to the plant are able to grow because thiamine is supplied to them by the leaves. Thus, when girdles were made across the stem or leaf petioles of a tomato plant, thiamine accumulated between the girdle and the leaf blades. The same seems to be true for pyridoxin. Although these substances are usually thought of as vitamins or as coenzymes (Chapter 11), they clearly act as hormones in these cases.

Most monocot roots cannot be cultivated in the excised condition nearly as long as can dicot roots, even with the addition of thiamine, niacin, and pyridoxin, although techniques are being developed for the long-term growth of wheat roots. Other unknown chemical factors supplied by the shoot are probably involved in growth of these roots.

21.4 CYTOKININS

In 1913 G. Haberlandt, an Austrian scientist, discovered that soluble substances present in phloem tissues could cause cell division in parenchyma cells of wounded potato tubers. This was perhaps the first demonstration of substances in plants capable of stimulating cytokinesis, compounds now called **cytokinins**. Many years later (1954) Carlos Miller, working in the laboratory of Folke Skoog at the University of Wisconsin, was attempting to find chemicals that would stimulate division in pith cells from tobacco they were growing as a tissue culture. Indoleacetic acid stimulated the early growth of the tissue by increasing the size of the

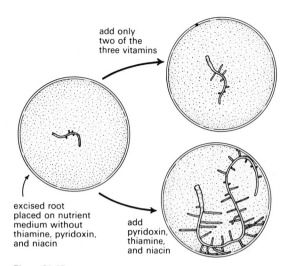

add only
two of the
three vitamins

excised root
placed on nutrient
medium without
thiamine, pyridoxin,
and niacin

add
pyridoxin,
thiamine,
and niacin

Figure 21-15

Tissue culture of excised roots requiring thiamine, pyridoxin, and niacin for growth. If only two of the three vitamins are provided, the roots often may make little, if any, growth, since the third is then the limiting factor.

cells but did not allow continued cell division. Aged or autoclaved DNA from herring sperm did stimulate cell divisions, and the active part of the DNA was soon found to be a degradation product. This substance was called **kinetin** because of its ability to bring about cytokinesis, and in 1955 it was identified as **6-furfurylamino-purine** (Fig. 21-16).

Kinetin itself has never been found in plants, although related purine derivatives are present, and other similar compounds that stimulate cytokinesis, some of them probably not formed by plants, have been chemically synthesized. Such substances were at first referred to simply as **kinins**, but animal physiologists had previously used this term for a certain group of polypeptides causing muscle contraction. As a result, the term **cytokinins** (or sometimes **phytokinins**) is now used for the substances effective upon plants.

Research by J. Van Overbeek and coworkers in the 1940s had previously suggested the

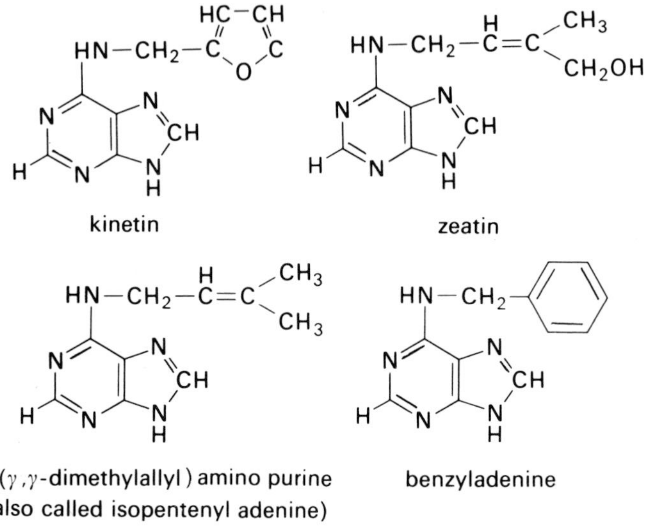

Figure 21-16

Structures of cytokinins. Except for benzyladenine, all are naturally occurring compounds.

presence of cytokinins in plants. They were attempting to grow immature *Datura* embryos to maturity in tissue culture and found that the nutritive liquid endosperm from coconuts (coconut milk) possessed substances that would stimulate cell division in these embryos. In the 1950s, F. C. Steward and colleagues at Cornell University began work attempting to discover what these substances were. They found that liquid endosperms from other plants contained similar compounds. In the coconut milk, they found no cytokinins with structures similar to kinetin or to any purine, but they did find that **myo-inositol, 1,3-diphenylurea**, a **leucoanthocyanin** (colorless), and an arabinose ester of indoleacetic acid called **IAA arabinose** were present and active (see Chapter 22).

From young plum fruits and from corn (*Zea mays*) endosperm at the milky stage, a cytokinin named **zeatin** was isolated and identified in 1964 by D. S. Letham in New Zealand and by Carlos Miller at Indiana University. This compound,

6-(4-hydroxy-3-methylbut-*trans*-2-enyl)-aminopurine, has a structure similar to that of kinetin (Fig. 21-16). Similar or identical cytokinins have been found in other fruits and in seeds. One of these was obtained but not rigorously identified by Folke Skoog and others at the University of Wisconsin in 1965. They obtained the material by purification of 6,900 liters of blanching water used to process 25 tons of peas in a commercial cannery.

Zeatin and a cytokinin almost identical in structure to zeatin called 6-(γ,γ-dimethylallyl) amino purine or **isopentenyl adenine** (Fig. 21-16) occur as unusual bases in certain transfer RNA molecules. Isopentenyl adenine is also present in *Corynebacterium fascians*, a pathogenic bacterium causing rapid cell division leading to irregular growths on certain dicots. It is likely that these growths are due to the cytokinins in the bacteria. It is presently assumed that cytokinins are widespread in plants, and that they act as hormones, although their translocation throughout plants has not yet been thoroughly studied. Based on experiments with synthetic kinins, cytokinin movement through the phloem is thought to be much slower than that of auxins and gibberellins.

21.4.1 Bioassays for Cytokinins

Steward developed the first commonly used bio-assays for the detection of cytokinins in his studies of coconut milk. He isolated tissue from a millimeter or two outside the cambial ring of a carrot root, and when this was cultured aseptically on an artificial medium, he found that coconut milk would cause a tremendous increase in the cell divisions occurring. Letham used this test and found it sensitive to amounts as low as 0.1 microgram (one ten-millionth of a gram) of zeatin per liter of medium.

Another even more sensitive test is one used by Miller and involves measuring the increase in growth of callus tissue obtained from soybean cotyledons. A concentration of zeatin of 0.01 microgram per liter causes a measurable growth response. A third type of bioassay came from the discovery by K. Mothes, in Germany, that kinetin and synthetic cytokinins could delay the breakdown of chlorophyll, protein, and nucleic acids in excised leaves, seeming to act as anti-senescence factors. A. C. Chibnall in England discovered in the 1930s that detached leaves soon lose their normal green color even when cultured on media containing nutrients and other possibly essential organic substances. Chibnall noticed that roots sometimes formed at the base of the petioles on leaves, and that the leaf blades then remained green and high in protein. He suggested that roots normally supply some antisenescence hormone to the leaves that allows them to synthesize proteins and chlorophyll properly.

When it was later discovered that kinetin delays protein and chlorophyll breakdown in detached leaves, suggestions were made that cytokinins produced in roots and translocated through the xylem to the shoot normally act as antisenescence hormones. In the early 1960s, several plant physiologists found compounds in roots or root xylem exudates that would both prevent chlorophyll loss when added to excised leaves and stimulate cell division in the soybean callus test. Some of these substances have purine-like structures, and at least one is similar to zeatin. It appears, then, that leaves may depend upon roots for at least part of their cytokinins, and that cytokinins would thus meet the trans-location test for hormonal substances.

Various bioassays taking advantage of the ability of cytokinins to retard chlorophyll breakdown in detached leaves have been established. One uses leaf discs cut from mature cocklebur (*Xanthium*) leaves with a cork borer just as they are beginning to lose chlorophyll, while other more sensitive tests use young leaves of cereal grain seedlings such as oat or barley. The chlorophyll is extracted and measured from some of the tissue at the time the unknown extract thought to contain a cytokinin is added, then after a few days' treatment the chlorophyll from remaining discs is similarly determined. Control leaf tissue treated only with water contains less chlorophyll at the end of the treatment period than does tissue treated with a solution containing a cytokinin. Within limits, the inhibition in chlorophyll breakdown is quantitatively related to the cytokinin content of the solutions used; with barley leaves the remaining chlorophyll is proportional to the logarithm of kinetin concentration from 0.003 to 3 ppm. This hormonal control of the delay of senescence is not a unique property of cyto-kinins, because auxins act in the same manner in leaves of *Prunus serrulata*, while gibberellic acid is effective in *Taraxacum officinale* (dandelion) and *Tropaeolum majus* (nasturtium). Cytokinins are active in far more plants than the other two hormones, however.

21.4.2 Synthetic Cytokinins and Potential Uses

Kinetin is perhaps the best known synthetic cytokinin, but another, **benzyladenine** (benzylaminopurine, Fig. 21-16), is now commercially synthesized and is active in all of the common bioassays. These compounds are sometimes used to prolong the market acceptability of cut flowers and fresh fruits and vegetables. In some of these the increased storage life is accompanied by, and may be partially due to, a decreased respiration rate.

21.4.3 Other Physiological Effects of Cytokinins

21.4.3A Nutrient mobilization and rejuvenation responses

Accompanying the prevention of breakdown of chlorophyll, nucleic acids, and proteins in leaves is an interesting ability to retain organic and inorganic solutes. In mature leaves that become yellow while attached to the plant, many of the breakdown products are translocated into younger leaves. In excised leaves the products not lost through respiration are transported into the petioles. If cytokinins are added in droplets to the leaf blades, these treated areas not only remain green due to a slower rate of degradative processes, but syntheses are sometimes actually stimulated. This effect does not depend upon the ability of cytokinins to increase cell division. The treated areas of the yellowing leaves sometimes actually become greener; they are rejuvenated. The green areas are strictly localized in the treated portions of the leaf, suggesting little translocation of cytokinin through living cells.

Accompanying this rejuvenation is a transport of amino acids and certain other nutrients *into the treated areas* through the phloem from untreated parts of the leaf blade, as shown by autoradiography following addition of ^{14}C-labeled substances such as amino acids (Fig.

21-17). This accumulation of nutrients apparently is not simply due to their being bound by conversion into large polymers, however, since amino acid analogues or natural amino acids not converted into proteins are similarly accumulated. Much more must be learned about the ability of various physiologically active tissues to mobilize nutrients from more mature tissues, but the high concentrations of cytokinins in endosperm and in young fruits are correlated with the ability of developing seeds and fruits to act as nutrient sinks.

21.4.3B Interactions with light

Kinins cause at least two effects similar to responses caused by light. Leaves of etiolated dicot seedlings do not enlarge in the absence of light, largely because of a very slow rate of cell division. Cytokinins stimulate the growth of such dicot leaves, but they do so by increasing the size of the cells rather than by stimulating cytokinesis as light does.

Certain seeds that require light to germinate have a need for far less light in the presence of proper amounts of cytokinins (see Chapter 23).

21.4.3C Other effects of cytokinins

These substances have the property in common with auxins and gibberellins of stimulating the formation of seedless fruits in the Calimyrna fig (*Ficus carica*) and in Black Corinth grapes (*Vitis vinifera*). They are ineffective with most other fruits, however.

Cytokinins also overcome apical dominances in some plants and prevent the inhibition of lateral bud development caused by adding an auxin to the decapitated shoot apex. They actually stimulate growth of these buds, at least partly because they encourage cell divisions necessary to join the young vascular bundles of the buds to those of stems, thus increasing the nutrient supply to the buds. In these experiments the kinins must be applied directly to the lateral buds. Application even within a few millimeters

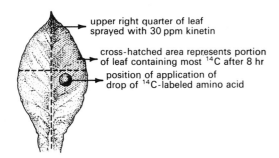

upper right quarter of leaf
sprayed with 30 ppm kinetin

cross-hatched area represents portion
of leaf containing most ^{14}C after 8 hr

position of application of
drop of ^{14}C-labeled amino acid

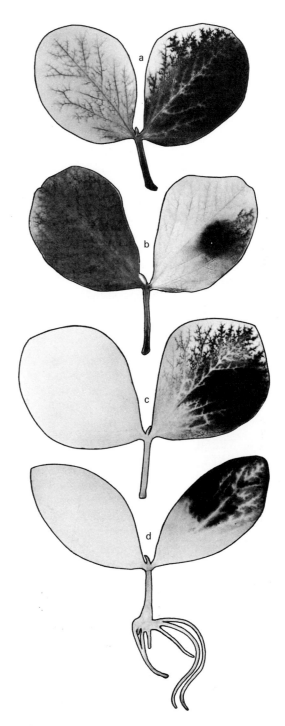

Figure 21-17

(above) Accumulation of ^{14}C-labeled amino acids in parts
of a tobacco leaf sprayed with kinetin. (After K. Mothes and
L. Engelbrecht, 1961, *Phytochem.* 1:58.) (right) Radio-
autographs showing the influence of kinetin upon distribution of ^{14}C-glycine in broad bean (*Vicia faba*) leaves. Except
for the control leaves in (a), leaves were sprayed three times
with 30 mg/l kinetin while still attached to the plants. Two
days after excision, 0.2 microcurie ^{14}C-glycine was added
in a droplet to each right leaflet. (a) Control leaf. ^{14}C spreads
throughout the right leaflet and gradually into the left,
(b) Left leaflet only sprayed with kinetin. It attracts glycine
from the right leaflet. (c) Right leaflet only sprayed with
kinetin. It retains glycine. (d) This leaf was rooted before
kinetin and glycine applications. Kinetin was added to the
left leaflet, yet glycine did not move from right to left,
possibly because of the relatively high amount of endogenous cytokinin provided by the young roots forming at
the base of the petiole. (Photographs courtesy of K. Mothes,
Halle/Saale, East Germany.)

of these buds is not effective, again demonstrating the poor movement of kinins through living
cells. This suggests that lateral branching is
controlled by a delicate balance between auxins
translocated to these buds from the apical bud
or the young, uppermost leaves and a cytokinin
synthesized in the buds or transported there
through the xylem from the roots. Other
demonstrated functions of cytokinins include an
effect upon leaf fall (abscission) and an influence
upon the transport of auxins.

21.5 FLOWERING HORMONE

In Chapters 24, 25, and 26 we shall discuss the
initiation of flowers in response to certain en-

vironmental factors, especially temperature and
the relative length of day and night. In these
discussions, evidences for the synthesis of a
special chemical substance in response to the
suitable environmental stimulus will be presented. When the leaves of a cocklebur, for
example, are exposed to long nights, they
apparently produce a compound that is subsequently translocated to the buds where it
initiates the development of flower buds. In the
promotion of flowering by cold (vernalization),
the buds themselves detect and respond to the
low temperatures, and hence the criterion of
translocation may not be met. Nevertheless,
grafting experiments seem to implicate hormonal materials even in vernalization. The
term **vernalin** has been suggested for the hypothetical substance produced as a result of
vernalization, and **florigen** for the flower-initiat-
ing material arising in response to treatment
with the proper daylength. Present evidence
seems to indicate that several substances, promoters and inhibitors, may be involved in both
cases, but in spite of many attempts, these have
not been isolated to everyone's satisfaction.

21.6 TUBER- AND BULB-FORMING HORMONES

Some plants produce underground storage
reserves, such as tubers or bulbs, organs that
may perpetuate the species through a long, cold
season (Chapter 25). The physiology of the
formation of tubers in the potato and bulbs in
the onion has received most study. Tubers are
formed by a swelling of adjacent internodes of
a stem, usually underground. The nodes become the eyes of a potato tuber. Onion bulbs
result from a swelling of the bases of young
leaves, rather than of internodes.

The formation of both tubers and bulbs
may be influenced by the photoperiod, the
leaves again acting as the detecting organs. At
relatively high temperatures, potato tubers are

formed more readily under short than under
long photoperiods. Onion bulbs are usually
initiated by relatively long photoperiods. Since
the potato leaves may detect the photoperiod
(or low temperature) and the underground
stems respond, this suggests that a hormone
messenger is involved. The same might be true
for bulb-producing plants, such as the onion.

21.7 BUD DORMANCY HORMONE

In many woody plants growing appreciable
distances from the equator, the buds become
dormant prior to the time the cold or dry
season begins (Chapter 25). Bud dormancy in
most species that have been studied is stimulated
by the short days and long nights arriving in
late summer, although there is usually an interaction of daylength with low temperatures. The
fact that the leaves perceive the daylength while
the buds respond by becoming dormant again
suggests the participation of a hormone.

Although dormancy hormones have not
been definitely identified, a substance called
dormin was isolated from sycamore leaves by
P. F. Wareing and coworkers in Wales in 1964.
Since then, it has been found in a number of
plants. Dormin causes dormancy in buds of
sycamore, black currant, maple, and birch trees,
and perhaps of many other species. Its structure
(Fig. 21-18) is somewhat similar to that of
vitamin A and is identical to that of another
substance isolated from cotton bolls that is
capable of causing senescence and leaf and
flower abscission in a number of plants. This
abscission-stimulating substance was called
abscisin II by F. T. Addicott and his colleagues
at the California Agricultural Experiment Station in Davis, who discovered it in 1965. It has
now been agreed to use the name **abscisic acid** to
replace the terms dormin and abscisin II.

The fact that a single substance can cause
both bud dormancy, senescence of leaves, and
their abscission is made particularly interesting

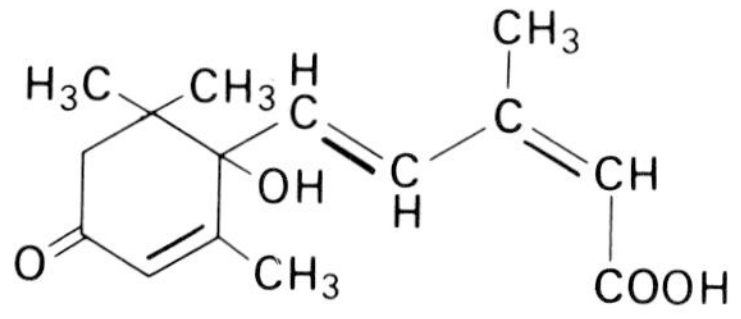

Figure 21-18

The structure of abscisic acid (also called dormin or abscisin II). The molecule contains one asymmetric carbon atom, but only the dextrorotatory enantiomorph apparently exists in plants.

when one observes that leaves usually begin to fall from trees at about the same time (or shortly after) the buds become dormant.

Abscisic acid causes other interesting responses in various species, including an increased rate of senescence (as measured by chlorophyll breakdown) in leaves of some species, inhibition of seed germination, production of flowers in certain species that otherwise require short days, and inhibition of flowering in others that require long days. Future research will undoubtedly show this compound to be an important growth-regulating substance.

21.8 ETHYLENE, A MATURATION AND FRUIT-RIPENING SUBSTANCE

The ability of certain gases to stimulate fruits to ripen has been known for many years. Even the ancient Chinese knew that their picked fruits would ripen more quickly in a room containing burning incense. F. E. Denny found in 1924 that ethylene stimulated the ripening of lemons, while others showed that a gas emanating from ripe oranges stimulated bananas to ripen, and that gaseous products from ripe apples hastened the maturity of green apples. R. Gane soon found (1935) that ethylene was abundant in ripe bananas, and that this gas hastened the climacteric respiratory rise (Chapter 15) of unripe bananas.

Ethylene has now been identified as a product of many ripening fruits. It is very effective in causing ripening, and picked fruits, such as lemons and oranges, that tree-ripen and do not normally undergo a respiratory climacteric do so in the presence of ethylene. Sensitive techniques for detection of ethylene (principally gas chromatography) showed that ethylene production slightly precedes the ripening process. It is believed that just before the respiratory climacteric sets in, the internal content of this gas increases to a level (near 0.1 to 1.0 ppm) that leads to the beginning of ripening. Other factors are undoubtedly involved, since a few fruits, such as peaches and apricots, are not greatly affected by ethylene.

If fruits are placed in a partial vacuum or in a stream of flowing air low in oxygen, the ethylene escapes rapidly, and fruits may be stored successfully for longer periods of time. For example, bananas have been kept for three months under a stream of cool, humid air, while under normal room conditions they lose their eating qualities in a few days. The presence of carbon dioxide is also helpful in fruit storage, and this is probably because it acts as a competitive inhibitor of ethylene action.

Ethylene seems, then, to act as a senescence factor in fruits. It is produced (perhaps from methionine) by many other plant parts, however, and has various effects upon vegetative tissues. One effect, perhaps related to its ability to hasten senescence, is its stimulation of abscission of leaves and flower petals. It also causes some flowers to lose their color more rapidly, which is probably associated with the stimulation of abscission. Ethylene at 1 ppm prevents the opening of flower buds of carnation and causes the inrolling or "sleep" disease of flowers that have already opened. As little as 0.002 ppm injures orchid flowers by causing the sepals to separate from one another.

Another response it causes is the phenomenon known as **leaf epinasty**, in which the

Figure 21-19

Epinasty in cocklebur. Plant on the left is an untreated control. Plant on the right was dipped into a solution of NAA ($1.0 \times 10^{-3}M$) about two days before the photograph was taken. Epinasty in response to ethylene is very similar. (Photograph by F. B. Salisbury.)

upper side of the petiole (especially at the base) grows more rapidly than the lower, and the leaves bend downward as a result. Figure 21-19 shows epinasty as caused by application of an auxin. Ethylene interferes with normal geotropic responses of seedlings, and when these are placed on their sides in the presence of this gas, both the roots and stems continue to grow horizontally. The biochemical explanations for ethylene action remain unknown, but one probable causative factor is an interference with the polar transport of auxin. This could account for its interference with geotropism of seedlings and for leaf epinasty, because the normal angle of leaves is partially controlled by the ratio of auxins on the upper and lower sides of the petioles.

It was discovered in about 1935 by P. W. Zimmerman and F. Wilcox at the Boyce Thompson Institute that auxin applications stimulate ethylene production from plants. More recent work of Fred B. Abeles and Bernard Rubenstein and by Stanley and Ellen Burg and others showed that several of the responses obtained when auxins are applied can be duplicated by exposure of the plants to ethylene, including stimulation of adventitious root initiation, inhibition of flowering in the cocklebur and promotion of flowering in the pineapple, inhibition of root elongation, stimulation of leaf abscission, and inhibition of opening of the hook in the hypocotyls of bean seedlings (see Chapter 23). Many other responses presently attributed to auxins will undoubtedly prove to be due to ethylene or at least to be inducible by ethylene.

21.9 INHIBITORY SUBSTANCES

The growth and development of plants is highly dependent upon the quantities of various hor-

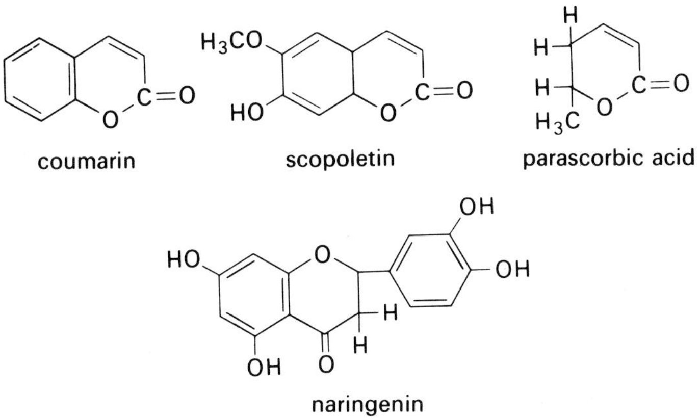

Figure 21-20

Molecular structures of some germination inhibitors found in seeds (see also Fig. 25-7).

mones or other growth-stimulating substances they contain, and upon their sensitivity to these at various stages in their lives. In certain stages the ability of a plant to survive depends upon its becoming dormant. Growth of many plant parts stops or becomes greatly reduced at other times, too. The cessation of growth could come about simply due to reduction in synthesis of growth-stimulating substances. Considerable evidence suggests, however, that the plant produces small amounts of inhibitory compounds that interfere with growth. If they are translocated from one part of the plant to another where they cause a response, these potent compounds should be considered hormones. They could act by inhibiting the production or stimulating the breakdown of other hormones, they could interfere with their action, or they might act independently of other hormones.

21.9.1 Germination Inhibitors

A. Köckemann (1934) found germination inhibitors in seeds still inside fleshy fruits and suggested that premature germination of such seeds might normally be prevented by such inhibitors. Since then, many unidentified compounds inhibitory to seed germination and to growth in oat coleoptile or pea stem section tests, for example, have been detected in seed coats or other parts of the seed. Some of these are **unsaturated lactones**, such as **coumarin**, **parascorbic acid**, and **scopoletin** (Fig. 21-20). The inhibiting action of some ripe fruits upon germination of the seeds they contain is at least partly due to their unsaturated lactone content. Abscisic acid may also be involved.

Beneficial effects of germination inhibitors also appear in the seed coats of certain desert plants. These germinate only after heavy rains have washed out the inhibitors and at the same time have wet the soil enough to allow plants to develop fully (Chapter 25).

21.9.2 Inhibitors in Dormant Buds

Evidence that dormancy of buds may be due to a high concentration of growth inhibitors was first obtained by Torsten Hemberg of Sweden in 1949. He found that dormant buds of potato tubers and of ash (*Fraxinus*) trees contained large amounts of unidentified inhibitors that declined when dormancy was broken. The buds of many woody plants are caused to become dormant when the days become short and the nights become long. J. P. Nitsch in France and Wareing in Wales showed that in at least some of these, dormancy may be due to an accumulation of abscisic acid or similar molecules in the buds as a result of short-day treatment. Abscisic acid may be considered an inhibitor in this case, since the inhibition of further development of the dormant buds is associated with its presence.

Charles H. Henderschott, a graduate student of David R. Walker, who was then at North Carolina State University, found another coleoptile-inhibiting substance in dormant flower buds of peach. This proved to be **naringenin** (Fig. 21-20), a flavonoid (Chapter 18). It has subsequently been found by Walker and his students at Utah State University in dormant peach seeds (Chapter 25). Naringenin and coumarin each induce a requirement for light in seeds of certain varieties of lettuce that normally germinate in darkness. This effect of these compounds is overcome by gibberellic acid. The influence of the unknown inhibitory compound or group of compounds upon sprouting of potato tuber buds can also be overcome by GA_3, and here, too, gibberellins break bud dormancy. The dormancy-breaking effects of gibberellins in seeds and buds may result in part from the ability of these hormones to raise the level of α-amylase and other enzymes, which then initiate starch breakdown and increase the sugars available for bud development. This is not always true, though, and so the gibberellins must also have another mechanism of action.

Both abscisic acid and the unknown β-inhibitor of potato buds (discussed below) inhibit α-amylase activity, and it is now established that these two substances are identical. It is interesting that naringenin is one of the monophenolic compounds that can stimulate IAA oxidase, and part of its inhibitory action might arise from destruction of this auxin by the oxidase.

21.9.3 The β-Inhibitor

When one-dimensional chromatographs of many plant extracts are prepared, certain portions of the chromatogram are found to contain one or more inhibitory compounds. One such portion contains compounds widely known as the **β-inhibitor complex** or simply as the **β-inhibitor**. The complex inhibits growth in most bioassays and also prevents sprouting of some buds. Since its discovery in 1953, plant physiologists have made various attempts to identify chemically the compounds present in the β-inhibitor zone, and the first suggestions were that phenolic compounds were responsible. Some phenolics that are toxic to plants (Chapter 18) are present in this zone. Possibly abscisic acid may prove to be the most active component present.

21.9.4 Inhibitors of Pollen Tube Development

Sexual reproduction in higher plants requires the pollen grain to germinate and send a pollen tube carrying the male gametes down through the style of the flower and into the embryo sac (Fig. 20-9). In some plants the growth rate of this pollen tube is very rapid. In certain species of *Oenothera* (Evening Primrose), for example, pollen tubes sometimes penetrate to the ovary, a distance of approximately 4 centimeters, in two hours.

In many species of angiosperms the pollen produced by a particular flower is not capable of fertilizing the egg in the same flower. This is an example of **self-incompatibility**, and its operation increases the chance that the plant will be fertilized by another with a slightly different genetic constitution, leading to an increase in vigor of the progeny. Self-incompatibility is often caused by a failure of pollen to germinate on the stigma of the same flower or by the inability of the pollen tube to grow through the style toward the embryo sac. It is likely that chemical inhibitors exist in the stigma and styles of such plants, and that these prevent self-fertilization by retarding pollen tube formation and development. Such inhibitors have been chromatographically separated from some flowers but have not yet been identified.

21.9.5 Other Growth Inhibitors

Some growth inhibitors are leached by rain water from the leaves, stems, or fruits of plants into the soil, and these may interfere with the growth of surrounding plants. Such inhibitors may also be incorporated into the soil when abscission occurs. The first to be discovered is produced by leaves of the black walnut tree (*Juglans nigra*) and was named **juglone**. The toxic **trans-cinnamic acid** is produced by guayule, and evidence of Elroy Rice at Oklahoma University and of others indicates that many other inhibitors exist, most of which are aromatic or phenolic compounds. These may play important roles in determining the ecological distribution of vegetation in certain plant communities.

21.10 POSSIBLE MECHANISMS OF ACTION OF PLANT HORMONES

Great effort has been and is being made to attain a biochemical understanding of the manner in which plant hormones exert their spectacular effects. As yet no definite mechanism has been positively uncovered, although recent research indicates that the auxins and gibberellins, at least, may act partly through effects upon nucleic acid transformation. One of the difficulties in solving the mechanism of hormone action has been the multitude of different kinds of physiological responses they control. Insufficient knowledge is available to indicate how auxins, for example, could influence through

a common chemical reaction, tropistic responses, fruit growth, adventitious root formation, lateral bud development, meristematic activity, and abscission of leaves and flowers. Perhaps hormones have more than one primary mechanism of action.

Early hormone research was guided by the thought that auxins might act as coenzymes for specific enzymes, much as do the vitamin hormones required by roots. One of the reasons for suspecting a catalytic activity is that hormones cause such marked effects when present in extremely small concentrations. A tremendous amplification of the initial triggering response clearly occurs, one molecule of hormone affecting the production of many molecules. Such an amplification could result if hormones were necessary for certain enzymes to function. Although both auxins and gibberellins influence the activity of several enzymes when added to plants, they have not been shown to act as specific coenzymes. They may, however, regulate enzyme activity by causing allosteric transitions and by preventing breakdown of certain isozymes into inactive subunits. The animal hormone thyroxine and certain steroid hormones are already known to cause similar changes in the enzyme glutamic dehydrogenase when in the presence of NADH. In this case, however, the enzyme dissociates into subunits when these hormones are applied, a dissociation that is reversed by certain amino acids or by ADP.

An amplification could also result if hormones stimulate the synthesis of certain enzymes that in turn lead to the physiological effects observed. This could occur through promotive effects on formation of any of the kinds of RNA necessary for enzyme production or by an inhibition of RNA breakdown. The influence of individual plant hormones upon various processes and their relation to functions at the cellular and molecular level are described in the following paragraphs.

21.10.1 Auxins

To determine the mechanism of action of auxins, it is useful to determine the kinds of cells affected by these substances. In general, parenchyma cells in stems of higher plants are most sensitive to added auxins. Bacteria, fungi, and algae respond little if at all, even though members of each group contain IAA. Parenchyma cells of higher plants differ from bacterial, fungal and some algal cells in containing a primary wall rich in cellulose, hemicellulose, and pectic compounds. Some proteins are also present (Chapter 12). These cells still possess the ability to grow, while mature xylem elements and others with secondary walls cannot.

The increased growth of parenchyma cells in excised sections, such as those taken from pea stems or from coleoptiles, has been studied in great detail. Growth stimulation due to auxins requires metabolic energy, as shown by the requirement for proper temperatures, oxygen, and by the inhibition due to respiratory poisons. No important effects of auxins on isolated mitochondria, the centers of aerobic respiration, were at first observed, and animals that contain mitochondria very similar to those of plants are not affected. These facts indicated that growth stimulation by auxins simply depends upon some respiratory product, but that they do not cause growth by stimulating the mitochondria. Plants treated with growth-stimulating auxin concentrations often respire somewhat faster, but this was thought to be because the growth process uses up some respiratory product such as ATP, whose accumulation otherwise limits respiration. For example, the accumulation of ATP can prevent rapid respiration, because ADP and Pi are necessary for the mitochondrial electron transport system, but both become combined in the ATP molecule. Utilization of ATP in growth processes, such as the formation of proteins or cell wall materials, regenerates ADP and Pi,

which then allow respiration and ATP production to continue. This is another example of feedback control.

The above ideas about the way in which growth-promoting concentrations of auxin increase respiration in plants may be true, but more recent evidence of Igor Sarkissian and Robert McDaniel at West Virginia University indicates that one auxin, IAA, can directly influence mitochondrial reactions. Working with mitochondria from cotyledons of inbred lines of corn, they found that 1×10^{-10} M IAA nearly doubles the rate of oxygen uptake due to oxidative phosphorylation. Sarkissian also observed that the condensing enzyme, which forms citric acid from oxaloacetic acid and acetyl coenzyme A in the mitochondria, is much more effective in the presence of IAA than in its absence. It was suggested that this auxin acts as an allosteric effector of the condensing enzyme and perhaps of others involved in ATP production. If this proves to be true of other auxins and with other plants, stimulations of growth by these hormones could be at least partly attributed to an increased energy supply in their presence.

The greater size of cells in the presence of auxins is due primarily to a greater content of water. The components of water potential of Chapter 5 can be used to determine how more water could be absorbed, remembering that $\psi = \psi_\pi + \psi_P$ and that for water uptake to be promoted by auxins, water potential (ψ) inside the cell must be more negative than outside, and the membranes must be sufficiently permeable so as not to prevent water movement. Now ψ could become more negative either because the osmotic potential (ψ_π) becomes more negative or because the pressure potential (ψ_P) decreases. If resistance of the wall to stretching decreases, the wall will yield, and both pressure and pressure potential will decrease. Cells whose growth is stimulated by auxins sometimes contain increased amounts of salts and growth products such as proteins, nucleic acids, and cell wall substances. It was suggested that an increase in cell size might result simply from the ability of auxins to cause an increased rate of uptake of solutes, making osmotic potential of the cells more negative and resulting in a consequent increased water uptake and cell expansion. If this occurs, it is not essential, however, since auxins stimulate growth of oat coleoptile sections even in distilled water where solute uptake cannot be involved.

That expansion occurs because auxins cause a decrease in the resisting properties of the wall was first demonstrated by A. N. Heyn in 1930 in Holland. He showed that the walls of oat coleoptile sections became more easily irreversibly deformable (became more plastic) in the presence of IAA. He added a weight near the ends of treated coleoptiles, measured the bending that resulted, and then removed the weight and observed the extent to which the coleoptiles returned to their original positions (**elastic deformation**) and the extent to which they remained deformed (**plastic deformation**) (Fig. 21-21). An increased plastic bending occurs in IAA-treated coleoptiles. The extent of plastic deformation caused by IAA is quantitatively similar to the effect of this auxin upon growth of oat coleoptiles. As the cell walls become more plastic, they more easily stretch in response to the cell's internal turgor pressure; this reduces the turgor pressure, and more water can diffuse in because of the more negative water potential. Osmotic potential remains essentially constant, although it would increase slightly due to dilution.

Active attempts were undertaken to determine how auxins might increase the plasticity of cell walls. They were found to increase the synthesis of pectic compounds, hemicellulose, and sometimes of cellulose, and it was supposed that addition of new sugar units to cellulose or pectic chains would lengthen them and would in some way lower their restrictive force upon

cell elongation. However, much of the addition of wall materials during growth occurs by the formation of new layers (microfibrils) appressed against the old (by **apposition**), and it would seem that this should decrease the plasticity. It is likely, then, that the increased production of cell wall materials is only a process *accompanying* growth and is not its *cause*. We conclude that during growth some individual bonds must be broken in whatever molecules give rigidity to walls, so that the cellulose chains can slide past one another. Some evidence exists that the restrictive bonds are between the hydroxyproline-rich structural protein found in many cell walls and the cellulose, or between the cellulose and pectic substances. Perhaps the quantitatively important hemicelluloses are involved.

Changes in plasticity of cell walls surely involve reactions catalyzed by enzymes, and there is no evidence that auxins act as coenzymes for these. How, then, do they effect such changes? Could auxins increase the production of certain enzymes affecting cell wall plasticity, rather than simply stimulating the action of those already present? Evidence first obtained by plant physiologists in the United States and Japan suggests that growth-stimulating concentrations of various auxins do act through influences upon enzyme production.

In 1963, L. Nooden and K. V. Thimann showed that such compounds as the antibiotics **chloramphenicol** (chloromycetin), and **puromycin**, and the phenylalanine antimetabolite **p-fluorophenylalanine**, all of which are known to be inhibitors of enzyme synthesis, interfered with stimulation of growth caused by IAA in oat coleoptiles and pea stem sections. **Actinomycin D**, an inhibitor of RNA formation (Chapter 17), was also inhibitory to growth promotion by IAA. The next year Joe Key, at Purdue University, observed that actinomycin D and puromycin inhibited the growth of excised soybean hypocotyls caused by the

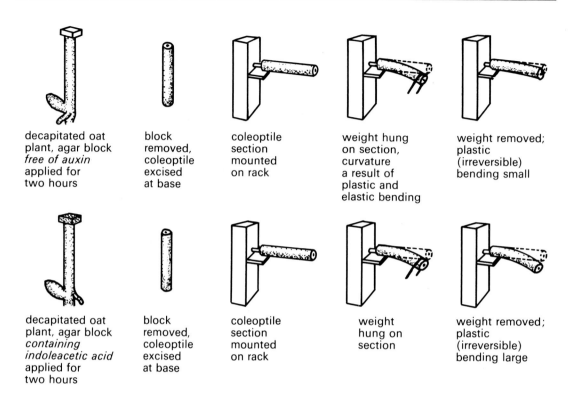

Figure 21-21
Increase in plasticity of coleoptile sections by IAA. (From *Principles of Plant Physiology* by James Bonner and Arthur W. Galston. W. H. Freeman and Company, p. 363. Copyright © 1952. Used by permission.)

auxin 2,4-D. Since then, several workers have found similar results with other plant parts. It is thought that the kind of RNA needed for auxins to increase cellular growth is messenger RNA, since the production of transfer and ribosomal RNA can be inhibited in soybean hypocotyl sections by 5-fluorouracil with little effect on messenger RNA formation or upon growth. The cells presumably have enough transfer RNA and ribosomes to support growth but are limited by messenger RNA molecules, which code for the synthesis of enzymes needed to make the cell walls expand easier (Fig. 21-22).

Suppression of auxin action by RNA synthesis inhibitors such as actinomycin *D* does not conclusively prove that the auxin normally *directly* affects RNA formation, since auxins could act upon some other process which, in turn, then affects the RNA. Some of the stimulating responses caused by auxins, such as the effect on protoplasmic streaming, appear to occur too rapidly to depend upon prior RNA synthesis. Nevertheless, it is likely that auxins do act inside the nucleus, since they sometimes accumulate there. Figure 21-23 shows the accumulation of ^{14}C-labeled IAA in the nucleus of a root tip cell of onion. Attachment of IAA and 2,4-D directly to the chromosomes of other cells has also been demonstrated. Furthermore, it should be mentioned that Arthur Galston

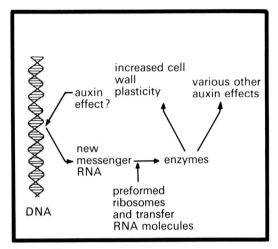

Figure 21-22

A postulated mechanism of how auxin acts directly upon DNA with a resulting synthesis of enzymes.

and his coworkers at Yale University have shown that IAA becomes connected to certain transfer RNA molecules. This attachment may influence enzyme production in ways that have not yet been defined. Finally, in 1967, B. D. Patterson and A. J. Trewavas demonstrated that IAA induces changes in the kinds of proteins synthesized in etiolated pea stem sections, a tissue in which growth is also increased by this hormone. This is further evidence supporting the theory that auxins increase cell expansion through prior effects on enzyme synthesis. Which enzymes are thus responsible for growth remains to be discovered.

21.10.2 Gibberellins

Some scientists have suggested that gibberellins act by promoting auxin production, or through some other interaction with auxin. There are examples in which responses caused by gibberellins are accompanied by increasing auxin levels inside the plant, but many cases are also known in which this is not true. Gibber-

ellins thus have specific effects different from those of auxins, and again these effects may result from influences upon the formation of specific RNA and enzyme molecules. Excellent evidence that this is so comes from research upon barley seeds, although similar processes probably occur in seeds of many other members of the grass family.

The embryo (germ) of seeds of cereal grains is surrounded by food reserves present in the essentially nonliving cells of the endosperm. The endosperm is surrounded by a thin layer of living cells high in protein content called the **aleurone layer** (Fig. 21-24). When germination occurs, primarily in response to increased moisture, the aleurone cells provide the hydrolytic enzymes that digest the starch, proteins, RNA, and some cell wall materials present in the endosperm cells. The smaller soluble compounds produced are then used by the embryo as it develops into a seedling. Some of the necessary enzymes for these digestion processes include β-amylase (already present in the aleurone layer), α-amylase (synthesized in this layer as germination begins), ribonuclease, and various proteases (some of which are also newly synthesized upon germination). If the embryo is removed from the seed, germination must fail, of course, but the important observation was made that even in response to added moisture, the aleurone cells do not produce hydrolytic enzymes, especially α-amylase, in the absence of the embryo. This suggests that the embryo normally provides some hormone to the aleurone layer, which stimulates it to manufacture these enzymes.

Harugoru Yomo, a Japanese scientist, and L. Paleg, an American working in Australia, each suggested in 1960 that the hormone provided by the embryo was a gibberellin. GA_3 at concentrations as low as $2 \times 10^{-11}\,M$ was then found to induce an increase in the content of α-amylase and of proteases in the aleurone layers of seeds from which the embryos are

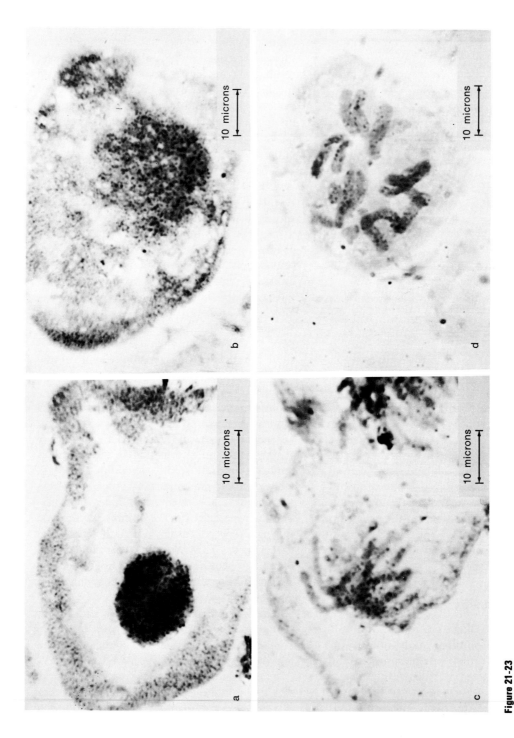

Figure 21-23

(a) Autoradiograph of *Allium cernuum* root tip cell after exposure to IAA-methyl ^{14}C for 6 hours, showing nuclear and cytoplasmic labeling. (b) *Vicia faba* root tip cell after exposure to 2,4-D-carboxyl-^{14}C for 1 hour. *Vicia faba* cells which had absorbed 2,4-D-^{14}C for 1 hour and then had grown without 2,4-D-^{14}C for 72 hours (c) or 120 hours (d). The auxin remains attached to chromosomes. (Photographs courtesy of R. H. Hamilton; from S. Liao and R. H. Hamilton, 1966, "Intracellular localization of growth hormones in plants," *Science*, 151:822. Copyright 1966 by the American Association for the Advancement of Science. Used by permission.)

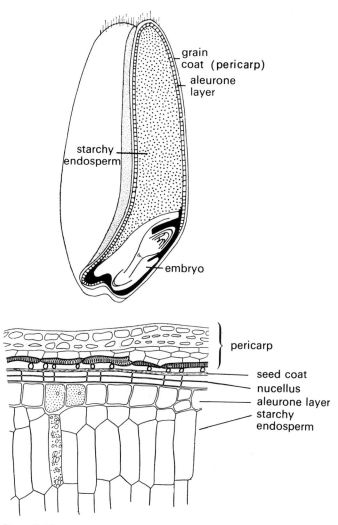

Figure 21-24

The aleurone layer in wheat seeds. (top) Longitudinal section showing position of aleurone layer in the seed relative to the embryo and endosperm. (From A. Fahn, 1967, *Plant Anatomy*, Pergamon Press, New York, p. 478. Used by permission.) (bottom) Enlarged cross section of a small portion of a mature wheat grain. (From H. E. Hayward, 1938, *The Structure of Economic Plants*, Macmillan Company, New York, p. 151. Used by permission.)

removed. It also activated the β-amylase already present. Joseph E. Varner in the United States proved that the increase in measurable quantity of α-amylase is actually due to a greater production of this enzyme in the presence of gibber-

ellic acid, rather than to an activation by this hormone of preexisting enzyme molecules. He did this by providing ^{14}C-labeled phenylalanine to excised aleurone layers. If GA_3 was present, he found, using chromatographic techniques for separating the proteins, that α-amylase contained much ^{14}C. This showed that it had been synthesized in the presence of the hormone after the labeled phenylalanine and the GA_3 were added. This stimulation of enzyme synthesis could be blocked by adding inhibitors of protein formation, such as the antibiotics puromycin and chloramphenicol, or p-fluorophenylalanine, which inhibits incorporation of phenylalanine into the protein chain. Inhibitors of RNA synthesis such as actinomycin D also prevent the GA_3 stimulation. Abscisic acid is also effective. The tentative conclusion is that gibberellins normally act by causing formerly repressed genes to become active, resulting in new messenger RNA molecules and then new enzymes responsible for digesting and releasing products of the endosperm.

The striking stimulation of α-amylase production by gibberellins is taken advantage of in a very sensitive bioassay for these hormones (21.2.1). Barley seeds are sterilized in calcium hypochlorite to kill microorganisms, cut in half transversely, and one or more endosperm pieces are placed in a vial containing about one ml of a gibberellin solution. After 24 to 48 hours soaking at 30°C, the content of reducing sugars in the solution is measured. These sugars are produced when α-amylase acts upon the stored starch in the endosperm, and they leak into the solution during the soaking period. Figure 21-25 shows the influence of four gibberellins upon reducing sugar production in this bioassay. GA_3 and GA_1 are effective at concentrations between 10^{-11} and 10^{-7} grams per ml, while GA_5 and GA_6 are much less effective at the lower concentrations.

This action of gibberellic acid upon gene activation in endosperm of cereals is similar to the way in which auxins are thought to act before they increase cell elongation. Several other examples are also known and are presently being discovered in which the responses caused by gibberellins are prevented by compounds

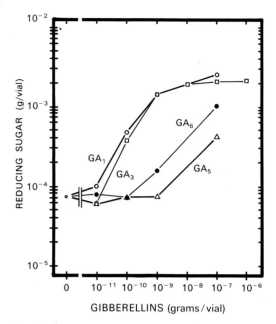

Figure 21-25

Influence of various gibberellins upon release of α-amylase from endosperm of barley seeds. Amylase release was measured by the ability of this enzyme to hydrolyze endosperm starch to reducing sugars. The latter were measured by an alkaline-copper reagent in which the cupric ion was reduced to cuprous oxide. (Data of B. G. Coombe et al., 1967, *Plant Physiol.* 42:113. Used by permission.)

capable of blocking RNA or protein synthesis, consistent with the theory of hormonal action upon messenger RNA formation. Further research must solidify this interpretation and clarify the manner in which auxins and gibberellins might activate genes. As discussed previously, both these compounds and the cytokinins sometimes stimulate cell divisions, and little information is yet available about how they might do this. It is possible that they could influence the activity of repressor proteins (Chapter 20) through allosteric transitions, but this is presently only speculation. There are many examples known in which auxins must be present in order for gibberellins or kinins to act, and this, too, must eventually be explained on a biochemical basis.

Finally, there is some evidence that in order for cells to grow, they must be synthesizing DNA during the growth period. This is somewhat surprising, since it has commonly been assumed that DNA synthesis is concerned only with cell division, and not with expansion. J. P. Nitsan and Anton Lang, now at Michigan State University, discovered in 1965 that 5-fluorodeoxyuridine, a compound that interferes with DNA synthesis, strongly inhibits elongation of epicotyl cells of lentil (*Lens culinaris*) seedlings. This inhibition was completely overcome by simultaneously adding thymidine, a precursor of thymidylic acid in DNA, but not by uridine, a precursor of RNA uridylic acid. It was then found that these cells normally synthesize DNA during the elongation period, and that GA_3, which stimulates their growth, also increases DNA synthesis. Nitsan and Lang concluded that GA_3 increases the rate of production of certain DNA molecules somehow essential to growth. The way in which these might act is unknown. There is no evidence that growth processes that are stimulated by auxins require DNA formation.

21.10.3 Cytokinins

Even less is known about the mechanism of action of hormones other than the auxins or gibberellins. It is known that synthetic cytokinins, at least, are incorporated into transfer RNA of some plants, although only to a small extent. Any incorporation of kinins into RNA is presumably preceded by conversion of the purine ring to the nucleoside and nucleotide levels (addition of ribose and phosphate), and the nucleoside and nucleotide derivatives of zeatin have been found in plants.

If cytokinins must be incorporated into RNA before they cause physiological responses, one might predict that the nucleoside and nu-

cleotide derivatives of zeatin and isopentenyl adenine would be even more active cytokinins than the free bases, assuming they penetrate the target cells equally well. There is, in fact, some evidence that this is true. Furthermore, Folke Skoog and his colleagues at the University of Wisconsin found that the transfer RNA molecules from yeast, liver, and bacteria had cytokinin activity, which proved to be largely due to the zeatin present. Later, in Buffalo, New York, Ross Hall and his colleagues found isopentenyl adenine in the transfer RNA of yeast, calf liver, and finally of sweet corn kernels.

Although these facts suggest that cytokinins somehow exert their effects as a result of their presence in transfer RNA molecules, there is reason to believe otherwise. The isopentenyl group from which the side chains of zeatin and isopentenyl adenine in transfer RNA are derived is probably added to RNA molecules already synthesized. It is likely that isopentenyl pyrophosphate (produced via the mevalonic acid pathway, Chapter 18) reacts directly with the amino group of adenine molecules in preformed transfer RNAs. Thus the preferred way of synthesizing cytokinins in RNA would not be by prior conversion of the free bases to the nucleosides and nucleotides and then into RNA, but would instead be via a secondary reaction involving isopentenyl pyrophosphate. This might mean that natural or synthetic cytokinins added as free bases cause effects completely independent of their incorporation into RNA. Nevertheless, because of the large amplifying effects involved, an influence upon RNA formation as occurs with auxins, gibberellins, and certain animal hormones is certainly suspected.

21.10.4 Abscisic Acid

The manner in which abscisic acid causes the many responses now being discovered is unknown. Some indirect evidence suggests that it interferes with the normal action of gibberellins or gibberellin synthesis. In addition, J. van Overbeek and colleagues then in California found that it strongly interferes with growth in the duckweed (*Lemna minor*), and that this effect is overcome by the synthetic cytokinin benzyladenine. Abscisic acid also inhibited both RNA and DNA synthesis in this plant, but the influence upon DNA seemed to occur first. They further observed that the cytokinin reversed this inhibition of nucleic acid formation. Their results suggest that a primary site of action of abscisic acid may be upon DNA; but, as usual, more research is needed.

Many interesting discoveries await plant physiologists interested in the field of hormone research.

22

Differentiation

The difference between the mass of thin-walled cells in a tumor (or even the cells in the apical meristem) and a fully developed plant is the specialization of individual cells. This occurs in exactly the appropriate places in relation to all the other cells in the plant, at the proper times during the life cycle, and sometimes as an appropriate response to external environmental conditions. The process of development of meristematic cells into others having specialized structures and functions is called **cellular differentiation**. The final shape of a plant is controlled not only by cellular differentiation, but also by the planes of cell divisions in the meristems, including the vascular cambium. As the cells grow in volume, divisions parallel to the surface (**tangential** or **periclinal**) will tend to result in a greater diameter of a plant stem or root, while divisions parallel to the cross section (**transverse**) are necessary for sustained elongation. Divisions of the cambium are tangential, producing from one highly elongate, narrow cell two others even narrower. These expand and differentiate into xylem (inside) or phloem (outside).

Sometimes a certain amount of differentiation is apparent even at cell division, so that the two daughter cells may not be exactly alike. Most commonly, however, the daughter cells are virtually identical, and differentiation occurs subsequent to division. From the meristematic cells arise all others including epidermis, cortex, phloem, vascular cambium, xylem, and pith cells (Fig. 22-1). Secondary wall formation is a differentiation process that contributes to production of the intricate wall patterns of the tracheids and vessel elements of the xylem or even bizarre forms such as the multi-branched sclereid cells found in various tissues. Ray cells, resin ducts, endodermis, xylem and phloem parenchyma, lenticels, guard cells, and palisade and spongy parenchyma constitute, among others, products of differentiation. These cells grouped together also account for the intricate final forms of leaves, roots, stems, flowers, and fruits.

The mature plant is the ultimate example of differentiation. It is the tissue and organ summation of cellular differentiation. Here the relative rates of growth and differentiation between the various plant parts determine the final form. For example, the rates of growth of the various veins in a leaf, as well as the interveinal tissue, will determine the shape of the leaf.

22.1 SEPARATION OF GROWTH AND DIFFERENTIATION

It is not difficult to find examples in which growth and differentiation are fairly well sep-

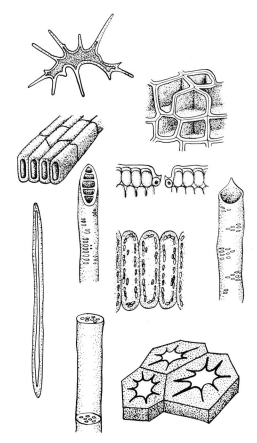

Figure 22-1
A variety of cell types, illustrating the diverse products of the process of cellular differentiation.

arated (Chapter 19). In growth of the endosperm during seed development, for example, cells divide and enlarge somewhat, but there is little, if any, differentiation. This is also true of tumor growth and to some extent growth of amorphous tissues such as pith and fleshy fruits. There are also stages of differentiation without growth, as in development of the embryo sac.

One of the most spectacular separations of growth and differentiation occurs in the slime molds. These organisms reproduce by the production of many spores. As the spores germ-

inate, they grow into amoeboid cells that live independently, dividing and growing, until their population number has increased considerably. This is the growth stage, and there is little, if any, sign of differentiation. At some signal this population of amoeboid cells (hardly plantlike!) begins to congregate toward a single center, forming a small, sluglike organism, perhaps only two or three mm long. This little slug then crawls along the forest floor until a suitable site for sporulation has been reached, usually a relatively dry, elevated point. It then begins differentiating into a spore-producing body (Fig. 22-2). Some of the cells in the slug provide a base. Others form a stalk. The rest migrate up this stalk, some of them increasing its length by becoming part of it. Finally, the remaining cells form a ball-shaped, clearly plantlike structure and become differentiated into spores. During all of this differentiation there has been no growth (increase in size). Soon after the slug has been formed, some of the cells have already been "determined" to be certain parts of the mature sporangium. This is shown by staining and by grafting and excision experiments.

It has long been considered a rule of thumb, particularly in agriculture, that high nitrogen levels and excess moisture promote growth of plants at the expense of differentiation, while low nitrogen, low moisture and high levels of accumulated carbohydrate promote differentiation. Careful studies have indicated that this generalization is oversimplified and often not true, although it still has valuable applications in agriculture. We shall refer to it again in our discussions of the physiology of flowering.

The basic problem of differentiation asks: how is differentiation within the mature organism controlled in time, space, and in response to environment? In the following sections, we shall first consider some principles of modern technology as they might apply to the problems of differentiation. We shall then consider descriptive data relating to differentiation, begin-

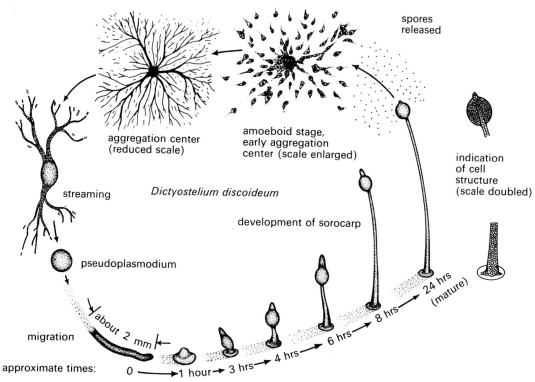

spores
released

aggregation center
(reduced scale)

amoeboid stage,
early aggregation
center (scale enlarged)

indication
of cell
structure
(scale doubled)

streaming

Dictyostelium discoideum

development of sorocarp

pseudoplasmodium

about 2 mm

migration

approximate times:

0 ——→ 1 hour ——→ 3 hrs ——→ 4 hrs ——→ 6 hrs ——→ 8 hrs ——→ 24 hrs (mature)

Figure 22-2

The life history and morphogenesis of a cellular slime mold.

ning with the complex case of the entire organism and working toward differentiation in single cells. At the mature-organism level, virtually all of the information is descriptive. At the single-cell level more is known about mechanisms. We shall consider the question of potency. How can a single cell, for example, contain the genetic program for the development of an entire plant?

22.2 DIFFERENTIATION AND PRINCIPLES OF MODERN TECHNOLOGY

Engineering science, both electrical and mechanical, is discovering principles that may help in our understanding of how the plant machinery

might function. In a few cases the component systems of modern electronic and mechanical devices are clearly performing functions identical to some performed by perfectly analogous components in the plant. In other cases it is not known how the plant actually functions, but understanding the operation of a given machine may provide insight into plant function. This is the approach of formulating **conceptual models**. The double-osmometer system, used by Münch to illustrate the principle of solute translocation by pressure flow (Chapter 9) is an example of such a conceptual model that could actually be constructed in the laboratory. The two connected rooms containing perfectly elastic balls in motion, used to illustrate diffusion

(Chapter 3), represent a model that cannot be constructed but is nevertheless conceptually valid. Control systems, logic circuits, and other aspects of modern electronic technology, especially as applied in computers, are presently providing us with new possibilities for conceptual models that may even help us to understand the process of differentiation.

We will introduce three general principles of technology and consider these in terms of differentiation. We will then find occasions in the remainder of the book to refer to these principles. The general approach is an exciting one that will surely suggest profitable experiments for the future.

22.2.1 Transducers, Language, and Translation

A **transducer** is a device that will respond to some environmental parameter, converting this to some form usable in a measurement or control system. A thermocouple, for example, produces an electric current proportional to temperature, and this current may be used in a device that records the temperature or in one that controls temperature by controlling heating or cooling devices. Living cells clearly contain transducers. A number of examples were given in Chapter 20. The rate of an enzymatic reaction may be controlled by temperature, and thus the enzyme may be thought of as a transducer for temperature. The pigment system phytochrome, to be discussed in the next chapter, transduces a light stimulus resulting in the control of stem elongation, leaf expansion, flowering, germination, and many other plant processes.

We are concerned here with the concept of language or information. **Language** is the *form* of information, and **translation** is the conversion from one form to another. We have discussed an excellent example in Chapter 17. The order of arrangement of nucleotides in DNA constitutes information. This order of arrangement is translated into the order of arrangement of amino acids in proteins. While the DNA language is effective in reproduction, it is completely ineffective in the control of metabolic processes; yet protein language (enzymes) is highly effective in control of metabolism but not in reproduction.

It is valuable to consider the various kinds of language involved in plant growth and in the plant's response to its environment. *First* might be the language of **environment**, the physical and chemical parameters to which the plant is exposed. We translate these into numbers having arbitrary units (e.g., degrees Celsius, moles/liter, etc.), and this helps us to understand and work with them, but we must not confuse the numbers (*our* language) with the actual parameters themselves.

The *second* language might be that of the **responding systems** within the organism. These transducers translate the language of environment into terms more "understandable" to the cell itself.

Third is the **DNA-RNA-protein system**. At this level we are probably concerned with enzyme inducers and repressors, operator genes, and structural genes, as introduced in Chapter 20. In a sense, the transducers translate the "environment" language into the language of the DNA-RNA-protein system.

Fourth is the **"metabolic" language**. Most of Section II in this book is concerned with discussing this language. Here, under control of the enzymes, the various intermediary metabolites are translated (converted) from one to another.

Fifth must be a **"whole-organism" language**. It, again, deals with the environment. The organism grows, reproduces, and performs all of the functions (many of them translations) studied in an introductory biology course. An end result of all of this might even be the ability of man and perhaps other animals to "enjoy life."

Another language is worth considering. The actual languages of the living system are known to us only very imperfectly in terms of our **human languages** of symbols. We use analogies, often highly anthropomorphic, to convey this understanding. For instance, we stated above that the transducers translate the environment language into one more "understandable" to the cell itself. The term understandable does not imply that the cell thinks but that it may respond to the product of the transducers when it might have been incapable of responding to the environment itself. If we realize the limitations of our human languages, the analogies and the anthropomorphisms can often be highly valuable.

22.2.2 Control Theory

Often plant responses seem to be accurately controlled by some internal mechanism. Present work with control systems is beginning to give us insight into how this might occur. We may consider **homeostasis**, in which the *level* of some response is controlled (e.g., rate of growth, intensity of respiration, etc.). Or the *kind* of response may be controlled (e.g., the seed germinates or does not, the plant flowers or grows vegetatively, etc.).

Control in the level of a given response may be brought about through a **feedback system** (Fig. 22-3). In such a system the response being controlled is monitored by a transducer of some sort. The signal from the transducer is compared to some preset value in the system, and the level of the response is then controlled in such a way that the returning signal from the transducer will more closely approach the preset value. Usually there is an amplification of response between the incoming signal from the transducer and the response being monitored. Control of temperature by a thermostat provides a good example. Heating coils may warm the air in a room, or cooling coils may cool it. A thermometer (transducer) measures the air temperature, and the signal from the thermometer is com-

pared with some preset value. In the simplest mechanical system, the value is preset by the positioning of a switch. Expansion (movement) of a bimetallic thermometer may cause the switch to be activated when the temperature is higher than the preset value. Such activation of the switch might turn on a cooling unit, providing the amplification. This is necessary, because the energy required for cooling will greatly exceed the energy involved in activation of the switch by the thermometer.

The stomatal control mechanism proposed in Chapter 6 is an excellent example of a feedback system. Stomatal apertures control the concentration of carbon dioxide inside the leaf. Some as yet unknown transducer detects this concentration and compares it with some desirable preset value. The response is an opening or a closing of the stomates, leading to an increase or a decrease in the carbon dioxide level within the leaf. It is not difficult to imagine such feedback control systems in the various growth and metabolic processes of the plant, and several have already been discussed, especially in Chapter 20.

Logic circuits are essential to the function of a modern computer. They may control kind rather than level of response. In such a circuit, a given condition leads to a response; lack of this condition leads to lack of response. In symbolic terms: If *A*, then *B*. Such a so-called **logic gate** may be set up with three incoming wires. If all are charged, then the current will pass through the gate to a fourth wire. If any one of the three is not charged, then no current will pass through the gate. Alternatively, the gate may not pass current if any one of the first three wires is charged. There are several possibilities.

Such a logic circuit allows the function of **testing**. The gates described above test for the presence of current in particular wires. The principle of testing could be very important in differentiation. A gene may test for the presence of an auxin, for example. If the auxin is present,

A SIMPLE FEEDBACK SYSTEM:

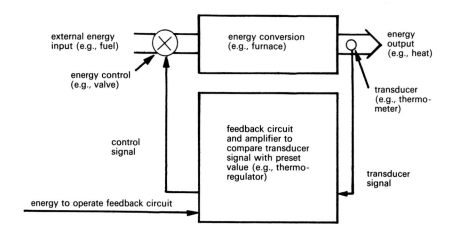

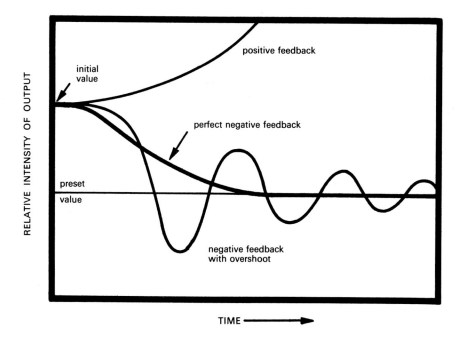

Figure 22-3

A generalized diagram of a simple feedback system and the expected outputs as a function of time for positive and negative systems.

the gene is activated, if not, then it is repressed (or vice-versa). The results of such testing could be **switching**. The presence or absence of auxin may, by its effect on the gene, switch growth on or off. The phenomenon of **induction** was described in Chapter 20. This might be a matter of switching in response to tests, possibly through gene activation or repression as described here.

22.2.3 The Program

In a computer the **program** consists of a series of tests and controlled events designed to attain an ultimate end result. The program is the heart of the operation of a computer. Usually the program is fed into the **memory** of the computer in sequential form. For example, the program for evaluation of data relating to students in a university may be fed into the computer. The student data are punched onto cards, and the cards are then examined one by one by the computer. According to the program, A grades punched on the cards are multiplied by 4, B grades by 3, etc. The total may be divided by the number of credits recorded on the card to obtain the grade-point average. The cards may be tested for various factors. Grades of boys may be placed in one part of the memory, those for girls or some other special group in another. **Subroutines** may be introduced to calculate average grades for boys or girls, standard error of the averages, relationship between grade-point average and home town, or a myriad of other possibilities.

As James Bonner has pointed out in recent years, living organisms may be closely comparable. In the plant the **morphogenetic program** is contained in the **genome**, which consists of a complete set of the cell's genetic material (the two sets of chromosomes plus perhaps other nonchromosomal DNA). The master program must control the life cycle of the plant, and it must contain subroutines relating to time of flowering, response to gravity or to injury, and a host of others. There is much testing of transducer signals and switching in response to environmental factors.

There are apparent differences between a cell and a computer, however. In a digital computer, steps are always sequential (cards are read one by one), but this must not be the case in the plant. Many tests and controlled steps seem to be going on simultaneously. Nevertheless, the end result of the plant program is growth of the plant through the sequential steps of its life cycle (Fig. 22-4). It may well be that in operation the morphogenetic program has little in common with the programs of modern digital computers. Yet the conceptual model seems to be a good one, and it may apply even better to some of the analog computers being developed. *Concepts* developed in relation to computers seem to have their counterparts in morphogenesis. The idea of a life-cycle program with its various subroutines can be valuable in our study of growth and development.

22.3 DIFFERENTIATION IN THE WHOLE PLANT

There are many correlation phenomena in the entire organism, and these may be thought of in terms of the over-all problem of differentiation. We shall consider four broad examples. The point of our discussions will not be to present detailed physiological mechanisms, since these are not yet known; it is simply to indicate the problems involved in finding such mechanisms. An ultimate objective would be to understand how the mechanisms of cellular differentiation act in concert, ultimately to determine the final form of the plant.

22.3.1 Polarity

As indicated in previous chapters, the ultimate form of the plant is dependent upon the property

FLOW CHART, PRELIMINARY TO WRITING PROGRAM: LIFE CYCLE

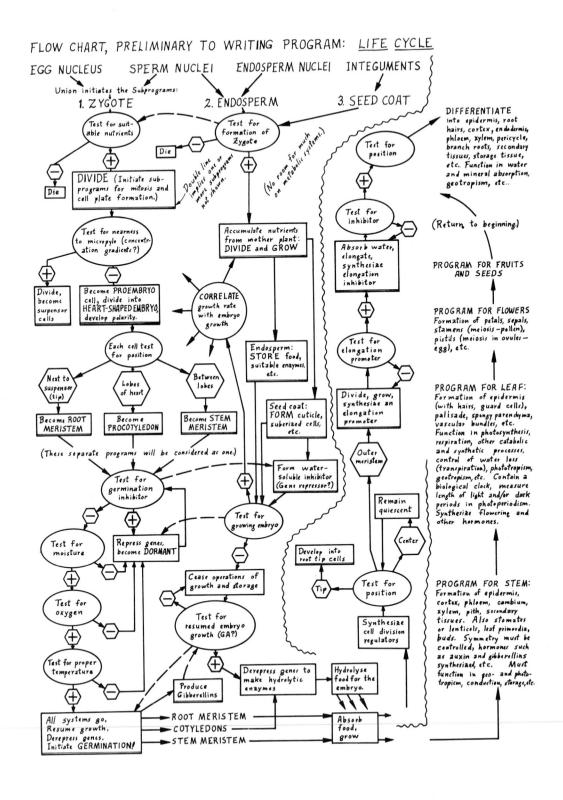

of polarity. It appears, as Vöchting suggested, that the phenomenon is common to all tissues and possibly even to individual cells. Polarity may be observed in several ways, such as by the polar movement of auxin discussed in the previous chapter. It appears early in the life cycle, usually after the first division of the zygote.

Polarity has been studied by adventitious bud and root formation on stem cuttings. As Vöchting showed, a section cut from a willow stem always produced roots at the end that was originally basal, even though the section is inverted (Fig. 21-11). The willow has been widely used, but most other species respond similarly. In a few species, such as *Hibiscus*, however, roots will form at the physiologically apical end. With some of these species this occurs readily when the stem section is inverted, and with others it can be caused to occur with special treatments. A branch may be bent down from a mature plant and its leafy end buried in the soil. Roots will form in the soil, and the branch may then be cut off from the mature plant. Shoots will then arise from what was physiologically the basal end, while roots are growing at the morphologically apical end. It would appear that polarity has been reversed. It is easy to show, however, that if a section is cut out from such a stem and laid horizontally, roots form at the original basal end, while shoots form at the apical end. In such a case it is possible to *mask* polarity but not to *reverse* it.

We are faced not only with understanding the nature of polarity but also with understanding its original induction. Apparently gravity is important, and this seems reasonable because the polar nature of higher plants is typically displayed in relation to gravity. In some situations, however, other environmental influences may be more important than gravity. Light, for example, has been shown to induce polarity in developing *Fucus* zygotes.

22.3.2 Reaction Wood and Plagiotropism

While polarity may be partly a gravity phenomenon, geotropism is by definition a response to gravity. The topic was introduced briefly in the previous three chapters. Coleoptiles and most stems grow away from the source of gravity, while roots grow toward it. Evidence indicates that this response, in stems, at least, is due to a redistribution of auxin. Higher concentrations of auxin on the lower side of a stem placed horizontally make the cells grow more rapidly, thereby causing the stem to bend upward. The gravity receptors, the so-called statoliths, have not been identified, nor does anyone have more than preliminary suggestions about how they could function. In this section we will consider the important complication of lateral branch growth. Most studies of these phenomena have utilized gymnosperms. F. Hertmann in Germany (1942–1943) and Edmund W. Sinnott at Yale University (1952) have been particularly active in this field. In gymnosperms the lateral branches grow out at an angle that remains fairly constant in relation to the direction of the gravitational force. This phenomenon is referred to as **plagiotropism**. As the weight of the limb increases, it might be expected to bend downward. This does occur in many species, but

---

Figure 22-4

The results of Frank B. Salisbury's attempt to devise, one evening, the elements of a flow chart preliminary to writing a program for the life cycle of a higher plant. It soon became apparent that space and time limitations made this an almost impossible task. Such a program rapidly becomes far more complex than might be imagined. It should be evident that nearly any of the boxes in the figure could be expanded on the basis of information in this book to a flow chart as complex as this one. The authors would be interested in seeing student corrections of the errors in this chart and student attempts to develop programs.

there is a tendency to resist this bending by a
build-up of wood on the bottom of the limb.
This **reaction wood** is under compression, and
it tends to push the limb toward a more upright
position, *maintaining the proper angle.*

What could be the mechanism controlling
the formation of reaction wood? Is it a matter
of auxin moving toward the bottom of the
branch in response to the movement of some
statolith? Or is it a response of the wood to the
compression on the bottom of the branch?
There are reasons to doubt that either explanation, by itself at least, is sufficient. For example,
if the branch is bent upward rather than downward (e.g., by tying it with a cable), then the
reaction wood forms on the *top* of the branch.
Clearly this is not a simple gravity response.

The trunk will also make reaction wood if
it is held in some position other than vertical.
A simple experiment indicates that the response
is not merely to compression. The young leader
of a pine tree may be wrapped into a complete
vertical loop. In this case (Fig. 22-5), the reaction
wood forms on the under side of both the upper
and the lower parts of the loop. The under side
of the upper part of the loop is clearly under
compression, but the lower side of the bottom
part of the loop is clearly under tension.

Whatever the mechanism, reaction wood
tends to maintain the normal position of either
branches or main stems in relation to gravity.
In the loop mentioned above, the branches do
not grow out at a constant angle to the stem
but at an angle essentially constant in relation
to the direction of the gravitational field. So
we are obviously dealing with a gravity response,
but one considerably more complex than a
simple movement of growth hormones in
response to gravity.

James Finn, working for the North American
Aviation Company in Southern California,
studied the related phenomenon of leaf petiole
angle. He constructed a device in which he
could simulate gravitational fields of any value

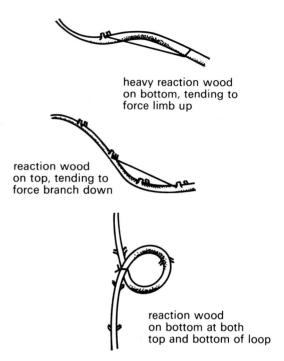

Figure 22-5
Summary of experiments on reaction wood.

from zero g to values considerably above 1 g
by placing horizontal clinostats upon a large
centrifuge. The shoot tips of the plants on the
clinostats were directed toward the center of
the centrifuge. When the centrifuge was stationary but the clinostats were revolving, the plants
would be subjected to simulated zero g. By
controlling the speed of rotation of the centrifuge, the plants would be subjected to simulated
gravitational fields at any desired level. Finn
referred to the angle between the leaf petiole
and the main stem (using cocklebur, pepper,
and various other plants) as the **liminal leaf
angle**. Figure 22-6 shows the results of his experiments. The liminal leaf angle was inversely proportional to the strength of the simulated
gravitational field. Figure 22-6 also shows the
results of an experiment in Biosatellite II, the

first extensive biological experiment of the United States carried out in space.

In plagiotropism we are apparently dealing with a true directional response to gravity. It is as though the cells are programmed to assess their position in relation to gravity and react accordingly. Perhaps they react by redistributing auxin or by some other mechanism, causing growth in whatever manner might be required to reorient them into their proper position.

Another interesting aspect of this morphogenetic program is its ability to be switched in some species. In spruce and in many other species with an **excurrent growth habit** ("pine tree" form), if the leader is cut off, the lateral branches in the upper whorl begin to grow in a more vertical direction. Finally one (or sometimes two) of these becomes predominant, and the others then assume their specific angles. It is as if the branches are programmed to grow at some certain angle as long as they are receiving a message from the leader shoot that it is definitely active and growing vertically. Their program must also include the information that if the message from the leader stops coming, then the branch itself is to grow vertically until it can send its own message or until it begins to receive a more powerful message from another shoot.

Is the message an auxin? We know that auxins are important in the apical dominance of many species. It is difficult, however, to see how they might operate here. If auxins are involved in the growth itself, for example, then the messages from the branch and from the leader shoot might become confused. Also, the auxins would apparently have to move up the branch in the acropetal direction (contrary to the usual polar movement) if they were the message from the leader.

A few species are known in which a lateral branch does not become a leader upon removal of the main shoot. Lateral branches of *Araucaria excelsa* maintain their plagiotropic growth habit

even if they are removed from the plant and rooted as cuttings. Such a horizontal tree has been growing in the Botanical Garden in Munich, Germany, for over 60 years. The program in the cells of *Araucaria* must include information about plagiotropic growth but nothing about the response to a message from the leader shoot.

In angiosperms, virtually all of the same responses may be observed, although these have been considerably less studied than in gymnosperms. In angiosperms the reaction wood forms on the *top* and pulls the branch or stem toward the vertical position by *tension*. Many angiosperm trees have a **deliquescent growth habit**, in which no clear leader can be discerned, but several large branches grow almost vertically. The program relating to apical dominance is obviously somewhat modified here in relation to gymnosperms. In shrubs, it is even more modified.

22.3.3 Regeneration

The phenomenon of regeneration, both in plants and in animals, offers a number of fascinating and instructive examples of differentiation and morphogenesis. The process is almost a standard research tool, as in the formation of roots on cuttings. This is because the processes involved in regeneration are very similar or identical to the normal processes of differentiation.

There has been some problem in the definition of the term regeneration. We shall use the following rather broad definition by Sinnott. **Regeneration** is the tendency shown by developing organisms to restore any part that has been removed or physiologically isolated and thus *to produce a complete whole*. It is important to note that the tendency to restore the whole is always a conspicuous aspect of the regeneration process.

The kind of regeneration called **reconstitution** is frequently observed in animals. A lizard's

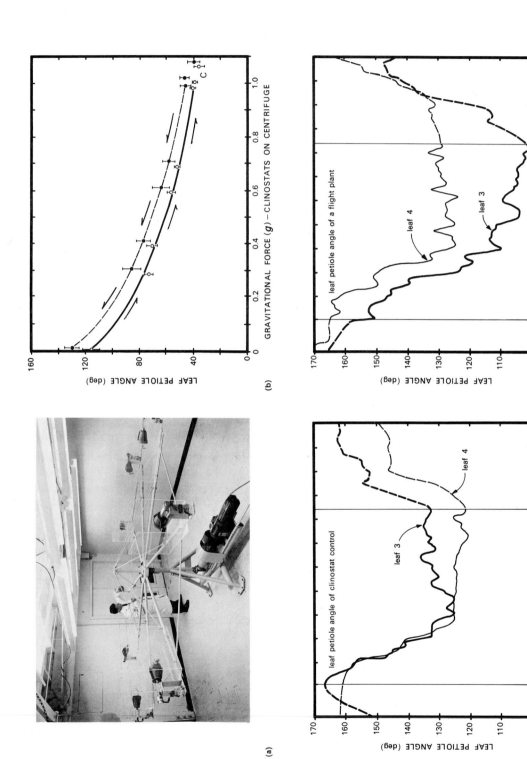

(a)

(b)

LEAF PETIOLE ANGLE (deg)

GRAVITATIONAL FORCE (g) — CLINOSTATS ON CENTRIFUGE

(c) PRELAUNCH   LAUNCH AND ORBIT (hrs)   RECOVERY PHASE

leaf petiole angle of clinostat control

leaf 3

leaf 4

LEAF PETIOLE ANGLE (deg)

(d) PRELAUNCH   LAUNCH AND ORBIT (hrs)   RECOVERY PHASE

leaf petiole angle of a flight plant

leaf 4

leaf 3

LEAF PETIOLE ANGLE (deg)

tail may be easily detached, but it is subsequently replaced by the growth of a new one from the remaining stub. While this process is relatively rare in plants, there are several good examples. One may remove 0.50 to 0.75 mm of a root tip, for example, and a new tip will be formed from the remaining cells. This will also occur upon removal of the terminal portion of the shoot tip, but in the species studied only the upper 80 μ of the dome-like structure could be removed if regeneration was to occur. When more than these quantities are removed from either the root or the shoot apices, callus usually forms, and new meristems may develop in this. It has been shown that the meristem of either roots or shoots may be split lengthwise (in the experiments of Ernest Ball with *Lupinus* stems, into as many as six strips), and new meristems will be constituted from the separated segments. Various workers have also isolated a central core of the shoot tip, showing that this will also form a reconstituted apical meristem.

Tissue patterns are often reconstituted following wounding (Fig. 22-7). If a lateral incision is made into a stem, the vascular elements that have been severed will often reform around the wound. That is, cortex and other cells are **redifferentiated** into vascular cells. There appear to be at least two factors that determine which cells become redifferentiated. Typically, the vascular elements

develop downward in connection with existing vascular tissue above the wound. Something might flow from this original vascular tissue, controlling the formation of new vascular elements in continuity with the old. Several experimental approaches indicate that this is probably auxin (see tissue culture discussions below). Distance from the cut surface also appears to be important. Perhaps formation of xylem elements depends upon some specific oxygen (or carbon dioxide) concentration found only at certain distances below the surface. Such a hypothesis could be tested by observing reconstitution of vascular elements in tissues placed in atmospheres having different oxygen concentrations. Low oxygen should result in formation of vascular elements near the surface.

There is an all-or-none aspect to tissue reconstitution. Either a cell becomes a xylem element or it does not. This might indicate that only one or a few genes within the cell nucleus might be in control of this kind of differentiation. Either this gene is activated or it is not, apparently depending upon conditions such as auxin and oxygen concentrations.

There are other examples of reconstitution, such as the formation of a new epidermis following wounding. In a few instances (e.g., Kohlrabi), the reformed epidermis is remarkably similar to the original, having the same kind of stomates, etc. There are also a few

---

Figure 22-6

Effects of gravity on leaf petiole angle. (upper left) The large centrifuge with its clinostats developed at North American Aviation, Inc., Downey, California. The investigator is J. Finn. This apparatus is functionally comparable to the 2-Pi clinostat shown in Fig. 20-8. (upper right) Data obtained by Finn using the apparatus shown on the left. Plants rotated on the clinostat when the centrifuge is not moving have leaf petiole angles of about 120° (heavy line − upper left at zero *g*). Since *g* force increases as the centrifuge begins to rotate more and more rapidly, leaf angle decreases (heavy line) until it is about equal to that of control plants not on the apparatus (points labeled *C*). As the centrifuge is slowed in its rotation (light line), leaf angle again increases until, with the clinostat still in operation but the centrifuge stationary, it reaches about 130°. (lower left) Leaf petiole angle as a function of time for two leaves grown on a clinostat in a manner designed to simulate the gravity profile of Biosatellite II. That is, *g* = 1 during prelaunch and recovery, and zero *g* is simulated during most of orbit (*g* exceeds 1 for a brief period during launch and recovery). For other brief intervals during course correction, *g* is above zero but less than 1. (lower right) Leaf petiole angle as a function of time for two leaves of plants in Biosatellite II. Data compare reasonably well with those obtained on the clinostat control. (Photograph and data courtesy of the project engineer for this Biosatellite experiment, the late S. P. Johnson, North American Aviation, Inc., Downey, California.)

examples of true reconstitution of leaves and other organs, but these are quite rare.

A much more typical kind of regeneration in plants is called **restoration**. The spruce lateral branch which becomes a leader following removal of the original leader is a good example. The wounded surface does not reconstitute a new organ, but a new organ may be formed from some nearby tissue that was not wounded. In the simplest cases a lateral branch or an axillary bud may grow out to produce a leader shoot. Adventitious buds may also form near a wound, frequently in callus tissue that develops on or near the wound.

The most common example of restorative regeneration is vegetative propagation by rooting of stem cuttings. Somewhat more rare is sucker (adventitious bud) formation on root cuttings. In either case, a new plant is formed by restoration of the part missing from the cutting. Leaves may also be used as cuttings depending upon the species, (e.g., African violets), and in a few rare instances flower parts or even fruits may produce adventitious buds or roots.

Sometimes vegetative regeneration of the whole plant is the *rule* under natural conditions, rather than the result of special treatment such as that necessary to produce cuttings. *Bryophyllum* plants, for example, produce small **foliar embryos (plantlets)** on the edges of their leaves. This often occurs in response to various environmental conditions, particularly long days. Sinnott referred to this process as **reproductive regeneration**, but since it is not in response to a missing part, it would not fit his definition of regeneration given above.

We seem again to be dealing with a specialized program within the cells. As long as all is "normal" in relation to the immediate environment of a given cell, this cell remains what it is, but when such factors as oxygen or auxin concentration, or available inorganic and organic nutrients change radically, then the cell responds to the "message." In the cases of

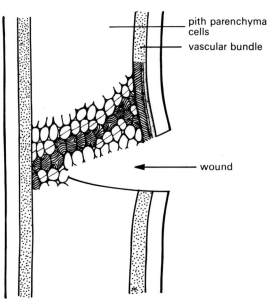

Figure 22-7
Redifferentiation of xylem cells around a wound in a geranium stem. Stippled area indicates vascular bundles and is drawn essentially to scale, but pith cells have been greatly enlarged to show the secondary wall formation. Note new cell walls in the cells adjacent to the redifferentiating xylem cells and parallel to the line of redifferentiation. (Based on E. W. Sinnott, 1960, *Plant Morphogenesis*, McGraw-Hill Book Company, New York, Toronto, London.)

regeneration, the message arises because some given part is missing. Apparently the cell is programmed to respond to this message by initiating a new subprogram that will result in restoration of the lost part.

22.3.4 Symmetry

Three tendencies, correlated with each other and with growth in general, are important in producing the final plant form: polarity, symmetry, and spirality (spiral growth). We might think of **spirality** as a special manifestation of symmetry, but in an exact definition this would not hold, since **symmetry** implies that the object in question can be equally divided into identical mirror-image halves by at least one

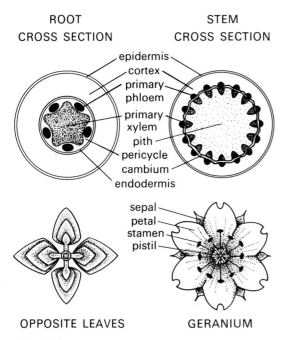

ROOT
CROSS SECTION

STEM
CROSS SECTION

epidermis
cortex
primary phloem
primary xylem
pith
pericycle
cambium
endodermis

sepal
petal
stamen
pistil

OPPOSITE LEAVES

GERANIUM

Figure 22-8

Some examples of radial symmetry. (Note that geraniums normally have five petals. The drawing was made from a photograph of a geranium with six petals before the discrepancy was noted. See Fig. 1-5, F. B. Salisbury and R. V. Parke, 1964, *Vascular Plants: Form and Function,* Wadsworth Publishing Company, Inc., Belmont, Calif.)

plane of division, a requirement that is not met by a spiral structure.

In **radial symmetry** there is an axis of rotation around which symmetry is uniform (Fig. 22-8). There may be two longitudinal planes of symmetry at right angles to each other, as in the case of a stem with alternating pairs of opposite leaves, or there may be a large number of planes of symmetry (infinite for a smooth circle). There are many examples in the plant kingdom. Virtually all roots exhibit this kind of symmetry, as does the internal anatomy of most vertical stems. Many flowers exhibit radial symmetry. Sometimes the axis is somewhat compressed or flattened, so that there are two planes of symmetry, but these are not quite equal. This

is known as **bilateral symmetry**, and it is somewhat rare in plants. Certain stems of cacti, leaves of iris, and grass stems do exhibit this kind of symmetry.

More typically, the flattening is so extensive that only one plane of symmetry remains. The two sides may be alike, but top and bottom (or in a vertical organ, the other two sides) are not. This is known as **dorsiventral symmetry**, and it is very common in plants. The great majority of leaves exhibit it, as do many flowers and branches. Sometimes dorsiventral or even radial symmetry is highly complex, as in the special case of **anisophylly** (Fig. 22-9). Here the individual leaves or other plant parts may be asymmetric (e.g., one half larger than the other half), but their placement on the branch is such that the branch itself exhibits dorsiventral symmetry. This is a particularly interesting aspect of symmetry from the standpoint of differentiation. Figure 22-9 indicates the floral arrangement of *Stellaria aquatica*. Here the individual flowers are somewhat asymmetrical, yet their placement in the cyme is such that a high degree of radial symmetry results. Each flower has its opposite counterpart in the inflorescence. Note particularly the placement of the "odd" sepal. What mechanisms at the cellular level can account for such an intricate integration of organismal growth?

There are a great many examples of spirality in nature. D'Arcy W. Thompson, in his monumental book *On Growth and Form* published in 1942, made a special point of this, citing numerous examples from both the plant and animal kingdoms. In the plant kingdom, most study has been devoted to the problems of leaf arrangement on the stem, the **phyllotaxy** (Fig. 22-10). Phyllotaxy poses some very valid problems of differentiation. Many workers, including certain mathematicians, have investigated the problems.

The simplest leaf arrangement is a truly alternate one in which the successive leaves

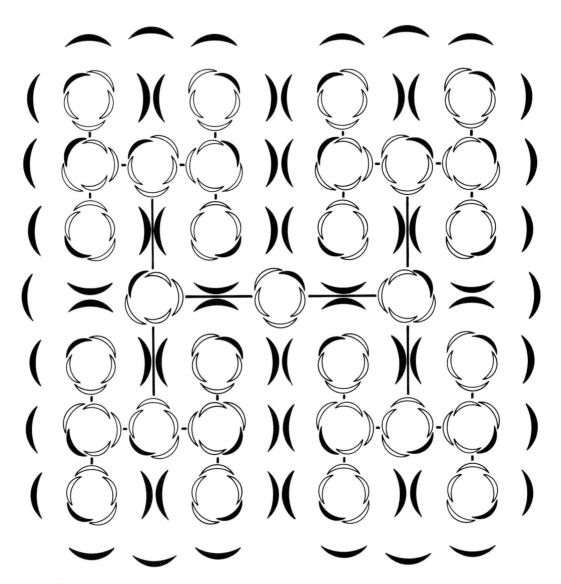

Figure 22-9

A complex example of symmetry. Diagram of an inflorescence of *Stellaria aquatica*. In the center is the terminal flower; at its right and left are the two which arise just below it; and below each of these, in turn, are two others. The "odd" sepal has been darkened in the floral diagrams. Note the extent to which even this is symmetrical in its placement in the inflorescence. Only in the terminal flower does this sepal lack a counterpart in another flower. (After E. W. Sinnott, 1960, *Plant Morphogenesis*, McGraw-Hill Book Company, New York, Toronto, London.)

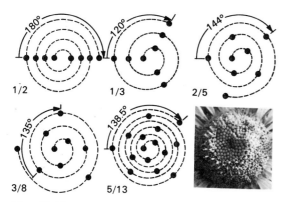

Figure 22-10

Several examples of spiral phyllotaxy. Photograph is of the center part of the inflorescence of *Hymenoxys grandiflora*. Note complex spiral arrangement of disk flowers.

are 180° apart around the stem. To pass from a leaf to one directly below it involves one circuit of the stem and two leaves. This may be expressed by the fraction $\frac{1}{2}$. On other plants the spiral passes once around the axis for each three leaves, a condition represented by $\frac{1}{3}$. Another example is the $\frac{2}{5}$ type in which two circuits involving five leaves are completed before one leaf occurs directly above another. The kinds of leaf arrangements that have been observed fall into the following series: $\frac{1}{2}$, $\frac{1}{3}$, $\frac{2}{5}$, $\frac{3}{8}$, $\frac{5}{13}$, $\frac{8}{21}$, $\frac{13}{34}$, $\frac{21}{55}$. The fractions represent that fraction of the circumference of the axis traversed by the spiral in passing from one leaf to the next. The series is identical to a mathematical series known as the **fibonacci series** which is generated by summing the numerators and the denominators of two fractions to obtain the next fraction in the series. The higher fractions become more nearly uniform, approaching the limit of 0.38197 or the angle, 137° 30′ 28″, the so-called ideal angle.[1]

If successive leaves were formed at just this angular distance around the stem, no leaf would ever be exactly above any other leaf. It is perhaps not surprising that artists, mathematicians, mystics and other nonbiologists have been interested in leaf phyllotaxy!

Two theories have been suggested to account for the order of formation of leaf primordia at the apical meristem.[2] The first of these theories holds that the presence of a developing leaf primordium at the apical meristem inhibits the formation of other primordia near it. Thus, the next primordium to be formed will occur as far from the last one as possible. If the inhibitory effects were rapidly dissipated, primordia might be expected simply to alternate at opposite positions along the stem as in the $\frac{1}{2}$ arrangement. If this inhibitory effect remains longer, however, the formation of a new primordium will be influenced not only by the last one but by the ones formed even earlier. The fibonacci angle may be the ideal angle when the inhibitory effect remains the longest.

Robert and Mary Snow, a husband-and-wife team working in England, have done a number of experiments on the induction of leaf primordia at the apical meristem. Some of their experiments seem to be incompatible with the inhibitor idea. If they removed the last primordium to be formed, the next primordium still appeared at the place where it might have been expected, as though its formation were not at all dependent upon the last primordium.

The second theory holds that the primordium will form where there is the most available space. The Snows found evidence for this idea. They isolated with incisions the area where the next primordium was expected

[1] The fraction (0.38197) is the so-called golden mean. If a line is divided by that fraction, the small portion of the line will bear the same relation to the larger portion that the larger portion bears to the original line.

[2] Actually the arrangement of leaf primordia at the meristem does not follow the fibonacci series but a closely related one which approaches the difference between the ideal angle and one: 0.61803. For more detailed discussion, see: Edmund W. Sinnott, 1960. *Plant Morphogenesis*. McGraw-Hill, New York.

and found that it would form only if the area were large enough. If the area were too small, it still appeared to grow normally, but no leaf primordium was formed. Of course, one can always suggest that the surgical treatment is a severe one, and that normal developmental processes may be upset by it. In spite of these evidences, several workers still believe that elements of both explanations may actually apply; that is, inhibitors and available space are both important.

Can we understand symmetry in terms of the concept of programming? We could probably devise schemes to account for our observations in these terms. They would become fairly complex and would imply extremely sensitive responses to various levels of hormones and environmental factors. We can imagine that a given cell will grow and/or differentiate in a manner exactly determined by such factors, accounting for the production of symmetries by cellular processes. This is far beyond our present knowledge, however; so far beyond that we cannot help but be a bit uncomfortable with the theory. Would it not be very easy to upset symmetries by slight changes in environmental factors such as oxygen pressures, temperatures, etc.? Often the form of the mature plant is only slightly influenced by such things. If we cannot apply such an explanation, however, then what does account for these phenomena?

22.4 DIFFERENTIATION AND APICAL MERISTEMS

Figure 22-11 shows the organization of a stem and a root apical meristem. Plant anatomists have for many years attempted to understand apical meristems in terms of specific zones and the functions of these zones. The **tunica corpus concept** is one of the most widely applied interpretations of shoot apical meristem zonation in angiosperms. It appears that the tunica gener-

ates the epidermis from which the leaves and buds arise, while the corpus generates the rest of the stem tissues. Other interpretations are also applied (e.g., the cytohistological zonation theory for gymnosperms). In virtually every case, the **apical initial cells** are a readily apparent aspect of the shoot meristem due to their large nuclei, thin walls, and dense cytoplasm. Their possible role will be discussed below.

As was indicated in Chapter 20 growth takes place by the division, enlargement, elongation, and differentiation of cells. Many workers have attempted to describe root meristems in terms of **zones of division**, **elongation**, and **differentiation**. In a very general way, such zones do exist, but even in the root they overlap considerably. Differentiation of xylem elements may begin, for example, simultaneously with, or shortly after, initiation of elongation. In the stem the overlap is so great that such zones cannot be distinguished. Divisions occur several centimeters below the stem tip, and elongation will sometimes continue as much as half a meter below the apex. In the root, elongation of cells typically stops within a millimeter or two of the root tip.

All apical meristems do appear to have at least two things in common: a capacity for self-maintenance and the ability to generate a vascular axis with its appendages (roots, branch roots, leaves, branches, flowers, etc.). The problems related to these abilities of the meristem provide an area of research for the botanist interested in morphogenesis. Do the already-differentiated tissues induce the further differentiation of similar tissues? Or is the meristem **totipotent** in that it is by itself capable of generating an entire plant? Other questions relating to meristems have already been discussed above, including the effect of the meristem on the differentiation of axillary roots and buds and the initial generation of meristems.

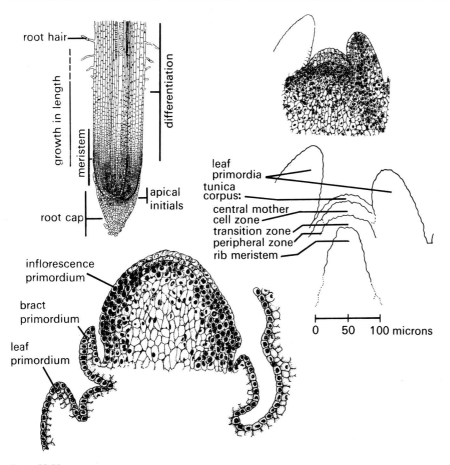

root hair

growth in length

meristem

differentiation

root cap

apical initials

leaf primordia

tunica

corpus:

central mother cell zone

transition zone

peripheral zone

rib meristem

0   50   100 microns

inflorescence primordium

bract primordium

leaf primordium

Figure 22-11

Apical meristems. Upper left is a root meristem, upper right is the vegetative meristem of *Xanthium strumarium*, below is a line diagram indicating the various zones. Lower figure is an early stage in development of the flower of *Xanthium strumarium*. (*Xanthium* meristems from F. B. Salisbury, 1963, *The Flowering Process*, Pergamon Press, New York. Used by permission.)

22.4.1 The Differentiation of the Vascular Cylinder and Other Stem Tissues

Differentiating primary xylem and phloem, cortex, and other cells in the stem occur in close conjunction with similar cell types that have already been differentiated. That is, differentiation in the primary apical meristem occurs in an acropetal direction. This might imply that differentiation of xylem cells, for example, is in response to the immediate presence of already-differentiated xylem cells. Alternatively, some influence from above might cause xylem cells to be differentiated one on top of the other. There is evidence that the latter idea may be the true one. As a lateral bud forms, cells close to the epidermis divide to produce the new meristem, and there is initially no vascular connection with the vascular elements in the main stem. Xylem and other vascular elements then begin to form in the newly differentiated bud, and these connect by differentiation in a basipetal direction with the vascular stele in the stem.

Tissue culture experiments also support the concept that dividing cells provide a stimulus for vascular differentiation. Usually such cultures contain random, scattered tracheids, vessels, and sieve tube elements. If a bud is grafted onto the tissue culture, cells in the culture differentiate to produce vascular elements in a somewhat more organized way. As Fig. 22-12 indicates, the organization is far from perfect, but there is a tendency to form a vascular cylinder that can connect with the one present in the grafted bud. Auxin appeared to be the active factor from the bud, since similar results were obtained by implanting a block of agar containing auxin into such a tissue culture. More recent experiments of Ralph H. Wetmore and John P. Rier of Harvard and Howard Universities (1963) have indicated that, providing auxin is present, sugar (sucrose or glucose) *concentration* controls the formation of xylem or phloem. Low sugar results in xylem formation; high, in sieve tube (phloem) formation; and intermediate levels (2.5–3.5 percent) produced both xylem and phloem with a cambium between. Direct application of auxin and sugar to the callus surface of six species resulted in formation of a vascular nodule in the callus. High auxin (IAA or NAA) concentrations resulted in large nodules with much pith compared to those produced by low auxin concentrations. Xylem occurred toward the inside of the nodules with phloem outside. Since sugar would arrive at the meristem via the already-formed vascular elements below, while auxin is synthesized in the meristems, it is easy to see how both the meristem and the

Figure 22-12

Effects of grafting an apex of lilac into a piece of lilac callus. Note that most of the developing vascular strands tend to be scattered, but that their general orientation seems to be strongly influenced by the presence of the bud and, in one case at least, a strand in the callus has become continuous with the bud. The approximate size of the callus is about 1 cm. (From R. H. Wetmore and S. Sorokin, 1955, *J. Arnold Arboretum* 36:305–317.)

preformed stem tissue might combine to control differentiation of the stem.

Frequently, as was mentioned in the section on regeneration above, the distance from the surface appears to be important in the differentiation of xylem and other vascular elements. Oxygen or carbon dioxide concentrations in the tissue might be in control, but of course other factors could interact or even be responsible. Sugar concentration might be highest toward the outside, for example.

The cells might include a program relating to differentiation of xylem or other vascular tissues. The program might contain the following information: "If auxin, sugar, and gas concentrations are at some given level, differentiate into a xylem element. If sugar and gas concentrations are relatively high, then become a sieve tube. If surrounded on one side by a xylem element and on the other by a phloem element or if sugar and gas concentrations are intermediate, then remain a meristematic cambial cell."

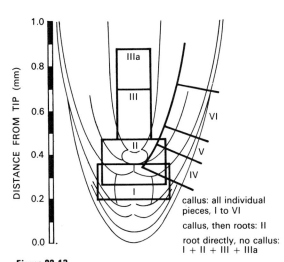

Figure 22-13

Schematic illustration of a root meristem, showing the sections removed and cultured by Reinhard (1954). Results are indicated at the lower right. The combined sections, including areas I, II, III, and IIIa, continue to grow directly into a root.

22.4.2 Is the Organized Apex Totipotent?

We have already indicated and will discuss again below the evidence for the totipotency of individual cells, including embryonic ones such as those in the meristem. But what about the organized meristem itself? Can it, without losing its organization, regenerate an entire plant?

The reconstitution of a meristem after isolation by vertical incisions indicated that this might be expected. There was always a connection with the plant, however, so this experiment was not conclusive. A more direct approach was to attempt to grow isolated meristems on artificial nutrient media. If the meristem would grow into an organized stem, then totipotency was demonstrated. If only a callus was produced, then totipotency must be absent. In 1948, Ernest Ball showed with *Lupinus albus* that such an isolated meristem

was totipotent. He even found that small pie-shaped sections of the meristem regenerated an entire shoot with its adventitious roots, thus forming an entire plant. Since these pioneering experiments, several other workers have succeeded with several other species. Nutrients are always important in such experiments, since the isolated meristems will not grow without them, but in some cases only the inorganic nutrients (and often sugar) were required. In other cases success of the experiment depended upon the presence of certain special substances, such as leaf extracts or coconut milk.

Success with isolated root tips was somewhat slower in coming. Initial studies seemed to indicate that unless some differentiated tissue were included in the meristem explant, only a growth of callus would result. John Torrey at Harvard University in 1954 and E. Reinhard in Germany in the same year were finally able to obtain mature roots by culturing only a very small portion of the root meristems that contained no fully differentiated cells. The complete organization of the root apical *meristem* did have to be present, however (Fig. 22-13). If the piece of root was too small, then it would grow into callus, but roots would subsequently be regenerated from this callus. In Reinhard's experiment, the sterile nutrient agar medium contained sucrose, the macronutrient salts, thiamine, cysteine, and IAA.

In considering the importance in differentiation of the meristem versus the already differentiated tissue, we must always conclude that both are important, since the meristems produce the differentiated tissues, and these, in turn, produce nutrients for the meristems. These experiments seem to indicate, however, that the role of the already-differentiated tissues is *only* the production of nutrients, and that *organization* of these tissues is not essential for further differentiation of cells produced by the meristems.

Leaf primordia, by proper surgical experiments, can be shown to be **multipotent**. That is, a leaf primordium, once formed, will not grow directly into an entire shoot system (it is not totipotent), but it will grow into several different kinds of leaves (various shapes, bracts, etc.).

The cells produced by root or shoot meristems must be acting under the directions of the stem or root information subprograms. Subroutines to these subprograms must include organization into the meristem, the formation of leaf primordia, the differentiation of the vascular cylinder, and other functions of developing roots and shoots. Maintenance of the program in the meristems depends upon nutrients coming from the body of the plant (sugars, minerals, and possibly special vitamin-like substances, depending upon the species). If the suitable nutrient supply is available, then the program operates and its totipotency is manifested, both in roots and in shoots.

22.5 CYTOCHEMISTRY AS A RESEARCH TOOL

Using micromethods, the concentration and localization of various metabolites and other substances may be directly observed in developing meristems, and the results may tell us something about the biochemistry of differentiation.

22.5.1 Quantitative Histochemistry

Toward the end of the 1940s, Kay Linderstrom-Lang and Heinz Holter in Copenhagen, Denmark, developed methods to analyze extremely small pieces of tissue. These methods were further developed by William Jensen, now at the University of California in Berkeley. The rationale was essentially as follows: in the root tip, the regions of division, elongation, and differentiation are usually sufficiently distinct to justify a biochemical analysis of sequential cross sections. Known methods of biochemical

analysis were adapted by many special techniques to allow their operation on a microscale. It is important to preserve the substances within the tissues in which they exist, so the root tip is frozen at the temperature of liquid nitrogen and then dehydrated under vacuum. In this dry condition, materials are much less likely to migrate within the tissues or to be changed. After embedding the root tip in paraffin, it is cut into cross sections (e.g., 100μ thick) on a microtome, and these are placed in small tubes. After removal of the paraffin, substances such as the nucleic acids may be extracted by standard techniques, using micropipettes and microburettes. The ultraviolet absorption of these solutions may then be determined with a special microattachment on a standard spectrophotometer, indicating the nucleic acid concentrations. Essential to this analysis is a detailed anatomical study of the root to reveal, among other things, the number of cells in each section. It is then possible to express the amounts of substances such as DNA on a per-cell basis.

The results of such an analysis for DNA in onion root tips are shown in Fig. 22-14, along with the percent of the cells in each section that were dividing when the sections were made. The DNA increases at first, since chromosomes are being duplicated for cell division, but there is another such increase *after* cell division has nearly ceased. This proves to be an increase in the chromosome number within differentiating cells, a phenomenon previously described by various workers. This development of **cellular polyploidy** may, as we shall see later, be correlated with cellular differentiation.[3]

Many other substances besides DNA have been studied by micromethods. These include RNA, total proteins, many of the cell wall

---

[3] The polyploid cells are apparently unable to give rise to secondary roots, according to observations of John Torrey. Application of kinetin induces these cells to divide, reducing their ploidy level.

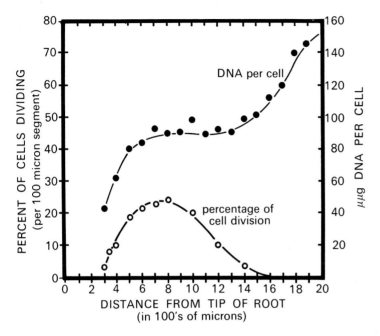

Figure 22-14

The amount of DNA per cell as measured in consecutive 100-micron segments of the onion root tip. Also plotted on the graph is the percentage of cell divisions per 100-micron segment. (From W. A. Jensen, 1966. In W. A. Jensen and L. Kavaljian (eds.), *Plant Biology Today*, Wadsworth Publishing Company, Inc., Belmont, California. Used by permission.)

components, certain enzymes, and other materials. In spite of the interesting information yielded by the method, it is limited by its level of operation. Overlap in the zones is the principal limitation, and in a stem meristem the zonation that exists is concentric, so that such an approach is virtually impossible. Figure 22-15 illustrates the complexity of the problem even in roots. The organized meristem is really a highly complex system, and a cross section is far from homogeneous.

22.5.2 Microscopic Histochemical Methods

The approach used to overcome the above problem is to localize materials within the individual cells. Again, many special techniques have been developed. The traditional histological stains are important, because they indicate the nature of the cellular constituents that absorb them. Freeze drying of the tissue prior to staining is especially important to restrict the movement of cellular materials. It has been possible to utilize radioactive tracers (primarily tritium) at the micro level. An unexposed, liquid photographic emulsion is poured onto the slide over the tissue section containing the radioactive tracer. It gels there, and as the radioactive atoms disintegrate, some of the grains in the emulsion are exposed. These can be developed, and the location of a radioactive particle determined by tracing the line of silver grains back to their origin at some point within the cell.

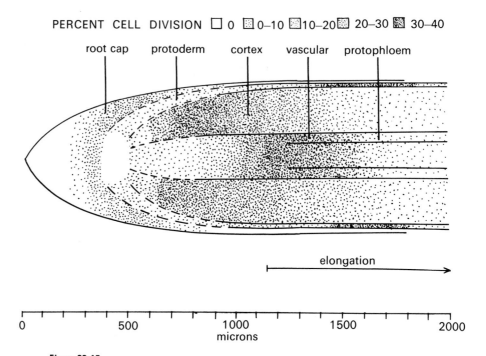

PERCENT CELL DIVISION ☐ 0 ▨ 0–10 ▨ 10–20 ▨ 20–30 ▨ 30–40

root cap   protoderm   cortex   vascular   protophloem

elongation

0   500   1000   1500   2000
                        microns

Figure 22-15
The distribution of mitotic figures in the root, showing the absence of divisions in the region
of the apical meristems. (From W. A. Jensen, 1966. In W. A. Jensen and L. Kavaljian (eds.),
Plant Biology Today, Wadsworth Publishing Company, Inc., Belmont, California. Based on
data from "An analysis of cell morphology and the periodicity of division in the root tip of
Allium cepa," *Amer. Jour. Bot.* 45:370, 1958. Used by permission.)

Let us consider the results of microscopic histochemical studies relating to DNA as they compare to those obtained by quantitative histochemical methods. The Feulgen stain reacts very specifically with DNA, and thus the quantity of DNA at any point within the cell can be approximated by measuring the intensity of this stain with a microspectrophotometer. The incorporation of tritiated thymidine into DNA has also been utilized as a measure of DNA synthesis.

One of the most striking findings of this approach was the quiescence of the apical initials in the root meristem. Figure 22-15 indicates the distribution of mitotic figures, and the synthesis of DNA as shown by tritiated thymidine incorporation produces the same kind of picture. There is virtually no DNA synthesis in the large apical initial cells. Other studies indicate that they synthesize almost no RNA or protein, either. The role of these cells in normal development of the root is yet to be determined, but it is known that they are less sensitive to injury than other meristematic cells, providing perhaps a source of regeneration following such injury.

DNA in the cortex cells was found to follow the pattern of polyploidy development determined by quantitative histochemical techniques (Fig. 22-14). It is reasonable that these latter methods would· indicate primarily the contribution of cortex cells, since they make up the main volume of the root. In the epidermis, however, no polyploidy has been found to develop during the period of differentiation. In the vascular tissue the development of polyploidy is even more extensive than in the cortex. Clearly then, when the microscopic histochemical methods can be applied, they are superior to the quantitative histochemical techniques in providing us with detailed information about differentiation. Unfortunately, they cannot yet be used for study of many substances, such as amino acids or most enzymes.

It is an important observation that even in individual cells DNA increases, and this increase is correlated with differentiation. This may well be related to the observation of Nitsan and Lang (21.10.2) that cell elongation is dependent upon DNA synthesis.

22.5.3 Development of Specific Cell Types

These methods have led to a better understanding of the differentiation of specific cell types. Two examples are of interest. *First*, lignin is an important component of xylem cells, and as these cells begin to develop there is a noticeable build-up in peroxidase enzymes (indicated by a histochemical color reaction). These enzymes are probably important in the formation of lignin, and they sometimes arise in response to auxin application. Following their appearance, lignin builds up strongly within the cells.

Second, Charlotte Avers studied extensively the formation of root hairs from epidermal cells. She observed early in her work that when an epidermal cell divides unequally the short daughter cell is the one that develops into a root hair. Using microscopic histochemical methods to measure such enzymes as cytochrome oxidase, succinic dehydrogenase, and acid phosphatase, she showed that this short cell is far more active metabolically than the

other cell. Although only a slight difference in size was apparent, the two daughter cells were already strongly differentiated from each other in a metabolic sense.

22.5.4 Transformation to the Reproductive Bud

An excellent example of switching to a new morphogenetic subprogram is the conversion of the vegetative apical meristem into a flower bud. As is discussed in later chapters, this is apparently controlled by the arrival of a specific substance synthesized in the leaves and referred to as florigen or the flowering hormone. There has been notable interest in application of microscopic histochemical techniques to an understanding of this transformation. Descriptive studies were required first. Certain species are known in which the transformation can be absolutely controlled by the environment. The cocklebur plant, for example, remains vegetative as long as it is not exposed to a period of darkness longer than about 8.3 hours. Exposure to one longer dark period causes formation of the flowering hormone in the leaf· and subsequent transformation of the bud to the floral state. The Japanese morning glory and a few other species are equally sensitive to night length and thus their flowering is easy to control.

L. Plantefol, R. Buvat, and H. Camefort in France proposed in the 1940s that the apical initials of the shoot tip were quiescent, as in the case of the root meristem, and that they remained quiescent until arrival of the flowering hormone, at which time they then developed into the floral bud. This group of initials was referred to as the "meristem-in-waiting" (*meristeme d'attente*). Several investigators, including Ralph Wetmore at Harvard University and a number of French and Belgian scientists (A. Nougarede, G. Bernier and others), investigated this proposal extensively. Little evidence for the meristem-in-waiting has been found, but our understanding of transformation to the reproductive state has been increased considerably. Wetmore and his coworkers found that the cells immediately below the apical initials were the first to become active upon arrival of the flowering hormone. They could detect no special role of the apical initials themselves. The French and Belgian workers described a series of stages through which the meristem must develop before flowers are formed. Unless a so-called intermediate stage is reached, transformation will not occur. In some plants this stage develops rapidly, while in others several months may be required for complete development. Exposure of the plant to the suitable environment may often hasten the development.

Based upon these descriptive studies, various workers, including particularly Earnest Gifford, of the University of California at Davis, and Jensen and his former graduate student Patrick Healey, were able to apply the microscopic histochemical approach. They showed that synthesis of RNA and proteins (especially sulfur-containing proteins) increased markedly upon arrival of the flowering hormone.

Gifford observed a clear increase in the histone proteins in the cytoplasm upon arrival of florigen. In his initial experiments there was a decrease in nuclear histones, but this finding was not substantiated by later work. Hydrolytic enzymes, such as acid phosphatase, increase rapidly upon arrival of florigen. Electron microscope studies on Japanese morning glories indicated that the number of ribosomes in the apical meristematic cells doubled within a very short interval (about 12 hours) after the assumed synthesis of the flowering hormone in the leaf. This is almost less time than was thought necessary for translocation of the hormone to the bud. A further observation that the endoplasmic reticulum exhibited marked increases in complexity in the cytoplasm within only three hours after the assumed end of florigen synthesis is even more perplexing.

The importance of these changes to flowering remains unclear, but an activation of the DNA-RNA-protein system seems to be indicated. In any case, the microhistochemical approach to an understanding of differentiation should help in our attempts to discern the details of the morphogenetic program of apical meristems.

22.6 DIFFERENTIATION AND THE CULTURE OF SINGLE CELLS

The single cell that most normally develops into a mature organism is the zygote. How special is this cell? Is its ability to produce an embryo and an entire plant due to a special information program initiated only by the union of sperm and egg? Or could the program be initiated in any cell? Current evidence seems to indicate that any cell or group of cells can be made to act like a zygote by isolating and surrounding the cell with the proper environment.

Such experiments were performed in the laboratory of F. C. Steward at Cornell University. We have alluded to them in the previous chapter in relation to the cytokinins. Steward used small explants from carrot roots. These were grown in liquid media containing the essential minerals plus an energy source, usually sucrose. In this basic medium the explants would only about double their size and then stop growing. Steward found that by the addition of coconut milk they could be made to grow much more rapidly. An 80-fold increase in size within 20 days was not uncommon. Coconut milk is a liquid endosperm, and Steward found that other liquid endosperms obtained from immature horse chestnuts, corn, bananas, and walnuts were also effective. He also demonstrated activity in extracts of plant tumors.

After several years of extractions and fractionations, the active materials in these liquid endosperms and other materials seem to fall into four general classes. *First* is a source of reduced or organic nitrogen. A mixture of amino acids is quite effective (e.g., casein hydrolyzate). *Second* is a so-called neutral fraction. This consists of certain synergists that, by themselves, have no activity but are essential to full activity of the inducers of cell division. The neutral fraction consists of sugar alcohols and myo-inositol and related alcohols. *Third* are the inducers of cell division. These include such substances as 1,3-diphenylurea and a leucoanthocyanin (a colorless anthocyanin). A compound of IAA with the sugar arabinose is also effective. (Kinetin would be in this class, although it is only slightly active in Steward's bioassay.) *Fourth* are inhibitors that may be extracted from certain tissues. Potato tubers, for example, contain a substance that appears to antagonize the effects of coconut milk. Dormant maple buds also yield an extract containing a coconut milk antagonist (abscisic acid). After their dormancy has been broken by exposure to an extended period of low temperatures (see Chapter 25), these maple bud extracts are no longer inhibitory in the carrot bioassay.

Steward suggests that the proper balance of these classes of substances (and probably others, such as the auxins and gibberellins) may be controlling in normal plant growth. Such substances are apparently essential to the normal growth of the zygote and the embryo, and they may be produced by the endosperm. When the cell division inducers are at a high level, embryonic growth may even be induced in already-differentiated cells (**dedifferentiation**). An overbalance of such promoters may cause the development of tumors. This might come about in response to certain environmental factors, such as the presence of the tumor-inducing bacteria (*Agrobacterium tumefacians*) effective in the formation of crown gall tumors. Normal differentiation and maturity (even

Figure 22-16
Rotated nipple flasks used in tissue culture. (Photograph courtesy of F. C. Steward and New York State College of Agriculture, Cornell University, Ithaca, New York.)

senescence) may come about as the inhibitors build up to a point where they overbalance the effect of the promoters. We might think of the cellular subprograms as responding to these chemical factors.

Steward hoped to make his system more efficient by using large nipple flasks (Fig. 22-16) rather than individual flasks as in his earlier work. The flasks were rotated, and the rate of rotation, the degree of aeration, and perhaps the clinostat effect combined with gentle washing were apparently all exactly suitable for the production of individual cells. His culture medium became milky as single cells were gently washed off the tissue cultures. He could then grow the cells of higher plants much as bacteria may be cultured.

Microscopic examination indicated that the cells in his cultures grew in several ways. Some cells were apparently haploid; others were triploid or exhibited various levels of ploidy, being in some cases giant polyploids with many nuclei. In these giant cells, protoplasmic streaming was quite evident. Sometimes the cells developed tubular outgrowths that finally became filaments resembling certain algal cells. Occasionally certain cells would bud in a manner similar to yeast cells.

Steward reports that when these various kinds of single cells were removed from the rotating flasks, certain ones began to grow like young carrot embryos, exhibiting the polarity of the root and shoot ends. These cells were always diploid. The entire course of development was very much like that observable in growth of the normal embryo, and eventually an entire, completely normal-appearing plant was the result. Steward suggested that when a single cell was removed from direct contact with its neighbors and placed in a proper nutrient environment, it acted like an embryo. Indeed, a normal embryo might be broken down into a number of single cells, and each of these would in turn act like a zygote and grow into an embryo. Approximately 100,000 embryoids were produced from a single embryo

in this manner! Since Steward's initial discovery with carrot cells, similar demonstrations have been made with several other species and by several investigators. J. Reinert in Germany has been especially active in this field, as have investigators at the Institute of Plant Physiology in Moscow and at the University of Wisconsin.

So it appears that to reinitiate the zygote subprogram in an already differentiated cell, two things must be accomplished: *First*, the cell must be separated from its neighbors. Steward suggested that removing the protoplasmic connections between the cells, the plasmodesmata, is especially important in this respect. When they are broken, a cell is ready to act like a zygote, providing the *second* condition is met; namely, the availability of the proper environment, especially the nutrient environment. In more recent work in Steward's laboratory, the proper sequence of utilization of substances in this environment has been partially solved.

Several problems remain to be clarified. Some workers (notably Walter Halperin, then at the University of California at Berkeley) have suggested that the embryos arise from clumps of cells much more readily than from single cells, and that the coconut milk factors are not essential to such development. In any case, it appears to be possible by some manner other than union of sperm and egg nuclei to reinitiate the zygote program, even in already-differentiated cells. Hopefully, future research can accurately define the requirements.

23

Photomorphogenesis

Growth and development of plants are influenced by a number of environmental factors, including light. Water and nutrient availability, gas composition of the atmosphere, and temperature ordinarily influence growth in a quantitative way by determining the maximum attainable size of the plant. These factors do not generally influence morphogenesis, except for the effects of temperature upon flowering and dormancy. The influence of light acting through photosynthesis is similarly largely a quantitative effect.

Light causes several responses other than photosynthesis, however, and these greatly influence the course of plant development and the final plant appearance. They are photomorphogenetic responses, and many seem to provide ecological advantages to the plants in which they occur. For example, the seeds of several plants fail to germinate unless they are exposed to light. This probably helps perpetuate some species, since only a fraction of the seeds present in the soil may be disturbed and exposed to light in a given season. An unfavorable growing year might otherwise destroy all of the plants. Germination only in light also more nearly assures that the seedlings will have light to grow.

Phototropic responses of seedlings and of leaves of mature plants, which become positioned to absorb the sun's rays maximally, are also beneficial photomorphogenetic processes. Another apparent advantage occurs with dicot seedlings that germinate in darkness or in very weak light. These have poorly developed leaves and elongated stems. They are said to be **etiolated** (French, *étioler*: to grow pale or weak). Most of the substances required for their growth are used for stem elongation and are not wasted upon leaf expansion until the plants are tall enough to intercept greater amounts of sunlight. The lack of leaf growth in dicot seedlings in darkness also prevents an interference by these organs in penetration of the germinating seedling through the soil. The leaves of monocot seedlings also do not usually expand appreciably until they reach the soil level and the elongation of the coleoptile that encloses them ceases. Figure 23-1 compares the shoots of etiolated corn and bean seedlings with those grown in light. In the dark-grown bean, note the much greater length of the stems, the absence of well-developed leaves, and the presence of the epicotyl hook. The dark-grown corn has become elongated through expansion of the first internode (the **mesocotyl**) above the endosperm.

Photomorphogenic responses are also important to older plants. Many respond to the relative lengths of day and night by forming

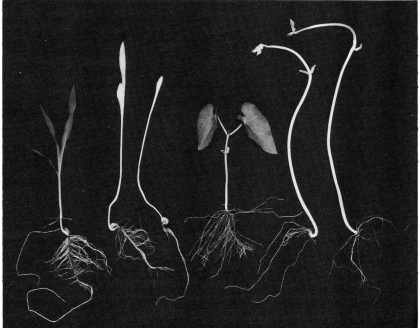

Figure 23-1

Etiolation in dicots and monocots. (top) Plants on the left were grown in the greenhouse under normal conditions, while those in the pot on the right were grown in total darkness for eight days. (bottom) The bean and corn plants shown in the top of the figure have been removed from the soil and placed on a black background, where differences in root development also become apparent. Note in the etiolated plants: pale color, elongated stems, reduced leaves, reduced root systems, and hooks on bean seedlings. (Photographs by F. B. Salisbury.)

reproductive structures or by forming dormant buds that can resist a cold winter (Chapters 25 and 26). With the exception of the process of phototropism, where it was known that blue and violet rays were most effective, almost no research into the colors of light causing photomorphogenic responses had been undertaken until the 1930s. It was commonly assumed that the phototropically active light and the red and blue wavelengths causing photosynthesis were responsible for all photomorphogenetic processes. Since then, we have discovered that at least one other pigment is involved, and that it causes inductive effects that greatly influence the direction of plant development. In this respect it is similar to the phototropic pigment system that causes a response only after an inductive time lag, but it is different from protochlorophyll and chlorophyll, which lead to rather immediate effects when irradiated.

Several of the results of activating this new pigment, named **phytochrome**, are summarized in Table 23-1, along with some effects brought about by other known photoactive pigments in plants. The most effective colors are also given. In this chapter, the individual processes caused by irradiation (except for chlorophyll formation, photosynthesis, photoperiodism, and phototaxis mentioned in other chapters) will be discussed in detail. Studies of the effects of light on living organisms constitute the field of **photobiology**.

23.1 PHOTOTROPISM

The bending of plant organs toward light is known as **phototropism**. The bending is caused by a more rapid growth of cells on the shaded than on the illuminated side. The experiments of Frits Went and other European scientists discussed in Chapter 21 showed that in the case of grass coleoptiles the effective light is absorbed by the tip, and this somehow causes more auxin to be accumulated in the shaded side than in the

side absorbing the light. This auxin then diffuses polarly down through the shaded parenchyma cells of the coleoptile and causes these to expand. The resulting more rapid growth in that side is directly responsible for the bending process.

This interesting phenomenon has been studied intensively. Early workers such as A. H. Blaauw in Holland (1909) were aware that blue light was most effective and that red was inactive in causing phototropism, but a good action spectrum was first measured by F. Bachmann and F. Bergann in 1930. The effectiveness of blue light suggested that a yellow pigment, probably either a carotenoid or a riboflavin-containing compound, was the active agent involved. In the late 1950s and early 1960s, the action spectrum was carefully refined (Fig. 23-2), especially in the ultraviolet part of the spectrum, and this was compared with the absorption spectra of certain carotenoids and flavins known to exist in coleoptiles. The two peaks in the visible part of the spectrum approximately match those of the carotenoids, but the peak in the ultraviolet corresponds to that of riboflavin. One must remember, however, that the absorption spectrum of pigments *in vitro* is often somewhat different than *in vivo* (Chapter 13). On the basis of the data, one pigment cannot be chosen over the other, and it is possible that both take part.

Arthur Galston and his colleagues found that blue light absorbed by a solution of riboflavin and IAA caused the destruction of this auxin, and they suggested that this destruction also occurred in the lighted side of coleoptile tips. However, more recent work by K. V. Thimann and by Winslow Briggs confirmed the suggestions of Went that a true redistribution of auxin is involved and not just a light-catalyzed destruction. Some results of Briggs showing that just as much auxin can be collected from coleoptile tips exposed to light as from those kept in darkness appear in Fig. 23-3. Thimann

TABLE 23-1

SOME PHOTOMORPHOGENETIC PROCESSES, PROBABLE PHOTORECEPTORS, AND EFFECTIVE COLORS OF LIGHT INVOLVED[a]

Process	Photoreceptor	Effective colors	Reference example
phototropism	carotenoid or flavin?	blue	Briggs, W. *Plant Physiol.* 38:237, 1963.
photoreactivation	unknown	blue	Mellor, R. and F. Salisbury, *Plant Physiol.* 40:506, 1965.
polar differentiation of rhizoids in germinating spores	unknown	blue	Haupt, W. *Planta.* 49:61, 1957.
conversion of fern protonemata into prothallia	riboflavin?	blue	Mohr, H. *Biol. Rev.* 39:87, 1964. Yeoh, O. and V. Raghavan. *Plant Physiol.* 41: 1739, 1966.
anthocyanin production in milo (*Sorghum vulgare*) seedlings	unknown	blue	Downs, R. and H. Siegelman, *Plant Physiol.* 38:25, 1963.
stimulation of cytoplasmic streaming	chlorophyll?	blue and red	Virgin, H. In *Photophysiology*, A. C. Giese, ed. Academic Press, 1964, p. 299.
phototaxis of chloroplasts	unknown	blue and sometimes red	ibid.
phototaxis of the chloroplast of the alga *Mougeotia*	phytochrome	red	Haupt, W. *Planta.* 53:484, 1959.
seed germination	phytochrome	red	Borthwick, H. et al. *Proc. Natl. Acad. Sci.* 38:662, 1952.
fern spore germination	phytochrome	red	Mohr, H. *Planta.* 46:534, 1956.
dicot leaf growth	phytochrome	red	Downs, R. *Plant Physiol.* 30:468, 1955.
inhibition of stem and of grass mesocotyl elongation	phytochrome	red	Downs, R. et al. *Botan. Gazette* 118:199, 1957.
rapid stimulation of closing (turgor change) of *Albizzia* and *Mimosa* leaflets	phytochrome	red	Hillman, W. and W. L. Koukkari, *Plant Physiol.* 42:1413, 1967 and J. Fondeville, et al. *Planta* 75:228, 1967.
temporary stimulation of grass coleoptile elongation	phytochrome	red	Hopkins, W. and W. Hillman, *Planta* 65:157, 1965.
hypocotyl or plumular hook opening in some dicot seedlings	phytochrome	red	Withrow, R. et al *Plant Physiol.* 32:453, 1957.
unfolding of leaves of grass seedlings	phytochrome	red	Virgin, H. *Physiologia Plantarum* 15:380, 1962.
elongation of fern rhizoids	phytochrome	red	Miller, J. H. and Pauline Miller, *Plant Cell Physiol.* 4:65, 1963.
chloroplast replication (division)	phytochrome	red	Hahn, L. and J. H. Miller, *Physiologia Plantarum* 19:134, 1966.
initiation and differentiation of dicot leaves	phytochrome	red	Mohr, H. *Photochem. Photobiol.* 5:469, 1966.
anthocyanin formation	phytochrome	red	Downs, R. and H. Siegelman, *Plant Physiol.* 38:25, 1963.
inhibition of flowering of short-day plants	phytochrome	red	Borthwick, H. et al. *Proc. Natl. Acad. Sci.* 38:929, 1952.
stimulation of flowering of long-day plants	phytochrome	red	Downs, R. *Plant. Physiol.* 31:279, 1956.
formation of palisade layers in leaves	unknown	unknown	Watson, R. *New Phytologist* 41:206, 1942.
inhibition of hypocotyl elongation	unknown	blue, far-red	Evans, L. et al. *Planta* 64:201, 1965.
anthocyanin production	unknown	blue, red, far-red	Hendricks, S. and H. Borthwick, *Botan. Gazette* 120:187, 1959.
opening of *Mimosa* pinnae	unknown	blue, far-red	Fondeville, J. et al. *Planta* 75:228, 1967.
control of flowering in *Hyoscyamus*	unknown	blue, far-red	Schneider et al. *Amer. J. Bot.* 54:1241, 1967.
opening of plumular hook of lettuce seedlings	unknown	blue, far-red	Mohr, H. and A. Noble, *Planta* 55:327, 1960.

[a] For some other responses, see Fig. 23–13.

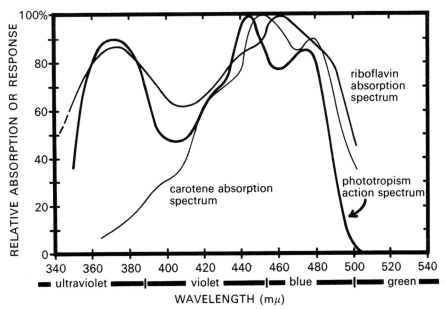

Figure 23-2

The action spectrum for phototropism and the absorption spectra of riboflavin and carotene. Note that the absorption spectrum of carotene matches the action spectrum quite well in the visible part of the spectrum (slight shifting of the peaks often occurs upon extraction with special solvents) but fails to account for the peak in the ultraviolet—a peak nicely accounted for by riboflavin, which has only a poor match of peaks in the visible portion of the spectrum. (From W. Shropshire, Jr., 1958, *Plant Physiol.* 33: 360–365.)

has repeatedly indicated that a carotenoid is the probable receptive pigment, but a final choice cannot yet be made. We know little about how light absorption could cause the lateral redistribution of auxin.

Even before the action spectrum was studied, workers had investigated the quantitative problems of phototropism. To begin with, the picture is complicated considerably by the fact that curvature is not always increased by increasing light exposure. Above a certain exposure level, *less* curvature occurs, and the coleoptiles sometimes even bend in the opposite direction so that there is a *negative* **curvature** (away from the light), followed by a **second positive curvature** at still higher levels. Figure 23-4 shows curvature of coleoptiles as a function of the logarithm of exposure.

Curves such as those in Fig. 23-4 involve an assumption that the response follows the so-called **reciprocity law**, which states that as long as the product of light intensity and exposure time (the total energy applied) remains constant, the photochemical effect of the light should also remain constant. In photography, constant exposure is achieved when exposure time is shortened by increasing the lens opening to allow more light to pass through. The problem of reciprocity in phototropism was investigated by P. Fröschel in 1908 and by Blaauw in 1909. They found the law to be valid for the first positive curvature over an enormous range of intensity-time combinations. Others had found the negative curvature and second positive curvature not to obey reciprocity.

In recent years, Winslow Briggs at Stanford

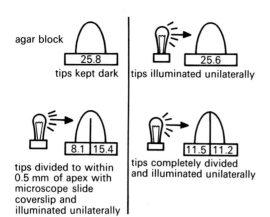

agar block

25.8

tips kept dark

25.6

tips illuminated unilaterally

8.1 | 15.4

tips divided to within
0.5 mm of apex with
microscope slide
coverslip and
illuminated unilaterally

11.5 | 11.2

tips completely divided
and illuminated unilaterally

Figure 23-3

Experiments showing that unilateral illumination of corn coleoptile tips leads to a transport of auxin from the illuminated to the shaded side of the tips and does not cause a destruction of auxin. Numbers on the agar blocks represent the degrees of curvature caused by application of the blocks to decapitated oat coleoptile stumps. In the partially split tips, part of the auxin was transported laterally above the dividing barrier, but in the completely split tips this was not possible. (After W. R. Briggs, 1963, *Plant Physiol.* 38:241. Used by permission.)

University, using oat and corn coleoptiles, reinvestigated the entire problem, particularly the negative and second positive curvature. His work is supported by that of various other investigators, and representative results are indicated in Fig. 23-4. Reciprocity holds for the first positive and negative curvatures but fails for the second positive curvature except at high intensities and short exposure times. The exposure time is more important, and by making certain assumptions, curvature could be accounted for on the basis of exposure time independent of intensity. Furthermore, blue light-stimulated curvatures beyond the first positive were found to be strongly influenced by previous exposure to red light. The sensitivity of the systems resulting in the first positive and the negative curvatures were greatly reduced by previous exposure to red light, but the sensitivity

of the system controlling second positive curvature was increased considerably by red light.

The stems of green plants also exhibit phototropism, and the shoot apex is thought to respond in the same way that coleoptiles do. The leaves are also involved in the process, though, since their removal greatly reduces the phototropic curvature. Shue-Lock Lam and A. Carl Leopold at Purdue University studied the role of leaves in phototropism of sunflower seedlings. Sunflower plants normally turn toward the east in the morning and to the west in the evening of sunny days. They found that if only the stems were exposed to unilateral light, bending did not occur, but if one of the two cotyledons was shaded, the stem bent in the direction of that receiving the greatest amount of light (Fig. 23-5). It was shown that this phototropism was probably due to a greater transport of an auxin to the stem from the shaded than from the well-illuminated cotyledon. This difference in auxin supply from the two cotyledons presumably caused the difference in growth rate in the two sides of the stem. Perhaps phototropism in stems of green plants is then due primarily to inhibitory effects of light on auxin production in the leaves closer to the sun, or to a greater auxin transport from shaded leaves, although the stem normally does show some response by itself. We assume that the blue rays are most effective as in the case of coleoptiles, although the action spectrum in the case of green plants has not yet been studied.

23.2 DISCOVERY AND PROPERTIES OF PHYTOCHROME—THE RED, FAR-RED PIGMENT SYSTEM

23.2.1 Early Physiological Experiments

In 1934 it was found at the United States Department of Agriculture Research Station in Beltsville, Maryland, that red light stimulated the germination of lettuce seeds. Three years

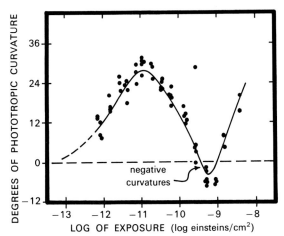

Figure 23-4

Phototropic responses (first positive, negative, and second positive curvatures) of oat coleoptiles as caused by increasing energies of blue light at 4,358 Å. Intensity was 1.4×10^{-12} einsteins/cm²/sec, and exposure times varied to give the total exposures indicated along the abscissa. (From B. K. Zimmerman and W. R. Briggs, 1963, *Plant Physiol.* 38:248. Used by permission.)

later in a careful study by L. H. Flint and E. D. McAlister, in Washington, D.C., it was found that blue and far-red wavelengths were inhibitory. Far-red includes those wavelengths just longer than the red, covering approximately the range 700 to 800 mμ. (Those longer than about 760 mμ are invisible to humans and are, therefore, actually infra-red.) It was known that certain plants flower in response to long dark periods (see Chapters 24 and 27). In 1938 it was shown by Karl Hamner and James Bonner at the University of Chicago that a light interruption of such long nights prevented short-day plants from flowering. Researchers in Beltsville began attempts to discover the most effective wavelengths for these effects in 1944.

To determine an action spectrum adequately, it was necessary to build a large spectrograph which would break up a brilliant beam of white light produced by a large carbon arc into the individual component wavelengths. Various plants were then exposed in different experiments to uniform intensities of the different colors. M. W. Parker, H. Borthwick, S. B. Hendricks, and N. Scully found red light of about 670 mμ to be most inhibitory when interrupting long nights otherwise capable of inducing short-day cockleburs and Biloxi soybeans to flower, and to be most effective for causing normal growth of pea leaves. An energy level of 3×10^4 ergs/cm² was enough to cause a detectable inhibition of flowering. This is an energy equivalent to applying an intensity only about 1/2,000 that of full sunlight for one minute.[1] Calculations show that these energy levels could activate only a small portion of the already dilute pigment molecules present and indicate that the light effects must be greatly amplified to cause the observed results. These and other facts suggest that the pigment is an enzyme.

The same red light was also most effective in *stimulating* flowering of Wintex barley and other long-day plants when used to interrupt nights that were otherwise too long. (The response of long-day plants is exactly opposite to that of short-day plants.) Collaborating with E. H. Toole and other plant physiologists interested in seed germination, the Beltsville group discovered that many light-requiring seeds germinated best under red wavelengths and then, in 1952, that these effects were reversed by immediately following the red treatment with far-red (maximum effectiveness near 730 mμ). By repeatedly alternating red and far-red treatments, they found that the light applied last determined whether the seeds germinated or not, red promoting and far-red inhibiting the promotion by red.

It was immediately shown that the influences upon flowering were similarly reversible, and it was concluded that a blue pigment capable

---

[1] Full sunlight on a June day at sea level is near 8,000 foot-candles, 1.4 cal/cm²/min, or 5.9×10^7 ergs/cm²/min, which are equivalent to approximately 100,000 μwatts/cm².

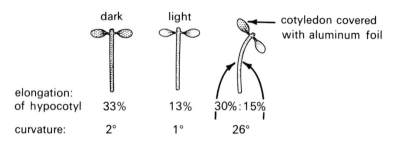

Figure 23-5

Effect of shading on growth and phototropism in sunflower seedlings. The seedling kept in darkness (left) did not bend appreciably but did elongate 33 percent in a 24-hour period. The seedling kept in light did not bend and elongated less than half as much as the one in darkness. The seedling on the right exhibited phototropism. The side below the darkened cotyledon elongated almost as well as the seedling in darkness, while the side below the illuminated cotyledon elongated about the same as did the hypocotyl of the seedling exposed to light. (Data of S. Lam and A. C. Leopold, 1966, *Plant Physiol.* 41:847. Used by permission.)

of existing in two interconvertible forms existed in plants. One form was thought to absorb red light and to be changed into a form of a slightly different color, which was then capable of absorbing mostly far-red. The far-red-absorbing form was believed to be changed back to the red-absorbing pigment as it absorbed far-red light. The form produced by red light was apparently the active one, promoting seed germination and influencing flower formation, while the other form was inactive or active only in certain cases. This interpretation, which proved correct, explains the reversible influences of these colors upon germination and flowering and also upon a large number of other physiological responses.

23.2.2 Demonstration, Separation, and Properties of Phytochrome

Attempts to demonstrate directly the presence of this pigment in plants and to extract it from them soon began. The problem was a difficult one because the pigment is very dilute in plant tissues, while similar, interfering pigments such as chlorophyll are often present in large quanti-

ties. Measurement is also difficult because passing a beam of red light through the sample to measure the amount of pigment that absorbs it converts the pigment to a form that does not absorb it nearly as well. The same is true for a beam of far-red light. Finally, in 1959, K. H. Norris, an engineer; W. L. Butler, a biophysicist; S. E. Hendricks, a chemist; and H. W. Siegelman, a plant physiologist, attacked the problem at Beltsville. These scientists realized that phytochrome could be detected by taking advantage of its reversible absorbance by red and far-red light. They employed a special spectrophotometer to solve the problems. This instrument was capable of measuring very slight differences in absorption in very dense samples (e.g., a two-inch piece of pine wood!), so they could use whole tissues of corn or certain other plants. These plants were grown in darkness so that chlorophyll could not interfere. Absorption of two low-intensity beams of light, one red and one far-red alternating with each other several times a second, was measured. If the sample had been previously irradiated with intense red light, absorption of the red beam was low compared to that of the far-red beam,

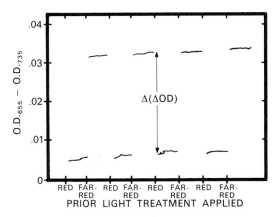

Figure 23-6

Influence of red and far-red light treatments upon subsequent absorption of these wavelengths by a phytochrome-containing solution extracted from corn shoots. After red exposure (e.g., as shown near origin), the absorption of red light at 655 mμ is very low compared to the absorption of far-red at 735 mμ. However, after a far-red treatment, the absorption of red light compared to that of far-red increases greatly, since the far-red treatment converts phytochrome into the red-absorbing form. (From W. L. Butler et al., 1959, *Proc. Natl. Acad. Sci.*, 45:1703. Used by permission.)

and vice-versa if the sample had previously been irradiated with intense far-red light. The differences in absorption (optical density, or O.D.) that they observed in extracts from shoots of corn seedlings after successively irradiating the extracts with strong red and far-red light are shown in Fig. 23-6.

Further evidence that such a photoreversible pigment exists even in green plants was thus obtained by this differential spectrophotometric technique. The quantities of the pigment present are indicated by (can be calculated from) the difference in height between the upper and lower lines shown in graphs like Fig. 23-6. This difference is referred to as the $\Delta(\Delta O.D.)$, which equals $(O.D._{670\,m\mu} - O.D._{730\,m\mu})$ after far-red irradiation minus $(O.D._{670\,m\mu} - O.D._{730\,m\mu})$ after red irradiation. Assuming that the far-red-absorbing form of the pigment might be an enzyme, they attempted to remove and

purify it using techniques of protein separations (Chapter 11). Initial success came in 1959, and the pigment was then named **phytochrome**.

The red-absorbing form of phytochrome proved to be blue-green, and the far-red-absorbing form, light-green colored. In 1966, it was reported that the chromophoric group giving the protein the two colors is an open-chain tetrapyrrole pigment similar to the phycobilin **allophycocyanin**. It is not yet known what reversible changes occur in the chromophoric group upon irradiation. The protein itself was highly purified from oat seedlings by F. E. Mumford and E. L. Jenner at Wilmington, Delaware, who measured its molecular weight to be about 60,000 g/mole. It probably contained no essential metals, although traces of copper and aluminum were associated with it, likely as contaminants. Whether the protein contains more than one polypeptide chain and whether it can undergo allosteric transitions as the chromophoric group is changed by light is an interesting problem, since these properties could be important in its function. There is some evidence that the protein of *Secale* (rye) is composed of monomeric chains with molecular weights of about 36,000.

The absorption spectrum of each form of phytochrome is compared with action spectra for certain physiological responses in Fig. 23-7. Remembering that small shifts in the absorption spectra can result when pigments are removed from the compounds with which they are associated in plant cells, excellent agreement between the absorption by phytochrome and the action spectra for these reactions is seen. Principal absorption maxima occur in the red and the far-red portions of the spectrum, and both forms have a weaker absorption peak in the blue-violet. Both absorb in the ultraviolet, but this is probably due to absorption by the tyrosine, phenylalanine, and tryptophan in the protein and not to the chromophoric group. The two are interconvertible even when a

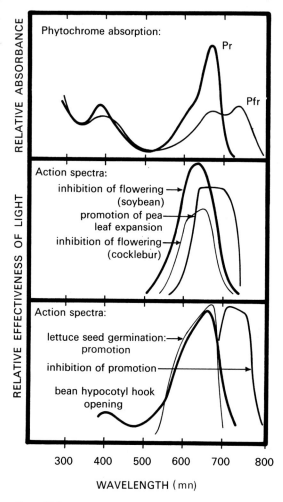

Figure 23-7

A comparison of the absorption spectrum of both forms of phytochrome with action spectra for various physiological processes. (Absorption spectra for Pr and Pfr purified from oats are data of W. L. Butler et al., 1965. In T. W. Goodwin (ed.), *Chemistry and Biochemistry of Plant Pigments,* Academic Press, New York, p. 203. Action spectra shown in the middle graph were redrawn from data of M. W. Parker et al., 1949, *Amer. J. Bot.* 36:194. Action spectra for promotion of bean hypocotyl hook opening shown in the lower graph were redrawn from R. B. Withrow et al., 1957, *Plant Physiol.* 32:453. Action spectra for stimulation and subsequent inhibition of lettuce seed (Grand Rapids variety) were redrawn from data of S. B. Hendricks, 1960, *Comparative Biochemistry of Photoreactive Systems,* Academic Press, New York, p. 307. All data were used by permission.)

partially purified solution of phytochrome is illuminated:

$$ \text{Pr} \underset{\text{far-red (730 } nm)}{\overset{\text{red (660 } nm)}{\rightleftharpoons}} \text{Pfr} $$

Pr and Pfr represent the red- and far-red-absorbing forms, respectively.

When both wavelengths strike the pigment system simultaneously, as when sunlight or an artificial white light source is used, an equilibrium is reached in which both pigments are present. The ratio of the two forms produced depends upon the intensity of each wavelength, the extent to which it is absorbed by each (absorption constant), and the extent to which the molecules absorbing the light can react (quantum yield). The absorption constant and the quantum yield for Pr were each estimated to be about 1.5 times as high as for Pfr; so Pr is converted to Pfr nearly 2.3 fold (1.5×1.5) as easily by 660 mμ radiation as the reverse occurs when Pfr is illuminated at 730 mμ. Thus, even in sunlight or in incandescent light, both of which are somewhat richer in far-red, there is more Pfr than Pr present in the plant, and so white light acts primarily as a red source. This explains why sunlight, artificial light, and red light all act the same in influencing processes such as seed germination and the induction of flowering. It is thought that both Pr and Pfr occur in roughly equal amounts under blue light.

Sometimes, however, sunlight and incandescent light bulbs cause responses showing that they allow appreciable amounts of Pr to be present. For example, both sunlight and incandescent sources cause stems to become longer than does an equal energy of artificial fluorescent light, which is almost entirely lacking in far-red wavelengths (Fig. 6-12). Most growth chambers for physiological experiments therefore contain both incandescent and fluorescent bulbs, the latter being an economical source of visible light, yet with very little of the infrared wavelengths that cause overheating of the chambers.

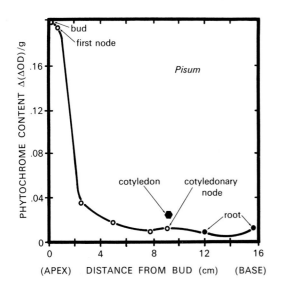

Figure 23-8

Distribution of phytochrome along the axis of pea seedlings. (From W. R. Briggs and H. W. Siegelmań, 1965, *Plant Physiol.* 40:934. Used by permission.)

The quantitative nature of the effect of the light source depends to a large extent upon the ratio of Pr to Pfr that is established, since, with sunlight or any white artificial source, both pigments are present.

Actually, both forms will be present at some ratio under constant illumination with *any* wavelength, since both forms absorb at all visible wavelengths to some extent. This is well illustrated by prolonged treatment of plants with far-red light. This sometimes causes effects identical to those of shorter treatments with red. An example is found in the flowering of short-day plants (see Fig. 26-10). Interruption of their long night with a few seconds of red light is reversed by short periods of far-red immediately following the red, but if this far-red treatment is too long, it is also inhibitory. This inhibition apparently results from the fact that the red-absorbing form, Pr, absorbs some of the shorter far-red wavelengths and is par-

tially transformed into Pfr (see Fig. 23-7). The low amounts of Pfr formed in this manner are inhibitory to flowering of short-day plants when present for long periods of time. If the illumination period is very short, the Pfr will be metabolically removed in the dark before it can be inhibitory (see below).

23.2.3 Distribution and Transformation of Phytochrome in Plants

Phytochrome is probably present in all photosynthesizing plants, with the possible exception of some of the algae. The influences of red and far-red light upon phototaxis of chloroplasts (Chapter 15) showed that it is present in certain green algae. Then, in 1967, A. O. Taylor and Bruce Bonner at the University of California at Davis isolated the pigment from the green alga *Mesotaenium caldariorum*. The absorption peaks for this phytochrome differ from those of higher plants in being shifted about 15 mμ toward the blue. Phytochrome has apparently not yet been extracted from gymnosperms, although there is physiological evidence suggesting its presence in such plants. The phytochrome content of various parts of higher plants has been compared only in dark-grown seedlings where interference due to chlorophyll is not a problem. In general, meristematic or differentiating tissues high in protein contain the largest amounts of this pigment. This is illustrated for the pea plant in Fig. 23-8. Phytochrome occurs in roots, even though the total amount in these organs is small. The greatest quantities here, as in the stems, are in the apices.

Nearly all of the phytochrome in dark-grown plants or germinating seeds is present as the Pr form. Exposure of the plants to light causes a large but incomplete conversion to Pfr accompanied by a destruction of some of the Pfr produced. This destruction goes on in both light and darkness but is more rapid in light because more Pfr is continuously produced from

Pr. In some plants (especially dicots) there is also a slow decay (reversion) of Pfr back to Pr even in darkness. The discovery and study of phytochrome has been based upon the assumption that photomorphogenetic processes are strongly influenced by phytochrome levels in the plant. Hence these reactions of phytochrome may be highly significant in plant morphogenesis.

The Pr form of phytochrome appears to be that first synthesized by developing seedlings. This synthesis seems to be inhibited by light, at least in corn seedlings. The lower total phytochrome content of seedlings grown in the light than in darkness therefore appears to be due both to a slow but continuous destruction of Pfr as it is formed in light from Pr and to an inhibition of Pr formation. The transformations of phytochrome may be summarized as follows:

$$\text{Pr} \underset{\text{far-red (730 }nm)}{\overset{\text{red (660 }nm)}{\rightleftharpoons}} \text{Pfr}$$

synthesis   metabolic destruction

dark reversion in some plants

23.3 EFFECTS OF VISIBLE LIGHT ON PLANT DEVELOPMENT

As outlined in Table 23-1, light has many morphogenetic influences upon plants distinct from photosynthesis. Some of the phytochrome responses most clearly understood will be discussed below, although detailed treatment of the role of light in photoperiodic responses is postponed until Chapter 26.

23.3.1 Growth of Dicot Leaves

In the absence of light, dicot leaves fail to develop, although grass leaves usually grow, for a time, as rapidly in darkness as in light once they break through the coleoptile. The stimulating effect of red light on leaf growth was studied in the 1940s (an action spectrum was determined), and soon after the discovery of the reversibility of red effects by far-red, the same phenomenon was demonstrated for the expansion of discs cut from dark-grown leaves.

It was reported that this expansion in response to the formation of Pfr was due primarily to increased cell division, and that the final size of the cells was not appreciably different from those kept in the dark. In intact leaves, at least of the pea, bright light causes a more rapid rate of cell division, elongation, and differentiation compared to those grown under low-intensity light. There seems, then, to be a general stimulating effect of light upon development and maturity of leaves, especially of dicots. Light has little influence upon the length of grass leaves, although it does cause them to become slightly wider. It is not known whether this is due to increased cell division, expansion, or both.

23.3.2 Unfolding of the Plumular (Epicotyl) Hook

Etiolated dicot seedlings contain a plumule (epicotyl) that is usually recurved to form a hook (Fig. 23-1). This hook (initially in the hypocotyl) readily penetrates the soil as the seed germinates but then unfolds in the presence of light. This straightening is due to an increased enlargement of the cells on the lower side of the hook and is typically controlled by the phytochrome system. Weak intensities of green and blue wavelengths have almost no effect on this process, while weak red light causes unfolding.

Not all dicots form such a hook in darkness. Hans Mohr, in Germany, found in 1960 that Grand Rapids lettuce seedlings do not normally produce an epicotyl hook but do so if phytochrome is activated with red light. This situation is therefore opposite to that with such other dicots as the pea and bean. Now if the lettuce hook formed in weak red light is exposed to high intensities of either blue or far-red radia-

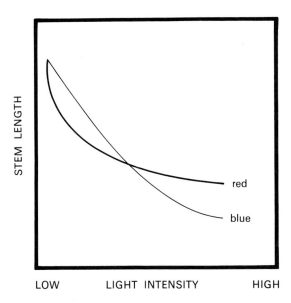

Figure 23-9
Both blue and red light are inhibitory to stem extension in some plants. At low intensities, red is often more effective, while at higher intensities blue becomes more inhibitory. (From J. A. Lockhart, 1963, *Adv. Frontiers Plant Sciences* 7:1; after G. Meijer, 1959, *Acta Botanica Neerlandica* 8:189. Used by permission.)

23.3.3 Stem Growth

Julius Sachs, in 1852, was probably the first to record observations that the stems of many species do not elongate as rapidly during the daytime as at night. Sachs correctly recognized this as a light inhibition of growth. Furthermore, grass coleoptiles do not become as long in the light as in darkness (even though their growth rate is initially faster, at least in red light); the embryonic leaves break through the coleoptile more rapidly in light, and the elongation of the mesocotyl of most grasses is retarded by light.

23.3.3A Effective wavelengths The effect of colored light upon stem growth of many dicots was investigated by Dutch plant physiologists in the early 1950s. They germinated some of the plants in sunlight and then covered the seedlings with filters transparent to only one region of the visible spectrum. High intensities of blue light were most inhibitory to elongation, while approximately equal intensities of red caused elongated plants. On the other hand, when they exposed plants previously germinated in darkness to low intensities of the same colors, the red region was most inhibitory, blue less so, and green almost without effect. Further research now seems to explain their different results. At low energies red is more inhibitory than blue light, but with greater intensities a cross-over point is reached and blue becomes more effective (Fig. 23-9).

Figure 23-9 shows that an intensity of red light can be applied which saturates the inhibition system, and further intensities then cause no more effect. With blue light the retardation of stem elongation is increasingly severe as intensities increase, suggesting that the two colors act on different pigments. Perhaps the red acts through the phytochrome system, while the blue influences either a different pigment or activates the phytochrome in a manner not yet understood. The high-intensity blue may act

tion, it reopens. The closing process in lettuce is caused by a greater expansion of cells on the top of the stem, while opening is due to enlargement of those on the lower side. In nature the lettuce seedlings are exposed to high intensity sunlight containing both blue and far-red wavelengths. These colors predominate over the red, which would tend to cause hook formation, and no hook is formed. The opposite effects of sunlight and weak red light here suggest that the blue and far-red components to which plants are exposed in nature may have far greater morphogenetic influences than does activation of phytochrome by low-intensity red radiation. It also raises the question of whether another, unknown pigment activated by blue or perhaps by far-red radiation may be present in plants. More will be said of this later.

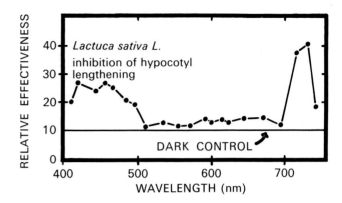

Figure 23-10

An action spectrum showing inhibitory effects of blue and far-red light upon elongation of lettuce hypocotyls. (After H. Mohr and M. Wehrung, 1960, *Planta* 55:438. Used by permission.)

through the same mechanism here as it does in the lettuce plumular hook discussed above.

Mohr found that growth of lettuce hypocotyls was barely influenced by red radiation, but high intensities of either far-red or blue were quite inhibitory (Fig. 23-10). Nearly 2.7×10^7 ergs/cm^2 (2.7 joules/cm^2) of far-red light are required to inhibit growth of the lettuce hypocotyl by 40 percent. Other plants respond most to either low-intensity red or to greater intensities of far-red or blue. Because much higher energies of these blue and far-red wavelengths are necessary than for phytochrome activation and because of other morphogenetic effects due to these colors, Mohr initially suggested that a high-energy reaction system distinct from phytochrome is present, and he abbreviated this as the **HER**. In general, energies greater than 1×10^7 ergs/cm^2 are required to cause these responses, while significant phytochrome effects can be caused by 1×10^5 ergs/cm^2 or less. Figure 23-11 summarizes a number of plant responses to various light energies.

Inhibitory effects of red light, which are reversible with far-red and thus clearly due to

the phytochrome system, can be demonstrated in stems of various etiolated dicot seedlings. Absorption of weak red light by phytochrome can also be shown to inhibit the final length of the coleoptile and mesocotyl in grass seedlings. We may conclude that either low intensities of red or much higher intensities of blue and far-red wavelengths can retard stem growth. It remains to be seen which of these is most important in causing the natural light inhibition of growth observed by Sachs. In any case, it is likely that the increased elongation of stems of many plants in the shade of a forest canopy compared to those growing in open areas may be due to a filtering out of blue and red wavelengths by the chlorophyll in the plant tissues above.

23.3.3B Interaction of the HER with phytochrome A difficulty in assessing the influence of radiation upon stem growth is that the time of day the particular color of light is applied is important. A pinto bean plant remains short when grown under high intensities of artificial fluorescent light rich in red but poor in far-red wavelengths, and if incandescent light rich in far-red is given at the same time, it becomes only

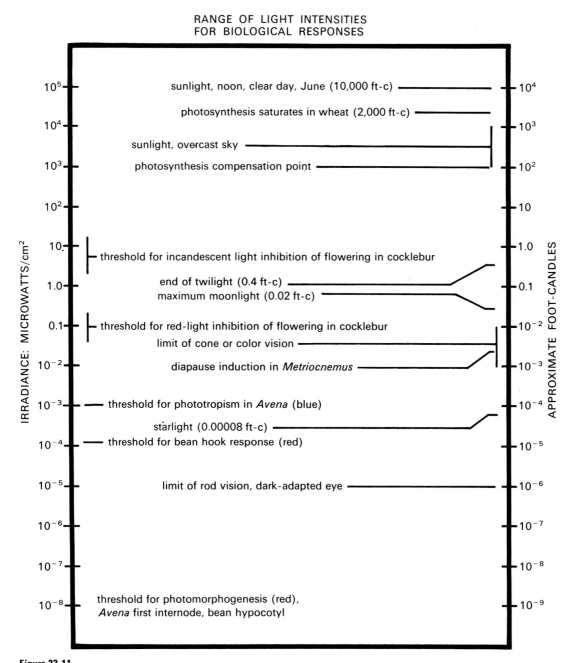

Figure 23-11

The light intensities capable of bringing about certain biological responses. Note that the range of effective light intensities extends over 13 orders of magnitude. (From F. B. Salisbury, 1963, *The Flowering Process*, Pergamon Press, Oxford, London, Paris, New York. Used by permission.)

slightly taller. If, however, as shown by R. J. Downs at Beltsville, the incandescent lights are turned on during all or the early part of what is the normal dark period, the internodes become greatly elongated. The greater length is due both to increased cell division and to increased cell expansion. This stimulation of stem elongation by weak far-red light is reversed by following with red, showing that phytochrome participates. The Dutch scientists observed that with other dicots, too, far-red applied at the end of the day results in elongated stems, and they suggested that the red light received during the day predisposes plants to elongate when subsequently irradiated with far-red just before darkness. This could also be an interaction with the circadian rhythms discussed in the next chapter, and it could be quite important to the plant in nature.

The Beltsville group found somewhat similar results with hypocotyl elongation in petunia and lettuce seedlings. Short periods of high-intensity blue or far-red wavelengths were inhibitory, although other colors, including red, had little effect. The red was strongly inhibitory, however, if applied just after the period of blue or far-red radiation. In this case the inhibition of elongation due to red was additive to the blue or far-red effects. If these high-intensity blue or far-red light periods were followed by a very brief period of far-red radiation, no inhibition of hypocotyl growth was noted. This ability of low-intensity far-red to overcome the retarding influence of high-energy blue and far-red was reversed by following the far-red treatment with a period of red, again demonstrating the importance of the phytochrome system after the HER has acted. They suggested a model to explain the fact that phytochrome is effective only after prior activation of the HER. This model, shown in Fig. 23-12 in a modified form, suggests that prior action by the HER leads to the formation of some metabolite that can be acted upon by Pfr to cause hypocotyl growth

inhibition. A dependence of action by the HER upon subsequent Pfr formation in causing dicot leaf growth and anthocyanin formation also exists, and these influences are illustrated in the model. As outlined, the model does not account for responses that can be caused by the HER alone, and it must be assumed that one or more of the metabolites formed by the HER are somehow responsible for these responses.

23.3.3C   Mechanism of light inhibition of stem growth
The way in which light retards stem elongation is not yet understood, but James Lockhart, then at the University of Hawaii, provided evidence that it reduces the effective gibberellin supply in the growing regions. *First*, in some species the application of gibberellic acid to the stems completely overcomes the inhibition caused by low-intensity red light or by the HER system. *Second*, bean plants, which normally are taller when shaded than when in full sunlight, grow taller in sunlight than in shade when treated with gibberellin. It is presumed that in sunlight the gibberellin content is low but photosynthesis is more rapid than in shade, and, if exogenous gibberellin is supplied, growth is then fastest. *Third*, plants whose stems are stimulated to elongate by shading generally also respond markedly to gibberellin, while plants whose height is not increased by shading show little response to this hormone. This correlation is best illustrated in the dwarf and normal corn varieties mentioned in Chapter 21. The height of normal corn plants is not appreciably increased by shading or by adding gibberellin, while the dwarf plants grow taller with either treatment. *Fourth*, light reduces cell wall plasticity, while gibberellin prevents this reduction.

Lockhart showed that for light acting through the phytochrome system to inhibit stem elongation of beans, the young trifoliate leaves had to be present, but it was necessary to expose the growing part of the stem to light,

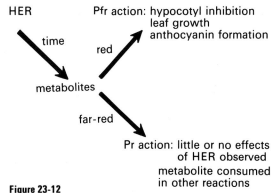

Figure 23-12
Possible relationship between high-energy reactions caused by blue or far-red light and subsequent influence by phytochrome. (After L. T. Evans et al., 1965, *Planta* 64:201. Used by permission.)

thus demonstrating a role for both organs. If the stem was treated with GA_3, it then elongated normally even if the young leaves were removed and the stem was irradiated. It was suggested that the leaves normally supply a gibberellin precursor to the stem and that light blocks the precursor's conversion to an active gibberellin, thus preventing synthesis of the hormone that would otherwise increase stem elongation.

Some results nevertheless indicate that light cannot control stem extension through gibberellin, because light is still inhibitory to elongation of some species even if GA_3 is added. However, these plants might depend upon one of the other native gibberellins rather than upon GA_3, or perhaps light has an additional inhibitory effect in these plants. The influences of light upon certain other morphogenetic processes and upon anthocyanin formation (discussed below) are not affected by GA_3 application either, and here light is clearly acting through some other process. The ability of either light or GA_3 to overcome dormancy in certain seeds suggests either that their action is similar or that light stimulates the synthesis or effectiveness of endogenous gibberellin. In Germany, Diethard Köhler recently showed that

red light causes increased production of gibberellins in germinating pea seeds and that far-red reverses this effect. This suggests that other responses controlled by phytochrome might be mediated through changes in levels of gibberellins or closely related compounds.

23.3.4 Formation of Anthocyanin and Other Flavonoid Compounds

Many plants form colored anthocyanins in one or more of their organs. Production of these pigments requires an adequate supply of soluble sugars often provided directly by photosynthesis. Light has additional promotive effects upon anthocyanin synthesis, however, and man has probably long realized that apples become red faster on the south than on the north side of the trees, and that the red colors of autumn leaves are often more brilliant in those directly exposed to the sun. Some plants, such as red cabbage seedlings, synthesize visible quantities of these pigments in darkness, but even here light is almost always greatly promotive. In others, such as apple fruits, turnip seedlings, and several milo varieties *(Sorghum vulgare)*, light is essential for production of these pigments. Blue wavelengths are effective in each case. The response to longer wavelengths varies considerably, depending upon the species. In the milo seedlings, red radiation alone is not effective but action peaks are observed at 650 mμ in apple skins, 690 mμ in red cabbage seedlings, and about 725 mμ in turnip *(Brassica rapa)* and mustard *(Sinapis alba)* seedlings (Fig. 23-13). The action spectra curves are not typical of those in which phytochrome is usually considered to function; furthermore, much higher intensities of light are needed. This suggests that the HER system is participating. The pigment responsible for anthocyanin formation under these rather high light intensities is not known, except in the apple skin, where it appears that the blue and red peaks are due to photosynthesis. In the other plants, photosynthesis is not responsible for the stimulation in pigment synthesis, and the necessary soluble sugars are provided by translocation or by starch breakdown in the cells involved.

Clever experiments have shown that the phytochrome system does participate in anthocyanin production in plants, however. If milo seedlings, for example, are irradiated with high-intensity blue light for a few hours and then are kept dark, the content of cyanidin gradually builds up. But if the plants are exposed for a brief period with a low level of far-red radiation just after the blue, only about half as much pigment develops. This inhibiting effect of far-red is repeatedly reversed by red radiation. A phytochrome influence after a period of high intensity also exists in seedlings of *Impatiens balsamina, Sinapis alba, Fagopyrum,* and in turnip roots and apple fruit skins.

The synthesis of flavonoids other than anthocyanins is often stimulated by visible radiation. Examples include the formation of quercetin in buckwheat seedlings and the formation of a yellow flavonoid in the skin of various tomato fruits. The presence of this pigment in the skin superimposed over the pink or reddish color of the fruit gives the orange-red appearance typical of normal field-ripened tomatoes.

Like the flavonoids and anthocyanins, lignins are also formed from the shikimic acid pathway. In many seedlings, or in young parts of other plants undergoing xylem differentiation or synthesis of xylem from the vascular cambium, it is observed that the accumulation of lignin is stimulated by visible radiation. This is partially responsible for the stiffness of plants grown in the light whose etiolation and excessive stem lengthening have been inhibited by this environmental factor.

23.3.5 Influences upon Seed Germination

After seeds have imbibed water, their germination is often affected by light (Table 23-2).

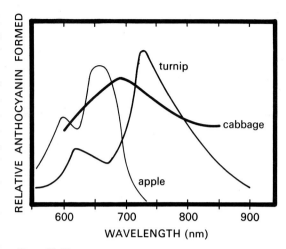

Figure 23-13

Partial action spectra for anthocyanin formation in apple skin, turnip, and red cabbage seedlings. Light energy applied to the apple skins was 26 joules/cm^2; that to the turnip seedlings was 10 joules/cm^2; that to the red cabbage seedlings was 5 joules/cm^2. All responses thus require considerably more energy than do phytochrome-caused processes. (From H. W. Siegelman, 1964. In J. B. Harborne (ed.), *Biochemistry of Phenolic Compounds*, Academic Press, New York, p. 447. Used by permission.)

Among several hundred species in which its role has been investigated, approximately half require light for maximum germination, especially if they are sown immediately after harvest. Those affected are frequently small seeds, and few of our large-seeded garden crops are influenced. Germination of many others is also unaffected by light, while in some, light is inhibitory. In still others, short periods of light are promotive, but continuous irradiation is inhibitory.

As in many processes affected by light, there is some interaction with temperature. The temperature of imbibition is important, but the temperature of the radiation period itself is not critical, since the photoreceptor can be properly excited only by light and not by thermal energy. Some plants are known (e.g., certain lettuce and tomato varieties) in which

TABLE 23-2

EFFECTS OF LIGHT ON GERMINATION

Germination promoted by low-energy red light (660 nm), effect reversed by far-red light (730 nm)[a]

pimpernel *(Anagallis arvensis foemina)*
mouse-ear cress *(Arabidopsis thaliana)*
beggar-ticks *(Bidens radiata)*
airbrom *(Billbergia elegans)*
lettuce, Grand Rapids *(Lactuca sativa)*
lettuce, Great Lakes, Reine de Mai *(Lactuca sativa)* Red promotes only after prolonged irradiation with far-red
virginia pepper weed *(Lepidium virginicum)*
smilo grass *(Oryzopsis miliacea)*
puya *(Puya beteroniana)*
brazilian wittrockia *(Wittrockia superba)*

Germination inhibited by blue (440 nm) and far-red (710 nm), applied at relatively high intensities and long intervals of time (e.g., several hours)[a]

beggar-ticks *(Bidens radiata)*
lettuce, Reine de Mai *(Lactuca sativa)*
smilo grass *(Oryzopsis miliacea)*

Germination requiring or favored by light[b]

Florida strangular fig *(Ficus aurea)*
cardinal flower *(Lobelia cardinalis)*

common tobacco *(Nicotiana tabacum)*
top primrose *(Primula obconica)*
flannel mullein *(Verbascum thapsus)*
carrot *(Daucus carota)*
cultivated rubber plant *(Ficus elastica)*
common evening primrose *(Oenothera biennis)*
American mistletoe *(Phoradendron flavescens)*
curly dock *(Rumex crispus)*
many grasses *(Gramineae)*

Germination prevented or retarded by light[b]

campion *(Lychnis pallonica)*
showy primrose *(Primula spectabilis)*
jimsonweed *(Datura stramonium)*
tomato *(Lycopersicum esculentum)*
many lilies *(Liliaceae)*

Germination indifferent to light or dark[c]

European wood anemone *(Anemone nemorosa)*
giant summer hyacinth *(Hyacinthus candicans)*
rush *(Juncus tenagea)*
toad flax *(Linaria cymbalaria)*
horseshoe pelargonium *(Pelargonium zonale)*
meadow salsify *(Tragopogon pratensis)*

[a] Various sources, summarized in P. L. Altman and Dorothy S. Dittmer. 1966. *Environmental Biology.* Fed. Amer. Soc. for Expt. Biol., Bethesda, Maryland.

[b] W. Crocker. 1936. "Effect of the visible spectrum upon the germination of seeds and fruits." In: B. M. Duggar (ed.), *Biological Effects of Radiation.* 1:791-828. Summarized in: R. F. Daubenmire. 1947. *Plants and Environment,* John Wiley & Sons, New York.

[c] W. Kinzel. 1926. *Frost und Licht.* Neue Tabellen, Euger Ulmer, Stuttgart. Summary in: A. M. Mayer and A. Poljakoff-Mayber. 1963. *The Germination of Seeds,* Pergamon Press, Oxford, London, New York, Paris.

light has no influence when the seeds are moistened at one temperature, but in which it is necessary if the temperature is raised somewhat. For example, Great Lakes lettuce germinates very well in the dark at 20°C, but only about 10 percent of the seeds will do so when soaked at 35°C.

It was discovered in 1954 that seeds exist in which germination depends upon the length of the photoperiod. Some of these have requirements for one or more days longer than some critical length after they are moistened (i.e., *Eragrostis ferruginea, Begonia evansiana*). Others

require days shorter than some critical amount (i.e., *Veronica persica*). Even in these cases light often interacts with temperature in an important way. For example, at 15°C seeds of birch *(Betula pubescens)* require eight long-day cycles to induce germination, while at 25°C they germinate well following a single 8- to 12-hour photoperiod.

These examples clearly point out the complicated relationships among light, temperature, and time in seed germination. Current research suggests that varying photosensitivity of seeds may depend somewhat on changing ratios of

Pr to Pfr as affected by time and temperature. As mentioned earlier in this chapter, the phytochrome system plays a direct and critical role in the light sensitivity of seeds. Whether the postulated HER pigment system is also involved is not evident, although blue and far-red radiations are inhibitory to germination of some seeds.

In several species, soaking the seeds in gibberellic acid (GA₃) solutions overcomes the light requirement for germination. Even in seeds unaffected by light, this hormone is sometimes stimulatory. Köhler showed that red light increased the gibberellin content of soaked pea seeds, that far-red reduced the level of this hormone, and that each wavelength could reverse the effect of the other in the usual manner, indicating that the phytochrome system is involved. It is possible that this increased hormone production is important in seeds whose germination is affected by light. One of the effects of gibberellins is to increase the production of α-amylase and certain other digestive enzymes in cereal grain seeds (Chapter 21), although germination of these is not light dependent. If hydrolytic enzyme production is activated in other seeds, these hormones may then stimulate embryo development by increasing the food supply to the embryo. Since GA₃ increases the production of invertase in certain tubers, involvement of this enzyme should be considered. The sugars and other solutes produced from breakdown of larger molecules could then increase water absorption into the embryo by osmosis, and the radicle and plumule could break through the restricting endosperm and seed coat more rapidly.

23.4 THE MECHANISM OF ACTION OF PHYTOCHROME

Many experiments have been performed to determine the manner in which light controls so many different responses in plants. Research

at Yale University by Arthur Galston and co-workers suggests that one of the biochemical effects of the phytochrome system is upon the hydroxylation of flavonoid compounds. Their work indicates that red light causes the introduction of an additional hydroxyl group into compounds such as kaempferol to form such products as quercetin. Generally similar results have been observed by Helen Stafford, who studied the influence of light upon the anthocyanins and other flavonoids formed in sorghum seedlings.

These findings provide basic biochemical information concerning effects of phytochrome, but in many other situations the influence of phytochrome is not to control hydroxylation patterns in flavonoids. The general stimulation by light of anthocyanin formation and of synthesis of products arising from intermediates of the shikimic acid pathway suggests an earlier role for radiation on the production of these compounds. One might suspect that the general synthesis stimulations of compounds formed from the shikimic acid pathway result indirectly from influences of light upon photosynthetic products, which in turn provide, by respiration, the phosphoenolpyruvate and erythrose-4-phosphate necessary for shikimic acid formation. This may account for the influence of high-energy radiation on anthocyanin formation in apple skins where there are small amounts of chlorophyll in the cells just below the skin, but in many other instances effects due to high-energy radiation have been clearly separated from influences upon photosynthesis. Mohr suggested that radiation influences some "basic metabolic change in the cell" responsible for many different effects, and influences on flavonoid hydroxylation patterns presumably represent only one such change.

Some research by K. V. Thimann and co-workers suggested a possible basic change that might be influenced by phytochrome. They showed that a wide variety of inhibitors of nucleic acid synthesis blocked the light stimulation of anthocyanin production in *Spirodela oligorrhiza* (a duckweed). This suggests that nucleic acid formation is essential to the normal changes brought about by phytochrome activation and, in addition, that the nucleic acids may be necessary for production of certain specific enzymes, which then cause the observable physiological stimulations due to light. Several research groups studying various species found that red light induces increases in activity of phenylalanine deaminase. This enzyme catalyzes the conversion of phenylalanine to trans-cinnamic acid (see section 18.2.2) in the pathway leading to synthesis of ring *B* of the flavonoids. This is probably one of the enzymes involved in the light-stimulated production of anthocyanins and other flavonoids.

Mohr and others have obtained much information supporting the assumption that RNA synthesis is necessary for the mediation of certain phytochrome effects. They observed that actinomycin *D*, which blocks DNA-dependent RNA formation, and puromycin, which interferes with protein synthesis, both inhibit the normal light stimulation of several different physiological responses in plants. Most of their work has been performed with white mustard (*Sinapis alba*) seedlings. Figure 23-14 illustrates the appearance of these seedlings when grown in light and in darkness and also lists 17 responses in them caused by light. In certain of the positive responses, such as opening of the plumular hook and enlargement and development of the cotyledons into effective photosynthetic structures, Pfr stimulates the production of new enzymes. In the case of the cotyledons, the breakdown of storage proteins is stimulated by Pfr, and the resulting soluble nitrogen compounds released (amino acids and amides) are more rapidly converted into enzyme proteins and into structural proteins of leucoplasts. In the presence of photosynthetically active light, these leucoplasts are quickly transformed into functional chloro-

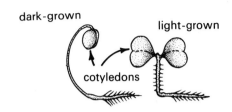

Figure 23-14

Photoresponses induced by Pfr: (1) enlargement of cotyledons, (2) straightening of the hypocotyl hook, (3) inhibition of hypocotyl elongation, (4) hair formation along the hypocotyl, (5) increase of the negative geotropic reactivity, (6) anthocyanin production in epidermal cells, (7) formation of tracheary elements in hypocotyl vascular bundles, (8) formation of leaf primordia and differentiation of the primary leaves, (9) increase of protein synthesis in leucoplasts of cotyledons, (10) stimulation of breakdown of cotyledonary storage proteins, (11) differentiation of stomata, (12) changes in respiration rates, (13) increase of RNA synthesis in the cotyledons, (14) increase in the rate of protochlorophyll formation, (15) increased synthesis of ascorbic acid, (16) changes in the rate of fat breakdown, (17) synthesis of phenylalanine deaminase—an enzyme involved in anthocyanin production. Processes influenced by the phytochrome system in white-seeded mustard (*Sinapis alba*) seedlings. Several of these responses are also elicited by high-energy far-red or blue light. (After H. Mohr, 1961, "Effects of ionizing radiation on seeds," International Atomic Energy Agency, Vienna. Used by permission.)

plasts. Furthermore, D. P. Holdgate and T. W. Goodwin in Wales showed that irradiation of rye seedlings with red or far-red light does cause measurable changes in the levels of RNA, and Mohr and coworkers obtained similar results with other plants. Therefore, it was suggested that phytochrome effects are initiated after an unknown activation of genes that code for specific messenger RNA molecules, and that these, in turn, code for specific enzymes necessary to cause the biochemical changes leading to several observed physiological responses. This hypothesis is outlined in Fig. 23-15. The mechanism by which Pfr might activate genes awaits further discoveries about the general process of gene activation as discussed in Chapter 20 and about the phytochrome protein and chromophore.

As contrasted to the theory that the primary mechanism of phytochrome action involves gene activation (or repression), there is evidence that certain responses due to red or far-red light are too rapid to be explained this way. Several legumes fold their leaves or leaflets together at the end of the daily light period. These responses are examples of **sleep movements**, or **nyctinastic movements**. If the leaflets are exposed to far-red light just before darkness, the closing is much slower than that of plants immediately placed in darkness. Red light applied just after the far-red treatment reverses the effect of the latter, showing that the phytochrome system is involved. In some of the plants, a difference in closing between leaflets treated with red as opposed to far-red can be seen in as little as five minutes. It is believed that this time period is too short to allow gene activation, messenger RNA synthesis, enzyme formation, and enzyme action. Furthermore, the response is not inhibited by actinomycin *D*, again indicating that messenger RNA synthesis is not involved. It is considered likely that Pfr in these cases rapidly increases permeability of membranes to solutes, thus allowing water movement and turgor changes in the leaf pulvini which cause the observed closing movements. If an effect upon membrane permeability should prove to be a primary process in all effects of phytochrome, then this must somehow subsequently influence gene activation or repression, because new enzymes are certainly involved in most of the morphogenetic processes affected by phytochrome.

Finally, further research by Mohr, Karl Hartmann, and their coworkers suggests that the effects caused by high-energy, far-red radiation, previously thought to involve an unknown pigment, may be due solely to absorption by phytochrome, after all. The explanation for the fact that the various colors of light given for short time periods can act differently from when they are given for long time periods involves the overlapping absorption spectra of Pr and Pfr and effects of light on synthesis and destruction of Pr or Pfr. When plants are exposed to far-red light for long enough time periods, some Pfr is present (although in small amounts) because Pr absorbs far-red to some extent. This Pfr then has time to act in the same way as when it is formed from a low-energy red light treatment. We suspect, then, that at least some of the physiological influences due to far-red light, which were previously attributed to the HER, are instead due to activation of phytochrome. Present evidence suggests that the HER responses caused by blue light are due to absorbance by a riboflavin-containing pigment.

23.5 EFFECTS OF ULTRAVIOLET LIGHT: PHOTOREACTIVATION

The existence of ultraviolet rays was discovered as early as 1801, and they were characterized by their ability to bring about photochemical changes, particularly destructive ones, by titles such as "chemical" or "actinic" light rays. Photons in this short-wavelength part of the spectrum have relatively high energies, and many kinds of molecules can be activated, leading to several different kinds of chemical reactions, but particularly to dissociations and other essentially destructive reactions. The photobiological implications of ultraviolet light have long been of interest. The role of the ultraviolet light (UV) of sunlight in sunburn was recognized in 1858, and its ability to kill bacteria was known in 1877.

23.5.1 Possible Ecological Effects of Natural Ultraviolet Light

Probably the most clear-cut example of a biological response to the ultraviolet portion of the solar spectrum at the earth's surface is the synthesis of Vitamin D in human skin. Several possibly important roles for the UV in sunlight have also been suggested for plants, but for the most part, we remain in doubt about the actual

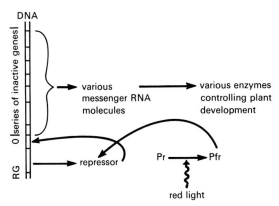

Figure 23-15

A hypothesis which might account for the multiple developmental effects caused by phytochrome. Assuming that regulator genes (RG), operator genes (O), and repressors exist in plants, as in certain bacteria, it is possible that red light induces an allosteric change in the structure of phytochrome. The resulting Pfr might then be able to inhibit action of the repressor, thus preventing it from blocking messenger RNA transcription beginning at the operator gene. In this way, a series of genes might become activated.

significance of these responses. It was suggested, for example, that the stunting of alpine plants is due to the increased intensities of UV at high elevations. A little reflection makes this seem quite unlikely, however, since the same species are found with essentially the same growth habits at far northern latitudes growing close to sea level where UV is even less intense than it is at sea level near the equator. Furthermore, laboratory experimentation has failed to confirm the proposed stunting effects. There have also been reports that UV might influence various processes, such as flowering. This may well be the case, but studies so far have not been sufficiently detailed to allow us to assess the importance of such mechanisms in nature. One reason for the ambiguities becomes apparent when we realize that most of the solar UV (especially the shortest wavelengths) is absorbed by ozone in the earth's upper atmosphere, so that only a small portion reaches the surface. Differences in intensities at different elevations

are not extremely great. Sunburn is somewhat more severe at higher elevations, however, and thus we do have some precedent for a biological significance of natural UV as a function of elevation.

Martin Caldwell, working on a doctoral degree with W. Dwight Billings at Duke University (1967), studied the effects of UV on growth of alpine plants in the Colorado Rockies. He carefully measured UV intensities in the field, excluded solar UV from plots on the tundra, and irradiated alpine plants with UV in the laboratory. He confirmed that the increase in UV with increasing elevation is rather modest (26 percent from 1,670 m to 4,350 m above sea level). Direct solar UV does increase markedly, but UV reflected from the atmosphere (sky UV), which makes up at least half of the total, actually decreases. He strongly confirmed that natural UV has little effect upon growth of plants in the field when proper controls are used. There was, however, a statistically significant (5 percent level) promotion of flowering in *Trifolium dasphyllum* by exclusion of UV during the first season, but flowering was actually reduced by this treatment during the second season. He found no greater resistance of alpine plants to UV than of plants from lower elevations, but he did obtain data indicating that photoreversal by visible light of UV damage might play a significant role in nature (see 25.5.3).

A current question concerns the possible importance of UV on the surface of Mars for the possible existence of some form of life there. The lack of ozone in the thin Martian atmosphere and recent measurements of Mars from rockets above the earth's atmosphere indicates that solar UV would not be appreciably attenuated at the surface of Mars.

23.5.2 Ultraviolet Damage

Of far more interest to the physiologist is the response of organisms to fairly high intensities of UV produced in the laboratory by sources such as a xenon arc lamp or a mercury vapor lamp. (The mercury emission line at 2,537 Å is a common source of laboratory ultraviolet light.) Using such sources, it soon becomes apparent that virtually all living organisms are adversely affected by irradiation with UV. Many organisms, particularly microbes, are killed by relatively short exposure to the so-called germicidal UV (2,537 Å). Higher plants may also be killed, although longer exposures are typically required. Damage of various kinds appears on the leaves of many higher plants even with relatively low doses. Ultraviolet light penetrates only a very thin layer of living tissue, and consequently, flowers and leaves are much more sensitive than are stems and other thicker organs. A typical response in leaves after irradiation is a bronzing or darkening of the surface tissue, and the epidermis may appear shiny. Several days may be required for full development of these symptoms.

Several action spectra for the deleterious effects caused by different wavelengths of UV have been determined. There is usually a peak at about 2,600 Å corresponding to the absorption peak of nucleic acids. This was first noticed in relation to the accelerated mutation rates induced by UV, particularly in microorganisms, and it was cited as early evidence that gene mutations were related to DNA. In general, UV effects may be effects upon the nucleic acids. There are a few significant exceptions, however, such as an action spectrum peak comparing to the absorption peak of protein (the immobilization of ciliary action in protozoa).

In higher plants, a considerable variability in resistance to UV occurs (Fig. 23-16). In a survey of some 67 species, for example, it was found that some are highly sensitive to UV, being killed after exposure to only three or four hours of the UV intensities to be expected on the surface of Mars. These included a wide variety of species, such as tomato, pea, bean, sugar beet,

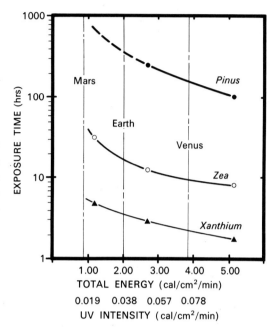

Figure 23-16

Leaf survival time under different intensities of simulated extraterrestrial solar radiation (xenon lamp). The values on the upper scale refer to the total simulated solar energy as measured, whereas those below refer only to the middle UV portion ($\lambda = 200-290$ *nm*). (From M. G. Cline and F. B. Salisbury, 1966, "Effects of ultraviolet radiation on the leaves of higher plants"; data from *Radiation Botany* 6:151–163.)

clover, and even horsetail (*Equisetum arvense*). Other species were less sensitive, and some were highly resistant. Species requiring 60 to 100 hours of exposure for leaf kill included Englemann spruce, rye, wheat, and corn. A few species were highly resistant, particularly the Austrian pine (*Pinus nigra*—635 hours without kill) but also a century plant (*Agave sp.*), other pines, and a cactus (*Opuntia sp.*). The Austrian pine, which was studied in the most detail, could withstand the UV intensities thought to be encountered on Mars for the equivalent of a Martian growing season.

Careful examination revealed no single mechanism of resistance in the resistant species.

Rather, a number of morphological modifications seemed to be responsible. Grass leaves, for example, are resistant partially because their leaves are rather vertical, consequently receiving less irradiation per unit area from an overhead source. Conifer leaves are protected by several layers of thick-walled, subepidermal cells. The cactus contains a network of tightly-packed, globular crystals in the epidermis, which probably reflects and absorbs much of the impinging UV radiation. The century plant is well fortified with large bundles of fibers just below the epidermis. Plants might become adapted by a variety of mechanisms to a UV environment such as may have once occurred on earth and seems now to occur on Mars.

23.5.3 Photoreactivation

Albert Kelner at the Carnegie Laboratories at Cold Spring Harbor, New York, discovered in 1948 that the survival rate for certain soil microorganisms (actinomycetes) was improved by a factor of several thousand when UV irradiation was followed by exposure to an intense source of visible light. The phenomenon was termed **photoreactivation** (or **photoreversal**). Since its discovery, the finding has been extended to a great many other organisms and kinds of UV damage. The most intensive research has been devoted to the bacteria, in which the phenomenon is clearly demonstrable and easily studied, but quite comparable effects occur with the bronzing of the leaves of higher plants and even with certain forms of ultraviolet damage in mammals and other higher animals. There are some rather interesting special cases. Bean plants, for example, subjected to short periods of UV radiation, fail to exhibit the usual epinastic responses caused by 2,4-D, providing they are placed in the dark following UV irradiation. If they are placed in the light, however, they then exhibit the normal epinastic responses. Thus, UV seems to destroy the plant's

ability to respond to 2,4-D (this is true whether UV is given before or after the 2,4-D), and visible light will reverse the UV effect so that the plant responds normally to the chemical. Gene effects might be implicated.

It is logical to ask whether the visible light in sunlight normally reverses biological responses to solar UV. Reversal will occur to some extent, but at higher intensities reversal due to concurrent radiation with visible light is relatively slight compared to reversal brought about by subsequent exposure to visible light in the absence of UV. That is, photoreactivation is more effective when the visible radiation is given following the UV than when it is given at the same time, even though the intensity of the concurrent radiation may be much higher.

To understand photoreactivation, we must first understand the mechanisms of damage by UV irradiation. Many mechanisms have been proposed, such as the production of organic peroxides that inhibit numerous metabolic processes. Many of these various possibilities might be realized in the many organisms damaged by UV, but present evidence is strongly in favor of the idea that most UV damage can be accounted for on the basis of effects on DNA. In recent years, it has been possible to define some of these effects quite exactly. When two thymine bases occur next to each other in one of the DNA strands, these pyrimidines may form bonds between adjacent carbons (two in each molecule—Fig. 23-17). The resulting molecule is called a **thymine dimer**. The other pyrimidines might also form dimers, but apparently thymine is especially important. The presence of dimers in the DNA strands prevents normal replication, and it might also interfere with the normal control of RNA and protein synthesis by DNA, thus accounting for various kinds of damage, such as the bronzing in the leaves of higher plants.

If this is the mechanism of UV damage, then what is the mechanism of photoreactivation?

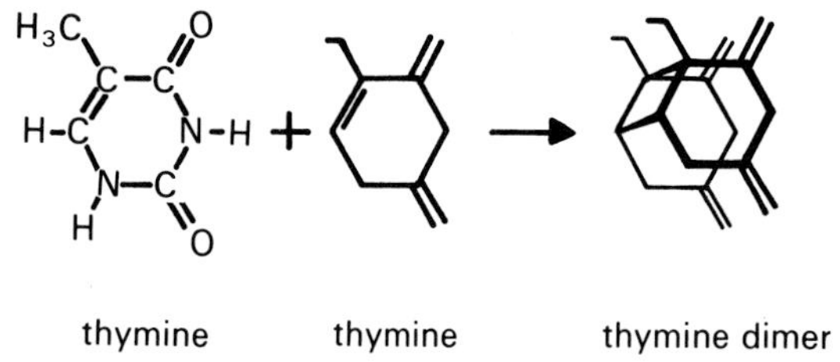

thymine　　　　thymine　　　　thymine dimer

Figure 23-17

Formation of thymine dimers by reaction between two thymine molecules. Reaction occurs across the double bonds in the two rings of the two thymine molecules.

Again, several action spectra have been determined, and in the great majority of cases, it is apparent that blue light is most effective in photoreactivation. Indeed, wavelengths that are only slightly too long to produce ultraviolet damage are especially effective in photoreactivation. Wavelengths in the yellow or longer are usually quite ineffective. Detailed studies, primarily with the bacterium *Escherichia coli*, indicated that an enzyme which has the ability to repair the damaged DNA strands is activated by photoreactivation. The role of visible light is only to provide energy for the activation of this enzyme (the response is direct and neither induced nor amplified). Elevated temperatures are also sometimes effective. The enzyme apparently functions by removing the thymine dimers and replacing them with normal thymine molecules. Actually, it appears that the enzyme is capable of repairing various kinds of damage in the DNA chains, responding to slight distortions in the chain, rather than only to the presence of specific anomalies such as the

thymine dimers. The mechanism of repair is not yet completely clear, but it appears that the distorted section of the DNA chain may simply be removed, beginning a few nucleotides before the occurrence of the dimer and ending a few nucleotides after its occurrence. As the chain is removed, proper nucleotides are inserted into place, these being determined by those present in the complementary strand. Only the redundancy of the double-stranded DNA structures makes this possible. If a section were removed from an unpaired single strand, the information relating to order of arrangement of the nucleotides would be lost forever.

This finding of the mechanism for the repair of anomalies in the DNA chains could be of far broader biological significance than might be implied by its initial discovery in relation to UV damage and photoreactivation. It has been estimated, for example, that the genes in a bacterium may be duplicated as many as one hundred million times before there is a 50–50 chance that even one gene will be altered. Such an extremely accurate copying process would certainly seem to require some mechanism for detecting and correcting occasional errors. No modern manufacturing process could mass produce an object without such mechanisms. The enzyme discovered by studies on photoreactivation might constitute this mechanism in living things. That it applies more generally than just to photoreactivation of UV damage is implied by its ability to correct errors introduced by agents other than UV, such as the so-called nitrogen mustards and other mutation-inducing agents.

24

The Biological Clock

24.1 INTRODUCTION AND HISTORICAL SUMMARY

The leaves of many species exhibit one position during the daytime (typically nearly horizontal) and another position in the middle of the night (typically nearly vertical). This observation was made at least as early as 400 B.C. by Androsthenes, who was the historian of Alexander the Great. In 1729, the French astronomer DeMairan was perceptive enough to recognize a fundamental problem in relation to this diurnal cycle of leaf movements in plants. He wondered if the movement occurred in response to changes in the environment (the daily light-dark cycle), or if it might be controlled by some time-measuring system within the plant. Using the sensitive plant (*Mimosa sp.*), DeMairan could observe the movements even after the plants had been placed in deep shade, and so he concluded that these motions do not require intense sunlight during part of the 24-hour cycle. He suggested that the movements might occur in response to some *internal* time measurement, even when conditions remained constant.

A few other early workers, including Charles Darwin and Julius Sachs, were also interested in these rhythms and published preliminary studies relating to them. But the investigator who devoted the most time and effort to this topic was Wilhelm Pfeffer, who, from 1875 to 1915, wrote many papers about the leaf movements of the common bean plant (*Phaseolus vulgaris*). Much of his extensive work is still of real interest. When he began, he was skeptical of the existence of an internal timing system, but by the end of his researches he became convinced that such a "clock" within the plant must exist. Ironically, however, he was unable to provide experimental data sufficiently convincing to convert other scientists to this idea.

Not only were the leaf movement rhythms being studied, but various workers such as A. Kiesel (who published in 1894) were observing and reporting various rhythms in animals. Diurnal rhythms of activity were particularly noticeable.

24.1.1 Endogenous Timing and the Free-running Rhythms

Through all of these early researches, the fundamental problem of an internal (**endogenous**) timing system remained unanswered. The real breakthrough came in the mid-1920s. Professor Friedrick Dessauer was the director of the Institute for the Study of the Physical Basis of Medicine at the University at Frankfurt, Germany. He was interested in any biological response to physical factors of the environment,

searches they were able to show, however, that Rose Stoppel's factor *X* was simply the dim red safe light she had used at the same time each day to water the plants in her darkroom. Since plants exhibit no phototropic curvature in response to red light, most plant physiologists of that period had assumed red to be a safe color for work with plants in a darkroom. We now know that red light is the most effective wavelength for influencing the diurnal rhythms of plants and even of some animals.

When Bünning and Stern carried out their experiments in total darkness and constant temperature (recording the position of the leaves as indicated in Fig. 24-1 by a lever arrangement and a marker on a revolving drum), they were able to show that Stoppel's original prediction was valid. Under these constant environmental conditions, the leaf movement rhythms did differ from the daily rhythm of the diurnal environment outside the darkroom. As a matter of fact, individual plants proved to have leaf movement cycles of various lengths. One plant, for example, might complete a cycle in 22 hours, while another would require nearly 27. After four or five days these two plants would be fully out of cycle (out of phase) with each other. The length of a plant's cycle, expressed under such constant conditions that it seems to be uninfluenced by any cyclical variation in environment, is called the **free-running period**.

This seemed to settle the question of endogenous versus exogenous timing. If the plants under the same conditions had different free-running periods, so that they would drift out of

particularly subtle physical factors. Since it seemed reasonable that plants might offer certain advantages in the study of such factors, Dessauer called two young botanists to his Institute. These doctoral students were Erwin Bünning and Kurt Stern.

In surveying the literature, Bünning and Stern became interested in some experiments of Rose Stoppel in Hamburg, who had reinvestigated some of the findings of Pfeffer. In her studies she had become convinced that the clock was *not* endogenous, since a given position of the leaves occurred at the same time each day, even though the plants were maintained under constant temperature and in a darkroom. She reasoned that if the clock were truly endogenous it would not be that accurate, and that one might expect the plant cycle after a while to get out of phase with the daily environmental cycle. Since the leaf movement cycle remained *exactly* in phase with the daily cycle, Stoppel postulated that some subtle **factor *X*** in the environment (*other than temperature and light*) was responsible for the phasing of the leaf movements.

Dessauer was interested in the ionic content of the air, and since he knew that the concentration and charge of ions in the air varied according to a diurnal cycle, he postulated that Stoppel's factor *X* might be the changing ionic content of the atmosphere.

Bünning and Stern set out to investigate this hypothesis. They artificially controlled the ions of the air and were soon able to demonstrate conclusively that these had no effect upon the diurnal leaf movements. In their further re-

---

Figure 24-1

Methods of recording leaf movement. (top) The method used in the laboratory of Bünning in Germany. Note that both stem and petiole are maintained in a rigid position with a bamboo framework. Only the blade is allowed to move. (bottom) Time-lapse photography used with plants for which the top method does not work well. Cocklebur plants, for example, have stem elongation and nastic movement such that they cannot be conveniently tied to a framework, and recording on a drum fails to give satisfactory results (see Fig. 24-2). In the time-lapse system, plants are photographed in the usual way during the light period and silhouetted against a dim green light panel (using relatively long time exposure) during the dark period (or infrared photography is used). Position of the leaves on a developed film is measured and plotted as on the figure at the bottom left. This may be facilitated by a gridwork behind the plants. (Three plants are shown, but usually six are used.)

METHODS OF MEASURING LEAF MOVEMENTS

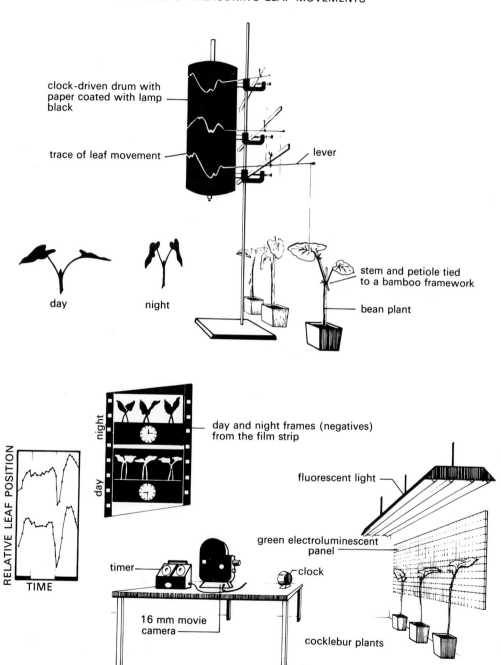

clock-driven drum with paper coated with lamp black

trace of leaf movement

lever

day

night

stem and petiole tied to a bamboo framework

bean plant

day and night frames (negatives) from the film strip

fluorescent light

green electroluminescent panel

RELATIVE LEAF POSITION

TIME

night

day

timer

clock

16 mm movie camera

green electroluminescent panel

cocklebur plants

phase with each other, how could they be responding to a single, unrecognized factor X in the environment?

It is interesting to note that Antonia Kleinhoonte, working quite independently in Delft, Holland, arrived at exactly the same conclusions as those of Bünning and Stern. The experiments of Bünning and Stern, and of Kleinhoonte were published between 1928 and 1932. Stern later immigrated to America and did not continue his work on the biological clock; Kleinhoonte also lost interest. Bünning, however, has continued his work until the present time, providing an extensive and detailed body of literature relating to biological time measurement.

24.1.2 Basic Concepts and Terminology

It is helpful to use the terminology applied to physical oscillating systems, although it is sometimes used in a rather special sense in relation to the rhythms. The oscillations as indicated in Fig. 24-2 may be thought of as having three characteristics: *first*, the **period** is that specific time between comparable points on the repeating cycles. Typically, the maxima of the curves are observed and measured because they show the sharpest changes in slope. Sometimes minima provide a more accurate measurement, or for that matter some other point on the cycle might be considered. The term **phase** is used in a specialized sense as any point on a cycle, recognizable by its relationship to the rest of the cycle. In a more general sense, it may be used as a recognizable *part* of a cycle, for example, as the part that may normally fall during the light period, the photophil phase (see Chapter 26). Using phase in the technical sense, the period is the time between comparable phases on the repeating cycles.

Second, the **amplitude** is the degree to which the observed response varies from the **mean**, as indicated again in Fig. 24-2 (the **range** is the difference between the maximum and the minimum

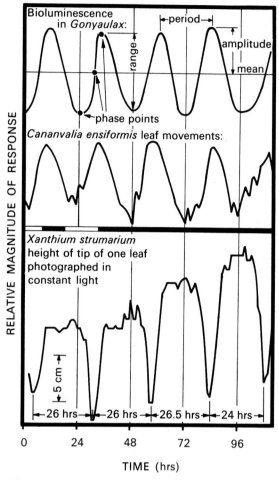

Figure 24-2

Some representative data for various circadian rhythms. (top) Bioluminescence in *Gonyaulax* measured for plants kept under constant conditions of dim light. Characteristics of circadian cycles are indicated (phase points, range, period, amplitude, and mean). (middle) A leaf movement record from *Cananvalia ensiformis*. Light and dark conditions are indicated by the bar. Note gradual shift of the peak as the cycles progress. (bottom) Leaf movements of cocklebur (*Xanthium strumarium*) recorded by the time-lapse photography method illustrated in Fig. 24-1. Period lengths between the troughs are indicated. Note increase in absolute height of the leaves, particularly at the peaks, but also at the troughs. This is largely due to growth of the stem during the course of the experiment, but the increase in range of leaf movement is also very apparent. Light was entirely from fluorescent lamps.

values). *Third*, one might consider the **pattern** of the cycle. Usually, the common sine wave comes to mind, but there are many variations. A short maximum might be accompanied by a broad minimum, for example, or the slope of the curve approaching the maximum might be very steep, while that approaching the minimum might be much less so.

Free-running rhythms that approximate but seldom if ever exactly equal 24 hours in their periodicity were referred to by Franz Halberg during the 1950s as being **circadian** (*circa*, approximately; *diem*, day). Since the rhythms are not exactly *diurnal*, nor are they *daily*, the term circadian is more accurate than either of these terms, which were previously used.

When plants or animals are exposed to an environment that fluctuates according to some period, and the rhythms exhibit the same period, they are said to be **entrained** to the environment rather than to be free-running. That is, the phases are controlled by environment. As we shall discuss below, this **entrainment** to the environment can be brought about by several factors, particularly an oscillating light environment, such as the red "safe" light of Stoppel. Such entraining environmental cycles are called **synchronizers** or **Zeitgebers**, a German word meaning time-giver. The term entrainment is used when the *Zeitgeber* is a fluctuating environment with several regular cycles. If an environmental stimulus is given only once (e.g., a single flash of light), and the period of the rhythms is shifted in response to it, the rhythm is said to have been **phase-shifted** or **rephased**.

24.1.3 Time Memory

While Bünning and Stern were discovering the endogenous nature of the biological clock as it occurs in plants, Ingeborg Beling in Germany (1928) was making an important discovery about the clock in honeybees. She found that it was possible to train honeybees to feed at a certain time during the day. It is as though the clock in the honeybee can have a "rider" attached to it, indicating the time of day and informing the honeybee 24 hours later that it is time to eat. It remains to be seen whether this is the same clock that controls circadian rhythms.

Man has a comparable time-measuring system. Time memory in man is most frequently manifested by his ability to wake up at a predetermined time. This is particularly impressive, since he must translate an abstract idea into some form that will "adjust the rider" on his biological clock.

24.1.4 Recent Developments: Celestial Navigation and Temperature Independence

In spite of the extremely intriguing discoveries of the 1920s and 1930s, only a small minority of biologists showed any great interest in this phenomenon until the early 1950s. At that time American botanists began to become interested in the work of Bünning, because it seemed to bear a direct relationship to the physiology of flowering (photoperiodism—see below and Chapter 26). Indeed, Bünning had proposed a theory to correlate photoperiodism and the circadian rhythms. Zoologists, particularly Colin S. Pittendrigh at Princeton University, also began to take notice of Bünning's discovery and other work going on in Europe.

Two very important discoveries were made during this period. They caught the attention of biologists all over the world and resulted in a surge of interest in the biological clock. First, Gustav Kramer, K. von Frisch, and others working primarily in Germany found that certain birds and other animals could tell direction upon the earth's surface by the position of the sun in the sky. Since this position changes, the organism must be able to correct for the time of day, apparently by the use of some kind of clock. Up until this time, many of the manifestations of the clock (e.g., the leaf movements) did not seem to be of much value to the organism. In the case of **celestial navigation**, the clock clearly is used, and this discovery stimulated interest considerably.

This was one of the observations that particularly aroused the interest of Pittendrigh in the biological clock and led to the *second* discovery. He realized that the clock could be of little value to an organism in functions such as celestial navigation if the rate at which it ran were strongly dependent upon temperature, as are most metabolic functions. He had also heard of the eclosion rhythm of *Drosophila* pupae,[1] discovered by H. Kalmus in Germany. Pittendrigh (1954) studied this rhythm at several temperatures and found the period to be nearly constant over a wide temperature range. Thus **temperature independence** of the biological clock was discovered.

Frank Brown and Marguerita Webb at Northwestern University in Chicago had also independently discovered this phenomenon in 1948. A color change observable in the fiddler crab exhibited a period length that was temperature independent, but Brown and Webb did not deduce from their data a temperature-independent clock. Rather they considered their results to be evidence *against* an endogenous clock (see below, 24.6). Bünning had investigated the temperature question in 1931, but with leaf movements of his beans, temperature independence was not as clear-cut as in the animal examples. Bünning did indicate that the temperature response was unexpectedly low.

24.2 PHOTOPERIODISM

Even before the work of Bünning and Stern and Kleinhoonte, the biological clock had clearly been demonstrated as a component of living plants, although the discovery has not been

recognized as such until rather recently. W. W. Garner and H. A. Allard were two scientists working in the Plant Breeding section of the United States Department of Agriculture research laboratories at Beltsville, Maryland. They had made two observations that they could not explain. Maryland Mammoth tobacco grew at that latitude to a height of 10 or 12 feet during the summer months but never came into flower, although it flowered profusely in the greenhouse in the winter. This was important to their breeding program, because it was essential to have flowers readily available for cross-pollination. They had also noticed that all the individuals of a certain variety of soybean would flower at the same time in the middle of the summer regardless of when they had been planted during the spring. That is, the large plants sown in early spring came into flower at the same time as the smaller plants sown only in early summer. Garner and Allard wondered if some factor of the environment might be responsible for flowering in these two species.

They executed a series of experiments that were a model of the scientific method. In regard to the tobacco, they carefully considered all of the environmental factors that might differ between the summer fields and the winter greenhouses at Beltsville, Maryland. They tested relative humidity, light intensity, temperature, soil moisture, and particularly soil nutrient conditions. George Klebs, the great German plant physiologist who had been specializing in problems of growth and development for several decades, was a strong proponent of the idea that flowering was brought about in response to nutrient conditions. He and other workers around the world believed that when nitrogen was high in the soil but when photosynthesis was somewhat restricted, plants would remain vegetative, but when nitrogen was low and photosynthesis produced large quantities of carbohydrate, flowering would occur. Garner

[1] The time of day at which adults emerge from the pupae exhibits a circadian rhythm.

and Allard were aware of these ideas and considered them carefully in their experiments.

In spite of their expectations, no combinations of temperature, light intensity, humidity, soil moisture or soil nutrient conditions that they studied resulted in flowering of the tobacco plants. One other factor included in their experimental setup did prove to be controlling: the daylength. Garner and Allard realized that daylength varied throughout the season, as well as being a function of latitude, and they tested what must have seemed like the remote possibility that this could control flower formation. It did. When the days were shorter than some maximum length, the tobacco plants began to bloom. When the days were shorter than some other maximum length, the soybean plants also began to bloom. Garner and Allard named the discovery of flowering in response to photoperiod **photoperiodism**.[2] Subsequent work seemed to indicate that the length of the dark period was in some ways even more important than the photoperiod. All of these intricacies are to be discussed in Chapter 26. The point here is, however, that these plants were capable of *measuring the length of the light and/or the dark period*. Here, then, was a clear-cut demonstration of biological time measurement. Completely comparable responses were subsequently discovered in animals, including effects on insect life cycles, fur color (arctic hare), breeding times (gonad size), and migration of many birds and other animals.

As indicated in the previous chapter in the discussion of the discovery of phytochrome, some organisms respond when the daylength *exceeds* some minimum. Garner and Allard called plants such as Wintex barley and spinach, which flower in response to days longer than some critical length, **long-day plants**, and those

such as tobacco and soybean, which flower when the daylength is *less* than some maximum, **short-day plants**. Some of the species they studied showed *no response to daylength*, and these they called **day-neutral plants**.

Historically, Garner and Allard deserve credit for the discovery of biological time measurement. Their use of the term photoperiodism implies their understanding of the significance of their discovery. Incidentally, Klebs and others had observed effects of daylength on flowering before Garner and Allard, but they failed to grasp the significance of their observations, explaining their results principally in terms of nutrients but overlooking the implications of time measurement.

24.3 CIRCADIAN RHYTHMS

There are several modern areas of knowledge that clearly belong in the field of *biology* rather than in *botany* or *zoology*. These would include the principles of inheritance, various respiratory pathways, and the cell theory. The circadian rhythms discussed in the ensuing paragraphs apply with only a few exceptions equally well to both plants and animals.

It can now be said that the circadian rhythms have been observed in representatives of all groups of living things with the possible exception of the bacteria. Viruses also fail to show such rhythms. One can almost conclude that wherever careful search has been instigated, the rhythms have been discovered.

Rhythms clearly exist in single-celled organisms. Phototaxis in the green alga *Euglena* and a mating reaction in *Paramecium* have been studied extensively. Among single-celled organisms, the biological clock has probably been most thoroughly studied in *Gonyaulax polyedra*, a dinoflagellate. This organism is mobile, having two flagellae. Beatrice Sweeney and J. Woodland Hastings, then located at the Scripps Insti-

---

[2] They acknowledge in a footnote in their second paper that the term was suggested by A. O. Cook, a colleague at Beltsville.

tute of Oceanography at LaJolla, California, were the first to work intensively with this organism. They have carefully documented three separate rhythms. Most spectacular is a rhythm of **bioluminescence** observable when these organisms are disturbed. That is, when a suspension of *Gonyaulax* cells is tapped or otherwise jarred, the organisms emit light, but the quantity of light they emit follows a circadian rhythm. Under normal conditions, the peak of the rhythm occurs near midnight. There is a rhythm in **cell division** with the maximum occurring near dawn. The third rhythm is in **photosynthesis**. The quantity of carbon dioxide fixed with a given illumination varies according to a circadian rhythm, with the maximum usually occurring near noon. It is interesting to note that we are dealing here with a population of organisms, rather than with individuals as in Bünning's original studies.

Among the fungi, there is a rhythm in growth of *Neurospora* exhibited as a series of zones of mycelia on the culture plate, and a rhythm in spore discharge in *Pilobolus* has been observed and studied somewhat. Many rhythms besides leaf movements have been observed in higher plants. These include petal movements, rates of growth of various organs, concentrations of pigments, discharge of perfume from flowers, times of cell division, metabolic activity (particularly respiration), and such other responses as the volume of the nucleus, which was observed to fluctuate according to a circadian rhythm. This last observation could be highly significant (volume doubled from the minimum to the maximum phase), but it requires confirmation and has not been further investigated.

Several insects exhibit rhythms convenient for study. The eclosion of *Drosophila* mentioned above provides an intensively studied example, as does the activity of the cockroach. **Activity or running cycles** have also been studied in birds and rodents. These rhythms are particularly valuable to the biologist because they typically continue for long intervals (months or even years—Fig. 24-3) and they are relatively easy to study. Various automatic devices may be installed in the cage allowing for continuous recording of the activity of the organism. A microswitch attached to the perch can indicate bird activity, for example, and electrically monitored running cages are often used for rodents.

Many circadian cycles have also been studied in man, although in some ways man is a difficult object because he may be entrained by such *Zeitgebers* as his wristwatch! Nevertheless, detailed studies seem to indicate that the circadian rhythms of man (e.g., urinary excretion, temperature, pulse frequency, etc.) follow the same general principles developed for the rhythms of other organisms. A particular feature of one study was that certain of the cycles could be rather easily entrained while others were somewhat more resistant.

Although much study remains to be done, many biologists are intrigued with noncircadian rhythms. Metabolism, color, and activity of fiddler crabs and other organisms have shown cycles in a laboratory closely matched to the tides of the bay where the organisms were collected. Lunar rhythms are often related to tidal rhythms. The grunion (*Leuresthes tenuis*) is a small fish living off the coast of Southern California that spawns from late February to early September during three to four nights at the new and the full moon and during the descending tidal series. Rhythms related only to the moon have also been observed, and, because of the similarity in the periods, various workers have speculated about the relationship of the human menstrual cycle to these lunar rhythms. In certain ground squirrels held under constant conditions, entrance into and termination of hibernation has been shown to follow an annual rhythm of about a year. Amount of daily wheel-running activity of these animals also follows such a cycle. Germination of certain seeds appears to be best at certain times during the

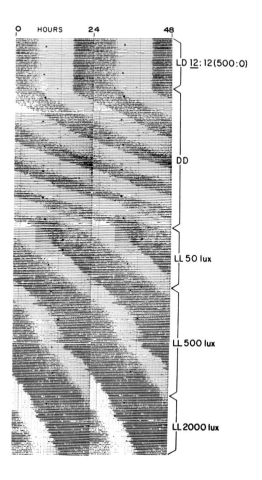

O HOURS 24 48

LD 12:12(500:0)

DD

LL 50 lux

LL 500 lux

LL 2000 lux

Figure 24-3

The chart is a record of activity rhythm in a blind sparrow measured over a period of 251 days. In this experiment birds with eyes removed were kept in cages under controlled conditions of light and temperature. The perch in its cage was wired to a recorder so that whenever the bird was active, short vertical lines appeared on the record. These records may be cut out and pasted together as in the figure. Each line on the record represents two days (48 hours). The second of these two days is the same as the first of the two days in the line below. If the beginning of activity comes at the same time each day, a vertical line can be drawn through the first marks for each day. In such a case, the period lengths are exactly equal to 24 hours. If this line has a negative slope, as in the figure, a delay each day is indicated (the period exceeds 24 hours). The more the negative slope deviates from the vertical, the greater the delay (the longer the period). Light conditions are indicated on the right. At the top, 12 hours of darkness were alternated with 12 hours of 500 lux

light intensities. Lights came on about the time indicated by the beginning of activity. DD signifies constant darkness. Note that the bird, even though blind, was entrained by the light–dark cycle, but had a period exceeding 24 hours in constant dark. In constant light (LL 50 lux) the period still exceeds 24 hours, but less so than in constant darkness; that is, the clock appears to be running faster. As light intensities increase (LL 500 lux), the clock runs still faster (after a few days of adjustment), illustrating Aschoff's rule that rate of running of the clock is proportional to light intensity. This effect was no longer clearly noticeable at 2,000 lux. Aschoff's rule also states that the ratio of activity to rest time increases as light intensity increases, and this prediction was also borne out. (Figure courtesy of M. Menaker, University of Texas. See *1968 Proc. Natl. Acad. of Sci.*, 59(2):414–421.)

year, even though the seeds have been stored under conditions of constant temperature, light, and moisture. Considerably more work must be done before the implications of these apparent annual rhythms become clear.

24.4 SOME CHARACTERISTICS OF THE RHYTHMS

As in any attempt to understand the operation of the natural universe, a first assignment is to obtain descriptive data. Many investigators have expended a great deal of effort in obtaining data relating to the biological clock, particularly as it is exhibited by circadian rhythms. A vast amount of detail has accumulated, far too much for extensive discussion here. An important characteristic of the rhythms is their circadian free-running periods introduced above in relation to the work of Bünning and Stern. We will summarize three other general characteristics in the following paragraphs.

24.4.1 The Response to Light

With the discovery that the rhythms had free-running periods usually not equal to 24 hours, it became apparent that they must be entrained by varying conditions in the external environment to account for the normal 24-hour periodicity. The work of Bünning and Stern indicated that these conditions might be as subtle as a rather weak red light; so light was obviously of interest as a possible *Zeitgeber* or synchronizer.

One approach was to see if the rhythms could be entrained to some light-dark cycle other than a 24-hour one. It was readily apparent that this could be done. The rhythms could be entrained by shorter cycles of 20 to 22 hours (in rare cases, even 10 to 16 hours) or longer cycles of 28 to 38 hours.

Another approach is to allow a rhythm to become strongly established by a cycling environment, and then to let it run free under constant environmental conditions, usually in the dark. A brief interruption of light may be given at various times during the free-running rhythm. With plants and many animals (especially nocturnal ones), when the flash of light is given during **subjective day**, there is virtually no effect upon the rhythm. That is, if light comes during the phases typical of day in a natural cycling environment, the following phases of the cycle are not influenced much. When the light interruption comes during early **subjective night**, the rhythm is typically **delayed** (e.g., the maximum comes later than would have been expected). It is as though the flash of light were acting as **dusk**, but by coming later in the day, a delay resulted. As the light flash is given later and later during subjective night, the extent of the delay increases until a certain point is reached where the flash of light suddenly results in an **advance** of the rhythm rather than in a delay (e.g., the maximum comes earlier than expected). The flash of light is acting as **dawn** rather than as dusk. This response is illustrated in Fig. 24-4.

Typically, the delay or advance occurs gradually over several cycles, called **transients** before the new phase relationships become firmly established. The transient cycles are more commonly observed with animal than with plant rhythms. Pittendrigh and Victor Bruce sug-

gested that the transients could be understood if the rhythms are actually under the control of two clocks. The first may be readily phase-shifted by the light flash; it in turn then entrains the other, which actually controls the rhythms. Entrainment of the second may require several days, accounting for the transients.

By carefully studying curves, like that in Fig. 24-4, and knowing the amount of delay or advance caused by a light flash given during otherwise constant conditions at various times during a free-running cycle, it is possible to account for the phenomenon of entrainment. That is, one might consider the advancing effects of dawn (when the lights come on) and the retarding effects of dusk (lights out), and by so doing predict the phases of a rhythm in relation both to the normal 24-hour cycles and to cycles other than 24 hours in length. Pittendrigh and his coworkers have pioneered in this approach.

They have also introduced the elegant technique of using the **skeleton photoperiod**. Pittendrigh's group used *Drosophila*, but other organisms, including plants, respond as well. Controls are exposed (at constant temperature) to a light-dark cycle with a photoperiod of say 10 hours and a dark period of 14 hours, but the treated plants receive, rather than the photoperiod, two short light interruptions (5 minutes to an hour or so) and otherwise continuous darkness (also constant temperature). When one light interruption comes at the same time as the beginning of the photoperiod for the controls (dawn), and the other comes at the same time as the end of the photoperiod (dusk), the rhythm is the same for the treated organisms as for the controls. That is, the rhythms can be entrained by a skeleton photoperiod as well as by a photoperiod consisting of continuous light.

An interesting discovery was made in relation to the skeleton photoperiods (Fig. 24-5). The time at which "dusk" occurs may be progressively delayed, and in response to this the phases of the rhythm are also delayed (by the

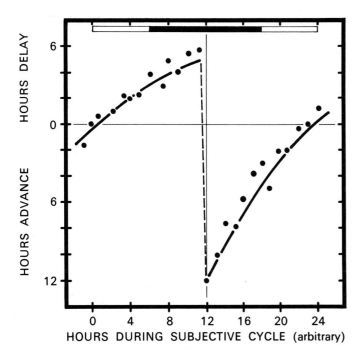

Figure 24-4

Phase shift in petal movements of *Kalanchoë blossfeldiana* following two-hour exposures to orange light given at various times during an extended period of continuous darkness. Bar at the top indicates subjective status of the rhythm; i.e., dark part of the bar indicates petal closure or subjective night. As light interruption approaches the middle of subjective night, there is an increasing delay; following the middle of subjective night, there is an advance which decreases as subjective day is approached. (Data after R. Zimmer in E. Bünning, 1964, *The Physiological Clock*, Springer-Verlag, Berlin, Göttingen, Heidelberg, p. 61.)

predictable amount according to entrainment and rephasing studies). This progresses as the dawn and dusk light breaks become more and more separated until the separation reaches a critical length, typically about 14 hours. When this occurs, there may be a relatively sudden shift, and the phases of the rhythm become reversed, so the two light breaks of the skeleton photoperiod act in an opposite way. "Dawn" acts as "dusk" and vice-versa. Of course, this shift would not occur under a normal light-dark cycle with dusk being delayed each day; so light during the photoperiod does have an influence on timing. Pittendrigh further investigated such problems with **asymmetric skeleton photoperiods** (light breaks of different duration), or with three interruptions each 24 hours, but we will not further pursue the matter here.

Entrainment by light is clearly a photobiological process. Certainly some photoreceptor pigment is absorbing the light, and by this absorption it is changed in such a way that it leads to an advance or a delay of the clock. It would be extremely interesting to understand the photobiochemical mechanism of this response. A first step would be identification of the photo-

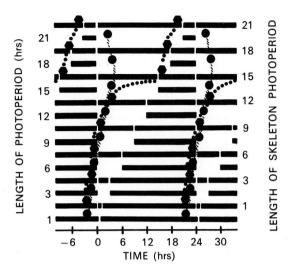

Figure 24-5

Position of the peak in the eclosion rhythm of *Drosophila* for insects exposed to continuous photoperiods or to comparable skeleton photoperiods. Hexagon indicates position of the peak in relation to the skeleton photoperiod illustrated by the bar below the hexagon. Peaks are connected by dots. Circles indicate position of the peak for control photoperiods, as indicated by the bars below the circles. Circles are connected by slanting lines. In the control photoperiods, peaks come before dawn for short photoperiods and up to three or four hours after dawn for the longest photoperiods. Skeleton photoperiods have peaks close to those of the control photoperiods until the skeleton photoperiods exceed 14 hours, at which time there is a sharp shift, and subjective dusk becomes subjective dawn. (Data from C. S. Pittendrigh and Dorothea H. Minis, 1964, *The American Naturalist* 98:261–294.)

receptor pigment, and this is usually initially undertaken by a determination of the action spectrum for the response (see Chapters 13 and 23). Flashes of light of carefully controlled spectral qualities are given at various times to test their effectiveness on entrainment.

For a long time zoologists working on the biological clock did not perform experiments of this type. They simply assumed that the receptor was the eye of the animal with which they were working. There are indications, however, that the situation might not be that simple. To begin

with, light effects have been studied on certain organisms after masking or removal of the eyes. It was shown in the 1950s that gonads of ducks would develop in response to long days (a photoperiodism response) even though the eyes were removed. It appeared that the hypothalamus (the forebrain) responded to the light. Enough light, especially red light, penetrated the skull to be effective. Recently, Michael Menaker at the University of Texas in Austin has shown that blind sparrows (both eyes removed) could be entrained in their activity rhythm by light signals. He also confirms with blind sparrows the development of testes in response to long days, as observed in blind ducks. Furthermore, he has shown that a weak green light has an effect upon the activity rhythm of his birds (normal eyes), but that it does not influence the photoperiodism response. Much information of this type is needed, and various zoologists are presently becoming interested in the action spectrum approach.

Action spectra have been determined for the various rhythms of *Gonyaulax* and also for the mating rhythm of *Paramecium*. In both cases, ultraviolet light is highly effective in bringing about entrainment, but in *Gonyaulax* red and blue light are also effective. The responses to ultraviolet are not identical in the two organisms, and the observation has yet to be followed by a search for the photoreceptor pigment, but one might suspect proteins or the nucleic acids. The action spectra for responses in these two organisms (Fig. 24-6) constitute the best data presently available relating to the quality of light most effective in synchronization of the biological clock.

Lars Lörcher, working in Bünning's laboratory in Tübingen, Germany, attempted to determine an action spectrum for the leaf movements of the bean plant. Using dark-grown plants, he found that the rhythms were most effectively established by red light and that this establishment could be reversed by an immediate exposure to far-red light. This would seem to implicate the phytochrome system. Lörcher found, however, that other wavelengths were also effective in entrainment, providing the plants had been grown in the light rather than in the dark. Action spectra clearly indicate that phytochrome is not the photoreceptor in fungi or animals, and we lack any evidence that phytochrome even exists in these organisms. We do have one other suggestive observation relating to phytochrome and the rhythms in higher plants, however. The leaf movement rhythms will often continue for several days when the plants are maintained at a constant temperature and under continuous light, providing the light is rich in red wavelengths but contains none of the far-red part of the spectrum. When far-red light is present, the rhythms tend to damp out rather rapidly. Therefore, the phytochrome system does seem to be involved, although some other pigment (perhaps one that absorbs blue light) may be of even greater importance.

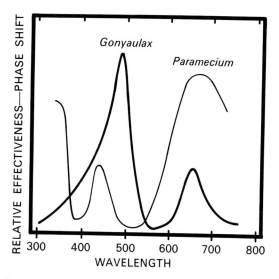

Figure 24-6

Approximate action spectra for phase shifting in the rhythms of *Gonyaulax* and *Paramecium*. (From C. F. Ehret, 1960, *Cold Spring Harbor Symposium on Quantitative Biology* 15: 149–158.)

24.4.2 Temperature

We are faced with somewhat of a paradox in our discussion of temperature effects on the biological clock. Sharp changes in temperature may synchronize the rhythms (act as a *Zeitgeber*), and temperature may also strongly influence the amplitude of the response. On the other hand, the period of the free-running rhythm is relatively temperature-insensitive (it remains quite constant over a wide range of temperatures). So some aspects of the clocks are sensitive and others are insensitive to temperature.

The temperature insensitivity is especially interesting. In *Gonyaulax* the Q_{10} for the effect of temperature on period length is slightly *less* than one (as temperature increases, the free-running period becomes slightly longer), whereas it is equivalent to about 1.3 for the leaf movements of the bean. Various workers have observed Q_{10}s that approach 1.00 very closely.

For example, the value is approximately 1.02 for biological time measurement in the flowering of cocklebur (see 26.3.3). Because the bean plant has a relatively high Q_{10} and because there may be a strong temperature effect during the first one or two cycles after temperature is radically changed (due to entrainment by temperature and subsequent transients?), Bünning had overlooked or at least failed to emphasize this fascinating aspect of the biological clock.

As Pittendrigh pointed out in relation to celestial navigation, temperature independence of the clock is certainly reasonable from an ecological standpoint. If the clock is used in any ecological way, resistance to temperature changes would obviously be essential, since temperatures fluctuate considerably in nature both diurnally and seasonally, and seasonal differences would surely upset any physiological time measurement not exhibiting temperature independence.

In spite of this, temperature independence of the clock is somewhat surprising, since the Q_{10} for most biochemical reactions is appreciably greater than one. How, one might ask, if the living organism is fundamentally a biochemical system, can one account for temperature independence?

One can envision certain feedback systems. The products of one reaction may inhibit the velocity of an earlier one. Such feedback inhibition systems are well known in living organisms (Chapter 20). As temperature increases, the velocity of the first reaction (the time-measuring reaction) might be expected to increase, but the inhibitory product would then increase at a proportional rate, and consequently the reaction would maintain a near constant rate over a wide range of temperatures. The Q_{10} value of less than one observed in *Gonyaulax* could be accounted for by such a scheme, assuming that the inhibitory product were produced somewhat faster with increasing temperature than the time-measuring reaction is accelerated. So such a feedback system (possibly overcompensating as in *Gonyaulax*) could be invoked in a temperature-independent system of time measurement based upon biochemical reactions. Furthermore, some simple enzyme systems are now known that have temperature coefficients close to one.

Britton Chance and his coworkers at the University of Pennsylvania have recently (1967) been experimenting with suspensions of yeast cells and with extracts from these cells that exhibit the properties of oscillating systems. Concentrations of glycolytic intermediates, for example, oscillate in these cell-free extracts for several minutes to an hour with period lengths on the order of a minute. The oscillations depend upon feedback reactions in the metabolic pathways. By controlling rate of glucose infusion into the system, it is possible to control the period length within limits, shift the phases, etc. In spite of the differences (e.g., period length), the properties of these systems have generated considerable enthusiasm, since their study could lead to an eventual understanding of the biochemical basis for the biological clock.

On the other hand, some investigators have suggested that the biological clock consists of some physical system. Such systems are far less sensitive to temperature than are chemical ones (an hourglass, a pendulum, or a balance-wheel clock are highly temperature-insensitive compared to even the best examples of the biological clock). But what kind of a physical time measuring system could exist within the cell? Could it be some kind of molecular oscillation? But how could this vibrating system with a period length of microseconds or shorter account for a circadian clock with a period length approximating 24 hours? What in the cell might be analogous to the gear train connecting the balance wheel to the hands of the clock? If the biological clock is physical, some unexpected breakthrough will surely be required to discover it.

24.4.3 Chemical Inhibitors

If we could find some chemical that would clearly inhibit biological time measurement, then by our speculations about its mode of action we might gain some insight into the operation of the biological clock. Many chemicals have been studied in an attempt to find an inhibitor of time measurement, but one must be careful in interpreting the results. A given chemical might, and often will, influence the *amplitude* of the rhythm without influencing its *period* (the actual indication of time measurement). That is, the physiological manifestation of time measurement (leaf movements or activities, etc.) may be rather easily influenced by some substance such as a powerful respiration inhibitor, although the clock is more resistant (Fig. 24-7). There are some instances in which the amplitude may be completely damped out, yet when the inhibitor is removed the cycle will be seen to be in phase

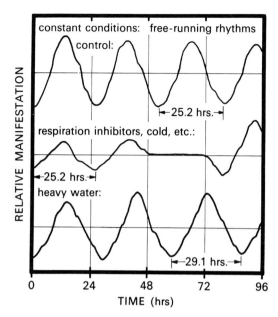

Figure 24-7

Effects of various chemicals and other factors upon free-running rhythms. Most compounds that inhibit metabolism reduce the amplitude but do not affect the period (compare center record with control above). Heavy water increases the length of the period (29.1 hours compared with 25.2 hours for eclosion in *Drosophila*). (Curves are schematic and do not represent actual data.)

with control organisms having the same period and to which no inhibitor was applied. This is one aspect of the general problem of **masking**.[3]

Bünning reported several instances in which the effect of a given chemical inhibitor applied to bean plants appeared to be directly upon the clock itself, rather than upon its manifestation. In these cases, the period was lengthened somewhat, and the amplitude was unaffected or only somewhat decreased. Materials such as colchicine, ether, ethyl alcohol, urethane (ethyl car-

---

[3] Masking of a rhythm by some overriding environmental influence may occur in several ways. In a somewhat more subtle example, animal activity may begin as soon as the lights come on, but when animals are transferred to constant darkness, activity begins some hours later than the expected time. The daily photoperiod is said to mask the actual cycle.

bamate), and other materials seemed to have this effect. The work has been extended in a few cases to other organisms, but usually with negative results.

In *Gonyaulax* it was reported that the photosynthesis rhythm disappeared upon treatment with actinomycin-*D*, although the over-all level of photosynthesis was not influenced. Thus it was possible to postulate that the clock itself and not its manifestations was being influenced. Since actinomycin-*D* is known to inhibit the production of RNA in the nucleus, this observation seemed to tie the biological clock to the genetic control of protein synthesis. Unfortunately, when the situation was looked into somewhat more closely, enthusiasm tended to wane. To begin with, although the photosynthesis rhythm is repressed or eliminated by this material, the luminescence rhythm is not. Furthermore, some attempts to repeat the original observation with actinomycin-*D* have indicated the usual decrease in amplitude without a change in period. It was also possible to account for the original observation by assuming that some coupling link between the clock and photosynthesis depended upon something which is inhibited by actinomycin-*D* (most likely synthesis of RNA), but that the clock itself is not dependent upon this step.

More recently (1967), Jerry F. Feldman, working in Pittendrigh's laboratory, reports that the period length of the rhythm of phototactic response in *Euglena* is increased by cycloheximide, an inhibitor of protein synthesis. Experiments on phase shifting by light seemed to implicate the clock itself rather than some "coupling" mechanism. Feldman discussed the difficulties of concluding with any certainty that operation of the clock depends upon protein synthesis, but this possibility will surely be considered in future research.

Another clear-cut effect of some chemical substance upon time measurement itself is that of heavy water, deuterium oxide. Treatment with this substance causes a considerable increase in the phototaxis period of *Euglena* and also of bean leaf movements. Heavy water seems to slow the time measurement in photoperiodism, as indicated by rather recent studies of Bünning. The observation is an interesting one, but we are still left with little in the way of concrete proposals to account for the mechanism of the clock. Heavy water might be expected to influence a great many processes within the plant, and so there is little we can say about how it may influence the clock.

In any case, we would appear to be justified in concluding that a simple description of the characteristics of the biological clock as exhibited in the various manifestations of circadian rhythms have not been sufficient to give us a clear-cut understanding of how the clock operates.

24.5 THE BIOLOGICAL CLOCK IN NATURE

It is not difficult to imagine advantages conferred upon the organism by possession of a biological clock. Rhythms of activity in animals, for example, allow a species to occupy a niche not only in space but also in time—two animals might use the same space but at different times (e.g., nocturnal and diurnal animals). The rhythms in flower opening may also confer an adaptation to the time factor of natural environments, and the time memory of the honeybees might be an adaptation to this feature of plants. The phenomenon of photoperiodism confers upon the organism possessing it the ability to occupy a particular niche in *seasonal* as contrasted to *diurnal* time. The several species which flower in response to photoperiodism may do so at different times and in sequence throughout the season, providing a rather constant source of nectar for insect pollinators throughout an entire growing season. Given a time during the season with minimal flowers but high availability of pollinators there would be a selective advantage to any species able to flower during that time.

What are the ecological advantages of the leaf movements? Pfeffer asked this question and settled it in his mind by tying the leaves fast to a bamboo framework so that the movements could not occur. Since the plants exhibited no apparent ill effects from this treatment, he concluded that the movements were some artifact of the evolutionary process and not something of selective value to the plant. More recently, however, Klaus Raschke in Germany has suggested that the typical horizontal leaf position during day and vertical position during night might have some value in heat transfer between the plant and its environment (Chapter 6). That is, the horizontal leaf is in the best position for the reception of sunlight during the day, but this is a poor position for the retention of heat at night. Heat is simply radiated from the horizontal leaf surfaces into space. Vertical leaves in a plant community, however, would radiate more to each other than would horizontal leaves. Whether the resulting difference in leaf temperature is significant remains to be determined, but fairly simple experiments might be performed to settle the question.

Celestial navigation could be our most spectacular and clear-cut application of the biological clock among animals. In such a case, the clock is clearly used.

The circadian rhythms of man and his other time-measuring abilities are of importance in certain obvious ways, and they may clearly increase in importance in a negative way as our modern life becomes ever more complex. Jet air travel across time zones, for example, has a strong effect upon the internal timing systems of the passengers. Various current studies are concerned with these problems, and we can expect to hear more about this subject as time goes on.

The ability of man to measure intervals of time without external cues is most clearly exhibited with subjects placed under hypnosis, applying the principle of posthypnotic suggestions. In many such cases, suggested intervals of time may be estimated with a high degree of accuracy.

Janet Harker in England performed some experiments with cockroaches which, if they are substantiated and their implications apply to plants and other animals including man, could be of considerable significance in future research. A special nerve center called the suboesophageal ganglion had been shown to be in control of the activity rhythm of this organism. In Harker's experiments, two insects were entrained with light-dark cycles completely out of phase with each other. When the ganglion from one insect was transplanted to the second insect without removal of the second ganglion, the second cockroach began to exhibit symptoms of severe stress, including cancerous malignancies of the gut. Could such dire consequences result when our own circadian rhythms are internally out of phase?

24.6 SOME PROBLEMS

A most important problem concerns the mechanism of operation of the biological clock. Direct study has so far been impossible, but experiments may be suggested by the establishment of conceptual models (Chapter 22). The two-clock model of Pittendrigh and Bruce, for example, provides a way to understand their data on transients. Bünning suggested that the clock acts like a relaxation oscillator, in which energy is introduced into the system during one phase, and relaxation occurs during the following phase. Yet in spite of these models, the problem remains unsolved, and we must simply await further research for satisfying answers.

We have long wondered about the location of the biological clock. It obviously can exist in a single cell, as evidenced by its manifestations in Gonyaulax and other single-celled organisms. Where is it located within the cell? Bünning suggested several years ago that it might be located in the nucleus. He pointed out that some of his chemical inhibitors (e.g., colchicine) were known to influence nuclear processes, and it was a

student of his that discovered the circadian rhythm in volume of the nuclei in Phaseolus (section 24.3). Workers in America conceived an experiment designed to test the importance of the nucleus. Using the large, single-celled alga, Acetabularia, they showed that a photosynthesis rhythm persisted after removal of the nucleus. They concluded that the clock could not be located in the nucleus. In more recent experiments with Acetabularia, however, the nucleus from an organism entrained to one cycle was transplanted to an enucleated second organism entrained to another cycle. The second organism immediately assumed the rhythm of the organism from which it had received its transplanted nucleus (Fig. 24-8). (These experiments are quite analogous to the transplantation experiments of Janet Harker.) The conclusion might be that the clock does indeed reside within the nucleus, but that in the highly special organism, Acetabularia, vestiges of the clock may also reside in the cytoplasm.

In animals the clock controlling certain rhythms can sometimes be located in a specific organ such as the suboesophageal ganglion of the cockroaches utilized by Harker. She was also able to show that other rhythms were apparently controlled by timing mechanisms in other parts of the organism. We have no specific evidence indicating that the clock might be localized in any particular plant part. Certain rhythms of respiration, carbon dioxide fixation, and other manifestations can be readily observed in tissue cultures utilizing cells taken from various parts of the plant.

One problem seems to arise again and again in our study of the biological clock. It is basically the problem of factor X suggested several decades ago by Rose Stoppel. For virtually all workers in the field, the problem has been solved. They find it difficult to interpret the circadian nature of the rhythms in any way other than an endogenous biological timer. Frank Brown at Northwestern University, however, has persisted in arguing for an external factor X as the

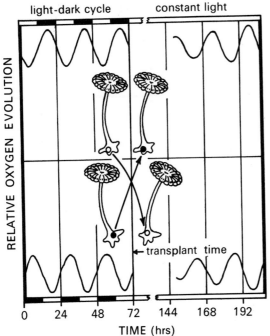

light-dark cycle   constant light

RELATIVE OXYGEN EVOLUTION

←transplant time

| 0 | 24 | 48 | 72 | 144 | 168 | 192 |

TIME (hrs)

Figure 24-8

Effects of transplantation of the nucleus ·in *Acetabularia* upon its rhythm of photosynthesis. Following transplantation, the rhythm becomes adjusted to match that of the plant from which the nucleus was obtained, although it cannot be observed for about three days. (Curves are hypothetical. For actual data, see E. Schweiger et al., 1964, *Science* 146:658.)

ultimate source of time measurement for the biological clock. He suggests that the rhythms might have circadian free-running periods, because the translation of the external oscillation to the manifestation of the organism might be imperfect. An electric clock, as used in the United States, keeps time by responding to the 60 fluctuations per second in the current coming from the power station. That is, its time measurement is exogenous and not endogenous as is a spring-driven clock. An electric clock could, however, be made to run either fast or slow. As a matter of fact the 60-cycle fluctuation of the current could be translated into any period. Studying respiration in potato-tuber and carrot-root slices, Brown observed slight deviations in clock manifestations that came at the same time for different samples, even though these samples were in separate controlled-environment chambers. Temperature, humidity, light, and in some cases even barometric pressure have been maintained constant in these various chambers. Brown suggests that some other factor (magnetic field, cosmic rays, etc.?) might penetrate and be fluctuating within these chambers and accounting for biological time measurement.

Several tests of Brown's contentions have been devised. Time measurement has been found to progress even in organisms carried to the bottoms of deep salt mines where the cosmic ray flux has dropped to an extremely low level. Time measurement even managed to continue when organisms were placed on turn-tables on the South Pole which were rotating in a direction opposite to the earth, so that the organism was not rotating with the earth. In certain experiments, honeybees were trained to feed at a given time in a constant-light laboratory in Paris and were then flown by trans-Atlantic jet to an identical laboratory in New York City. They continued to feed according to Paris time. Brown pointed out, however, that in some of his experiments fiddler crabs transported over 2,000 miles westward were soon entrained to the time at the new location, even though they had not been exposed to any obvious *Zeitgeber*.

We have noted a continuation of certain circadian rhythms in astronauts who have orbited the earth for fairly extensive periods of time. This would seem to be a conclusive evidence against Brown's suggestions, and future experiments planned for satellites could settle the problem. In the meantime we nevertheless wonder about the subtle environmental factors that could account for the fluctuations in Brown's data. They may not serve as an exogenous cue for time measurement, but they could be a highly interesting feature of natural environments so far unrecognized by biologists.

25

Responses to Low Temperature and Related Phenomena

The general plant response to temperature has been well known for many years. We usually think of it in terms of enzyme reactions in which two opposing factors seem to operate. With increases in temperature, the increased kinetic energy of the reacting molecules results in an increased rate of reaction, but at the same time, increasing temperature results in an increased rate of enzyme denaturation. The result is a typical, somewhat asymmetrical bell-shaped curve (Fig. 25-1), indicating that the rate of the reaction builds up from a minimum temperature to a certain optimum after which it then drops off to a maximum temperature. The general curve also applies to growth, respiration, photosynthesis, and many other plant responses.

After the student has become familiar with the general positive responses of plants to increasing temperature (until temperatures are too high), it may come as somewhat of a surprise to learn that certain other processes are promoted as the temperature *decreases* toward zero. In the **vernalization** process, exposing plants to low temperatures for a few weeks results in the formation of flowers, usually after plants are returned to normal temperatures. The dormancy of certain seeds, as well as bud dormancy in various woody plants, is also broken by exposing them to an extended period of low temperature. This is exactly

opposite to the induction of dormancy, which may also be promoted by cold. If we oversimplify dormancy induction by thinking of it in a *negative* sense as a simple slowing down of plant processes at decreased temperatures, then we must surely consider the breaking of dormancy in an opposite, *positive* sense. This is the interesting dilemma of the low-temperature response.

In this chapter we will be concerned with five different positive responses to low temperature. The *first* of these, vernalization, has been studied extensively. The *second* is the breaking of seed dormancy by exposure of moist seeds to low temperatures. This treatment is referred to as **stratification**.[1] The *third* process is very similar to stratification. It is the breaking of winter dormancy in the buds of perennial woody plants. The *fourth* process has been studied less, and we will devote a minimum of space to it here. It is the induction by low temperature of the growth of underground storage organs such as tubers, corms, and bulbs. The *fifth* process has been studied even less. Indeed, most of what we know is based only upon rather casual observation.

---

[1] It is easy to confuse vernalization and stratification, since in both cases moist seeds may be exposed to low temperature.

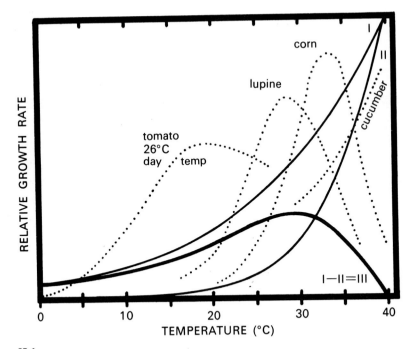

Figure 25-1

Effects of temperature on plant growth. I. Rate of a reaction with a Q_{10} of 2. II. A reaction with a Q_{10} of 6, such as denaturation of protein. III. The expected curve for rates of an enzymatically controlled reaction based upon subtracting the curve for enzyme destruction from the curve for enzymatically controlled reaction rate. Dotted lines show representative plant growth curves as a function of temperature. Note that optimum temperatures are extremely dependent upon species. (In tomato, day temperature was constant and night temperature varied.)

This is the effect of low temperatures upon the vegetative form and growth of certain plants.

In each of these five processes, we are concerned mostly with inductive (delayed) effects upon some developmental plant process. Such effects may also be observed in response to the length of day and perhaps to other environmental factors as well. In fact, low temperature and daylength effects are frequently interrelated in the five plant responses, but especially in vernalization. Since all of the five positive plant responses to low temperature have much in common, we might ask if the mechanism involved is the same in each case? The answer is unavailable, but we will consider the question in a general way.

Ultimately, the low-temperature response must be a matter of the activation of specific genes—a switching of the morphogenetic program in response to low temperatures. Could the genome response to low temperature be somewhat more direct than we have so far imagined? Does the low temperature in some way result directly in the activation of particular genes? If not, what are the transducers? Could they be located in the cytoplasm or perhaps even the nuclei of the cells in which the program is readjusted? At this stage of our research, our answers are far from final, but the questions could guide future research.

25.1 VERNALIZATION

In the 1920s, the term **vernalization** came into use. It is a Latin derivation from a Russian near-equivalent, **jarovization**, coined by T. D. Lysenko, the geneticist who, during the reign of Stalin, was allowed to exercise absolute political control over Russian genetics. Vernalization would be translated into English as "springization," the implication being that winter varieties are converted to the summer varieties by cold treatment. We realize (although apparently Lysenko didn't) that the genetic makeup is not changed by the low-temperature treatment. The cold period supplied artificially by the experimenter simply substitutes for the natural cold of winter (Fig. 25-2).

The term vernalization has been widely misused. Sometimes, any effects of cold on plant growth have been referred to as vernalization. On the other hand, any promotion of flowering by any treatment (even daylength) has also been called vernalization. In this textbook, we will restrict use of the term **vernalization** to *a low-temperature promotion of flowering*. Some workers would prefer to restrict the term even further to the *inductive* low-temperature promotion of flowering. This would eliminate examples in which some flower formation occurs even before plants are removed from the cold (e.g., Brussel sprouts); so we will use the broader definition, which includes such noninductive examples.

25.1.1 The Response Types

In terms of our broad definition, it is possible to observe a great variety of flowering responses to low temperature, depending not only upon species but frequently upon varieties within species and sometimes even individuals within recognized varieties. In classifying the response types, there are several factors to consider (indicated by italics). To begin with, we may differentiate between *inductive* and *noninductive* responses. The majority of the plants that have been studied respond inductively.

A profitable way to classify the response types is according to the *age* at which the plant is sensitive to cold. The **winter annuals** constitute one large category that has been studied by workers all over the world, but particularly in Russia and by G. Gregory and O. N. Purvis at Imperial College in London. These plants respond as very young seedlings or even as seeds, providing that sufficient moisture is present. Petkus rye (*Secale cereale*) has been studied perhaps more than any of the other examples. Seeds of these species are normally planted in the fall of the year, and then they begin to germinate, spending the winter as small seedlings. In an artificial situation, they may be exposed to low temperatures as moist seeds or small seedlings for a period of only a few weeks, after which they form flowers at normal temperatures in approximately seven weeks. Without the low-temperature treatment, approximately 14 weeks are required to form flowers, but ultimately flowers do form. Since the cold requirement is a **quantitative** one (low temperatures result in *faster* flowering) but not a **qualitative** one (in which flowering *absolutely depends* upon the low temperatures), we have another basis for classification. The winter annuals are inductive and quantitative in their response.

In the case of Petkus rye, there is an interesting complication: short-day treatment will often substitute to a certain extent for the low-temperature requirement. There is another important interaction with daylength. After rye plants have been exposed to the low temperature and have begun to grow, their flowering is strongly *promoted by long days*. All of the winter annuals that have so far been studied

| 1.8 to 2.7 | −0.8 to 0.7 | 1.3 to 3.2 | 6.2 to 7.6 | 9.5 to 10.2 | 2.7 to 3.4 |

Figure 25-2
Effect of different storage temperatures upon flowering (bolting) in a sugar beet variety. Roots were stored for 53 days at the temperatures indicated and then returned to a warm greenhouse, where they were grown for 56 days before photographing on November 8, 1939. In this variety, maximum flowering occurs following storage at relatively high temperatures, 2.7° to 10.2°C. Unfortunately, no purely vegetative control plants were included in the picture. (Photograph courtesy of M. Stout. See *Jour. of Agr. Res.* 72:49–68, 1946.)

are not only promoted in rate of flowering by low temperatures, but they are also promoted by subsequent long days.

The **biennials** constitute the second intensively studied category, investigated mostly during the 1940s in Germany by Georg Melchers and Anton Lang. By definition, biennials live two growing seasons, then flower and die. In nature this usually means that they germinate in the spring, form a vegetative plant, which is typically a rosette, and spend the winter in this condition. With the coming of the second spring, a flowering shoot begins to elongate from the center of the rosette. This rapid elongation of the flowering shoot is referred to as **bolting**. Flowering during the second season is dependent upon the exposure to low temperature during the preceding winter. If most biennials do not experience several days to several weeks of temperatures slightly above the freezing point, they remain vegetative indefinitely. Hence, they have a qualitative or **absolute** requirement for cold as contrasted to the quantitative or **facultative** winter annuals. Flowering of many biennials is also promoted by long-day treatment following the low temperatures, and some may absolutely require this treatment, such as *Hyoscyamus niger*, the European henbane, used in the studies of Melchers and Lang. Other biennials are day-neutral following vernalization. Various biennials have been studied to greater or lesser extents, including several varieties of beets, cabbages, kales, Brussel sprouts, carrots, celery, and foxglove.

There are many species of cold-requiring plants that do not fall readily into the categories of winter annuals or biennials. Flowering of several perennial grasses, for example, may be promoted by cold. Some of these have a subsequent short-day requirement for flowering. The chrysanthemum is a short-day perennial that has been studied extensively because of its photoperiodism response. It also has a cold requirement that must be met once before the plants can respond to the short days. This was overlooked because plants are propagated vegetatively, and cuttings carry the vernalization effect with them. Other perennials (e.g., a *Geum*, studied by P. Chouard in Paris), which do not have the grass-growth habit of the winter annuals or the rosette form of the biennials, may still flower in response to a low-temperature treatment, and several annual garden vegetables will flower somewhat earlier in the season if they

are exposed to a short vernalization treatment. Thus we see that many different kinds of plants are stimulated to flower by cold periods, that in some cases there is a quantitative and in others a qualitative effect, and that flowering of some species also requires or is promoted by a suitable daylength.

25.1.2 The Location of the Low-Temperature Effect

It is the meristematic cells in the bud that respond to the cold. If a hormonelike substance is produced, this occurs in the same cells in which it acts. Several experimental approaches have been taken that demonstrate this fact. The most straightforward is simply to cool various parts of the plant while leaving the other parts at normal temperatures. This is not easy, but it can be done with small cooling coils.

With plants that may be vernalized as seeds, the embryos may be excised and grown on an agar medium. Removal of cotyledons or endosperm, although sometimes delaying the vernalization process, does not otherwise hinder it. In some cases, this delay can be avoided by supplying carbohydrate in the agar medium.

Still another way to investigate the site of response is to vernalize a plant and then to graft various parts of it onto an unvernalized plant. If the meristem itself is so transplanted, it will ultimately flower, indicating that it had been vernalized. If a meristem from an unvernalized plant is grafted onto a vernalized plant after removal of the vernalized meristem, the transplanted, unvernalized meristem remains vegetative as it grows out. Vernalization is clearly limited to the meristematic tissues themselves.

For a while there appeared to be an exception to this generalization. S. J. Wellensiek in Holland found that excised *Lunaria biennis* leaves could be vernalized. Upon closer examination, however, he discovered that new buds were formed on the leaf petioles, and that these meristematic tissues had to appear before the low-temperature treatment was effective. Wellensiek has since suggested that vernalization requires not only the presence of a meristem but that actively dividing cells are also essential to the process. Several studies support this conclusion, but one fact seems opposed. This is the response of certain seeds, even at temperatures a few degrees below the freezing point. Cell division at such temperatures seems unlikely, and microscopic investigations failed to reveal it. If Wellensiek's suggestion, or the modification that DNA must be replicating whether cells are dividing or not, nevertheless proves to be true, it could be of considerable significance. The switching of the morphogenetic program in the vernalization process would seem to depend in some way upon nuclear division—or perhaps upon replication of DNA previous to nuclear division. There is an indication that if the apical meristem of Japanese morning glory is to respond to flowering hormone produced in response to a long night, DNA in the apical cells must be replicating. DNA synthesis is inhibited by 5-fluorodeoxyuridine, which inhibits flowering of Japanese morning glories only when applied to the buds at the time flowering hormone arrives at the apical meristem cells. Its effect is fully reversed by DNA precursors, such as thymidine.

The vernalization process evidently requires energy. It will not proceed in the absence of oxygen, and an energy substrate, such as sucrose, is apparently essential. A certain amount of water must also be available, since dry seeds will not respond to the low temperature. In some cases the required water content is quite minimal. (Forty percent may be sufficient, whereas 80–90 percent may be required for active growth.)

25.1.3 Physiological Experiments Relating to Vernalization

Although plant physiologists wish to understand plant function in terms of physics and chemistry, we often have not identified the molecules involved or how they might act. This is particularly true in vernalization and photoperiodism. In such cases we must take a much more indirect approach to solving the problems. Experiments are performed by manipulating whole plants in various ways, observing the results, and making deductions based upon our general understanding of plant function at the biochemical and biophysical level. Experiments of this type are called **physiological experiments** as contrasted to more specific biochemical experiments.

An initial physiological investigation on vernalization might involve a determination of optimum temperatures. Figure 25-3 indicates the results of a typical experiment of this type with Petkus rye. Vernalization proceeds at a maximum rate over a fairly wide range of temperatures from slightly above freezing to 8° or 10°C. Of course, the exact temperature curve depends upon the species, but a broad optimum is quite typical. The upper limits vary from about 9° to 17°C for several tested species. Vernalization will occur even at a few degrees below freezing. Usually the lower limit is set by the formation of ice crystals within the plant tissues.

Another important study determines the most effective vernalization times. Again, this varies considerably with species. Minimum lengths vary from four days to eight weeks for the first observable effect. Saturation times vary from three weeks for winter wheat to three months for henbane. In a few cases a slight drop in the level of vernalization attained by the plant occurs with extremely long vernalization time (several months). This phenomenon is referred to as **oververnalization**.

In the course of such studies, an interesting phenomenon was discovered. If the plant, immediately following its exposure to vernalizing temperatures, is exposed to high temperatures, the vernalized condition may be reversed, and the plant does not flower. This

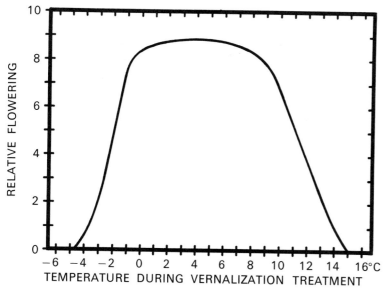

Figure 25-3

Final relative flowering response as a function of temperature during vernalization. The data represent response of Petkus rye to a six-week period of treatment. (Original data of Purvis and of Hänsel. From F. B. Salisbury, 1963, *The Flowering Process*, Pergamon Press, Oxford, London, Paris, New York. Used by permission.)

phenomenon is referred to as **devernalization**. To be really effective, devernalizing temperatures must be about 30°C or higher, and they must be applied immediately after the plants are removed from the low-temperature treatment. Careful studies have shown, however, that a certain degree of devernalization can be observed when the plants are exposed to any temperature higher than that which will cause vernalization. In winter rye, for example, 15°C is the neutral temperature. Any temperature below this will increase the level of vernalization in the plant, and any temperature above this, applied immediately following low-temperature treatment, will cause some reduction in the level of vernalization.

Devernalization is essentially ineffective after four or five days (in winter rye) during which time the plants are held at the neutral temperature. That is, the vernalized condition becomes stabilized at the neutral temperature, and this stabilization becomes maximally effective after four or five days of exposure to the neutral temperature.

25.1.4 Vernalin and Gibberellins

The experiments indicating that the apical meristem itself responds to low temperatures do not suggest a translocated flowering stimulus, a hormone. Yet experimental results exist that do indicate formation of such a hormone as one result of vernalization. The evidence is based upon grafting experiments and was reported as early as 1937 by Melchers. Recently the work has been extended somewhat in Russia. The basic finding is that a plant induced to flower by proper cold treatment will, in turn, induce flowering in a vegetative receptor plant (that has never experienced the low-temperature treatment) to which it is grafted. Beyond this basic experiment, in which plants of a single variety were used, it has been found that dissimilar response types will also transmit the flowering stimulus across a graft union. Cold-requiring plants may be induced without the cold period by being grafted to a noncold-requiring variety, for example. The reverse, though less clear-cut, will also occur.

Considerable attention has been given to the translocation properties of the vernalization stimulus. *First,* a living graft union must be formed between the two plants if movement of the stimulus is to occur from one to the other. *Second,* conditions favoring transport of carbohydrates also favor transport of the stimulus. If the receptor is defoliated, for example, while leaves are left on the donor, then the receptor must obtain its sugars and other foodstuffs from the donor, and this favors movement of the vernalization stimulus across the graft union. If the receptor is darkened, the same effect may be observed.

Melchers suggested that a vernalization stimulus exists and termed this hypothetical substance **vernalin**. The logical thing to do would be to isolate and identify it. Many attempts have been made to do this (25.6.2), but so far these have not been completely successful, although results with gibberellins show that their properties are similar to those expected for the vernalin of Melchers.

It was found in the mid-1950s by Lang, by then located at the University of California in Los Angeles, that when gibberellins were applied to certain cold-requiring species, these plants would be induced to flower without a low-temperature treatment (Fig. 25-4). This was essentially the result expected for the vernalin postulated by Melchers. Following these initial observations, several workers began to investigate the problem, and Lang, with a number of assistants and collaborators, also pursued the matter intensively. It could be shown, using several cold-requiring species, that natural

Figure 25-4

Two Comet radish plants maintained under short days (10 hours) at 50° to 55°F. (left) Control plants. (right) Plants treated with 100 mg of gibberellic acid per plant on October 10, 1956 (photograph taken on February 5, 1957). The flowering plants are essentially identical to those produced by growing the plants on long days. Results are also typical of Lang's experiments with cold-requiring plants (see text). (Photograph courtesy of S. H. Wittwer, Michigan State University, East Lansing.)

gibberellins build up within the plant during exposure to low temperature. Furthermore, the gibberellins extracted from induced plants (or more typically from other higher plant sources) could be reapplied to vegetative plants, causing them to flower.

Is gibberellin then to be considered equivalent to vernalin? For various reasons, plant physiologists have been reluctant to accept this conclusion. When gibberellins are applied to a cold-requiring rosette plant, the first observable response is the elongation of a vegetative shoot. Soon thereafter, this shoot begins to develop flower buds. When the plants are induced to flower by exposure to low temperatures, however, the flower buds are apparent from the very beginning. Furthermore, it is clear that gibberellin is not the general flowering hormone, since many species (particularly short-day plants) do not respond to it. Lang suggested that gibberellins might act pharmacologically rather than physiologically; that is, they may act like a pick-lock rather than a key designed to fit the lock. It is conceivable that gibberellin could induce certain changes within the plant which, in turn, lead to flowering or possibly even to production of vernalin, even though the gibberellin were not itself the vernalin. Couldn't several molecules influence the morphogenetic program in the same way? On the other hand, the changes in the native gibberellin levels during induction appear significant, and we are not ready to eliminate the gibberellins as being involved in some way in the vernalization process.

It has been suggested, primarily by M. Kh. Chailakhyan in Russia, that there are two substances involved in flower formation, one a gibberellin or a gibberellin-like material, and the other something else. He suggests that low-temperature and long-day requiring plants lack sufficient gibberellin until they have been exposed to the inducing environment, while short-day plants may contain sufficient gibberellin but lack the other flower-inducing substance. An elegant experiment performed many years ago by Melchers supports this point of view. A noninduced short-day plant (Maryland Mammoth tobacco) was grafted to a noninduced cold-requiring plant (henbane), causing the latter to flower. It appeared that each contained one of the essential substances for the flowering process but had to obtain the other from the plant to which it was grafted. (This succeeded for the henbane but not for the tobacco.)

25.1.5 Vernalization and the Induced State

Vernalization is an excellent example of a process leading to the induced state. Development of flowers typically follows the cold period by days or weeks. How permanent is this switching of the morphogenetic program to the induced state? One variety of henbane requires both low temperatures and subsequent long days for flowering. It is possible to vernalize the plants but to postpone flowering for a desired interval of time by withholding long days. Plants maintained in this condition showed no loss of the vernalization stimulus after 190 days, even though all of the original leaves exposed to the cold had died. Only after 300 days was there any sign of loss of the vernalized condition. There are many other examples in which the induced state appears to be a very stable one. Certain cereal seeds, for example, can be vernalized while in a moist condition and then dried out and maintained for various intervals of time (months to years) without loss of the vernalized condition. It is important to note, however, that there are several other species in which the induced state is far less permanent.

25.2 THE DORMANCY AND GERMINATION OF SEEDS

One of the most interesting and thoroughly studied plant responses to low temperature is the breaking of seed dormancy, but the topic is far broader than a simple positive response to low temperature, since many factors besides temperature influence seed germination. The effect of light has already been discussed in Chapter 23, but we will consider other factors influencing germination in the following paragraphs.

25.2.1 Seed Viability and Life Span

It is an impressive idea that a living organism can go into a sort of suspended animation, remain alive but not grow for a long period of time, only to begin active growth when conditions are finally suitable. Stories have been circulated to the effect that certain seeds found in some of the ancient tombs of Egypt or the deserted pueblos of the southwestern United States were capable of growth, even though they were hundreds or even thousands of years old. Careful investigation has completely failed to support any of these stories, but the life span of some seeds is very great, often far exceeding the life span of a human being.

In discussions of this topic, it is convenient, first, to define the term **viable**. Seeds that remain alive and capable of **germination** (growth of the embryo and penetration of the seed coat) when all of their environmental requirements have been met are said to be viable. Seeds absolutely incapable of germination under any circumstances are dead.

Table 25-1 lists the longevities of several seeds. Some of these figures were determined by T. Becquerel, who studied seeds stored in the national museum in Paris. *Mimosa glomerata* seeds remained viable for some 221 years, but from these and other studies we can conclude that a rather typical life span of seeds is from 10 to 50 years. The documented record for seed survival appears to belong to a lupine (*Lupinus arcticus*). Viable seeds of this species at least 10,000 years old were found in lemming burrows deeply buried in permanently frozen silt of the Pleistocene Age in the central Yukon.

Storage conditions always influence seed viability. Moisture content during storage is extremely critical. Increased moisture usually results in a more rapid loss of viability, but some seeds live longest submerged in water. High temperatures also shorten longevity. There is evidence that some seeds remain alive longer when buried in the soil than when stored in jars on a laboratory shelf. A few seeds are characterized by a very short life span. Seeds of *Acer saccharinum*, *Zizana aquatica*, *Salix japonica*, and *S. pierotti* lose their viability within a week if kept in air, and oxygen is generally detrimental to seed life spans. Seeds of several species may remain viable anywhere from a few months to less than a year.

25.2.2 Dormancy: The Concepts and Terminology

A seed may remain viable but still not grow for several reasons. Seed physiologists have attempted to distinguish between two general causes of lack of germination: *First, external environmental conditions* may be limiting, or *second*, some *internal situation* within the seed may keep it from germinating even when no obvious environmental factor would otherwise limit it. The example of an internal situation most easy to understand pertains to the seed that fails to germinate because the embryo inside has not reached a morphological maturity capable of germination (e.g., in certain members of the Orchidaceae, Orobancheae, or the genus *Ranunculus*). Only time will allow this maturity to develop, and no environmental treatments will induce germination (at least of normal seedlings), although proper conditions are required for maturity to develop. Germination of seeds of wild plants may often be limited in this or some other internal way. On the other hand, the seed may be quite capable of germination, but it simply lacks sufficient moisture, or the temperature is incorrect. This is typical of the seeds of many domestic plants.

To distinguish between these two different situations, the seed physiologists have utilized two terms: **quiescence** is the condition of a seed when it is unable to germinate because the environmental conditions normally required for growth are not present, and **dormancy** is the condition of a seed when it fails to germinate even though the environmental conditions usually considered necessary for active growth are present.

TABLE 25-1

SOME REPRESENTATIVE LIFE SPANS FOR SEEDS[a]

Species	Viability (%) Initial	Final	Age at test	Notes
1. sugar maple *(Acer saccharinum)*	—	—	<1 week	
2. wild rice *(Zizania aquatica)*	—	—	<1 week	
3. willows *(Salix japonica* and *S. pierotti)*	—	—	<1 week	
4. English elm *(Ulmus campestris)*	—	—	ca. 6 mos	
5. American elm *(Ulmus americana)*	70	28	10 months	dry storage
6. *Hevea, Boehea, Thea,* sugar cane, etc.	—	—	<1 year	
7. wild oats *(Avena fatua)*	70	9	1 year	buried 8″ in soil
8. bald brome grass *(Bromus racemosus)*	100	12	6 yrs	buried 8″ in soil
9. alfalfa *(Medicago sativa)*	85	1	6 yrs	buried 8″ in soil
10. smooth dandelion *(Taraxacum laevigatum)*	86	7	6 yrs	buried 8″ in soil
11. yellow foxtail *(Setaria lutescens)*	56	4	10 yrs	buried 8″ in soil
12. narrow leaved plantain *(Plantago lanceolata)*	83	4	10 yrs	buried 8″ in soil
13. cocklebur *(Xanthium strumarium)*	50	15	16 yrs	buried 8″ in soil
14. alsike clover *(Trifolium hybridum)*	90	1	21 yrs	buried 8″ in soil
15. Canada thistle *(Cirsium arvense)*	57	1	21 yrs	buried 8″ in soil
16. Kentucky blue grass *(Poa pratensis)*	91	1	30 yrs	buried 8″ in soil
17. purslane *(Portulaca oleracea)*	83	1	30 yrs	buried 8″ in soil
18. red clover *(Trifolium pratense)*	90	1	30 yrs	buried 8″ in soil
19. white clover *(Trifolium repens)*	85	1	30 yrs	buried 8″ in soil
20. tobacco *(Nicotiana tabacum)*	89	13	30 yrs	buried 8″ in soil
21. chrysanthemum *(Chrysanthemum leucanthemum)*	96	4	30 yrs	buried 8″ in soil
22. button clover *(Medicago orbicularis)*	—	—	78 yrs	herbarium
23. clover *(Trifolium striatum)*	—	—	90 yrs	herbarium
24. big trifoil *(Lotus uliginosus)*	—	1	100 yrs	dry storage
25. red clover *(Trifolium pratense)*	—	1	100 yrs	dry storage
26. loco weed *(Astragalus massiliensis)*	—	—	100–150 yrs	herbarium
27. sensitive plant *(Mimosa glomerata)*	—	—	221 yrs	herbarium
28. Indian lotus *(Nelumbo nucifera)*	—	—	1040 yrs	peat bog

[a] From various sources. See summaries in: P. L. Altman and Dorothy S. Dittmer (editors). 1962. *Growth, including Reproduction and Morphological Development.* Fed. Amer. Soc. for Expt. Biol., Washington, D.C., A. M. Mayer and A. Poljakoff-Mayber. 1963. *The Germination of Seeds.* Reprinted with permission of Pergamon Press, Oxford, London, New York, Paris.

The terms meet with some difficulties. Dormant seeds may frequently be induced to germinate by some specific change in the environment such as light or a period of low temperature. Where do we draw the line on conditions "normally" necessary for growth? The approach of defining dormancy as failure to germinate due to internal conditions, and quiescence as failure due to external conditions, also meets with some difficulty. In a sense, it is always the internal conditions that are limiting.

(If lack of water is limiting, it is lack of water in the cells of the embryo inside the seed.) In another sense it is the external conditions that always allow germination. The external conditions influence the internal ones.

The terms are very valuable, but the definitions must be somewhat more precise, stating conditions rather than depending upon the word "normally." **Dormancy** is better defined as the condition of a seed when it fails to germinate, even though ample external *moisture* is available, the seed is exposed to *atmospheric conditions* typical of those found at the earth's surface, and *temperature* is within the range usually associated with physiological activity (say 10° to 35°C). (A seed physiologist might define conditions still more precisely.) **Quiescence** is the condition of a seed when it fails to germinate *unless the above conditions are available.*

Another difficulty in terminology is encountered. In relation to seeds, agreement about the terms is fairly widespread, but dormancy is common to other plant systems, notably the buds of perennial plants. We have fairly good reason to believe that the mechanisms of response may be the same or similar in these various cases, but other terms have been used for the same concepts. Specifically, researchers concerned with fruit trees (**pomologists**) have employed a different terminology. The concept of dormancy defined above is called **rest**, while the term dormancy is used in exactly the same sense as quiescence. The **rest period** refers to the period during which the seed or other plant part is in rest (dormancy). It is common in European countries to use the word rest (e.g., the German *Ruhe*), while the term dormancy may not be commonly used in these languages. The student should be on guard as he studies the topic in the literature, especially for the term dormancy, which may be used in either sense. An excellent compromise would be to drop the term dormancy and use only quiescence and rest. This will depend upon acceptance by the scientists working in these areas. In this text, the term dormancy is never used in the sense of quiescence.

One other term has been widely used in studies in this area. **After-ripening** refers to the changes that go on within the seed (or the bud) during the breaking of dormancy.

25.2.3 Stratification

Several seeds, particularly rosaceous species, such as the stone fruits (peach, plum, cherry),

will not germinate until they have been exposed in the moist condition in the presence of oxygen for weeks to months (depending on the species; e.g., 6 weeks for peaches) to low temperatures (0° to 10°C). In a few rare cases, very similar effects may be observed by exposing the moist seeds to high temperatures. The practice of layering the seeds during winter in moist flats has been referred to as **stratification**. The phenomenon is of ecological importance. The requirement for exposure to an extended period at low temperatures protects the seed from precocious germination in the fall or during the winter months in response to an unseasonal warm period.

What goes on within the seed during stratification, allowing it subsequently to germinate when it is presented with optimum moisture, atmospheric, and temperature conditions? Careful observations of several seeds failed to reveal any morphological change during stratification. Changes must have been taking place, but they appeared in these cases to be at the chemical rather than the morphological level.

In recent years, however, anatomical changes during stratification have become apparent in other seeds. Figure 25-5 indicates the results of studies with cherry seeds carried out by Bruce Pollock and H. O. Olney then at Beltsville, Maryland. There was a clear-cut elongation of the embryos in those seeds exposed to low temperatures, but not in the control seeds held (in the moist condition) at room temperature. Chemical studies were also carried out, and it was found that many changes occurred. There were shifts in the concentrations of nitrogen and phosphorus between the various parts of the seed. Constituent amino acids, organic acids, and enzymes also shifted during stratification. Such observations have also been made with other species. In Rosaceae seeds, for example, the cyanogenic glycosides that are quite prevalent decompose during stratification to produce hydrocyanic acid. In several studies, it has been found that potentially important changes in the

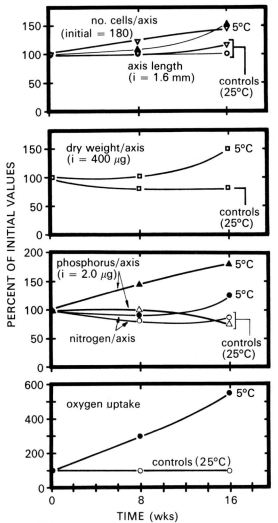

Figure 25-5

Changes during storage in cherry seeds. Data refer to the embryonic axis. Changes during storage at 5°C as compared to storage at 25°C are evident in the several factors illustrated. (Data from B. M. Pollock and H. O. Olney, 1959, *Plant Physiol.* 34:131, and H. O. Olney and B. M. Pollock, 1960, *Plant Physiol.* 35:970.)

concentrations of various growth regulators (both promoters and inhibitors) can be observed (see below 25.6.2).

If the changes within the dormant organ (seed, bud, etc.) are purely chemical, then the effect is inductive. Morphological changes would, according to the definition we have used (Chapter 20, section 20.6.1; see also 22.2.2 and 29.3.3) make the effect a noninductive one.

While the phenomenon may not be directly related to the cold requirement for germination, it is important to note that germination of some seeds is strongly promoted by alternating daily temperatures. This could be another manifestation of the biological clock, although little is known of the mechanism involved.

25.2.4 Impaction and Scarification

In seeds of many species, germination may fail because of a hard seed coat. Water or oxygen may be unable to penetrate, or the seed coat may be so hard that it restricts the growth of the embryo. This is common in members of the Leguminosae family, although it is not true of beans or peas, exemplifying that dormancy mechanisms are not common in domesticated species. Sometimes water and oxygen are unable to penetrate certain seeds because entry is blocked by a cork-like filling (the **strophiolar plug**) in a small opening (the **strophiolar cleft**) in the seed coat (Fig. 25-6). Vigorous shaking of the seeds will sometimes dislodge this plug allowing germination. The treatment is called **impaction**, and it has been applied to seeds of *Melilotus alba, Trigonella arabica,* and *Crotallaria egyptica.*

The seed coat barrier may be broken in several ways, and the process is referred to as **scarification**. Mechanical means such as knives, files, sandpaper, etc., have been used. In nature the abrasion may come about by microbial action, passage of the seed through the digestive tract of a bird or other animal, exposure to alternating temperatures, movement by water across sand or rocks, or by other means. In the laboratory and in practical agriculture (when needed), scarification may be carried out with alcohol or other fat solvents (which apparently dissolve the waxy materials sometimes re-

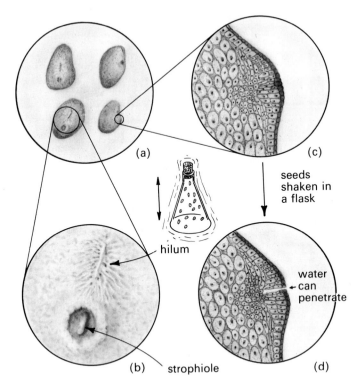

Figure 25-6

Impaction in white sweet clover (*Melilotus alba*). (a) Seeds placed with strophiole facing upward on the left; on the right, strophiole faces right. (b) An enlargement of the hilum and strophiole part of the seed. (c) A cross section through the strophiole. When the seeds are shaken, the strophiole breaks (d), allowing penetration of water and subsequent germination. (After D. H. Hamly, 1932, *Botan. Gaz.* 93:345–375.) .

sponsible for the inability of water to penetrate) or by concentrated acids. Seeds of some species (e.g., cotton) may be soaked briefly (e.g., a few minutes to an hour) in concentrated sulfuric acid, and then washed to remove the acid, after which germination is greatly improved.

In some cases the seed coat may be permeable to water but not to gases. Such a seed coat is a very unusual kind of membrane. The most frequently cited case of impermeability to oxygen is that of the seed coat of cocklebur (*Xanthium strumarium*). The fruit contains two seeds that differ in their requirements for external oxygen. The upper seed requires a concentration of oxygen much higher than normal in the external atmosphere (higher partial pressure), but if the seed coat is broken, germination occurs readily at normal oxygen pressures. P. F. Wareing and his student H. A. Foda in Aberystwyth, Wales, demonstrated the presence of an inhibitor in the seed coats of the upper seed and showed that this inhibitor was destroyed by high oxygen pressures.

A requirement for scarification could also be of considerable ecological importance. Frequently an interval of time is required for scarification to be completed by some natural means, and this again protects against premature germination in the autumn or during unseasonal warm periods in winter. Dean Vest, then at the University of Utah, was able to demonstrate an interesting symbiotic relationship between a particular fungus and the seeds of shadscale (*Atriplex confertifolia*). The fungus used the seed coats as a substrate for growth, at the same time scarifying them so germination could occur. The fungus would grow only when temperatures and moisture conditions were suitable, and these occurred only in the early spring in the deserts of the Great Basin, the most likely time for survival of the seedlings.

Fire is another important natural means of scarification. Several seeds, particularly in situations such as the chaparral vegetation type of Mediterranean climates (e.g., Southern California), are very effectively scarified by the fires so common in these situations. The result is a relatively rapid recovery of the area following the fires.

25.2.5 Chemical Inhibitors

What prevents the seeds in a ripe tomato from germinating inside of the fruit? Temperature is usually ideal, and there would seem to be plenty of water surrounding the seed. Oxygen is usually not limiting. If the seeds are removed from the fruit, dried, and planted, they usually will germinate rapidly, indicating that they are mature enough for germination. Apparently they fail to germinate because of the presence of certain germination inhibitors within the fruit (Chapter 21, 21.9). An alternate possibility, and one that apparently does play a role in many fruits, is an osmotic inhibition. The osmotic potential of the fruit juice is too negative to permit germination. The situation with the tomato still remains to be settled. Some workers claim that caffeic and

ferulic acids are the inhibitors; others claim that the inhibition is only osmotic.

There are also chemical inhibitors present in the seeds themselves, and often these must be leached out before germination can occur. This kind of dormancy is again of ecological importance. If enough rain falls to leach the inhibitor from the seed, the ground will then be adequately wet for survival of the new seedling. This is especially important in the desert where moisture is far more limiting than are other factors such as temperature. In shadscale, Vest found a chemical inhibitor of this type in the seed. It proved to be sodium chloride, but frequently the material is more complex. M. Evenari in Israel has made an extensive survey of naturally occurring germination inhibitors and found representatives of a wide variety of organic classes (Fig. 25-7). Some are cyanide-releasing complexes (especially in Rosaceous seeds), while others are ammonia-releasing substances. Mustard oils are common in the Cruciferae, and many other organic compounds may also be important including organic acids, unsaturated lactones (especially coumarin, parasorbic acid, and protoanemonin), aldehydes, essential oils, alkaloids, and phenolic compounds. These substances may occur not only in the seeds but also in leaves, roots, and other parts of plants. Even there they may play an important ecological role by inhibiting the germination of seeds in the near vicinity of the parent plant. Germination inhibitors produced by other plants (or conceivably even animals) may be referred to as **antibiotics**, using the term in its broadest sense as in Chapter 18 (substances produced by one organism and harmful to another).

In relation to the antibiotics, we are not dealing with dormancy in the usual sense of the word. Furthermore, some of the compounds produced by other organisms may actually act as germination promoters. Nitrate is one of the most commonly used germination promoters

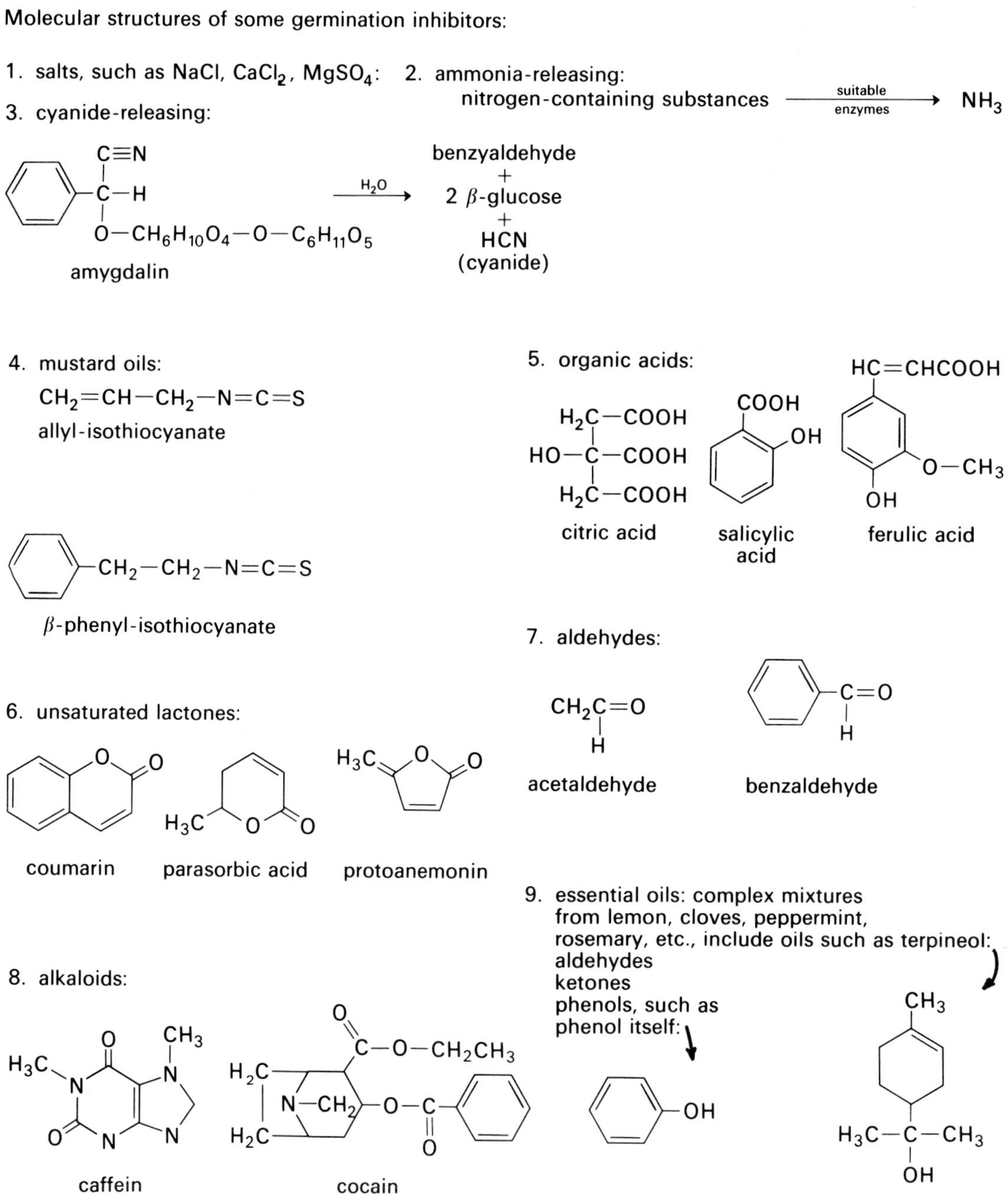

Molecular structures of some germination inhibitors:

1. salts, such as NaCl, $CaCl_2$, $MgSO_4$:

2. ammonia-releasing:

nitrogen-containing substances $\xrightarrow[\text{enzymes}]{\text{suitable}}$ NH_3

3. cyanide-releasing:

amygdalin

benzaldehyde
+
2 β-glucose
+
HCN
(cyanide)

4. mustard oils:

$CH_2=CH-CH_2-N=C=S$

allyl-isothiocyanate

β-phenyl-isothiocyanate

5. organic acids:

citric acid

salicylic
acid

ferulic acid

6. unsaturated lactones:

coumarin   parasorbic acid   protoanemonin

7. aldehydes:

$CH_2C=O$ with H below

acetaldehyde

benzaldehyde

8. alkaloids:

caffein   cocain

9. essential oils: complex mixtures
from lemon, cloves, peppermint,
rosemary, etc., include oils such as terpineol:
aldehydes
ketones
phenols, such as
phenol itself:

Figure 25-7

A summary of germination inhibitors showing representative molecular structures. (See also Fig. 21-20.)

in seed physiology laboratories. Nitrate is produced by decay of virtually any plant or animal residue, and its role in promotion of germination could be significant.

Before leaving the topic completely, we should note that many known compounds that are not natural products may strongly influence germination one way or the other. These include many of the growth regulators presently of commercial importance (e.g., 2,4-D, dalapon, etc.).

25.2.6 Light

In Chapter 23 (Photomorphogenesis), effects of light on seed germination were discussed, particularly as these effects are mediated through the phytochrome system. Daylength responses were also discussed there.

25.3 BUD DORMANCY IN PERENNIAL PLANTS

In temperate regions, plants commonly become dormant during the cold part of the year. This is true not only of deciduous trees but also of evergreens, which may grow much more slowly with the approach of fall and exhibit virtually no growth during the winter months. Some plants become dormant (or quiescent) during a hot and dry summer. We will again utilize the term dormancy (or rest) to refer to the condition of the plant when it will not grow immediately, even though it is exposed to suitable conditions of temperature, moisture, and atmosphere, while quiescence is the plant's condition when its growth is limited only by temperature, moisture, or atmospheric conditions. As indicated above, the student should be aware that pomologists utilize the term dormancy as we have defined quiescence and use rest as we have defined dormancy.

25.3.1 The Induction of Dormancy

Apparently several environmental factors will cause a plant to become dormant. We have a number of almost casual observations relating to this phenomenon, and we can draw a few general conclusions, but it appears that the exact interactions and details of the induction of dormancy remain to be discerned. Two factors, temperature and daylength, are of primary importance.

The development of bud dormancy often goes hand in hand with the appearance of fall color and the senescence of leaves. The two processes should not be confused, however. Buds of many trees are completely dormant in midsummer, exhibiting some growth again in late summer before going into fall dormancy. The leaves remain green and photosynthetically active until early autumn. The factors responsible for leaf senescence are discussed in Chapter 27.

Bud quiescence and dormancy are induced in many species by low temperatures, but it is possible in many if not most woody species to demonstrate a clear-cut control of the phenomenon by daylength, especially providing that temperatures remain high. With several deciduous trees studied at Beltsville, short-day treatment resulted in formation of a dormant terminal bud (typically a number of greatly foreshortened internodes within the bud scales or stipules that act as bud scales) and cessation of internode elongation and leaf expansion but often a retention of the leaves. Long nights, each interrupted by an interval of light, acted the same as long days. The leaves are usually the organs that detect the relative lengths of day and night, although the dormancy phenomenon is observed by changes in the buds. Perhaps this correlative phenomenon, like others, is caused by a hormone. The buds of birch (*Betula pubescens*), however, detect the daylength directly. There are always a number of interactions in the induction of dormancy. In the study with deciduous trees, the daylength response was induced at temperatures of 21° to 27°C, but at temperatures of 15° and 21°C, there was little growth of the plants, and consequently daylength effects were not readily apparent.

Withholding of water will frequently also accelerate the development of dormancy, as will the restriction of mineral nutrients, particularly nitrogen. This is probably important in enabling some species to withstand the high temperatures and drought occurring in dry climates.

Situations are also known in which dormancy develops in response to *changing* daylength (and even to changing soil temperature). This is also true for certain developmental processes in birds.

In any case, dormancy seldom appears immediately. Typically, a gradual development of rest can be observed by attempting to induce active growth with moderate temperatures and long days (or continuous light). As rest first begins to develop, it can easily be reversed by these treatments. The plant is then only in the initial stages of a quiescence and is not truly dormant. Gradually, however, attempts to induce active growth completely fail, and at this time the plant is said to have reached true dormancy or rest. Frost hardiness and fall leaf color usually develop concurrently with autumn dormancy. Again, short days promote the effects, as do reduced temperatures.

25.3.2 The Breaking of Dormancy

Overcoming the rest period also appears to be a function of temperature or daylength or both. The daylength effect was recognized only within the past decade or so. Leaves were known to respond to the daylength in the *induction* of dormancy and in flowering, and so it seemed reasonable to imagine that leaves always are the only organs that respond to daylength. There

seemed to be no reason to suspect that the buds themselves would respond. Nevertheless, it is known that dormancy can be broken by long days in several species of trees that have no leaves during the dormant period, such as beech, birch, larch, yellow poplar, sweetgum, and red oak; although, except for beech, these species also respond to cold periods. In other cases, cold periods must be followed by long days.

A midsummer dormancy occurs in some species (especially evergreens) during which the stems cease to elongate for a period of time. This is typically broken by exposure to more long days. It appears that even in midwinter certain deciduous species will respond to long-day treatment (particularly continuous light). What is initially responding in these cases? Apparently enough light penetrates the bud scales to bring about the response within the primordial leaf tissues inside the bud. We have reason to believe that both the short-day induction of dormancy and the long-day breaking of dormancy are phytochrome responses, but at this time the case has not been as thoroughly documented as is desirable. Certain recent studies do indicate phytochrome participation in the short-day induction of dormancy, since red light is most effective in the night interruption, and its effect may be reversed somewhat by far-red light.

It has long been known that bud rest may be broken by exposure to low temperatures. Days to months may be required at temperatures below 10°C. In a recent study with fruit trees at Utah State University, 5–7°C proved to be more effective than 0°C. Considerable work has been done with many species, particularly commercial fruit trees, to determine the minimum period of dormancy. The length of this period varies considerably with species and varieties. Apples, for example, depending upon the variety, may require 1,000 to 1,400 hours below 7°C to break their dormancy. Considerable headway

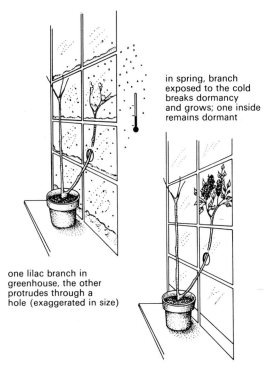

in spring, branch
exposed to the cold
breaks dormancy
and grows; one inside
remains dormant

one lilac branch in
greenhouse, the other
protrudes through a
hole (exaggerated in size)

Figure 25-8

Illustrating the experiment in which a lilac branch was
allowed to protrude through the greenhouse wall during the
winter, breaking its dormancy in the spring, while the remainder of the plant, not exposed to the low temperatures
of winter, remained dormant.

has been made in selecting peach varieties for a
shorter chilling requirement, allowing certain
varieties to be cultivated farther south where
the winters are warmer.

The effects of chilling upon the breaking of
dormancy are not translocated within the plant
but appear to be localized within the individual
buds. A dormant lilac bush, for example, may
be placed in the greenhouse with one branch
protruding outside through a small hole in the
wall (Fig. 25-8). The branch exposed to the low
temperatures of winter will leaf out early in the
spring, while the rest of the bush inside of the
greenhouse remains dormant.

Several chemical treatments will break dormancy. 2-Chloroethanol[2] ($ClCH_2CH_2OH$) has
been used with success for many years. It breaks
dormancy of fruit trees when applied in the vapor
form. A rather simple treatment that results in
the breaking of dormancy is immersion of the
plant or plant part in a warm water bath
(40–55°C). Often a very short exposure (15
seconds) to these elevated temperatures will
break dormancy.

In recent years, it has been discovered that
applied gibberellins break the dormancy of a
great many deciduous plants. Since this chemical
will also break the dormancy of some cold-
requiring seeds (e.g., peach—but not apple) and
induce the flowering of cold-requiring plants,
we have another good reason to suspect that
the positive plant responses to low temperature
may have a single metabolic mechanism in
common.

As we shall see from the discussion below,
there are a number of other possibly significant
breakthroughs in this area. A number of growth-
regulating compounds, such as naringenin and
abscisic acid (Chapter 21) have recently been
extracted from dormant seeds and buds.

25.4 UNDERGROUND STORAGE ORGANS

Several phenomena unique to such underground
storage organs as bulbs, corms, and tubers are
related to the general topic of this chapter. In
some cases, certain temperature conditions induce the formation of the underground storage
organ; and, in other cases, dormancy may be
broken or subsequent growth influenced by
storage temperatures. Daylength may also affect
the formation of the specific organs.

---

[2] This compound was called ethylenechlorohydrin in
many earlier plant physiology books.

25.4.1 The Potato

Under usual greenhouse conditions, potato tubers form in response to short days. All the expected features of photoperiodism are present (including a critical night and the inhibitory effect of a light interruption during the dark period—see Chapter 26). Tuber formation does not *require* short days, however, but will proceed at any daylength (a day-neutral response) if the night temperature is below 20°C. Tuberization is optimal at night temperatures of about 12°C. This interaction between photoperiodism and temperature (Fig. 25-9) is not uncommon, as we saw in relation to vernalization.

Scientists have postulated that a "tuber-inducing" principle exists. Obviously, the leaves must respond to the short days, since the underground stems are dark, and so something produced in response to short-day treatment must be translocated to the **stolons** (underground stems) where tuber formation is induced. Low temperatures stimulating tuberization are also detected by the *tops* of the plants, rather than the underground parts. This is demonstrated by maintaining the two parts at different temperatures. On long days no tubers will form at any soil temperatures unless the tops are exposed to low temperatures. It might be suggested that tubers form in response to some nutritional change brought about by the low temperatures, rather than in response to a specific tuber-inducing hormone, yet the tops are capable of exporting the tuber-inducing stimulus for several days after they have been removed from the cold, as can be shown by grafting them at intervals following cold treatment to a root system with no tubers, resulting in tuber formation. Such an effect is more easily explained in terms of a hormone than in terms of nutrition.

It might be noted that the stolons form over a wide range of soil and air temperatures and daylengths, but only the conditions described above cause these to develop into tubers.

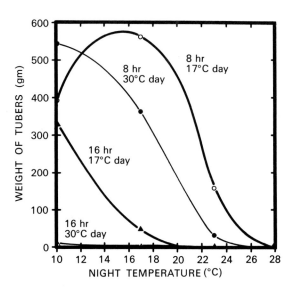

Figure 25-9

Effects of night temperature at two day lengths and two day temperatures upon weight of tubers produced by Kennebec potato plants. Low temperatures and short days promoted tuber formation. (Data from L. E. Gregory, 1965, "Physiology of tuberization in plants," *Encyc. of Plant Physiology*, W. Ruhland (ed.), Springer-Verlag, Berlin, 15/1:1328–1354. By permission of L. E. Gregory.)

The potato tuber is an underground stem and exhibits the expected characteristics of stems. The eyes on a potato are the axillary buds, and they remain dormant in response to the presence of the apical bud. When the potato is cut up to produce seed pieces, this apical dominance is lost, and the axillary buds become active and grow if dormancy has been broken. There are practical reasons for wanting both to prolong and to break tuber dormancy. The longer the tubers can be stored during winter and spring in the dormant condition, the higher their price when they are sold for food. In potato "seed" certification, it is desirable to break dormancy prematurely. The period of time normally required to break dormancy is somewhat shorter when the tubers are stored at about 20°C than at lower temperatures, but there is no clear-cut temperature effect. Certainly there is no cold requirement as in the cases discussed above.

It is possible to break dormancy in a potato tuber by certain chemical treatments, typically those that are effective in breaking the bud dormancy of above-ground stems (2-chloro-ethanol, gibberellins, hot water, etc.). Thiourea also causes sprouting but may result in as many as eight sprouts from a single eye rather than the usual single sprout. Dormancy may also be induced or prolonged by treatment with such growth regulators as naphthalene-acetic acid, maleic hydrazide, or CIPC (Chapter 28). These compounds are sometimes sprayed on the foliage before harvest or on the tubers after harvest to prevent premature sprouting in storage. Storage temperature is also very important. Tubers sprout somewhat prematurely at high temperatures, and their starches turn to sugars at low temperatures. The ideal compromise seems to be 10°C.

25.4.2 Bulbs and Corms

Although very little has been done toward investigating the induction of bulb, corm, and rhizome formation, a great deal of work has been done in Holland, supported largely by the Dutch bulb industry, on the optimum storage conditions for these underground organs. It is important for the industry to understand the storage conditions (primarily the storage temp-erature as a function of time) that will result in the formation of leaves, flowers, and stems with the desirable properties. Their approach was to observe the morphology of the bulb carefully in the field during a normal season, and then to repeat this using bulbs stored under accurately controlled temperature conditions. This work has been going on now for well over 40 years. It was originally under the direction of A. H. Blaauw, but Annie Hartsema has also contributed a great deal. In the Encyclopedia of Plant Physiology, she recently reviewed the results of 40 years of investigation.

A few generalizations can be summarized here. Bulbs must reach a critical size, which may require two or more years, before they begin to respond to temperature storage condi-tions by the formation of flower primordia. In some cases (e.g., tulip), leaf primordia are formed before the flowers, or sometimes leaf and flower formation may be nearly simul-taneous. Specific temperatures may be required for flower initiation or subsequent stem elonga-tion. The course of change and the optimum temperatures usually match closely the climate at the location native to the bulbs.

A number of different patterns are exhibited: in some cases, flower primordia form before the bulbs can even be harvested. In these situa-tions little control can be exercised during storage conditions; these have not been studied extensively. In other cases, the flower primordia form during the storage period after harvest in the summer but before replanting in the fall. Extensive work has been done with plants in this category. Optimum temperatures as a function of time are shown for tulips in Fig. 25-10. The object here is to cause rapid flowering in time for Christmas. It can be noted that the temperatures inducing flowers are relatively high compared to those discussed above in the section on vernalization. Nevertheless, there is a parallel response.

In most bulbous irises (Fig. 25-10) the actual flower primordia appear during the low temperatures of winter (9° to 13°C optimum), but it was found that a high temperature (20° to 30°C) pretreatment was essential if flower formation was to occur at all. This would be a true inductive effect very similar to vernaliza-tion except that the response is to high rather than low temperatures.

25.5 VEGETATIVE GROWTH

Growth of the vegetative parts of the plant is always strongly influenced by temperature, sometimes in rather specific and even inductive ways. This is often closely associated with flowering, as in the case of the bolting of rosette plants in response to vernalization and/or long-day treatment. Stratification of seeds sometimes has a strong inductive effect on growth, in addition to its dormancy-breaking action. If the embryos of peach seedlings are excised from their cotyledons, they germinate without stratification, but the seedlings produced are frequently stunted and highly abnormal (Fig. 25-11). If these excised embryos are exposed to a period of low temperature, they then grow into normal seedlings. Apparently it is not the presence of the cotyledons that insures their normality, but the stratification process. Since stunted growth is now often associated with lack of gibberellin-like growth promoters, we suspect that the accumulation of gibberellins might be an important aspect of the responses to stratification.

Frits Went described a phenomenon that appears to be of widespread occurrence and that is clearly of importance in our understanding of plant growth. This is the phenomenon of **thermoperiodism**. He found, for example, that fruit set on tomato plants was strongly influenced by the night temperature. Vegetative growth was often influenced, whether fruit set or flower formation were affected or not. Effects were particularly adverse if constant temperature was accompanied by continuous light. The effect is direct and not typically inductive.

One of the most spectacular examples of thermoperiodism involved *Baeria charysostoma*, a small annual composite commonly seen during spring in California. This plant normally occurs in mountain valleys and foothills and occasionally in the west Mojave Desert. It is very sensitive to night temperature. Grown under short-day conditions, plants survive only for two months when the night temperature is 20°C. At lower temperatures they grow for at least 100 days. They die rapidly at night temperatures of 26°C.

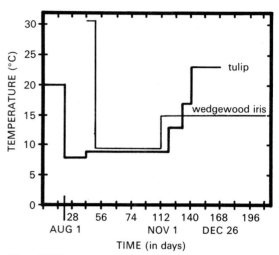

Figure 25-10

Temperature treatment for early flowering of *Tulipa gesneriana* W. Copland and of *Iris xiphium* Imperator. With the tulip, flower initiation begins and is well under way during the 20°C treatment. Moving to storage rooms at 8° and 9°C provides an acceleration in blooming, so that flowers are produced at Christmas. Continuous 9°C treatment gives equal earliness, but quality is poor unless the 20°C treatment is given first. The bulbs are planted in a controlled temperature greenhouse about midway during the low-temperature treatment. The temperature is first raised when the leaf tips are visible, then again when they are 3 cm long, and finally again when they are 6 cm long. With iris, the short period at high temperature is completely essential to flowering, although actual initiation of flower primordia does not occur until the bulbs have been moved from low temperature to 15°C, at which time the sprouts are about 6 cm long. Again, the 9°C treatment is to ensure earliness. At temperatures much above 15°C during the last part of the treatment, abnormal flowers may be produced. Low light intensities will also result in "blasted" flowers at this time, especially if the temperatures are not right. If extremely high temperatures (38°C) are used during the first flower induction period, flower parts are increased or decreased, or tetramerous, pentamerous, or dimerous flowers result. (Data from Annie M. Hartsema in F. B. Salisbury, 1963, *The Flowering Process*, Pergamon Press, Oxford, London, Paris, New York. Used by permission.)

The concept of 26°C as a lethal temperature is an unexpected one. Many species do not grow particularly well at night temperatures this high, but it is difficult to imagine what kind of mechanism might account for death due to this

Figure 25-11
Normal and dwarf peach seedlings (Sullivan Elberta). The seed that produced the plant at left
was stored at 19°C while the seed that produced the plant at right was stored at 27°C. Embryos
were excised, allowing germination. (Photograph courtesy of B. M. Pollock, National Seed
Storage Laboratory, Fort Collins, Colorado.)

temperature. The *Baeria* plants flourish when
the day temperature is well above 26°C, providing only that the night temperature is low
enough. Other plants native to California acted
similarly in Went's experiments.

Thermoperiodism is not a phenomenon
common to all species. Many plants (e.g., some
varieties of the cocklebur) will grow well when
the day and the night temperatures are identical,
even when they are subjected to continuous
light.

It is of importance to note that these temperature responses frequently interact with the light
environment. Sometimes this may be a response
to photoperiodism, while in other cases it may
be due to the action of light intensity or light
quality (e.g., the balance in the phytochrome
system).

25.6 THE MECHANISMS OF THE LOW-TEMPERATURE RESPONSE

How are we to understand the positive plant
responses to low temperature? We might be
dealing with some kind of metabolic block. If
a seed fails to germinate until it has been exposed
to low temperatures, the treatment could remove
some block to germination. Vernalization could
remove a flowering block. Several investigators
have discussed the responses in these terms.
These blocks could be inhibiting substances or
the *lack* of some necessary metabolite or condition within the plant.

Are the mechanisms the same in the several
responses we have described above? Surely the
diversity is great enough that we wouldn't
expect a common mechanism for all, but in

many cases there are striking similarities, and similarities in mechanism seem reasonable. A growth regulator may arise at low temperatures, for example, and this, in turn, may influence flowering, germination, subsequent seedling growth, etc. There is evidence to indicate that the mechanisms might be similar in at least two processes. M. Black and P. F. Wareing have studied germination of birch seeds and the breaking of dormancy of buds on the mature trees. They observed a number of close parallels, including the presence of a specific growth inhibitor (abscisic acid).

In the following paragraphs we will examine a few ideas relative to the mechanisms of the low-temperature response.

25.6.1 The Production of a Growth Regulator by a Compensated System

As we have seen above, there is much evidence for a chemical promoter, a hormone of some type that arises in response to cold and that may influence the various responses. This was shown by Melchers and others with grafting and other experiments related to vernalization, and the hypothetical potato tuber-inducing principle is another good example. Growth promoters may also be influencing the other phenomena described above. Gibberellins often seem to play a role.

But here we are faced with a paradox. Low temperature is known to reduce the rate of chemical reactions, and yet we are thinking of an *increased* production of some substance in response to low temperature. Melchers and Lang, in Europe, and Gregory and Purvis, in England, simultaneously proposed a scheme designed to solve this problem. They suggested that there might be two interacting reactions, one with a fairly low temperature coefficient and the other with a higher temperature coefficient. The principle is illustrated in Fig. 25-12, which shows not only the reactions but their relative

rates (purely hypothetical) plotted as a function of temperature. The idea is simply that the products of one reaction (I) are acted upon by a second reaction (II). If the rate of reaction I exceeds that of II, then the product of reaction I will accumulate, while if the reverse is true, there will be no accumulation. If the temperature coefficient of reaction I is relatively low, but the reaction progresses at low temperatures more rapidly than reaction II, then we can explain the accumulation of product at low temperatures but not at high temperatures. With increasing temperature, the rate of reaction II increases much more rapidly than the rate of reaction I, and at some critical temperature, product will be utilized faster than it is produced and hence will not accumulate. The devernalization response seems to give evidence for this mechanism (reaction II would be devernalization), and the fact that devernalization fails after two or three days at the neutral temperature seems to indicate a third reaction (III), which stabilizes the product.

The compensated feedback systems discussed in the previous chapter in relation to temperature independence in the biological clock could also account for an over-all reaction with a negative temperature coefficient. In that system, rather than two sequential reactions with different temperature coefficients as above, the product of one reaction might inhibit the *rate* of another. At low temperatures, a substance might accumulate because another compound inhibiting its production might not. Again, different temperature coefficients would be required.

Inherent in these schemes is the idea that a promoter of some kind is produced by the low-temperature experience. If gibberellin-like substances are the promoters leading to the breaking of dormancy, bolting of vernalized stems, and other similar reactions, then the gibberellins may be equivalent to the products of reactions I or III in the first scheme.

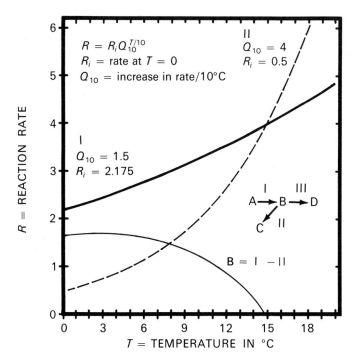

Figure 25-12

Sample curves showing hypothetical reaction rates as a function of temperature for reactions with Q_{10} values of 1.5 or 4.0. If the reaction with $Q'_{10} = 1.5$ is considered to be reaction 1 in the formula in the text, and the reaction with $Q'_{10} = 4.0$ to be reaction 2, then the hypothetical product B will be proportional to curve 2 minus curve 1, as shown (curve B). Compare the shape of curve B with the curves in Figs. 25-1 and 25-3. (From F. B. Salisbury, 1963, *The Flowering Process,* Pergamon Press, Oxford, London, Paris, New York. Used by permission.)

But what if we are dealing with the *destruction of an inhibitor* rather than with the production of some promoter? We have only to reverse the roles of the two reactions. The destruction (or conversion) reaction must have the fairly rapid rate at low temperatures and the low temperature coefficient. The synthesis of the inhibitor, on the other hand, must be low at low temperatures but have the high temperature coefficient. These schemes are, of course, only hypothetical, but it is likely that something similar does indeed occur in plants during the induction of low-temperature responses.

It is also possible that the genes themselves respond to temperature, becoming derepressed at low temperatures and producing an enzyme that controls synthesis of our hypothetical promoter. At the moment, we have no evidence for such a mechanism.

25.6.2   Evidences for the Participation of Growth Regulators

Several workers have reported various degrees of success in extracting vernalized seeds, applying the extracts back to unvernalized seeds, and causing early flowering. This has been done with winter rye, and in one case the extracts were effective not only on the winter rye but also on a variety of pea. Extracts from the pea seeds were also effective on the rye. Comparable results have been obtained using extracts of mature vernalized plants (e.g., *Rudbeckia*).

The real breakthrough in this area came with the discovery that gibberellins could replace the vernalization (or long-day) treatments required for the flowering of several species. We have discussed this above (25.1.4). Of course, the response is strongly dependent upon the species. With *Samolus parviflorus* a total of 20 micrograms of GA_3 per plant (1 microgram per day for 20 days) was very effective, and 100 micrograms gave a maximum effect. On the other hand, about 900 micrograms (5 micrograms per day for 6 months) was only partially effective on parsley. It is important to realize that only 0.001 microgram per plant will often give a significant stem elongation response.

A well-defined pattern is evident in the results of experiments in which gibberellins are applied to different species. Flowering of many cold-requiring plants with a rosette form is promoted in the absence of cold by gibberellins, but if the plant also has a long-day requirement, effects of gibberellins are best observed under long-day conditions. Only a few species requiring both cold and long days have been promoted to flower with gibberellins alone, and usually rather large quantities are required. Long-day plants without a cold requirement are frequently promoted to flower with gibberellins. In a long-short-day species of *Bryophyllum*, which flowers only in response to long days followed by short days, application of gibberellin under short days promptly results in flowering, but application under long days does not. Thus, gibberellins can substitute for cold or for a long-day requirement, but seldom for both. Applied gibberellins do not cause flowering in short-day plants under long-day conditions. Gibberellins seldom promote the flowering of caulescent plants (as contrasted to rosette plants) whether these plants have a cold or a long-day requirement or not, and the winter annuals seldom respond to applied gibberellins either.

These generalizations hold fairly well, but there are exceptions, depending upon species, and furthermore, the particular gibberellin used is often of considerable importance. It was possible to show, for example, that some of the most common gibberellins had little influence upon the flowering of certain species but readily promoted the flowering of others. We conclude that these substances could indeed play an important role in the flowering of some plants but that the situation is rather complex. Most plant physiologists are optimistic about the possibilities that the gibberellins do represent an extremely important aspect of low-temperature and long-day promotion of flowering.

Gibberellic acid also promotes germination in the dark of lettuce seeds that normally require light (Chapter 21). It is also effective in substituting for stratification in some species (e.g., peach and apricot), although not in others, and there are promotive effects of gibberellins upon the dormant buds of deciduous plants (e.g., effective on peaches but not on apple).

Several breakthroughs are being made by extracting various inhibitors from dormant seeds or buds. For example, F. C. Steward extracted from dormant maple buds antagonists of coconut milk as studied in his carrot-tissue bioassay. As the dormancy of the buds is broken by cold, the antagonists disappear. Naringenin (5,7,4'-trihydroxyflavanon, 21.9.2) has proved to be an inhibitor in the *Avena* straight-growth test, and its occurrence in dormant peach flower buds correlates fairly well with their dormancy. As dormancy is broken, the level of inhibitor drops. Abscisic acid (dormin) is a similar compound having similar effects. Recently, David Walker and Teh'hsiu Liao at Utah State University have followed the levels of three *Avena* growth promoters and one inhibitor (apparently naringenin) during stratification of peach seeds (Fig. 25-13). As seed dormancy was broken, the three promoters gradually increased, and the inhibitor decreased.

This may well be the general picture we face in our attempts to understand dormancy. Growth promoters and growth inhibitors may be interacting, possibly in a complex series of reactions, not too unrelated to the temperature-compensated systems described above. There has always been discussion among plant physiologists as to the relative roles of inhibitors or promoters. The henbane, for example, which requires long days for flowering, will flower under short-day conditions if the leaves are continually removed. Apparently the leaves produce some inhibitor under short-day conditions. Yet there is evidence for flowering promoters in grafting experiments with this same plant. In the dormancy of the vascular cambium, auxin by itself had little promotive effect, but when applied in conjunction with kinetin, dormancy was broken. There is evidence that dormancy-breaking treatments, such as stratification or exposure to long days, destroy inhibitors in the seed coats of several species besides the peach studied by Walker and Liao. There is also evidence that growth promoters are formed in many of these seeds. Several investigators (particularly Wareing in Wales and Nitsch in France) commonly observe areas on chromatograms that contain growth promoters and other areas that contain growth inhibitors. This is true almost regardless of the tissue being studied, but it is particularly true for dormant tissues.

We would appear to be justified, then, in concluding that the phenomena discussed in this chapter may typically be responses to balances in various growth regulators, some of which are promotive in their actions and others of which are inhibitory. The reactions producing these compounds would be the transducers

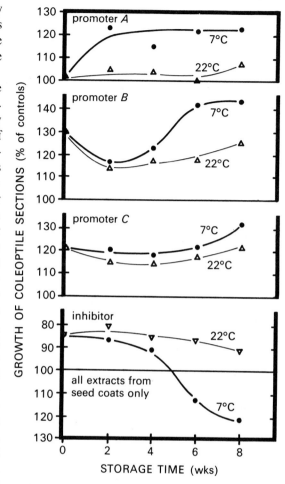

Figure 25-13

Relative levels of three *Avena* coleoptile growth promoters and one inhibitor in peach seeds stored at 7°C and at 22°C. "Promoters *A, B, C*," and "inhibitor" refer to positions on chromatographs of extracts from the peach seeds. Data shown are for seed coats only. Results are given as growth of coleoptile sections expressed as percent of control sections not treated with extract. Germination occurred in chilled seeds after eight weeks. (Data from Teh-Hsiu Liao, 1966, master's thesis, Utah State University, Logan.)

of the environment, and translation to final response might well involve activation and repression of specific genes.

25.6.3 Dormancy and the Temperature Range for Growth

A. Vegis in Sweden has been concerned with the phenomenon of dormancy for many years. In a recent review, he took a somewhat different approach from that usually taken (and that we have taken here). Apparently many investigators have not considered as wide a range of environmental conditions as might be desirable. Thus, Vegis was able to show that, in several supposedly dormant seeds as well as deciduous buds, growth could be immediately induced, providing only that the proper temperatures were applied. The buds were not truly dormant but had simply developed *a narrow temperature range that would allow active growth.* A ripening seed on the plant, if immediately removed, would germinate over a fairly wide range of temperatures, but if tested at later times, the temperature range that would permit germination became increasingly narrowed. The same was true for the growth of deciduous perennials. With the approach of fall the range over which they would grow was very wide but became progressively more narrow. In some cases, this finally culminated in a condition in which the seeds would not germinate (or the shoots would not grow) at any temperature. Vegis called this **true dormancy.** He was able to show that in several apparent cases of dormancy, as defined earlier in this chapter, seeds or plants were simply not tested with a sufficient number of narrow temperature ranges.

With the coming of spring; dormancy was broken by a reversal of the initial process—that is, the temperature range allowing germination or growth became progressively wider. Often the period of true dormancy was relatively brief.

Vegis described three possible variations on this condition, as illustrated in Fig. 25-14. *First,* the range for growth narrows as the maximum temperature allowing growth gradually decreases, while the minimum remains constant.

In the spring, dormancy is broken by a reversal of this process: the maximum temperature increases gradually from a low value. *Second,* in the opposite situation the maximum temperature remains relatively constant, but the minimum temperature gradually increases as plants approach dormancy. In the case of true dormancy, the maximum and the minimum finally converge, after which no growth at all occurs at any temperature. *Third,* both the minimum and the maximum temperatures may change, approaching each other at some middle value. Again, they may or may not actually meet. When they do, Vegis's true dormancy is achieved.

Vegis discussed the ecological adaptations of these various possibilities. In the first instance, the plant would be well adapted to a warm climate, and its dormancy may be a protection against a hot period of drought. The second case might be more typical of temperate climates, in which the increase in the minimum temperature for growth results in the plant's remaining quiescent (or perhaps truly dormant) throughout a cold winter. The third type is the most common, providing an adaptation to two unfavorable seasons, a hot and arid summer and a cold winter.

Vegis extended this general descriptive approach to several situations. For example, Bruce Pollock found that the abnormal growth of peach seedlings developing from embryos from which the cotyledons had been removed was a function of the germination temperature. The abnormal growth was quite apparent at germination temperatures above 23°C but less and less so at temperatures below this value. At 19°C, growth was quite normal. It was not that unchilled embryos would not grow normally at *any* temperature, but rather that these seedlings would grow normally only at *a more narrow range* of temperature.

Vegis discussed his observations in terms of the growth-regulator ideas considered in

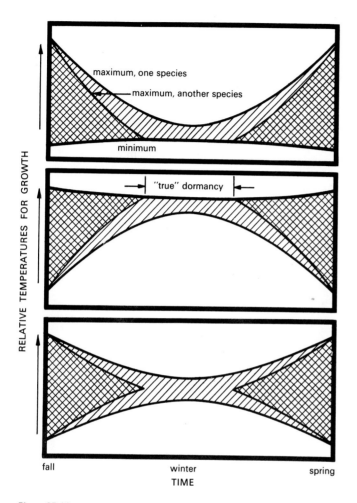

Figure 25-14

An illustration of Vegis' theory on dormancy and the temperature range allowing growth.

previous sections. Such an approach may be entirely reasonable. Rather than thinking in all-or-none terms (i.e., either the seed germinates or it doesn't; the plant flowers or it doesn't; the deciduous buds grow or they don't), we must simply quantitate our observations somewhat, considering the range of conditions under which the organism will respond. We recognize that the quiescent situation is somewhat more common than we had previously assumed. The gibberellins, auxins, cytokinins, naringenin, and other compounds may have their effects upon this temperature range, or conversely, the temperature range may have its effect upon or via these compounds. Normal seedling growth, for example, may depend upon the presence of adequate gibberellins. At 25°C the organism's metabolism may be quite unable to synthesize these compounds. At 17°C, however, synthesis goes on readily, accounting for the observations of Pollock.

The real question is changed only slightly. Before, we may have thought that the question was concerned primarily with various kinds of metabolism at various temperature levels. We are now in a position to consider the question of how the temperature range permitting metabolism of various compounds may be gradually changed as a function of time. That is, the factors that induce dormancy may do so by an effect upon the limiting temperature range for a given reaction. Perhaps if this is a matter of temperature-compensated reactions, as indicated above, then dormancy induction is a matter of shifting the balance in these various reactions, perhaps shifting the relative concentrations of enzymes available.

25.6.4 Interaction of Cold with Other Environmental Factors

As should be evident from the discussion in this chapter, many (if not most) of the phenomena described here can be caused not only by low temperatures but also by a host of other factors, including particularly daylength, as well as by more subtle effects such as special light qualities (the phytochrome system), the removal of the seed coat, and high oxygen partial pressures. Surely, since this is a very general sort of observation, we might expect it to tell us something about the nature of the phenomenon under consideration.

It is reasonable to assume that in all of the cases being studied here, we are dealing, as suggested in the first part of this chapter, with the activation and repression of certain genes, the morphogenetic program. For example, if the temperature range allowing a given response is a function of the balances between the various components of a temperature-compensated reaction complex, then this might, in turn, be controlled by the balances in the activated and repressed genes that produce the enzymes that are in control of this complex. James Bonner and Dorothy Tuan were indeed able to show that the number of activated genes in dormant potato buds was greatly reduced compared to active potato buds. This being the case, then our assignment is to discover the transducers and their mechanisms, the control systems, the steps in translation, and finally the morphogenetic program.

Photoperiodism and the Physiology of Flowering

26.1 INTRODUCTION

Two powerful mechanisms of plant response to environment have already been introduced. The low-temperature responses with their possibility of compensated reaction rates were discussed in the preceding chapter. Photoperiodism was mentioned in earlier chapters and then defined and briefly outlined in Chapter 24 on the biological clock. It was also often mentioned in the low-temperature chapter, since there is such a frequent interaction between the response to low temperature and photoperiodism. Often the same plant response may be mediated through either mechanism. In this chapter we will consider photoperiodism in detail.

The characteristic feature of photoperiodism is the biological measurement of the relative lengths of day and night, and this could involve a single mechanism for the various processes occurring in different species. In a broad sense, the mechanism of photoperiodism is the transducer that responds to the environment. Yet the ultimate manifestations (dormancy, germination, flowering, etc.) surely indicate a biochemical diversity. That is, there are several translational possibilities. The best-understood response is the flowering process. Following the response to photoperiod itself, there appears to be a synthesis of a flowering hormone, its translocation to the buds, and (in response to this) a switching of the morphogenetic program to reproductive development.

During the first part of this chapter, we will consider in some detail the general phenomenon of photoperiodism as it is exemplified by measurement of the relative lengths of day and night in the flowering process. We will then consider further aspects of the physiology of flowering in response to photoperiodism.

26.2 THE PHENOMENON OF PHOTOPERIODISM

26.2.1 Some Examples

Examples of photoperiodism are summarized in Table 26-1. Examples from the plant kingdom include reproductive initiation in higher plants and certain comparable examples in lower plants. The remaining categories include effects upon both vegetative and reproductive growth, germination of certain seeds, and the induction and breaking of dormancy. Several examples from the animal kingdom are also of considerable interest.

26.2.2 A Basic Characteristic: Ripeness to Flower

All plants that are induced to flower by photoperiodic treatment do not respond to such

TABLE 26-1

SELECTED EXAMPLES OF PHOTOPERIODISM IN PLANTS AND ANIMALS

Organism	Short-day	Long-day	Response promoted by indicated day length
Bryophytes:			
Sphagnum plumulosum[a]	x(?)		development of reproductive structure
Marchantia polymorpha[a]		x	development of reproductive structure
Preissia quadrata[a]		x	development of reproductive structure
Conocephalum conicum[a]		x	development of reproductive structure
Lunularia cruciata[a]		x	development of reproductive structure
Gymnosperms:			
loblolly pine *(Pinus taeda)*[b]		x	stem growth
Angiosperms:			
monocots:			
bluestem grass *(Andropogon gerardi)*[c]	x		flower formation
wild oats *(Avena sativa)*[c]		x	flower formation
onion *(Allium cepa)*[d]		x	bulb formation
orchid *(Cattleya trianae)*[d]	x		bud elongation
orchid *(Cattleya trianae)*[c]	x		flower formation
dicots:			
soybean *(Glycine max)*[c,d]	x		flower formation (see Table 26-2 for many examples)
sugar beet *(Beta vulgaris)*[c,d]		x	flower formation (see Table 26-2 for many examples)
radish *(Raphanus sativus)*[d]	x		root thickening
radish *(Raphanus sativus)*[c,d]		x	flower formation
strawberry *(Fragaria chiloensis)*[d]		x	runner development
strawberry *(Fragaria chiloensis)*[c,d]	x		flower formation
coneflower *(Rudbeckia spp.)*[d]		x	stem elongation
coneflower *(Rudbeckia spp.)*[c,d]		x	flower formation
cucumber *(Cucumis sativus)*[d]	x		pistillate flowers increased
cucumber *(Cucumis sativus)*[d]		x	staminate flowers increased
alfalfa *(Medicago sativa)*[d]	x		winter hardening
potato *(Solanum tuberosum)*[d]	x		tuber development
yam *(Dioscorea alata)*[d]	x		tuber development
dahlia *(Dahlia spp.)*[d]	x		storage root development
dahlia *(Dahlia spp.)*[d]		x	fibrous root development
bryophyllum *(Bryophyllum pinnatum)*[d]		x	development of foliar plantlets
bryophyllum *(Bryophyllum pinnatum)*[c,d]	x		flower formation
kalanchoë *(Kalanchoë blossfeldiana)*[e]	x		dark fixation of CO_2
Insects:			
mite *(Metatetranychus ulmi)*[f]		x	uninterrupted development
mite *(Metatetranychus ulmi)*[f]	x		initiation of diapause
mulberry silkworm *(Bombyx mori)*[f]		x	female lays diapause eggs
mulberry silkworm *(Bombyx mori)*[f]	x		female lays developing eggs
pitcher-plant midge *(Metriocnemus knabi)*[g]	x		initiation of diapause
pitcher-plant midge *(Metriocnemus knabi)*[g]		x	termination of diapause (pupation)
Fish:			
European minnow *(Phoxinus phoxinus)*[h]		x	egg maturation
bridled shiner *(Notropis bifrenatus)*[h]		x	egg maturation

TABLE 26-1 continued

SELECTED EXAMPLES OF PHOTOPERIODISM IN PLANTS AND ANIMALS

Organism	Short-day	Long-day	Response promoted by indicated day length
Reptile:			
lizard *(Xantusia vigilis)*		x	accelerated gonadal growth
Birds:			
junco *(Junco hyemalis)*[j,k] (Rate of gonadal development is proportionate to day length in many species of birds—no critical day length.)		x	increase in body weight, marked deposition of fat, gonadal recrudescence, migratory behavior
willow ptarmigan *(Logopus logopus)*[k]	x		white winter plummage
turkey *(Meleogris gallopavo)*[k]		x	acceleration of sexual maturation in young birds
female domestic fowl *(Gallus gallus)*[k]		x	same as turkey, stimulation of egg production
Mammals:			
goat *(Capra spp.)*[k]	x		induction of estrus
sheep *(Ovis spp.)*[k]	x		estrus; spermatogenic activity, hair growth
snowshoe rabbit *(Lepus americanus)*[k]		x	spring molt, summer pelage, estrus, and testicular development
snowshoe rabbit *(Lepus americanus)*[k]	x		induction of autumn molt and winter pelage
ermine *(Mustela erminea cicognani)*[k]		x	induction of summer pelage
ermine *(Mustela erminea cicognani)*[k]	x		induction of winter pelage
raccoon *(Procyon lotor)*[k]		x	estrus, reproductive activity of males
red fox *(Vulpes fulva)*[k]	x		autumn molt, winter pelage, spermatogenesis and female reproductive system

[a] Kathryn Benson-Evans. 1961. *Nature* 191:255–260.

[b] R. J. Downs. 1959. In: R. B. Withrow (ed.). *Photoperiodism and Related Phenomena in Plants and Animals.* AAAS, Washington D.C., p. 129.

[c] P. L. Altman and Dorothy S. Dittmer (eds.). 1962. *Growth, including Reproduction and Morphological Development.* Fed. Amer. Soc. For Expt. Biol., Washington D.C.

[d] W. S. Spector (ed.). 1956. *Handbook for Biological Data.* W. B. Saunders Co., Philadelphia and London.

[e] I. Spear. 1959. In: R. B. Withrow (ed.). *Photoperiodism and Related Phenomena in Plants and Animals.* AAAS, Washington D.C., p. 289.

[f] A. D. Lees. 1959. In: R. B. Withrow (ed.). *Photoperiodism and Related Phenomena in Plants and Animals,* AAAS, Washington D.C., p. 285.

[g] O. H. Paris, Jr. and C. E. Jenner. 1959. In: R. B. Withrow (ed.). *Photoperiodism and Related Phenomena in Plants and Animals,* AAAS, Washington D.C., p. 601.

[h] R. W. Harrington, Jr. 1959. In: R. B. Withrow (ed.). *Photoperiodism and Related Phenomena in Plants and Animals,* AAAS, Washington D.C., p. 651.

[i] G. A. Bartholomew. 1959. In: R. B. Withrow (ed.). *Photoperiodism and Related Phenomena in Plants and Animals,* AAAS, Washington D.C., p. 669.

[j] D. S. Farner. 1959. In: R. B. Withrow (ed.). *Photoperiodism and Related Phenomena in Plants and Animals,* AAAS, Washington D.C., p. 717.

[k] P. L. Altman and Dorothy S. Dittmer. 1966. *Environmental Biology.* Fed. Amer. Soc. for Expt. Biol., Washington D.C.

treatment equally well. To begin with, only a few will respond when they are very small seedlings. One such example, the Japanese morning glory (*Pharbitis nil*), responds in the cotyledonary stage, and *Chenopodium rubrum* will even respond to short days and flower as a minute seedling on filter paper in a petri dish. Most, including the much studied cocklebur (*Xanthium strumarium*)[1] must attain a somewhat larger size. Henbane (*Hyoscyamus niger*) must be ten to thirty days old before it will respond. Some trees will not flower until they are five to forty years old. Clearly, the exact age depends upon the species. Georg Klebs recognized this diversity of response by suggesting a name for the condition a plant must achieve before it will flower in response to the environment. He called this condition **ripeness to flower**.

Individual leaves, even on mature plants, must also reach an apparent ripeness to flower before they will respond to daylength. In several species, the leaf is maximally sensitive when it is first mature (fully expanded). With the cocklebur, which requires only a single long, dark period for the induction of flowering, leaves less than one cm in length will not respond, while the half-expanded leaf, the one growing most rapidly, is most sensitive. As we shall see, in experiments with this plant, it is sometimes convenient to remove all of the leaves except this most sensitive one.

Plants also vary in the number of cycles required for induction. A few short-day plants, notably cocklebur, Japanese morning glory, *Chenopodium rubrum*, *C. amaranticolor*, and a duckweed (*Lemna*) variety, will respond to a single long, dark period. *Lolium temulentum*, *Brassica campestris*, and *Sinapis alba* are long-day plants that will respond to a single cycle. These plants are very convenient for certain experiments, but most species require several

---

[1] Often referred to in the past as *Xanthium pen(n)-sylvanicum.*

cycles for induction. Examples and their response types are listed in Table 26-2. In many species, the number of required cycles decreases as the plant gets older. Sometimes the plant finally flowers independently of the photoperiod; that is, it becomes day-neutral.

26.2.3 The Critical Day and the Critical Night

In all cases of photoperiodism studied under the usual conditions of a light-dark cycle totaling 24 hours, it is possible to speak of both a critical day and a critical night. The sense of the terms always depends upon whether we are dealing with short-day or with long-day plants. This is well illustrated by Fig. 26-1, in which the relative number of days from the beginning of treatment to the appearance of flowers is plotted as a function of the hours of light per 24-hour cycle. In a truly day-neutral plant, the time to the appearance of flowers is independent of daylength, and a horizontal line appears in the figure. If there is a long-day response, the curve has a negative slope. If flowering will occur at any daylength but more rapidly at long days, then we say that the plant is a **quantitative or facultative long-day plant**. In an **absolute or qualitative long-day plant**, no flowering will occur when the days are less than some particular value dependent upon the species. This value is equivalent to the **critical day length**. Days shorter than this will not result in flowering, whereas longer days will (curve number 5, Fig. 26-1).

The **critical night** is that period of darkness which, comparable to the critical day, must be exceeded before the first perceptible sign of flowering can be observed in short-day plants or *not* observed in long-day plants. In the long-day plant, the critical night represents a maximum period: if flowering is to occur, the *dark period* must be *shorter* than the critical night. With short-day plants (curve 6, Fig. 26-1—note

TABLE 26-2

REPRESENTATIVE PLANTS HAVING LONG-, SHORT-, AND NEUTRAL-DAY LENGTHS, AND THE CRITICAL DAY LENGTH (LIGHT PERIOD NECESSARY FOR FLOWERING) FOR LONG- AND SHORT-DAY SPECIES.[a]

Long-day plants	Critical day length in hours		
Althea *(Hibiscus syriacus)*	>12	Lespedeza *(Lespedeza stipulacea)*	<13.5
Barley, winter *(Hordeum vulgare)*	>12	Poinsettia *(Euphorbia pulcherrima)*	<12.5
Bentgrass *(Agrostis palustris)*	>16	Rice, winter *(Oryza sativa)*	<12
Bromegrass *(Bromus inermis)*	>12.5	Strawberry *(Fragaria chiloensis)*	<10
Canary-grass *Phalaris arundinacea)*	>12.5	Tobacco, Maryland Mammoth	
Clover, red *(Trifolium pratense)*	>12	*(Nicotiana tabacum)*	<14
Coneflower[b] *(Rudbeckia bicolor)*	>10	Violet *(Viola papilionacea)*	<11
Dill *(Anethum graveolens)*	>11		
Henbane[b] annual *(Hyoscyamus niger)*	>10	**Day-neutral plants**	
Oat *(Avena sativa)*	> 9	Cucumber *(Cucumis sativus)*	
Orchardgrass *(Dactylis glomerata)*	>12	Euphorbia *(Euphorbia peplus)*	
Ryegrass, early perennial		Buckwheat *(Fagopyrum tataricum)*	
(Lolium perenne)	> 9	Strawberry, everbearing *(Fragaria chiloensis)*	
Ryegrass, Italian *(Lolium italicum)*	>11	Cape jasmine *(Gardenia jasminoides)*	
Ryegrass, late perennial		Globe-amaranth *(Gomphrina globosa)*	
(Lolium perenne)	>13	Cotton, one variety *(Gossypium hirsutum)*	
Sedum *(Sedum spectabile)*	>13	Artichoke, one variety	
Spinach *(Spinacia oleracea)*	>13	*(Helianthus tuberosus)*	
Timothy, hay *(Phleum pratensis)*	>12	English holly *(Ilex aquifolium)*	
Timothy, pasture *(Phleum nodosum)*	>14.5	Balsam *(Impatiens balsamina)*	
Wheatgrass *(Agropyron smithii)*	>10	Honesty *(Lunaria annua)*	
Wheat, winter *(Triticum aestivum)*	>12	Tobacco, one variety *(Nicotiana tabacum)*	
		Lima bean, one variety *(Phaseolus lunatus)*	
Short-day plants		String bean, one variety *(Phaseolus vulgaris)*	
Bryophyllum *(Bryophyllum pinnatum)*	<12	Bluegrass, annual *(Poa annua)*	
Chrysanthemum		Azalea, coral bell *(Rhododendron spp.)*	
(Chrysanthemum spp.)	<15	Scrofularia *(Scrofularia peregrina)*	
Cocklebur[b] *(Xanthium strumarium)*	<15.6	Senecio *(Senecio vulgaris)*	
Cosmos, Klondyke		Potato, one variety *(Solanum tuberosum)*	
(Cosmus sulphureus)	<14	Viburnum *(Viburnum spp.)*	
Kalanchoë *(Kalanchoë blossfeldiana)*	<12	Corn or maize *(Zea mays)*	

[a] Various sources. See summary in F. B. Salisbury. 1963. The Flowering Process, Pergamon Press, Oxford, London, Paris, New York.

[b] Weeds, the seeds of which must be collected in the field. Seeds or plants of the other species are available commercially. (>12 hr should be interpreted as 12 hours or more; <12 hr, as 12 hours or less. In many cases, critical day lengths are approximations.)

positive slope), the situation is exactly the opposite: the *day* must be *shorter* than the critical day if flowering is to occur, and the *night* must be *longer* than the critical night. It is important to note the complete difference between long- and short-day plants. The classi-fication has nothing to do with the arbitrary daylength at which the plant will flower but whether flowering occurs when the daylength is *more* or *less* than the critical. In Fig. 26-1, flowering of *both* the species represented by curve number 5 and that represented by curve

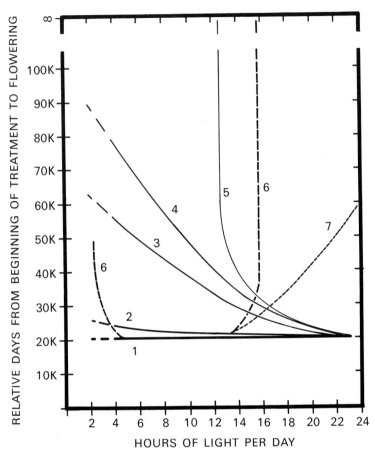

Figure 26-1

Representative flowering responses to different day lengths, plotted as time required for appearance of flowers. *K* following the numbers on the ordinate indicates that these numbers are arbitrary. Curve 1 is for a true day-neutral plant. Curve 2 would also be considered a day-neutral response, although flowering is slightly promoted by long days. Curves 3 and 4 represent quantitative long-day plants, but 4 is more sensitive to day length than 3. Curve 5 is a true (absolute) long-day plant. Curve 6 is a true (absolute) short-day plant, with its minimum day (about 2.5 hours) indicated on the left and its minimum night (8.5 hours, a 15.5-hour day) on the right. Curve 7 is a quantitative short-day plant. (Modified after F. B. Salisbury, 1963, *The Flowering Process*, Pergamon Press, Oxford, London, Paris, New York. Used by permission.)

number 6 would occur at daylengths between about 12.5 and 15.7 hours. Quantitative short-day plants are represented by curve 7.

In some cases the critical day or night for a population of plants can be determined within rather narrow limits (only five to ten minutes in the most spectacular cases). In other cases the limits are far less exact and may spread out over an hour or two. In cocklebur, at least, the greater the number of inductive cycles given, the more exact is the critical day or night.

Often, particularly with short-day plants, the critical night remains constant even when it is determined on artificial cycles that do not total

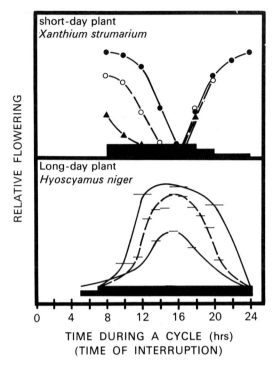

Figure 26-2

Effects of a light interruption given at various times during dark periods of various lengths on subsequent flowering of a short-day plant and of a long-day plant. Interruptions with *Xanthium* were 60 seconds; with *Hyoscyamus*, for times indicated by length of data lines. (Data for *Xanthium* from F. B. Salisbury and J. Bonner, 1956, *Plant Physiol.* 310:141–147; data for *Hyoscyamus* from H. Claes and A. Lang, 1947, *Z. Naturforschung* 26:56–63.)

24 hours. That is, even though the hours of light vary considerably, the critical night may continue to exhibit the same values. When the experiment is performed in this way, a critical or an optimum day that is fairly constant for various night lengths may also be evident; but, as we shall see below, the interpretation of this result is somewhat more complex.

26.2.4 The Night-Interruption Phenomenon

A common and important aspect of photoperiodism is the so-called **night-interruption phenomenon**. Interruption of the night with a rather brief interval of light (depending upon species) is equivalent to exposure to long day. That is, most short-day plants so treated do not flower, whereas most long-day plants do (Fig. 26-2). There is much to study in the night-break phenomenon, and we will have occasion to refer to many of the experiments that have been performed. To summarize, the *intensity* of light that is effective depends upon the *time* over which it is applied: light of extremely high intensity may be applied for only brief intervals to obtain a given effect; light applied over very long intervals is effective even at extremely low intensities (e.g., three to ten times the light from the full moon, 0.02 ft-c). The *time during the dark period* when the light break is applied is also important. That is, at certain times the plant is much more sensitive to the light break than at other times. With most plants that have been studied, *red light* is considerably more effective than other wavelengths, and its effect is typically reversed by *far-red light*, implying participation of the phytochrome system (Chapter 23). Indeed, participation of the phytochrome system was demonstrated in flowering immediately following its discovery in germination of lettuce seeds.

It is important to note that no "day-interruption" phenomenon comparable to the night-interruption response is known. A period of darkness given during the day has very little or no effect. This fact, along with the relatively constant critical night (compared to the critical day), has led many investigators to emphasize strongly the role of the dark period in photoperiodism. It was suggested during the 1940s, for example, that the terminology of Garner and Allard should be modified so that one spoke of long-night plants rather than short-day plants (or short-night plants rather than long-day plants). The term photoperiodism could be replaced by the term nyctoperiodism (*nycto*; of night). Presently accumulating evidence, however, favors the idea that both the day and the night are important in the time-measurement aspects of photoperiodism, and so the Garner and Allard terminology appears to be as appropriate as any.

26.2.5 The Flowering Response Types

Representative long-day, short-day, and day-neutral plants are shown in Fig. 26-3, and these three basic response types observed by Garner and Allard still form the foundation for any kind of classification of plant flowering response type to photoperiod. We have already encountered a few embellishments on this simple scheme, however, and we shall consider a few more in this section.

Figure 26-1 illustrated the concept of absolute or facultative response to photoperiod. It should also be evident from this figure that it is not always possible to be absolutely certain of our classifications. Curve 1 is clearly representative of a day-neutral plant, but what about curve 2? It would certainly seem to describe a day-neutral plant also, even though there is a slight acceleration of flowering by long days. The criteria used in measurement of flowering might also be important. If the number of flowers on a plant were plotted as a function of daylength, a different curve may be produced from the one plotting time to the first appearance of flowers as a function of daylength. Such a situation is known to hold for at least two plants (*Leucanthemum cebennense* and *Saxifraga rotundifolia*), in which the plant appears to be day-neutral in terms of time to the appearance of the flowers but is clearly a quantitative long-day plant in terms of the number of flowers.

In addition to these complications added to Garner and Allard's scheme, there appear to be a number of valid categories at least nearly equal in importance to those of Garner and Allard. To produce flowers, a few species require long days followed by short days (a situation normally encountered in late summer and fall). When maintained under continuous long days or con-tinuous short days, they remain vegetative. In contrast to these **long-short-day plants**, there are their counterparts, the **short-long-day plants**, which require for flowering short days followed by long days (the normal condition in spring-time). There are one or two species at least (e.g., certain varieties of sugar cane) that flower only on **intermediate daylength** and remain vegetative when days are either too short or too long. C. Ch. Methon and M. Stroun in France have even demonstrated their counter-parts. Such plants remain vegetative on inter-mediate daylength, flowering only on longer or shorter days. The discoverers called this re-sponse type **ambiphotoperiodism**. The example they studied was *Media elegans*. Table 26-2 in-cludes examples of the principal response types.

It is important to be aware of the extreme plasticity in response types, even within a given species. In three separate studies, representatives of *Chenopodium album*, cocklebur, and *Oxyria digyna* (an alpine plant) were collected at various latitudes throughout North America and (in the case of *Oxyria*) the Arctic and studied in relation to their flowering, considering especially the critical daylength. The first two are short-day plants, the third a long-day plant. The critical day varied for each species, becoming longer for individuals collected farther north. Often no morphological differences could be detected between individuals having a greatly different flowering response. Varieties of many other species (e.g., cotton, soybean, chrysanthemum) have also been compared, although not from a wide latitudinal range, and the same diversity has become apparent. These results indicate the importance of using a carefully standardized variety in a continuing scientific study, and they also indicate that classifications of response types, such as given in Table 26-2, are at best only approximations.

There are several interesting interactions between photoperiod and temperature, as we have indicated in previous chapters. In the cases already discussed, a low-temperature requirement may be followed by a requirement for long days. In some very interesting cases, a plant may act like one response type at one temperature but not at another. It may, for example, exhibit a clear-cut qualitative or quantitative short-day response at temperatures above, say, 20°C but be essentially day-neutral at temperatures below this. Two examples (poinsettia, *Euphorbia pulcherrima*, and morning glory, *Ipomoea purpurea*) that are absolute short-day plants at high temperature and absolute long-day plants at low temperature have been reported. They are day-neutral only at the intermediate temperature. This striking response would certainly seem to merit further study.

There are also cases in which a given temperature will apparently substitute for a given photoperiodic treatment, or vice-versa. This was first discovered by S. G. Wellensiek in Holland, and it is referred to as **Wellensiek's phenomenon**. He used *Campanula medium* (canterbury bells) in his studies. The necessity for vernalization was fully replaced by exposure to short days. In either case, subsequent long days were required for flowering. Even Petkus rye exhibits a certain degree of this type of response, since short days will substitute to a certain extent for the low-temperature requirement. In one study, considering all of the possible combinations of the response types described here, it was suggested that at least 777 different types might be expected! Forty-eight examples of these different types were found in the literature. Of course, of the approximately 285,000 species of angiosperms, only a few hundred have been studied.

The classification situation is not quite as hopelessly confusing as it may appear. It is possible to account for most of the known types by considering certain differences in the action of only a few relatively simple mechanisms. It is known, for example (see below), that even a short-day plant with its clear-cut critical night may also, under certain conditions, exhibit the response typical of a long-day plant. That is, even in short days a *minimum* daylength must be exceeded if flowering is to occur (left-hand part of curve 6 in Fig. 26-1). This is normally overlooked because the *maximum* critical daylength (e.g., for cocklebur) may be as high as 15.6 hours, whereas the *minimum* critical daylength may be as short as only three or four hours (see 26.3.4 and Fig. 26-17). Nevertheless, we suspect that both the long- and the short-day responses exist in all plants, and that the peculiarities described in the above paragraphs, including day-neutral plants, can be accounted for by specific interactions and overlappings of the critical minimum and maximum lengths of day and night for these various species (Fig. 26-4).

26.3 TIME MEASUREMENT

As indicated above, the really unique thing about photoperiodism is the time measurement involved in the detection of day and night lengths. The term photoperiodism is highly appropriate, since we are dealing both with light (or its absence) and with time. The special aspects of time measurement we will discuss in relation to the photoperiodic control of flowering may well prove to be valid for such other responses as the induction of dormancy. Future research will be required to demonstrate whether this is true.

26.3.1 The Partial Processes: The Concept of Hour-Glass Timing

Beginning around 1940, Karl C. Hamner, then at the University of Chicago, began to develop an approach to the study of photoperiodism in which the process for short-day plants was segmented into a series of component steps. This is an example of the fundamental scientific process of **analysis**. It has been extremely

SHORT DAY | LONG DAY

Ca. 110 days

TOMATO

LD → SHORT DAY | LONG DAY

Ca. 110 days

PIGWEED

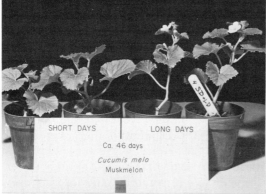

SHORT DAYS | LONG DAYS

Ca. 46 days

Cucumis melo
Muskmelon

SHORT DAY | LONG DAY

Ca. 35 days

JAPANESE MORNINGGLORY

SHORT DAY | LONG DAY

Ca. 60 days

COCKLEBUR

SD | SD→LD | LD→SD | LD

54 days total
27 SD, 27 LD

Petunia sp.
Petunia

Figure 26-3

Some representative day-neutral (tomato), short-day (pigweed, Japanese morning glory, and cocklebur), and long-day (henbane, radish, muskmelon, petunia, barley, and spinach) plants. In tomato, note strong effects of day length on vegetative form although both plants are flowering. (Photographs by F. B. Salisbury; tomato, pigweed, Japanese morning glory, barley, spinach, henbane, and radish previously published in F. B. Salisbury, 1963, *The Flowering Process*, Pergamon Press, Oxford, London, Paris, New York. Used by permission.)

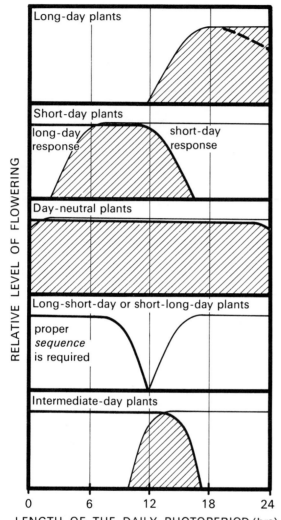

Figure 26-4

A scheme to account for the various response types based upon a long-day and a short-day requirement in all plants. According to the scheme, flowering would occur on day lengths indicated by the shading. In the case of the long-short-day or short-long-day plants, flowering never occurs in response to a single day length, but a proper sequence is required. The scheme is imperfect in that there is no evidence in most plants for short-day response in long-day species. Flowering increases as day length increases up to and including continuous light. This is not true for some long-day species, however, and in the case of short-day plants, a long-day response has been clearly demonstrated.

valuable in many fields of science, and it seemed to Hamner that it might help here as well. The result was a fairly simple scheme that was subsequently enlarged and modified, particularly by James Bonner and two of his graduate students, James L. Liverman and Frank B. Salisbury, at the California Institute of Technology. In the following paragraphs, we will describe in terms of current information such a system of partial or component processes as it may be applied to short-day plants, particularly the strain of cocklebur (*Xanthium strumarium*) originally collected near Chicago, Illinois. With minor modifications, most of the scheme applies equally well to long-day plants and to other short-day plants. To facilitate discussion, each of the component steps will be given a formal title, and this will be capitalized to imply that the title refers specifically to the flowering process and not to more general manifestations such as biological time measurement.

26.3.1A The high-intensity light process It
seems logical that the flowering of a short-day plant, apparently dependent upon an uninterrupted period of darkness exceeding the critical night, would also require high-intensity light during the preceding light period to provide ample photosynthetic substrates for the subsequent reactions. Obviously, the plant must have such high-intensity light if it is to grow adequately. Is there a more specific requirement for high-intensity light preceding the inductive dark period?

Hamner devised a clever experiment to answer this question (Fig. 26-5). He exposed the plants to an extended period of darkness, during which time they would presumably become depleted of their photosynthetic reserves. To keep this period of darkness from being effective in the induction of flowering, he interrupted it at three-hour intervals with a brief period of relatively low-intensity light. The light interrup-

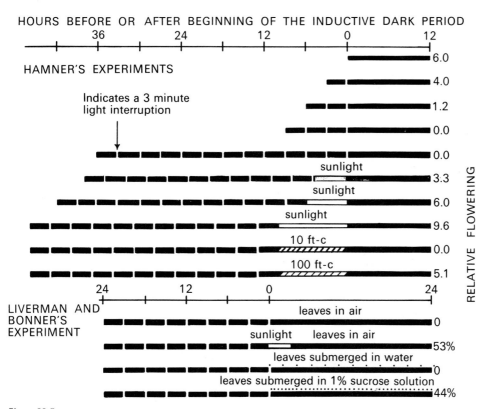

Figure 26-5

Some of the experiments of K. C. Hamner, showing the effects on cocklebur flowering of intermittent light and dark periods and other treatments preceding a dark period of normally inductive length; and experiments of J. Liverman and J. Bonner showing effects of sugar applied during a long dark period preceded by intermittent light and dark periods. Liverman and Bonner present data only for the percent of the treated plants which flowered. Before and after treatment, plants were subjected to long days in the greenhouse. Buds were examined after three weeks. Solutions were applied by immersing the leaf in the solution during the entire inductive dark period. In other experiments, solutions were applied by putting cuttings into the solutions at the beginning of the long dark period. Three-minute light interruptions were 200 ft-c (Hamner) or 50 ft-c (Liverman and Bonner). (See references at end of book. Figure from F. B. Salisbury, 1963, *The Flowering Process*, Pergamon Press, Oxford, London, Paris, New York. Used by permission.)

tion was ample to inhibit the flowering process but hardly significant in terms of photosynthesis. Following such a treatment, exposure of the plants to a long, uninterrupted dark period, normally quite adequate to induce flowers, was ineffective in flower induction. If the period of so-called **flashing light** (three-hour dark periods) was followed by three hours of sunlight, then the subsequent long, uninterrupted dark period was quite effective in bringing about floral induction. Liverman and Bonner further tested this idea by showing that the three-hour interval of sunlight could be replaced by a treatment with sucrose or other energy substrates (Fig. 26-5).

This seemed clearly to show that the high-intensity light process did indeed exist (that it was essential for subsequent steps in the flowering process) and that it was equivalent to photosynthesis.

In section 26.3.4 we shall have occasion to reexamine this conclusion and discover that it is not entirely correct. Photosynthesis is certainly essential for growth of the plant, and an interval of light is also completely essential preceding the inductive dark period, but only under special circumstances such as those used by Liverman and Bonner (an exceptionally long period of flashing-light treatment—24 hours at least) is this high-intensity light period essential. Usually photosynthetic substrates remain amply high in cocklebur plants over relatively long intervals of time, even in the dark, and the requirement for light is much more closely related to the actual time-measurement processes.

26.3.1B Reactions of the dark period

In an analysis of the reactions taking place during the inductive dark period, an experiment studying the quantitative response to night length proves to be particularly instructive, and examination of this experiment in some detail will introduce the reader to some of the methodology of this field.

Using the cocklebur plant, it is possible to make quantitative studies of flowering by inducing groups of plants with a single dark period, and then examining their flowering conditions several days later. More than one dark period may be used, but for many experiments, the ability to use only one is extremely useful or even essential. It is convenient to examine plants under a dissecting binocular microscope (about 36 power magnification) some nine days after the inductive dark period and to classify the conditions of their apical meristems according to a system of **floral stages** like that devised by Salisbury (Fig. 26-6). As the apical bud

develops into the staminate (male) inflorescence, typical of the cocklebur (female flowers develop into burs in the leaf axils), a number of easily recognizable stages become apparent. The *rate* at which this development occurs depends upon the degree of previous induction, and thus measurement of these stages at a constant interval following induction indicates the developmental rate, which in turn indicates the initial level of induction.

In addition to the one utilizing floral stages, several other quantitative methods exist for measuring flowering. Two of these have already been implied above: The interval of time between induction and the first visible appearance of flowers can be observed, or one may simply count the number of flowers on the plant after they have developed fully. With two species widely used in studies on photoperiodism [Biloxi soybean (*Glycine max*) and Japanese morning glory], the number of nodes bearing flowers is counted. This may be done after flowers have developed, or plants may be dissected under the binocular microscope a few days after induction, and the flowering nodes detected by the presence of floral primordia. In some species, the height of a bolting vernalized shoot may be measured. It has been valuable in some studies to compare the number of flowers to the number of leaves, giving a kind of **floral index**, which is thought by some to be less influenced by the environmental conditions during floral bud development. Using all methods other than the floral index, it is absolutely essential to have at least two kinds of control plants, one that remains vegetative (never exposed to inducing conditions) and one that is induced in a standard way. Treatments may then be compared with these controls.

To return to the experiment in which flowering of cockleburs is studied as a function of length of the inductive dark period, plants are exposed to a single period of darkness, which

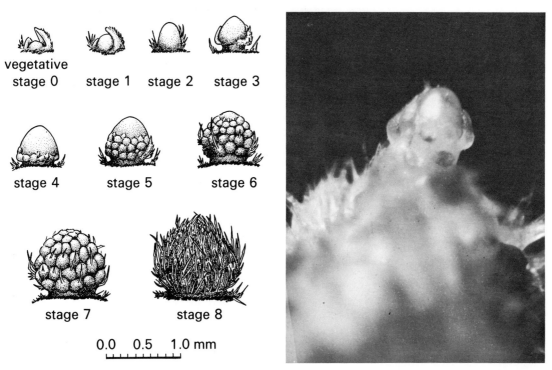

vegetative
stage 0   stage 1   stage 2   stage 3

stage 4   stage 5   stage 6

stage 7   stage 8

0.0   0.5   1.0 mm

Figure 26-6

(left) Drawings of the developing terminal inflorescence primordium (staminate) of cocklebur, illustrating the system of floral stages devised by Salisbury (*Plant Physiol.* 30:327–334, 1955). (right) A photograph through a dissecting microscope of a cocklebur inflorescence primordium at stage 3.

may vary in length from eight to sixteen or more hours. Nine days later, floral stages for the plants in a given treatment (receiving a given night length) are determined, averaged, and plotted as a function of night length (Fig. 26-7). The critical night is quite apparent in an experiment of this type. With dark periods longer than the critical, the degree of flowering increases in an almost linear way (a fortunate aspect of the chosen floral stages) until saturation is reached at about twelve hours. Figure 26-7 implies that there are at least two reactions of the inductive dark period in short-day plants. *First* is the time measurement, accounting for the critical night. *Second* are the metab-

olic processes, which account for the increased level of flowering with increased exposure to darkness. As we shall document below, a flowering hormone is apparently synthesized within the leaves following completion of the critical night. Hence, we can think of at least two component reactions of the inductive dark period: **Time Measurement** and **Synthesis of Flowering Hormone**. Since the flowering hormone has been called florigen, we can shorten the title of the second reaction to **Florigen Synthesis**.

As indicated, an interruption of the inductive dark period by light makes it ineffective (acts as a long-day treatment). The pigment system that

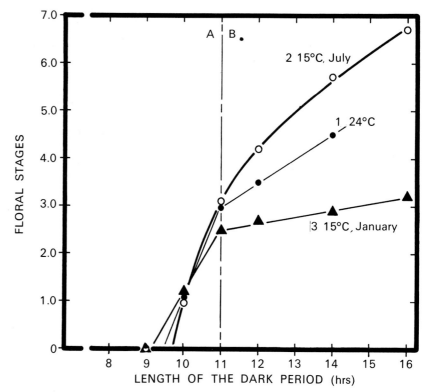

Figure 26-7
Some examples of cocklebur flowering response to different night lengths. (From F. B. Salisbury, 1963, *Planta* 59:518–534.)

responds to the night interruption has been identified as the phytochrome system. Since red light is most effective in the night interruption, the phytochrome system must be in the red-receptive form (Pr) at the time of the interruption, and the far-red-receptive form (Pfr) must be most effective in inhibition of flowering during the dark period. At the beginning of the dark period, however, the system will be primarily in the Pfr form (Chapter 23). If the pigment is in the Pfr form at the beginning of the dark period and the Pr form some time later, there might be a *conversion* in the dark from one form to the other. Alternatively, Pfr might be *destroyed* in the dark while Pr is being *synthesized.*

Evidence exists that the latter possibility is true in many situations, although the former one appears to account for a few others. In either case, a shift in the ratio of Pr to Pfr occurs. This change in the status of the pigment taking place after plants are put in the dark has been referred to as **Pigment Conversion**. In view of the probability that we are dealing with a destruction and synthesis rather than a true conversion, the term **Pigment Shift** will be used to include conversion and/or synthesis and destruction.

Does Pigment Shift account for Time Measurement? If the time required for completion of Pigment Shift is equal to the critical dark period, then Pigment Shift might indeed account for the critical night. Salisbury, working with Bonner, measured in cocklebur the level of inhibition brought about by light interruptions of different durations given at different times during the inductive dark period (Fig. 26-8). He found that the **saturation levels** (maximum inhibition caused by a light break) were strongly dependent upon the time during the inductive dark period at which the light break was given. The *quantity of light required for saturation*, however, appeared to be essentially constant regardless of when the light break was given. This was true even for light breaks given only a few hours after the beginning of darkness. He reasoned that the saturation light quantity (exposure time with a given source) was an indication of the amount of available Pr. The quantity of light required to convert the pigment should be a measure of the amount of pigment available for conversion. Since it appeared that the amount of pigment was already constant beginning just a few hours after the initiation of darkness, he proposed that Pigment Shift was complete in considerably less time than Time Measurement. He suggested that the interval unaccounted for might be referred to as **Preparatory Reaction(s)**. We now suspect that the time between Pigment Shift and Florigen Synthesis represents **Time Measurement**.[2] We shall return to the question and further evidence bearing upon it.

A number of questions may be asked about the nature of the Reactions of the Dark Period. One of these asks whether the light-break phenomenon exhibits the expected photochemical property of reciprocity. We have already indicated (26.2.4) that at least an approximate reciprocal relationship does exist: with longer exposure times lower intensities are required to bring about a given effect. If **reciprocity** holds, exposure time multiplied by intensity will yield a constant for a given effect. In the night-break phenomenon, this is only very roughly true, although the relationship is valid enough with relatively short exposure times to allow its application in experimental studies. For example, the intensity may be maintained constant and only the exposure time varied.

The question might also be asked as to the length of time required for inhibitory action by Pfr. This may be determined by exposing short-day plants to an inhibitory quantity of red light as a night interruption, and then by attempting to reverse this effect by applying far-red light at various intervals of time thereafter. As Fig. 26-9 indicates, if far-red light is given more than 30 minutes after red light, reversal is impossible in cocklebur plants. We suppose that the inhibitory action of Pfr is complete by the end of 30 minutes. With other species, the time may vary from this considerably. It is about the same for soybeans, but much longer (about four hours) for chrysanthemums and much shorter (seconds or minutes) for Japanese morning glory. With some plants having a long time requirement, a single, short red-light interruption of the dark period is not effective. Pfr decays before inhibition is complete. Either a long (several-hour) interruption or several short interruptions over a period of several hours must be given.

Another phenomenon is of considerable interest in relation to action of the pigment. Apparently Pfr is highly active even in the presence of large percentages of Pr. Such a situation is common due to the overlapping in the absorption spectra of the two forms of phytochrome (Fig. 23-6 and section 23.2.2). For example, far-red light is absorbed not only by Pfr but also to a considerably lesser degree by Pr. Thus, when a plant is illuminated with far-red light, the majority of the pigment will be converted to Pr, but a certain small proportion will always be converted back to Pfr by the

---

[2] Actually, the measurement of time (e.g., critical night) might include both Pigment Shift and Time Measurement, but the formal term Time Measurement as used here does not include Pigment Shift.

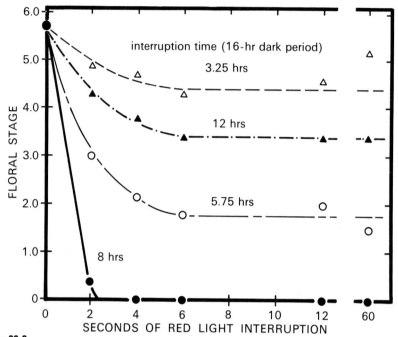

Figure 26-8

The effects upon flowering of light interruptions given for various durations at various times after the beginning of a 16-hour dark period. Saturation time is about six seconds, but when the interruption is given at eight hours, the maximum inhibition is obtained with only slightly more than two seconds. (Data from F. B. Salisbury and J. Bonner, 1956, *Plant Physiol.* 31:141–147.)

absorption of far-red light by Pr. If a plant is illuminated for only a brief interval of time with far-red light, then only a small portion of pigment will exist in the form of Pfr, and this will soon be metabolically destroyed or converted during the ensuing darkness. If the far-red illumination is applied over a fairly long interval of time, however, then a certain low level of Pfr will be maintained over that interval in the plant. We might expect long illuminations with far-red light to be equivalent to short illuminations with red, and such a response can indeed be observed (Fig. 26-10). This complication of illumination time must always be watched for in photobiological experiments of this type. Other examples were given in Chapter 23.

26.3.1C The second-high-intensity light process In studies by Hamner and James Lockhart, then his graduate student at the University of California in Los Angeles, it was possible to demonstrate the importance of high-intensity light *following* the inductive dark period. They showed that a brief interval of light terminating the inductive dark period and followed by a short period of darkness (e.g., four hours) was *sometimes* inhibitory compared to treatments in which the second period of darkness was replaced by high-intensity light. They suggested that high-intensity light was required for stabilization of florigen in the leaf following its initial synthesis during the dark period, and they spoke of the **Second High-Intensity Light Process**.

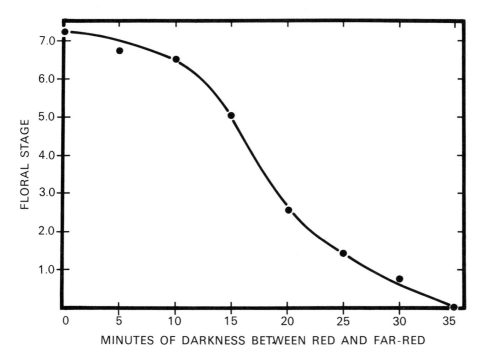

Figure 26-9

The effects of far-red light (3 minutes) given at various times after interruptions with red light (2 minutes) given near the middle of three 12-hour dark periods. (Data from R. J. Downs, 1956, *Plant Physiol.* 31:279.) The flowering stages of Downs have been converted to the floral stages used in other figures. (From F. B. Salisbury, 1963, *The Flowering Process*, Pergamon Press, Oxford, London, Paris, New York. Used by permission.)

Alternatively, the leaf might sometimes be capable of destroying florigen, and this ability might be removed by high-intensity light. D. J. Carr, then in Australia, was able to replace the requirement for a second high-intensity light period by treating the leaves with sucrose. Sugars, produced by photosynthesis, might facilitate the translocation of florigen out of the leaf, but some protection of the hormone is apparently also afforded. Sucrose eventually appears in the leaf following the second dark period, and if the hormone is not destroyed in the meantime, then its export might simply be delayed but not prevented by the second dark period.

The arguments here illustrate exceptionally well the intricacies that can appear when one attempts to understand physiological processes in terms of experiments with whole plants. With careful thought, one can almost always devise a number of possibilities to explain an initial observation, and distinguishing between these may require many carefully designed and executed experiments plus the further mental effort required to understand them.

26.3.1D Translocation of florigen With plants that flower in response to photoperiod, it is possible to show that it is nearly always the leaves that detect the daylength. A short-day

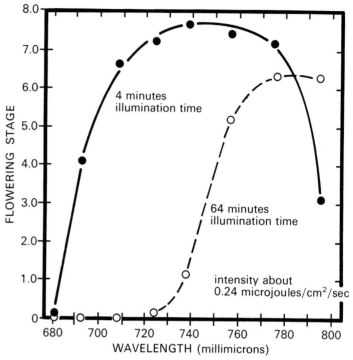

Figure 26-10

Action spectra for far-red reversal of red inhibition of flowering in *Chenopodium rubrum*, showing effects of either 4 or 64 minutes of far-red illumination. (Data from S. B. Hendricks and H. A. Borthwick, 1963, "Control of plant growth by light," in L. T. Evans (ed.), *Environmental Control of Plant Growth*, Academic Press, New York and London, p. 252. Figure from F. B. Salisbury, 1963, *The Flowering Process*, Pergamon Press, Oxford, London, Paris, New York. Used with permission.)

plant maintained under long-day conditions, for example, will flower when only the leaves are exposed to a long, dark period (e.g., by enclosing them in a black paper bag), but there is no response if the buds (which will actually become flowers) or the stems are given a long dark period while the leaves remain under long day. Thus, our postulated florigen must arise in the leaf.

With such species as cocklebur and Japanese morning glory, it is possible to chart the translocation of florigen out of the leaf by defoliating plants at various times following a single inductive dark period. If the leaves are removed immediately at the end of the night, plants will usually remain vegetative. If leaves are removed several hours later, plants will flower nearly as well as those from which the leaves are not removed at all. Removal at intermediate times results in intermediate levels of flowering (Fig. 26-11).

We may think of **Florigen Translocation** as the partial process following the Reactions of the Dark Period or perhaps following the Second High-Intensity Light Process. It may be that Translocation and the Second High-Intensity Light Process are different manifestations of a single process. This must be determined by future research.

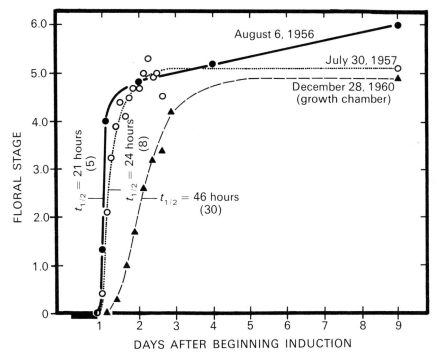

Figure 26-11
Three translocation curves obtained by defoliation of plants at various times following a 16-hour inductive dark period. Times of defoliation are shown, with floral stages of all plants being determined on the ninth day. Numbers on the abscissa represent noon of the indicated day, while the bar on the abscissa indicates the inductive dark period. Approximate times when half the stimulus was out of the leaf are indicated by $t_{1/2}$. The figures represent half-times after beginning of the dark period; the figures in parentheses represent half-times after end of the dark period. Dates refer to the day plants were subjected to the dark treatment. Plants represented by the $t_{1/2} = 46$ hour curve were kept under 2,000 ft-c of fluorescent light in the growth chambers (23°C). (From F. B. Salisbury, 1963, *The Flowering Process*, Pergamon Press, Oxford, London, Paris, New York. Used by permission.)

Using the defoliation technique, it is possible to study the effects of various environmental factors upon Florigen Translocation. Fig. 26-12 summarizes the effects of time of year. In experiments conducted with cocklebur plants in a greenhouse at Pasadena, California, translocation was much slower in winter than in summer. Daylength was maintained about the same in both cases, as was temperature. We suspect, then, that translocation rate is a function of light intensity, although other more subtle factors could also be responsible. Temperature clearly does have a measurable influence upon Translocation, and the Q_{10} for the effect is in the neighborhood of 1.5 to 2.5, a rather typical value for metabolic reactions.

26.3.1E Differentiation Upon arrival of florigen at the apical meristem, the course of meristematic development changes from the vegetative to the reproductive mode. This switching in the morphogenetic program has already been discussed in Chapter 22. Information relative to the cytohistochemical studies being carried out in relation to this switching was presented there (22.5.4).

26.3.1F Hourglass implications of the partial process approach

In view of the postulated component steps in the flowering process as outlined above, one explanation for Time Measurement seems to be apparent. If flowering is a matter of one step leading to the next, Time Measurement would logically seem to be equal to the time required for the completion of one or more of these steps. As the sand runs through an hourglass to measure time, so some chemical reaction might run to completion, measuring time in the flowering process. Following the hourglass analogy, initiation of timing would require an input of energy into the system (inverting the hourglass), and once the reaction had gone to completion (the sand had run out), timing would be halted until it was reinitiated (perhaps by the High-Intensity Light Process). But under constant conditions only one interval of time could be measured. With an oscillating system, analogous to a pendulum rather than to an hourglass, intervals of time (the period of the pendulum) are measured repeatedly, even under constant conditions.

With the discovery of phytochrome conversion (Pigment Shift), the mechanism of time measurement seemed to be explained, as was indicated above. Pigment Shift was quite analogous to the hourglass and not to the pendulum. Salisbury had rejected this mechanism as the ultimate explanation for Time Measurement in cocklebur simply because it seemed to go to completion in less time than the critical night. He assumed, however, that Time Measurement was indeed of an hourglass type, and to maintain this assumption in view of the absence of a phytochrome clock, he postulated another analogous hourglass reaction [Preparatory Reaction(s)]. Until about 1962, Harry Borthwick and

Sterling Hendricks at Beltsville held to the idea that phytochrome conversion accounted for Time Measurement. They were partially responsible for the initial discoveries relating to phytochrome, and their opinions on phytochrome Time Measurement were quite influential.

26.3.2 Rhythmical Manifestations: An Oscillating Timer

In the early 1930s, Erwin Bünning became interested in photoperiodism as it might relate to his studies on circadian rhythms. It occurred to him that the oscillating timer responsible for these rhythms might logically also be responsible for time measurement in photoperiodism. After all, he reasoned, why should the plant be bothered with more than a single time-measuring system if a single one would do? Bünning proposed a theory involving the same clock for circadian rhythms and for Time Measurement in photoperiodism. The theory held that the metabolism of the plant oscillates between two separate modes. During one of these phases[3] (the **photophil phase**), light promotes plant processes, including flowering and several other manifestations. The opposite phase (the **skotophil phase**) is one in which light was inhibitory to plant processes, including flowering.

Bünning was able to cite considerable evidence in favor of such oscillating phases, but how could he account for the striking difference between short-day and long-day plants? He proposed that in short-day plants the photophil phase came immediately following dawn, and that, if anything, it was somewhat advanced, so that darkness had to be present sooner in the day throughout the entire period of the skotophil phase. With long-day plants, the photophil

---

[3] Here the term phase is used as a *part* of a cycle rather than in its more correct sense as a *point* on a cycle.

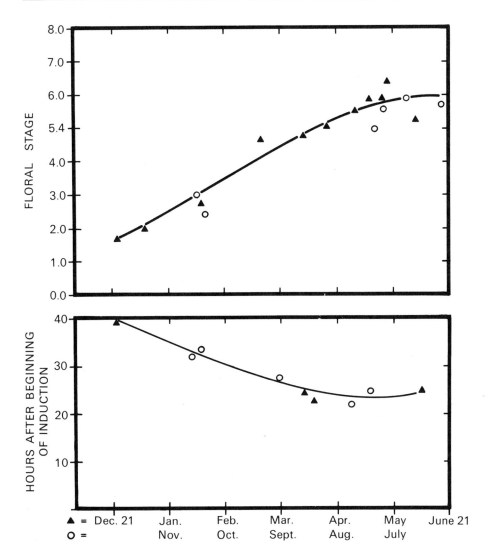

Figure 26-12

Relationship between flowering (floral stage), translocation (hours after beginning of induction), and time of year. Translocation times refer to half-times. All groups of plants were induced with a 16-hour dark period. (From F. B. Salisbury, 1955, doctoral dissertation, California Institute of Technology, Pasadena, California.)

phase was considerably delayed following the dawn signal, so that the plant had to be exposed to light for an extended period if light were to coincide with the photophil phase.

Important details of the theory, especially relating to shifting of the phases, subsequently had to be rejected. For example, how could we explain the rather sharply defined critical day and critical night, especially in such plants as the cocklebur, which can be exposed to several days of continuous light at constant temperature and then flower in response to a single long night but in the absence of another dawn signal? Bünning himself could observe no significant and consistent differences in shifting of the phases (e.g., for leaf movements) following the dawn signal between short-day and long-day plants. The controversy relating to shifting of the phases lasted until the end of the 1950s, but we may now return to the basic question of hourglass versus oscillator time measurement in photoperiodism. Is there evidence for *alternating phases* of sensitivity to light, and do these phases relate to time measurement in photoperiodism? Is the time-measuring system in photoperiodism comparable to an oscillator, as in the case of the circadian rhythms, or is it comparable to an hourglass?

Two kinds of experiments seem to imply an oscillating timer in photoperiodism in some species. The *first* has been performed by many workers with a number of species. An example using Hamner's data is shown in Fig. 26-13. Plants are exposed to several cycles, each including a period of extended darkness, perhaps as long as 64 to 72 hours. Light interruptions are given at various times during this extended period of darkness, and results are plotted showing flowering as a function of the time of the light interruptions. With species in which the experiment indicates an oscillating timer in flowering, peaks of promotion may be observed to occur separated by approximately 24 hours, and peaks of inhibition also exhibit a 24-hour cycle. That is, the curves exhibit a cyclical sensitivity to light reminiscent of the cyclical leaf movements or other circadian rhythms and of Bünning's suggestion that plants have such an alternating sensitivity to illumination.

The experiment is usually most definitive with plants that require more than one cycle. Only when other conditions are met (see below)

can we observe such a rhythmical response in cocklebur. The response does show up rather nicely in *Chenopodium rubrum*, however, and studies with this "single-cycle" genus were carried out extensively (although not initially) at Beltsville. The fairly unequivocal results obtained there convinced the Beltsville discoverers of phytochrome that an oscillating timer may indeed be a part of the photoperiodism response.

The *second* kind of experiment is also illustrated in Fig. 26-13. Plants may be given a light period of constant duration and a dark period that varies in length (or vice-versa). When subsequent flowering is plotted as a function of the total cycle length, it is apparent with some species that cycles totaling 24 hours or multiples thereof are maximally promotive of flowering, while cycles totaling 36 hours or 24-hour intervals beginning at 36 hours are maximally inhibitory (minimally promotive). Again, the rhythmical manifestations are apparent.

So there is evidence for an oscillator in photoperiodism. We shall note four similarities between Time Measurement in photoperiodism and timing in the circadian rhythms. The above experiments constitute the *first* of these similarities: rhythmical manifestations even under extended periods of continuous light or dark may be observed in both phenomena.

26.3.3 Further Experiments on the Critical Night

The critical dark period is one manifestation of Time Measurement in photoperiodism. It has been studied rather intensively from this viewpoint.

A fundamental question concerns the influence of temperature upon the critical night. Figure 26-14 shows the results of two attempts to study this. In cocklebur the effect of temperature upon the critical night is very minor, although there is a marked effect upon the maximum (saturation) level of flowering observable

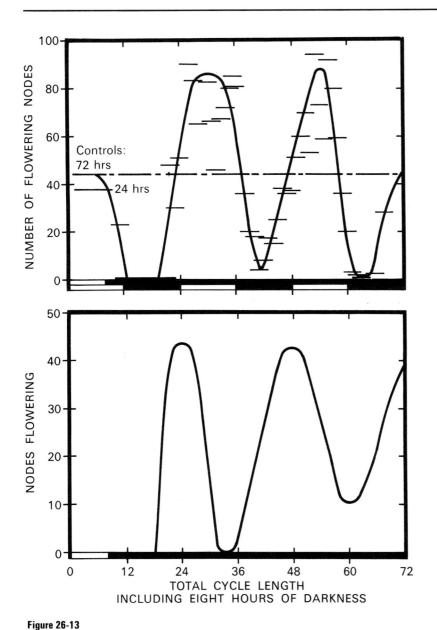

Figure 26-13

Rhythmical responses in flowering to Biloxi soybean. (top) Flowering response of soybean to 4-hour interruptions (indicated as scattered horizontal lines) applied at various times during the 64-hour dark period. Plants received 7 cycles of 8 hours of light followed by 64 hours of darkness, as indicated by the top bar at the bottom. Bottom bar shows postulated photophile and skotophile phases. (bottom) Flowering response of soybeans to 7 cycles, including 8 hours of light and different dark periods to provide the total cycle lengths as indicated. (Data for both figures from various publications of K. C. Hamner. Figures from F. B. Salisbury, 1963, *The Flowering Process*, Pergamon Press, Oxford, London, Paris, New York.)

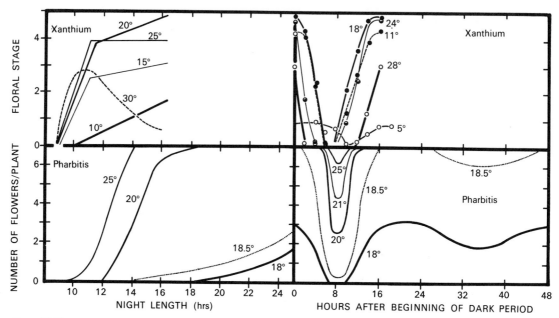

Figure 26-14

Effects of temperature on time measurement in cocklebur (*Xanthium*) and Japanese morning glory (*Pharbitis*). Left figures indicate flowering response as a function of night length. Note the small effects of temperature upon critical dark period in cocklebur, but the large effects in Japanese morning glory. Right figures indicate flowering response of plants induced with a long dark period and interrupted at various times with a brief interval of light and at various temperatures as indicated. Time of maximum sensitivity to the light flash is quite independent of temperature in Japanese morning glory and relatively independent in cocklebur. (Japanese morning glory data from A. Takimoto and K. C. Hamner, 1964, *Plant Physiol.* 39:6, 1025. Critical dark period data for cocklebur from F. B. Salisbury, 1963, *Planta* 59:518–534. Light interruption data for cocklebur obtained by a graduate plant physiology class at Colorado State University, 1964, previously unpublished.)

for plants induced at the various temperatures. The effect on level of flowering must be an effect on Florigen Synthesis, but the lack of effect on critical night implies that Time Measurement in the flowering of cocklebur is relatively temperature independent. Calculations for Q_{10} yield values of 1.02 for Time Measurement. Figure 26-14 also shows the results of a similar experiment using Japanese morning glory. With this plant, both the final level of flowering and the critical night are highly temperature sensitive. The responses to slight temperature changes are very striking.

Such an experiment does not conclusively demonstrate temperature dependence of Time

Measurement in Japanese morning glory, however, since the effect of temperature upon Florigen Synthesis might mask an effect upon Time Measurement. At the lower temperatures, Time Measurement may go to completion as at higher temperatures, but insufficient hormone may be synthesized to produce a perceptible level of flowering. An alternative and more definitive approach to the study of Time Measurement is to study the effects of a light interruption applied at different times during the dark period. This kind of an experiment, with temperature as a variable, is also illustrated in Fig. 26-14 with both cocklebur and Japanese morning glory. In both cases the time of max-

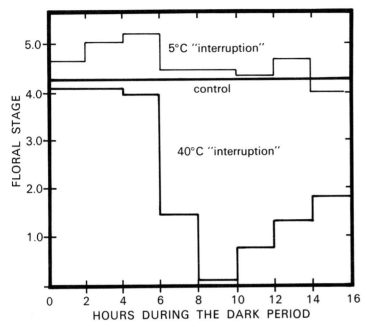

Figure 26-15
Flowering response to high- or low-temperature "interruptions" applied for 2-hour intervals at various times during a 16-hour inductive dark period (23°C). (From F. B. Salisbury, 1963, *Planta* 59:518–534.)

imum sensitivity to light remains quite constant over a wide range of temperatures. Interestingly enough, this is more clearly illustrated with Japanese morning glory than with cocklebur. Indeed, with cocklebur there is an apparent slowing of Time Measurement at 5°C.

In any case, Time Measurement in photoperiodism is quite independent of temperature. A few supporting studies have been performed with species other than those indicated. A temperature-independent clock is highly characteristic of the circadian rhythms, and so this constitutes the *second* property of Time Measurement in photoperiodism, which is similar to that of the circadian rhythms.

The point is also illustrated by "interrupting" an inductive dark period with intervals of abnormally high (or low) temperature (Fig.

26-15). There is virtually no effect during Time Measurement, although a high degree of sensitivity to elevated temperatures is exhibited during Florigen Synthesis. If effects at two-hour intervals of low temperature (10°C) on critical night (cocklebur) are studied, it becomes apparent that the entire response (lengthening of critical night by about 30 minutes) is due to low temperatures during the first two hours—during Pigment Shift. Again, Time Measurement is temperature independent but Pigment Shift acts like a typical metabolic reaction.

It was found in another experiment with cockleburs and low temperatures by two groups of workers in the mid-1950s that the critical night might be shortened somewhat if about half of the daily *light* period (using several inductive cycles) was given at temperatures just a few degrees above freezing. That is, plants would flower with only 8.0 hours of darkness (8.3 normally required) if 8 hours of the light period were given at low temperatures. Salisbury was subsequently able to show that the effect could not be observed if plants were given only a single dark period followed by the low-temperature treatment. In such a case, the critical dark period was actually extended somewhat. With multiple cycles, however, he was able to observe critical nights as short as 6.5 to 7 hours. Apparently, this effect depended upon the low-temperature light periods' coming *before* the inductive dark period rather than after. Plants seemed to be conditioned in some way by the low-temperature treatment so that they responded to shorter dark periods (see the last two paragraphs of 26.3.4). Incidentally, a very similar phenomenon can be observed when high pressures of carbon dioxide are given during the light period in a multiple-cycle induction.

Perhaps one of the most meaningful experiments designed to study Time Measurement involves observation of the critical night under so-called **threshold light**. This refers in a specialized sense to the intensity of light that will inhibit flowering about 50 percent when it is applied during the entire inductive dark period.[4] Figure 26-16 shows the results of an experiment in which the critical night was determined for plants placed under threshold light conditions. Although the level of flowering is inhibited, as required by our definition of threshold light, Time Measurement remains uninfluenced. The

figure shows an equivalent experiment in which the time of maximum sensitivity to a light interruption of the dark period was determined for plants under threshold light conditions. Again, there is a clear inhibition in the level of flowering but no effect upon Time Measurement. This experiment would seem to eliminate Pigment Shift as the mechanism of Time Measurement in flowering of cocklebur. Under threshold light conditions, Pigment Shift can apparently not go to completion. The fact that flowering is inhibited by the threshold light implies that an effective amount of Pfr must exist at all times.

The above experiment does raise an interesting question. If Pigment Shift never goes to completion, how can Time Measurement of the dark period originally be initiated? We have assumed that the link between the time-measuring system and the light environment is provided by the phytochrome system with its potential for Pigment Shift. Several possible answers remain to be investigated. It is conceivable that some completely new pigment system is involved in providing this coupling between Time Measurement and the environment. We have no evidence for such a system, however. It is more likely that the coupling may be achieved when Pigment Shift has only progressed to a slight degree, while subsequent flowering (the biochemistry of Florigen Synthesis) is far more sensitive to the Pfr resulting from Pigment Shift. These are intriguing questions which imply various avenues for future research.

26.3.4 Experiments on the Light Period

Two rather simple observations suggest an interesting problem. To begin with, it is well known that twelve hours of darkness will bring about a nearly maximum level of flowering in a cocklebur under the usual experimental conditions, yet a light flash given eight hours after the beginning of a twenty-hour inductive dark period leaves plants in a completely vegetative condition. Why should twelve hours of darkness

[4] Threshold light is determined by placing plants at different distances from a low-wattage lamp (7.5 watts, incandescent, is appropriate for cocklebur), leaving them there for 16 hours or some other appropriate time, and subsequently determining their flowering. Plants closest to the light may be inhibited completely, while plants at a sufficient distance are not inhibited compared to control plants in constant darkness and at the same temperature. At an intermediate distance, plants are inhibited about 50 percent (the intensity is approximately equivalent to that provided by the full moon).

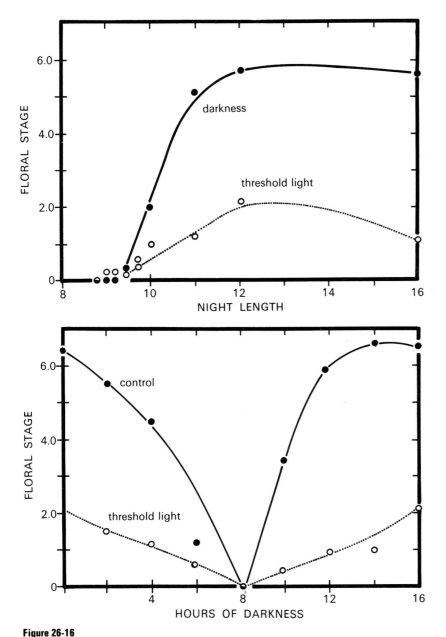

Figure 26-16

Effects of threshold light upon time measurement in flowering of cocklebur. (top) The flowering response to night length as influenced by incandescent light of about 10 microwatt/cm². (bottom) Effect of a brief light interruption during an inductive dark period given either in total darkness or under threshold light. (Critical dark period data from F. B. Salisbury, 1963, *Planta* 59:518–534. Light-interruption data from H. D. Papenfuss, 1966, doctoral dissertation, Colorado State University, Fort Collins.)

be so effective in floral induction when given after several hours of light but so completely ineffective when it follows a light flash given after eight hours of darkness? Actually, a little further thought reveals that this depends upon the length of the light interruption. If it lasts only a few seconds, then flowering is inhibited, but if it lasts sixteen hours, then the following twelve hours of darkness are fully effective in inducing flowering. That is, plants given eight hours of darkness, a normal sixteen-hour day, and then twelve hours of darkness will flower at a near maximum level. What is the difference to the plant between a few seconds of light and sixteen hours?

To study this problem, Salisbury in 1962 initiated a series of experiments based upon the following scheme. Plants were placed in a growth chamber under continuous light and at constant temperature for several days (three or more) until their circadian leaf movements had nearly disappeared and they had become essentially arhythmic. They were then exposed to a single interval of darkness less than the critical night (often 7.5 hours) referred to as the **phasing dark period**. This period of darkness was then terminated by an interval of light referred to as the **intervening light period**. The effectiveness of the treatment was then observed by subjecting the plants to a **test dark period** long enough to induce flowering (conveniently twelve hours). The properties of the intervening light period were then studied in several ways.

The question posed above may first be answered by studying flowering in response to a constant test dark period as a function of the length of the intervening light period, as shown in Fig. 26-17. Intervening light periods from a duration just sufficient to saturate the phytochrome system (a few seconds) up to about five hours in length were completely inhibitory to flowering. As the intervening light period became longer, however, flowering increased until a saturation level was reached at about twelve

hours. The analogy to the critical night is evident. Here we are apparently measuring the critical day, but *in the sense of a long-day plant* (flowering is produced by days *exceeding* a minimum). It is much shorter than the critical night, only three to five hours in duration, although the optimum day is about twelve hours (as is the optimum night—adding again to the optimum 24 hours total cycle length).

Figure 26-18 summarizes a number of other experiments designed to study the properties of the intervening light period. *First*, the effect of intensity was investigated. A little study makes it clear that the intervening light period investigated in this way is in principle equivalent to the High-Intensity Light Process of Hamner, hence the desirability of studying the intensity requirements. Various levels of relatively high-intensity light (100 to 4,000 foot-candles) were initially used, but no effect of intensity could be observed. Threshold light was then determined in an experiment analogous to that used in measurement of the inhibitory effects of threshold light applied during the inductive dark period. Here, promotive effects during the intervening light period were the subject of study. Such promotive effects could be observed when plants were separated by about 1.5 meters from a 25-watt incandescent bulb. While this is a somewhat higher intensity than that required for inhibition of flowering when applied during the dark period, it is nevertheless within the same order of magnitude. The High-Intensity Light Process proves then to be a Low-Intensity Light Process! We are dealing with intensities of the order of those required to influence the phytochrome system.

This suggested the *second* study, the determination of the most effective quality (an action spectrum) for the intervening light period. This was done by Salisbury using a monochromater installation in Bünning's laboratory in Tübingen, Germany. Red light proved to be most effective in the promotion during the intervening light

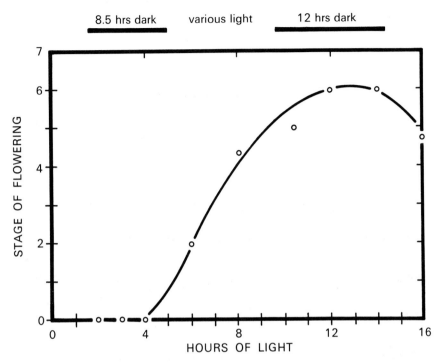

Figure 26-17

Flowering response as a function of length of the intervening light period in an experiment symbolized by the bars above the figure. (Data from F. B. Salisbury, 1965, *Planta* 66:1–26.)

period, and far-red light was most inhibitory. While detailed reversal studies have not been carried out, the results, nevertheless, clearly imply that Pfr is *promotive* to flowering when it is present during the *light* period but (as has long been known) highly *inhibitory* when present during the *dark* period. Thus, Bünning's early suggestion that plants go through two phases, during one of which light is inhibitory and the other, promotive, is fully substantiated by these experiments using the cocklebur, the one species that previously seemed to resist explanation in terms of Bünning's idea. At the time that Salisbury was carrying out these experiments with cocklebur, a number of other laboratories using various other species were performing comparable and even quite different experi-

ments, all of which seemed to lead to the same conclusion: that a changing cyclical sensitivity to Pfr exists in the flowering process. The experiments discussed above, which involve interruption of extended dark periods (Fig. 26-13), sometimes use red and far-red light and constitute good examples. Some of the other approaches are too involved for further discussion here.

This conclusion that plants do go through phases opposite in their sensitivity to red light constitutes the *third* similarity between time measurement in the circadian rhythms and in photoperiodism.

Third, Salisbury studied the sensitivity to temperature during the intervening light period and found a temperature independence in time

HOURS BEFORE OR AFTER BEGINNING OF INDUCTIVE DARK PERIOD

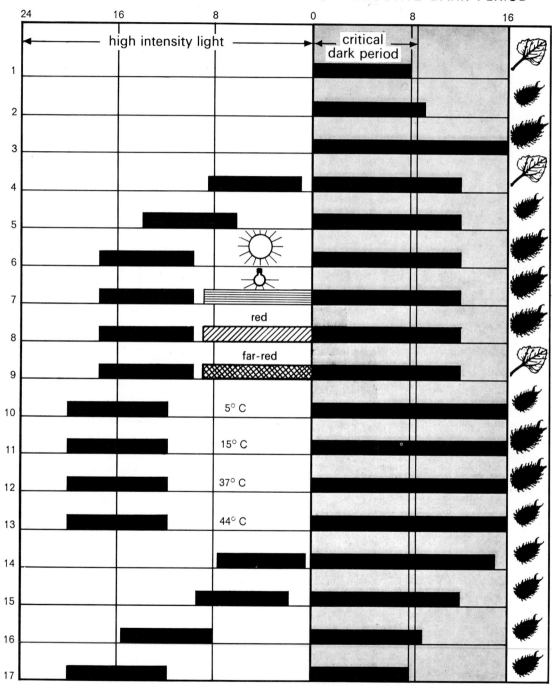

measurement equivalent to that observed during the dark period. This is further support for the second common characteristic.

Fourth, an interesting complication was observed. Interaction between length of the intervening light period and the subsequent test dark period was studied in a multiple factorial experiment (Fig. 26-19). It became apparent that as the intervening light period became longer and longer, the critical night (test dark period) became shorter and shorter. The value of the critical night approached the usual 8.3 hours but went considerably below this value, reaching its lowest point at about 6.5 hours when the intervening light period was 12 hours in duration. As the intervening light period increased in length, the critical dark period then also increased to its usual value of 8.3 hours.

Why should the critical dark period actually be less than its usual value, providing only that the intervening light period is twelve hours long? Two possible explanations come to mind. Perhaps an inhibitor is formed during the light period when this light period exceeds about twelve hours in length, requiring a longer subsequent dark period to overcome its effect. If this is the case, the experiments involving low temperatures or high carbon dioxide pressures during the day (described in section 26.3.3) might be explained on the same basis. Perhaps these treatments prevent the formation of this inhibitor. On the other hand, it is possible that this is also a function of the biological clock. Its tendency to oscillate may be so strong that it

begins to go into the "dark" phase after say nine or ten hours of light. If plants are then placed in darkness, the oscillation will continue into the dark phase—but have a "head start" of two or three hours. If plants continue in the light, this may rephase them back to the light phase. Low temperatures or high carbon dioxide could slow the clock during the original light phase.

26.3.5 Studies on Clock Setting and Rephasing

Based upon the experiments described above, Herbert Papenfuss (a graduate student) and Salisbury studied the properties of clock setting and rephasing in Time Measurement in the flowering of cocklebur. Atsushi Takimoto and Hamner performed at the same time somewhat similar experiments with Japanese morning glory. The results aid somewhat in understanding the problems outlined in the above section.

In some of Papenfuss's experiments, the length of the phasing dark period was allowed to vary while the intervening light period remained constant and very short, and the test dark period also remained constant. As the phasing dark period was increased to about five hours in length, effectiveness of the test dark period decreased only slightly. With an increase in length of the phasing dark period to six hours, however, the test dark period suddenly became markedly ineffective.

Another and more fruitful approach is illustrated in Fig. 26-20. A long interval of dark-

Figure 26-18

Some effects of the intervening light period upon flowering of cocklebur. (1) Dark periods less than the critical do not induce flowering. (2) Dark periods slightly longer than the critical result in a low level of flowering, while (3) dark periods much longer than the critical result in high levels of flowering. (4, 5, and 6) As the intervening light period at high intensity increases, flowering increases. (7) Low-intensity light during the intervening light will also result in high levels of flowering, as will red light (8), while far-red is inhibitory (9). (10, 11, 12, and 13) Temperature during the intervening light period has little effect upon flowering, at least between 15° and 37°C. (14, 15, 16, and 17) Comparable levels of flowering are obtained with decreasing inductive dark periods, providing length of the intervening light period increases. Finally, when the intervening light period is 12 hours long (17), flowering is induced with dark periods slightly less than the critical. (From F. B. Salisbury, 1966, *Naturwissenschaft und Medizin* 12:48.)

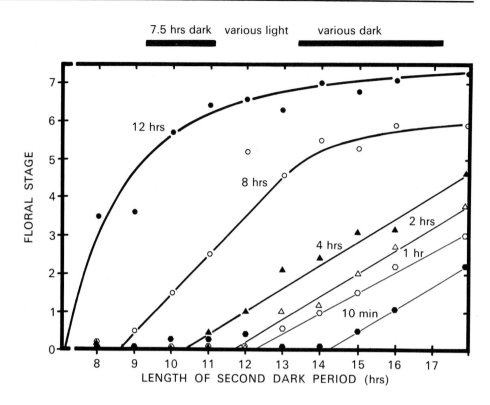

Figure 26-19

Effects of length of the intervening light period upon critical night for the test dark period (experimental plan indicated above the figure). As the intervening light period increases in length, flowering response to a given test dark period increases, and critical dark period for the test dark period decreases in length. (Data from F. B. Salisbury, 1963, *Planta* 59:518.)

ness was given, and this was interrupted first after two, four, or six hours (phasing dark periods of two, four, or six hours). A second interruption was then given at various times during the ensuing darkness to determine the time of maximum sensitivity to light. As the figure indicates, the time of maximum sensitivity remained essentially constant with two- and four-hour phasing dark periods but was shifted ten hours following a six-hour phasing dark period. There appears to be some effect of the two- and four-hour phasing dark periods, and this is even easier to observe when the phasing dark period is followed by test dark periods of various

lengths, so that the critical night is determined. The critical night is shifted an hour or two, although the time of maximum sensitivity to a light flash is not clearly shifted but only broadened. We can imagine that the effect of a light interruption given some time before five hours of darkness is essentially a *delay* approximately equivalent to the hours of darkness that have elapsed before the light flash is given. That is, the light flash, although not completely effective, is acting somewhat like the *dusk signal* received by the plants when they are first put in the dark. The easily noticeable shift in maximum sensitivity following the light flash

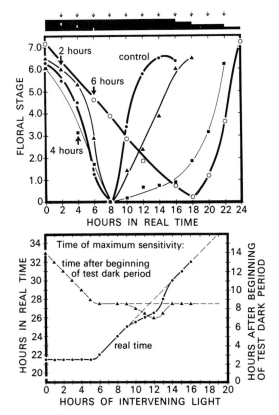

Figure 26-20

Aspects of clock resetting in flowering of *Xanthium*. (top) Effects of a light interruption given at various times during long test dark periods that followed phasing dark periods of various lengths. Arrows above the bars at the top indicate times when light interruptions were given and correspond to the data points. Of course, a given set of plants receiving a given test dark period received only one light interruption during the test dark period and following the interruptions at 0, 2, 4, or 6 hours. (bottom) Time of maximum sensitivity during the test dark period as a function of the length of the intervening light period. Heavy line corresponds to left ordinate and indicates time of maximum sensitivity in terms of real time. Lighter line shows time of maximum sensitivity in terms of time after beginning of the test dark period (right ordinate). Dashed lines are interpolations and extrapolations. (From H. D. Papenfuss and F. B. Salisbury, 1967, *Plant Physiol.* 42:1562.)

after six hours, however, seems to indicate a completely different kind of effect from that observed following the two- and four-hour light flashes. Rather than a simple **delay**, there seems

to be a complete **rephasing**. The six-hour light flash appears to be acting more like a *dawn signal* than a dusk signal.

The properties of rephasing by a dawn signal as well as delay by a dusk signal, the actual effect depending upon the time when the light flash is given, have their closely analogous counterparts in the properties of the circadian rhythms. This constitutes the *fourth* and last common characteristic exhibited by the circadian rhythms and the photoperiodism clock.

Papenfuss performed a number of experiments in which a constant 7.5-hour phasing dark period was given. This was followed by intervening light periods of various lengths, and the subsequent test dark period was interrupted at various times to determine the time of maximum sensitivity to the light flash. That is, termination of a 7.5-hour phasing dark period would, according to the above conclusions, act as a dawn signal and result in a rephasing and very noticeable shift (typically 14 hours) in the time of maximum sensitivity. Papenfuss found (Fig. 26-21) that the time of maximum sensitivity during the test dark period was essentially uninfluenced as the intervening light period increased from a very short duration (seconds) to about five hours. In terms of Time Measurement, light is essentially without effect (innocuous) during the first five hours following the dawn signal. Following intervening light periods of five hours or longer, the time of maximum sensitivity tended to come about eight hours after the beginning of the test dark period, as is the usual case when it is determined under normal conditions. That is, there is no effect of dawn, only dusk. The clock seems to be held in some sort of **suspension** in its daytime phase, and the beginning of darkness acts as a true dusk signal **restarting** the operation of Time Measurement during the inductive dark period. Between about nine and fourteen hours, there is an interesting dip in the curve that is apparently related to the effect described above (last two paragraphs of 26.3.4). That is, with a twelve-

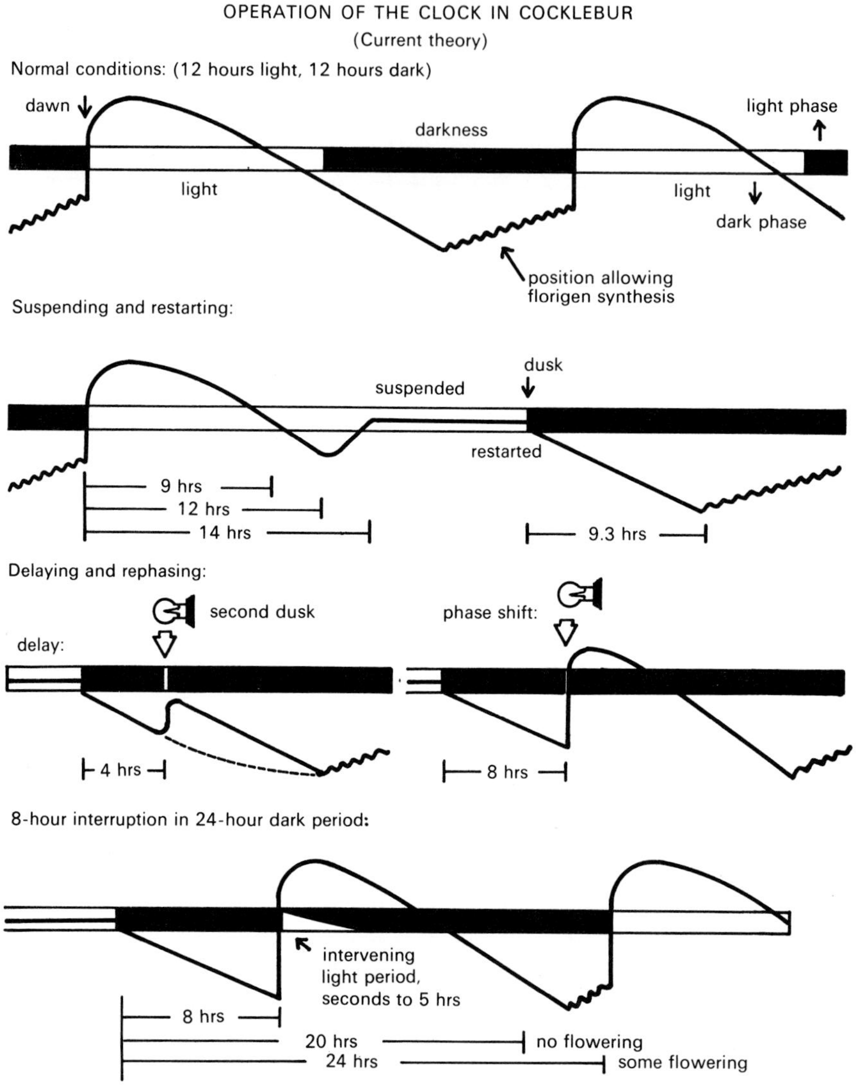

OPERATION OF THE CLOCK IN COCKLEBUR
(Current theory)

Normal conditions: (12 hours light, 12 hours dark)

dawn ↓   darkness   light phase ↑

light   light ↓

dark phase

position allowing
florigen synthesis

Suspending and restarting:

dusk ↓
suspended

restarted

├─ 9 hrs ─┤
├─ 12 hrs ─┤
├─ 14 hrs ─┤   ├─ 9.3 hrs ─┤

Delaying and rephasing:

second dusk   phase shift:

delay:

├ 4 hrs ┤   ├─ 8 hrs ─┤

8-hour interruption in 24-hour dark period:

↖ intervening
light period,
seconds to 5 hrs

├─ 8 hrs ─┤
├─── 20 hrs ───┤ no flowering
├──── 24 hrs ────┤ some flowering

Figure 26-21
A schematic representation of the features of time measurement in flowering of cocklebur as discussed in the text. (From H. D. Papenfuss and F. B. Salisbury, 1967, *Plant Physiol.* 42:1562.)

hour intervening light period, the time of maximum sensitivity occurs only about six hours after the beginning of the test dark period, and this gradually increases to eight hours as the intervening light period increases from twelve to

fourteen hours. Are we indeed dealing with an overriding tendency for the clock to oscillate into the dark phase? This idea does seem to fit the data.

This study has considerably illuminated the

properties of the photoperiodism clock in cocklebur: it may be *delayed* somewhat by light flashes coming less than five hours after the beginning of darkness. It may be *rephased* by a dawn signal coming after about five hours of darkness or more. It may be *suspended* during intervals of light longer than five hours. It may be *restarted* at the beginning of darkness by a true dusk signal following five hours or more of light. It may well be that cocklebur (and perhaps other plants induced by a single cycle) owes its ability to respond to a single inductive dark period to the ability of its photoperiodism clock to be suspended and then reinitiated by a true dusk signal. These properties might be unique to such plants; at least they have surely complicated their study.

The results presented here shed some light on another question: what is the physiological effect of an inhibitory light flash? Does an interruption of the dark period inhibit flowering to an extent determined by the status of the clock? (Is the effect of Pfr a function of the status of the clock?) Or can the effects of a light flash be explained *strictly* on the basis of effects on the clock? Previously, we had thought that the only effect on the clock would be a delay, and this did not seem to explain all effects of a light flash. In such a scheme, the flash after eight hours in a twenty-hour dark period should not inhibit. After all, the twelve remaining hours should provide plenty of time to start over and produce plenty of florigen. Knowing about rephasing, however, it is easy to see how a flash at eight hours can inhibit. Things must begin from dawn, not dusk. Considering these new concepts, it appears possible to understand essentially all of the previous experiments with light interruptions of dark periods given to cocklebur by assuming that florigen is synthesized only when the clock is in a suitable state, and that light may either delay or rephase the clock. Further tests of these ideas will be required.

26.4 THE BIOCHEMISTRY OF FLOWERING: FLORIGEN

The above discussion of the role of the photoperiod in flowering and the influence of low temperature (vernalization) mentioned in Chapter 25 indicate strong environmental control over sexual reproduction in many species. As with other physiological processes, we wish to understand flowering in terms of the essential chemical processes involved.

26.4.1 Evidences for a Flowering Hormone

Three evidences for the existence of a hormone that stimulates flowering are well recognized. *First*, the leaf detects and somehow responds to the proper photoperiod, although the bud ultimately becomes a flower (26.3.1D). *Second*, removal of the leaves at various times after an inductive photoperiod influences flowering in a manner suggesting that translocation of a flowering stimulus out of the leaves is being measured (see Fig. 26-11). The *third* evidence, previously considered in relation to vernalization, is that a vegetative plant grafted to one that has been induced will itself then flower, even though it is never exposed to the suitable vernalization or photoperiodic treatment.

Flowering can also be caused in many species that have not received photoperiodic induction by grafting them to others that have. Mh. Chailakhyan, a Russian, performed the first such grafts in the 1930s and suggested that the name **florigen** (flower maker) be given to the hormone he believed was involved. Many successful grafting experiments similar to those shown in Fig. 26-22 have been performed among short-day plants, long-day plants, and day-neutral plants, and among members of several diverse families. In one study, five vegetative cocklebur plants were grafted in series to one at the end of the chain, and that one was then induced by short-day treatment. Flowers formed

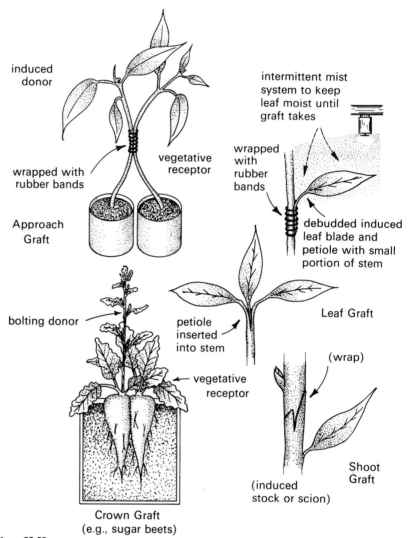

Figure 26-22

Some techniques of grafting used in the study of the flowering process.

on all plants, further indicating the contagious nature of the induced state.

A conclusion from these studies is that florigen may be similar or identical in all plants and that the various response types differ not in their requirement for such a hormone but in the influence that environment has upon its produc-

tion. The requirement of some species for both a cold treatment and proper daylength can, however, be interpreted to indicate that more than one substance is involved in the flowering stimulus, one perhaps being a precursor of another.

Jan A. D. Zeevaart, then in the Netherlands

(1957–1958), performed some interesting grafting experiments with short-day *Perilla* and cocklebur plants, in which he wished to know whether a single leaf could donate florigen. He found that a *Perilla* leaf from a flowering plant could be grafted first to one vegetative plant of the same species and then to others, with flowering the result of each graft. Results with cocklebur were also successful. He then determined whether detached leaves of these species could be induced by proper photoperiods, as evidenced by their ability to cause flowering in vegetative plants to which they were grafted. Detached *Perilla* leaves could be induced, but those of the cocklebur could be induced only very weakly. More recently, others have also found that cocklebur leaves can be weakly induced in this way, but they are never very effective in causing flowering of noninduced plants, perhaps because they deteriorate (become senescent) so rapidly when excised from the plant.

The above experiments suggest that the transmissible substance or substances act in a positive manner to promote differentiation of vegetative buds into flowering buds. We suspect that florigen acts in the buds by activating previously repressed genes, which then lead to flower formation. From this standpoint, a new portion of the plant's morphogenetic information program is called upon.

Is it possible that photoperiodic induction does not produce a positively acting florigen, but instead simply prevents the formation of a flowering inhibitor otherwise produced in the leaves? Our definition of plant hormones (Chapter 21) says only that these regulate physiological processes but does not imply that they cannot do this by inhibition of certain biochemical reactions, so an inhibitor might also be a hormone. The results from grafting experiments, especially those of Zeevaart in which single leaves were used, strongly indicate, however, that induction in many species leads to synthesis of a positively acting hormone, rather than to

termination of inhibitor production. Nevertheless, as we shall see later, various studies do indicate that flowering is controlled by a proper balance of transmissible inhibitors and promoters, both of which are synthesized in leaves.

26.4.2 Extraction and Identification of Florigen

Shortly after evidence for the existence of a florigen was obtained, several investigators began attempts to extract and identify the active compound or compounds. Various substances were extracted from flowering plants using different solvents, and these were then added to vegetative plants to determine whether these alone would cause flowering. Although indications of positive responses were often obtained, the first clearly repeatable experiments were announced by Richard G. Lincoln, Darwin L. Mayfield, and Alan Cunningham in 1961. They found that flowering cocklebur plants growing in the Los Angeles area yielded a methanol-soluble substance that caused noninduced plants of this species to flower. It was then reported that even leaves from reproductive sunflowers contained a substance with similar properties capable of causing flowering of the cocklebur under unfavorable daylengths. Further fractionation indicated that the active compound in the cocklebur is an unknown water-soluble organic acid. Extracts from vegetative plants will not cause the same response. Perhaps this substance will prove to be the elusive florigen of Chailakhyan, but flowering has thus far been produced only when the active substance is added to the leaves of the vegetative plants. If it is indeed a flowering hormone, it should cause reproductive buds to form when added directly to vegetative buds. The possibility remains that it is not florigen itself, but that it only causes the production of florigen in the leaves of vegetative plants, in which case it would still be a highly interesting and valuable material.

26.4.3 Evidences for Flowering Inhibitors

If a plant is induced by exposing only one or a few leaves to the proper photoperiodic conditions while the others are in unfavorable photoperiods, flowering is frequently poor. It was also noted that when an induced plant is grafted to a vegetative one, the presence of leaves on the latter reduces its flowering response. In such cases, as in vernalization (Chapter 25), these results can often be explained on the basis of translocation effects. Florigen apparently moves primarily in the assimilate stream. A leaf in the light may not be exporting an inhibitor but only acting as a source of assimilates that reach the bud more readily than those from darkened leaves synthesizing florigen. Several experiments with radioactive tracers (^{14}C-labeled sugars) have produced results in agreement with this concept.

These explanations do not account for several experiments, however. In some short-day plants, for example, an inhibition is exerted not only if some of the leaves are kept in continuous light during the time the others are darkened, but even if these are given a dark period interrupted by a short light break, which should not influence assimilate export very much. In addition, in the case of the cocklebur, at least, the presence of leaves that are too old to cause flowering (when they alone are given short days) is inhibitory compared to the response of plants in which these leaves have been removed. S. C. Bhargava, then in the Netherlands, recently obtained good evidence that such inhibitors are formed in the short-day plants *Salvia occidentalis* and *Perilla crispa* under noninductive conditions, and that they exert their influence directly in the buds. Finally, when mature leaves are removed from the long-day henbane plant (*Hyoscyamus niger*), it will flower even under short days. Certain short-day varieties of strawberry (*Fragaria* sp.) also flower under improper daylengths if their leaves are removed. These results, and others, all indicate that inhibitors as well as promoters are produced in leaves and that the flowering response depends upon the balance between them. In strawberry and henbane inhibitory substances appear to be controlling, while in the cocklebur and many other species the powerful promotive substances are probably of primary importance.

26.4.4 Influence of Growth Regulators upon Flowering

26.4.4A Auxins In view of the many physiological effects influenced by auxins, it was reasonable for early investigators to suspect that these substances play an important role in flowering. Chailakhyan and L. Zhdanova investigated the auxin content of a number of long-day and short-day plants as early as 1938 but found that auxins were more abundant on long days than on short days in both groups. They concluded that it was unlikely that floral induction was due to changes in auxin content, and this has been supported by more recent work.

There is at least one plant, the pineapple (*Ananas comosus*), in which auxins can control flowering. H. E. Clark and K. R. Kerns reported, in 1942, that sprays of certain synthetic auxins stimulated flowering of this species. Indoleacetic acid is not effective (it is rapidly destroyed by enzymes in the plant), but naphthaleneacetic acid (10–50 ppm) causes earlier and more uniform fruit production. As a result, mechanical harvesters can be used in pineapple production. The unsaturated gases ethylene and acetylene also stimulate flowering in pineapple, and there is evidence that the auxin treatments may simply be acting indirectly by increasing ethylene production. As mentioned in Chapter 21, ethylene release is stimulated by auxin application in many plants, including the pineapple. If ethylene is indeed the active agent in the present case, an important problem is to determine how it acts.

In short-day plants, applied auxins usually inhibit flowering, especially when added during Florigen Synthesis and during Florigen Translocation. F. Abeles discovered that it is likely that this auxin effect, like several others[5] (Chapter 21), may be due to the ethylene they cause the plant to produce in greater amounts. He found that when cocklebur leaves were sprayed with IAA, the ethylene production more than doubled and that ethylene itself was inhibitory to flowering of this plant. In a few cases auxins have stimulated flowering of long-day plants, but only when these are given photoperiods nearly long enough to induce flowering anyway. It is unlikely that endogenous auxins normally play a decisive role in flowering, but they will probably prove to modify somewhat the effects of compounds that do.

26.4.4B Gibberellins

The first extensive study of gibberellin effects upon flowering was performed by Anton Lang in 1957, when he demonstrated that GA_3 substituted for the vernalization treatment required by several biennials (sections 25.1.4 and 25.6.2 and Fig. 25-4). Certain long-day plants also flowered on short days when similarly treated, but short-day plants were not appreciably influenced. Lang's studies have been extended by many plant physiologists, and more than 30 long-day species from at least 17 families are now known to be either promoted or induced by GA_3. A few species have failed to respond, but perhaps they require one of the other known gibberellins. Some gibberellins are far more effective upon some plants than are others. For example, GA_7 is more effective with *Silene armeria* than is GA_3, and both GA_7 and GA_4 surpass GA_3 activity with *Crepis parviflora*. It should be noted, however, as Roy Sachs has emphasized, that GA_3 inhibits flowering of several plants, both short-day and long-day.

A few long-short-day species have been investigated, and it appears that gibberellins can substitute for the long-day requirement but not for short days. No qualitative short-day plants have yet been induced in unfavorable daylengths by application of any gibberellin, so we may conclude that their florigen is not a gibberellin, at least not one of those presently known.

The influence of gibberellic acid (GA_3) upon the flowering of certain trees has also been investigated. Most trees do not flower until they are several years old and must first go through what is often called a juvenile stage. Y. Kato, in Japan, found in 1958 that a number of conifer species in the families Taxodiaceae and Cupressaceae "flowered"[6] much earlier after being sprayed with GA_3. A particularly striking example is that of sugi (*Cryptomeria japonica*) which "flowered" in its second summer after GA_3 treatment. Since then, Richard Pharis, now at the University of Calgary, and others have discovered that Arizona cypress (*Cupressus arizonica*), which normally produces staminate strobili when four or five years old, does so when as young as 55 days old if sprayed with GA_3. Pharis also forced Western red cedar, a conifer native to the Pacific Northwest, to "flower" when the seedlings were only 4 cm tall (three months old) by this treatment. The economically

---

[5] As this manuscript is in proof, a controversy is developing about which compound has the primary effect, ethylene or auxin. If auxin causes ethylene production, does ethylene cause auxin production? Or could *both* activate genes in some independent manner? In a recent study it was shown that auxin (IAA) inhibition of pea root growth remained reversible upon transfer to IAA-free solutions after several hours, but ethylene inhibition was not reversible. Ethylene response exhibited a lag period (3 to 6 hours), while auxin response did not. IAA promoted ethylene production, but conditions which inhibited this did not affect the growth inhibition due to IAA. (Data of W. A. Andreae, M. A. Venis, F. Jursic, and T. Dumas in press in *Plant Physiology* at the time of this writing.)

[6] Reproductive structures in the gymnosperms are not flowers but male and female strobili or cones.

more important pines and firs have not responded to GA₃ by "flowering," but they might do so if treated with one of the several other known gibberellins when supplies of these become more abundant.

The striking effects of applied gibberellins upon flowering of long-day plants and certain conifers suggests that these hormones may be directly involved in flowering of these species. Several workers have, using various bioassay techniques, followed endogenous gibberellin changes in long-day plants during induction. Just after photoinduction the gibberellin levels consistently increase. It is not yet certain whether these increases reflect the synthesis of new gibberellins or are simply due to changes in the ratios of those already present. In either case, the view that endogenous gibberellins do play a critical role in flowering is strengthened. Furthermore, such plant parts as seeds, known to be rich in gibberellins, yield extracts also capable of inducing flowering in long-day species.

It is not yet clear why gibberellins are effective in long-day plants but not in short-day plants, especially when the grafting experiments discussed above suggest that their florigens are the same. Lang has suggested that gibberellins are not flowering hormones, but that when these are present in proper amounts, florigen is synthesized. It is possible, then, that gibberellins are precursors to florigen on as yet unidentified biosynthetic pathways. Or they might activate genes which control synthesis of florigen. Zeevaart found that certain antigibberellins such as CCC (cycocel) inhibit induction of the Japanese morning glory (*Pharbitis nil*), that they reduce endogenous gibberellin production, and that applications of GA₃ reverse the effect upon flowering. R. D. Bennett, S. T. Ko, and Erich Heftmann then found that ¹⁴C-labeled kaurene, a metabolic precursor of gibberellins, was converted into two or more compounds in *P. nil* buds that were undetectable in vegetative buds. These were not gibberellins but were probably isoprenoids somewhat similar to these hormones. They were transported from the cotyledons (which produce florigen in this plant) to the buds, suggesting that they might play an important role in flowering. This indicates that gibberellins or substances related to gibberellins may be even more directly involved in the induction process than has been thought. In addition, both gibberellins and auxins influence the sex expression of flowers on monoecious and dioecious plants (see next chapter).

26.4.4C Abscisic acid Since the discovery of abscisic acid in 1964, P. F. Wareing and others have performed experiments to determine whether it might play a role in flowering, as well as in dormancy and abscission. They found that black currants will both flower and become dormant under long days when abscisic acid is sprayed on the leaves, even though about a week of short days is usually needed to cause these responses. A few other short-day plants, including *Pharbitis nil* and *Chenopodium rubrum*, also flowered under long days when they received prolonged treatments of abscisic acid, but the cocklebur, Maryland Mammoth tobacco, and a short-day soybean variety did not. Abscisic acid is inhibitory to flowering in the long-day plants *Lolium temulentum* and spinach. In fact, this compound seems to have certain properties in common with an inhibitor produced in *L. temulentum* leaves kept on short days. We may conclude that, although abscisic acid does sometimes exhibit flower-promoting ability, it (like the auxins) is probably not a florigen but may influence the production or action of florigen.

26.4.4D Metabolic inhibitors Because of the difficulty in directly identifying florigen, several researchers have attempted to learn something about it by studying the processes leading to its synthesis. Most of this research has been performed with the short-day cocklebur and Japanese morning glory (*P. nil*), but Lloyd T. Evans in Australia has also intensively investigated the long-day *L. temulentum*, and some information about other species is also available.

S. Nakayama, in Japan, discovered about 1955 that respiratory poisons such as fluoride, azide, and cyanide inhibited induction in *P. nil* if applied during the long, dark period. These results indicated that respiration is needed for florigen synthesis but gave no clues to explain why. Salisbury extended and improved these techniques in studies with the cocklebur. Particular interest has been given to the relation of any inhibition found to the individual partial processes of induction listed earlier in this chapter. Inhibitory compounds are discovered by dipping plants (which have been trimmed to a single remaining florigen-donating leaf and a single florigen-receptive bud) in various concentrations of the compound just before an inductive dark period. In subsequent experiments an effective compound is then applied to different groups of plants at different times during and after the induction period to determine whether the inhibition is due to a specific influence upon induction or whether it simply prevents flower development (Fig. 26-23). The results of these **time of application** studies are then related to the partial processes of Pigment Shift, Time Measurement, Florigen Synthesis, Translocation of Florigen, and Flower Development. Specific effects upon Time Measurement are determined by measuring the *critical night* in the presence and absence of the chemical. If the critical night is lengthened, Time Measurement may be affected, but to make sure, the dark periods given treated and untreated plants are interrupted with brief inhibitory light periods. If the time of maximum sensitivity to a light interruption is affected, Time Measurement is presumed to be influenced. So far, only one substance affecting Time Measurement has been found, and this is the cobaltous ion (Co^{++}), which seems to slow the process. Its effects, along with those of two compounds that extend the critical night but do not affect the time of maximum sensitivity to light, are shown in Fig. 26-24. The specific chemical reactions necessary for flowering that are influenced by cobaltous ion have not yet been elucidated.

Certain herbicides, including 2,4-D, maleic hydrazide, and dalapon (2,2-dichloropropionic acid), inhibit flowering of the cocklebur regardless of when they are applied. They have rather general growth-retarding effects and block development of the flower buds. They may also interfere with earlier, inductive partial processes, but, if so, these effects are masked by the inhibition of growth and development. Dinitrophenol, an uncoupler of oxidative phosphorylation (i.e., ATP formation—see Chapter 15), also inhibits flowering, but it does so only when applied before the end of the inductive dark period. This suggests that ATP is needed for florigen synthesis, but this is not surprising since so many biosynthetic processes do require ATP as an energy source.

26.4.4E Antimetabolites

Salisbury decided in the late 1950s that considerably more could be learned about the biochemical processes essential to flowering if inhibitors were used to block one or only a few known reactions by interfering with normal metabolism of cell constituents. Several such **antimetabolites** are known, many of which act as competitive enzyme inhibitors, and their sites of action are usually easier to pinpoint than those of herbicides and other nonspecific inhibitors. Salisbury and James Bonner discovered that 5-fluorouracil (Fig. 26-25), a compound that blocks reactions leading to RNA and DNA synthesis, inhibits flowering of the cocklebur, but only if added before the end of the inductive dark period. They then discovered that it was more inhibitory if added to the bud than to the leaf, even though it was assumed that during the dark period the

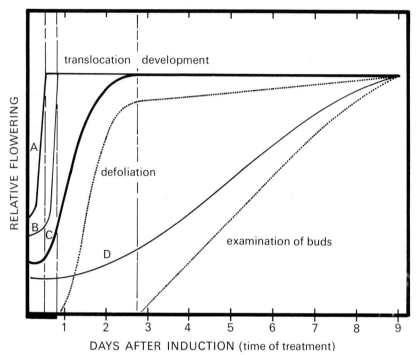

Figure 26-23

Summary curves showing the effects upon flowering (cocklebur) of inhibitory chemicals as a function of the times when they are applied in relation to a single inductive dark period (indicated by bar on the abscissa). (A) Represents compounds effective only when applied before the end of the critical night (time measurement); (B) compounds effective only when applied before the end of the dark period (synthesis of flowering hormones); (C) compounds that inhibit if they are applied before translocation of the hormone from the leaf is complete; and (D) compounds that inhibit floral development regardless of when they are applied. (From F. B. Salisbury, 1963, *The Flowering Process*, Pergamon Press, Oxford, London, Paris, New York. Used by permission.)

essential inductive processes occurred only in the leaf.

It was possible to overcome (reverse) the inhibition of fluorouracil by simultaneously applying orotic acid, a precursor of RNA and DNA pyrimidines but not by applying thymidine, a precursor only of DNA (Fig. 26-26). This suggested that RNA synthesis is the essential process with which fluorouracil interferes, and further work by Bonner and Zeevaart seems to have confirmed this. They also found that the site of inhibition is indeed in the bud, and that

any influence in the leaf is of lesser importance. Fluorouracil does block RNA synthesis in cocklebur buds and is itself incorporated into RNA molecules (presumably in place of uracil), perhaps creating fraudulent RNA in the buds. More recent studies by Joe Cherry at Purdue University indicated that fluorouracil interferes primarily with formation of ribosomal RNA, rather than with messenger RNA in this plant. It is presumably inhibitory because the necessary enzymes leading to flower bud production cannot be made. It is still unclear why RNA

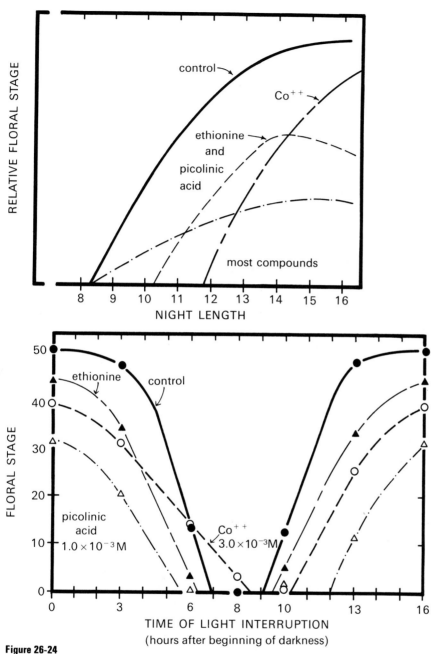

Figure 26-24

Effects of chemicals upon time measurement in cocklebur: (top) Effects upon critical night. Most compounds inhibit flowering but do not change the critical night, while Co^{++}, ethionine, and picolinic acid extend the critical dark period. (bottom) Effects of compounds upon flowering response to a light interruption during a single 16-hour inductive dark period. Inhibitory effects of the ethionine and picolinic acid are *additive* to the inhibitory effect of the light flash, regardless of when the flash is given. Co^{++}, on the other hand, shifts the time of maximum sensitivity past the usual 8 hours, so that at 6 and at 8 hours, effects of Co^{++} and the light flash are clearly not additive. (From F. B. Salisbury, 1963, *The Flowering Process*, Pergamon Press, Oxford, London, Paris, New York. Used by permission.)

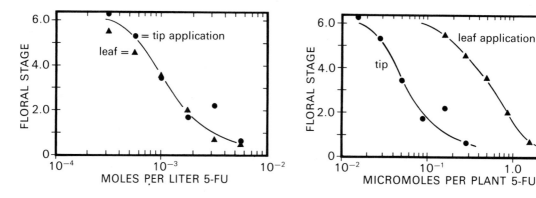

Figure 26-25

Flowering response of plants treated with various concentrations of 5-fluorouracil applied either to the leaf or to the tip. (From F. B. Salisbury and J. Bonner, 1960, *Plant Physiol.* 35:173–177.)

synthesis must be occurring in the buds even before florigen is translocated there from the leaves. Perhaps the buds do respond in ways stimulating flowering when dark, even though induction in this plant will not occur if *only* the bud is dark and will occur if it is in continuous light and only a single leaf is darkened for a period longer than the critical night. Or some "preflorigen" may be translocated to the buds soon after beginning of the dark period, influencing RNA synthesis upon its arrival.

In hemp (*Cannabis sativa*), *L. temulentum, P. nil*, and a few other species, RNA synthesis probably also is necessary for induction. The remarkable inhibitory effect of fluorouracil upon flowering of *P. nil* is shown in Fig. 26-27. Another potent RNA synthesis inhibitor, actinomycin D (Chapter 17) blocks flowering in the latter two species when added to the buds during and just after the inductive cycle, further supporting the belief that RNA formation is essential. Actinomycin D, even at high doses (5 mg/ml), has no influence upon flowering or growth of the cocklebur when the plants are dipped in it in the usual manner, but this is because it does not enter the cells. If, however, a string dipping in the solution is threaded

through the leaf petiole, flowering is inhibited and the plant is injured by the chemical. R. F. Watson and R. E. Matthews, in New Zealand, found that actinomycin D would not normally penetrate the short-day plant *Chenopodium amaranticolor* either, but if the antibiotic was injected during or before an inductive dark period into a slit cut in the stem below the apical bud, flowering and RNA synthesis in the bud were strongly inhibited.

RNA formation during induction is thought to be essential, because these molecules are needed to form essential enzymes. If this is true, substances that block enzyme synthesis should retard flowering. Research by the authors and by Walter Collins and Joseph Miller, when graduate students, suggests that this is true. Ethionine, an antimetabolite of the amino acid methionine, and *p*-fluorophenylalanine, an antimetabolite of phenylalanine, both inhibit induction of the cocklebur, perhaps by interfering with synthesis and transport of florigen (Fig. 26-28). Effects of each are reversed by the corresponding amino acid metabolite, suggesting that phenylalanine and methionine somehow participate in induction. Both inhibitors interfere with protein synthesis, and Miller and Ross

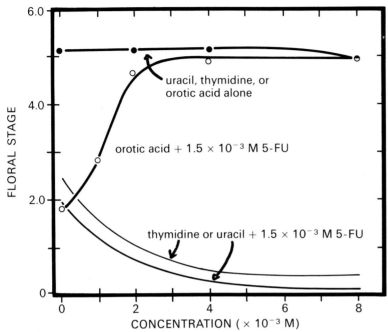

Figure 26-26

Effects upon flowering of 5-fluorouracil (5-FU) applied in the presence of increasing concentrations of uracil, thymidine, or orotic acid, as compared to effects of the metabolites applied alone. The metabolites alone have no significant effect, and only the orotic acid overcomes the inhibitory effect of 5-FU. (Modified after F. B. Salisbury, 1963, *The Flowering Process*, Pergamon Press, Oxford, London, Paris, New York. Used by permission.)

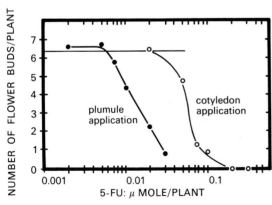

Figure 26-27

Inhibition of flowering in the Japanese morning glory by 5-FU. 5-FU was more inhibitory when added to the plumules (which respond to the floral stimulus) than to the cotyledons (which produce the stimulus). (From J. A. D. Zeevaart, 1962, *Plant Physiol.* 37:296. Used by permission.)

found that fluorophenylalanine is incorporated into cocklebur leaf proteins, perhaps in place of phenylalanine. Ethionine also blocks flowering of *P. nil* and *L. temulentum*.

It is assumed that these antimetabolites inhibit flowering because they interfere with enzyme synthesis, but we can never be certain that they do not block other reactions that are instead essential to flowering. (The same ambiguity exists in the studies with antimetabolites that prevent nucleic acid synthesis, of course.) Miller and Ross showed that fluorophenylalanine is primarily inhibitory to flowering because it blocks processes occurring in the florigen-synthesizing leaves, although a small effect in the buds was also noted. Preliminary experiments suggest that ethionine acts in a

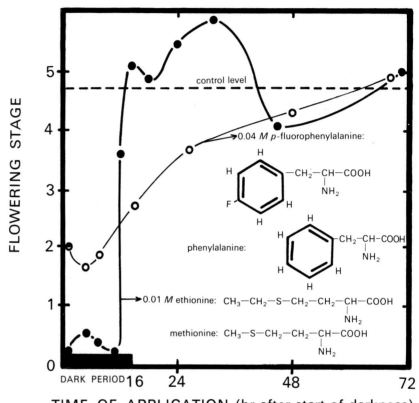

Figure 26-28

Time-of-application curves for inhibition of flowering in cocklebur with DL-ethionine or DL-*p*-fluorophenylalanine. Structures of these antimetabolites and of the amino acids with which they are known to interfere are shown on the graph. Ethionine was added both to the receptive apical bud (in which the floral response was later measured) and to the single remaining leaf capable of producing the floral stimulus (unpublished data of W. T. Collins and F. B. Salisbury). Fluorophenylalanine was added only to the leaf (unpublished data of C. Ross). Dashed line indicates the average floral stage of untreated control plants. Curves have been normalized, since results with the two inhibitors were obtained in separate experiments. Both inhibitors are most effective when applied to the plants during the inductive dark period; both become inactive when applied later.

similar way. These studies thus indicate that synthesis of new proteins must occur in leaves during the long dark period if the cocklebur is to be induced to flower, and that both RNA and protein synthesis may be essential in the buds. According to the theory for flow of genetic information (Chapter 17), if new enzymes specific to flowering are produced in the leaves during induction, new messenger RNA molecules should also be required. No compounds that block RNA synthesis have yet been clearly shown to interfere with inductive processes occurring in the leaves of any plant, although actinomycin *D* may prove to do so. Various

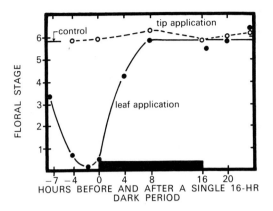

Figure 26-29

Effects of time-of-application of SKF-7997 upon flowering of the cocklebur. Either the shoot-tip (containing the responding bud, upper curve) or the leaf (lower curve) was dipped in a solution of the chemical at the times indicated. Solid dark line on the abscissa represents the 16-hour inductive dark period. (From J. Bonner et al., 1963, *Plant Physiol.* 38:81. Used by permission.)

other compounds preventing RNA formation inhibit flowering when added to these organs, but radioactive tracer studies show that they are quickly transported to the buds, where they may be inhibitory. From the present data we may conclude either that enzyme synthesis is not an essential part of florigen production, or that enzyme formation is essential but that RNA synthesis is not, or that both are required even though it has not yet been possible to demonstrate clearly a need for RNA synthesis. Because phytochrome seems to control other photomorphogenetic responses through gene activation and the resulting RNA and enzyme synthesis (Chapter 23), we suspect that both of these macromolecules are essential to induction of flowering, which, of course, is a process also strongly influenced by phytochrome.

Bonner and Zeevaart, working with a steroid chemist, Erich Heftmann, suspected that florigen might be a steroid, just as are many hormones controlling sexual reproduction in higher animals. They found that certain compounds known to block cholesterol synthesis in animals were effective inhibitors of flowering. The compound tris-(2-diethylaminoethyl) phosphate trihydrochloride, (abbreviated SKF-7997) a product of Smith, Kline, and French Laboratories, was especially effective, and its inhibition was restricted to the leaves of both the cocklebur (Fig. 26-29) and *P. nil*. They showed that it also blocks steroid production in plants, since the conversion of ^{14}C-labeled acetate and mevalonate into various sterols separated by column chromatography was reduced. However, they were not able to reverse its inhibition with any sterol or with mevalonic acid. They also investigated the endogenous sterols produced in induced, vegetative, and SKF-7997-treated plants without finding any large differences. It is possible that florigen is a minor sterol that escaped detection, or that this inhibitor blocks flowering because of interference with other unknown reactions. It would be interesting to determine whether SKF-7997 influences gibberellin production in plants, since both steroids and gibberellins are derived from mevalonic acid.

26.4.5 The Nature of the Induced State

The length of time that the induced condition caused by photoperiodic treatment exists varies considerably among different plants. In soybeans the number of flowers produced on a plant is proportional to the number of short days given after the first short day, but as soon as long days are given, the plant reverts to vegetative growth, and subsequent developing buds are not reproductive. This is also apparently true of certain long-day plants.

Cocklebur plants act quite differently, because once induction is accomplished, virtually all of the subsequent buds produce flowers. If only one short day is given, approximately the same number of flowers develops, but at a slower rate than if several short days are given.

Between these two extremes are found many other species in which the induced state persists for various lengths of time. In most of these, some vegetative reversion eventually occurs.

The induced state persists for long periods in certain species of *Perilla* just as it does in the cocklebur, but there are differences between these types in the parts that retain this condition. *Perilla* leaves, once induced, can be grafted to several vegetative receptor plants and will cause flowering in all, as mentioned earlier. But the leaves of these now reproductive plants cannot themselves cause flowering of other vegetative individuals when grafted to them. Thus, although a single induced leaf retains this state as long as it lives, the leaves not exposed to the proper short days do not themselves become induced even when on a flowering plant. In the cocklebur, on the other hand, even the very young leaves can be induced by exposing the older ones to short days, and they can then also donate florigen to still other individuals. We suppose that the proper part of the morpho-genetic information program of the cocklebur can be switched on by this environmental stimulus, that it remains on and is capable of turning on this program in other leaves. With *Perilla*, the information program remains turned on until the leaf becomes senescent and dies, but there is no way of switching on the program in other leaves not exposed to the proper environment. Thus, the induced state, like other characteristics of the flowering process, differs considerably among various species of plants.

Reproduction, Maturation, and Senescence

The completion of the life cycle of an angiosperm involves the production of flowers, fruits, and seeds. Usually accompanying seed production is a maturation and senescence of the leaves, flowers, and fruits. A large number of physiological changes other than those discussed in the previous chapter occur during the transition from vegetative to reproductive growth. Many of these changes are still only poorly understood.

We have introduced (Chapter 25) the concept of **annual plants**, which produce flowers during the same year in which they germinate and then die. We have also considered the **biennials** and the **winter annuals**, which germinate and develop vegetatively during one season, become dormant, and produce flowers and seeds the next year, usually in response to the low temperatures of the winter between the two growing seasons. Those that flower each year for a number of years are called **perennials**. Since many biennials can be thought of as cold-requiring annuals, and since several annuals behave as perennials in more tropical climates, some scientists have suggested that species be classified either as perennials or as **monocarpic plants**. The latter group would include the true annuals, biennials, and others, all of which flower only once before death. The bamboos and the century plant (*Agave americana*), which may live up to 50 and 20 years, respectively, but which die upon fruiting, are included in the monocarpic group. We shall employ both classifications in the present chapter.

27.1 PHYSIOLOGY OF FLOWER DEVELOPMENT

The length of time after germination before flowers are produced varies greatly among various plants. In certain species of *Plantago* (plantain), the complete life cycle requires only eight to ten weeks, while in the above-mentioned bamboos and the *Agave*, flower production is delayed for several years. Ultimately one or more of the buds, often the apical bud, develops into a flower. In some species the meristem initiates a primordium of only a single flower, while in others an inflorescence bearing a number of flowers develops. A tulip is a familiar example in which only a single flower develops from one meristem, while the grass and Compositae families exemplify those producing an inflorescence. Flowers may develop from the shoot apical bud, from lateral buds, or from both.

27.1.1 Male and Female Flowers

Most plants produce bisexual or **perfect flowers** containing functional female and male parts.

Other species such as spinach, date palms, willows, and maples are **dioecious** and contain staminate (male) and pistillate (female) flowers only on different individual plants. **Monoecious** plants such as corn, squash, pumpkins, and many hardwood trees contain staminate and pistillate flowers at different positions along the axis of the stem.

In the squash (*Cucurbita pepo*) there appears to be a quantitative progression toward femaleness from the lower toward the upper flowers. Only male flowers are formed at first, then both, then only female. The ratio of male to female flowers can be increased by long-day treatment and decreased by short days. This is also true for corn and other species, but with spinach (*Spinacea oleracea*) and *Silene pendula* var. *compacta*, both photoperiodically long-day plants, the opposite effect is observed. The night temperature is even more important than daylength with cucumbers, cool nights decreasing and warm nights increasing the production of female flowers. In several other monoecious and dioecious plants, however, warm temperatures favor staminate and cold temperatures, pistillate development.

Application of auxins or gibberellins and other chemicals influences the ratio of male to female flowers in certain monoecious species. In both cucumber and squash this ratio is decreased by auxins, sometimes markedly. For example, a 0.1 percent paste of NAA added to the debladed petiole of the second leaf of cucumber caused a fifteenfold increase in the number of female flowers produced over the first seven nodes. Unsaturated gases, including ethylene, acetylene, and carbon monoxide also stimulate the formation of female flowers in the cucumber. The demonstration that high concentrations of auxins increase ethylene production suggests that these substances are effective because of the ethylene released. Gibberellic acid (GA_3) has an effect opposite to that of auxins, i.e., it increases the ratio of male to female flowers in the cucumber.

Apparently, then, hormones have rather marked influences upon sexuality in plants, just as they do in animals. Much more research is needed to determine whether auxins and gibberellins are the usual agents affecting sexuality or whether other, unknown hormones are responsible. Löve and Löve reported in 1945 that certain animal sex hormones influenced sex expression in *Melandrium dioicum*. The male hormone testosterone caused the development of rudimentary stamens in the female flowers, while the female hormones estrone and estradiol led to ovaries in the flowers of male plants. These observations still need to be investigated further, although subsequent research has shown that such compounds were not effective on other plants.

27.1.2 General Development of the Flower

Growth and development of the individual parts composing the flower follow closely the initiation of flower buds. Many careful studies indicate that optimum environmental conditions for flower initiation are often different than for subsequent development, and that various floral parts may have individual requirements for optimal development. The difference in responses of tulip flowers to temperature depending upon their stage of development was demonstrated by Blaauw and coworkers in the Netherlands. Development of flower primordia in the bulb could be divided into at least three separate stages with varying temperature optima (Fig. 25-10). Initiation occurs well only near 20°C; then cell growth occurs during about the next thirteen weeks and proceeds best at 8–9°C, while a final stage has an optimum gradually increasing to 23°C.

In other plants the photoperiod needed for induction and initiation of flowers is sometimes different from that needed for flower development. Furthermore, some plants have different requirements for development of various flower parts, an example being *Silene pendula* cultivar *rubberrima.* Either long days or auxins will reduce petal and stamen growth in this plant, but they stimulate growth of the ovary. Factors which increase development of the petals often also stimulate that of the stamens. These correlations have not been satisfactorily explained, but it is interesting that students of evolution have pointed out a phylogenetic relationship between petals and stamens.

As the flower reaches maturity, several physiological changes occur. The peduncle ceases to grow, the rate of water uptake into the flower decreases greatly (perhaps due to observed decreases in diffusible auxin), and there is a large increase in rate of respiration. The respiration of flowers is so intense that the heat released sometimes causes a significant rise in temperature. In fact, the mechanism of respiration has been intensively investigated in inflorescences (spadices) of the genus *Arum* because of the unusual rapidity of the process there (Fig. 27-1). Until the flowers open at anthesis there is also a rapid accumulation of both inorganic and organic solutes in the various parts. In *Lilium croceum*, sugars move into the petals until they contain so much that they excrete these molecules through the nectaries. At anthesis more than 30 percent of the dry weight of the petals may be due to reducing sugars. These rapidly disappear after anthesis.

27.1.3   Rhythms in Flower Opening

The opening of flowers is often a spectacular phenomenon and is usually associated with full attainment of their color and scent. This has probably stimulated observations of the rhythmic behavior of opening in some species. While many plants have flowers that, once opened, remain so until they abscise, others have flowers that open and close at certain times of the day. This opening and closing may continue for several days.

The opening and closing processes are often influenced to some extent by temperature and atmospheric vapor pressure, but the primary controlling factor seems to be either the time of the dawn or the dusk signal (Chapter 24). Flowers of various species of *Oenothera* (evening primrose) normally open in the evening about twelve hours after dawn. They can be rephased by reversing the light-dark cycle. The light influencing the response in this plant is absorbed by the flowers themselves.

The opening and closing and odor production of *Cestrum nocturnum* (night-blooming jasmine) flowers also show a circadian rhythm when the plants are held in either constant light or darkness. This is true for certain other species, too. The rhythm usually continues for a longer period of time in continuous darkness than in light. *Calendula arvensis* and *Bellis perennis* are examples of species in which anthesis appears to be controlled by a dusk signal, and opening occurs in the morning.

The cause of flower opening is usually due to differential growth of the inner and outer sides of the part involved. Changes in turgor (hydrostatic pressure) that cause the movement of leaves upon many plants do not seem to be involved in flower movements.

27.1.4   Death of the Corolla

After the flower opens and pollination occurs, the petals eventually wither, die, and abscise. In some species, withering rapidly follows anthesis. In *Portulaca grandifolia* anthesis occurs in the morning, and the corolla withers the afternoon of the same day. In the tropical perennial herb *Turnera ulmifolia*, withering follows flower opening by only three or four hours, and the petals abscise the next morning. Some 60 percent of the dry matter of the perianth parts was found to be transported to other regions of this plant before abscission. An extensive reutilization of nitrogen compounds also occurs in several other species. In fact, death of the sepals and petals is usually preceded by a rapid loss of mineral salts and organic substances. These are

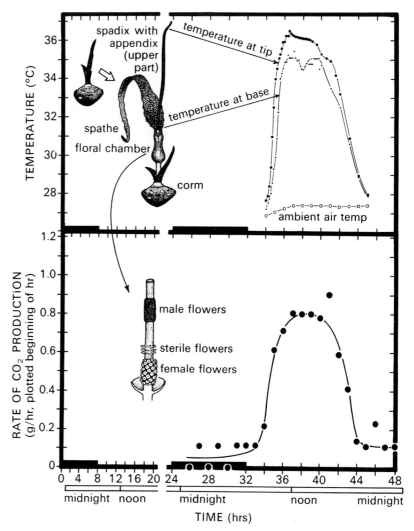

Figure 27-1

Respiration and temperature of a spadix of *Sauromatum guttatum* shott as a function of time. *Sauromatum* is a Pakistani and Indian genus in the Araceae family. Growth from the corm to a structure about 50 cm tall may occur in about 9 days (drawings at upper left), with a maximum growth rate of 7 to 10 cm/day. If this occurs in constant light, the spathe remains wrapped around the spadix, but after the "normal" time for flowering has passed, a single period of darkness, if it is long enough (bar on the abscissa—two 8-hour dark periods were given in this experiment), will initiate opening of the spathe and a burst in CO_2 production (note extremely large quantities) with a concurrent rise in temperature. The heat apparently serves to volatilize various compounds (especially amines and ammonia), which give an odor of rotting meat. Carrion flies and beetles are attracted and serve in pollination. They enter the floral chamber (lower drawing; somewhat schematic). (Original data. Experiment kindly performed for use in this text by B. J. D. Meeuse, R. C. Buggeln, and J. R. Klima of the University of Washington, Seattle.)

transported into the ovary where growth soon leads to fruit development, or else they are transported to other parts of the plant. Water is often, but not always, extensively lost from the petals, probably by transpiration. In cotton there is a fairly large import of phosphorus, nitrogen, potassium, magnesium, and chlorine into the corolla during the night before anthesis. This is followed by a corresponding export through the peduncle and into the stem the following night, transport in each case being through the phloem. In addition, there is often a rapid breakdown of protein and other cellular constituents from the sepals and petals. In *Hydrocleis nymphorides* (Butomaceae family) the flowers are very ephemeral, and in one case 28 percent of the original protein was broken down in a 45-minute period shortly after anthesis. On the other hand, certain species of *Dahlia* and *Rosa* are examples in which the petals are still turgid and contain most of their original protein when they fall. The factors controlling these responses have not been well studied, but it is likely that they are triggered by hormone changes.

It is interesting that many flowers give off small amounts of ammonia or various organic amines, including ethylamine, trimethylamine, isobutylamine, or amylamine. These are among the many compounds contributing to the odor of flowers.

27.2 EMBRYO SAC, EMBRYO, AND SEED DEVELOPMENT

27.2.1 Anatomical Development

After germination of the pollen grains, the extension of a pollen tube through the style and into the embryo sac seems to be controlled by chemotropic substances as discussed in Chapter 21. One of the two nuclei in the pollen grain, the **generative nucleus**, often divides mitotically into two **sperm nuclei** before entry of the tube

into the embryo sac, while the **tube nucleus** undergoes no such division. Upon entry of the pollen tube (usually through the **micropyle**), the end of the tube usually disintegrates and releases the two sperm nuclei. The tube nucleus and the **synergid cells** and **antipodal cells** of the embryo sac serve no known function in the fertilization process and soon are broken down in the embryo sac. Meanwhile, in many species of angiosperms, fertilization of the **egg cell** by one sperm nucleus is occurring about the time the other sperm unites with the two **polar nuclei** in a fusion which forms the triploid **primary endosperm nucleus**. This participation of both sperm nuclei in the process of **double fertilization** is unique to the angiosperms. Some of the processes described above are outlined in Fig. 27-2.

The zygote remains inactive for some time but eventually undergoes a series of mitoses, producing a row of cells called the **proembryo**. The uppermost cell of these (that farthest from the micropyle) then divides by forming walls parallel to the axis of the row of cells below. Further divisions of these two daughter cells gives rise to a group of eight cells in two tiers of four cells each. The embryo largely develops from these eight cells while those in the row below develop into the **suspensor** (Fig. 27-2). The suspensor seems to function by pushing the developing embryo into the abundant endosperm developing around and above it. Soon the suspensor disintegrates.

Development of the zygote into a mature embryo is dependent upon surrounding tissues for energy sources, and, at least in some plants, upon growth hormones produced by the surrounding endosperm cells. Cytokinins are among the hormones provided the young embryos by the endosperm. The endosperm in many plants consists originally of a group of free triploid nuclei resulting from mitosis of the primary endosperm nucleus. This process usually begins rapidly after fertilization, and

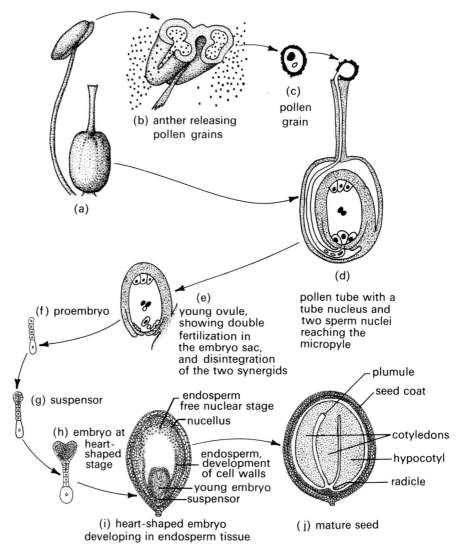

(b) anther releasing
pollen grains

(c)
pollen
grain

(a)

(d)

pollen tube with a
tube nucleus and
two sperm nuclei
reaching the
micropyle

(f) proembryo

(e)
young ovule,
showing double
fertilization in
the embryo sac,
and disintegration
of the two synergids

(g) suspensor

(h) embryo at
heart-
shaped
stage

endosperm
free nuclear stage
nucellus

endosperm,
development
of cell walls
young embryo
suspensor

plumule
seed coat

cotyledons

hypocotyl

radicle

(i) heart-shaped embryo
developing in endosperm tissue

(j) mature seed

Figure 27-2

Pollen grain release, fertilization, and embryo development in an angiosperm. Drawings from
(a) to (f) represent specific stages in embryo development of cabbage (*Brassica oleracea*).
Several different patterns of embryogenesis occur in other species. (Redrawn from *Botany*,
4th ed., by Carl L. Wilson and Walter E. Loomis. Copyright 1952, © 1957, 1962, 1967 by
Holt, Rinehart and Winston, Inc. Reproduced by permission of Holt, Rinehart and Winston,
Inc.)

development of this tissue precedes that of the
embryo. Eventually, walls form around most
of these endosperm nuclei. The cells then
expand rapidly, and during this stage various
subcellular bodies such as plastids, mitochondria, the endoplasmic reticulum, and the golgi
apparatus are clearly visible. Soon, however,
the cells become filled with starch grains and

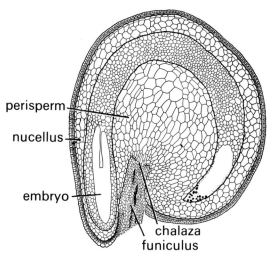

Figure 27-3

Section through immature ovule of sugar beet, showing relation of perisperm to the embryo and other parts of the seed. (From H. E. Hayward, 1938, *The Structure of Economic Plants*, Macmillan Company, New York, p. 251. Used by permission.)

protein granules, which mask most of the other ultrastructural features. The milk of coconuts and the milky tissue in immature corn kernels contain endosperm still in the free nuclear stages. The physiological factors initiating wall formation around the nuclei at a particular time are not understood.

In many species, of which the cereal grains are good examples, the endosperm persists, enlarges, and becomes the primary food storage tissue of the seeds. The peripheral layer of endosperm cells lining the embryo sac remains alive and becomes the **aleurone layer**. As seed development proceeds in many other species, nearly all of the endosperm tissue is absorbed, presumably at the expense of the growing embryo. In this case food is deposited in the cotyledons, which may become greatly enlarged as in the bean, pea, and peanut. In still other plants the **nucellus** (central part of the ovule in which the embryo sac originates) undergoes extensive development to produce the **peri-**

sperm (Fig. 27-3). The perisperm represents a significant food-accumulating tissue in beet, coffee, and spinach seeds, for example.

27.2.2 Biochemical Changes in Developing Seeds

Some attention has been given to the carbohydrate, protein, and fat changes that occur during the development of seeds in economic crops such as the legumes and cereal grains. In most plants that have been analyzed, there is an accumulation of sugars, including sucrose, fructose, and glucose, in the ovules until the endosperm nuclei become surrounded by cell walls. These soluble sugars then begin to decrease as wall formation begins. Presumably they are utilized to form the cellulose and other complex carbohydrates of the endosperm walls. Most of the nitrogen present in such immature seeds is in the form of amino acids and amides. These compounds often decrease with maturation of the seeds as storage proteins are built up in the endosperm, cotyledons, or perisperm. Soluble sugars also decrease as starch and protein deposition occurs, and the amino acids present in the proteins are believed to arise both from the amino acids and amides already present and from the disappearing sugars. Of course, soluble precursor compounds are being imported during most of seed development.

Anatomical and ultrastructural observations have been performed upon developing grains of wheat, in which starch and proteins are stored in the endosperm, and of peas, in which these substances accumulate in the cotyledons. In the pea, both polymers exist as large granules enclosed by a membrane, while in wheat some of the protein granules are not enclosed. Figure 27-4 shows an electron micrograph of a cell of a pea cotyledon. Note the large number of protein bodies and the presence of few but large starch grains. Figure 27-5 illustrates the relative changes in starch, protein, sucrose, and reducing sugars

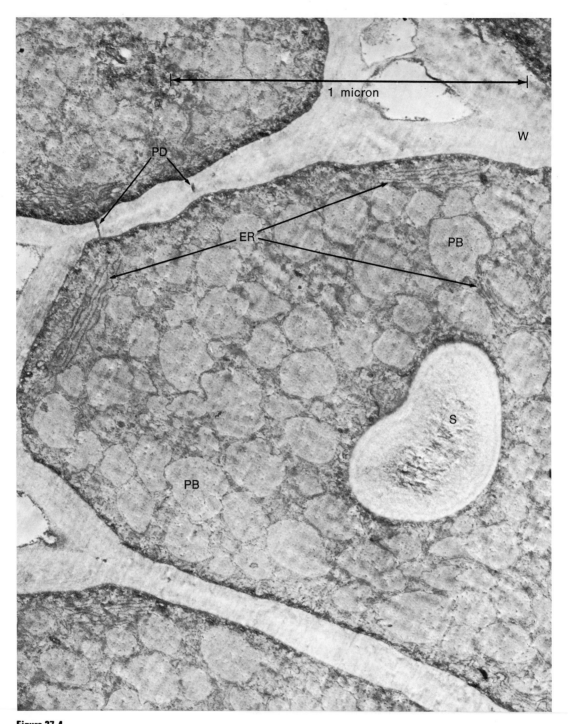

Figure 27-4

Electron micrograph of part of a mature pea seed after 18 hours' imbibition of water. Protein bodies (PB) are abundant. A few starch grains (S), the endoplasmic reticulum (ER), plasmodesmata (PD), and cell walls (W) are also visible. (From J. E. Varner, 1965. In J. Bonner and J. E. Varner (eds.), *Plant Biochemistry*, Academic Press, New York, p. 775. Used by permission.)

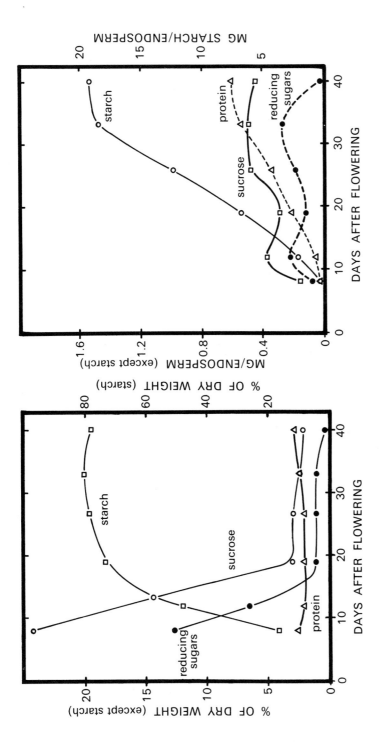

Figure 27-5

Changes in sucrose, reducing sugars, starch, and protein in endosperm of developing wheat seeds. (left) Expressed as percent of dry weight, suggesting that starch is formed at the expense of disappearing sugars. (right) Expressed as mg per endosperm, showing that the absolute amount of sucrose does not decrease, although amounts of reducing sugars do. Apparently the accumulation of starch and protein occurs at the expense of sucrose transported from leaves to the endosperm and not strictly from sugars already present. Note that data for starch are measured by the right-hand-side ordinates only. (Data of A. C. Jennings and R. K. Morton, 1963, *Australian J. Biol. Sci.* 16:318. Used by permission.)

in wheat endosperm from shortly after its formation until harvest. The endosperm accounts for about 75 percent of the dry weight of mature wheat grains, the remaining 25 percent being due to the embryo and the seed coat plus ovary wall (**pericarp**).

A few studies of nucleic acid changes in developing seeds have been made. In the mature wheat grain there is about 10 times as much RNA as DNA, and neither appears to be an important storage product. Increases in DNA content in various seeds have been used as indications of the time at which cell divisions cease. In wheat there is little cell division in the seed coat and pericarp following fertilization, and mitosis ceases in the endosperm when the seeds are nearly half mature. It is probable that seeds contain different kinds of messenger RNA molecules than do other organs of the plant because of their rather unique proteins.

An important development during formation of seeds is the loss of water. This desiccation is the principal factor causing the finally dry seeds to respire very slowly, and it allows their preservation through drought and cold periods, often for several years. Associated with desiccation are important but poorly understood changes in the physical properties of the cytoplasm.

27.3 FRUIT GROWTH AND DEVELOPMENT

During the time of seed development, the surrounding ovary tissue also grows and matures, accompanied by several physiological changes. Fruit growth may involve primarily an enlargement of the ovary itself, as in the drupes, or of the ovary and accessory tissues, as in the apple (Fig. 27-6). Most studies have been made using fleshy fruits, since these are frequently of greatest horticultural and economic interest. The nonfleshy fruits of most species have received little attention from physiologists.

27.3.1 Growth Rates

The fruits studied usually have growth curves of the sigmoid (e.g., apple, strawberry, pear, avocado, pea, tomato) or of a double sigmoid type (e.g., cherry, olive, apricot, raspberry, peach, grape, plum), as described in Chapter 19 (Fig. 19-4). In the double sigmoid type, two rapid growth periods are separated by a period of little growth. During the first period, the ovary itself and the nucellus and integuments of the enclosed ovules account for the growth shown. In the second phase the endosperm and embryo grow, but the ovary increases but little in size, so the over-all growth of the fruit is very small. When the embryo becomes fully grown in the second period, growth of the ovary begins again in the third phase.

The cause for the period of suspended growth of the ovary shown in the midportion of the double sigmoid curve is not well understood. It has been suggested that there is a competition among various parts of the fruits showing this kind of growth kinetics, and that the over-all curve results from this competitive effect. For example, the embryo often begins to grow most rapidly at the time the larger pericarp tissue starts to reach its period of suspended growth. Perhaps the embryo is then using and thus competing for growth factors that otherwise are used in expansion of the pericarp.

27.3.2 The Importance of Seeds for Fruit Growth

Development of many fruits is dependent upon germination of pollen grains on the stigma of the pistils or upon this process and subsequent fertilization. Some data of the French plant physiologist, J. P. Nitsch, illustrate the effect of fertilization upon growth of cucumber (*Cucumus anguria*) fruits (Fig. 27-7). Fruits from unpollinated flowers did not grow. However, extracts of pollen grains when applied to certain flowers will cause swelling of the ovary and wil-

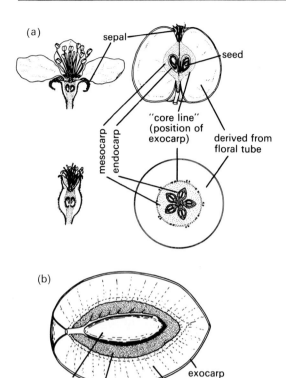

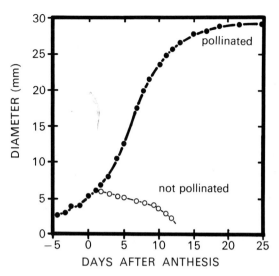

Figure 27-7
Growth of pollinated ovaries of *Cucumis anguria* and lack of growth in unpollinated ovaries. (From J. P. Nitsch, 1965, *Encyc. Plant Physiology*, W. Ruhland (ed.), Springer-Verlag, Berlin, 15/1, p. 1580. Used by permission.)

Figure 27-6
Fleshy fruits. (a) Development of the edible portion of an apple from accessory tissues (floral tube) attached to the receptacle. (b) Longitudinal section through an olive fruit (a drupe) showing exocarp, mesocarp, and endocarp, all derived from ovary tissues. (From *Botany*, 4th ed., by Carl L. Wilson and Walter E. Loomis. Copyright 1952, © 1957, 1962, 1967 by Holt, Rinehart and Winston, Inc. Reproduced by permission of Holt, Rinehart and Winston, Inc.)

ting and abscission of the petals in a manner simulating natural pollination and fertilization.

The presence of developing seeds is usually essential for normal fruit growth. For example, if seeds are present only in one side of a young apple fruit, only that side of the fruit will develop, resulting in a deformed apple. Apparently, one of the factors controlling fruit growth is a normal supply of auxins. There are several possible reasons for this belief: *First*,

the auxin content is very high in germinating pollen grains; *second*, the auxin content in the various tissues of the pistil sometimes increases progressively as the pollen tube germinates through it; *third*, young seeds are rich sources of auxin; and *fourth*, the retarding effect of seed removal upon growth of some fruits can be overcome by adding an auxin to the ovaries. Nitsch demonstrated the stimulating role of seeds in the growth of strawberry fruits and their replacement by auxin (Fig. 27-8).

Some plants normally produce fruits lacking seeds. These are called **parthenocarpic fruits**. Parthenocarpic fruit development is especially common among fruits that produce many immature ovules, such as bananas, melons, figs, and pineapple. Parthenocarpy may result from normal ovary development without any pollination, from fruit growth stimulated by pollination but in which fertilization does not occur, or from growth of fruits in which fertilization has occurred but in which the embryos abort. Parthenocarpy following embryo abortion occurs in various grapes, peaches, and cherries. Certain orchids are examples of the second case in which pollination does not lead to fertilization, while the seedless citrus, banana, and pineapple fruits develop even without pollination.

F. G. Gustafson (1936) first demonstrated that seedless fruits could be produced by adding auxins to the ovaries of flowers in which pollination was prevented (Fig. 27-9). Subsequently it was found that many species, especially members of the Solanaceae and Cucurbitae families, will produce parthenocarpic fruits in response to applied auxins. We cannot conclude that auxins alone control fruit development, however, for various reasons. *First*, with most plant species studied, auxins fail to stimulate parthenocarpic fruit development. In some of these (grapes, apples, pears, cherries, apricots, peaches) gibberellins such as GA$_3$ are more active, and these hormones are also effective with some of the species quite responsive to auxins (e.g., tomatoes and figs). *Second*, many investigations have failed to find the proper corelation between auxin content and growth rate of fruits. The fact that seeds are unusually high in gibberellins suggests that these hormones may be among the active substances causing fruit enlargement, but proof for this is lacking. The presence of cytokinins in some fruits may implicate these substances, too. It is likely that a proper balance among the auxins, gibberellins, cytokinins, and other undiscovered growth substances is responsible for normal fruit development.

27.3.3 Chemical Changes in Developing Fruits

27.3.3A Carbohydrates and nitrogen compounds
Young fruits often have chloroplasts, synthesizing part of the sugars needed for growth. Nevertheless, both fruits and seeds

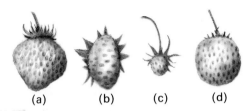

Figure 27-8

The influences of seeds (achenes, which are dry, true fruits) and auxin on the development of the edible portion of strawberries (tissue derived from the receptacle). (a) Normal "fruit," (b) disk-shaped "fruit" resulting from removal of achenes on two sides early in development, (c) "fruit" from which all achenes were removed, and (d) "fruit" from which all achenes were removed but which was treated with a lanolin paste containing an auxin. (Redrawn from J. P. Nitsch, 1950, "Growth and morphogenesis of the strawberry fruit as related to auxin," *Amer. Jour. Bot.* 37:211. Used by permission.)

attract carbohydrates and nitrogenous materials from other organs of the plant and depend primarily upon these as energy sources for development. As these transportable sugars are received, they may be completely respired; partially respired so that organic acids accumulate; or they may be converted into fats, starch, or cell wall materials. Citric and malic acids are abundant in the vacuoles of many immature fruits, giving these their sour taste, but they decrease in concentration as the fruits mature. Other acids may predominate in certain fruits, as, for example, tartaric acid in grapes and isocitric acid in blackberries. A dark fixation of carbon dioxide by reactions with phosphoenolpyruvic or pyruvic acid is essential for accumulation of these acids, since operation of the Krebs cycle alone does not allow for this (see Chapter 15). Finally, the absorption of sugars and nitrogen compounds is essential for protein synthesis in seeds and fruits. During respiration the sugars are transformed into organic acids and other compounds from which amino acids are built. The latter are then presumably converted into proteins according to the reactions discussed in Chapter 17.

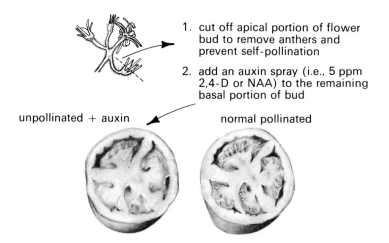

1. cut off apical portion of flower bud to remove anthers and prevent self-pollination

2. add an auxin spray (i.e., 5 ppm 2,4-D or NAA) to the remaining basal portion of bud

unpollinated + auxin   normal pollinated

Figure 27-9

Production of seedless fruits by removal of anthers and application of an auxin to ovaries of tomato plants. (Fruits redrawn from *Botany*, 4th ed., by Carl L. Wilson and Walter E. Loomis. Copyright 1952, © 1957, 1962, 1967 by Holt, Rinehart and Winston, Inc. Reproduced by permission of Holt, Rinehart and Winston, Inc.)

Protein formation in fruit cells is probably continuous during growth, but mature fleshy fruits generally have only small percentages of protein compared to other living parts of the plant. Protein content varies from approximately 0.3–0.4 percent of the fresh weight for apples and pineapples to 1.7 percent for avocados.

A number of studies upon the chemical composition of edible fruits and the transformation of carbohydrates accompanying the ripening of these have been made. The dry matter content of most mature fleshy fruits is about 10–20 percent of the total fresh weight, and this is largely due to carbohydrate material. The content of starch in apple or other fruits increases to a maximum and then decreases until little is present at harvest, while the sugar content of apples steadily rises up to and after picking. In both apples and pears, fructose is the most abundant sugar, while lesser amounts of sucrose, glucose, and sugar alcohols are also present. Bananas also show decreases in starch during ripening accompanied by increases in fructose, glucose, and sucrose. During the period in which the fruit of bananas changes from green to yellow, the starch may decrease from 20 percent of the fresh weight to less than 1 percent, while the sugar content rises from 1 to 15 percent. Hemicelluloses decline in bananas, apples, and pears during ripening, one study showing a fourfold decrease occurring in bananas.

During ripening of oranges, grapes, grapefruits, pineapples, and various berries, the organic acids decrease and the sugars increase. Lemons do not show the same changes as oranges and grapefruits, inasmuch as the acids continue to increase during ripening, and the pH decreases. Lemon fruits do not contain appreciable amounts of starch at any time in their development. Significant changes in amounts of cellulose do not appear to be common in developing fruits, but the pectic substances do undergo changes. Ripening often involves a decrease in the length of the molecular chains and removal of methyl groups from the galacturonic acid residues to which they are esterified. In apples and pears the protopectin content decreases, and this is accompanied by an increase in pectin during ripening.

27.3.3B Pigment and flavor changes

Although chlorophylls are present in many young fruits, these pigments usually disappear when the fruits are mature. This loss of chlorophyll from the plastids is often followed closely by an increase in carotenoids, and the chloroplasts differentiate into chromoplasts whose color depends primarily upon the kinds and amounts of carotenoids present.

The content of anthocyanins in various fruits is increased by light (as mentioned in Chapter 23), giving them a desirable color. Other flavonoids also undergo changes that may or may not be appreciably influenced by light. The total flavonoid content of various citrus fruits increases for some time and then becomes rather constant. On the other hand, the content of the bitter-tasting catechol tannins, chemically related to the flavonoids, decreased about eightfold during the ripening and maturation of peaches.

Studies of flavoring compounds other than sugars in ripening fruits are of great commercial importance but are often made difficult because these substances occur only in very small quantities. We do know that many flavoring substances are aliphatic or aromatic esters, alcohols, and carbonyl compounds. Bananas, for example, contain amyl acetate and other similar aliphatic esters that give these fruits their odor and presumably influence their flavor, too. Citrus fruits owe their aromas and part of their flavors to terpenoid essential oils and to coumarin derivatives (Chapter 18). Progress toward controlling the flavor of fruits is a goal of plant breeders, but this will probably first necessitate identification of the compounds

involved and clarification of the biosynthetic pathways from which they arise.

27.4 RELATIONS BETWEEN VEGETATIVE AND REPRODUCTIVE GROWTH

Gardeners have long practiced the technique of removing flower buds from certain plants to maintain vegetative growth. A commercial example of this practice is found in the growth of tobacco plants, where "topping" (removal of flowers and fruits) is performed to encourage leaf production. A. E. Murneek, working at the University of Missouri in the 1920s, made extensive studies of the growth rates of tomato plants as affected by flowering and fruiting. The growth of plants allowed to set fruits, that of plants from which flowers were removed, and that of defruited plants are shown in Fig. 27-10.

We are aware that there is a competition for nutrients among vegetative organs and flowers, and that developing flowers and fruits (especially young fruits) possess a large "drawing power" for mineral salts, sugars, and amino acids. During the accumulation of these substances by the reproductive organs, there is often an approximately corresponding decrease in the amounts present in the leaves. When leaves of garden peas (*Pisum sativum*) were treated with radioactive phosphate and CO_2, up to 90 percent of the labeled products was recovered in the young seeds and in the pod that developed from the bud present in the axil of the treated leaf. Other examples with radioactive tracers are known, showing that nutrient accumulation in developing flowers, fruits, and tubers occurs largely at the expense of materials in the leaves or other adjacent photosynthetic tissues. Nevertheless, we cannot positively conclude that the retardation of leaf, stem, and root growth by reproductive organs is due only to a competition for nutrients. It is entirely possible that flowers and fruits may produce some

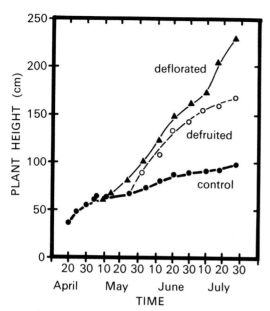

Figure 27-10

Increase in rate of elongation of tomato plants after removal of flowers or fruits. (From A. E. Murneek, 1926, *Plant Physiol.* 1:3, after A. C. Leopold, 1964, *Plant Growth and Development*, McGraw-Hill Book Company, New York, p. 199. Used by permission.)

inhibitor that is transported into the vegetative organs.

There is usually a competitive action among individual fruits of the same plant for nutrients. This is evidenced by decreases in fruit size with increasing number of fruits allowed to form on tomato plants or apple trees, for example. The mechanism by which fruits can divert nutrients out of the leaves and into their own tissues, sometimes against apparent concentration gradients, and simultaneously interfere with vegetative growth is not understood. It is probable that various hormones (especially cytokinins— Chapter 21) are somehow involved.

We have observed, then, that reproductive processes can interfere with vegetative growth and that, if reproduction is prevented, the remaining organs of the plant grow faster. There is also evidence that factors that stimulate shoot growth retard flower, tuber, and fruit development. Klebs and others were aware around the turn of the century that high nitrogen promoted vegetative growth, but the work of E. J. Kraus and H. R. Kraybill in 1918 is often cited. They observed that high nitrogen fertilization caused luxuriant growth of stems and leaves of tomatoes but did not allow much fruit development, while moderate nitrogen levels led to less stem and leaf growth and more fruit development. Similarly, excess nitrogen fertilization prevents normal growth of potato tubers or apple fruits while stimulating shoot expansion.

We might now ask whether the converse process occurs; that is, whether processes interfering with vegetative growth will stimulate flower development. A few experiments suggest that this is true. Certain antigibberellins or other growth retardants such as phosphon D, CCC, Amo-1618 (see Chapters 21 and 28), and B995 (*N*-dimethylamino succinamic acid), inhibit growth of stems and cause stunted plants. This stunting is sometimes accompanied by increased flowering, as measured by more rapid initiation of flower buds or a greater number of flowers per plant. In other plants, however, the flowering response is inhibited by these chemicals. Heavy pruning, tying branches to the ground, various other mutilation procedures, or restraining growth by certain physical treatments also occasionally effectively stimulate flowering. In a Japanese variety of radish (*Raphanus*), it was reported that imbedding the upper part of the seedling in gypsum promoted bolting and flowering of unvernalized seedlings.

In other species, such as cocklebur, if the proper photoperiodic conditions to induce flowering have been provided, environmental factors, including high nitrogen levels that promote luxuriant vegetative growth, will also promote flowering.

27.5 SENESCENCE

Senescence has been defined as the deterioration that ends the functional life of an organism or an organ. Although meristems do not undergo senescence and can perhaps be considered potentially immortal, all of the cells produced from these undergo aging, which eventually leads to death. Senescence occurs in leaves, flowers, fruits, stems, and roots, but it commonly occurs at different times in these organs. In many perennial herbs, such as alfalfa, essentially the entire aboveground system dies each year, but the crown and root systems remain largely viable. In deciduous woody perennials, the leaves die, but much of the root and stem tissues remain alive. Another pattern of senescence is seen in several herbaceous annual species (monocarpic plants), such as beans, tomatoes, and the cereal grains. Here there is a progressive senescence of the leaves from the older to the younger, followed by death of both the stem and roots after flowering.

27.5.1 Chemical Changes Accompanying Senescence

Studies of chemical changes accompanying senescence of organs of higher plants have been performed primarily with leaves and fleshy fruits. Measurements show that young leaves have, on a fresh weight basis, more rapid rates of respiration, more synthesis of RNA and protein, a higher content of growth hormones, and less transport of solutes through the phloem to other organs than do full-grown leaves. On the other hand, the photosynthetic capacity usually becomes maximal at about the time the leaf is completely expanded. With the approach of autumn and the onset of senescence, the contents of starch, chlorophyll, protein, and RNA in leaves all decline, and the hydrolytic breakdown products are transported to younger regions of the plant (Fig. 27-11). These processes can be stimulated by elevated temperatures, short days, nutrient deficiencies (especially nitrogen), and drought periods.

The brilliant fall leaf colors are partly due to an unmasking of the yellow and orange carotenoid pigments as chlorophyll is lost. The bright red colors are due to an accumulation of anthocyanin pigments, primarily cyanidin. This accumulation is favored by bright, clear days and moderately cool temperatures. The stimulating effects of light intensity upon anthocyanin formation were discussed in Chapter 23. The favorable influence of cool temperature is not understood, but it may be that this causes the conversion of starch to sugar as it does in potato tubers, for example. Respiration of the sugar then provides the erythrose-4-phosphate, phosphoenolpyruvate, and acetyl coenzyme A which are the important flavonoid precursors. Synthesis of anthocyanins during the time that nitrogen and phosphate are transported out of the leaves is consistent with the observation that soil deficiencies of these elements cause accumulation of such pigments in a number of species (Chapter 10).

27.5.2 Possible Causes of Senescence

Various plant physiologists have suggested several possible explanations for the reasons senescence occurs, some of which are discussed below. None of these seems adequate to cover all situations.

27.5.2A Competition for nutrients An early theory proposed by H. Molisch (1928) suggests that senescence is imposed upon vegetative parts of the plant by the nutrient-depleting action of sexual reproduction. He showed that removal of flowers or fruits of several species delayed senescence. Experiments with similar results have been performed numerous times since then, confirming this effect of reproductive appendages. Senescence in fruits would presum-

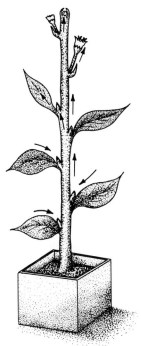

Proteins, starch, chlorophyll, nucleic acids, etc., are degraded in senescing leaves, and the products are transported (apparently through phloem) to young leaves, flowers, and buds.

Figure 27-11
Some processes involved in leaf senescence.

ably occur as the nutrient supply of the plant becomes exhausted. This theory is consistent with the fact that flowering of monocarpic plants leads to their death, but it does not account for several observations below.

27.5.2B Production of inhibitors
Carl Leopold and his colleagues at Purdue University found in 1959 that senescence in soybean leaves is caused by the presence of young flowers, even though these are not large enough to deplete the leaves of nutrients. Furthermore, the presence of ripening fruits also caused senescence, even though translocation into these organs was nearly completed. They also found that the production of male flowers on staminate spinach plants induced senescence as effectively

as did the development of both flowers and fruits on female plants, and that the removal of flowers of either sex delayed senescence.

It seems, then, that a simple competition for nutrients alone cannot satisfactorily explain senescence. It is possible that reproductive organs produce substances that are transported to vegetative tissue, where they cause senescence. It has been found that flowering of wheat plants causes sudden and striking decreases in photosynthetic capacity, not only of old leaves and mature leaves, but even of the young ones. Perhaps this is due to the production of some inhibitor or other hormonal regulator by the flowers. There is evidence that buds of germinating dicot seedlings produce growth substances that move into the cotyledons and induce senescence and abscission of these food storage organs. Removal of the epicotyl and the buds formed in the axils of the cotyledons greatly extends their active life. Thus, there is ample evidence of a correlative influence of both vegetative and reproductive buds and of fruits upon other parts of the plant, but no information is yet available concerning the nature of possible hormonal substances that might be involved in this correlation.

27.5.2C Changes in enzyme patterns

M. Dixon, a British biochemist, briefly described living matter as "a system of unstable catalysts being kept in existence by the occurrence of the reactions which they catalyze." With the instability of these catalysts (enzymes) in mind, aging has been referred to as an unfavorable change in the ability of protoplasm to maintain itself. This implies that factors that accompany aging somehow increase the ratio of catabolic to anabolic enzymes. Various researchers have shown that senescence does involve a loss in power of assimilation along with the breakdown of various cell constituents. An increase in the ratio of breakdown to synthetic reactions could be due to an increase in the former or a decrease in the latter, or both. Decreased assimilation could perhaps be caused by inhibitors that are gradually accumulated in the cells or are provided by other organs, as mentioned above. Some evidence indicates that senescence is indeed primarily due to a lower capacity for synthesis, rather than to a greater capacity for catabolic reactions. It appears that this comes about by an impairment in the ability of the cells to produce the necessary assimilative enzymes, rather than to influences of inhibitors upon the action of these enzymes.

Let us consider certain chemicals known to retard senescence and investigate the manner in which they seem to act. As mentioned in Chapter 21, cytokinins very effectively delay senescence in the leaves of various plants. Dov Sitton and Chanan Itai, in Israel, and Hans Kende in the United States obtained evidence that a decreased cytokinin transport from roots to shoots may lead to senescence of the shoots. Thus, when sunflower plants were growing most rapidly the cytokinin content of root exudates was high, but when the plants reached their final size the content of this hormone in the exudates decreased tenfold. Certain auxins also retard leaf senescence in some species, while gibberellins are effective with still other species. One of the processes affected in common by these three classes of hormones seems to be the gene-directed synthesis of messenger RNA and of protein molecules. Daphne Osborne and colleagues in England demonstrated that these hormones probably retard senescence through the same mechanism. J. E. Sacher in California studied the influence of auxins and kinetin upon senescence in excised bean pods. In this case, kinetin did not delay senescence and had little influence upon synthesis of either RNA or protein, while auxin treatment did delay senescence. The auxin effect was accompanied by a large stimulation in RNA synthesis and an increase in protein formation.

Sacher, Osborne, and others have considered that such antisenescence compounds prevent the usual loss in ability to form RNA, and that this maintains protein synthesis at near normal rates. The continued action of genes in the presence of the proper hormone level presumably maintains the synthesis of RNA and the enzymes necessary to produce chlorophyll, DNA, and other components that otherwise disappear during the senescence process. Abscisic acid counteracts the effects of these hormones upon leaf senescence and accelerates the process. It is probably significant that this compound inhibits RNA synthesis in the affected leaves. In many edible fruits ethylene also acts as a senescence stimulator and, in fact, is believed to be a hormone responsible for fruit ripening (see Chapter 21).

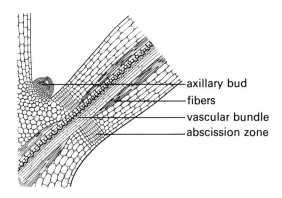

Figure 27-12

The abscission layer. (From F. T. Addicott, 1965, *Encyc. Plant Physiology*, W. Ruhland (ed.), Springer-Verlag, Berlin, 15/2, p. 1098. Used by permission.)

We tentatively conclude that senescence is the result of an altered hormone balance that prevents the genes from continuing to code for the same enzymes as when the cells were younger. Considered in this way, senescence may be thought of as a final stage of differentiation, which itself is continuous from juvenility to death. It is the culmination of the morphogenetic information program. More complete explanation awaits advances in understanding the relation between hormones and gene activation and repression.

27.6 ABSCISSION

Soon after senescence occurs, some plant organs are lost by **abscission**. The physiology of this process is best understood in the case of leaves, flowers, and fruits. The longevity of flowers ranges from three or four hours in *Hibiscus trionum* and *Calandrinia compressa* up to three or four months in *Phalaenopsis schilleriana*. Leaves are generally longer lived. Those of most herbaceous annuals are never shed and live as long as the plant, those of deciduous woody dicotyledons remain intact one growing season,

and the needles of certain gymnosperms are retained from about one year to seven or eight years, depending upon the species and growth conditions. Most fruits are lost during the season in which they are formed.

Abscission appears to benefit plants in various ways. Injury or disease often causes the abscission of the afflicted organ. The plant thus rids itself of a useless part or of a potential infection source. A second important advantage is in the dissemination of reproductive bodies, such as pollen and seeds. We shall see that abscission is another example of a correlative phenomenon, since it is influenced by other organs of the plant.

27.6.1 Anatomical Changes Accompanying Abscission

In many plants, abscission of leaves or fruits is preceded by the production of an **abscission layer** or **zone** at the base of the organ involved. In leaves this zone is formed across the petiole near its junction with the stem (Fig. 27-12). Abscission usually occurs here, although in some plants the leaves break off even though no such layer is produced.

Pioneering work on the structure of the abscission layer of leaves was performed in 1901 by A. Tison, who described the layers of 105 woody species. It consists of a group of thin-walled cells formed from anticlinal (transverse) divisions across the petiole that often occur even before the leaf is fully grown. The development of these cells is then arrested until abscission occurs. At this time the middle lamella between certain cells in the **distal region** (that farthest from the stem) of the abscission zone is often digested. It is likely that other degenerative changes occur here, too, and in a few cases the entire protoplasm seems to lose its structure, and the cells become waterlogged. Separation occurs between these cells, and the vascular system is soon broken by wind or other mechanical forces. Preceding or soon following abscission, cell divisions occur in the stump, and suberin and other substances are deposited in the walls and intercellular spaces. These processes protect the plant against excessive water loss and entry of pathogenic organisms.

27.6.2 Physiology of Abscission: The Influence of Growth Regulators

Abscission is delayed as long as the organ is physiologically active and occurs only if the normal metabolic processes are completed or are interrupted by injury or disease. Removal of the blade of the leaf causes the remaining petiole to abscise much sooner than it otherwise would. The process is not entirely controlled by the organ itself, however, since other regions of the plant often influence the time of retention. Leaf abscission is usually stimulated by the younger leaves above, and one of the causative factors supplied by these is an auxin, perhaps IAA. Auxins (or ethylene) applied to the proximal side of the abscission layer (that closest to the stem) often promote abscission. If auxins are added to the distal side, abscission is often delayed. Another fact implicating auxins is the common observation that levels of these hormones decrease inside the leaves during senescence.

These auxin relationships led F. T. Addicott and his colleagues to suggest during the 1950s that abscission might be primarily determined by the *gradient* of auxin across the abscission zone. When the leaf is young and·producing auxin, the distal/proximal ratio is high, and when senescence or injury occurs the ratio decreases and the organ is shed. This theory was consistent with many observations, but the problem remained of how an auxin gradient could control the abscission process. More recent data have considerably modified ideas about the relationship of auxins to the process. Leopold and coworkers found that these sub-

stances sometimes promoted leaf loss when added to the distal side and inhibited this action when applied on the proximal side, depending upon the *concentration* used. They also noticed that opposite results could be obtained depending upon *how long* before abscission the auxins were added. The simple auxin gradient theory cannot fully explain the phenomenon, and, as we have observed with most functions, other hormones are almost surely involved. For example, exposure of plants to ethylene usually stimulates abscission of leaves, flowers, or fruits; and F. Abeles demonstrated that the auxin-induced abscission of bean leaves probably is due largely to ethylene production (Chapter 21). In addition, cytokinins were implicated by the discovery that kinetin and benzyladenine (synthetic cytokinins) prevented senescence in leaves.

A compound that stimulates abscission regardless of the side of the layer to which it is added was found by Daphne Osborne (1955) in extracts from senescent leaves of a number of species. This substance was not identified, but in 1961 W. C. Liu and H. R. Carns of the United States Department of Agriculture found either the same abscission-accelerating compound or one with similar properties in cotton fruits, which they named **abscisin**. A second and different abscission stimulator from cotton fruits was later identified by F. T. Addicott and colleagues (1965) and named abscisin II (now abscisic acid, Chapter 21). Abscisic acid content of cotton fruits was found by Carns to be most abundant at about the onset of fruit drop, and varieties that characteristically lose their fruits more easily had higher concentrations of this substance. Abscisic acid stimulates abscission of leaves in a number of species besides cotton. It appears, then, that abscisic acid and perhaps other chemically related abscisins play important roles in the loss of leaves, of fruits, and probably of flowers. It does not seem likely that these are the abscission accelerators produced by younger tissues, however, since most of the evidence obtained from studies with cotton fruits and various leaves indicates that abscisins accumulate only in senescent tissue. Abscisic acid also hastens senescence of leaves, and it might act by repressing certain genes, thus causing a loss in RNA, protein, and chlorophyll. The transport of these substances out of the blade of the leaf and perhaps even out of the abscission zone may then lead to abscission.

Osborne obtained evidence that abscission is closely dependent upon senescence of the abscission layer when she found that kinetin retarded the process if added directly to the layer but stimulated it if added close by on either side. Recognizing that cytokinins usually cause the tissue in which they occur to act as a sink for translocatable solutes, she concluded that kinetin treatment of the abscission layer prevented its senescence. Addition of kinetin to either side of the layer, however, probably caused the export of essential metabolites from it, resulting in abscission. Results consistent with the interpretation that leaf abscission may be considered as being due to a localized senescence in the distal tissue were obtained by P. C. Scott and Leopold. They found that abscission was preceded by a loss of dry weight, chlorophyll, protein, phosphate compounds, and RNA from the distal tissue of bean petioles. These substances accumulated in the region just proximal to the abscission layer. This removal of metabolites presumably contributes to the senescence of cells at the separation zone and hastens abscission.

Applications of Plant Physiology

28

Plant Physiology in Agriculture

In this textbook, plant physiology has been discussed essentially as a basic science, and plant function is certainly a challenging and rewarding intellectual pursuit. Yet there are several solid practical reasons for studying plant physiology. Experts on population are agreed that the world is rapidly running out of food. Plant physiology has contributed and must increasingly contribute to the feeding of the world's population.

This contribution in **agriculture** is probably the most important application of knowledge in plant physiology, but it could also be important to man to understand the balances and interactions of the living organisms on the earth's surface. Only a small portion of this surface can ever be covered with agricultural crops, but plants and animals will continue to occupy much of the rest. The responses of these living organisms to their environment are physiological in nature, and thus plant physiology may be applied in the relatively new borderline science of **physiological ecology**.

Not of immediate importance but conceivably of some future interest to mankind is the question of life on planets other than the earth. The science developing around this question has been called **exobiology**. Such a new science must rely heavily upon already-established sciences including plant physiology. We must

ultimately be prepared to understand possible life forms that might be encountered in the exploration of space. It is the purpose of this last section to summarize a few examples of applied plant physiology in agriculture, ecology, and exobiology.

28.1 PLANT PHYSIOLOGY IN AGRICULTURE

The population explosion is a topic of high current interest. Approximately 3 percent of the earth's surface is presently under cultivation. Considering the deserts, savannahs, scrub forests, and other areas (particularly in the tropics) that may be brought under cultivation in the future, this figure can probably be increased to about 5 percent. The rest of the earth is covered with water, ice, extreme desert, or rocks (mountains), or it is otherwise unsuitable for cultivation. At the moment about 1 percent of the world's food supply comes from the oceans, and the most optimistic estimates indicate that even intensive efforts to increase this will just allow this percentage to remain about constant as the population increases.

Beginning at the time of Christ, 1,600 years were required for the population to double. It doubled again in the next 200 years and again in only 60 years. The present (1969) world population slightly exceeds 3 billion persons. It is estimated that this figure will double again to 6 billion by the year 2000. This last doubling will have required only about 35 years. Right now, about 1.5 billion people, or half of the world's population, are either malnourished or are actually starving. Clearly, this situation can become much worse as the population continues to increase unless food production increases at an equal rate. To solve the immediate problem, food production must be increased at a more rapid rate than population. Yet in a world with finite area, population itself must have an ultimate limit.

Increasing food production by bringing new land under cultivation is one important approach, but obviously it is not the ultimate solution. As indicated by the figures above, there simply is not enough land available. The approximately 2.5 billion acres of potentially arable land will require in many cases tremendous advances in technology and large expenditures of funds to be brought into production. These acres include many tropical regions, for example, and while we feel that they are potentially productive, we have not as yet solved the problem of high rainfall, which leads to leaching of the soil and luxuriant growth of unwanted plants. To bring water to the desert areas, while within the realm of our present technology, will be in most cases extremely costly. Purification of sea water may be required, for example.

At the same time, many acres of highly productive agricultural land are continually being taken out of production to make room for the expanding population. Factories, suburbs, highways, and other human developments are rapidly occupying much of this land. In the state of California alone, some 250 acres are going out of production every day. Furthermore, the industries, homes, and other developments that are occupying this land are utilizing much of the water needed for agricultural production.

Clearly the solution to the world's food problem will require a combination of many approaches. Birth control is one often-discussed aspect. The technology of land reclamation is another. Education of underdeveloped peoples so that presently available knowledge can be applied is very important. Probably the present starvation in the world could be eliminated if knowledge already available could be properly applied everywhere. Principles of plant physiology have the potential of contributing some important components to the solution of the world food problem.

In fact, the contributions of plant physiology to the revolution in agriculture that led to the overabundance of food in the United States and other technologically advanced nations have been profound. Knowledge of the mechanisms of plant growth applied in conjunction with the principles of engineering has allowed modern agriculture to develop to the point where one person can produce the food for about 37 others, while as recently as 1920 one person could produce food for only about eight others. In this chapter we will discuss some of the principles of plant physiology that have led to the agricultural revolution, and we will also suggest some of the areas of research in plant physiology that must be actively pursued if the agricultural revolution is to continue its expansion.

An extremely important aspect of this revolution is **mechanization**. With the increasing level in the standard of living, the cost of labor has risen to high levels, and if food were now produced by the laborious hand methods of the past, its cost would limit the increase in the standard of living. Thus mechanization has become an essential part of modern agriculture and has necessitated a great many innovations in agricultural practice. In many cases these innovations involve the plant itself. To harvest tomatoes mechanically, for example, determinate varieties have had to be developed that produce ripe fruit all at one time rather than continually throughout the last part of the growing season. Plant form also had to be modified to allow mechanical harvesting. A number of other examples are presented in the following paragraphs.

Changes in the plant constitute examples of **biological engineering**, not in the traditional sense of the engineering concerned with the development and construction of proper farm machinery (**agricultural engineering**), but in the sense that principles of plant physiology and genetics are applied to control the growth and development of the plant itself. This is done by adjusting the plant's genetics through breeding, manipulating and controlling the environment in which it grows by suitable cultural practices, and in more recent years by influencing the plant's metabolism directly through the application of specific growth-regulating chemicals. As the engineer applies physical principles in the invention and construction of machines, so the modern agriculturist can apply comparable principles of plant growth to produce and control plants in a manner that will allow maximum production of food on minimal land area with minimum expenditure of water, of agricultural chemicals (including fertilizers), and perhaps above all, of human labor.

28.2 PLANT BREEDING AND GENETIC SURGERY

Man has undoubtedly always selected in his agricultural practices for those varieties best suited to his needs. During the 20th century, however, the practice of plant breeding for desirable varieties has become a highly developed applied science, and its impact upon agriculture has been great. This has been, for the most part, the practical application of genetics rather than plant physiology, but plant physiology has always played an essential role in specifying the features for which the plant breeder must select. Actually, much of plant breeding has been dictated by the problems of disease. Thus the wheat breeders of the north-central United States have devoted a major effort to developing rust-resistant strains of wheat to keep pace with new pathogenic races of the rust organisms that continue to appear. Conceivably, other means of disease control will be found in the future, in which case aspects of plant physiology concerned with yield will become of increasing importance to the breeder.

In the practice of plant breeding, the breeder rearranges the genetic material by various crossing procedures, attempting to obtain the most desirable combinations. He is always limited by the genes available to him. He frequently attempts to find new genetic material by using in his crosses some of the wild relatives of cultivated plants, and in more recent years he has attempted to increase the genetic variation with which he can work by mutational processes such as irradiation with ultraviolet light or gamma rays.

Imagine the potentials for biological engineering if we *really* understood the genetic code! Presumably an ultimate understanding of the role of enzymes in plant function and of the significance of the molecular structure of enzymes would allow the biological engineer to suggest a specific enzymatic structure for a specific desirable plant function. This might then be translated into a specific molecular structure of DNA. Ultimately this newly synthesized gene might be inserted into the genome of a given plant by some future microsurgery. So many technical difficulties are involved in such genetic surgery that it is presently completely beyond the realms of feasibility. The principles discussed in this book, however, make it possible for us to conceive of such futuristic schemes as this. It may be centuries before we can insert the essential genes for the production of a given antibiotic, for example, but scientific predictions in the past projected over centuries have sometimes been fulfilled within decades.

28.3 CULTURAL METHODS

This is the area where applied plant physiology has been of real value in modern agriculture. By understanding the plant's response to environment, it has been possible to modify the environment in such a way that crop production has increased. Even the most ancient "plant physiologists" recognized that most plants grew better if they were provided with supplemental water. In more recent years we have been able to recognize several more subtle possibilities.

Much of the modern revolution in agriculture has come about because of our understanding of the **mineral nutrition** of plants. This understanding has led to extensive revisions in the practices of applying fertilizers. It has been realized that, if soil conditions permit availability and uptake, the mineral elements are equally effective whether they are applied as organic fertilizers or simply as inorganic salts. Using knowledge of plant physiology, it has been possible to specify more accurately the times during the growing season when application of fertilizer is most appropriate and the forms of the fertilizer which may lead to most efficient crop production. From the standpoint of agriculture, one of the most significant discoveries of plant physiology was the finding of Kraus and Kraybill that high levels of available nitrogen in the soil result in extensive vegetative growth of many species with little growth of the fruits, seeds, or other storage organs that may be the desirable part of the crop (22.1). Even in species in which flower *initiation* may not be inhibited by high nitrogen levels, fruit development often is retarded by excess nitrogen. With these crops it is most prudent to apply the fertilizer early in the season, leading to rapid leaf growth, since this photosynthetic structure must later in the season produce the materials that will be stored in the appropriate organs. We are not always dealing with *size* of the organ. In the

fall of the year, there is an inverse relationship between available nitrogen in the soil and percent of sugar stored in the sugarbeet root.

In recent years, several highly efficient and novel ways of applying fertilizers have been devised. Seeds may be coated with sufficient fertilizer to give the seedling an early stimulation. Anhydrous ammonia is inserted into moist soil where it is soon oxidized to nitrate. Nitrogen may also be applied as urea, as, for example, is often done in the pineapple fields of Hawaii. Several minor elements (or even urea) may be applied directly by spraying on the leaves. It has become possible, because of changes in irrigation practices, to apply some fertilizers in the irrigation water. This is particularly convenient in greenhouses where there is a minimum waste of applied water.

In much of the world where rainfall is limited, **irrigation** has been a major part of the agricultural revolution. Irrigation was important a century ago when the water was simply flooded onto the fields or run onto the fields through a system of ditches and furrows. It has assumed an even greater role with the development of special irrigation systems such as overhead sprinkler systems or underground sub-irrigation systems. Here, as in most examples being discussed in this section, plant physiology has combined with engineering and other sciences including soil science. Through plant physiological research, it is possible to inform the engineer of the optimum quantities of water required and the optimum times for its application.

The engineering revolution has been especially striking in recent years with the development of sprinkler irrigation systems that require an absolute minimum of human labor. In some cases, nearly an entire section of land (a square mile) may be irrigated by a single moving system of pipes and overhead sprinklers. Water is introduced at the center, and the pipe forms the radius of a large circle, continuously rotating in the field. Of course, the amount of water delivered at each sprinkler must be carefully controlled, since the pipe moves much more slowly near the center than at the periphery. These new systems have become so efficient and dependable that many farmers in exceptionally dry areas such as Arizona and parts of southern California now consider every rainstorm to be a hindrance rather than a help to their farming operations. They can produce crops more efficiently when they have absolute control over the amount of moisture delivered to the plants.

There are many relatively minor developments, all of which add together to make up the revolution in cultural practices. It has become a fairly common practice in certain areas, for example, to spray a band of **asphalt** over a row where seeds of plants such as tomato have been planted. This black material absorbs more energy from the sun than the normal lighter-colored soil. The result is an increase in temperature of a few degrees, enough to shorten significantly the germination time of the seeds. This can be very important in marginal areas where the growing season is just long enough to allow for crop production. The asphalt may also prevent crusting of the soil, thus enhancing emergence of small seedlings.

It is interesting to note the degree to which the introduction of **plastics** has increased efficiency in agricultural practices. Many aspects of the new agricultural machinery depend upon the use of plastics, and in some cases plastic is also used in the field. Whole areas may be covered with plastic. Such crop plants as strawberries are placed in small holes cut in the plastic material. The result is a greatly reduced water loss by evaporation from the soil and a near lack of weeds.

These practices, as well as the control of pests, are leading to profound revisions in our approaches to ancient agricultural problems. We are moving toward the cultivation of a population of plants consisting of only a single species on a large area (**pure-stand culture**), and

we are striving for ultimate efficiency in terms of yield per unit area and cost of production, especially labor. Many traditional practices may prove to be quite inappropriate in light of these trends. We must recognize that we are no longer limited by the natural nutrient levels in the soil or by natural precipitation patterns. The limitations due to insects, diseases, and weeds have been greatly reduced and may ultimately be completely eliminated. In many crops it is already possible in a production sense to have a completely weed-free environment, and, if present trends continue, this will be true for virtually all crops.

The most important limitation proves in many circumstances to be the ability of the photosynthesizing plants to absorb sunlight. Traditionally, plants have been planted in rows, allowing for movement of cultivators through the growing crop to control weeds. Often the width of these rows was established for horse-drawn cultivators but has not been readjusted with the advent of tractors. Now it appears that we should reconsider the row concept itself. By the use of chemical weed controlling agents, applied at planting time or from air-planes, it may be that machines will be brought onto the fields only at the times of planting and harvest. Thus very narrow rows might be possible, or in some cases seed could even be broadcast. In any case, the result might be a much denser population, capable early in the season of absorbing a much higher percentage of the sunlight that falls on the field.

In many cases the varieties presently in use are not adapted well to such an approach, since they have been developed under the system of much wider rows. They spend a considerable part of the growing season producing a large amount of foliage before they finally produce the harvested part of the crop such as the kernels of corn or wheat or the seeds of soybeans. It appears that yield per unit area of land can be increased in certain crops by using varieties that produce only a minimum of foliage before initiating production of fruit or seed. Short-season varieties adapted to the northern growing seasons already have many of the desirable characteristics. These are placed close together by increasing planting rates so that maximum utilization of sunlight is possible. The fruits or seeds are produced relatively early in the season when intensity levels of sunlight are highest. A further future development might be the discovery of chemicals to inhibit photo-oxidation of chlorophyll or otherwise increase the field efficiency of the photosynthetic mechanism itself.

In any case, it appears that the agricultural revolution is just beginning with many crops where new production techniques make new approaches possible and desirable.

Many sound principles of plant physiology are applied in the growth of horticultural crops, including ornamentals. Fruit trees or grape vines may be **girdled**, for example. If this is done properly, photosynthate in the translocation stream may be directed into the developing fruits so that larger fruits are produced. Apple trees are also brought into production sooner by this practice. **Pruning procedures** are widely applied in fruit production and in the growth of ornamentals in the greenhouse. A knowledge of the principles of plant growth often lies at the basis of these practices. Pinching of terminal buds of chrysanthemums, for example, removes apical dominance, allowing lateral buds to become active and produce flowers. Most recently, some of the same end results can be obtained by application of suitable chemicals (see below).

A sort of ultimate in control of environment for maximum production is the growth of crops in **greenhouses**. This approach has long been used for horticultural species such as cut flowers. The discoveries of photoperiodism and vernalization, which allow control of flowering time by control of daylength and temperature, have thoroughly revolutionized the greenhouse

culture of many species, such as lilies, poinsettias, and chrysanthemums. Both covering greenhouse benches with black cloth to shorten the light period and extending daylength with supplementary lights are now common practices. In many regions it now appears feasible to grow certain specialty food crops like tomatoes under the highly artificial conditions of a greenhouse. In regions with relatively short growing seasons, several annual crops can be obtained from a given land area by this approach. Ultimate efficiency in agricultural production could depend upon this nearly total control of environment in terms of the principles of plant physiology.

28.4 PEST CONTROL: INSECTS AND PLANT DISEASES

Three classes of pests greatly reduce the yield of agricultural crops: insects, plant diseases, and weeds. Even insect control borders upon plant physiology. Certain new insecticides, for example, enter the plant and are translocated **systemically** so that the insect is killed when it feeds upon the plant. These will become more efficient as we learn more about the mechanisms of translocation in plants. Certain aspects of **biological control** are also related to plant physiology, whether the agriculturist is controlling insects, diseases, or weeds. Breeding for resistant species constitutes the best example, but sometimes one species may be used as a predator against another.

Plant pathology, the study of plant diseases, is closely related in many important ways to plant physiology. To begin with, a pathologist is concerned with a number of so-called **physiological diseases**, such as those caused by insufficient quantities of an essential nutrient element in the soil or toxic quantities of elements like boron or sodium. Even when the pathologist deals with viral, bacterial, or fungal plant pathogens, his studies of the host-parasite relationship are fundamentally physiological in nature. Much of the recent work on plant viruses contributed directly to our knowledge about the genetic code, for example.

The problem of the host-parasite relationship remains almost completely unsolved. At the moment we are unable even to speculate intelligently about the nature of plant resistance except in a few rather restricted cases. Why, for example, can a given plant pathogen infect only a handful of the nearly 300,000 species of Angiosperms? It appears that resistance to most pathogens is the overwhelming rule in the plant kingdom, while susceptibility is a rare exception. Perhaps if we could understand the mechanisms of resistance and susceptibility, it would be possible to utilize these in the control of plant disease. In any case, research in this area is essentially research in a highly specialized phase of plant function.

28.5 PEST CONTROL: WEEDS

The science of weed control, initially an almost insignificant branch of agronomic plant physiology, has now developed into a healthy and thriving subscience, blending principles of both plant physiology and plant ecology with agronomic practice. Until the years immediately following World War II, weed control was primarily a matter of cultivation and other crop management practices. It was concerned with the application of ecological principles (competition, etc.) to crops. Certain chemicals were used as soil sterilants (e.g., on industrial lands), but most control of weeds was at best a 20th century mechanized version of ancient cultivation practices. Many of these practices are still important in modern agriculture, but the discovery of 2,4-D (2,4-dichlorophenoxyacetic acid—Chapter 21) during World War II has changed all of this. It was found that 2,4-D would kill many broadleaf weeds in a field of wheat or corn without harming the crop

itself. Thus it became possible by the expenditure of a few cents per acre for the chemical to remove many important weeds completely from this kind of a crop.

It is important to realize that the discovery of 2,4-D was a direct outgrowth of work on growth regulators following the discovery of auxin. Since that time many highly effective relatives of 2,4-D have been discovered. Selective and highly powerful compounds, chemically unrelated to 2,4-D, have also been found and introduced into agricultural practice. In recent years textbooks discussing them have been written, and so the summary in the next few pages will be relatively brief. Furthermore, this is one of the most rapidly advancing frontiers of modern biology, and many things written at any given time are bound to be superseded by continuing discoveries within a few years or sometimes even months thereafter. A number of weed-killing compounds are listed in Table 28-1 along with their chemical names. The molecular structures of many of these are illustrated in Fig. 28-1.

28.5.1 Soil Sterilants and Contact Herbicides

The **soil sterilants** used several decades before the discovery of 2,4-D are still important in certain applications. Inorganic salts including **chlorates, borates, arsenicals**, and others have been used for this purpose. Nearly any of the weed killers described in the following sections may act as soil sterilants, providing only that they are applied at high enough concentrations. It is important to recognize that herbicidal action is always a function of concentration of the **herbicide** (weed-killing chemical). 2,4-D will kill many broadleafed plants at concentrations harmless to such monocots as wheat and corn, but at higher concentrations it may also kill the wheat and corn.

Other nonselective herbicides include certain

TABLE 28-1

SOME COMMONLY USED HERBICIDES[a]

Soil sterilants

chlorates-sodium chlorate-$NaClO_3$
borates-sodium tetraborate-$Na_2B_4O_7$
arsenicals-arsenic trioxide, sodium arsenite
$\qquad$ As_2O_3 $\qquad$ Na_3AsO_3

Contact herbicides

diquat (6,7-dihydrodipyridol[1,2-a:2',1'-c]=
pyrazindinium salt)

Auxin-type herbicides

chlorophenoxy herbicides
$\quad$ 2,4-D (2,4-dichlorophenoxyacetic acid)
$\quad$ 2,4,5-T (2,4,5-trichlorophenoxyacetic acid)
$\quad$ MCPA (2-methyl-4-chlorophenoxyacetic acid)
benzoics
$\quad$ dicamba (2-methyl-3,6-dichlorobenzoic acid)
picolinic acid derivatives
$\quad$ picloram (Tordon) (4-amino-3,5-trichloro-
$\quad\quad$ picolinic acid)

Chlorinated aliphatic acids

TCA (trichloroacetic acid)
dalapon (2,2-dichloropropionic acid)

Aminotriazoles

amitrole (3-amino-1,2,4-triazole)

Substituted dinitrophenols

DNBP (4,6-dinitro-o-sec-butylphenol)

Triazines

simazine (2-chloro-4,6-bis[ethylamino]-6-
$\quad$ triazine)
atrazine (2-chloro-4-ethylamino-6-isopropyl-
$\quad$ amino-1,3,5-triazine)

Substituted ureas

monuron 3(4-chlorophenyl)1,1,dimethyl urea

Carbamates

IPC (isopropyl N-phenylcarbamate)

Acetanilides

propachlor (2-chloro-N-isopropylacetanilide)
chloro-IPC (isopropyl N-[3-chlorophenyl]-
$\quad$ carbamate)

Thiocarbamates

EPTC (ethyl N, N-dipropylthiocarbamate)

Substituted uracils

bromacil (5-bromo-3-sec-butyl-6-methyluracil)

Miscellaneous compounds

trifluralin (N,N-di-n-propyl-2,6-dinitro-4-
$\quad$ trifluoromethyl aniline)
diphenamid (N,N-dimethyl, 2,2-diphenyl
$\quad$ acetamide)
dacthal (dimethyl-2,3,5,6-tetrachlorotere-
$\quad$ phthalate)
chlordane (mixture of isomers, the most insecticidal
$\quad$ of which is 1,2,4,5,6,7,8,8-octachloro-4,7-
$\quad$ methano-3a,4,7,7a-tetrahydroindane. Used as
$\quad$ an insecticide and as a herbicide against crab
$\quad$ grass)
endothal (7-oxabicyclo[2,2,1]heptane-2,3-
$\quad$ dicarboxylic acid)

For more information, see Hull, H. M. (Editorial chairman). 1967. *Herbicide Handbook of the Weed Society of America*. W. F. Humphrey Press, Inc., Geneva, New York.

light oils that are sprayed on the plants, killing any plant tissues they contact. Such weed killers are logically referred to as **contact herbicides**. Other materials in this class include compounds of **dinitrophenol**, which are fre-

quently used in industrial and noncrop areas where the desired purpose is simply to eliminate all plants from a given area. Quaternary ammonium compounds such as **diquat** are also used for this purpose.

28.5.2 Translocated Herbicides

The translocated herbicides are often considered in contrast to the soil sterilants or contact weed killers. These compounds may enter either the roots or the foliage and are translocated to other parts of the plant. These cause damage or death not only to the tissues that absorb them but to other tissues as well. In many cases the root-absorbed compounds may be applied as **pre-emergent herbicides**. That is, they may be applied to the soil in the upper layers where weed seedlings may absorb them during the process of germination. In some cases, their selectivity against the weeds and in favor of the crop would be a matter of their not being absorbed by the crop plants such as established, deep-rooted perennial crops (e.g., fruit trees). In other cases these pre-emergent herbicides may have a **physiological selectivity**, in which they are absorbed both by the crop and the weeds but damage only the weeds. Of course, foliar-absorbed herbicides must be applied as post-emergent sprays; that is, after germination and development of the foliage which will absorb them.

28.5.3 Auxin-type Herbicides

The three groups of herbicides discussed in this section are all more effective against broad-leaved (dicotyledonous) than against narrow-leaved (monocotyledonous) plants. It is important to realize, however, that each compound has its own **spectrum of plants** against which it may be toxic. Even closely related molecular structures prove to be more toxic to certain species than to others, although as implied above, certain taxonomic groups may be more susceptible to a given compound than other comparable groups.

The following three groups of compounds have one other feature in common. At certain concentrations they are active in tests such as the *Avena* section growth test, eliciting responses common to those caused by the auxins. Whether their herbicidal activity is closely and directly related to their auxin activity will be discussed below, but this question has not been completely solved to everyone's satisfaction. Nevertheless, these compounds are frequently referred to as auxin-type herbicides or even as hormone-type herbicides. If they are active in the standard auxin tests, then they do qualify for the term auxin according to the definition given in Chapter 21 (21.1). Unless they are synthesized by the plant, however, they do not qualify as hormones. In any case, they fulfill the definition of **growth regulators**, and this is true of any compound that influences plant growth by its herbicidal activity.

28.5.3A The chlorophenoxy herbicides As indicated above, 2,4-D was the first of the organic selective herbicides to be discovered and applied widely, and it is still one of the most important commercial herbicides. In practice it may be used as the acid, esters, or it may be used as a salt produced by neutralization of the acid with a base. The salts (commonly sodium or ammonium) are highly soluble in water, whereas the undissociated acid has a low water solubility. The amine form is soluble and widely used at present. Even the acid is used at such high dilutions that the quantities soluble in water are extremely effective. During the early years of its use, one formulation was the methyl ester. This form proved to be extremely volatile, however, often drifting from one field to nearby areas where valuable crop plants or horticultural species were damaged. Less volatile esters have since been developed, and the methyl ester is seldom used any more. The amine formulation is not volatile and may penetrate certain species better than the acid or the salt formulations.

2,4,5-T is used widely because of its high toxicity toward woody species such as sagebrush, mesquite, or other undesirable shrubs of

NaClO₃
sodium chlorate

Na₂B₄O₇
sodium tetraborate

As₂O₃
arsenic trioxide

Na₂AsO₃
sodium arsenite

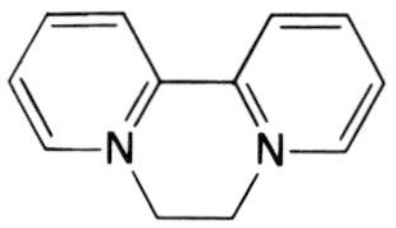

diquat

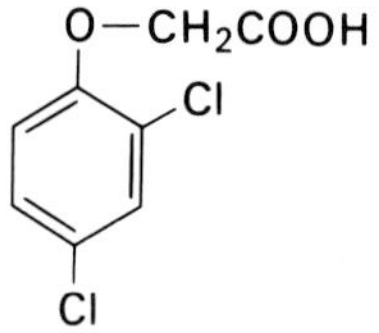

2,4-D

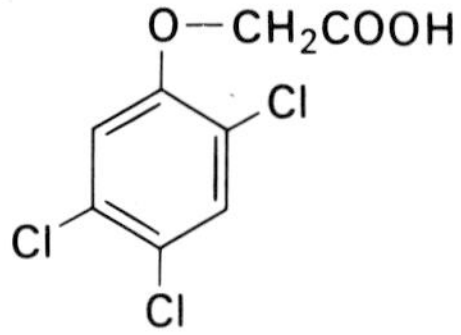

2,4,5-T

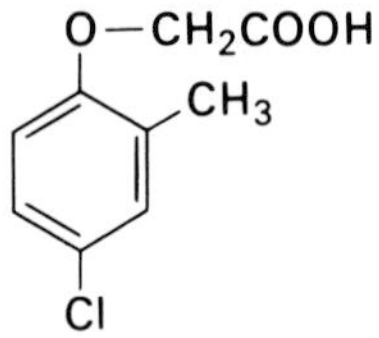

MCPA

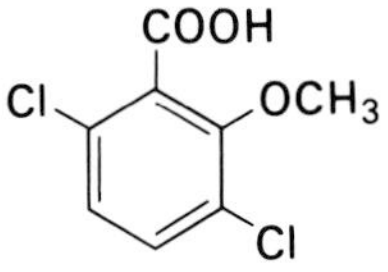

dicamba

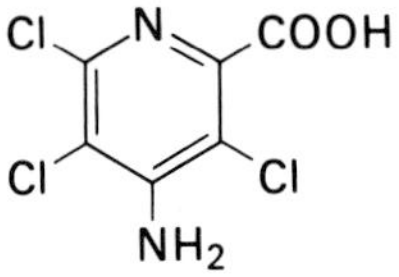

tordon (picloram)

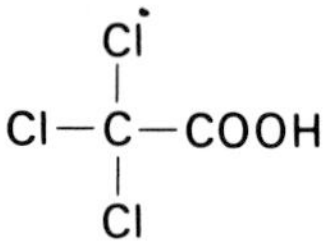

TCA

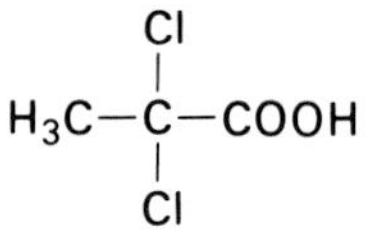

dalapon

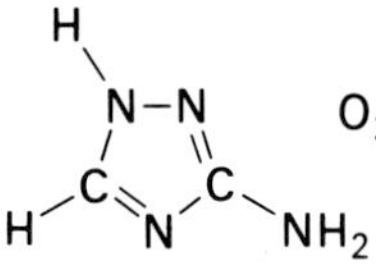

amitrole

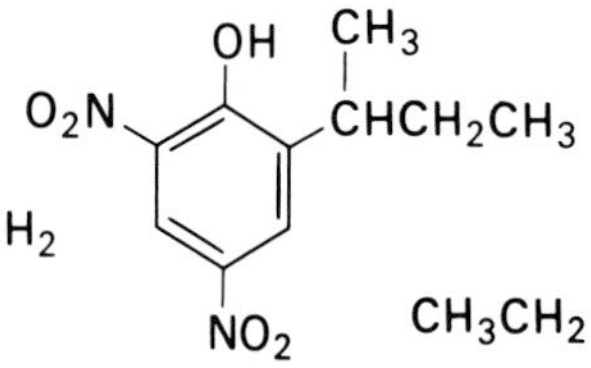

DNBP

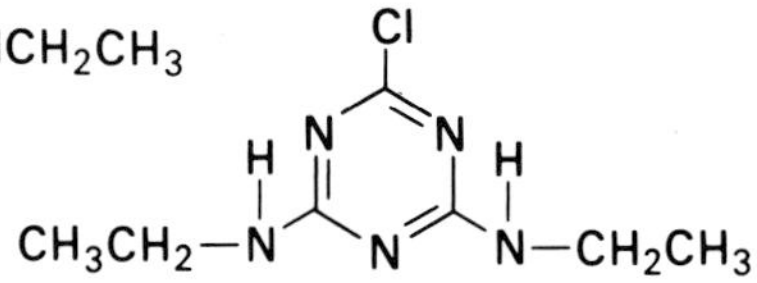

simazine

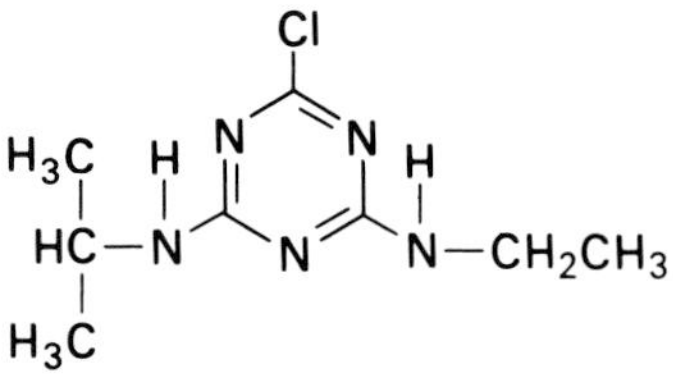

atrazine

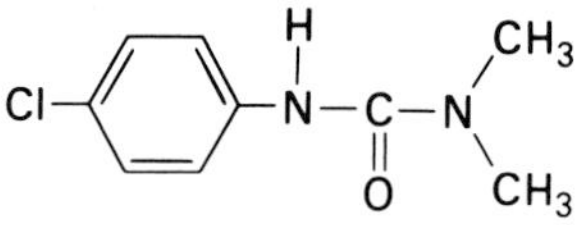

monuron

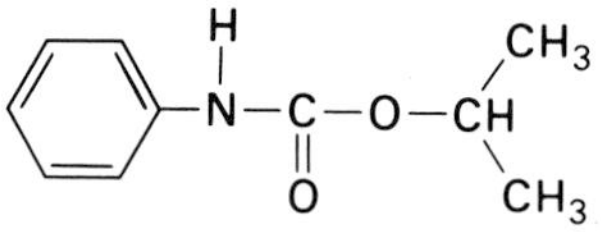

IPC

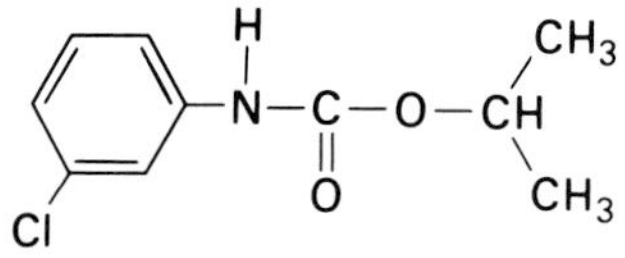

chloro-IPC

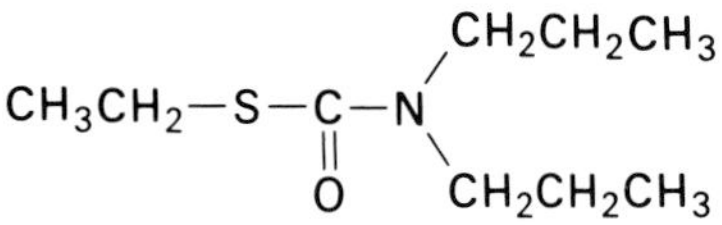

EPTC

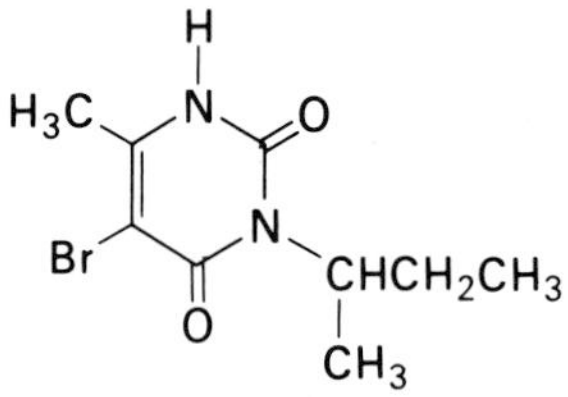

bromacil

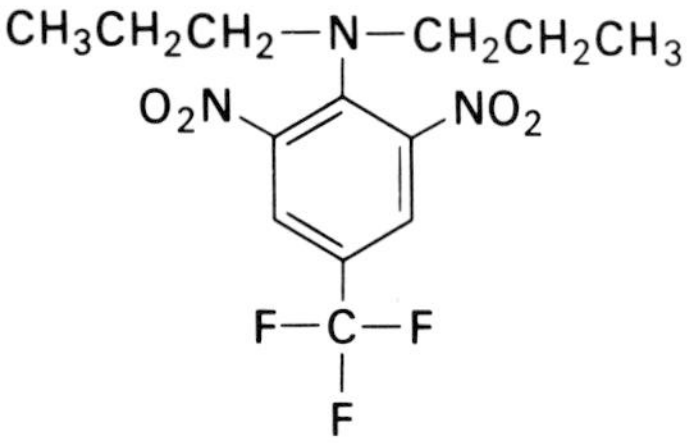

trifluralin

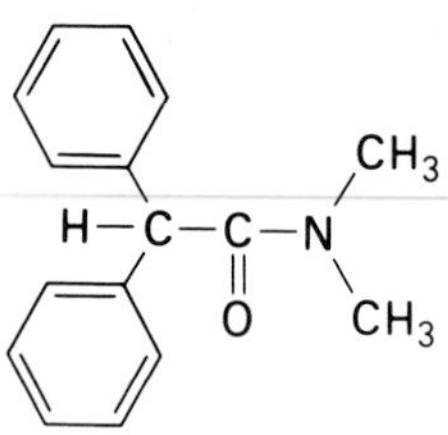

diphenamid

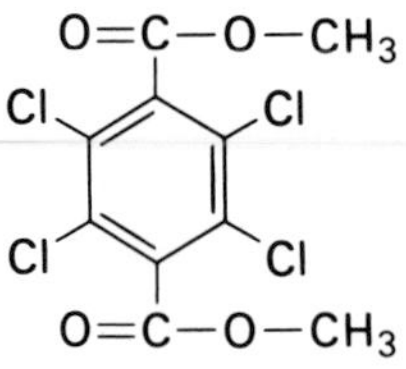

dacthal

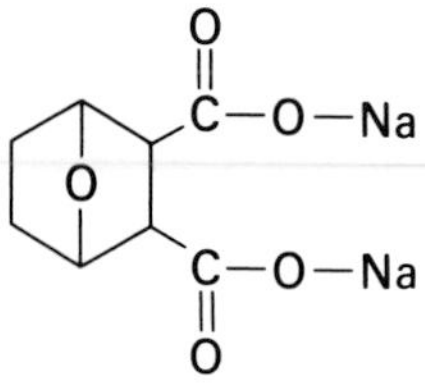

endothal

the Southwest. **MCPA** is also used, as are phenoxy derivatives of propionic and other acids. These, like 2,4,5-T, are valuable in certain applications.

28.5.3B Benzoics Several derivatives of benzoic acid (e.g., **dicamba**) have powerful herbicidal activity. The benzoics are particularly effective against deep-rooted perennials like field bindweed (wild morning glory—*Convolvulus arvensis*) or Canada thistle (*Cirsium arvense*), plants that are quite resistant to 2,4-D.

28.5.3C Picolinic acid derivatives Derivatives of picolinic acid also prove in some cases to be powerful herbicides. **Picloram**, the compound referred to by the trade name of **Tordon**, is as powerful as any herbicide known today. That is, it is effective as a weed killer at lower concentrations or smaller quantities per plant than most of its competitors.

28.5.3D Mode of action of auxin-type herbicides When 2,4-D was first discovered and its auxin activity became apparent, it was stated that this compound simply caused plants "to grow themselves to death." A few years later, however, more detailed curves for growth as a response to auxin concentration (Chapter 21, Fig. 21-6) were determined. It became apparent that 2,4-D might be killing plants not by causing them to grow by an inordinate amount but by acting on the high-concentration part of the curve where increasing concentrations of auxin result in decreasing growth. The curve drops all the way to the level of no growth, and presumably 2,4-D was acting by causing metabolic inhibitions even beyond those that would allow no observable growth. The result was death of the plant. This part of the curve was explained at that time by the proposal that

two molecules attached to a single auxin substrate at each of two postulated active sites instead of one auxin molecule attaching at both substrate sites. The two molecules attached to one substrate formed an ineffective complex.

From the very beginning, efforts were made to find an enzyme system that was adversely affected *in vitro* by 2,4-D. Levels of metabolites within the plant were also followed as a function of time of treatment with 2,4-D. The results were disappointing, but not because they were negative; rather they were disappointing because so many responses could be observed that nothing relating to a specific enzyme could be said about the mode of action of the compound. Many metabolites appeared to change in response to treatment with 2,4-D, and several enzyme systems were inhibited, although this work is not definitive, since concentrations of the herbicide in the test tube were often higher than might be expected within the plant after the usual spray treatment.

It became evident from several other studies, however, that the explanation of growth inhibition was not satisfactory in every case. Plants did not die as though their growth were simply being stopped. Rather they exhibited a callus formation and epinastic bending as though growth were indeed being accelerated.

In recent years a more general mode of action for 2,4-D has been suggested. The broad effects on the many different metabolites provide the first clue. Several workers, including John B. Hanson and his students at the University of Illinois, found a rapid increase in RNA, DNA, protein and in the number of mitochondria, ribosomes, and several other cell constituents following treatment of young meristematic tissues with 2,4-D. Often this is most readily observable in roots and stems and less so in leaves. Merrill Ross, working with us

Figure 28-1
Molecular structures of some herbicides.

as a graduate student at Colorado State University, studied the effects of several herbicides upon ATP levels, respiration rates, and incorporation of several metabolic intermediates, particularly acetate. He found with dinitrophenol, as might be expected, that ATP levels decreased following treatment, although oxygen uptake increased.[1] With most other compounds, including 2,4-D, Ross found an *increase* in ATP levels, respiration, and incorporation of metabolites immediately following treatment. After several days as the plant approached death, these levels would, of course, drop below the controls.

The observations of Hanson, Ross, and others make it possible to postulate that 2,4-D is acting upon the DNA-RNA-protein system. It is as though 2,4-D indiscriminantly activated many otherwise repressed genes. The result might be a rapid synthesis of enzymes and a consequent increase in general metabolic turnover rates. Such an indiscriminate increase in metabolism could not be sustained with limited available substrates. Furthermore, balances would be upset in serious ways. The result would be an uncontrolled metabolism and death of the plant. Indeed, such rapid rises in metabolic levels might be a general characteristic of approaching death, as Ross and others have shown for plants simply pulled out by the roots and allowed to die on the greenhouse bench by desiccation.

Even if the action of 2,4-D in causing death is about to be solved by recourse to our understanding of the DNA-RNA-protein system, we still remain essentially without understanding of the mechanisms of selectivity of this compound. For a time it was thought that 2,4-D

might kill broadleaf plants rather than grasses simply because there was more leaf area to absorb the compound. In the sections below, we shall discuss several compounds, however, that are toxic to grasses but not to broadleaf plants. Furthermore, it could be shown that considerable 2,4-D did penetrate the grasses. There is evidence that 2,4-D is metabolically inactivated more rapidly in resistant than in susceptible plants. It is presently thought that selectivity will ultimately be understood primarily on the basis of differential penetration, translocation, and detoxification in susceptible and resistant species.

28.5.4 Chlorinated Aliphatic Acids

Compounds such as **TCA** and **dalapon** prove to be effective grass killers (especially annual grasses). Such compounds are important in agriculture, since grass can be a serious weed in several crops, such as sugar beets, beans, and even corn. Sometimes these compounds are applied as pre-emergent herbicides, but more often they are applied to the mature foliage. As in the case of other herbicides, these compounds will kill all types of plants at high concentrations, but they are more lethal to grasses at a given low concentration than they are to broadleaf plants. Unfortunately, the difference between concentrations lethal to grasses and those lethal to broadleaf plants is fairly small, and so the selectivity can be utilized only in limited cases and with very accurate control of the applied concentrations. Thus these compounds have had their widest application in situations where it is desirable to kill virtually all of the plants, and where grasses may be very predominant.

The mode of action of the chlorinated aliphatic acids has not been determined. Several suggestions have been made. Dalapon, for example, resembles pyruvic acid, an important metabolite. Perhaps it acts as an antimetabolite

---

[1] This effect was much more apparent for plants left in the dark than for those in the light. Incidentally, Ross's method for ATP measurement was not exactly specific for ATP except in a few instances in which chromatography was used.

for this compound. It has been shown that it will inhibit *in vitro* pantothenic acid metabolism in microorganisms. Although selectivity would not be explained, it has also been suggested that the chlorinated aliphatics may be acting simply as enzyme denaturants, since they are highly effective as protein denaturants at high enough concentrations. (Could concentrations become high enough by accumulation close to the enzymes?) Merrill Ross found increases in metabolic rates as described above when these compounds were applied. Is it possible that these molecules are also activating genes indiscriminately?

28.5.5 Aminotriazole

Amitrole (the commercial name) is basically nonselective, but it has proved to be valuable in several agricultural applications. It is broken down fairly rapidly in soil and hence is most effective as a foliar herbicide. By directed spraying it can be used for weed control in orchards, vineyards, and similar situations. In the case of aminotriazole, the immediate plant response is a severe bleaching of the tissue. The nearly white plants are very striking. Amitrole inhibits the development of leaf plastids, but the resulting chlorosis may be independent of the growth-inhibiting actions responsible for herbicidal actions. Amitrole also probably inhibits biosynthesis of histidine, riboflavin, and it possibly also inhibits nucleic acid and purine metabolism.

28.5.6 Substituted Dinitrophenols

The so-called **dinitros** (e.g., **DNBP**) are used largely as contact herbicides in nonselective weed control. When used with an oil carrier, the dinitros are nonselective. When formulated with a water carrier, DNBP will selectively control weeds in certain crops, such as peas, which have a waxy "bloom" on the foliage to

which the spray material does not readily adhere, and in bean seedlings while they are in the "crook" stage.

As indicated above, the mode of action of the dinitros does seem to be fairly clear. **Dinitrophenol** itself has long been known as an uncoupler of oxidative phosphorylation, a fact often referred to in the chapters on metabolism. Apparently the dinitro herbicides also act by uncoupling phosphorylation, so that ATP cannot be synthesized (15.4.4). Salisbury, Merrill Ross, and another graduate student, Robert Mellor, studied the response to dinitrophenol when applied to plants in the light or to plants in the dark. Dinitrophenol and other dinitro herbicides were much more effective when applied to plants in the dark. Ross was able to show that ATP levels dropped much more in response to this compound when plants were in the dark than when they were in the light. Thus it appears that dinitrophenol is more effective as an uncoupler of respiratory phosphorylation than as an uncoupler of photosynthetic phosphorylation.

28.5.7 Triazines and Substituted Ureas

These compounds are also not very selective, killing both annual grasses and broadleaf plants. An important exception is corn, which is unusually resistant to the triazines.

It has been shown by several studies that these compounds are effective inhibitors of the Hill reaction in photosynthesis. Thus they are more damaging to plants left in the light than to those placed in the dark. The picture is complicated somewhat, however, by the fact that damage will also occur to some extent in tissues that do not contain chlorophyll and that do not photosynthesize. Nevertheless, the effects on photosynthesis appear to be an important aspect of the mechanism of herbicidal action of these compounds.

It has recently been shown by Stanley Ries at Michigan State University that levels of protein increase markedly in response to the triazines applied at low concentrations. Thus these compounds used at proper concentrations might promote protein production (in such crops as soybean) rather than acting as herbicides. Again it would seem logical to suspect an effect upon the DNA-RNA-protein system.

28.5.8 The Carbamates and Thiocarbamates

IPC, **chloro-IPC**, and **EPTC** are effective against grasses and a few other plants. They are normally used as pre-emergent herbicides, and they are particularly effective against germinating weed seeds. Often they are selective enough to be used in certain crops. Their mechanism of action is not fully understood, but they are known to inhibit mitosis. The thiocarbamates are volatile and need to be incorporated into the soil prior to weed seed germination. Absorption appears to be through the developing epicotyl.

28.5.9 Substituted Uracils

These compounds (e.g., **bromacil**) have also been used as herbicides in recent years, especially in industrial weed control. Presumably their mode of action might be related to their activity as nucleotide antimetabolites. Studies with microorganisms suggest that they do not interfere appreciably with pyrimidine metabolism as one might expect. They appear to inhibit photosynthesis, since strong inhibition of the Hill reaction of isolated chloroplasts has been noted.

28.5.10 Miscellaneous Compounds

There are several other compounds that do not yet fit readily into the classification scheme used for the above paragraphs. In some cases these are compounds new to agricultural practice at the time of this writing, but they may well constitute important groups in the near future.

Trifluralin is effective against germinating weeds in cotton and also in tomato fields that have been established by transplanting. **Diphenamid** has a similar action but may be used in direct seeded tomatoes. **Dacthal** is a pre-emergent herbicide with almost no activity against emerged weeds or crops. All three of these compounds must be incorporated into the soil in arid regions.

Several compounds (e.g., dacthal) are known which will kill crabgrass without damaging established bluegrass. In a few cases there is even a selectivity during germination so that bluegrass may germinate and grow while crabgrass will not. Such selectivity between closely related species is indeed remarkable. Various arsenicals have been used in crabgrass control, as have such unlikely compounds as **chlordane**, a rather complex molecule containing several atoms of chlorine. It is used primarily as an insecticide, but it was noticed that application of crude preparations of this compound to control insect pests in lawns also controlled the crab grass.

Several compounds, such as **endothal**, are known to be effective against aquatic weeds. Endothal is readily absorbed and translocated, but little is known of its mode of action. It does not harm fish.

28.6 GROWTH REGULATORS

Some of the most exciting potential for the future application of basic plant physiology in agriculture involves the growth regulators discussed in Chapter 21 and other chapters. Several of these compounds are already in regular use, but much remains to be done in this field as we learn more about the mode of action of the various natural plant growth regulators and as we discover more compounds that will influence plant growth and morphogenesis. At the moment, most of the available plant growth regulators can be classified as auxins or auxin-related materials, gibberellins, cytokinins, or growth retardants. They are summarized in Table 28-2 and Fig. 28-2. We will discuss the use of some representatives of these various groups.

28.6.1   Auxins and Auxin-related Compounds

These were some of the first compounds to be used in agriculture. Indoleacetic acid, probably the native auxin of several species, has not been used widely because most plants contain enzyme systems that destroy this compound rather rapidly. **Naphthalene acetic acid** (NAA), **indolebutyric acid** (IBA), *p*-**chlorophenoxyacetic acid** (PCPA), **2,4,5-trichlorophenoxypropionic acid** (2,4,5-TP), 2,4,5-T, and even 2,4-D have been used widely. Many of these compounds are utilized in the fruit-growing industry, since they will induce thinning of the crop when applied early during the growing season, but conversely they result in prevention of fruit drop when applied close to the time of harvest. The mechanism of this interesting response is not yet understood, although several hypotheses have been proposed.

The auxin-type herbicides have been used in the induction of parthenocarpic or seedless fruit. They will also cause fruit set under otherwise adverse conditions, and in some cases, they will reduce the alternate-bearing habit of certain fruit trees such as apples. **Triiodobenzoic acid** (TIBA) has been used for this purpose, and this compound is also effective in increasing the yield of soybeans by as much as 30 percent. TIBA is normally considered to be an antiauxin, and many plants treated with TIBA no longer transport auxin only in the polar direction.

TABLE 28-2

SOME REPRESENTATIVE GROWTH REGULATORS

Auxins and auxin-related compounds

NAA (naphthalene acetic acid)
IBA (indolebutyric acid)
PCPA (p-chlorophenoxyacetic acid)
2,4,5-TP or silvex (2-(2,4,5-trichlorophenoxy)-
    propionic acid)
2,4,5-T (2,4,5-trichlorophenoxyacetic acid)
2,4-D (dichlorophenoxyacetic acid)
TIBA (2,3,5-triiodobenzoic acid)

Gibberellins (See Fig. 21-13)
Cytokinins (See Fig. 21-16)
Growth retardants

B-9 (N-dimethylamino succinamic acid)
CCC ([2-chloroethyl]-trimethyl-ammonium
    chloride)
phosphon (tributyl-2,4-chlorobenzylphos-
    phonium chloride)
maleic hydrazide
CIPC (isopropyl-N-[3-chlorophenyl]carbamate)
TCNB (tetrachloronitrobenzene)

As indicated in the discussion in Chapter 21, since the auxins induce formation of roots on cuttings, they have often been used for this purpose in agriculture and horticulture. Many ornamental species are commonly propagated as cuttings, and the considerable promotion in root formation on these cuttings by applied auxins has been very valuable. Fruit trees and other fruit-producing species are also in some cases propagated with cuttings.

28.6.2   The Gibberellins

Although the gibberellins caused a great deal of excitement in the 1950s at the time of their introduction to the western world, practical application in agriculture has been somewhat limited. They are widely used in the grape industry (Fig. 28-3). Applied at the proper time and at the appropriate concentrations, gibberellins cause the bunches of grapes to elongate somewhat so that they are less tightly packed

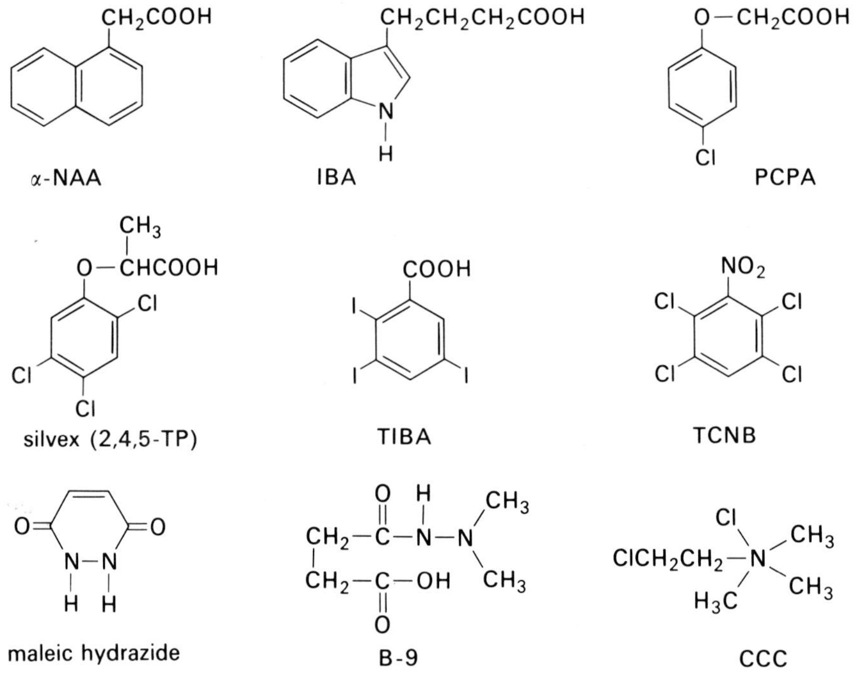

Figure 28-2
Molecular structures of some representative growth regulators used in agriculture.

and hence less susceptible to diseases or fungi. The individual grapes are also larger and more elongated, features that prove to be commercially desirable. Gibberellins also tend to increase celery production, although this has been somewhat sporadic, and storage quality is adversely affected. They have been used in the citrus industry (e.g., to delay ripening in lemons), and in some cases they have increased yields in cotton. Because of their effects on the flowering of long-day or cold-requiring species, they can be used to induce bolting in plants that might otherwise require two years to flower. This has been of considerable value in certain breeding projects (e.g., in sugar beets), and it is applied somewhat in commercial seed production. The effects on formation of amylase enzymes in the aleurone layer of barley as discussed in Chapter 21 have been applied in the brewing industry. Treatment of the mash with gibberellins increases malting.

28.6.3 Cytokinins

So far the cytokinins have had virtually no application in practical agriculture. They may prove to be valuable in extending the shelf-life of lettuce, as might be expected from their effects on leaf senescence discussed in Chapters 21 and 27. The response of cuttings to the balance between auxin and cytokinins could also be of value. African violet leaves, for example, will readily form roots when the petiole is placed in a moist medium as a cutting.

BLOSSOM SPRAY JUNE 13   GIRDLING JUNE 23
SHATTER SPRAY JUNE 23   GRAPES HARVESTED AUGUST 3

UNTREATED   BLOSSOM SPRAY   SHATTER SPRAY   BLOSSOM & SHATTER SPRAYS

GIRDLED   GIRDLED, BLOSSOM SPRAY   GIRDLED, SHATTER SPRAY   GIRDLED, SHATTER & BLOSSOM SPRAYS

Figure 28-3

Effects of gibberellin and girdling on growth of Thompson seedless grapes. (Photograph courtesy of J. LaMar Anderson, Utah State University, Logan.)

The subsequent formation of buds is sometimes considerably delayed, however, but this can be overcome by application of cytokinins. Surely this is a very minor use of these materials, of importance only to those ornamental horticulturists who are interested in the propagation of African violets. But we may confidently expect that several uses for these materials will become evident as they are further studied by plant physiologists and agriculturists.

28.6.4 Growth Retardants

As indicated in previous chapters, growth inhibitors are of common occurrence in higher plants. Nevertheless, the compounds to be discussed in this section are, for the most part, synthetic materials rather than naturally occurring substances, as is implied by the terms auxin, gibberellin, and cytokinin. But then the vast majority of auxins that are actually used in practical agriculture are also synthetics.

A number of growth inhibitors are utilized in ornamental horticulture, because they will retard the height of ornamentals such as chrysanthemums, Easter lilies, petunias, *Coleus*, poinsettias, etc. The result is a more compact and desirable plant (Fig. 28-4). Important current compounds include **B-9**, **CCC**, and **phosphon**. These growth retardants appear to be valuable in other aspects of agriculture such as in fruit production where they may be effective in retarding preharvest drop and in other ways.

Other examples of growth-retardant compounds that have been utilized in agriculture are those that inhibit the formation of sprouts, particularly on potatoes but in certain other

Figure 28-4

Effects of CCC on poinsettia growth. Plants were propagated August 2, 1961, and first treated September 21. Plant on the left is the untreated control; plant on the right was treated with 8 fluid ounces of CCC at approximately $1/2$ ounce to 3 quarts of water on September 21 and November 2. Photographs taken on December 1. (From R. S. Lindstrom, 1962, "Poinsettia response to CCC," *Florists' Review*, March 8:17–18, 44–48. Photo courtesy of R. S. Lindstrom.)

instances as well. Premature sprouting in stored potatoes may be prevented by application of materials such as **maleic hydrazide**, **CIPC**, and **TCNB**.

It is important to realize that probably less than half of the currently important compounds have been mentioned in this brief survey, and that the number of available compounds will certainly continue to increase at a rapid rate. Some of the search for new compounds of value in agriculture is being carried out by university and United States Department of Agriculture scientists. By far the most research of this type, however, is going on in the laboratories of large industrial chemical corporations. The introduction of a new compound into agriculture requires extensive and costly testing, not only for the compound's effectiveness in the desired cropping practice, but also to determine its safety from the standpoint of human health, even as this might be indirectly influenced by its effects on plants and animals in the ecosystem. Several million dollars are involved in the testing and finally bringing into production of a new agricultural chemical. Hence this procedure requires the support of a large industrial organization if it is to be carried to a successful completion.

28.7 SEED PRODUCTION

Modern agriculture is highly dependent upon the availability of high-quality seed. This implies not only the proper genetic composition, but also high viability and freedom from weed seeds. Much plant physiology is involved in the production of such seed. This is especially apparent in seed certification laboratories, where samples are tested for purity. The most advanced agricultural techniques must be applied in the fields where pure seeds are produced. The production of certified seed potatoes is an excellent example. A detailed and involved technology has developed, involving cooperation between the land-grant universities and the growers. The United States Department of Agriculture and the food processors are also involved.

28.8 FOOD TECHNOLOGY

The problem of food production extends beyond the challenges encountered in producing the food to those concerned with its preservation and preparation for final consumption. The methods that have been developed by the science of **food technology** have not only helped a great deal in feeding the hungry people of the world, but they have also added a high degree of quality to the food consumed in the more advanced nations. The importance of food technology becomes clear when we realize that even now, 25–50 percent of the fruits and vegetables produced spoil before they can be consumed. Yet in our technological society, such large cities as New York would begin to face starvation within one or two weeks if it were not for the principles of food technology now being applied.

Many of the techniques of food processing, such as drying and pickling, were discovered long before the development of plant physiology. Modern food technology began to develop following the early discoveries of microbiology. Canning and freezing processes are direct applications of Pasteur's discovery of the ability of microorganisms to carry out decay processes. Most of the traditional methods serve the dual purposes of killing the microorganisms that result in decay and denaturing the enzymes that

otherwise cause continued aging and breakdown of important flavor and nutrient compounds in the fruit or vegetable. Modern food technology, applying principles of plant physiology and bacteriology, has made a number of important and valuable contributions to the traditional methods, and a considerable amount of plant physiological research is presently conducted as part of the science of food technology. Much of this belongs to the area of postharvest physiology which we have already examined in Chapter 27.

In recent years, a number of new preservation methods have been developed or at least investigated in the laboratory. The entire area of **containers** has been reexamined, for example. Fresh fruits and vegetables are stored in transparent **thin-film bags**. The increased carbon dioxide and lower oxygen (due to respiration of the food materials) contribute to extended life. If such bags are completely impervious to water and carbon dioxide, anaerobic conditions may become damaging, and so the most suitable films are those that do permit diffusion of limited quantities of gases. Flexible films such as polyethylene may also be used for canning instead of the usual iron can coated with tin. Fruits and vegetables may be subjected to the usual canning processes (high temperatures) after being sealed in these materials.

Recently considerable interest has developed in the process of **freeze-drying**, in which fairly large quantities of water are removed by evaporation at normal temperatures, after which the fruits are frozen, and much of the remaining water is removed by sublimation in vacuum. Foods may be frozen by high-capacity conventional freezers, or they may even be dipped into liquid nitrogen. In any case, the resulting products maintain much of the flavor and even the cell structure of the original material.

The preservation of such perishable fruits as apples, peaches, apricots, cherries, and plums has been revolutionized by a number of new techniques developed in recent years. Pre-harvest sprays and postharvest dips are being tested to control fungi and even respiration of the harvested fruits. Precooling in one method by placing fruits soon after harvest in ice-water (**hydrocooling**), is also valuable in extending life of the fresh fruit. Many growers and processors now store fruits at 0°C and 85 percent relative humidity, greatly extending their life. More recently, it has been found that high carbon-dioxide levels and low oxygen levels add another four to eight months to the normal cold-storage life. Furthermore, after fruits are removed from **controlled-atmosphere storage** they may last five to twenty times as long as fruits maintained in conventional cold storage. Special units burning natural gas or propane have been developed to produce and accurately to maintain the desired carbon-dioxide levels.

There are many other details of food storage, such as blanching with soft instead of hard water (water containing calcium may make fruits and vegetables tougher by reacting with pectins), and using artificial sweeteners to produce low calorie fruits and vegetables. Since the early 1950s, considerable effort has gone into the study of food preservation by **gamma irradiation**. These high-energy radiation treatments kill or inhibit the microorganisms and denature destructive enzymes so that foods may last much longer even at normal temperatures. Such a lethal treatment also prevents sprouting of potatoes. The process is not without difficulties, however, since tissues are changed somewhat (e.g., turn brown).

Some of the best plant physiological research in the area of food technology is concerned with the problem of quality. Thousands of acres of potatoes are sprayed annually with maleic hydrazide, for example. This not only prevents sprouting of the tubers in storage (25.4.1), but it also results in a much higher potato-chip quality when the tubers are finally used to produce chips. Tomatoes must be shipped green from southern areas into northern areas in the winter. Normal ripening often produces an inferior product, but treatment with ethylene may greatly improve the final ripened tomato fruits. In a further effort to improve flavor, texture, color, and nutrition of plant products, food technologists have been engaged in extensive research on the biochemistry of synthesis of the compounds responsible for the desired food characteristics.

It should become increasingly evident that both modern agriculture and the utilization of its final products are based firmly on principles of plant physiology, genetics, microbiology, and engineering. And it is also in agricultural plant physiology where the scientist can become a humanitarian.

29

Physiological Ecology

29.1 THE SUBJECT MATTER OF PHYSIOLOGICAL ECOLOGY

In the introductory chapter we discussed the levels of organization in biological science, as illustrated in Fig. 1-1. Ecology, the study of the interaction of plants and animals with their environment, occupies a level just above that of physiology. The borderline, constituting an area of interplay between these two sciences, is of considerable interest. It provides the ecologist with facts essential to the application of his science, and it provides the physiologist with some interesting new challenges.

29.1.1 What Is Physiological Ecology?

In an area as broad as the interaction between plants and environment, there is room for different approaches. Basically, **physiological ecology** attempts to gain answers to the problems of plant ecology through understanding plant functions. That is, the methodology, facts, and interpretations of plant physiology are applied to the study of the problems of plant ecology. Some workers prefer the terms **environmental physiology** or **ecological physiology**. These terms shift the emphasis slightly, imply-

ing that the scientist is somewhat more interested in studying plant response to environment than he is in studying the problems of plant ecology. This is also a valuable approach.

The plant ecologist has long utilized the term **synecology** as that part of his science concerned with the interactions of plants with each other. **Autecology** is concerned with the response of individual plants to their environment. Autecology is, then, essentially equivalent to physiological ecology or environmental physiology—but not quite. Physiological ecology, while concerned primarily with the responses of individual plants, may also be concerned with the several functions of several plants making up a plant community. That is, plant physiology may be applied (but seldom is) in the study of synecology as well as autecology.

In its fullest scope, physiological ecology includes far more than can be contained in a brief chapter in a plant physiology textbook. Furthermore, we have already provided numerous examples in previous chapters. These most obviously include our discussions of transpiration and heat transfer, photosynthesis in nature, vernalization, photoperiodism, and the biological clock. The physiological ecologist would also draw upon many other areas we have already discussed. In this final chapter we will examine this interesting and somewhat different approach to the question of plant physiology, and we will also be able to consider at least one important area that has so far not been discussed in detail (stress physiology).

29.1.2   What Are the Problems of Ecology?

If physiological ecology is the application of plant physiology to the problems of ecology, then we might validly ask: Just what is ecology? James Bonner has suggested that the problems of ecology may be expressed by the following three questions: *First*, who lives where and why? *Second*, who eats whom? *Third*, what is the physiology of togetherness? The problem of "where" is basically the problem of plant or animal distribution. It has provided an extremely active area of research in ecology ever since the study of natural history began to develop at the time of the Renaissance. It is still an active area of study. Ecologists are searching for data to help them decide whether plants and animals in natural habitats occur in **discrete communities**, or whether one group of plants blends into another so gradually that the term **continuum** better describes the true situation than does the term community.

  The question of "who eats whom" is the question of food chains and energy flow into, within, and out of a community[1] or **ecosystem**. This question has stimulated a considerable amount of new and valuable research in recent years. It includes, of course, the question of heat transfer discussed in Chapter 6. It is also

intimately concerned with the problem of the efficiency of photosynthesis as this might be influenced by species and environment (Chapters 13 and 14). Both aquatic and terrestrial communities have been studied by establishing energy balance sheets and considering in detail factors that influence the quantity and rate of flow of materials and energy through the ecosystem. We will not have space to consider this interesting approach in this chapter.

  The "physiology of togetherness" implies the study of the intimate interactions among plants and animals in nature. **Parasitism** and **symbiosis** constitute extreme examples of these kinds of interactions. **Competition** and **epiphytism** (one plant using another for support) are other less extreme examples. We are dealing in each case with functions of two organisms as they interact with each other.

29.1.3   Why Do Specific Plants Grow in a Specific Environment?

Bonner's question "why" is the real heart of physiological ecology. There must be at least three reasons why a given plant occurs at a given location on the earth's surface: *First*, it or its progenitors happened to get there. *Second*, it is capable of survival, growth, and reproduction under the existing environmental conditions. *Third*, it has not been crowded out or eliminated by animals or other plants.

  The physiological ecologist is not primarily interested in mechanisms of plant dispersal, nor has he been able to contribute much to the problem of competition or elimination by other species. His main contribution may be in the area of a plant's capability for survival, growth, and reproduction under a given set of environmental conditions. The practicing physiological ecologist is most directly concerned, perhaps, with three more questions: *First*, what is the nature of the environment to which the plant is exposed? *Second*, what are the plant's functions,

---

[1] The term community is valuable even if continuum is a better description. A community might be thought of as an interacting group of plants and animals that constitutes a point along a continuum. In its modern context, the term ecosystem avoids some of the difficult connotations of the term community and also strongly implies the study of energy flow.

its physiology? *Third*, how is the plant's physiology influenced by its environment? Eventually, he may ask how the plant in turn influences its environment.

Study of the nature of environment should not be a part of physiological ecology. This is properly the duty of climatologists, meteorologists, and soil scientists. The physiological ecologist is highly dependent upon soil science, but he is seldom able to use directly more than a token amount of the specific data produced by climatologists. Rather, the physiological ecologist must often himself measure the atmospheric environment where the plants in which he is interested are growing. If he continues his study in the laboratory by growing plants under controlled environments (and this is perhaps the primary modern approach), then he will be further concerned with the problem of measuring the environment he himself designed. Thus the measurement and control of environment is an important aspect of physiological ecology.

The science of plant physiology should contribute information about how the plant functions. It is quite possible, however, that new plant functions and responses must be studied in the attempt to answer the specific problem of physiological ecology that motivated the research in the first place. Or well-known physiological processes may have to be studied in new ways, dictated again by the ecological approach. In nearly every case, even if the functions are known for some species, they will have to be studied *using the particular species* being investigated. Unfortunately, very seldom is enough physiological information available about a given species to allow a solution of the ecological problems relating to this species.

The study of physiological responses in environment is the real heart of physiological ecology. In its present development, this approach utilizes controlled environments to a high degree. Plant response to environment is studied by observing plants under controlled conditions, often conditions in which only one environmental parameter is varied and an attempt is made to maintain all others constant. With the use of computers, it is becoming possible to study responses to several factors changing simultaneously. This becomes nothing but plant physiology, however, unless the ecological problem is kept in mind and unless some effort is expended to develop a classification and philosophy about the physiology of plant response to environment. This has already been done to a certain extent in Chapters 19 and 20, but we will devote a special section to such an approach. In every case, we must relate our knowledge of plant response to the basic questions of plant ecology, particularly the questions of plant distribution and, to a lesser extent, community dynamics.

A guiding principle in studies of physiological ecology has been the so-called **law of the minimum** or the **law of limiting factors**. Sometimes there are physical barriers over which plant propagules cannot cross, but more frequently limitations on plant distribution are not due to dispersal mechanisms. As a general rule, plants are well able to spread their seeds or other propagules beyond their present population boundaries. This being the case, these boundaries must be established by intolerance to the environmental factors beyond the population area.

It has been tempting to search for the single factor which might be most limiting to the plant. Justus von Liebig stated in his law of the minimum in 1840 that: "The growth of a plant is dependent upon the amount of foodstuff which is presented to it in minimum quantities." Sometimes it has been possible to find an environmental factor that, like Liebig's foodstuff, seemed to be the most limiting factor. This might be particularly true at a given point along the population boundary. Surely, however, the picture is far more complicated than might be implied from Liebig's simple law. If low temperatures establish a northern boundary, for example, high temperatures might be responsible for the southern limits of distribution. Conceivably soil factors, precipitation, daylength, and a host of other factors and interactions might be responsible for different segments of a population boundary.

Furthermore, the law of the minimum implies that reactions using Liebig's foodstuffs as substrates have equilibrium constants such that they always go all the way to completion. That is, the response curve (response to a given factor) shows two lines, the first with a constant slope and the second a horizontal line intersecting the first at saturation (Fig. 29-1). As consideration of equilibrium principles makes quite clear, if a reaction between two substrates goes to completion (the equilibrium constant is very small), then either one of the substrates may be completely limiting. But if the reaction does not go to completion (large equilibrium constant), then in a very real sense, both of the substrates may be limiting at once (Fig. 29-1). It is important to keep in mind the law of the minimum in studies on physiological ecology, but it is equally important to realize that the situation will almost always be more complex than this law might imply.

29.1.4 The Ecotype Concept

It has long been recognized that plants within a species may exhibit considerable morphological variability, or they may appear identical in morphology but nevertheless may vary widely from each other in physiology, as indicated by their response to environment.

Some attempt to define and better understand the variability within morphological species was made as early as 1846 by Alexis Jordan in France. He transplanted members of a given species that appeared to differ from each other to a common location and found that in a common environment they nevertheless maintained their apparent differences. Other workers, particularly Gaston Bonnier in France and Frederick Clements in the western United States, reported that plants transplanted from one location to another (e.g., from the lowlands to the alpine) would strongly change in their appearance. Results of Bonnier and Clements are difficult to evaluate and are not accepted by all workers, but the general principle seems to be valid, since some plants will indeed change

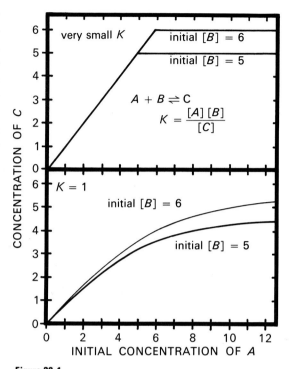

Figure 29-1

An illustration of the principle of limiting factors as it might be observed in a chemical equilibrium reaction. Concentration of a hypothetical product (C) is plotted as a function of initial concentration of one reactant (A) in the presence of two initial concentrations of the other reactant (B). (top) With a very small equilibrium constant, virtually all of the available (A) enters into the formation of (C) until (B) becomes limiting at its two concentrations. This is the ideal limiting factor response. If (K) is as large as 1 (bottom), then even at low concentrations, both (A) and (B) limit the amount of product formed.

radically in appearance when they are grown under another environment.

Göte Turesson in Sweden used the approach in the 1920s that had been established by the earlier workers. He transplanted individuals of a given species to a common environment (including a single soil type). In some cases he found that the differences apparent in the individuals growing at their original habitat were maintained when they were brought together to the common environment. These races within a species were referred to by Turesson as **ecotypes**. He defined these as genetically distinct races within a species, having a recognizable association with a given habitat. Ecotypes of a species were always completely interfertile. They might constitute a more basic unit of classification for the physiological ecologist than the species. It has since become apparent that genetically distinct ecotypes might appear identical in morphology but exhibit different physiological responses. One may flower earlier than another, for example.

In a few cases, members of species that appeared to be different at their original different locations developed an identical appearance when they were transplanted to a common environment. Turesson called these plants that were genetically similar but morphologically distinct in response to different environments **ecophenes**.

The concept of ecotypes and ecophenes strongly underscores a principle that is of the highest importance to the physiological ecologist: A great deal of genetic variability exists within species, leading to an almost astronomical number of plant and animal genotypes existing on the earth's surface. The plant physiologist has so far been much more concerned with a study of general principles of plant function as they may apply to all plants than the individual differences in plant response between genetically different individuals. Yet the physiological ecologist needs specific physiological information about individual ecotypes as they may occur in the system he is studying. Real development of physiological ecology will probably be dependent, then, upon an increasing interest in the physiology of individual species and their subunits, individual ecotypes.

29.2 THE MEASUREMENT AND CONTROL OF ENVIRONMENT

Environment is the unifying theme of physiological ecology. A modern course in this subject may devote as much as half of its allotted time to a discussion of the measurement and control of environment. This is also of increasing importance in all areas of plant physiology. After considering some principles and practices in this area, we will investigate the control of light and of temperature as examples of important problems and principles.

29.2.1 The Importance of Environmental Measurement and Control

If the guiding assumption of research in physiological ecology is that a plant is limited to its habitat by environment, then it is obvious that studies in this area must be vitally concerned with understanding natural environments, including the soil. Although many laboratory and greenhouse studies have led to broader understanding of environmental physiology, no investigation in physiological ecology can be complete without the field studies essential to a delineation and understanding of the problems at hand. After studying the plant or plants in which the investigator is interested and the environment in which these plants grow, he will investigate his hypothesis by experiments using controlled environments. Sometimes control of environment in the field will help (e.g., shading or application of fertilizers), but environment is usually controlled in the laboratory, maintaining a number of environmental factors at a constant level while varying only one.

This is the scientific process of **analysis**. As the organic chemist breaks down a molecule, studying it part by part to determine its structure, so the physiological ecologist may study the complex of response mechanisms in his test plant by investigating the effects of one environmental factor at a time. As the organic chemist has not really completed his task until he has assembled the facts gained by analysis, ultimately synthesizing the original molecule from its component parts, so the physiological ecologist must ultimately combine, in the process of **synthesis**, the facts he has learned about his plant to obtain a comprehensive picture of response in the field. He may well return to the field to make further observations, testing his laboratory hypotheses.

A certain level of environmental control can be achieved in a greenhouse, but most studies in physiological ecology require a more accurate control of temperature and light intensity than is available in most greenhouses. The result has been the development in recent years of **plant growth chambers**. Several commercial companies produce these facilities, and they vary considerably in detail (cost ranges from about $2,000 to over $10,000). They are becoming an important part of most plant research laboratories. Typically, temperature is controlled within one or two degrees, and artificial light is provided by a mixture of incandescent and fluorescent bulbs. Control of humidity is difficult and may nearly double the cost of a growth chamber. Temperatures may be set from values near freezing (or far below in some specialized units) to upper levels as high as might be desired (e.g., 40°C). Frequently the control system allows settings for separate day and night temperatures, and in some units temperature may be programmed to vary continuously throughout the 24-hour period. Light intensities are usually on the order of 700 to 1,500 ft-c, but in some installations, 3,000 to 5,000 ft-c or higher may be maintained over long periods of time. Frequently there is a plastic or glass barrier between the lights and the rest of the growth chamber, allowing removal of heat around the lights by a separate air-circulation system. In other units air from the chamber moves up directly through the lights, and the released heat must be removed by the cooling system in the chamber.

The ultimate development of the controlled environment facility is the **phytotron**.[2] This consists of an integrated series of growth chambers or growth rooms, involving usually a staff that includes several scientists, technicians, gardeners, and maintenance engineers. Phytotrons (most of them using the name in their official titles) now exist at many locations, including California, North Carolina, Australia, Canada, Belgium, France, South Africa, the Netherlands, Sweden, Germany, and Russia. A **biotron** has been built at the University of Wisconsin for the study of both plants and animals. A **climatron** was built by Frits Went at the Botanical Garden in St. Louis, Missouri. It consists of a large plexiglas dome in which temperature gradients were established, allowing warm days and warm nights, warm days and cool nights, and cool days and cool nights in different parts of the facility. Went made a number of interesting contributions to physiological ecology by the use of the Caltech Phytotron (officially the Earhart Plant Research Laboratory). Figure 29-2 summarizes some of the capabilities of this facility.

---

[2] The term phytotron was coined by James Bonner and Samuel Wildman at the California Institute of Technology where the first such facility was constructed under the direction of Frits Went. Caltech was building a cyclotron, and in jest these workers coined the term, saying that plant science should have a facility with an equally impressive name!

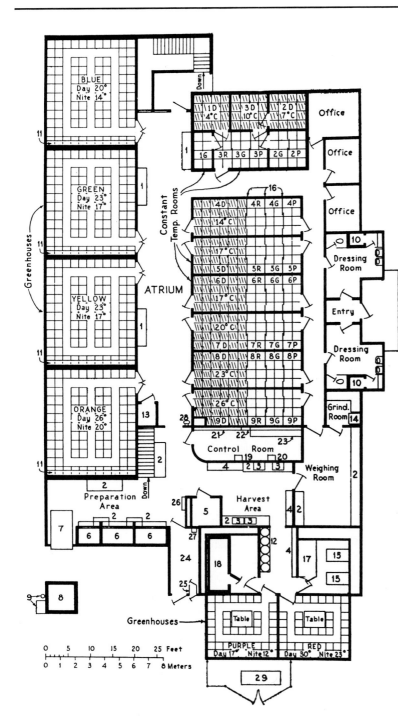

Figure 29-2

Floor plan for the upper floor of the phytotron built at the California Institute of Technology. The small squares represent trucks holding plants. Color names refer to the codes used for the various rooms. Day and night temperatures are indicated. Shaded areas indicate rooms maintained in continuous darkness. Data apply to the phytotron as originally operated under the direction of F. W. Went. Many changes have since been made. (From F. W. Went, 1957, *Experimental Control of Plant Growth*, Chronica Botanica Company, Waltham, Mass. Used by permission.)

29.2.2 The Control of Temperature

The control of temperature in a growth chamber, growth room, or even a greenhouse is an attempt to establish a level of kinetic energy of the molecules of air and ultimately the molecules within the plant cells. The principle of temperature control is simple: Temperature is detected, compared to a preset value, and heat is then either added or removed from the system. This is a classical feedback mechanism as discussed in previous chapters (6, 20, 22).

In practice two kinds of **thermal regulators** or **thermostats**[3] may be used in temperature control. In the first arrangement (Fig. 29-3), a temperature-sensing thermometer controls a simple **on–off switch**. If temperature is above the preset value, the switch may activate a cooling system; if temperature is below the preset value, a heating system may be activated. In any case, it should be apparent that no temperature control system can actually maintain an exact preset value. In order for heat to be removed or added to the system, temperature must vary by a detectable increment from the preset value. In a water bath it is possible for this variation to be as low as 0.001°, but in most growth chambers temperature may vary from 0.5° to 2.0° or more around the preset value. In the water bath the high specific heat of water allows for addition or removal of a relatively large quantity of heat (calories) with only a relatively small change in actual temperature. In a growth chamber containing air with its low specific heat, relatively small additions or subtractions of heat result in relatively large changes in temperature. In principle then, a fairly large unit with a large quantity of air and consequently a relatively high heat capacity

---

[3] The term thermostat originally meant the entire unit in which temperature was controlled (e.g. the growth chamber), but it has now become synonomous with the thermo regulator.

AN ON-OFF TEMPERATURE REGULATOR:

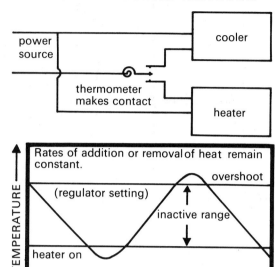

Figure 29-3

An on-off temperature regulator (top) and the expected variation in temperature (as a function of time) that might be produced by such a system (bottom). This is another portrayal of a negative feedback system.

for the system as a whole should be more stable than a smaller unit.

Temperature control is greatly complicated by the fact that plant growth requires a high intensity of light, and this acts as a continually high level of heat input into the system. The cooling system must work against this input of light energy.

The second kind of control system utilizes the principle of temperature **modulation** (Fig. 29-4). The switch that activates the heating or the cooling system in response to a difference in temperature between the measured and the preset value controls the *rate* of heating or cooling rather than simply turning it on or off. There are various ways that this may be accomplished. The switch may be connected with a rheostat, for example, in such a manner that as the temperature gets farther below the preset value, more electrical current is allowed to pass through an electrical resistance heater. In modulated cooling, chilled liquids are passed through cooling coils. As the temperature increases above the preset value, the valve allowing flow of the chilled fluid through the coils is opened wider so that the fluid flows more rapidly. Heating can use warm fluids. Such systems can be highly effective, allowing an accurate control of temperature in a growth chamber.

With an on–off system the rate of cooling or heating is nearly always the same. Refrigerant evaporating in coils in the air stream, or a suddenly activated heating system, results in sudden blasts of cold or hot air. In the modulated system the temperature of the cooling or heating liquid may itself be controlled accurately. Such a system utilizes the high specific heat of water (or other liquid such as ethylene glycol) to control the temperature of the gas with its relatively low specific heat.

In the control of plant temperature, it is imperative that the principles of heat transfer between the plant and its environment (Chapter 6) be kept in mind. Most growth chambers presently in operation depend exclusively upon convection as the cooling process. Air at controlled temperature is circulated at a velocity just high enough to remove heat by convection but not to shake the plants in the breeze. As a rule, it is simply assumed that plant temperature is equivalent to air temperature, and only air temperature is measured. If the incoming light is at a relatively low intensity (ca. 1,000 ft-c), then this assumption is reasonably valid (plant temperatures within one degree of air temperatures).

With high-intensity light sources, however, it is not safe to assume that plant and air temperatures are equal. As indicated in Chapter 6, leaves may be over 20°C warmer than the surrounding air. In such a growth chamber (and

few are presently in existence), leaf temperatures should be measured (by measuring infrared radiation emanating from the leaves or with minute thermocouples inserted into the leaves). The cooling system might conceivably utilize not only the principle of modulated air temperature control but also control of temperature of the growth chamber wall surfaces that are radiating to the plants. If these walls were cooled, they might act as a heat sink rather than a heat source, so that cooling of the leaves might be brought about by radiation to the walls as well as by convection to the air stream. These principles have been applied in a few studies utilizing wind tunnels in which all of the factors contributing to plant leaf temperature can be controlled or measured, including air temperature, humidity, and velocity; light intensity and quality; and temperature of the surrounding walls (Chapter 6, Fig. 6-18).

Several other principles and problems must be considered in temperature control for experiments in plant physiology. We will not further discuss these here, but they might include the direction and velocity of air movement (e.g., from below, from the side, or from above?), placement of the cooling and heating coils, and temperature-sensing devices in the air stream (temperature sensor should probably be placed among the leaves of the test plants); kinds of control systems (electrical or pneumatic?); kinds of heating and cooling systems; introduction of sufficient carbon dioxide into a recirculated air stream to allow proper photosynthesis; and safety devices that might be installed to prevent overheating or overcooling or failure of the light system.

29.2.3 Control of Light

In one sense, the control of light is simpler than the control of temperature. It is not as essential to monitor the levels produced, comparing the results with a preset level, and then changing

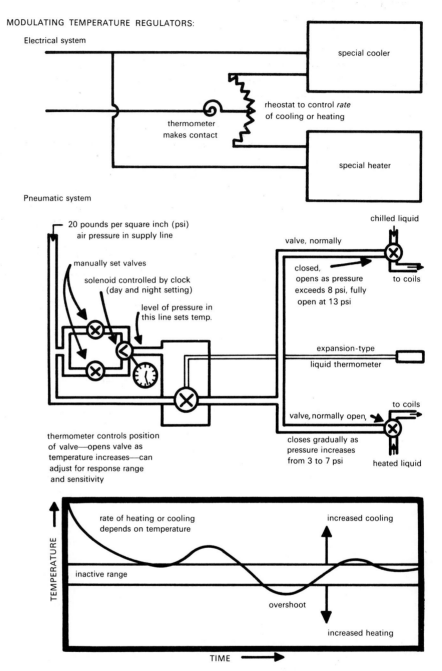

MODULATING TEMPERATURE REGULATORS:

Electrical system

special cooler

rheostat to control *rate*
of cooling or heating

thermometer
makes contact

special heater

Pneumatic system

20 pounds per square inch (psi)
air pressure in supply line

chilled liquid

valve, normally

manually set valves

solenoid controlled by clock
(day and night setting)

closed,
opens as pressure
exceeds 8 psi, fully
open at 13 psi

to coils

level of pressure in
this line sets temp.

expansion-type

liquid thermometer

to coils

valve, normally open,

thermometer controls position
of valve—opens valve as
temperature increases—can
adjust for response range
and sensitivity

closes gradually as
pressure increases
from 3 to 7 psi

heated liquid

rate of heating or cooling
depends on temperature

increased cooling

TEMPERATURE

inactive range

overshoot

increased heating

TIME

Figure 29-4

Two modulating temperature regulators (top and center) and the fluctuation in temperature
(as a function of time) that might be expected for such systems (bottom). In an electrical system,
rate of cooling or heating is governed by voltage or current, as this is controlled by a thermometer. In the pneumatic system, rate of cooling or heating is controlled by pressure in the
line to the valves controlling flow of hot or cold liquid. Pressure in the line is in turn controlled
by a valve that responds to a thermometer. The pneumatic system also includes an arrangement
whereby day and night settings can be controlled by a time switch. Such an additional feature
can also be added rather easily to the electrical system.

intensity in response to this (although such an approach could be used for highly accurate control). As a rule, we are dealing with light sources emitting at constant levels over long periods of time (or more typically the level decreases rather gradually with age of the source). Hence the main concern is the light source, and once this has been properly selected, then it is only necessary to renew it at intervals to overcome the effects of aging.

Basically we are concerned with the control of light intensity, quality, and levels of intensity and quality as a function of time (light duration). Intensity and quality will be controlled by the light source and the media (air, glass, special filter, etc.) between the source and the plants. Duration or changes in intensity or quality with time will be controlled by time switches that might even be of the modulating variety, changing with time the number of lamps operating or the level of intensity at which they operate.

Three fundamental principles of light emission are used in modern lamps, and all of these kinds of lamps have been utilized in growth chambers. *First* is the principle of **incandescence**. A filament, as in an incandescent bulb, or a plasma of gas as in an arc lamp, is heated to a high temperature so that it may act as a black body radiator, emitting light according to the principles discussed in Chapters 3 and 6. Carbon or xenon arc lamps reach temperatures equivalent to that of the surface of the sun, so that the spectral distribution of the light they emit approximates that of sunlight. (There are important differences. The surrounding hot glass of the xenon arc lamp, for example, produces a large quantity of infrared radiation.)

An incandescent lamp utilizing a tungsten filament, however, does not reach such high temperatures, and consequently the peak of emission is well into the infrared. (Less than 25 percent of the emitted radiant energy is in the visible part of the spectrum.) Nevertheless, these bulbs are much less expensive than the arc lamps,

and they are also much easier to operate. In recent years a few specialized studies have utilized xenon arc lamps, and in earlier years a number of laboratories made use of the carbon arc, but the overwhelming majority of growth chambers include incandescent lamps.

The main problem with the incandescent bulb is that the filament reaches a temperature at which the tungsten tends to sublime, precipitating on the inside of the bulb and causing it to darken. This, and final breakage of the filament, limits bulb life. With higher wattages, bulbs must be made larger so that heat can be more efficiently dissipated from the glass surface. In the late 1950s it was discovered that a small amount of iodine caused the tungsten to cycle from the filament to the glass surface and back to the filament. Small quartz tubes could be used, enclosing the filament in a much smaller volume than usual. These so-called **quartz-line lamps** can produce relatively large quantities of light from a small source (500 watts from a pencil-sized lamp). Their life is relatively long, but the tungsten is not recycled evenly, and finally the filament breaks. At least they do not lose intensity with age due to darkening of the inside of the glass envelope. They are relatively expensive, however, and they have not come into wide use in growth chambers.

The overwhelming amount of infrared energy produced by incandescent lamps is an important complication in the control of temperature in a growth chamber, but the presence of far-red and the general predominance of red wavelengths is very important to plant growth, and so they are used in the majority of chambers. Some workers use only fluorescent lamps (see below), but most authors report that this leads to abnormally shortened internodes on the test plants.

The *second* principle of light production is the passage of an electric current through a gas, exciting certain electrons and resulting in light emission as these return to the ground state. Neon, sodium-vapor, and mercury-vapor lamps operate on this principle. Neon lamps have been used to obtain certain desired light qualities, and mercury-vapor and sodium lamps have occasionally been used in plant growth studies. Since light emission depends not upon black-body radiation but upon an electron returning from a specific excited state to a specific ground level, light emission occurs in very narrow bands at specific wavelengths. In mercury lamps, these wavelengths are in the ultraviolet part of the spectrum. Ultraviolet lamps of this type are used in certain specialized plant studies.

The *third* principle of light emission involves the absorption of light by a so-called **phosphor**, the electrons of which then become excited, falling back to their ground state to emit light of a longer wavelength than that originally absorbed. This is the principle of **fluorescence**. It is utilized in the fluorescent tubes so widely used in growth chambers. Different salts can be mixed to produce the phosphors lining a fluorescent tube, providing the desired spectral properties. Mercury vapor is usually used to produce the wavelengths that excite the phosphor, and some of these may penetrate the phosphor in the tube, giving rise to the emission bands in the spectrum from a fluorescent lamp (Fig. 6-12, 6.7.1A(4)). These lamps are much more efficient in producing visible light than are incandescent lamps. They are more expensive than incandescent bulbs, requiring not a simple line voltage and current but a high voltage produced by so-called **ballasts**. The inefficiency which they do exhibit is due partially to heat losses from the ballasts. In recent years there have been a number of important improvements in fluorescent lamps, including particularly high-output lamps that provide relatively high intensities for a given lamp size.

Two important problems with the use of fluorescent lamps must be considered in growth chamber studies. *First*, no combination of phosphors has yet been produced that will provide light in the far-red part of the spectrum, and the red part is usually also rather weak. Considerable research has gone into this problem, and far-red-producing phosphors may be in the offing. At the time of this writing, however, no commercial lamps of any kind are available that will produce a spectral distribution of light properly balanced for plant growth.

Second, the intensity of light produced by a fluorescent tube is a function of its temperature. The mercury vapor condenses out on the surrounding glass envelope at a rate dependent upon temperature of the glass. This determines the pressure of the mercury vapor inside of the lamp and consequently the efficiency of its light emission. If the fluorescent lamps in the growth chamber are exposed to the air in the chamber, then the amount of light they emit will be influenced by the temperature at which the chamber is operated (Fig. 29-5). An investigator might think he was studying only the effects of air temperature, when actually he would be changing the light intensity along with air temperature. The most common solution involves the use of some kind of barrier between the lamps and the chamber. Mylar plastic is particularly suitable, but plexiglas and ordinary glass have often been used. Air temperature around the fluorescent tubes is then controlled separately from air temperature within the growth chamber. An important problem is the collection of dust particles on this barrier, which requires frequent cleaning.

In most growth chambers, a proper balance of light quality is obtained by combining 25 to 40 watts of incandescent illumination with each 60 to 75 watts of fluorescent light.

So, while light is easy to control in the sense that only the source must be controlled, available light sources probably constitute the most serious present limitation to the use of growth chambers. Temperature control, although difficult, can nevertheless be achieved within highly suitable limits, but light intensities in the field sometimes reach 10,000 ft-c, while

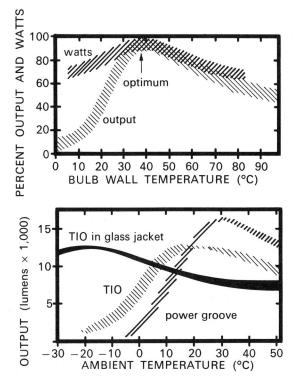

Figure 29-5

Light output of fluorescent lamps as a function of temperature (top) curves that apply to many fluorescent lamps expressed as light output and as watts consumed, both as a function of bulb-wall temperature, not air temperature. The curves are wide because other factors, such as age of the lamp, will influence them. (bottom) Light output as a function of ambient air temperature for three different kinds of lamps. The lamp in the glass jacket is made especially for outdoor applications where temperature would be expected to drop to low levels. (After General Electric Bulletin TP-111, "Fluorescent lamps." Large Lamp Department, Nela Park, Cleveland 12, Ohio. Used by permission.)

those obtainable in growth chambers are typically in the range of 1,000 ft-c. Light qualities are also limiting, and it is the experience of many investigators that plant growth in growth chambers is seldom equivalent in every important way to plant growth in the field. Use of xenon arc lamps with proper filtering systems provides intensities comparable to those in

nature, and qualities are not greatly different. These lamps with their starters and other accessories are expensive, however, and further study is required to ascertain their suitability.

29.3 PHYSIOLOGY OF RESPONSE TO ENVIRONMENT

In Chapter 20 we considered some of the mechanisms within the plant by which the plant responds to environment. We considered environmental effects upon enyzmes and upon the DNA-RNA-protein complex. In Chapter 23 we discussed responses to light, including direct-energy conversion as in photosynthesis and amplified responses as in the phytochrome system. We have also in previous chapters discussed the hormones and their role in environmental responses, acting often as translational factors between the environmental transducers and the enzymes or other systems that ultimately must take part in the plant's response to environment.

As background for studies in physiological ecology, it is instructive to classify plant responses to environment. The scheme utilized here is an elaboration of an outline presented by Anton Lang at the Annual Meetings of the American Institute of Biological Sciences held at Purdue University in 1961. The attempt at classification was considered a tentative one, and because of several difficulties, which we shall examine, the present amplification of Lang's original classification (partially through correspondence with Lang) must also remain highly tentative. The response categories as described seem reasonable enough, but actual plant responses (e.g., photoperiodism) often seem to resist falling into a single category.

29.3.1 Direct Environmental Effects

Several plant responses seem to depend directly upon an energy or material input from the environment. In Lang's definition, when the environmental factor is removed, then the effect disappears. If the factor changes in magnitude or intensity, then the response immediately changes (providing, of course, that the factor is limiting and not above saturation). Photosynthesis as dependent upon light or carbon dioxide provides one of the most obvious examples. Transpiration and leaf temperature or respiration and temperature may be other good examples, and plant growth as a function of water or nutrient supply would seem to fit in this category. There must be many metabolic processes in plants that would be rather easily classified here.

29.3.2 Triggered or On-Off Responses

This response differs from the direct response in that there is both a delay and an amplification. As a general rule, the response is initiated by the environmental stimulus but does not actually occur until some time after presentation of the stimulus. Furthermore, the energy provided by the incoming stimulus (light, temperature, nutrients) is typically not sufficient to account for the observed response. Seed germination may be one of the best examples of a triggered response. Either a seed germinates or it does not. (In a *population* of seeds, there is typically a quantitative response more closely analogous to the next category.) Rephasing of circadian rhythms may also fit in this category, as would wound healing and the induction or breaking of dormancy, although as we study these responses in more detail, we discover more and more quantitative aspects.

29.3.3 Modulated or Quantitative Responses

In the area of morphogenesis, modulated responses seem to be far more common. Not only does the environmental stimulus initiate a process that is then amplified, but the actual *level* of response will be proportional or related to the level of input from the environmental stimulus. This is closely analogous to the modulated temperature control system described above. As more unilateral blue light is presented to the coleoptile, the resultant bending increases in a roughly proportional manner. Of course, as should be evident from our discussions of these particular responses in previous chapters, these statements hold only over a part of the range of the environmental stimulus, namely before saturation (or even inhibition) is reached.

As in the triggered responses, there is not only an amplification between presentation of environmental factor and ultimate response, but there is a *delay in time*. In some cases this delay is relatively short. Geotropism will occur within a few hours after a plant is laid on its side. Typically, phototropic bending or many phytochrome responses also have short time delays. In a few other cases, the delay is much more extended, as in flowering, and development of fruit in response to photoperiodic induction. Days, weeks, and even months may elapse from the exposure of a cocklebur plant to a long dark period until mature fruits have developed. These **induced responses (induction)** are typically modulated, although at first glance they may resemble triggered effects. The rate of development of flowers and fruits in the cocklebur plant is proportional to the length of the original inductive dark period(s). The response, by being modulated and inductive, provides an example of **homeostasis.** In other cases (e.g., soybean) the development of flowers stops when plants are removed from the environmental stimulus that originally initiated the floral development. In these cases the response is not truly inductive, but it is clearly delayed, amplified, and modulated.

29.3.4 Conditioning Effects

In some cases a given set of environmental conditions causes a gradual change in the nature of the plant. The response may not be inductive in that if the environmental condition is removed, development of the plant response may stop (as in flowering of soybeans described above). In one sense the response may also be less delayed than in some of the above-mentioned examples. Each presentation of environmental stimulus may lead to a given increment in development of response, yet there may well be a requirement for amplifications of energy input. Frost and drought-hardening (29.4.1 and 29.4.3) may be examples of such a conditioning effect. Vernalization could be another good example. The long-day-requiring strain of henbane, for instance, is conditioned by exposure to the low temperature to respond to the subsequent long-day treatment. Long days by themselves will not result in flowering, nor will exposure to the low temperature. Only when the plant has been properly conditioned by low temperature does it become capable of responding to long days. In some cases the temperature of germination has an important effect upon subsequent growth and development of the plant (see Chapter 25). Again, environment during germination seems to be conditioning the plant so that it will respond to the subsequent environment in a given manner.

29.3.5 Carry-over Effects

In some interesting experiments of Harry Highkin, then working at the Caltech phytotron, it could be demonstrated that the environmental response during one generation was still evident in subsequent generations. Highkin found that if pea plants were grown under suboptimal temperature conditions (relatively low but constant day and night temperatures), plants became increasingly dwarfed from generation to generation until they had reached a highly dwarfed condition after about eight generations. Returning the offspring of this highly dwarfed generation to optimum conditions did not produce full-size plants; rather, another eight genera-

tions were required to achieve this status. Highkin was extremely careful to eliminate effects of selection as a cause of his observed results. For example, crossing of a dwarf with a normal pea plant resulted in intermediate progeny regardless of whether the dwarf was the male or the female parent. Since Highkin's original work (in the 1950s), his results have been duplicated by several other investigators. These results may well constitute a separate category of plant response to environment, and they are highly significant in terms of the ecotype concept discussed above.

In all of these categories of response, it is tempting to speculate about the role of the genome and the morphogenetic program. Except for direct responses, such as photosynthesis, it must almost always be the balance of activated and repressed genes that ultimately shifts in response to environmental change and brings about the observed morphogenetic response. How many of the delayed, induced, modulated, and amplified responses mentioned above are responses of the genome itself? Or does the morphogenetic program always require such transducers and translators as the pigments, hormones, enzymes, etc.? And a final question: How can our speculations and classifications contribute in the most meaningful way to a solution of the problems of physiological ecology?

29.4 STRESS PHYSIOLOGY

Biologists have long been interested in describing the environmental limits for the existence of life on earth. The physiologist is interested in understanding the mechanisms within plants and animals that establish these limits and how these mechanisms might break down under the stresses caused by environmental extremes. There are several ecological situations in which the stresses occurring at the extremes seem to control plant distribution.

Water is clearly one of the most important environmental factors from the standpoint of the plant's function. Because of this, it is of the utmost importance both to native plant distribution and to agriculture, and so water or the lack of it has long been studied as a stress factor. The ecologist classifies plants according to their response to water: **hydrophytes** are those plants that grow where water is available in super-abundance; **mesophytes** grow where amounts of water are intermediate; and **xerophytes** grow in dry regions. Presence of solutes strongly influences water potential, and ecologists further classify those plants that are sensitive to relatively high concentrations of salt in the surrounding liquid medium (body of water or soil solution) as **glycophytes** and those that are able to grow in the presence of such high concentrations of salt as **halophytes**.

During the 19th century and particularly during the first four decades of this century, water as a stress factor constituted one of the areas of primary interest in plant physiology. By the 1940s, interest had begun to wane, and few advances were being made. In very recent years, because of important advances in our understanding of the physics and chemistry of water, it has been possible to reinvestigate some of the old questions that were studied so actively for a century or more. In the following sections we will briefly examine some of the problems and some of the older as well as the newer work.

29.4.1   Drought

As pointed out by Jacob Levitt of the University of Missouri, who has contributed an exceptional amount of information to our understanding of water as a stress factor, we should differentiate in our discussions between **resistance** and **hardiness** to any given stress factor.

A plant may be *resistant* to low quantities of water in its environment by several mechanisms. **Annual plants** in the desert, for example, **escape** the drought (according to the terminology of

H. L. Shantz presented at the beginning of this century) by existing as dormant seeds during the dry season. When enough rain falls to wet the soil to a considerable depth, these seeds may germinate. (As pointed out in Chapter 25, they may do so in response to the removal by leaching of germination inhibitors.) Many of these plants are able to grow to maturity and set at least one seed before all soil moisture has been exhausted. They are eminently well-adapted to dry regions and thus are clearly xerophytes in the true sense of the word. Yet their active and metabolizing protoplasm is never exposed to a high water stress (highly negative water potential). Thus they resist the drought by escaping it.

Succulent species in dry regions, such as the cacti, *Agave* (century plant), and various others were, according to Shantz's terminology, **drought resisters**. They resisted the drought by storing water in their succulent tissue. As indicated in previous chapters, they are able to do this by a special so-called **succulent metabolism**. Organic acids are accumulated during the night when stomates are open admitting carbon dioxide, and then these organic acids are photosynthetically converted to carbohydrates during the day when stomates are closed. Enough water is stored in their tissue, and its rate of loss is so extremely low (due to an exceptionally thick cuticle and stomatal closure during the daytime) that they may exist for long periods of time without added moisture. D. T. MacDougal and E. S. Spaulding reported in 1910 that a stem of *Maximowiczia sonorae* (a desert succulent in the cucumber family) stored "dry" in a museum formed new growth every summer for eight consecutive summers, decreasing in weight only from 7.5 to 3.5 kg! In any case, the succulents resist the drought by storing moisture, and thus their protoplasm is also never subjected to extremely negative water potentials.

In addition to the annuals and the succulents, many of the plants of dry regions are **non-**

succulent perennials. Some of these (according to Shantz) **avoid** the drought by various anatomical modifications. The most effective of these modifications is a very deep root system extending to the water table. In such cases (e.g., alfalfa, mesquite), even though the plants are existing in areas of extremely low rainfall, they are always supplied with an ample quantity of water, and their tissues are never subjected to high water stress. Other modifications of this type, none of which are really as effective as roots that reach the water table, include extensive shallow root systems capable of absorbing surface moisture after a storm (common in cacti), reduction in size of leaf blades (which could be more important in increasing heat transfer by convection than in reduction of transpiration—Chapter 6), sunken stomates, and perhaps such other factors as heavy pubescence on the leaf surfaces. Although these modifications may indeed reduce the loss of water, they never completely prevent it and would, as a rule, by themselves be insufficient protection against extreme drought.

Among the nonsucculent perennials are those that simply (according to Shantz) **endure** the drought. That is, they lose exceptionally large quantities of water so that their protoplasm is subjected to very negative water potentials, and yet they are not killed. These are the so-called **true xerophytes (euxerophytes)**, and they exhibit the property of **hardiness** rather than merely of **resistance**, according to the terms suggested by Levitt. Plants that only resist drought are of interest to ecologists, but they do not hold the challenge to our understanding found in the euxerophytes, which are capable of enduring high levels of desiccation. Incidentally, it should be pointed out that many of the characteristics of drought avoiders such as small cells, sunken stomates, etc., also occur in the drought endurers. Yet in the euxerophytes the ultimate weapon against drought is the ability to endure it.

Drought hardiness has long been studied not only in the euxerophytes of desert regions, but in crop plants that may be drought hardy only in a relative sense compared to other crop plants but not to desert plants. In *Larrea divaricata* (Creosote bush), a desert shrub of both North and South America, the water content may drop to only 30 percent of the final fresh weight before leaves die. With most plants, levels of 50–75 percent are lethal.

In the study of drought hardiness, high temperature must always be considered. In such plants as watermelon, with deep root systems, transpiration levels may always remain high, so that leaf temperatures never exceed air temperatures by significant amounts. In the euxerophytes, however, when water levels have been greatly depleted, solar radiation will raise leaf temperatures to levels far above air temperatures. In many cases it can be shown that ultimate damage to the plant is brought about by the high temperatures rather than the negative water potential.

Physiologists have long studied the effects of desiccation in both drought-hardy and non-hardy plants. Protoplasmic viscosity usually increases with desiccation, often to a point where the protoplasm becomes brittle. Euxerophytes maintain protoplasmic elasticity to much higher levels of desiccation. Hydrolytic activities, including breakdown of metabolites in general but particularly the hydrolysis of starch and protein, increase during desiccation. This general increase in rate of metabolic breakdown is probably the most universal characteristic of high water stress. A result is a damage to and a destruction of the submicroscopic structure of protoplasm. There are also many other general plant responses to water stress (some of them discussed in Chapter 6). As might be expected, for example, there is a decrease in rate of translocation of solutes. According to the Münch hypothesis, translocation is a turgor phenomenon, and hence we would expect loss of water to result in loss of this function.

Agriculturists have long studied the induction of drought hardiness. Plants exposed to low water levels, high light intensities, and other factors, such as high phosphorus and low nitrogen fertilization become drought-hardy compared to plants of the same species not treated in this way. This is a good example of a conditioning effect. Russian scientists have reported that plants may be induced to become drought-hardy by soaking the seeds in water for two days and then air-drying them. After the seeds are planted, the resulting plants are said to be much more drought-hardy.

29.4.2 High Temperatures

Elevated temperatures typically accompany drought conditions and are an important environmental stress factor in themselves. The upper temperature limits permitting survival have long been of interest to biologists. Plants typically die when exposed to temperatures of 44° to 50°C, but some can tolerate temperatures above this. Stem tissue near to the soil line of plants in the desert, for example, may reach levels considerably above this. Certain bacteria and algae grow in the thermal waters of hot springs.

Thomas D. Brock (*Science*, 1967) studied the springs of Yellowstone National Park. He found bacteria actually growing at the boiling point (above 90°C at that elevation) and blue-green algae in waters of 73° to 75°C, about the "melting" point of DNA (the temperature at which the strands in the double helix disassociate). Microorganisms with nuclei (e.g., green algae) were not found at temperatures above 56° to 60°C.

The upper limit for animals seems to be about 45° to 51°C. Interestingly enough, many enzymes are denatured at temperatures below these, but apparently in the few organisms that can survive these temperatures, this is not the case. Bacteria have been found growing at the bottoms of oil wells at temperatures somewhat over 100°C, but at greatly elevated pressures. These organisms will repeat this performance in the laboratory (growth at high temperatures combined with high pressures) but will not grow at such high temperature levels when pressure is reduced. Several spores and even seeds of higher plants are known that will *survive* temperatures above 100°C. These do not actively *grow* at these temperatures, however.

Death of a plant in the field due to exposure to high temperatures may be due to several interacting factors. Commonly, two of these are especially important. Rapid warming results in a coagulation of protein and consequent disruption of protoplasmic structure. More gradual warming results in a breakdown of protein with a release of ammonia. Death may result from ammonia poisoning.

Plants which are hardy toward high temperatures exhibit high levels of bound water (water of hydration) and high protoplasmic viscosity, characteristics that are also exhibited by drought-hardy plants. High-temperature plants also are able to synthesize at high rates when temperatures become elevated, allowing synthetic rates to equal breakdown rates, and avoiding ammonia poisoning. P. A. Henckel, a Russian scientist who has recently reviewed drought and high-temperature hardiness, suggested that high levels of active nucleic acids may permit the rapid synthetic rate in high-temperature-hardy plants. He also reported that hardiness may be improved by the presowing drought-hardening procedure described above, as well as by exposure of mature plants to relatively elevated temperatures during a hardening period.

29.4.3 Low Temperatures

Hardiness toward low temperatures may be important in controlling the limits of distribution of a given plant. There are also many regions in the world where frost damage in agricultural crops is important.

Plant species vary considerably in their responses to low temperature. Certain tropical fruits such as bananas are damaged by a few hours below 13°C. Indeed, such chilling treatment may damage many crop plants normally grown in southern regions. In these cases exposure to 0.5–5.0°C is usually very damaging, but of course no signs of freezing are observed. On the other hand, winter-hardy plants, typically in the dormant condition, may easily survive exposure to temperatures of −20 to −30°C or lower depending upon species. As in the case of drought and high-temperature hardiness, frost hardiness may also be strongly induced by environmental treatments. Thus a winter rye plant will *grow* as a seedling under the snow, but during its active vegetative and flowering period in the following summer it will be killed by exposure to temperatures only a few degrees below freezing.

Apparently there is no lower temperature limit for survival of spores, seeds, and even lichens and certain mosses in the dry condition. Such test objects have been held within a fraction of a degree of absolute zero for several hours with no apparent damage. Even active tissue may survive these low temperatures if it is frozen and subsequently thawed rapidly enough and if it is frost hardy (see below). Certain bacteria are known that will actually grow at temperatures of −22°C. Molds have exhibited active growth in cold storage lockers at temperatures of −38°C, and spores have been formed by these organisms at temperatures of −47°C! These are unusual examples observed only rarely. (If they were common, cold-storage lockers could not be used.) Several higher plants such as winter rye will grow actively at the freezing point and perhaps a few degrees below. These include several species such as *Ranunculus adoneus* (snow buttercup), *Erythronium grandiflorum* (dogtooth violet or glacier

lily), and others which grow to the stage of flowering under snowbanks in the high mountains. A red-colored green alga (*Chlamydomonas nivalis*) also grows commonly in summer snowbanks in mountain regions. These responses are especially striking when compared with the extreme temperature sensitivity of tropical plants, such as the banana.

How does freezing kill plant tissue? A. Sakai and K. Otsuka in Japan have recently studied with the electron microscope tissue that was frozen at extremely rapid rates in liquid nitrogen or isopentane. They confirm theories of other scientists that have been developing for several decades, particularly those of B. J. Luyet and his coworkers. If cooling rates are extremely rapid, and warming is also rapid (tissue dipped into water at 30°C), then survival of frost-hardy tissue can be observed. Ice crystals in the protoplasm are extremely small, and cavities caused by ice-crystal formation are not observed in electron micrographs. If warming is slower, then the crystals grow during the warming period, damage occurs, and tissue does not survive. At intermediate cooling rates, large crystals form, cavities are apparent, and tissue is killed. At slow rates of cooling, crystals do not form inside the protoplasts but only in the intercellular spaces. This also allows survival of frost-hardy plants. The Japanese workers used frost-hardy mulberry stem tissue. Using mulberry stem tissue that had not been frost-hardened, death resulted from all three rates of freezing.

It was long thought that death of the plant resulted by its expansion upon freezing and subsequent disruption of cell walls and other anatomical features. Careful examination during the early decades of the 19th century made it clear, however, that plants actually contract rather than expand upon freezing. This is because ice crystals grow into the intercellular air spaces. Furthermore, ice has never been observed within the living cells of tissues that have frozen naturally. (It is observed in the dead xylem cells of trees in the winter.) Nor has damage to cells other than collapse ever been observed. There is no rupture of cell walls or even cell membranes. With very rapid cooling of tissue in the laboratory (e.g., 20°C in one hour), ice can be seen within the cells, and damage to cellular components can be observed. Such rapid cooling does occasionally occur in nature, and thus these phenomena may occur naturally, but apparently this is a relatively rare event, since literally thousands of observations have failed to disclose anything but ice in the intercellular spaces of naturally frozen tissue. The water potential inside the cells is more negative than it is outside, and thus freezing begins in the intercellular spaces. Apparently the surrounding lipophylic membrane as well as the small size of cells also act against freezing within the protoplasts. As ice crystals form in the intercellular spaces, the water potential at their surfaces becomes more negative than within the cells, and thus water begins to diffuse from the cells and condense on the ice crystals. A crystal may grow to a size several thousand times that of an individual cell.

In frost-hardy plants, as these ice crystals melt, the water goes back into the cells, and they resume their metabolism. In sensitive plants metabolism cannot be resumed, and the water does not reenter the cells completely. Again there are significant differences in protoplasm between hardy and sensitive plants. Hardy plants frequently contain higher concentrations of solutes; bound water is higher; and protoplasm is more elastic and remains more elastic during freezing.

Hardiness is measured in the laboratory by placing pieces of tissue at successively lower temperatures with intervals of one or two hours at each temperature (e.g., 5° intervals). As each lower temperature is reached, samples of tissue are removed, thawed out, and tested for viability. Several viability tests may be used. A common one is the application of colorless tetrazolium hydrochloride, which is reduced by active dehydrogenase in living cells to a bright red form.

Frost hardiness is typically induced by exposure to relatively low temperatures (e.g., 5°C) for several days. Short days also promote development of hardiness in several species, and there are indications that a stimulus may move from leaf tissue to the stems. The development of frost hardiness is a metabolic process requiring an energy source. Apparently this can be provided by light and photosynthesis. Low nitrogen levels also promote the development of hardiness.

29.4.4 Salt

Damage due to high salt concentrations in the external medium may commonly be due to two mechanisms: The reduced water potential makes it more difficult for the plant to obtain water, and in addition there may be specific effects due to the presence of specific ions. We will not discuss the ionic toxicity effects here.

In the study of salt hardiness, the **obligate halophytes** are particularly interesting. Several such species will grow only where salt levels in the soil are high as in deserts or near brackish waters on the sea coasts or close to the shores of extremely salty bodies of water such as the Great Salt Lake, where the salt content may be saturated at levels as high as 27 percent by weight. *Allenrolfea* (iodine bush), *Salicornia* (the pickleweed or samphire), and *Limonium* (sea-lavender, marsh-rosemary), are good examples. *Atriplex* (shadscale) and *Sarcobatus* (black greasewood) also grow in salty soils, and certain bacteria and blue-green algae live in the waters of the Great Salt Lake. In the case of the terrestrial halophytes, the osmotic potential of the cell sap is invariably highly negative. Values as negative as -200 bars have been observed in *Atriplex* species, for example, as contrasted to a normal -20 to -30 bars in most plants.

In some cases the xylem sap does not have a high osmotic potential but may be almost pure water. To obtain water from the surrounding soil, water potential within the xylem sap must then be greatly lowered by tension. This was demonstrated by Scholander and his coworkers for mangrove trees (7.4.2C and 7.5.3).

Some halophytes are referred to as salt **accumulators**. In these plants the osmotic potential continues to become more negative throughout the growing season as salt is absorbed. It should be noted, however, that even in these plants the soil solution is not taken directly into the plant. It is easy to calculate, based upon quantities of water transpired by the plant, that if the complete soil solution were absorbed, the plant would contain ten to one hundred times as much salt as is actually observed. Instead, water moves into the plant osmotically and not simply in bulk flow. The endodermal layer in the roots probably provides the osmotic barrier.

Halophytes in which the salt concentration within the plant does not increase during the growing season are known as salt **regulators**. Often the salt does enter the plant, but the leaves swell by absorbing water, so that concentrations do not increase. This leads to the development of **succulence** (a high volume/surface ratio), a common morphological feature of halophytes. Sometimes excess salt is exuded on the surface of the leaves, helping to maintain a constant salt concentration within the tissue. In certain halophytes there are readily observable salt glands on the leaves. Actually, it has been shown by several workers that large quantities of both organic and inorganic materials may be leached from the leaves of many plants, both halophytes and glycophytes. Some of the leaching brought about by washing the leaves may be due to removal of materials from within the tissue as well as washing off materials that have been exuded at the surface. In any case, these materials may be washed from the leaves to the soil and thus recycled within an individual plant and to other plants. This certainly has important ecological implications, particularly in relation to mineral nutrition.

Some crop plants (e.g., beets or tomatoes) are much more salt hardy than others (e.g., onions or peas), and salt hardiness can be increased somewhat by exposure to saline conditions.

29.4.5 Plant Response to Stress

Plant response to stress is obviously highly complex. It could involve specific enzymes, such as those that are most sensitive to high temperatures. Furthermore, there are also stress factors besides those we have discussed. These might include ultraviolet light (Chapter 23), herbicides (Chapter 28), and mechanical stresses, such as those brought about by high winds.

In the stress factors discussed in the above sections, however, water potential is almost always involved. We seem to be dealing with stress brought about by water potentials that are too negative. In drought, as water levels within the tissue decrease, osmotic and matric potentials become more negative. In frost, water is also removed from the cells, resulting in more negative water potentials within the protoplast. High salt concentrations have the same result. High-temperature damage is probably not related to negative water potentials, although it frequently accompanies drought. In every case effects upon protoplasm seem to indicate that we are dealing with the water adsorbed on the hydrating matrix, especially protein. Perhaps, as water is lost, the enzymes change shape so that structure of active sites becomes disturbed and enzymatic activity is lost.

Levitt proposed that high water stress (particularly in frost damage) results specifically in an effect upon the sulfhydryl groups of protein. He proposed that as the layer of water around protein molecules becomes thinner due to desiccation, sulfhydryl groups begin to contact each other in adjacent proteins. By removal of hydrogen (oxidation), these then form disulfide linkages (Fig. 29-6; see also Fig. 11-6). Upon rehydration, the disulfide linkages hold proteins together in such a way that the developing water layer results in strains and ultimate distortions of the molecules. Again, enzymatic activity is lost. Development of hardiness would be the development of a protection of the sulfhydryl groups, so that disulfide linkages are not formed. Levitt did find a decrease in sulfhydryl groups and an increase of disulfide linkages upon freezing.

Levitt's theory agrees with most of the observations relating to hardiness and stress, and it has provided a considerable impetus for new research into some old problems. There are several other possible approaches to the problem of stress, however. One of these concerns the research of Charles R. Olien at Michigan State University, which is related to the redistribution of water during freezing. Among other things, Olien studied the interference of freezing caused by large water-soluble polymers extracted from the cell walls of hardened plants. These substances interfered with freezing by competing with water molecules for sites in the ice lattice at the liquid interface. The result was that they tended to stop crystal growth, causing an imperfect ice mass to form. Polymers extracted from non-hardy winter cereals had little effect upon ice formation, but polymers from hardy varieties resulted in small, highly imperfect crystals within the plant. The polymers were mainly polysaccharides, containing large amounts of xylose and arabinose.

29.5 WORK ON DESERT STRESS PHYSIOLOGY

Much of the work summarized above was performed with desert species, and the desert

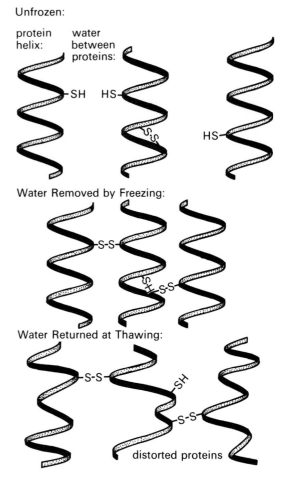

Figure 29-6

A schematic illustration of Levitt's sulfhydryl-disulfide hypothesis of frost injury and resistance in plants. (Based upon J. Levitt, 1962, *J. Theoretical Biology* 3:355–391.)

is certainly an ideal situation for the study of stress physiology. Many scientists have contributed to our present understanding of physiological ecology as it relates to plants in the desert, and we have already referred to much of this work above and in Chapter 25. A complete summary could easily fill a volume; so only a few projects can be mentioned.

Shantz was referred to above. His contributions during the first four decades of this century to our understanding of the water relations of desert plants constitute one of the earliest and best studies in physiological ecology.

Frits Went, beginning in the 1940s, has also contributed much to our understanding of the physiology of desert plants. He was long interested in the germination characteristics of desert seeds, carrying out his investigations in the Caltech Phytotron. His findings relating to interactions of temperature and rainfall (leaching of inhibitors) in germination of desert annuals were especially instructive from the standpoint of ecology. He is now at the Desert Research Institute of the University of Nevada. James Bonner and his students, also at Caltech, studied compounds that could be extracted from leaves of one plant and were inhibitory to the growth of others. These antibiotic unsaturated lactones and other compounds constitute the arsenal in a sort of plant chemical warfare in the desert.

M. Fireman and H. E. Hayward, located at the Salinity Laboratory in Riverside, California, carried out an interesting study in 1952 in the Escalante Desert of Utah (Fig. 29-7). They found that greasewood (*Sarcobatus vermiculatus*) markedly changed the pH and salinity of soil beneath it by bringing soluble salts from depths and depositing them on the surface, possibly by leaching from the leaves and certainly as the leaves are shed. Sagebrush (*Artemisia tridentata*), on the other hand, did not so change the soil characteristics. It had long been assumed that the occurrence of greasewood on salty soil must be due to a special physiology which allowed it to tolerate the salt—a physiology not shared by the sagebrush. Fireman and Hayward's work indicated that greasewood not only tolerated the salt but was, in some cases at least, partially responsible for salt in the upper layer of the soil.

The importance of soil in desert ecology was clearly shown in what is probably the most detailed and intensive study of desert ecology ever to be performed. This model investigation was carried out in the Great Salt Lake Desert (Dugway Valley) by the University of Utah under contract with the United States Army Chemical Corps. Beginning about 1952, it lasted over a decade, cost several million dollars, and involved about 32 scientists and many technicians from several disciplines (botany, zoology, microbiology). During much of its duration, it was under the direction of E. Dean Vest. Many of the interesting findings remain to be published.

Vest describes eight distinct plant communities (Fig. 29-8) with their concurrent animal (including insects, etc.) populations. Each is associated with a specific soil (Fig. 29-9). The sandy soils with the most available water have by far the largest number of plant and animal species with their associated pathogens. Topography and soil texture result in considerable surface redistribution of water, and this is also of importance in determining the communities. Of course, ultimate plant distribution is determined by the physiology of the plants involved—their ability to withstand highly negative water potentials. The physiology of the associated animals is equally important.

29.6 THE ALPINE TUNDRA

The **alpine tundra** is a developed vegetation type consisting of low, mostly herbaceous plants growing above timberline in high mountains. It offers another situation in which plants are under stress, in that environmental conditions approach the extremes for survival. There have been more studies on the physiological ecology of the alpine tundra than can be reviewed here, yet the surface has only been scratched, and more problems are evident than solutions. We will summarize a few ideas in the following paragraphs.

29.6.1 Environment

Austrian scientists, particularly Walter Tranquillini, Walter Larcher, and Arthur Pisek,

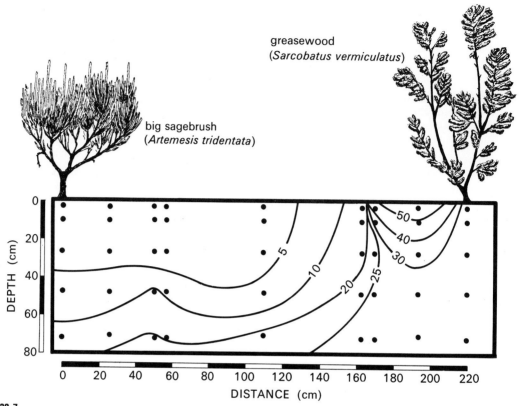

Figure 29-7

Salt concentrations in the soil (numbers in lines = percentage exchangeable sodium) as a function of position under a sagebrush plant and under a greasewood plant in the Escalante Desert of southern Utah. Note high sodium under greasewood. Dots are sampling points. (From M. Fireman and H. E. Hayward, 1952, *Botan. Gaz.* 114:143–154.)

have been particularly active in studying the physiology of plants at high elevations. Tranquillini has reviewed some of their findings rather recently, and much of the information in the following paragraphs is summarized from his review.

Two factors in the alpine tundra result from the increased elevations and are particularly important in controlling plant response: Light intensity increases due to a thinner layer of scattering atmosphere, and temperature decreases. Light intensities prove to be considerably higher than at lower elevations, even when the sky is overcast, because the clouds often

extend below the tundra level. The diffused light measurable within clouds shrouding the tundra is of much higher intensity than below the clouds in the valleys. Highest intensities are obtained when the sky is partly cloudy, so that the direct rays of the sun and reflected rays from the clouds fall on the same area. Intensities may be as high as 2.2 Cal./cm^2/min. (solar constant = 2.0 Cal./cm^2/min.), or 16,000 ft-c in one measurement when clear sky intensities equalled 13,000 ft-c.

Sufficiently warm air rises, expanding and cooling as it does so. The **adiabatic lapse rate**, or rate of cooling as dry air rises, is about −1.0°C/

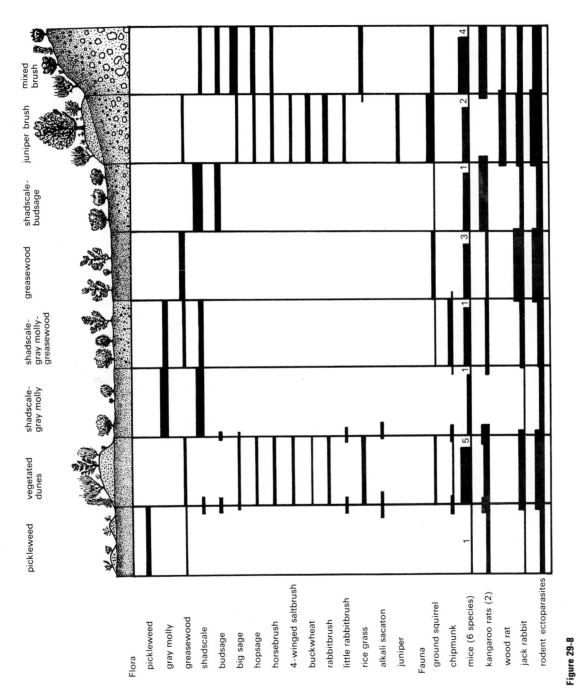

Figure 29-8

Distribution of plants and animals in the desert near Dugway, Utah. Note diversity of species on vegetated dunes, juniper brush, mixed brush. (Data from E. D. Vest, 1962, "Biotic communities in the Great Salt Lake Desert," Institute of Environmental Biological Research, Ecology and Epizoology Series No. 73. University of Utah, Salt Lake City.)

PLANT COMMUNITY

SOIL TEXTURE (percent, sand, silt, clay)

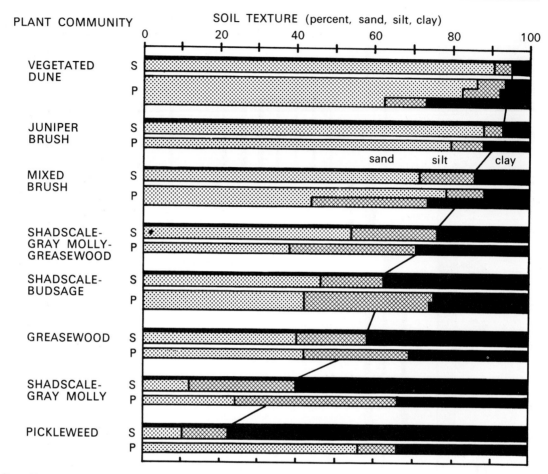

Figure 29-9

Soil textures for the desert communities of Fig. 29-8. S (with the heavy bar) refers to soil collected from exposed areas between the plants. P refers to soil collected under the plants, and in some cases more than one sample is shown. Slanted lines connect percentages of clay in samples taken from between the plants. (Data from E. D. Vest, 1962, "Biotic communities in the Great Salt Lake Desert," Institute of Environmental Biological Research, Ecology and Epizoology Series No. 73. University of Utah, Salt Lake City.)

100 meters. If the temperature gradient in the atmosphere is less than this, dry air will not rise due to convection (Fig. 29-10). For example, given air at one elevation at 20°C, atmospheric stability will be achieved if the temperature gradient is such that air 1,000 meters higher is 15°C or warmer. Hence air in high mountains can remain cooler than air in the valleys. Because the layer of air between contains moisture and carbon dioxide which absorb infrared radiation, plant and soil surfaces at high elevations will cool more rapidly by radiation into space, especially at night. As a result, alpine temperatures are virtually always lower than temperatures at lower elevations. Since plants in the arctic tundra closely resemble those in the alpine tundra, and low temperature is the factor most common to the two habitats, this

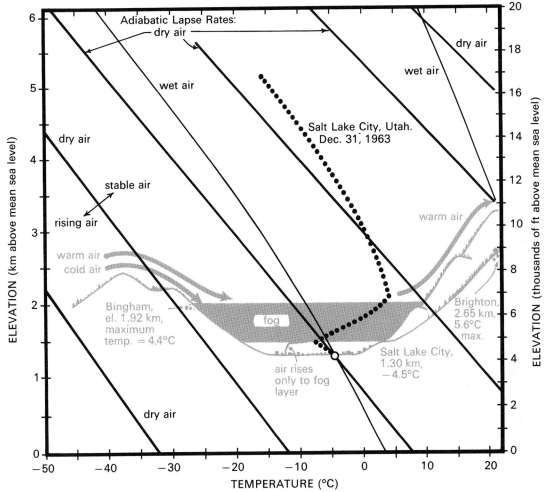

Figure 29-10

The adiabatic lapse rates. Unbroken lines indicate stable temperatures at various elevations. Note different slopes for lapse rates of wet and dry air. For wet air, the lines are slightly curved; for dry air, they are straight. Actual temperature data as a function of elevation are shown by the dotted line. Data were taken above Salt Lake City, Utah, on December 31, 1953. Gray part of the figure shows schematically conditions in the Salt Lake Valley and vicinity on that date. As indicated by the temperature, there is a strong inversion, and much of the valley was full of fog, although air movement occurred upward in the bottom part of the valley (to the bottom of the inversion layer). Winds were moving from the west (left to right on the figure). Cold air could penetrate the fog layer, but warm air moved above it. Nature of the inversion is strongly indicated by higher temperatures at Bingham and Brighton than in the Salt Lake Valley at a much lower elevation. (Curves from U.S. Department of Commerce, Weather Bureau chart supplied by A. Richardson, who also furnished the data. See also Lois M. Cox, 1967, *Utah Science* 28(2):53.)

low temperature may well be the factor most responsible for the tundra type of vegetation.

Frequent high winds are also characteristic of most alpine areas. They are typically gusty rather than constant, and such a variability in

level of a given environmental factor is also highly characteristic of alpine regions. Figure 29-11 shows typical temperature, light intensity, humidity, and wind data for an alpine area (see also Fig. 6-14). Temperatures often fluctuate

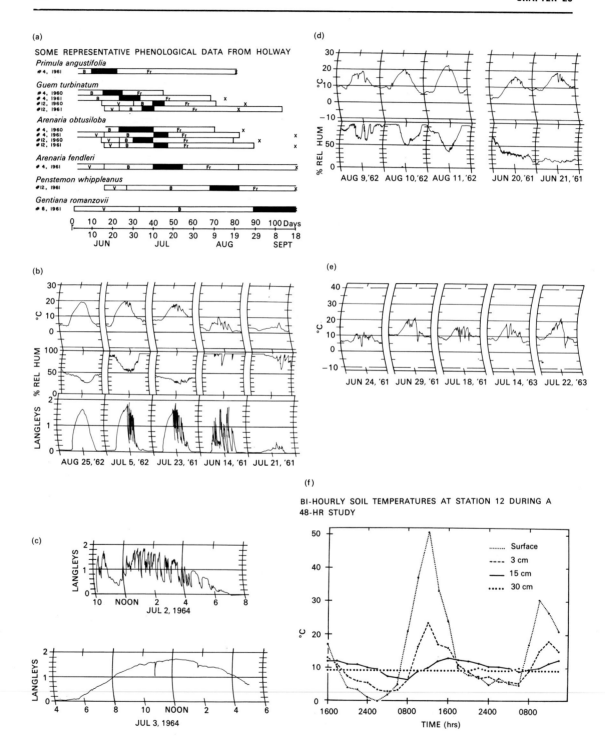

(a)

SOME REPRESENTATIVE PHENOLOGICAL DATA FROM HOLWAY

Primula angustifolia
4, 1961

Guem turbinatum
4, 1960
4, 1961
12, 1960
12, 1961

Arenaria obtusiloba
4, 1960
4, 1961
12, 1960
12, 1961

Arenaria fendleri
4, 1961

Penstemon whippleanus
12, 1961

Gentiana romanzovii
8, 1961

0   10   20   30   40   50   60   70   80   90 100 Days
    10   20   30   10   20   30   9   19   29   8   18
    JUN   JUL   AUG   SEPT

(b)

AUG 25,'62   JUL 5, '62   JUL 23, '61   JUN 14, '61   JUL 21, '61

(c)

10 NOON 2 4 6 8
JUL 2, 1964

4 6 8 10 NOON 2 4 6
JUL 3, 1964

(d)

AUG 9,'62   AUG 10,'62   AUG 11,'62   JUN 20,'61   JUN 21,'61

(e)

JUN 24, '61   JUN 29, '61   JUL 18, '61   JUL 14, '63   JUL 22, '63

(f)

BI-HOURLY SOIL TEMPERATURES AT STATION 12 DURING A 48-HR STUDY

········ Surface
‐ ‐ ‐ 3 cm
——— 15 cm
•••••• 30 cm

TIME (hrs)

over a wide range during each daily cycle and over considerable ranges within relatively short intervals during the day or night. Light intensity fluctuates extremely on partially cloudy days. We might well expect that response of alpine plants is strongly adjusted to this fluctuating environment.

In many alpine regions, water is seldom limiting, and frequently humidities are relatively high. In ranges far inland such as the Rocky Mountains, however, periods of drought lasting several weeks may occur. Winter snow accumulation has a profound effect upon alpine plant distribution, since snowbanks may last until late into the summer.

29.6.2 Transpiration and Water Balance

Depending upon specific habitat in the tundra, some plants transpire much larger quantities of water than others. In some plants, there is a decrease in transpiration rate around noon (Chapter 6). The actual amounts of water transpired are comparable to those transpired by lowland plants. In Austria, species that transpire the most still utilize only about one quarter of the water available throughout the year, and much precipitation falls during summer, so water is never limiting during the growing season. In the Colorado Rockies, however, periods of drought may limit plant growth. In later winter, water may become severely

limiting to some alpine plants because the ground is frozen. Plants particularly sensitive to desiccation may require snow protection to survive (e.g., *Rhododendron* spp.), while others can be exposed during the entire winter. Many plants in the Colorado Rockies can survive winter exposure, particularly cushion plants such as *Silene acaulis* and even *Geum rossii* (a perennial rosette plant) which may also grow in snow accumulation areas. Much of the Colorado tundra is blown free of snow during most of the winter and is snow-covered only after spring storms, during which wet and heavy snow falls without much wind.

29.6.3 Frost Resistance

It is difficult to separate the effects of winter drought from those of freezing. Frost hardiness may be relatively low in tundra plants during the summer. Although summer frosts are common, temperatures drop at most to only a few degrees below freezing. Frost hardiness increases from midsummer on, reaching a peak at midwinter. Sugar concentrations and osmotic potentials parallel this, osmotic potential becoming more negative with the development of frost hardiness. There are exceptions, however, indicating that frost hardiness is probably not caused by this increase in solute concentration.

Pinus cembra may withstand winter tem-

Figure 29-11

Some representative phenological and weather data from the alpine vegetation zone. (a) Phenological data applying to several species as indicated. B = buds, dark bar indicates flowering condition, Fr = fruits, V = vegetative, and X = shedding of seeds. Note that flowering occurs throughout the season depending upon species; that flowering may be strongly influenced by year (*Geum*) as well as position (stations no. 4, no. 12 at different elevations—both *Geum* and *Arenaria*). (b) representative temperature, humidity, and light intensity data for several days beginning with a cloudless day on the left and developing into an extremely stormy day on the right. (c) Light intensity data from Independence Pass, Colorado. Upper, partly cloudy conditions; lower, a nearly cloudless day. (d) Temperature and humidity for days when humidity is a virtual mirror image of temperature (left), and for days when humidity changes independently of temperature (right). (e) Rapid and extreme temperature changes. (f) Soil temperatures as a function of depth and time. Note the extreme fluctuation at the surface and the virtually steady temperatures at 30 cm depth. (Except for (c), data were from the False Mummy Pass area of alpine tundra on the northern border of Rocky Mountain National Park, Colorado. From F. B. Salisbury et al., 1968, *Botan. Gaz.* 129: 16–32.)

peratures of $-42°C$. Several other Austrian plants could withstand temperatures from -24 to $-38°C$, but others were severely damaged when temperatures dropped below $-20°C$. This latter group requires snow protection for survival.

29.6.4 Photosynthesis

Photosynthesis of alpine plants is highly efficient compared to plants of lower elevations (Table 29-1). Light intensities that bring about saturation are also unusually high, and they become higher with increasing elevations where temperatures are lower. Saturation values as high as 7,500–9,000 ft-c have been observed (compared to 1,000–3,000 ft-c for many lowland species). The optimum temperature for photosynthesis of alpine plants is also lower than that for lowland species. Values for tundra plants may range around 12–15°C, whereas plants of warmer climates photosynthesize optimally at 25–30°C. Minimum photosynthesis temperatures are usually around -5 to $-2°C$, but photosynthesis has been detected at $-14°C$. O. L. Lange in Germany reported that photosynthesis of lichens had an *optimum* at -10 to $0°C$! The minimum temperature value at which photosynthesis occurred was $-23°C$. The lichens live at higher elevations than any other plant (as high as 6,200 m). Alpine plants can also more efficiently utilize carbon dioxide at lower partial pressures than can lowland plants.

The net photosynthesis (photosynthesis compared to respiration) varies as might be expected, but Tranquillini found that photosynthetic levels are greatly reduced on days following exceptionally cold nights, particularly if frost occurred during the night. This response could establish the upper tree limit (timberline). If trees cannot assimilate by photosynthesis more carbohydrate than is used up in respiration, they cannot build new wood and therefore

TABLE 29-1

PHOTOSYNTHESIS OF ALPINE PLANTS COMPARED TO OTHERS[a]

Plant	Location	Range of photosynthetic rates (mg C/dm^2/hr)
Sieversia reptans, Doronicum Clusii, and *Ranunculus glacialus*	Alpine tundra (2,600 m. above sea level)	18–27
Sun plants	Low elevations	10–20
Shade plants	Low elevations	4–16
Cultivated plants	Low elevations	20–30

[a] Data from E. Cartellier, quoted by W. Tranquillini, *Ann. Rev. of Plant Physiol.* 15:345–362 (1964).

cannot survive. In the spring, respiration capacity is restored much more rapidly than is photosynthetic capacity.

A factor related to photosynthesis is the destruction of chlorophyll by high light intensities. In the winter, chlorophyll levels may drop to one-third of summer levels. The yellowing of such plants (e.g., *Pinus* spp.) is readily apparent.

29.6.5 Growth and Development

In recent years several scientists have begun to study morphogenesis of alpine plants as a function of environment. W. Dwight Billings at Duke University and his students have pioneered in these studies. In one investigation they collected examples of *Oxyria digyna* (mountain sorrel) from several latitudinal locations (Chapter 26). They discovered that all responded as long-day plants, but that those collected from more northern latitudes had much longer critical daylengths. George G. Spomer has worked with Salisbury on the physiological ecology of *Geum rossii*. He has demonstrated the importance of root temperature in growth of the plant and studied effects of light and temperature on dormancy and flowering. Plants would go into dormancy in response to daily average temperatures of 8°C or less, yet in the field the same dormancy symptoms became apparent during the middle of August when temperatures were at or near the maximum for the season. There was no daylength effect on dormancy or flowering. Flower primordia are formed in the field during July, and mature flowers appear immediately after plants begin to grow the following spring. Yet no combinations of temperature or daylength would result in flower primordia formation in growth chambers. There are several intriguing problems awaiting study in this area.

29.7 EXOBIOLOGY

In recent years interest has been developing in the possibility of life on other planets. It is apparent from developing theories in the field of astronomy that planetary systems must be the rule rather than the exception. This being the case, it has been estimated by several astronomers that there may be on the order of 10^{18} planets in the universe that would be very similar to the earth. Steven Dole estimated that there may be over fifty planets within 100 light-years of the earth that are similar enough to earth to support human life without any modification. There are clearly many different kinds of planets, as is evident from those in our own solar system. Surely life must exist somewhere besides on earth, and it could even be the rule in the universe. This growing conviction has had important implications for thinking in biology, resulting in a rapid broadening of past viewpoints. Previous research has been concerned with a definition and study of the *norm*; **exobiology** (the study of life on other planets) is concerned with the *extremes* permitting survival. Based upon what is known of the biology of organisms on earth, we can try to imagine life under other conditions.

We can start to formulate a science of exobiology by considering the question of whether there is life on Mars. This planet has an atmosphere, although a very thin one (pressures perhaps as low as 6–20 millibars). Carbon dioxide is present, but oxygen is not. Water is present in quantities large enough to form a polar cap, occasional clouds, and certain other phenomena visible through our telescopes. By our standards, however, available water on Mars is extremely limiting. The thin atmosphere would permit penetration of ultraviolet light from the sun and loss of infrared radiant energy at night. Temperatures may drop to tens of degrees below zero every night over the entire dark side of the planet. Daytime temperatures during the summer may reach levels as high as 20–30°C at the soil surface.

In spite of these extremely harsh environmental conditions (by our standards), Mars exhibits a phenomenon highly suggestive of the presence of life. Markings that fade out during the winter reappear with the coming of Martian spring, darkening occurring first next to the melting polar cap. A wave of darkening then progresses gradually toward the equator as the polar cap recedes, until full development is finally reached. Attempts to explain these observations in terms other than living organisms have not been very successful.

Our consideration of life on planets such as Mars must obviously be closely related to our study of the physiology of life under stress. It may be that Martian "plants" would not be stressed in their environment, but surely our plants would be extremely stressed if they were transplanted there. Since we can only think in terms of those organisms with which we are familiar, it is natural to consider what is known about stress physiology of earth plants in relation to the possibilities of life on Mars. This would also hold true for any other hypothetical planet very different from our own.

In view of our discussion above about the

ultimate lower temperature limits for survival, one may suppose that Martian "plants" might rather easily become adapted to the extremely low temperatures every night. The mechanism of adaptation would require frost hardiness equalling the best earthly precedents plus an ability to achieve maximum metabolism as soon as temperatures increased a few tens of degrees. The lack of oxygen probably requires other oxidation-reduction systems. This has stimulated some fascinating experiments carried out by Sanford Siegel, then at the Union Carbide and Carbon Chemical Laboratories in New York. Siegel found that winter rye and other plants would live surprisingly well under simulated Martian conditions. In some experiments, day temperatures were 25°C and night temperatures −20°C. Oxygen was absent, and total pressures (CO_2 and N_2) were around 16 millibars. Water was present only at extremely depressed vapor pressures (dew point −60°C). Under these conditions winter rye plants germinated and grew for several days, finally being killed by an infestation of common fungi that were normally only saprophytic and not parasitic. Siegel made the interesting observation that plants could withstand nightly freezing only in an oxygen-free atmosphere. The converse also seemed to be true; plants could stand a lack of oxygen only if they were frozen every night! These totally unexpected findings have broadened considerably our concepts of stress physiology. In further experiments, Siegel was even able to germinate several species of onion seeds in high-ammonia atmospheres. More recently he has found a fungus, previously unknown, which will grow in the presence of high levels of ammonia.

The low availability of water is a particularly interesting problem, yet we are finding examples of organisms that can obtain water from extremely dry atmospheres or from very high salt solutions. The thermodynamics of water movement, discussed in early chapters, is highly important in these considerations. Our hypothetical Martian organism might extract water from the atmosphere or retain with great tenacity that which has already been extracted from the atmosphere or the soil. In a practical situation a monomolecular film of such compounds as hexadecanol[4] will retard evaporation of water much more than passage of carbon dioxide and oxygen. Such a system could be of considerable value to a Martian organism, although experiments designed to see if earth plants could be covered with such materials, preventing transpiration but allowing photosynthesis and respiration, have so far met with only a very limited degree of success.

The ultraviolet radiation, long thought to be lethal to any kind of life on a planet such as Mars, may not be such a serious factor after all. As indicated in Chapter 23, even certain higher plants of earth (especially Austrian pine seedlings) could survive an entire growing season of the levels of ultraviolet present on the surface of Mars.

Exobiology will probably develop in future years, and of course if life is discovered on Mars (possibly as soon as the early 1970s), then the science will blossom rapidly. In the meantime, it has provided an interesting source of mental stimulation for the traditional biological scientist. In a sort of ultimate stretching of plant physiological theory, one contemplates new biochemistries and new life systems that will allow survival under the most extreme environmental conditions.

---

[4] Martin Blank, 1962. Monolayers: permeability to several gases. In: Victor K. La Mer (ed.), *Retardation of Evaporation by Monolayers: Transport Processes.* Academic Press, N.Y. and London. p. 94.

Advancing Frontiers

In plant physiology, so many workers at so many laboratories are publishing data that one or two authors cannot read and assimilate the material rapidly enough to produce a completely up-to-date and comprehensive textbook. This would be true even if textbook publication were instantaneous, but, of course, it is not. As the final stages of our book approached, we decided to ask help from over 50 of our colleagues, largely in the United States and some in Europe. Most answered our inquiries, sometimes with continuing correspondence. In general, the replies indicated a high current interest in growth regulators, phytochrome, photosynthesis, and photorespiration—in that order—but about 30 other topics were also mentioned. We updated as much as possible in galleys and pageproofs, but it seemed appropriate to discuss some topics further in a special section. Here we present a few new ideas, indicating the rapidly changing and developing status characteristic of certain areas of our science. A few selected references are included (nearly 700 were available in preparing this section), but searching for such references will primarily be the student's responsibility. Unless they are necessary in finding an article, titles and even authors' names are omitted here and journal names are abbreviated as much as possible.*

Pageproofs for the first few chapters were examined by Peter Ray. He brought up two matters which could not be corrected in proof. First, in the discussion of hydration of colloids in Chapter 4, hydrogen bonding should have been emphasized. Second, in Section 3.3.1A and Figure 3-4, we indicated that increasing temperature increases free energy and hence water potential, so that diffusion would occur

*AJB = *Amer. Jour. Bot.*
BBA = *Biochem. Biophys. Acta*
CJB = *Can. Jour. Bot.*
JBC = *Jour. Biol. Chem.*
N = *Nature*
PNAS = *Proc. Nat. Acad. Sci.*
PP = *Plant Physiol.*
S = *Science*

from areas of warm water toward areas of cooler water. Mathematical discussion of this topic requires irreversible thermodynamics, which were not introduced in this text, but it seems clear that water potential increases with temperature, since vapor pressure, a function of water potential, increases (Fig. 6-17). Yet Ray pointed out that some calculations apparently indicate a decrease in free energy with increasing temperature (see D. C. Spanner, 1964, *Introduction to Thermodynamics*, Academic Press, p. 247). We have since found that the topic is indeed controversial. The phenomenon of water movement across membranes in response to temperature differences and resulting in a buildup of pressure on one side was reported in the literature as early as 1907 and was called thermo-osmosis. Most experiments have been done with artificial membranes, but research for a master's thesis at Utah State University (1966, G. S. Campbell) used living potato tissue, as well as some other plant tissues. In the great majority of cases, water moved in such systems from warm to cool areas, as suggested in Figure 3-4 and by effects of temperature on vapor pressure. Many measurements of water movement in soils in response to temperature gradients have shown that movement occurs from warm to cool areas. The few exceptions reported are probably due to secondary effects of temperature on solutes. Some authors have suggested that the membrane might determine the direction of flow, but this is contrary to the thermodynamic generalization that the final states are independent of the path (unless energy is in some way expended by the membrane).

Stomatal mechanisms remain controversial. It now seems clear that stomatal opening in response to CO_2-free air and light specifically requires the presence of potassium ions (1969 *PP* 44:230; 1968 *PP* 43:1953; 1968 *S* 160:784). Experiments in which epidermal strips were floated on solutions indicated that the light-stimulated uptake of potassium plus a nonspecific anion was sufficient to account for the osmotic changes necessary for stomatal opening. Yet Levitt continues to champion his

709

modified classical theory (page 90), and in the potassium experiments a decrease in starch also correlated with stomatal opening. Potassium may act catalytically as well as osmotically. The highly specific requirement for potassium is indeed striking and certainly one of the first such highly specific physiological requirements for this cation known in plants. Incidentally, our statement on page 86 that plasmodesmata do not occur between guard cells and adjacent epidermal cells has been shown to be incorrect for some species (1968 *CJB* 45:1603).

Freezing of xylem sap in certain gymnosperms *can* occur without producing cavitation, although cavitation is produced when sap is frozen in the large vessels of various angiosperms (1967 *PP* 42:55).

Several interesting facts have been discovered in relation to membranes. For example, the plasmalemma has been confirmed as an important selective membrane (1969 *PP* 44:301) and seems (in contrast to evidence in Chapter 8) to be the site of both the low affinity and high affinity ion transport systems; enzymatic activities have been discovered within the vacuole, perhaps associated with membranes (1968 *Planta* 80:169); and membrane transport proteins are being detected and characterized (1968 *S* 162:632). Other effects, such as phytochrome localization on membranes and ATP formation in conjunction with membranes, will be discussed below.

Questions are being raised about the validity of the mass flow hypothesis for phloem transport. These are based primarily upon experiments with tritiated water, in which the water may move at rates only 1/40 those expected on the basis of mass flow (1968 *PP* 43:1845). We feel that the defense of mass flow presented in Chapter 9 remains convincing. Could the labelled water be exchanging with unlabelled water along the translocation pathway, accounting for the apparent discrepancy?

There is high interest in a protein called extensin, which is usually (1968 *AJB* 55:907) found almost exclusively in cell walls and which is very rich in hydroxyproline. This protein is thought to be attached to noncellulosic polysaccharides by glysocidic attachment of the hydroxyl groups of the hydroxyproline to arabinose of the polysaccharide (1967 *N* 216:1322). In this way, it could cross link much cell wall material, restricting cell expansion. The existence of such a protein is thus potentially interesting in relation to growth of cells and influences of auxin upon wall plasticity. The polysaccharide composition of cell walls is being more carefully defined, and the sugar residues are relatively constant within species and closely related varieties but vary considerably between unrelated species (1968 *PP* 43:914).

The chloroplasts and mitochondria are proving to be partially but not entirely genetically autonomous organelles (1967 *Progress in Nucleic Acid Research and Molecular Biology* 6:143). The DNA of each is distinct from that of the nucleus in base composition (no 5-methyl cytosine detected), density, and therefore in genetic information (1966 *S* 153:1269; 1966 *PNAS* 55:1600; 1969 *PP* 44:377). Each organelle contains a DNA polymerase capable of

replicating this DNA, an RNA polymerase capable of transcribing it into RNA, and the transfer-RNA and distinct ribosomes to translate messenger-RNA into specific enzymes. The DNA of mitochondria from cells of certain higher animals is in the form of a closed ring, as in certain bacteria, but this is apparently not true for mitochondrial DNA of fungi and higher plants (1968 *PNAS* 61:245). Chloroplast DNA seems to exist in fibrils, not rings (1968 *Jour. Mol. Biol.* 31:627). Interesting problems for the future are to determine how many separate molecules of DNA (how many "chromosomes" or nucleoids) exist in each organelle, whether these are all different from one another, whether gene control is similar to that in bacteria (which also lack histones), how DNA is partitioned between products of dividing chloroplasts and mitochondria, and what substances are normally provided to mitochondria and chloroplasts by decoding of nuclear genes; i.e., for what compounds these organelles are not autonomous. Finally, chloroplasts will continue to be critically compared to blue-green algae, and mitochondria compared to bacteria, perhaps especially by nucleic acid hybridization studies, to determine the possibility that evolution of such algae and bacteria inside prehistoric host cells may have led to what we now know as the subcellular organelles active in photosynthesis and in respiration.

The Mitchell chemiosmotic theory of how ATP is synthesized in chloroplasts and mitochondria is receiving increased support. The lack of evidence for high-energy phosphorylated protein intermediates participating in ATP synthesis is only one of the reasons for rejection of the classical chemical explanation. Further direct evidence for the chemiosmotic theory is also available. It is now clear that ATP can by synthesized from ADP and Pi in both mitochondria (1967 *Fed. Proc.* 25:1370) and in chloroplasts (1967 *Fed. Proc.* 25:1361) after experimentally creating pH gradients across the membranes by buffer treatment. According to this theory, ionization of water and expulsion of hydroxyl ions toward the low pH side of the membrane and of hydrogen ions toward the high pH side then apparently lowers the chemical potential of water in the membranes. This dehydration presumably facilitates, by mass action, the synthesis of ATP. In these experiments with buffers, the normal flow of electrons through the electron-transport systems is not essential for ATP formation; in isolated chloroplasts, for example, the process occurs in darkness. Inside the plant, of course, normal electron flow stimulates the ionization of water that leads to the pH gradient (1968 *Zeitsh f. Naturf.* 23:1571). We must still learn how the membrane components active in this process are arranged so that they can expel protons predominantly in one direction. Protons accumulate on the outside of mitochondrial membranes and on the inside of chloroplast grana membranes, yet we do not know why this difference exists. The action of uncouplers of oxidative or photosynthetic phosphorylation, formerly explained by the classical chemical hypothesis, can now apparently be accounted for by the chemiosmotic theory. Such uncouplers cause mitochondrial, chloroplast, plasmalemma, and artificial lipid membranes to become leaky to protons or monovalent cations, thus destroying the pH gradients responsible for ATP formation (i.e., 1968 *PNAS* 69:484).

A problem related to the chemiosmotic theory of phosphorylation is the likely function of membrane-imposed pH gradients upon solute absorption across the plasmalemma, tonoplast, and other cellular membranes, as well as the membranes of mitochondria and chloroplasts. If pH gradients can lead to ATP synthesis, it is likely that ATP hydrolysis can cause charge separations responsible for solute transport. Thus the known function of ATP in driving ion uptake in both plant and animal cells may eventually be explained, at least in part, on a chemiosmotic basis.

The Hatch and Slack photosynthetic pathway, in which the most important first product of CO_2 fixation is oxaloacetate, has been found in additional grass species which have originated in tropical climates (1968 *CJB* 46:207). These grasses belong to the panicoids, chloridoid-eragrostoid taxonomic groups, and include the agronomically important species corn (*Zea mays* L.). In addition to these grasses, some species of *Cyperus* (sedges) and of the dicotyledonous *Amaranthus* and *Atriplex* genera also depend primarily upon this pathway (1968 *Phyto. Chem.* 7:375). Several important differences in these plants compared to those depending mainly on ribulose-diphosphate carboxylase have been observed. The light intensities giving maximum photosynthetic rates are higher; the rates at light saturation are about twice as high; the compensation points are lower; the temperature optima for photosynthesis are higher (about 35° C vs. 10 to 25° C for other species); they photosynthesize much more effectively at low CO_2 concentrations (due to the greater affinity of phosphenolpyruvate carboxylase than ribulose-diphosphate carboxylase for CO_2); they have a well-defined chloroplast-containing sheath of cells surrounding the vascular bundles, which may increase their ability to translocate carbohydrates; and they do not exhibit increased respiration rates in light or in the presence of oxygen (i.e., they lack photorespiration).

Photorespiration should be contrasted with photooxidation, and is presently attributed to the oxidation by glycolic acid oxidase of glycolic acid formed during photosynthesis. Glycolate oxidation does not appear to occur in chloroplasts, as once was believed, but in small, recently discovered organelles, called peroxisomes or microbodies (1969 *PP* 44:242). Peroxisomes are much more abundant in species in which photorespiration and ribulose-diphosphate carboxylase are important than in species having the Hatch and Slack pathway. Apparently the breakdown of glycolic acid formed in chloroplasts in light decreases the net fixation of CO_2, thus reducing the over-all productivity of plants possessing active photorespiration. Genetic selection for greater conservation of fixed carbon to increase dry matter production among temperate grasses and other crops is now a reasonable goal (1969 *S* 163:78).

Further information about the way phosphoglycerate and other sugar phosphates are formed from oxaloacetate in such plants is needed. It now appears that carbon four (the carbon directly arising from CO_2) of oxaloacetate is transferred to an unknown acceptor to form 3-PGA, while the other three carbon atoms of oxaloacetate form pyruvate. Pyruvate regenerates phosphenolpyruvate in the presence of ATP by action of an enzyme named phosphopyruvatesynthetase, the reaction also releasing AMP and Pi (1968 *Phyto. Chem.* 7:375). Important to our understanding of the Hatch and Slack pathway is to learn which compound accepts the carboxyl group of oxaloacetate to form 3-PGA.

The mechanism of nitrogen fixation is being worked out in considerable detail (1968 *Ann. Rev. Biochem.* 37:331). Active cell-free extracts from several nitrogen-fixing bacteria, including bacteroids from root nodules, have been prepared (1968 *PP* 43:1906). Leghemoglobin is located outside the bacteroids, perhaps between these bodies and the membrane of host origin which surrounds them (1968 *Exp. Cell Res.* 49:148). Cell-free extracts from bacteroids do not require leghemoglobin to fix nitrogen, and the explanation for the close relation between the presence of this protein in root nodules and their ability to fix nitrogen must still be sought. The active cell-free extracts all contain two previously undiscovered proteins; one is a molybdenum- and iron-containing protein, molybdoferredoxin, and the other is a smaller iron-containing protein called azoferredoxin (1968 *BBA* 153:777). In the presence of these two proteins, magnesium ions, ATP, and an adequate source of electrons, such as reduced ferredoxin, nitrogen fixation occurs. Thus the essential components for fixation are now known, yet experiments are still needed to define their precise functions and the intermediates formed during reduction of the nitrogen molecule.

The 1966 discovery that the nitrogen-fixing enzymes also reduce acetylene to ethylene allows great opportunity for ecological studies of nitrogen fixation. The measurement of ethylene production from acetylene in water samples from seas, lakes, streams, and soils can be measured by gas chromatographic separation and measurement of ethylene. Compared to surveys with ^{15}N, the method is much easier, sensitive, and less expensive (1967 *PNAS* 68:2071). Information about rates of nitrogen fixation in various environments will now be much easier to obtain, and additional nitrogen-fixing organisms will undoubtedly be discovered (1967 *S* 158:1426).

The area of plant growth and development continues to be of high interest. Numerous workers are trying to discover how the Jacob-Monod model applies to development in plants, how genes are repressed and derepressed, how enzymes are induced or otherwise activated (1969, Filner, Ray, and Varner, Enzyme induction in higher plants. *Science*. In press.). We will discuss several aspects of these problems below, but there are numerous possibilities which we will not be able to discuss. The student might find interesting papers on development by perusing the titles of nearly any of the journals which publish plant physiological papers. Only a small portion of these papers is mentioned below.

At the level of the genes themselves, it has been discovered that many DNA nucleotide sequences (apparently genes) are repeated up to hundreds of times in a given nucleus (1968 *S* 161:529). The significance of this finding remains to be discovered.

If the genes are activated by removal of histones, as suggested in Chapter 17, then it is certainly of interest to discover that the amino acid sequences of one of six major histones is almost identical in pea plants and cows! Such an extremely high level of stability during evolutionary time must surely be of high physiological significance (1969 *JBC* 244:319).

The high current interest in our old friend auxin comes about because we may be on the verge of at last finding out something about its basic mode of action. This is discussed in Chapter 21 and in other chapters. Interest is heightened because of a controversy between those who suggest that auxins and other hormones act by derepression of genes with consequent RNA and enzyme synthesis, accounting for observed responses, and those who suspect that hormones act directly upon some cellular component(s) other than the genes (1969 *S* 163:1288; 1968, *Bioch. and Physiol. of Plt. Growth Substance*, Runge Press, Ottowa). Considerable evidence for an auxin stimulation of RNA synthesis now appears in the literature, but at the same time, auxin responses (including growth) observable within a few minutes after auxin application are being reported. This could hardly involve the synthesis of RNA. We may well have to decide that auxins act in various ways (as a single key may open several doors). Evidence concerning the mechanism of action of various animal hormones may well be applied to that of plant hormones. Several animal hormones are now known to cause physiological responses by way of a secondary messenger. This messenger, at least in most cases, is cyclic-AMP (a 3'–5' cyclic diester of AMP; 1968 *Ann. Rev. Biochem.* 37:149). The hormones stimulate production of cyclic-AMP from ATP at the plasma membranes. Cyclic-AMP then presumably moves to the nucleus, where it causes gene activation. A suggestion as to how such activation occurs is that it stimulates phosphorylation of histones, thus interfering with their repressive action. It is not yet clear how animal hormones, which are often more specific than plant hormones, can maintain their specificity if each act via the same secondary messenger, but differences in the physiological states of the responding target cells are undoubtedly involved.

Cyclic-AMP is also produced by bacteria, and, in fact, it appears to be the substance (acrasin) stimulating cell aggregation during the life cycle of slime molds (1967 *PNAS* 41:1152; Fig. 22-2). We expect to hear a report very soon as to whether higher plants also contain cyclic-AMP. If they do, we shall need to find out if it acts as a secondary messenger for plant hormones. There is evidence that the stimulation of RNA synthesis in isolated plant nuclei by both auxins (1968 Matthysse, *Plant Phys. Abstr.*) and gibberellic acid (1968 *PNAS* 59:269) requires the presence of some soluble substance, perhaps of cytoplasmic origin. It will be interesting to determine whether this substance could be cyclic-AMP. Regardless of its identity, the fact that auxins can cause very rapid responses prior to genetic transcription or translation might mean that hormones, in general, initially cause membrane changes. These changes might cause the known very rapid changes in protoplasmic streaming induced by auxins, and they might also lead to a secondary messenger which itself later activates genes. In any case, current researches finally offer hope of solving this old problem after 40 years of frustrated attempts.

The ethylene story continues to occupy the attention of many plant physiologists. Some workers had suspected that auxin acted only by stimulating ethylene production (Chapter 21). It is now recognized that the picture cannot be this simple. Ethylene is apparently evolved by plant tissues in response to a variety of inputs including damage. Ethylene has also been shown to cause the formation of particular enzymes, such as a peroxidase, and this apparently is via the derepression of genes. Numerous papers along these lines have been appearing in current issues of *Plant Physiology*, and much of the work was summarized at the abscission symposium at Fort Dietrick (Part B of September 1968 *PP*). It now appears that the damage caused by high concentrations of auxin is due to ethylene production (1969 *S* 163:1067). One absolute short-day plant (*Plumbago indica*) has been induced to flower in tissue culture with ethylene (1968 *Ann. Sci. Naturelles*, Botanique 12e Serie, 9:1–92). As a result of all of this work (and much more not mentioned here), ethylene has become a rather acceptable plant growth hormone.

If ethylene has become acceptable, certainly the same must be said for abscisic acid. We have already discussed most of the well-known findings related to this compound. Evidence is developing that abscisic acid is, as James Bonner suggests, a plant tranquilizer: a gene repressor. As indicated in the text, the gibberellins also appear to be acting at the gene level, although, as in the case of auxins, evidence is accumulating that they may act in other ways as well (e.g., on membrane permeability, 1968 *Biochem. Biophys. Res. Comm.* 33:2). In germination they may not be acting on genes (1969 *PP* 44:463); and even the effect on amylase in barley aleurone layers is now known to be only one of several such effects (1968 *Biochem. Biophys. Res. Comm.* 33:321). Plant physiologists now seem less preoccupied with the gibberellins and more concerned with the other growth-regulating substances and with the possibility that auxin action will finally be solved. Interest has been high in relation to the cytokinins (1968 *S* 161:974). It was thought that cytokinins acted by becoming a component of transfer-RNA, but it is now known that cytokinins which cannot be incorporated into RNA are still active, and their mechanism of action is not yet known (1969 *BioScience* 19:309; 1969 *S* 163:1288). At least one more native cytokinin is now known (dihydrozeaton), and other growth regulating compounds are becoming apparent (1967 *Planta* 72:258; 1969 *PP* 44:342).

Sometimes important plant physiological research is carried out in applied fields, remaining relatively unknown to most other plant physiologists. Such is the case with reaction wood. A friend supplied us with 37 abstracts of papers relating to this interesting topic (see Chapter 22). Virtually all of these papers were less than five years old. Reaction wood can be induced by a gravitational stimulus applied for a period as short as one day. Numerous studies relate to observations with light or electron microscopes. Cell wall hydration is being implicated in the phenomenon. Several experimental results indicate that tension wood may form in response to an auxin deficiency (or the presence of an auxin antagonist, such as TIBA), and that compression wood may form in response to high levels of auxin. There is evidence, however, that reaction wood forms not as a direct function of auxin concentration but rather in response to auxin gradients (1968 *Bot. Rev.* 34:51; 1965 *Planta* 64:224; 1968 *N* 208:406).

The problem of how phytochrome controls several morphogenetic processes is not solved, but information about it is accumulating rapidly. Phytochrome has been obtained in a highly pure state from etiolated annual rye (1968 *BBA* 168:46). It has a quaternary structure and appears to consist of a mixture of tetramers and hexamers of identical monomer polypeptide chains. These chains are apparently held together by non-covalent bonds. The amino acid composition has been determined, but the amino acid sequence has not yet been reported. This sequence is awaited with eagerness, because it will likely give clues as to some of the changes occurring upon absorption by phytochrome of red and far-red light. No cysteine or cystine molecules were found in this phytochrome, so no disulfide bridges can contribute to its secondary structure. Exposure of the molecule to red light did not cause any detectable decrease in the number of monomers associated as tetramers or hexomers, so the light effects apparently are not caused by a process involving association or dissociation of polypeptide chains. The transition from Pr to Pfr is accompanied by the formation of four detectable short-lived intermediates, two of which are thought to involve isomerization of the chromophore by a mechanism similar to that occurring during rhodopsin conversion in the visual process (1968 *PNAS* 61:1095). The other two intermediates might represent alternate structures of the protein itself. Unfortunately, the function of these four intermediates is not yet known, but the possibility will likely be investigated that they are involved in some of the high-energy reactions discussed in Chapter 23.

The intracellular location of phytochrome is being achieved. It appears that it is located on or in certain membranes (1967 *PNAS* 58:2130; 1969 *PP* 44:104). Earlier evidence indicated that it was located with the plasmalemma in algal cells, and it has more recently been found associated with the nuclear membrane of pea and oat seedlings (1968 *PNAS* 61:454). The plasmalemma location is consistent with a mechanism of action upon permeability, evidence for which was mentioned in Chapter 23. In addition to that evidence, it has recently been demonstrated that, in the presence of IAA, ascorbic acid, and certain cations, red light causes root tips to stick to negatively charged glassware (1968 *PNAS* 59:376). This effect can be observed within 30 seconds and is due to a change in electropotential of the root surfaces (1968 *S* 162:1016). Far-red light reverses this potential and, in the presence of ATP, causes the roots no longer to adhere to the glass (1968 *PP* 43:2070). Since the electropotential gradient must be due to alterations in the distribution of ions across the cellular membrane, it is clear that phytochrome affects membrane permeability, and that gene activation is not involved here. On the other hand, the association of phytochrome with the nuclear membrane causes us to suspect that the pigment here could indeed be influencing messenger-RNA and enzyme synthesis, perhaps by unknown effects on permeability of this membrane. In any case, if phytochrome should prove to be generally located on various cellular membranes, the varied influences that red and far-red light treatments have on different cells could be more easily explained. It is likely, for example, that light activation of the population of plasmalemma phytochromes will cause responses due to ion permeability changes only in cells which possess other properties necessary for these responses. In other cells, it may be that phytochrome molecules associated with the nuclear membrane or endoplasmic reticulum are the only ones capable of causing any detectable response. If this is true, it might help explain the frequent observation that the total extent of phytochrome conversion by red or far-red light does not correlate well with the magnitude of the physiological response being measured.

At least two interesting results relating to phototropism have been reported. It has been possible experimentally to reduce the carotenoids of coleoptiles to 20% of controls without reducing riboflavin. Phototropism remains unaffected, implying that riboflavin is the photoreceptor rather than carotene (1968 *Physiol. Plant.* 21:109). Secondly, it has been found that the action spectrum for second positive curvature is identical to that for first positive curvature, implying that the same pigment acts as the photoreceptor in both cases. This is interesting, since the kinetics for the two responses are quite different (1968 *PP* 43:1786).

In Chapter 24 on the Biological Clock, it was implied that Brown's hypothesis on exogenous timing had little evidence to support it. Brown's evidence now seems more impressive to us (1969 *CJB* 47:287).

It appears that a temperature-sensitive interconversion of gibberellin from a bound to a free form may control flowering in tulip bulbs (1969 *PP* 44:403). High Energy Light Reactions are being implicated in flowering (see abstracts of 1968 *Photobiology Congress*; 1967 *AJB* 54:241).

Unpublished work by David Gibby in Salisbury's laboratory strongly implies the significant participation of a flowering inhibitor in the cocklebur. Long-day leaf tissue (e.g., the basal half of a leaf) between short-day tissue (e.g., the tip half or a lower leaf) nullifies the effect of the short-day tissue, although it can be shown that the short-day tissue is producing florigen. Thus the long-day tissue may in some way interact with the florigen, resulting in its destruction. Effects cannot be explained simply on the basis of translocation.

We are also impressed with the extent to which knowledge of the physiology of flowering is being applied in fields such as ornamental horticulture (see USDA publications). In fact, numerous examples beyond those in Chapter 28 could be given to illustrate the application of basic plant physiology to agriculture. This applies particularly well to the area of photorespiration (see Widholm and Ogren, 1969 *Bot. Congress Abstracts*). Another example might be the chemical pruning of plants (1966 *S* 153:1382). Work is also continuing at an accelerated rate on mechanisms of plant disease resistance. An outstand-

ing development has been the production of a high lysine corn (1968 *Ag. Sci. Rev.* 6:1). Since this amino acid is essential for animal growth, this could be a significant finding in terms of the world food problem. Herbicide biochemistry is moving ahead rapidly. Support is accumulating for action of some herbicides at the gene level. For example, isolated chromatin (chromosomal material) from 2,4-D treated soybeans synthesizes RNA more rapidly than chromatin from controls (1968 *BBA* 169:35).

Work in physiological ecology also seems to be accelerating. Several papers on photosynthetic abilities of various native plants have appeared in recent issues of *Physiologia Plantarum*, for example. Levitt's sulfhydryl theory of frost resistance has been supported by at least one recent study (1969 *PP* 44:168). Another review on arctic-alpine physiological ecology has appeared (1968 *Biol. Rev.* 43:481). It should be apparent that the frontiers of plant physiology are advancing rapidly.

Bibliography

References to chapters in this book consist of general review articles, textbooks, and certain recent articles explaining or enlarging upon ideas in the chapters. No attempt has been made to include all recent references related to each topic, but with the aid of those included the student will be able to find much additional information.

A very important reference not inluded because of space limitations is the *Encyclopedia of Plant Physiology*, an 18-volume series of books edited by W. Ruhland. These books contain articles by many experts, treating in detail nearly all of the topics in this textbook. The student should also be aware of the *Annual Review of Plant Physiology*, which began in 1950. Most of the individual articles in the more recent reviews are cited under the chapters to which they are most related, but some of the older reviews are not cited. The *Annual Reviews of Biochemistry*, *Phytopathology*, and *Microbiology* usually also contain articles of interest to plant physiologists.

CHAPTER 1   REFERENCES

Other textbooks of plant physiology usually have discussions on the nature of life, science, and the role of plant physiology in modern life:

Bonner, J., and A. W. Galston. 1952. *Principles of Plant Physiology*. W. H. Freeman & Company, Publishers, San Francisco.

Curtis, O. F., and D. G. Clark. 1950. *An Introduction to Plant Physiology*. McGraw-Hill Book Company, Inc., New York.

Devlin, R. M. 1966. *Plant Physiology*. Reinhold Publishing Corporation, New York.

Ferry, J. F. 1959. *Fundamentals of Plant Physiology*. The Macmillan Company, New York.

Fogg, G. E. 1963. *The Growth of Plants*. Richard Clay and Co., Ltd., Bungay, Suffolk.

Galston, A. W. 1961. *The Life of the Green Plant*. Prentice-Hall, Inc., Englewood Cliffs, N.J.

James, W. O. 1963. *An Introduction to Plant Physiology*. Oxford University Press, London.

Leopold, A. C. 1964. *Plant Growth and Development*. McGraw-Hill Book Company, Inc., New York.

Levitt, J. 1954. *Plant Physiology*. Prentice-Hall, Inc., Englewood Cliffs, N.J.

Lundegårdh, H. 1966. *Plant Physiology*. American Elsevier Publishing Co., Inc., N.Y.

Meyer, B. S., D. B. Anderson, and R. H. Böhning. 1960. *Introduction to Plant Physiology*. D. Van Nostrand Company, Inc., Princeton, N.J.

Miller, E. C. 1938. *Plant Physiology*. McGraw-Hill Book Company, Inc., New York.

Ray, P. M. 1965. *The Living Plant*. Holt, Rinehart and Winston, Inc., New York.

Steward, F. C., A. D. Krikorian, and R. D. Holsten. 1966. *About Plants: Topics in Plant Biology*. Addison-Wesley Publishing Company, Inc., Reading, Mass.

Weevers, T. 1949. *Fifty Years of Plant Physiology*. Scheltema & Holkema's Boekhandel en Uitgeversmaatschappij N.V., Amsterdam.

Discussions of life and plant physiology can also be found in most modern textbooks of general botany or biology, such as the following:

Conquist, A. 1961. *Introductory Botany*. Harper & Row, Publishers, Inc., New York.

Platt, R. B., and G. K. Reid. 1967. *Bioscience*. Reinhold Publishing Corporation, New York.

Sinnott, E. W., and Katherine S. Wilson. 1963. *Botany: Principles and Problems.* McGraw-Hill Book Company, Inc., New York.

Sullivan, J. W. N. 1933. *The Limitations of Science.* The New American Library of World Literature, Inc., New York.

Walker, M. 1963. *The Nature of Scientific Thought.* Prentice-Hall, Inc., Englewood Cliffs, N.J.

Several books and articles also deal with the nature and origin of life:

Ehrensvard, G. 1961. *Life: Origin and Development.* University of Chicago Press, Chicago.

Mazia, D. 1966. "What is life?" In *Biology and the Exploration of Mars.* C. S. Pittendrigh, W. Vishniac, and J. P. T. Pearman [eds.]. pp. 25–40. Public. No. 1296, National Academy of Sciences, National Research Council, Washington, D.C.

Oparin, A. I. 1957. *The Origin of Life on the Earth.* (Translated from the Russian by Ann Synge.) Academic Press, Inc., New York.

Schrodinger, E. 1946. *What is Life?* The University Press, Cambridge, England.

Tax, S. [ed.]. 1960. *The Evolution of Life: Its Origin, History and Future.* University of Chicago Press, Chicago.

CHAPTER 2   REFERENCES

Bernal, J. D. 1965. "The structure of water and its biological implications." *Symposia of the Society for Experimental Biology* 19: 17–32.

Buswell, A. M., and W. H. Rodebush. 1956. "Water." *Scientific American* 194(4):76.

Christensen, H. N. 1964. *pH and Dissociation.* W. B. Saunders Company, Philadelphia.

Kohn, P. G. 1965. "Tables of some physical and chemical properties of water." *Symposia of the Society for Experimental Biology* 19:3–16.

Ling, G. N. 1967. "Effects of temperature on the state of water in the living cell." In *Thermobiology.* A. H. Rose [ed.]. pp. 5–24. Academic Press, Inc., New York.

Slatyer, R. O. 1967. *Plant-Water Relationships.* Academic Press, Inc., New York.

Wyllie, G. 1965. "Kinetic theory and transport in ice and water." *Symposia of the Society for Experimental Biology* 19:33–54.

CHAPTER 3   REFERENCES

The topics of this chapter are elaborated in general textbooks on physical chemistry, such as those listed below. Modern conventions of terminology and symbols should be studied in the more recent books, but concepts of interest to plant physiology often receive more attention in some of the older texts.

Castellan, G. W. 1964. *Physical Chemistry.* Addison-Wesley Publishing Company, Inc., Reading, Mass.

Daniels, F., and R. A. Alberty. 1955. *Physical Chemistry.* John Wiley & Sons, Inc., New York.

Glasstone, S. 1946. *The Elements of Physical Chemistry.* D. Van Nostrand Company, Inc., Princeton, N.J.

Noyes, A. A., and M. S. Sherrill. 1938. *A Course of Study in Chemical Principles.* The Macmillan Company, New York.

Rutgers, A. J. 1954. *Physical Chemistry.* Interscience Publishers, Inc., New York.

CHAPTER 4   BOOKS AND REVIEWS

Lyon, T. L., H. O. Buckman, and N. C. Brady. 1952. *The Nature and Properties of Soils.* The Macmillan Company, New York.

Marshall, C. E. 1935. *Colloids in Agriculture.* Edward Arnold and Company, London.

Meyer, B. S., D. B. Anderson, and R. H. Böhning. 1960. *Introduction to Plant Physiology.* D. Van Nostrand Company, Inc., Princeton, N.J.

Millar, C. E., and L. M. Turk. 1951. *Fundamentals of Soil Science.* John Wiley & Sons, Inc., New York.

Rich, C. I., and G. W. Kunze [eds.]. 1964. *Soil Clay Mineralogy: A Symposium.* University of North Carolina Press, Chapel Hill.

Russell, E. W. 1961. *Soil Conditions and Plant Growth.* John Wiley & Sons, Inc., New York.

Thorne, D. W., and H. B. Peterson. 1949. *Irrigated Soils, Their Fertility and Management.* The Blakiston Company, Philadelphia.

van Olphen, H. 1963. *An Introduction to Clay Colloid Chemistry.* Interscience Publishers, John Wiley & Sons, Inc., New York.

REFERENCE

Wiebe, H. H. 1966. "Matrix potential of several plant tissues and biocolloids." *Plant Physiology* 41:1439–1442.

CHAPTER 5   BOOKS AND REVIEWS

Bennet-Clark, T. A. 1959. "Water relations of cells." In *Plant Physiology.* Vol. II. *Plants in Relation to Water and Solutes.* F. C. Steward [ed.]. pp. 105–191. Academic Press, Inc., New York.

Briggs, G. E. 1967. *Movement of Water in Plants.* Davis Publishing Company, Philadelphia.

Crafts, A. S., H. B. Currier, and C. R. Stocking. 1949. *Water in the Physiology of Plants.* Chronica Botanica Company, Waltham, Mass.

Dainty, J. 1965. "Osmotic flow." *Symposia of the Society for Experimental Biology* 19:75–85.

—————. 1963. "Water relations of plant cells." *Advances in Botanical Research* 1:279–326.

Kozlowski, T. T. 1964. *Water Metabolism in Plants.* Harper & Row, Publishers, Inc., New York.

Kramer, P. J. 1949. *Plant and Soil Water Relationships.* McGraw-Hill Book Company, Inc., New York.

Meyer, B. S., and D. B. Anderson. 1952. *Plant Physiology.* D. Van Nostrand Company, Inc., Princeton, N.J.

Philip, J. R. 1966. "Plant-water relations: Some physical aspects." *Annual Review of Plant Physiology* 17:245–268.

Slatyer, R. O. 1960. "Absorption of water by plants." *Botanical Review* 26:331–392.

—————. 1962. "Internal water relations of higher plants." *Annual Review of Plant Physiology* 13:351–378.

—————. 1967. *Plant–Water Relationships.* Academic Press, Inc., New York.

REFERENCES

Barrs, H. D., and R. O. Slatyer. 1965. "Experience with three vapour methods for measuring water potential in plants." In *Methodology of Plant Eco-Physiology.* F. E. Eckhardt [ed.]. Proceedings of the Montpellier Symposium. UNESCO, Paris.

Boyer, J. S. 1967. "Leaf water potentials measured with a pressure chamber." *Plant Physiology* 42:133–137.

—————. 1967. "Matric potentials of leaves." *Plant Physiology* 42:213–217.

Boyer, J. S., and E. B. Knipling. 1965. "Isopiestic technique for measuring leaf water potentials with a thermocouple psychrometer." *Proceedings of the National Academy of Sciences* 54(4):1044–1051.

Clausen, J. J., and T. T. Kozlowski. 1965. "Use of the relative turgidity technique for measurement of water stresses in gymnosperm leaves." *Canadian Journal of Botany* 43:305–316.

Gaff, D. F., and D. J. Carr. 1964. "An examination of the refractometric method for determining the water potential of plant tissues." *Annals of Botany* 28:351–368.

Gardner, W. R., and C. F. Ehlig. 1965. "Physical aspects of the internal water relations of plant leaves." *Plant Physiology* 40:705–710.

Green, P. B., and R. W. Stanton. 1967. "Turgor pressure: Direct manometric measurement in single cells of *Nitella*." *Science* 155:1675–1676.

Knipling, E. B., and P. J. Kramer. 1967. "Comparison of the dye method with the thermocouple psychrometer for measuring leaf water potentials." *Plant Physiology* 42:1315–1320.

Kramer, P. J., and H. Brix. 1965. "Measurement of water stress in plants." In *Arid Zone Research 25.* F. Eckhardt [ed.]. pp. 343–351.

Kramer, P. J., E. B. Knipling, and L. N. Miller. 1966. "Terminology of cell water relations." *Science* 153:889–890.

Lang, A. R. G., and H. D. Barrs. 1965. "An apparatus for measuring water potentials in the xylem of intact plants." *Australian Journal of Biological Science* 18:487–497.

Ray, P. M. 1960. "On the theory of osmotic water movement." *Plant Physiology* 35:783–795.

Renner, O. 1915. "*Theoretisches und Experimentelles zur Kohäsionstheorie der Wasserbewegung.*" *Jahrbuch fur Wissenschaftliche Botanik* 56:617–667.

Scholander, P. F., H. T. Hammel, E. D. Bradstreet, and E. A. Hemmingsen. 1965. "Sap pressure in vascular plants." *Science* 148:339–346.

Shimshi, D., and A. Livne. 1967. "The estimation of the osmotic potential of plant sap by refractometry and conductimetry: A field method." *Annals of Botany* 31:505–511.

Slatyer, R. O., and S. A. Taylor. 1961. "Terminology in plant- and soil-water relations." *Nature* 189(4760):207–209.

Waring, R. H., and B. D. Cleary. 1967. "Plant moisture stress: Evaluation by pressure bomb." *Science* 155:1248–1254.

Wiebe, H. H. 1966. "Matrix potential of several plant tissues and biocolloids." *Plant Physiology* 41:1439–1442.

Wilson, J. W. 1967. "The components of leaf water potential. I. Osmotic and matrix potentials." *Australian Journal of Biological Science* 20:329–347.

—————. 1967. "The components of leaf water potential. II. Pressure potential and water potential." *Australian Journal of Biological Science* 20:349–357.

—————. 1967. "The components of leaf water potential. III. Effects of tissue characteristics and relative water content on water potential." *Australian Journal of Biological Science* 20:359–367.

CHAPTER 6 BOOKS AND REVIEWS

Briggs, G. E. 1967. *Movement of Water in Plants.* Davis Publishing Co., Philadelphia.

Brouwer, R. 1965. "Water movement across the root." *Symposia of the Society for Experimental Biology* 19:131–149.

Gates, D. M. 1966. "Transpiration and energy exchange." *Quarterly Review of Biology* 41:353–364.

Heath, O. V. S. 1959. "The water relations of stomatal cells and the mechanisms of stomatal movement." In *Plant Physiology,* Vol. II. F. C. Steward [ed.]. p. 193ff. Academic Press, Inc., New York.

Ketellaper, H. J. 1963. "Stomatal physiology." *Annual Review of Plant Physiology* 14:249–270.

Kozlowski, T. T. 1964. *Water Metabolism in Plants*. Harper & Row, Publishing, Inc., New York.

Kramer, P. J. 1959. "Transpiration and the water economy of plants." In *Plant Physiology*. Vol. II. F. C. Steward [ed.]. p. 607ff. Academic Press, Inc. New York.

Lemon, E. 1963. "Energy and water balance of plant communities." In *Environmental Control of Plant Growth*. Chap. 5. L. T. Evans [ed.]. Academic Press, Inc., New York.

Meidner, H., and T. A. Mansfield. 1965. "Stomatal responses to illumination." *Biological Reviews* 40:483–509.

Meyer, B. S., and D. B. Anderson. 1952. *Plant Physiology*. D. Van Nostrand Company, Inc., Princeton, N.J.

Pallas, J. E., Jr. 1966. "Mechanisms of guard cell action." *Quarterly Review of Biology* 41:365–383.

Rutter, A. J., and F. H. Whitehead [eds.]. 1961. *The water relations of plants*. A symposium of the British Ecological Society. John Wiley & Sons, Inc., New York.

Slatyer, R. O. 1963. "Climatic control of plant-water relations." In *Environmental Control of Plant Growth*. Chap. 4. L. T. Evans [ed.]. Academic Press, Inc., New York.

————. 1967. *Plant-Water Relationships*. Academic Press, Inc., New York.

Vaadia, Y., F. C. Raney, and R. M. Hagan. 1961. "Plant water deficits and physiological processes." *Annual Review of Plant Physiology* 12:265–292.

Weatherley, P. E. 1965. "The state and movement of water in the leaf." *Symposia of the Society for Experimental Biology* 19:157–184.

REFERENCES

Cook, G. D., J. R. Dixon, and A. C. Leopold. 1964. "Transpiration: Its effects on plant leaf temperature." *Science* 144:546–547.

Cox, L. M., and L. Boersma. 1967. "Transpiration as a function of soil temperature and soil water stress." *Plant Physiology* 42:550–556.

Drake, B. G. 1967. "Heat transfer studies in *Xanthium*." M.S. Thesis, Colorado State University, Fort Collins.

Idso, S. B., and D. G. Baker. 1967. "Relative importance of reradiation, convection, and transpiration in heat transfer from plants." *Plant Physiology* 42:631–640.

Jensen, R. D., and S. A. Taylor. 1961. "Effect of temperature on water transport through plants." *Plant Physiology* 36:639–642.

Lee, R., and D. M. Gates. 1964. "Diffusion resistance in leaves as related to their stomatal anatomy and microstructure." *American Journal of Botany* 51:963–975.

Levitt, J. 1967. "The mechanism of stomatal action." *Planta* 74:101–118.

Linacre, E. T. 1967. "Further studies of the heat transfer from a leaf." *Plant Physiology* 42:651–658.

Loomis, W. E. 1965. "Absorption of radiant energy by leaves." *Ecology* 46:14–17.

Mellor, R. S., F. B. Salisbury, and K. Raschke. 1964. "Leaf temperatures in controlled environments." *Planta* 61:56–72.

Raschke, K. 1960. "Heat transfer between the plant and the environment." *Annual Review of Plant Physiology* 11:111–126.

Salisbury, F. B., and G. G. Spomer. 1964. "Leaf temperatures of alpine plants in the field." *Planta* 60:497–505.

Slatyer, R. O., and J. F. Bierhuizen. 1964. "A differential psychrometer for continuous measurements of transpiration." *Plant Physiology* 39:1051–1056.

Stalfelt, M. G. 1964. "Reactions participating in the photoactive opening of the stomata." *Physiologia Plantarum* 17:828–838.

Tibbals, E. C., *et al.* 1964. "Radiation and convection in conifers." *American Journal of Botany* 51:529–538.

CHAPTER 7   BOOKS AND REVIEWS

Baver, L. D. 1948. *Soil Physics*. John Wiley & Sons, Inc., New York.

Briggs, G. E. 1967. *Movement of Water in Plants*. Davis Publishing Company, Philadelphia.

Briggs, G. E., and R. N. Robertson. 1957. "Apparent free space." *Annual Review of Plant Physiology* 8:11–29.

Devlin, R. M. 1966. *Plant Physiology*. Reinhold Publishing Corporation, New York.

Esau, Katherine. 1965. *Plant Anatomy*. John Wiley & Sons, Inc., New York.

Kozlowski, T. T. 1964. *Water Metabolism in Plants*. Harper & Row, Publishers, Inc., New York.

Kramer, P. J. 1949. *Plant and Soil Water Relationships*. McGraw-Hill Book Company, Inc., New York.

Kramer, P. J., and T. Y. Kozlowski. 1960. *Physiology of Trees*. McGraw-Hill Book Company, Inc., New York.

Leopold, A. C. 1964. *Plant Growth and Development*. McGraw-Hill Book Company, Inc., New York.

Meyer, B. S., D. B. Anderson, and R. H. Böhning. 1960. *Introduction to Plant Physiology*. D. Van Nostrand Company, Inc., Princeton, N.J.

Philip, J. R. 1966. "Plant-water relations: Some physical aspects." *Annual Review of Plant Physiology* 17:245–268.

Russell, R. S., and D. A. Barber, 1960. "The relationship between salt uptake and the absorption of water by intact plants." *Annual Review of Plant Physiology* 11:127–140.

Rutter, A. J., and F. H. Whitehead [eds.]. 1961. *The Water Relations of Plants*. A symposium of the British Ecological Society. John Wiley & Sons, Inc., New York.

Slatyer, R. O. 1967. *Plant-Water Relationships*. Academic Press, Inc., New York.

van Fleet, D. S. 1961. "Histochemistry and function of the endodermis." *Botanical Review* 27:165–220.

Zimmermann, M.H. 1965. "Water movement in stems of tall plants." *Symposia of the Society for Experimental Biology* 19:151–155.

REFERENCES

Crafts, A. S., and T. C. Broyer. 1938. "Migration of salts and water into xylem of the roots of higher plants." *American Journal of Botany* 25:529–535.

Hammel, H. T. 1967. "Freezing of xylem sap without cavitation." *Plant Physiology* 42:55–66.

Hu Yu, Grace, and P. J. Kramer. 1967. "Radial salt transport in corn roots." *Plant Physiology* 42:985–990.

Laties, G. G., and K. Budd. 1964. "The development of differential permeability in isolated steles of corn roots." *Proceedings of the National Academy of Sciences* 52:462–469.

Levitt, J. 1957. "The significance of 'apparent free space' (A.F.S.) in ion absorption." *Physiologia Plantarum* 10:882–888.

O'Leary, J. W. 1965. "Root-pressure exudation in woody plants." *Botanical Gazette* 126:108–115.

O'Leary, J. W., and P. J. Kramer. 1964. "Root pressure in conifers." *Science* 145:284–285.

Peel, A. J. 1965. "On the conductivity of the xylem in trees." *Annals of Botany* 29:119–130.

Wallace, A., R. T. Ashcroft, and O. R. Lunt. 1967. "Day-night periodicity of exudation in detopped tobacco." *Plant Physiology* 42:238–242.

Wray, F. J., and J. A. Richardson. 1964. "Paths of water transport in higher plants." *Nature* 202:415–416.

Zimmermann, M. H. 1964. "Effect of low temperature on ascent of sap in trees." *Plant Physiology* 39:568–572.

CHAPTER 8   BOOKS AND REVIEWS

Albers, R. W. 1967. "Biochemical aspects of active transport." *Annual Review of Biochemistry* 36:727–756.

Briggs, G. E., A. B. Hope, and R. N. Robertson. 1961. *Electrolytes and Plant Cells.* Blackwell Scientific Publications, Oxford, England.

Brouwer, R. 1965. "Ion absorption and transport in plants." *Annual Review of Plant Physiology* 16:241–266.

Brown, R. 1959. "The plant cell and its inclusions." In *Plant Physiology.* Vol. IA. F. C. Steward [ed.]. pp. 1–130. Academic Press, Inc., New York.

Buvat, R. 1963. "Electron microscopy of plant protoplasm." *International Review of Cytology* 14:41–155.

Cirillo, V. P. 1961. "Sugar transport in microorganism." *Annual Review of Microbiology* 15:197–218.

Collander, R. 1959. "Cell membranes: Their resistance to penetration and their capacity for transport." In *Plant Physiology.* Vol. 2. F. C. Steward [ed.]. pp. 3–102. Academic Press, Inc., New York.

———. 1957. "Permeability of plant cells." *Annual Review of Plant Physiology* 8:335–348.

Conway, E. J. 1955. "Evidence for a redox pump in the active transport of cations." *International Review of Cytology* 4:377–396.

Crane, F. L. 1961. "Structure and function of mitochondria." *Annual Review of Plant Physiology* 12:13–34.

Dainty, J. 1962. "Ion transport and electrical potentials in plant cells." *Annual Review of Plant Physiology* 13:379–402.

Epstein, E. 1956. "Mineral nutrition of plants: Mechanisms of uptake and transport." *Annual Review of Plant Physiology* 7:1–24.

Epstein, E., and R. L. Jefferies. 1964. "The genetic basis of selective ion transport in plants." *Annual Review of Plant Physiology* 15:169–184.

Frey-Wyssling, A., and K. Muhlethaler. 1965. *Ultrastructural Plant Cytology.* Elsevier Publishing Company, Amsterdam.

Giese, A. C. 1962. *Cell Physiology.* W. B. Saunders Company, Philadelphia.

Green, D. E., and R. Goldberger. 1967. "The membranes of the cell." *Molecular Insights into the Living Process.* Academic Press, Inc., New York.

Jennings, D. H. 1963. *The Absorption of Solutes by Plant Cells.* Iowa State University Press, Ames.

Laties, G. G. 1959. "Active transport of salt into plant tissue." *Annual Review of Plant Physiology* 10:87–112.

Sutcliffe, J. F. 1962. *Mineral Salts Absorption in Plants,* Pergamon Press, New York.

Troshin, A. S. 1966. *Problems of Cell Permeability.* Pergamon Press, Oxford.

Wallace, A. 1966. *Current Topics in Plant Nutrition.* Edwards Bros., Inc., Ann Arbor, Mich.

REFERENCES

Ahlgren, G. E. and T. W. Sudia. 1967. "Studies of the mechanism of the foliar absorption of phosphate." *Isotopes in Plant Nutrition and Physiology.* International Atomic Energy Agency, Vienna.

Atkinson, M. R., *et al.* 1966. "Salt accumulation and adenosine triphosphate in carrot xylem tissue." *Proceedings of the National Academy of Sciences* 55:560–564.

Bhide, S. V., and J. Brachet. 1960. "Study of the uptake of ribonuclease by onion root-tip cells." *Experimental Cell Research* 21:303–315.

Birt, L. M., and F. J. R. Hird. 1958. "The uptake and metabolism of amino acids by slices of carrot." *Biochemical Journal* 70:277–286.

Bradfute, O. E., and A. D. McLaren. 1964. "Entry of protein molecules into plant roots." *Physiologia Plantarum* 17:667–675.

Bradfute, O. E., Cicily Chapman-Andresen, and W. A. Jensen. 1965. "Concerning morphological evidence for pinocytosis in higher plants." *Experimental Cell Research* 36:207–210.

Elsas, L. J., and L. E. Rosenberg. 1967. "Inhibition of amino acid transport in rat kidney cortex by puromycin." *Proceedings of the National Academy of Sciences* 57:371–378.

Franke, W. W. 1966. "Isolated nuclear membranes." *Journal of Cell Biology* 31:619–623.

Frey-Wyssling, A., E. Grieshaber, and K. Muhlethaler. 1963. "Origin of spherosomes in plant cells." *Journal of Ultrastructural Research* 8:506–516.

Green, D. E. 1964. "The Mitochondrion." *Scientific American* 210(1):63–74.

Green, D. E., et al. 1967. "Formation of membranes by repeating units." *Archives of Biochemistry and Biophysics* 119:312–335.

Green, D. E., and J. F. Perdue. 1966. "Membranes as expressions of repeating units." *Proceedings of the National Academy of Sciences* 55:1295–1302.

Green, D. E., and O. Hechter. 1965. "Assembly of membrane subunits." *Proceedings of the National Academy of Sciences* 53:318–325.

Greenberger, N. J., and R. D. Ruppert. 1966. "Inhibition of protein synthesis: A mechanism for the production of impaired iron absorption." *Science* 153:315–316.

Gross, L. 1967. "Active membranes for active transport." *Journal of Theoretical Biology* 15:298–306.

Grun, P. 1963. "Ultrastructure of plant plasma and vacuolar membranes." *Journal of Ultrastructural Research* 9:198–208.

Hanson, J. B., and R. J. Miller. 1967. "Evidence for active phosphate transport in maize mitochondria." *Proceedings of the National Academy of Sciences* 58:727–734.

Hengstenberg, W., J. B. Egan, and M. L. Morse. 1967. "Carbohydrate transport in *Staphylococcus aureus*. V. The accumulation of phosphorylated carbohydrate derivatives, and evidence for a new enzyme-splitting lactose phosphate." *Proceedings of the National Academy of Sciences* 58:274–279.

Hiatt, A. J. 1967. "Relationship of cell sap pH to organic acid change during ion uptake." *Plant Physiology* 42:294–298.

Higinbotham, N., B. Etherton, and R. J. Foster. 1967. "Mineral ion contents and cell transmembrane electropotentials of pea and oat seedling tissue." *Plant Physiology* 42:37–46.

Jacoby, B. 1965. "Sodium retention in excised bean stems." *Physiologia Plantarum* 18:730–739.

Korn, E. D. 1966. "Structure of biological membranes." *Science* 153:1491–1498.

Luttge, U., and G. G. Laties. 1967. "Selective inhibition of absorption and long distance transport in relation to the dual mechanisms of ion absorption in maize seedlings." *Plant Physiology* 42:181–185.

McClurkin, Iola T., and D. C. McClurkin. 1967. "Cytochemical demonstration of a sodium-activated and a potassium-activated adenosine triphosphatase in Loblolly pine seedling root tips." *Plant Physiology* 42:1103–1110.

Miller, J., and C. Ross. 1966. "Inhibition of leaf processes by p-fluorophenylalanine during induction of flowering in the cocklebur." *Plant Physiology* 41:1185–1192.

Mitchell, P. 1967. "Proton current flow in mitochondrial systems." *Nature* 214:1327–1328.

Morre, D. J., and H. H. Mollenhauer. 1964. "Isolation of the golgi apparatus from plant cells." *Journal of Cell Biology* 23:295–305.

Nobel, P. S., and L. Packer. 1964. "Energy-dependent ion uptake in spinach chloroplasts." *Biochimica et Biophysica Acta* 88:453–455.

Pardee, A. B. 1966. "Purification and properties of a sulfate-binding protein from *Salmonella typhimurium*." *Journal of Biological Chemistry* 241:5886–5892.

Park, R. B. 1965. "Substructure of chloroplast lamellae." *Journal of Cell Biology* 27:151–161.

Parson, D. F. 1963. "Mitochondrial structure: Two types of subunits on negatively stained mitochondrial membranes." *Science* 140:985–987.

Pitman, M. G., and H. D. W. Saddler. 1967. "Active sodium and potassium transport in cells of barley roots." *Proceedings of the National Academy of Sciences* 57:44–49.

Sorokin, Helen P. 1967. "The spherosomes and the reserve fat in plant cells." *American Journal of Botany* 54:1008–1016.

Stiles, J. W., and F. L. Crane. 1966. "The demonstration of the elementary particles of mitochondrial membranes fixed with glutaraldehyde." *Biochimica et Biophysica Acta* 126:179–181.

Thomson, W. W. 1966. "Observations on the ultrastructure of the plasmalemma in oranges." *Journal of Ultrastructural Research* 16:640–650.

Ulrich, A. 1942. "Metabolism of organic acids in excised barley roots as influenced by temperature, oxygen tension and salt concentration." *American Journal of Botany* 29:220–227.

Viets, F. G., Jr. 1944. "Calcium and other polyvalent cations as accelerators of ion accumulation by excised barley roots." *Plant Physiology* 19:466–480.

Wallach, D. F. H., and P. H. Zahler. 1966. "Protein conformations in cellular membranes." *Proceedings of the National Academy of Sciences* 56:1552–1559.

Weier, T. E., *et al.* 1965. "The structural relationships of the internal membrane systems of *in situ* and isolated chloroplasts of *Hordeum vulgare*." *American Journal of Botany* 52:339–352.

Wright, D. E. 1962. "Amino acid uptake by plant roots." *Archives of Biochemistry and Biophysics* 97:174–180.

Yoo, B. Y., and S. T. Bayley. 1967. "The structure of pores in isolated pea nuclei." *Journal of Ultrastructural Research* 18:651–660.

CHAPTER 9   BOOKS AND REVIEWS

Bollard, E. G. 1960. "Transport in the xylem." *Annua Review of Plant Physiology* 11:114–166.

Crafts, A. S. 1961. *Translocation in Plants.* Holt, Rinehart and Winston, Inc., New York.

Esau, Katherine. 1965. *Plant Anatomy.* John Wiley & Sons, Inc., New York.

Esau, Katherine, H. B. Currier, and V. I. Cheadle. 1957. "Physiology of phloem." *Annual Review of Plant Physiology* 8:349–374.

Kramer, P. J., and T. T. Kozlowski. 1960. *Physiology of Trees.* McGraw-Hill Book Company, Inc., New York.

Kursanov, A. L. 1963. "Metabolism and the transport of organic substances in the phloem." *Advances in Botanical Research* 1:209–278.

Leopold, A. C. 1964. *Plant Growth and Development.* McGraw-Hill Book Company, Inc., New York.

McCready, C. C. 1966. "Translocation of growth regulators." *Annual Review of Plant Physiology* 17:283–294.

Nelson, C. D. 1963. "Effect of climate on the distribution and translocation of assimilates." In *Environmental Control of Plant Growth.* L. T. Evans [ed.]. pp. 149–174. Academic Press, Inc., New York.

Salisbury, F. B. 1966. "Translocation: The movement of dissolved substances in plants." In W. A. Jensen and L. G. Kavaljian [eds.]. *Plant Biology Today: Advances and Challenges.* Wadsworth Publishing Company, Inc., Belmont, California.

Swanson, C. A. 1959. "Translocation of organic solutes." In *Plant Physiology.* Vol. II.   F. C. Steward [ed.]. pp. 481–551. Academic Press, Inc., New York.

Zimmermann, M. H. 1958. "Translocation of organic substances in the phloem of forest trees." In *The Physiology of Forest Trees.* K. V. Thimann, [ed.]. The Ronald Press Company, New York.

—————. 1960. "Transport in the phloem." *Annual Review of Plant Physiology* 11:167–190.

REFERENCES

Biddulph, O., and R. Cory. 1957. "An analysis of translocation in the phloem of the bean plant using THO, P^{32} and $C^{14}O_2$." *Plant Physiology* 32:608–619.

Biddulph, O., and R. Cory. 1960. "Demonstration of two translocation mechanisms in studies of bidirectional movement." *Plant Physiology* 35:689–695.

—————. 1965. "Translocation of C^{14} metabolites in the phloem of the bean plant." *Plant Physiology* 40:119–129.

Biddulph, O., R. Cory, and Susann Biddulph. 1959. "Translocation of calcium in the bean plant." *Plant Physiology* 34:512–519.

Bouck, G. B., and J. Cronshaw. 1965. "The fine structure of differentiating sieve tube elements." *Journal of Cell Biology* 25:79–96.

Buttery, B. R., and S. G. Boatman. 1966. "Manometric measurement of turgor pressures in laticiferous phloem tissues." *Journal of Experimental Botany* 17:283–296.

De Morretes, Berta L. 1962. "Terminal phloem in vascular bundles of leaves of *Capsicum annuum* and *Phaseolus vulgaris*." *American Journal of Botany* 49:560–567.

Evert, R. F., and F. J. Alfieri. 1965. "Ontogeny and structure of coniferous sieve cells." *American Journal of Botany* 52:1058–1066.

Evert, R. F., and W. F. Derr. 1964. "Callose substance in sieve elements." *American Journal of Botany* 51:552–559.

Geiger, D. R. 1966. "Effect of sink region cooling on translocation of photosynthate." *Plant Physiology* 41:1667–1672.

Hartt, Constance E. 1965. "The effect of temperature upon translocation of C^{14} in sugar cane." *Plant Physiology* 40:74–81.

Hatch, M. D., and K. T. Glasziou. 1964. "Direct evidence for translocation of sucrose in sugar cane leaves and stems." *Plant Physiology* 39:180–184.

Mason, T. G., and E. J. Maskell. 1928. "Studies on transport of carbohydrates in the cotton plant. II. The factors determining the rate and the direction of movement of sugars." *Annals of Botany* 42:55–74.

Mortimer, D. C. 1965. "Translocation of the products of photosynthesis in sugar beet petioles." *Canadian Journal of Botany* 43:269–280.

Murmanis, Lidija, and R. F. Evert. 1967. "Parenchyma cells of secondary phloem in *Pinus strobus*." *Planta* 73:301–318.

—————. 1966. "Some aspects of sieve cell ultrastructure in *Pinus strobus*." *American Journal of Botany* 53:1065–1078.

Nelson, C. D. 1962. "The translocation of organic compounds in plants." *Canadian Journal of Botany* 40:757–770.

Nelson, C. D., H. J. Perkins, and P. R. Gorham. 1958. "Note on a rapid translocation of photosynthetically assimilated C^{14} out of the primary leaf of the young soybean plant." *Canadian Journal of Botany* 36:1277–1279.

Parker, J. 1965. "Strand characteristics in sieve tubes of some common tree species." *Protoplasma* 60:86–93.

Swanson, C. A., and D. R. Geiger. 1967. "Time course of low temperature inhibition of sucrose translocation in sugar beets." *Plant Physiology* 42:751–756.

Thaine, R. 1964. "The protoplasmic-streaming theory of phloem transport." *Journal of Experimental Botany* 15:470–484.

Thaine, R., M. C. Probine, and P. Y. Dyer. 1967. "The existence of transcellular strands in mature sieve elements." *Journal of Experimental Botany* 18:110–127.

Trip, P., C. D. Nelson, and G. Krotkov. 1965. "Selective and preferential translocation of C^{14} labeled sugars in white ash and lilac." *Plant Physiology* 40:740–747.

Webb, J. A. 1967. "Translocation of sugars in *Cucurbita melopepo*. IV. Effects of temperature change." *Plant Physiology* 42:881–885.

Webb, J. A., and P. R. Gorham. 1965. "The effect of node temperature on assimilation and translocation of C^{14} in the squash." *Canadian Journal of Botany* 43:1009–1020.

——————— 1964. "Translocation of photosynthetically assimilated C^{14} in straight-necked squash." *Plant Physiology* 39:663–672.

Webster, D. H., and H. B. Currier. 1965. "Callose: Lateral movement of assimilates from phloem." *Science* 150:1610–1611.

Wiersum, L. K. 1967. "The mass-flow theory of phloem transport: A supporting calculation." *Journal of Experimental Botany* 18:160–162.

Zimmermann, M. H. 1963. "How sap moves in trees." *Scientific American* 208(3):132–142.

———————. 1961. "Movement of organic substances in trees." *Science* 133:73–79.

CHAPTER 10   BOOKS AND REVIEWS

Ahlgren, G. E., and T. W. Sudia. 1967. "Studies of the mechanism of the foliar absorption of phosphate." *Isotopes in Plant Nutrition and Physiology.* International Atomic Energy Agency, Vienna.

Bollard, E. G., and G. W. Butler. 1966. "Mineral nutrition of plants." *Annual Review of Plant Physiology* 17:47–76.

Bonner, J., and A. W. Galston. 1952. *Principles of Plant Physiology.* W. H. Freeman & Company, Publishers, San Francisco.

Briggs, G. E., A. B. Hope, and R. N. Robertson. 1961. *Electrolytes and Plant Cells.* Blackwell Scientific Publications, Oxford, England.

Brouwer, R. 1965. "Ion absorption and transport in plants." *Annual Review of Plant Physiology* 16:241–266.

Broyer, T. C., and P. R. Stout. 1959. "The macronutrient elements." *Annual Review of Plant Physiology* 10:277–300.

Epstein, E. 1965. "Mineral metabolism." In *Plant Biochemistry.* J. Bonner and J. E. Varner [eds.]. pp. 438–461. Academic Press, Inc., New York.

Epstein, E., and R. L. Jefferies. 1964. "The genetic basis of selective ion transport in plants." *Annual Review of Plant Physiology* 15:169–184.

Evans, H. J., and G. J. Sorger. 1966. "Role of mineral elements with emphasis on the univalent cations." *Annual Review of Plant Physiology* 17:47–76.

Fried, M., and R. E. Shapiro. 1961. "Soil-plant relationships in ion uptake." *Annual Review of Plant Physiology* 12:91–112.

Hewitt, E. J. 1952. "Sand and water culture methods used in the study of plant nutrition." *Technical Communication No. 22.* Commonwealth Agricultural Bureau, East Malling, Maidstone, Kent, England.

Hoagland, D. R. 1948. *Lectures on the Inorganic Nutrition of Plants.* Chronica Botanica Company, Waltham, Mass.

Jennings, D. H. 1963. *The Absorption of Solutes by Plant Cells.* Iowa State University Press, Ames.

Meyer, B. S., D. B. Anderson, and R. H. Böhning. 1960. *Introduction to Plant Physiology.* D. Van Nostrand Company, Inc., Princeton, N.J.

Russell, R. S., and D. A. Barber. 1960. "The relationship between salt uptake and the absorption of water by intact plants." *Annual Review of Plant Physiology* 11:127–140.

Smith, P. F. 1962. "Mineral analysis of plant tissues." *Annual Review of Plant Physiology* 13:81–108.

Sprague, H. B. [ed.]. 1964. *Hunger Signs in Crops. A Symposium.* David McKay Company, Inc., New York.

Steward, F. C. 1963. *Plant Physiology.* Vol. III. *Inorganic Nutrition of Plants.* Academic Press, Inc., New York.

Steward, F. C., and J. F. Sutcliffe. 1959. "Plants in relation to inorganic salts." In *Plant Physiology.* Vol. II. F. C. Steward [ed.]. pp. 253–478. Academic Press, Inc., New York.

Stewart, I. 1963. "Chelation in the absorption and translocation of mineral elements." *Annual Review of Plant Physiology* 14:295–310.

Stiles, W. 1961. *Trace Elements in Plants.* University Press, Cambridge.

Sutcliffe, J. F. 1962. *Mineral Salts Absorption in Plants.* Pergamon Press, New York.

Truog, E. [ed.]. 1951. *Mineral Nutrition of Plants.* University of Wisconsin Press, Madison.

Wallace, A. 1966. *Current Topics in Plant Nutrition.* Edwards Bros., Inc., Ann Arbor, Mich.

Wallace, T. 1951. *The Diagnosis of Mineral Deficiencies in Plants by Visual Symptoms.* Her Majesty's Stationery Office, London.

Wittwer, S. H., and F. G. Teubner. 1959. "Foliar absorption of mineral nutrients." *Annual Review of Plant Physiology* 10:13–32.

REFERENCES

Barber, D. A., and M. G. T. Shone. 1966. "The absorption of silica from aqueous solutions by plants." *Journal of Experimental Botany* 17:569–578.

Cole, C. V., *et al.* 1963. "The effects of nitrogen on short-term phosphorus absorption and translocation in corn (*Zea mays*)." *Soil Science Society of America Proceedings* 27:671–674.

Dugger, W. M., Jr., T. E. Humphries, and Barbara Calhoun. 1957. "The influence of boron on starch phosphorylase and its significance in translocation of sugars in plants." *Plant Physiology* 32:364–370.

Findenegg, G., and E. Broda. 1965. "Mechanism of uptake of trace elements by plant roots." *Nature* 208:196–197.

Hewitt, E. J., and G. Bond. "The cobalt requirement of non-legume root nodule plants." *Journal of Experimental Botany* 17:480–491.

Hopkins, H. T. 1956. "Absorption of ionic species of ortho-phosphate by barley roots; Effects of 2,4-dinitrophenol and oxygen tension." *Plant Physiology* 31:155.

Johnson, D. L., and L. S. Albert. 1967. "Effect of selected nitrogen-bases and boron on the ribonucleic acid content, elongation, and visible deficiency symptoms of tomato root tips." *Plant Physiology* 42:1307–1309.

Lee, S., and S. Aronoff. 1967. "Boron in plants: A bio-chemical role." *Science* 158:798–799.

Marinos, N. G. 1962. "Studies on submicroscopic aspects of mineral deficiencies. I. Calcium deficiency in the shoot apex of barley." *American Journal of Botany* 49:834–841.

McIlrath, W. J. 1965. "Mobility of boron in several dicotyledonous species." *Botanical Gazette* 126:27–30.

Olsen, S. R., W. D. Kemper, and R. D. Jackson. 1962. "Phosphate diffusion to plant roots." *Soil Science Society of America Proceedings* 26:222–227.

Russell, R. S., and J. Sanderson. 1967. "Nutrient uptake by different parts of the intact roots of plants." *Journal of Experimental Botany* 18:491–508.

Toohey, J. I. 1965. "A vitamin B_{12} compound containing no cobalt." *Proceedings of the National Academy of Sciences* 54:934–942.

Wallace, A., E. Frolich, and O. R. Lunt. 1966. "Calcium requirements of higher plants." *Nature* 209:634.

Wiebe, H. H., and P. J. Kramer. 1954. "Translocation of radioactive isotopes from various regions of roots of barley seedlings." *Plant Physiology* 29:342–348.

Wilson, R. H., H. J. Evans, and R. R. Becker. 1967. "The effect of univalent cation salts on the stability and on certain physical properties of pyruvate kinase." *The Journal of Biological Chemistry* 242:3825–3832.

CHAPTER 11 BOOKS AND REVIEWS

Altschul, A. M., *et al.* 1966. "Seed proteins." *Annual Review of Plant Physiology* 17:113–136.

Asimov, I. 1962. *The Genetic Code.* The New American Library of World Literature, Inc., New York.

Bonner, J., and J. E. Varner. 1965. *Plant Biochemistry.* Academic Press, Inc., New York.

Boyer, P. D., H. Lardy, and K. Myrback. 1959–1963. *The Enzymes.* 8 volumes. Academic Press, Inc., New York.

Brandts, J. F. 1967. "Heat effects on proteins and enzymes." In *Thermobiology.* A. H. Rose [ed.]. pp. 25–72. Academic Press, Inc., New York.

Colowick, S. P., and N. D. Kaplan. 1955–1967. *Methods in Enzymology.* 12 volumes. Academic Press, Inc., New York.

Dixon, M., and E. C. Webb. 1964. *Enzymes.* Academic Press, Inc., New York.

Giese, A. C. 1962. *Cell Physiology.* W. B. Saunders Company, Philadelphia.

Mahler, H. R., and E. H. Cordes. 1966. *Biological Chemistry.* Harper & Row, Publishers, Inc., New York.

McElroy, W. D. 1964. *Cell Physiology and Biochemistry.* Prentice-Hall, Inc., Englewood Cliffs, N.J.

Neilands, J. B., and P. K. Stumpf. 1958. *Outlines of Enzyme Chemistry.* John Wiley & Sons, Inc., New York.

Paech, K., and M. V. Tracey. 1955. *Modern Methods of Plant Analysis* 4. Springer-Verlag, Berlin.

—————. 1963. *Modern Methods of Plant Analysis* 6. Springer-Verlag, Berlin.

—————. 1964. *Modern Methods of Plant Analysis* 7. Springer-Verlag, Berlin.

Pirie, N. W. 1959. "Leaf proteins." *Annual Review of Plant Physiology* 10:33–52.

Smith, L., and B. Chance. 1958. "Cytochromes in plants." *Annual Review of Plant Physiology* 9:449–482.

Stadtman, E. R. 1966. "Allosteric regulation of enzyme activity." In *Advances in Enzymology and Related Subjects of Biochemistry* 28. F. F. Nord [ed.]. pp. 41–154. Interscience Publishers, Inc., New York.

Stahmann, M. A. 1963. "Plant proteins." *Annual Review of Plant Physiology* 14:137–158.

Umbarger, H. E. 1963. "The integration of metabolic pathways." *Annual Review of Plant Physiology* 14:19–42.

Varner, J. E. 1965. "Enzymes." In *Plant Biochemistry.* J. Bonner and J. E. Varner [eds.]. pp. 14–20. Academic Press, Inc., New York.

Vennesland, Birgit. 1959. "Proteins, enzymes, and the mechanism of enzyme action." In *Plant Physiology.* Vol. IA. F. C. Steward [ed.]. pp. 131–205. Academic Press, Inc., New York.

Vogel, H. J., and Ruth H. Vogel. 1967. "Regulation of protein synthesis." *Annual Review of Biochemistry* 36(2):519–538.

Watson, J. D. 1965. *Molecular Biology of the Gene.* W. A. Benjamin, Inc., New York.

REFERENCES

Changeux, J. P. 1965. "The control of biochemical reactions." *Scientific American* 212(4):36–45.

Cleland, W. W. 1964. "Dithiothreitol, a new protective reagent for SH groups." *Biochemistry* 3:480.

Clements, R. L. 1965. "Fruit proteins: Extraction and electrophoresis." *Analytical Biochemistry* 13:390–401.

Keresztes-Nagy, S., and E. Margoliash. 1966. "Preparation and characterization of alfalfa ferredoxin." *Journal of Biological Chemistry* 241:5955–5966.

Light, A., *et al.* 1964. "Current status of the structure of papain: The linear sequence, active sulfhydryl group, and the disulfide bridges." *Proceedings of the National Academy of Sciences* 52:1276–1283.

Macko, V., G. R. Honold, and M. A. Stahmann. 1967. "Soluble proteins and multiple enzyme forms in early growth of wheat." *Phytochemistry* 6:465–471.

Margoliash, E. 1964. "The amino acid sequence of cytochrome C in relation to its function and evolution." *Canadian Journal of Biochemistry* 42:745–753.

Monod, J., J. P. Changeux, and F. Jacob. 1963. "Allosteric proteins and cellular control systems." *Journal of Molecular Biology* 6:306–329.

Morita, R. Y., and P. F. Mathemeir. 1964. "Temperature-hydrostatic pressure studies on partially purified inorganic pyrophosphatase activity." *Journal of Bacteriology* 6:1667–1671.

Phillips, D. C. 1966. "The three-dimensional structure of an enzyme molecule." *Scientific American* 215(5):78–90.

Shannon, L. M., E. Kay, and J. Y. Lew. 1966. "Peroxidase isozymes from horseradish roots. I. Isolation and physical properties." *Journal of Biological Chemistry* 241:2166–2172.

Stein, W. H., and S. Moore. 1961. "The structure of proteins." *Scientific American* 204:81–92.

Stevens, F. C., A. N. Glazer, and E. L. Smith. 1967. "The amino acid sequence of wheat germ cytochrome C." *Journal of Biological Chemistry* 242:2764–2767.

Tanaka, M., *et al.* 1966. "The amino acid sequence of Clostridium pasteurianum ferredoxin." *Biochemistry* 5:1666–1681.

Thompson, E. O. P. 1955. "The insulin molecule." *Scientific American* 192(5):36–41.

Wyckoff, H. W., *et al.* 1967. "The structure of ribonuclease-S at 6 Å resolution." *Journal of Biological Chemistry* 242:3749–3752.

Zuckerkandl, E. 1965. "The evolution of hemoglobin." *Scientific American* 212:110–118.

CHAPTER 12   BOOKS AND REVIEWS

Anderson, L., and K. E. Wolter. 1966. "Cyclitols in plants: Biochemistry and physiology." *Annual Review of Plant Physiology* 17:209–222.

Bonner, J. 1950. *Plant Biochemistry.* Academic Press, Inc., New York.

Buch, M. L. 1957. "*Bibliography of Organic Acids in Higher Plants.*" U. S. D. A. ARS Publication. U.S. Government Printing Office, Washington, D.C.

Côté, W. A., Jr. [ed.]. 1965. *Cellular Ultrastructure of Woody Plants.* Syracuse University Press, Syracuse, N.Y.

Davies, D. D., J. Giovanelli, and T. ap Rees. 1964. *Plant Biochemistry.* Davis Publishing Company, Philadelphia.

Esau, Katherine. 1965. *Plant Anatomy.* John Wiley & Sons, Inc., New York.

Frey-Wyssling, A., and K. Mühlethaler. 1965. *Ultrastructural Plant Cytology.* Elsevier Publishing Company, Amsterdam.

Gibbs, M. 1966. "Carbohydrates: Their role in plant metabolism and nutrition." In *Plant Physiology.* F. C. Steward [ed.]. pp. 3–115. Academic Press, Inc., New York.

Hassid, W. Z. 1967. "Transformation of sugars in plants." *Annual Review of Plant Physiology* 18:253–280.

Lamport, D. T. A. 1966. "Protein component of primary cell walls." In *Advances in Botanical Research* 2. R. D. Preston [ed.]. Academic Press, Inc., New York.

Mühlethaler, K. 1967. "Ultrastructure and formation of plant cell walls." *Annual Review of Plant Physiology* 18:1–24.

Newcomb, E. H. 1963. "Cytoplasm-cell wall relationships." *Annual Review of Plant Physiology* 14:43–64.

Nordin, J. H., and S. Kirkwood. 1965. "Biochemical aspects of plant polysaccharides." *Annual Review of Plant Physiology* 16:393–414.

Porter, H. K. 1962. "Synthesis of polysaccharides of higher plants." *Annual Review of Plant Physiology* 13:303–328.

Preston, R. D. 1964. "Structural plant polysaccharides." *Endeavour* 23:153–159.

Pridham, J. B., and T. Swain [eds.]. 1965. *Biosynthetic Pathways in Higher Plants.* Academic Press, Inc., New York.

Robinson, T. 1967. *The Organic Constituents of Higher Plants: Their Chemistry and Interrelationships.* Burgess Publishing Company, Minneapolis.

Roelofsen, P. A. 1965. "Ultrastructure of the wall in growing cells and its relation to the direction of the growth." *Advances in Botanical Research* 2:69–149.

Setterfield, G., and S. T. Bayley. 1961. "Structure and physiology of cell walls." *Annual Review of Plant Physiology* 12:35–62.

Siegel, S. 1962. *The Plant Cell Wall.* Pergamon Press, New York.

Wardrop, A. 1962. "Cell wall organization in higher plants. I. The primary wall." *Botanical Review* 28:241–285.

Wood, R. 1960. "Pectic and cellulolytic enzymes in plant disease." *Annual Review of Plant Physiology* 11:299–322.

REFERENCES

Ankel, H., *et al.* 1967. "Formation of UDP-D-xylose in algae." *Biochimica et Biophysica Acta* 136:172–175.

Bailey, R. W., and W. Z. Hassid. 1966. "Xylan synthesis from uridine diphosphate-D-xylose by particulate preparations from immature corncobs." *Proceedings of the National Academy of Sciences* 56:1586–1593.

Barber, G. A., A. D. Elbein, and W. Z. Hassid. 1964. "The synthesis of cellulose by enzyme systems from higher plants." *Journal of Biological Chemistry* 239:4056–4061.

Barber, G. A., and W. Z. Hassid. 1964. "The formation of guanosine diphosphate D-glucose by enzymes of higher plants." *Biochimica et Biophysica Acta* 86:397–399.

Brummond, D. O., and A. P. Gibbons. 1965. "Enzymatic cellulose synthesis from UDP-(^{14}C)-glucose by *Lupinus albus*." *Biochemische Zeitschrift* 342:308–318.

Dickerson, A. G., and J. Edelman. 1966. "The metabolism of fructose polymers in plants. VI. Transfructosylation in living tissue of *Helianthus tuberosus* L." *Journal of Experimental Botany* 17:612–619.

Frydman, Rosalia B., and C. E. Cardini. 1966. "Studies on the biosynthesis of starch. I. Isolation and properties of the soluble adenosine diphosphate glucose: Starch glucosyl transferase of *Solanun tuberosum*." *Archives of Biochemistry and Biophysics* 116:9–18.

King, N. J., and S. T. Bayley. 1965. "A preliminary analysis of the proteins of the primary walls of some plant cells." *Journal of Experimental Botany* 16:294–303.

McLennan, D. H., H. Beevers, and J. L. Harley. 1963. "Compartmentation of acids in plant tissues." *Biochemical Journal* 89:316–327.

McLendon, J. 1964. "Evidence for the pectic nature of the middle lamella of potato tuber cell walls based on chromatography of macerating enzymes." *American Journal of Botany* 51:628–633.

Murata, T., *et al.* 1966. "Enzymic mechanism of starch synthesis in ripening rice grains. III. Mechanism of the sucrose-starch conversion." *Archives of Biochemistry and Biophysics* 113:34–44.

Neal, G. E. 1965. "Changes occurring in the cell walls of strawberries during ripening." *Journal of the Science of Food and Agriculture* 16:604–611.

Nevins, D. J., Patricia D. English, and P. Albersheim. 1967. "The specific nature of plant cell wall polysaccharides." *Plant Physiology* 42:900–906.

Pickett-Heaps, J. D., and D. H. Northcote. 1966. "Relationship of cellular organelles to the formation and development of the plant cell wall." *Journal of Experimental Botany* 17:20–26.

Pressey, R., and R. Shaw. 1966. "Effect of temperature on invertase, invertase inhibitor, and sugars in potato tubers." *Plant Physiology* 41:1657–1661.

Preston, R. 1957. "Cellulose." *Scientific American* 197(3):157–168.

• Ray, P. M. 1962. "Cell wall synthesis and cell elongation in oat coleoptile tissue." *American Journal of Botany* 49:928–939.

Roberts, R. M., and V. S. Butt. 1967. "Patterns of cellulose synthesis in maize root tips: A chemical and autoradiographic study." *Experimental Cell Research* 46:495–510.

Scott, F. M. 1966. "Cell wall surface of the higher plants." *Nature* 210:1015–1017.

Trip, P., G. Krotkov, and C. D. Nelson. 1964. "Metabolism of mannitol in higher plants." *American Journal of Botany* 51:828–835.

Umemura, Y., M. Nakamura, and S. Funahashi. 1967. "Isolation and characterization of uridine diphosphate fructose from tubers of Jerusalem artichoke (*Helianthus tuberosus* L.)." *Archives of Biochemistry and Biophysics* 119:240–252.

Vickery, H. B. 1962. "A suggested new nomenclature for the isomers of isocitric acid." *Journal of Biological Chemistry* 237:1739–1741.

Villemez, C. L., T. Y. Lin, and W. Z. Hassid. 1965. "Biosynthesis of the polygalacturonic acid chain of pectin by a particulate enzyme preparation from *Phaseolus aureus* seedlings." *Proceedings of the National Academy of Sciences* 54:1626–1632.

Villemez, C. L., Jr., G. Franz, and W. Z. Hassid. 1967. "Biosynthesis of alkali insoluble polysaccharide from UDP-D-Glucose with particulate enzyme preparations from *Phaseolus aureus*." *Plant Physiology* 42:1219–1223.

CHAPTER 13   BOOKS AND REVIEWS

Allen, M. B. [ed.]. 1960. *The Comparative Biochemistry of Photoreactive Systems.* Academic Press, Inc., New York.

Arnon, D. I. 1965. "Ferredoxin and photosynthesis." *Science* 149:1460–1469.

Bogorad, L. 1966. "Photosynthesis." In *Plant Biology Today.* Wadsworth Publishing Company, Inc., Belmont, Calif.

Brookhaven Symposia Committee [eds.]. 1966. *Energy Conversion by the Photosynthetic Apparatus.* Brookhaven Symposia in Biology, Number 19. Biology Department, Brookhaven National Laboratory.

Clayton, R. K. 1963. "Photosynthesis: Primary physical and chemical processes." *Annual Review of Plant Physiology* 14:159–180.

——————. 1965. *Molecular Physics in Photosynthesis.* P. R. Gross [ed.]. Blaisdell Publishing Company, New York.

Devlin, R. M. 1966. *Plant Physiology.* Reinhold Publishing Corporation, New York.

Emerson, R. 1958. "The quantum yield of photosynthesis." *Annual Review of Plant Physiology* 9:1–24.

Frey-Wyssling, A., and K. Mühlethaler. 1965. *Ultrastructural Plant Cytology.* Elsevier Publishing Company, Amsterdam.

Gibbs, M. 1967. "Photosynthesis." *Annual Review of Biochemistry* 36(2):658–784.

Giese, A. C. 1964. *Photophysiology.* Academic Press, Inc., New York.

Goodwin, T. W. [ed.]. 1966 (Vol. 1); 1967 (Vol. 2). *Biochemistry of Chloroplasts.* Academic Press, Inc., New York.

——————. 1965. *Chemistry and Biochemistry of Plant Pigments.* Academic Press, Inc., New York.

Hill, R., and C. P. Whittingham. 1955. *Photosynthesis.* John Wiley & Sons, Inc., New York.

Hoch, G., and B. Kok. 1961. "Photosynthesis." *Annual Review of Plant Physiology* 12:155–194.

Japanese Society of Plant Physiologists [eds.]. 1963. *Studies on Microalgae and Photosynthetic Bacteria.* University of Tokyo Press, Tokyo.

Jensen, W. A., and R. B. Park. 1967. *Cell Ultrastructure.* Wadsworth Publishing Company, Inc., Belmont, Calif.

Kamen, M. D. 1963. *Primary Processes in Photosynthesis.* Academic Press, Inc., New York.

Kandler, O. 1960. "Energy transfer through phosphorylation mechanisms in photosynthesis." *Annual Review of Plant Physiology* 11:37–54.

Kirk, J. T. O., and R. A. E. Tilney-Bassett. 1967. *The Plastids.* W. H. Freeman & Company, Publishers, London.

Kok, B. 1965. "Photosynthesis: The path of energy." In *Plant Biochemistry.* J. Bonner and J. E. Varner [eds.]. Academic Press, Inc., New York.

Kok, B., and A. T. Jagendorf [eds.]. 1963. *Photosynthetic Mechanisms of Green Plants.* National Academy of Sciences–National Research Council, Publication No. 1145, Washington, D.C.

Krasnovsky, A. A. 1960. The primary processes of photosynthesis in plants. *Annual Review of Plant Physiology* 11:363–410.

McElroy, W. D., and B. Glass [eds.]. 1961. *A Symposium on Light and Life.* Johns Hopkins University Press, Baltimore, Md.

Menke, W. 1962. "Structure and chemistry of plastids." *Annual Review of Plant Physiology* 13:27–44.

O'h Eocha, C. 1965. "Biliproteins of algae." *Annual Review of Plant Physiology* 16:415–434.

Rabinowitch, E. I. 1945 (Vol. 1); 1951 (Vol. 2, pt. 1); 1956 (Vol. 2, pt. 2). *Photosynthesis and Related Processes.* Interscience Publishers, Inc., New York.

Rosenberg, J. L. 1965. *Photosynthesis.* Holt, Rinehart and Winston, Inc., New York.

San Pietro, A., and C. C. Black. 1965. "Enzymology of energy conversion in photosynthesis." *Annual Review of Plant Physiology* 16:155–194.

San Pietro, A., F. A. Greer, and T. J. Army [eds.]. 1967. *Harvesting the Sun.* Academic Press, Inc., New York.

Smith, J. H. C., and C. S. French. 1963. "The major and accessory pigments in photosynthesis." *Annual Review of Plant Physiology* 14:181–224.

Steward, F. C. [ed.]. 1960. *Plant Physiology.* Vol. IB. *Photosynthesis and Chemosynthesis.* Academic Press, Inc., New York.

van Niel, C. B. 1962. "The present status of the comparative study of photosynthesis." *Annual Review of Plant Physiology* 13:1–26.

Vernon, L. P., and M. Avron. 1965. "Photosynthesis." *Annual Review of Biochemistry* 34:269–296.

Vernon, L. P., and G. R. Seely [eds.]. 1966. *The Chlorophylls.* Academic Press, Inc., New York.

REFERENCES

Arnon, D. I. 1960. "The role of light in photosynthesis." *Scientific American* 203(5):104–118.

——————. 1967. "Photosynthetic activity of isolated chloroplasts." *Physiological Reviews* 47:317–358.

Arnon, D. I., H. Y. Tsujimoto, and B. D. McSwain. 1965. "Photosynthetic phosphorylation and electron transport." *Nature* 207:1367–1372.

Bishop, N. I. 1964. "Site of action of copper in photosynthesis." *Nature* 204:401–402.

Black, C. C. 1967. "Evidence supporting the theory of two sites of photophosphorylation in green plants." *Biochemical and Biophysical Research Communications* 28:985–990.

Branton, D., and R. B. Park. 1967. "Subunits in chloroplast lamellae." *Journal of Ultrastructure Research* 19:283–303.

Brody, S. S. 1965. "An experiment showing that P700 can be an aggregated form of chlorophyll *a*." *Archives of Biochemistry and Biophysics* 110:583–585.

Bültemann, V., H. Rüppel, and H. T. Witt. 1964. "Intermediary reactions in the water-splitting part of photosynthesis." *Nature* 204:646–648.

Clayton, R. K. 1965. "The biophysical problems of photosynthesis." *Science* 149:1346–1354.

Fujita, R., *et al.* 1965. "Effect of plastocyanin on plasto-phosphorylation in isolated chloroplasts." *Plant and Cell Physiology* 6:689–697.

Gest, H. 1966. "Comparative biochemistry of photosynthetic processes." *Nature* 209:879–882.

Gorman, D. S., and R. P. Levine. 1965. "Cytochrome *f* and plastocyanin: Their sequence in the photosynthetic electron transport chain of *Chlamydomonas reinhardi.*" *Proceedings of the National Academy of Sciences* 54:1665–1669.

Govindjee, R. G., and G. Hoch. 1964. "Emerson enhancement effect in chloroplast reactions." *Plant Physiology* 39:10–14.

Henninger, M. D., and F. L. Crane. 1966. "Electron transport in chloroplasts: A new redox protein, rubimedin." *Biochemical and Biophysical Research Communications* 24:386–390.

—————. 1967. "Electron transport in chloroplasts: III. The role of plastoquinone *c.*" *Journal of Biological Chemistry* 242:1155–1159.

Howell, S. H., and E. N. Moudrianakis. 1967. "Function of the 'quantasome' in photosynthesis: Structure and properties of membrane-bound particle active in the dark reactions of photophosphorylation." *Proceedings of the National Academy of Sciences* 58:1261–1268.

Kahn, J. S., and A. E. Purcell. 1965. "Enhancement by carotenoids of nicotinamide adenine dinucleotide phosphate photoreduction in isolated chloroplasts. I. Isolation and purification of active fractions." *Archives of Biochemistry and Biophysics* 112:355–360.

Kupke, D. W., and Judith L. Huntingdon. 1963. "Chlorophyll *a* appearance in the dark in higher plants: Analytical notes." *Science* 140:49–51.

Rabinowitch, E. I., and R. G. Govindjee. 1965. "The role of chlorophyll in photosynthesis." *Scientific American* 213(1):74–83.

Rumberg, B. 1964. "Evidence for the participation of chlorophyll *b* in the primary reaction of photosynthesis." *Nature* 204:860–862.

Wald, G. 1959. "Life and light." *Scientific American* 201(4):92–108.

CHAPTER 14   BOOKS AND REVIEWS

Bandurski, R. S. 1965. "Biological reduction of sulfate and nitrate." In *Plant Biochemistry.* J. Bonner and J. E. Varner [eds.]. Academic Press, Inc., New York.

Bassham, J. A. 1964. "Kinetic studies of the photosynthetic carbon reduction cycle." *Annual Review of Plant Physiology* 15:101–120.

—————. 1965. "Photosynthesis: The path of carbon." In *Plant Biochemistry.* J. Bonner and J. E. Varner [eds.]. pp. 875–902. Academic Press, Inc., New York.

Bassham, J., and M. Calvin. 1957. *The Path of Carbon in Photosynthesis.* Prentice-Hall, Inc., Englewood Cliffs, N.J.

Franck, J., and W. E. Loomis. 1949. *Photosynthesis in Plants.* The Iowa State College Press, Ames.

Gaastra, P. 1963. "Climatic Control of Photosynthesis and Respiration." In *Environmental Control of Plant Growth.* L. T. Evans [ed.]. Chap. 8. Academic Press, Inc., New York.

Gibbs, M. 1967. "Photosynthesis." *Annual Review of Biochemistry* 36(2):658–784.

Goodwin, T. W. [ed.]. 1966, 1967. *Biochemistry of Chloroplasts* 1 and 2. Academic Press, Inc., New York.

Hill, R., and C. P. Whittingham. 1955. *Photosynthesis.* John Wiley & Sons, Inc., New York.

Kirk, J. T. O., and R. A. E. Tilney-Bassett. 1967. *The Plastids.* W. H. Freeman & Company, Publishers, London.

Kramer, P. J., and T. T. Kozlowski. 1960. *Physiology of Trees.* McGraw-Hill Book Company, Inc., New York.

Leopold, A. C. 1964. *Plant Growth and Development.* McGraw-Hill Book Company, Inc., New York.

Meyer, B. S., D. B. Anderson, and R. H. Böhning. 1960. *Introduction to Plant Physiology.* D. Van Nostrand Company, Inc., Princeton, N.J.

Porter, H. K. 1962. "Synthesis of polysaccharides of higher plants." *Annual Review of Plant Physiology* 13:303–328.

Rabinowitch, E. I. 1945 (Vol. 1); 1951 (Vol. 2, pt. 1); 1956 (Vol. 2, pt. 2). *Photosynthesis and Related Processes.* Interscience Publishers, Inc., New York.

Rosenberg, J. L. 1965. *Photosynthesis.* Holt, Rinehart and Winston, Inc., New York.

San Pietro, A., F. A. Greer, and T. J. Army [eds.]. 1967. *Harvesting the Sun.* Academic Press, Inc., New York.

Stiller, M. 1962. "The path of carbon in photosynthesis." *Annual Review of Plant Physiology* 13:151–170.

Talling, J. F. 1961. "Photosynthesis under natural conditions." *Annual Review of Plant Physiology* 12:133–154.

Thomas, M. D. 1965. "Photosynthesis (carbon assimilation): Environmental and metabolic relationships." In *Plant Physiology.* Vol. IVA. *Metabolism: Organic Nutrition and Nitrogen Metabolism.* F. C. Steward [ed.]. pp. 9–202. Academic Press, Inc., New York.

Vernon, L. P., and M. Avron. 1965. "Photosynthesis." *Annual Review of Biochemistry* 34:269–296.

Umbreit, W. W., R. H. Burris, and J. F. Stauffer. 1964. *Manometric Techniques.* Burgess Publishing Company, Minneapolis.

REFERENCES

Hatch, M. D., and C. R. Slack. 1967. "Further studies on a new pathway of photosynthetic carbon dioxide fixation in sugar-cane and its occurrence in other plant species." *Biochemical Journal* 102:417–422.

————————. "The participation of phosphoenolpyruvate synthetase in photosynthetic CO_2 fixation of tropical grasses." *Archives of Biochemistry and Biophysics* 120:224–225.

Losada. M., and A. Paneque. 1966. "Light reduction of nitrate by chloroplasts depending on ferredoxin and NAD +." *Biochimica et Biophysica Acta* 126:578–580.

CHAPTER 15   BOOKS AND REVIEWS

Axelrod, B. 1965. "Mono- and oligosaccharides." In *Plant Biochemistry*. J. Bonner and J. E. Varner [eds.]. pp. 231–257. Academic Press, Inc., New York.

Axelrod, B., and H. Beevers. 1956. "Mechanisms of carbohydrate breakdown in plants." *Annual Review of Plant Physiology* 7:267–298.

Beevers, H. 1961. *Respiratory Metabolism in Plants*. Harper & Row, Publishers, Inc., New York.

Bonner, J. 1950. *Plant Biochemistry*. Academic Press, Inc., New York.

Bonner, J., and J. E. Varner. 1965. "The path of carbon in respiratory metabolism." In *Plant Biochemistry*. J. Bonner and J. E. Varner [eds.]. pp. 213–230. Academic Press, Inc., New York.

Bonner, W. D., Jr. 1966. "Electron transport systems in plants." In *Plant Biology Today: Advances and Challenges*. W. A. Jensen and L. G. Kavaljian [eds.]. pp. 135–147. Wadsworth Publishing Company, Inc., Belmont, Calif.

Bonner, W. D., Jr. 1965. "Mitochondria and electron transport." In *Plant Biochemistry*. J. Bonner and J. E. Varner [eds.]. Chapter 6. Academic Press, Inc., New York.

Davies, D. D., J. Giovanelli, and T. ap Rees. 1964. *Plant Biochemistry*. Davis Publishing Company, Philadelphia.

Ducet, G., and A. J. Rosenberg. 1962. "Leaf respiration." *Annual Review of Plant Physiology* 13:171–200.

Gibbs, M. 1959. "Metabolism of carbon compounds." *Annual Review of Plant Physiology* 10:329–378.

Giese, A. C. 1962. "*Cell Physiology*." W. B. Saunders Company, Philadelphia.

Green, D. E., and I. Silman. 1967. "Structure of the mitochondrial electron transfer chain." *Annual Review of Plant Physiology* 18:147–178.

Hackett, D. P. 1959. "Respiratory mechanisms in higher plants." *Annual Review of Plant Physiology* 10:113–146.

Hassid, W. Z. 1967. "Transformation of sugars in plants." *Annual Review of Plant Physiology* 18:253–280.

Jensen, W. A. 1962. *Botanical Histochemistry*. W. H. Freeman & Company, Publishers, San Francisco.

Lieberman, M., and J. E. Baker. 1965. "Respiratory electron transport." *Annual Review of Plant Physiology* 16:343–382.

Mahler, H. R., and E. H. Cordes. 1966. *Biological Chemistry*. Harper & Row, Publishers, Inc., New York.

Marre, E. 1961. "Phosphorylation in higher plants." *Annual Review of Plant Physiology* 12:195–218.

McElroy, W. D. 1964. *Cell Physiology and Biochemistry*. Prentice-Hall, Inc., Englewood Cliffs, N.J.

Millerd, A., and K. J. Scott. 1966. "Respiration of the diseased plant." *Annual Review of Plant Physiology* 13:167–174.

Pridham, J. B., and T. Swain [eds.]. 1965. *Biosynthetic Pathways in Higher Plants*. Academic Press, Inc., New York.

Ranson, S. L. 1965. "The Plant Acids." In *Plant Biochemistry*. J. Bonner and J. E. Varner [eds.]. pp. 493–525. Academic Press, Inc., New York.

Ranson, S. L., and M. Thomas. 1960. "Crassulacean acid metabolism." *Annual Review of Plant Physiology* 11:81–110.

Rowan, D. S. 1966. "Phosphorus metabolism in plants." *International Review of Cytology* 19:302–390.

San Pietro, A., F. A. Greer, and T. J. Army [eds.]. 1967. *Harvesting the Sun*. Academic Press, Inc., New York.

Stadtman, E. R. 1966. "Allosteric regulation of enzyme activity." *Advances in Enzymology* 28:41–154.

Steward, F. C. [ed.]. 1966. *Plant Physiology*. Vol. IVB. *Metabolism: Intermediary Metabolism and Pathology*. Academic Press, Inc., New York.

Stiles, W., and W. Leach. 1960. *Respiration in Plants*. John Wiley & Sons, Inc., New York.

Umbreit, W. W., R. H. Burris, and J. F. Stauffer. 1964. *Manometric Techniques*. Burgess Publishing Company, Minneapolis.

Zelitch, I. 1964. "Organic acids and respiration in photosynthetic tissues." *Annual Review of Plant Physiology* 15:121–142.

REFERENCES

Barker, J. 1965. "Studies in the respiratory and carbohydrate metabolism of plant tissues. XIX. The mechanism of oxygen poisoning of respiration in pea seeds." *New Phytologist* 64:210–223.

Barker, J., M. A. A. Khan, and T. Solomons. 1966. "Mechanism of the Pasteur effect." *Nature* 211:547–548.

Dennis, D. T., and T. P. Coultate. 1966. "Phosphofructokinase, a regulatory enzyme in plants." *Biochemical and Biophysical Research Communications* 25:187–191.

Goren, R., and E. E. Goldschmidt. 1966. "Peroxidase activity in citrus tissues." *Phytochemistry* 5:153–159.

Ishikawa, E., R. M. Oliver, and L. J. Reed. 1966. "α-Keto acid dehydrogenase complexes. V. Macromolecular organization of pyruvate and α-Ketoglutarate dehydrogenase complexes isolated from beef kidney mitochondria." *Proceedings of the National Academy of Sciences* 56:534–541.

Jones, J. D., A. C. Hulme, and L. S. C. Wooltorton. 1965. "The respiration climacteric in apple fruits: Biochemical changes occurring during the development of the climacteric in fruit detached from the tree." *The New Phytologist* 64:158–167.

Marre, E., R. Bianchetti, and S. Cocucci. 1966. "Rate limiting factors of glycolysis in higher plants." *Italian Journal of Biochemistry* 15:135–144.

Mitchell, P. 1967. "Proton-translocation phosphorylation in mitochondria, chloroplasts and bacteria: Natural fuel cells and solar cells." *Federation Proceedings* 26: 1370–1379.

Oppenheim, Ariella, and P. A. Castelfranco. 1967. "An acetaldehyde dehydrogenase from germinating seeds." *Plant Physiology* 42:125–132.

Palmer, J. M., and R. T. Wedding. 1966. "Purification and properties of succinyl-CoA synthetase from Jerusalem artichoke mitochondria." *Biochimica et Biophysica Acta* 113:167–174.

Poskuta, G., C. D. Nelson, and G. Krotkov. 1967. "Effects of metabolic inhibitors on the rates of CO_2 evolution in light and in darkness by detached spruce twigs, wheat and soybean leaves." *Plant Physiology* 42:1187–1190.

Robertson, R. N. 1967. "The separation of protons and electrons as a fundamental biological process." *Endeavour* 26:134–139.

Salas, M. L., *et al.* 1965. "Citrate inhibition of phosphofructokinase and the Pasteur effect." *Biochemical and Biophysical Research Communications* 19:371–376.

Stekhoven, F. M. A. H. S. 1966. "Studies on yeast mitochondria. I. Existence of three phosphorylation sites along the respiratory chain of isolated yeast mitochondria." *Archives of Biochemistry and Biophysics* 115:555–568.

Walker, J. 1964. "Studies on the enzymic browning of apples. II. Properties of apple polyphenoloxidase." *Australian Journal of Biological Science* 17:360–371.

Wang, J. H. 1967. "The molecular mechanism of oxidative phosphorylation." *Proceedings of the National Academy of Sciences* 58:37–44.

Young, R. E., and J. B. Biale. 1967. "Phosphorylation of avocado fruit slices in relation to the respiratory climacteric." *Plant Physiology* 42:1357–1362.

CHAPTER 16   BOOKS AND REVIEWS

Bandurski, R. S. 1965. "Biological reduction of sulfate and nitrate." In *Plant Biochemistry*. J. Bonner and J. E. Varner [eds.]. pp. 467–490. Academic Press, Inc., New York.

Bond, G. 1967. "Fixation of nitrogen by higher plants other than legumes." *Annual Review of Plant Physiology* 18: 107–126.

Bonner, J. 1950. *Plant Biochemistry*. Academic Press, Inc., New York.

Bonner, J., and A. W. Galston. 1952. *Principles of Plant Physiology*. W. H. Freeman & Company, San Francisco.

Burris, R. H. 1965. "Nitrogen fixation." In *Plant Biochemistry*. J. Bonner and J. E. Varner [eds.]. pp. 526–551. Academic Press, Inc., New York.

Carnahan, J. E., and J. E. Castle. 1963. "Nitrogen fixation." *Annual Review of Plant Physiology* 14:125–136.

Davies, D. D., J. Giovanelli, and T. ap Rees. 1964. *Plant Biochemistry*. Davis Publishing Company, Philadelphia.

Devlin, R. M. 1966. *Plant Physiology*. Reinhold Publishing Corporation, New York.

Ellis, R. J. 1963. "Cysteine biosynthesis in beet discs." *Phytochemistry* 2:129–136.

Fowden, L. 1967. "Aspects of amino acid metabolism in plants." *Annual Review of Plant Physiology* 18:85–106.

Kessler, E. 1963. "Nitrate assimilation by plants." *Annual Review of Plant Physiology* 14:57–72.

Kretovich, W. L. 1965. "Some problems of amino acid and amide biosynthesis in plants." *Annual Review of Plant Physiology* 16:141–154.

Lute, E. 1967. "Alkaloid biosynthesis." *Annual Review of Plant Physiology* 18:179–196.

Mahler, H. R., and E. H. Cordes. 1966. *Biological Chemistry*. Harper & Row, Publishers, Inc., New York.

McKee, H. S. 1962. *Nitrogen Metabolism in Plants*. Oxford University Press (Clarendon), London.

Meyer, B. S., D. B. Anderson, and R. H. Böhning. 1960. *Introduction to Plant Physiology*. D. Van Nostrand Company, Inc., Princeton, N.J.

Raggio, M., and N. Raggio. 1962. "Root nodules." *Annual Review of Plant Physiology* 13:109–128.

Reinbothe, H., and K. Mothes. 1962. "Urea, ureides and guanidines in plants." *Annual Review of Plant Physiology* 13:129–150.

Richards, J. H. 1965. "Alkaloid biogenesis." In *Plant Biochemistry*. J. Bonner and J. E. Varner [eds.]. pp. 526–551. Academic Press, Inc., New York.

Steward, F. C. 1964. *Plants at Work*. Addison-Wesley Publishing Company, Inc., Reading, Mass.

————. 1965. *Plant Physiology*. Vol. IVA. *Metabolism: Organic Nutrition and Nitrogen Metabolism*. Academic Press, Inc., New York.

Stewart, W. D. P. 1966. *Nitrogen Fixation in Plants*. The Athlone Press, University of London.

Thompson, J. F. 1967. "Sulfur metabolism in plants." *Annual Review of Plant Physiology* 18:59–84.

Virtanen, A. I. 1961. "Some aspects of amino acids, synthesis in plants and related subjects." *Annual Review of Plant Physiology* 12:1–10.

Webster, G. C. 1959. *Nitrogen Metabolism in Plants.* Row, Peterson and Company, Evanston, Ill.

Wilson, G. G. 1962. "Metabolism of sulfate: Sulfate reduction." *Annual Review of Plant Physiology* 13:201–224.

Yemm, E. W., and B. F. Folkes. 1958. "The metabolism of amino acids and proteins in plants." *Annual Review of Plant Physiology* 9:245–280.

Yocum, C. S. 1960. "Nitrogen fixation." *Annual Review of Plant Physiology* 11:25–36.

REFERENCES

Afridi, M., and E. Hewitt. 1964. "The inducible formation and stability of nitrate reductase in higher plants. I. Effects of nitrate and molybdenum on enzyme activity in cauliflower." *Journal of Experimental Botany* 15:251–271.

Bergersen, F. J. 1967. "Some properties of nitrogen-fixing breis prepared from soybean root nodules." *Biochimica et Biophysica Acta* 130:304–312.

Garcia-Rivera, J., and R. H. Burris. 1967. "Hydrazine and hydroxylamine as possible intermediates in the biological fixation of nitrogen." *Archives of Biochemistry and Biophysics* 119:167–172.

Goodchild, D. J., and F. J. Bergersen. 1966. "Electron microscopy of the infection and subsequent development of soybean nodule cells." *Journal of Bacteriology* 92:204–213.

Hess, J. L., and N. E. Tolbert. 1967. "Glycolate pathway in algae." *Plant Physiology* 42:371–379.

Joy, K. W., and R. H. Hageman. 1966. "The purification and properties of nitrite reductase from higher plants, and its dependence on ferredoxin." *Biochemical Journal* 100:263–273.

Kaneda, T. 1967. "Biosynthesis of long-chain hydrocarbons. I. Incorporation of L-valine, L-threonine, L-isoleucine, and L-leucine into specific branched-chain hydrocarbons in tobacco." *Biochemistry* 6:2023–2032.

Kennedy, I. R., C. A. Parker, and D. K. Kidby. 1966. "The probable site of nitrogen fixation in root nodules of *Ornithopus sativus.*" *Biochimica et Biophysica Acta* 130:517–519.

Koch, B., H. J. Evans, and S. Russell. 1967. "Reduction of acetylene and nitrogen gas by breis and cell-free extracts of soybean root nodules." *Plant Physiology* 42:466–468.

Mayer, A. M. 1967. "Subcellular location of sulphite reductase in plant tissues." *Plant Physiology* 42:324–326.

Oaks, Ann. 1965. "The synthesis of leucine in maize embryos." *Biochimica et Biophysica Acta* 111:79–89.

Paneque, A., and M. Losada. 1966. "Comparative reduction of nitrate by spinach nitrate reductase with $NADH_2$

and $NADPH_2$." *Biochimica et Biophysica Acta* 128:202–204.

Pate, J. S. 1965. "Roots as organs of assimilation of sulfate." *Science* 149:547–548.

Ritenour, G. L., *et al.* 1967. "Intracellular localization of nitrate reductase, nitrite reductase, and glutamic acid dehydrogenase in green leaf tissue." *Plant Physiology* 42:233–237.

Schaffer, A. G., and M. Alexander. 1967. "Partial purification of a legume nodulation factor present in coconut water." *Plant Physiology* 42:563–567.

Sinha, S. K., and E. A. Cossins. 1964. "The metabolism of (^{14}C) glycine by plant tissues." *Biochemical Journal* 93:27–33.

Splittstoesser, W. E. 1967. "The metabolism of glutamate and leucine by maize tissues." *Phytochemistry* 6:933–939.

CHAPTER 17   BOOKS AND REVIEWS

The Annual Review of Biochemistry each year contains one or more reviews concerning nucleic acids and their relation to protein synthesis.

Asimov, I. 1962. *The Genetic Code.* The New American Library of World Literature, Inc., New York.

Birnstiel, M. 1967. "The nucleolus in cell metabolism." *Annual Review of Plant Physiology* 18:25–58.

Bonner, J. 1965. "Development." In *Plant Biochemistry.* J. Bonner and J. E. Varner [eds.]. pp. 850–866. Academic Press, Inc., New York.

Carpenter, B. H. 1967. *Molecular and Cell Biology.* Dickenson Publishing Company, Inc., Belmont, Calif.

Chargaff, E., and J. N. Davidson. 1955 (Vols. 1 and 2); 1960 (Vol. 3). *The Nucleic Acids.* Academic Press, Inc., New York.

Cold Spring Harbor Symposia on Quantitative Biology. 1961. *Cellular Regulatory Mechanisms* 26.

———. 1963. *Synthesis and Structure of Macromolecules* 28.

———. 1966. *The Genetic Code* 31.

Davidson, J. N. 1965. *The Biochemistry of the Nucleic Acids.* Methuen and Company, Ltd., London; John Wiley & Sons, Inc., New York.

Davidson, J. N., and W. E. Cohn [eds.]. 1962 (Vol. 1); 1966 (through Vol. 5). *Progress in Nucleic Acid Research and Molecular Biology.* Academic Press, Inc., New York.

Holley, R. W. 1965. "Protein metabolism." In *Plant Biochemistry.* J. Bonner and J. E. Varner [eds.], pp. 346–360. Academic Press, Inc., New York.

Jordan, D. O. 1960. *The Chemistry of Nucleic Acids.* Butterworth and Company, Ltd., Washington, D.C.

Mans, R. J. 1967. "Protein synthesis in higher plants." *Annual Review of Plant Physiology* 18:127–146.

Oota, Y. 1964. "RNA in developing plant cells." *Annual Review of Plant Physiology* 15:17–36.

Steward, F. C. [ed.]. 1965. *Plant Physiology*. Vol. IVA. *Metabolism: Organic Nutrition and Nitrogen Metabolism.* Academic Press, Inc., New York.

Tso, P. O. P. 1962. "The ribosomes-ribonucleoprotein particles." *Annual Review of Plant Physiology* 13:45–80.

Watson, J. D. 1965. *Molecular Biology of the Gene.* W. A. Benjamin, Inc., New York.

Webster, G. C. 1959. *Nitrogen Metabolism in Plants.* Row, Peterson and Company, Evanston, Ill.

REFERENCES

Allende, J. E., and Maria Bravo. 1966. "Amino acid incorporation and aminoacyl transfer in a wheat embryo system." *Journal of Biological Chemistry* 241:5813–5818.

Barker, G. R., and J. A. Hollinshead. 1967. "The degradation of ribonucleic acid in the cotyledons of *Pisum arvense.*" *Biochemical Journal* 103:230–237.

Beevers, L., and F. S. Guernsey. 1966. "Changes in some nitrogenous components during the germination of pea seeds." *Plant Physiology* 41:1455–1458.

Bendich, A. J., and E. T. Bolton. 1967. "Relatedness among plants as measured by the DNA-agar technique." *Plant Physiology* 42:959–967.

Berg, P., *et al.* 1965. "Competition between RNA polymerase and DNA polymerase for the DNA template." *Biochemical and Biophysical Research Communications* 18:932–942.

Boardman, N. K., R. I. B. Francki, and S. G. Wildman. 1966. "Protein synthesis by cell-free extracts of tobacco leaves." *Journal of Molecular Biology* 17:470–489.

Chen, Jane L., and S. G. Wildman. 1967. "Functional chloroplast polyribosomes from tobacco leaves." *Science* 155:1271–1273.

Cherry, J. H., *et al.* 1965. "Nucleic acid metabolism in peanut cotyledons." *Plant Physiology* 40:582–587.

Cherry, J. H., and K. J. Lessman. 1967. "Comparison of nucleic acids in maize shoots and pea epicotyls." *American Journal of Botany* 54:181–188.

Ching, Te May. 1966. "Compositional changes of Douglas fir seeds during germination." *Plant Physiology* 41:1313–1319.

Clements, R. L. 1965. "Fruit proteins: Extraction and electrophoresis." *Analytical Biochemistry* 13:390–401.

Click, R. E., and D. P. Hackett. 1966. "Evidence that the two ribosomal RNA species of plant tissue are synthesized on different genetic loci." *Journal of Molecular Biology* 16:279–284.

——————. 1967. "Functional stability of messenger RNA in potato tuber slices." *Biochimica et Biophysica Acta* 142:403–409.

Commoner, B. 1964. "Deoxyribonucleic acid and the molecular basis of self-duplication." *Nature* 202:960–968.

Das, H. K., S. K. Chatterjee, and S. C. Roy. 1964. "Protein synthesis in plant mitochondria. I. Incorporation of amino acid in peptide linkage." *Journal of Biological Chemistry* 239:1126–1133.

Davern, C. I. 1966. "Isolation of the DNA of the *E. coli* chromosome in one piece." *Proceedings of the National Academy of Sciences* 55:792–797.

Fambrough, D. M., and J. Bonner. 1966. "On the similarity of plant and animal histones." *Biochemistry* 5:2563–2570.

Filner, P. 1965. "Semi-conservative replication of DNA in a higher plant cell." *Experimental Cell Research* 39:33–39.

Gibor, A., and S. Granick. 1964. "Plastids and mitochondria: Inheritable systems." *Science* 145:890–897.

Holley, R. W. 1966. "The nucleotide sequence of a nucleic acid." *Scientific American* 214(2):30–39.

Hotta, Y., M. Ito, and H. Stern. 1966. "Synthesis of DNA during meiosis." *Proceedings of the National Academy of Sciences* 56:1184–1191.

Huang, R. C., and J. Bonner. 1965. "Histone-bound RNA, a component of native nucleohistone." *Proceedings of the National Academy of Sciences* 54:960–967.

Ingle, J., D. Beitz, and R. H. Hageman. 1965. "Changes in composition during development and maturation of maize seeds." *Plant Physiology* 40:835–839.

Ingle, J., J. L. Key, and R. E. Holm. 1965. "Demonstration and characterization of a DNA-like RNA in excised plant tissue." *Journal of Molecular Biology* 11:730–746.

Jacob, F. 1966. "Genetics of the bacterial cell." *Science* 152:1470–1478.

Lengyel, P. 1966. "Problems in protein biosynthesis." *Journal of General Physiology* 49:305–330.

Marcus, A., and J. Feeley. 1965. "Protein synthesis in imbibed seeds." II. Polysome formation during imbibition." *Journal of Biological Chemistry* 240:1675–1680.

Maul, G. G., and T. H. Hamilton. 1967. "The intranuclear localization of two DNA-dependent RNA polymerase activities." *Proceedings of the National Academy of Sciences* 57:1371–1378.

Miller, J. H., and Henry M. Sobell. 1966. "A molecular model for gene repression." *Proceedings of the National Academy of Sciences* 55:1201–1205.

Monod, J. 1966. "From enzymatic adaptation to allosteric transitions." *Science* 154:475–483.

Nass, Margit M. K. 1966. "The circularity of mitochondrial DNA." *Proceedings of the National Academy of Sciences* 56:1215–1222.

Nass, Margit M. K., S. Nass, and B. A. Afzelius. 1965. "The general occurrence of mitochondrial DNA." *Experimental Cell Research* 37:516–539.

Nirenberg, M. W., and J. H. Matthaei. 1961. "The dependence of cell-free protein synthesis in *E. coli* upon naturally occurring or synthetic polyribonucleotides." *Proceedings of the National Academy of Sciences* 47: 1588–1602.

Parisi, B., and O. Ciferri. 1966. "Protein synthesis by cell-free extracts from castor bean seedlings. I. Preparation and characteristics of the amino acid incorporating system." *Biochemistry* 5:1638–1645.

Stent, G. S. 1966. "Genetic transcription." *Proceedings of the Royal Society*, B., 164:181–197.

Stout, E. R., and R. J. Mans. 1967. "Partial purification and properties of RNA polymerase from maize." *Biochimica et Biophysica Acta* 134:327–336.

Stutz, E., and H. Noll. 1967. "Characterization of cytoplasmic and chloroplast polysomes in plants: Evidence for three classes of ribosomal RNA in nature." *Proceedings of the National Academy of Sciences* 57:774–781.

Suyama, Y., and W. D. Bonner, Jr. 1966. "DNA from plant mitochondria." *Plant Physiology* 41:383–388.

CHAPTER 18   BOOKS AND REVIEWS

Benson, A. A. 1964. "Plant membrane lipids." *Annual Review of Plant Physiology* 15:1–16.

Bloch, K. 1965. "The biological synthesis of cholesterol." *Science* 150:19–28.

Bogorad, L. 1958. "The biogenesis of flavonoids." *Annual Review of Plant Physiology* 9:417–448.

Bonner, J. 1950. *Plant Biochemistry*. Academic Press, Inc., New York.

Bonner, J., and J. E. Varner. 1965. *Plant Biochemistry*. Academic Press, Inc., New York.

Brown, S. A. 1966. "Lignins." *Annual Review of Plant Physiology* 17:223–244.

Eglinton, G., and R. J. Hamilton. 1967. "Leaf epicuticular waxes." *Science* 156:1322–1335.

Goodwin, T. W. 1961. "Biosynthesis and function of carotenoids." *Annual Review of Plant Physiology* 12:219–244.

Goodwin, T. W. 1965. *Chemistry and Biochemistry of Plant Pigments*. Academic Press, Inc., New York.

Goodwin, T. W. [ed.]. 1966 (Vol. 1); 1967 (Vol. 2). *Biochemistry of Chloroplasts*. Academic Press, Inc., New York.

Harborne, J. B. 1964. *Biochemistry of Phenolic Compounds*. Academic Press, Inc., New York.

Heftmann, E. 1963. "Biochemistry of plant steroids." *Annual Review of Plant Physiology* 14:225–248.

Kolattukudy, P. E. 1968. "Biosynthesis of surface lipids." *Science* 159:498–505.

Kremers, R. E. 1959. "The lignins." *Annual Review of Plant Physiology* 10:185–196.

Mudd, J. B. 1967. "Fat metabolism in plants." *Annual Review of Plant Physiology* 18:229–252.

Neish, A. C. 1960. "Biosynthetic pathways of aromatic compounds." *Annual Review of Plant Physiology* 11: 55–80.

Porter, J. W., and D. G. Anderson. 1967. "Biosynthesis of carotenes." *Annual Review of Plant Physiology* 18:197–228.

Pridham, J. B. 1965. "Low molecular weight phenols in higher plants." *Annual Review of Plant Physiology* 16:13–36.

——————. [ed.]. 1967. *Terpenoids in plants*. Academic Press, Inc., New York.

Pridham, J. B., and T. Swain [eds.]. 1965. *Biosynthetic Pathways in Higher Plants*. Academic Press, Inc., New York.

Robinson, T. 1967. *The Organic Constituents of Higher Plants. Their Chemistry and Interrelationships*. Burgess Publishing Company, Minneapolis.

Schubert, W. J. 1965. *Lignin Biochemistry*. Academic Press, Inc., New York.

Stumpf, P. K., and C. Bradbeer. 1959. "Fat metabolism in higher plants." *Annual Review of Plant Physiology* 10:197–222.

Wolff, I. A. 1966. "Seed lipids." *Science* 154:1140–1149.

Zill, L. P., and G. M. Cheniae. 1962. "Lipid metabolism." *Annual Review of Plant Physiology* 13:225–264.

REFERENCES

Anderson, J. D., and T. C. Moore. 1967. "Biosynthesis of (−)-Kaurene in cell-free extracts of immature pea seeds." *Plant Physiology* 42:1527–1534.

Baisted, D. J. 1967. "Incorporation of label from Geraniol-^{14}C into squalene, β-amyrin and β-sitosterol in germinating pea seeds." *Phytochemistry* 6:93–97.

Bellis, D. M., M. S. Spring, and J. R. Stoker. 1967. "The biosynthesis of dicoumarol." *Biochemical Journal* 103: 202–206.

Bennett, R. D., Ellen Lieber, and E. Heftmann. 1967. "Biosynthesis of sterol from (−)-Kaurene." *Phytochemistry* 6:1107–1110.

Brodie, J. D., Gertrude Wasson, and J. W. Porter. 1964. "Enzyme-bound intermediates in the biosynthesis of mevalonic and palmitic acids." *Journal of Biological Chemistry* 239:1346–1356.

Burbott, Alice J., and W. D. Loomis. 1967. "Effects of light and temperature on the monoterpenes of peppermint." *Plant Physiology* 42:20–28.

Cooper, Carol Z., and C. R. Benedict. 1967. "Mevalonic acid kinase in *Euglena gracilis*." *Plant Physiology* 42:515–519.

Delmer, Deborah P., and S. E. Mills. 1968. "Tryptophan biosynthesis in cell cultures of *Nicotiana tabacum*." *Plant Physiology* 43:81–87.

Dennis, D. T., and C. A. West. 1967. "Biosynthesis of gibberellins. III. The conversion of (−)-Kaurene to (−)-Kauren-19-oic acid in endosperm of *Echinocystis macrocarpa* Greene." *Journal of Biological Chemistry* 242:3293–3300.

Gamborg, O. L. 1966. "Aromatic metabolism in plants. II. Enzymes of the shikimate pathway in suspension cultures of plant cells." *Canadian Journal of Biochemistry* 44:791–799.

Glennie, C. W., and B. A. Bohm. 1966. "Conjugates of hydroxycinnamic acids and glucose in some gymnosperms." *Canadian Journal of Biochemistry* 44:281–283.

Goad, L. J., and T. W. Goodwin. 1967. "Studies on phytosterol biosynthesis: The sterols of *Larix decidua* leaves." *European Journal of Biochemistry* 1:357–362.

Graebe, Jan. 1967. "Isoprenoid biosynthesis in a cell-free system from pea shoots." *Science* 157:73–75.

Griffiths, W. T., D. R. Threlfall, and T. W. Goodwin. 1967. "Nature, intracellular distribution, and formation of terpenoid quinones in maize and barley shoots." *Biochemical Journal* 103:589–600.

Hagen, C. W. 1966. "The differentiation of pigmentation in flower parts. I. The flavonoid pigments of *Impatiens balsamina* genotype 11HHPrPr and their distribution within the plant." *American Journal of Botany* 53:46–54.

Harris, R. V., and A. T. James. 1965. "Linoleic and α-linolenic acid biosynthesis in plant leaves and a green alga." *Biochimica et Biophysica Acta* 106:456–464.

Hawke, J. C., and P. K. Stumpf. 1965. "Fat metabolism in higher plants. XXVIII. The biosynthesis of saturated and unsaturated fatty acids by preparation from barley seedlings." *Journal of Biological Chemistry* 240:4746–4752.

Higuchi, T. 1966. "Role of phenylalanine deaminase and tyrase in the lignification of bamboo." *Agricultural and Biological Chemistry* 30:667–673.

Hillis, W. E., and K. Isoi. 1965. "The biosynthesis of polyphenols in *Eucalyptus* species." *Phytochemistry* 4:905–918.

Hitchcock, C., and A. T. James. 1966. "The mechanism of α-oxidation in leaves." *Biochimica et Biophysica Acta* 116:413–424.

Huelin, F. E., and K. E. Murray. 1966. "α-Farnesene in the natural coating of apples." *Nature* 210:1260–1261.

Johnson, D. F., R. D. Bennett, and E. Heftmann. 1963. "Cholesterol in higher plants." *Science* 140:198–199.

Kende, H. 1967. "Preparation of gibberellin A1 and its metabolism in dwarf peas." *Plant Physiology* 42:1612–1618.

Kirkham, D. S., and L. D. Hunter. 1965. "Studies of the *in vivo* activity of esters of o-coumaric and cinnamic acids against apple scab." *Annals of Applied Biology* 55:359–371.

Koukol, Jane, and E. E. Conn. 1961. "The metabolism of aromatic compounds in higher plants. IV. Purification and properties of the phenylalanine deaminase of *Hordeum vulgare*." *Journal of Biological Chemistry* 236:2692–2698.

Levin, E. Y., and K. Bloch. 1964. "Absence of sterols in blue-green algae." *Nature* 202:90–91.

Melchert, T. E., and R. E. Alston. 1965. "Flavonoids from the moss *Mnium affine* Bland." *Science* 150:1170–1171.

Minamikawa, T., and I. Uritani. 1967. "3-Deoxy-D-arabino-heptulosonic acid-7-phosphate synthase in sweet potato roots." *Journal of Biochemistry* 61:367–372.

Nagai, J., and K. Bloch. 1967. "Elongation of acyl carrier protein derivatives by bacterial and plant extracts." *Journal of Biological Chemistry* 242:357–362.

Pecket, R. C. 1966. "Development of anthocyanin pigmentation in flowers of *Lathyrus odoratus*." *Journal of Experimental Botany* 17:177–184.

Pierpoint, W. S. 1966. "The enzymic oxidation of chlorogenic acid and some reactions of the quinone produced." *Biochemical Journal* 98:567–580.

Simoni, R. D., R. S. Criddle, and P. K. Stumpf. 1967. "Fat metabolism in higher plants. XXXI. Purification and properties of plant and bacterial acyl carrier proteins." *Journal of Biological Chemistry* 242:573–581.

Stafford, Helen A. 1967. "Biosynthesis of phenolic compounds in first internodes of sorghum: Lignin and related products." *Plant Physiology* 42:450–455.

Steck, W. 1967. "Biosynthesis of scopolin in tobacco." *Canadian Journal of Biochemistry* 45:889–896.

Stoher, J. R. 1964. "The biosynthesis of coumarin in *Melilotus alba*." *Biochemical and Biophysical Research Communication* 14:17–20.

Varga, M., and E. Koves. 1959. "Phenolic acids as growth and germination inhibitors in dry fruits." *Nature* 4658:401.

Wong, E. 1965. "Flavonoid biosynthesis in *Cicer arietinum*." *Biochimica et Biophysica Acta* 111:358–363.

Yang, S. F., and P. K. Stumpf. 1965. "Fat metabolism in higher plants. XXI. Biosynthesis of fatty acids by avocado mesocarp enzyme systems." *Biochimica et Biophysica Acta* 98:19–26.

CHAPTER 19 BOOKS AND REVIEWS

Bonner, J., and A. W. Galston. 1952. *Principles of Plant Physiology.* W. H. Freeman & Company, Publishers, San Francisco.

Humphries, E. C., and A. W. Wheeler. 1963. "The physiology of leaf growth." *Annual Review of Plant Physiology* 14:385–410.

Klein, R. M. [ed.]. 1961. *Plant Growth Regulation.* Iowa State University Press, Ames.

Leopold, A. C. 1964. *Plant Growth and Development.* McGraw-Hill Book Company, Inc., New York.

Lockhart, J. A. 1965. "The analysis of interactions of physical and chemical factors of plant growth." *Annual Review of Plant Physiology* 16:37–52.

Loomis, W. E. [ed.]. 1953. *Growth and Differentiation in Plants.* The Iowa State College Press, Ames.

Meyer, B. S., D. B. Anderson, and R. H. Böhning. 1960. *Introduction to Plant Physiology.* D. Van Nostrand Company, Inc., Princeton, N. J.

Sachs, R. M. 1965. "Stem elongation." *Annual Review of Plant Physiology* 16:73–96.

Salisbury, F. B., and R. V. Parke. 1964. *Vascular Plants: Form and Function.* Wadsworth Publishing Company, Inc., Belmont, Calif.

Sinnott, E. W. 1960. *Plant Morphogenesis.* McGraw-Hill Book Company, Inc., New York.

—————. 1961. *The Biology of the Spirit.* The Viking Press, Inc., New York.

Steward, F. C., and H. Y. Mohan Ram. 1961. "Determining factors in cell growth: Some implications for morphogenesis in plants." *Advances in Morphogenesis* 1:189–266.

Thompson, D. 1966. *On Growth and Form.* J. T. Bonner [ed.], abridged edition. University Press, Cambridge. (Original edition, 1942).

Torrey, J. G. 1967. *Development in Flowering Plants.* The Macmillan Company, New York.

REFERENCES

Maksymowych, R. 1963. "Cell division and cell elongation in leaf development of *Xanthium pensylvanicum.*" *American Journal of Botany* 50:891–901.

Parke, R. V. 1959. "Growth periodicity and the shoot tip of *Abies concolor.*" *American Journal of Botany* 46:110–118.

CHAPTER 20   BOOKS AND REVIEWS

Atkinson, D. W. 1965. "Biological feedback control at the molecular level." *Science* 150:851–862.

Bonner, J. 1965. *The Molecular Biology of Development.* Oxford University Press, New York and Oxford.

Bonner, J., and J. E. Varner [eds.]. 1965. *Plant Biochemistry.* Academic Press, Inc., New York.

Cohen, G. N. 1965. "Regulations of enzyme activity in microorganisms." *Annual Review of Microbiology* 19:105–126.

Cold Spring Harbor Symposia on Quantitative Biology. 1961. *Cellular Regulatory Mechanisms,* 26.

—————. 1963. *Synthesis and Structure of Macromolecules* Vol. 28.

Fredrick, J. F., and E. M. Weyer [eds.]. 1967. "Plant Growth Regulators." *Annals of the New York Academy of Sciences* 144:1–382.

Haemmerling, J. 1963. "Nucleo-cytoplasmic interactions in acetabularia and other cells." *Annual Review of Plant Physiology* 14:65–92.

Johri, B. M., and I. K. Vasil. 1961. "Physiology of pollen." *Botanical Review* 27:325–381.

Linskens, H. F. 1964. "Pollen physiology." *Annual Review of Plant Physiology* 15:255–270.

Machlis, L., and Erika Rawitscher-Kunkel. 1963. "Mechanisms of gametic approach in plants." *International Review of Cytology* 15:97–138.

Maheshwari, P., and N. S. Rangaswamy. 1965. "Embryology in relation to physiology and genetics." *Advances in Botanical Research* 2:219–321.

Oota, Y. 1964. "RNA in developing plant cells." *Annual Review of Plant Physiology* 15:17–36.

Stadtman, E. R. 1966. "Allosteric regulation of enzyme activity." *Advances in Enzymology* 28:41–154.

Stern, H. 1966. "The regulation of cell division." *Annual Review of Plant Physiology* 17:345–378.

Torrey, J. G. 1967. *Development in Flowering Plants.* The Macmillan Company, New York.

Umbarger, H. E. 1963. "The integration of metabolic pathways." *Annual Review of Plant Physiology* 14:19–42.

Watson, J. D. 1965. *Molecular Biology of the Gene.* W. A. Benjamin, Inc., New York.

Wilkins, M. B. 1966. "Geotropism." *Annual Review of Plant Physiology* 17:379–408.

REFERENCES

Afridi, M., and E. Hewitt. 1964. "The inducible formation and stability of nitrate reductase in higher plants. I. Effects of nitrate and molybdenum on enzyme activity in cauliflower." *Journal of Experimental Botany* 15:251–271.

Brown, G. N., and A. W. Naylor. 1965. "Quantitative studies of nucleic acids in contrasting zones of tissue differentiation in germinating *Mimosa* seedlings." *Botanical Gazette* 126:167–174.

Burg, S. P., and Ellen A. Burg. 1967. "Lateral auxin transport in stems and roots." *Plant Physiology* 42:891–893.

Chadwick, A. W., and S. P. Burg. 1967. "An explanation of the inhibition of root growth caused by indole-3-acetic acid." *Plant Physiology* 42:415–420.

Changeux, J. P. 1965. "The control of biochemical reactions." *Scientific American* 212(4):36–43.

Dedolph, R. R., S. M. Naqvi, and S. A. Gordon. 1966. "Role of indole-3-acetic acid in modification of geotropic responses in clinostat rotated *Avena* seedlings." *Plant Physiology* 41:897–902.

Ghosh, H. P., and J. Preiss. 1965. "The biosynthesis of starch in spinach chloroplasts." *Journal of Biological Chemistry* 240:960–961.

Jacob, F., and J. Monod. 1961. "Genetic regulatory mechanisms in the synthesis of proteins." *Journal of Molecular Biology* 3:318–356.

Jensen, W. A. 1966. "The problem of cell development in plants." In *Plant Biology Today: Advances and Challenges.* W. A. Jensen and L. G. Kavaljian [eds.]. pp. 11–26. Wadsworth Publishing Company, Inc., Belmont, Calif.

Machlis, L., *et al.* 1966. "Production, isolation and characterization of sirenin." *Biochemistry* 5:2147–2152.

Mascarenhas, J. P., and L. Machlis. 1962. "The pollen-tube chemotropic factor from *Antirrhinum majus*: Bioassay, extraction, and partial purification." *American Journal of Botany* 49:482–489.

Monod, J., J. P. Changeux, and F. Jacob. 1963. "Allosteric proteins and cellular control systems." *Journal of Molecular Biology* 6:306–329.

Neumann, J., and M. E. Jones. 1964. "End-product inhibition of aspartate transcarbamylase in various species." *Archives of Biochemistry and Biophysics* 104:438–447.

Oaks, Ann. 1965. "The synthesis of leucine in maize embryos." *Biochimica et Biophysica Acta* 111:79–89.

CHAPTER 21   BOOKS AND REVIEWS

Audus, L. J. 1959. *Plant Growth Substances.* Leonard Hill (Books), Limited, London; Interscience Publishers, Inc. New York.

Ball, N. G. 1963. "Plant tropisms." *Vistas in Botany* 3:228–254.

Bentley, J. A. 1958. "The naturally occurring auxins and inhibitors." *Annual Review of Plant Physiology* 9:47–80.

Brian, P. W. 1966. "The gibberellins as hormones." *International Review of Cytology* 19:229–266.

Burg, S. P. 1962. "The physiology of ethylene formation." *Annual Review of Plant Physiology* 13:265–302.

Cathey, H. M. 1964. "Physiology of growth-retarding chemicals." *Annual Review of Plant Physiology* 15:271–302.

Crane, J. C. 1964. "Growth substances in fruit setting and development." *Annual Review of Plant Physiology* 15:303–326.

Fawcett, C. H. 1961. "Indole auxins." *Annual Review of Plant Physiology* 12:345–368.

Fogg, G. E. 1963. *The Growth of Plants.* Penguin Books, Baltimore, Md.

Fredga, A., and B. Åberg. 1965. "Stereoisomerism in plant growth regulators of the auxin type." *Annual Review of Plant Physiology* 16:53–72.

Fredrick, J. F., and E. M. Weyer [eds.]. 1967. "Plant Growth Regulators." *Annals of the New York Academy of Sciences* 144:1–382.

Galston, A. W., and W. K. Purves. 1960. "The mechanism of action of auxin." *Annual Review of Plant Physiology* 11:239–276.

Gruen, H. E. 1959. "Auxins and fungi." *Annual Review of Plant Physiology* 10:405–440.

Haupt, W. 1965. "Orienting growth and movement in lower plants." *Annual Review of Plant Physiology* 16:267–290.

Heslop-Harrison, J. 1963. "Plant growth substances." *Vistas in Botany* 3:104–194.

Klein, R. M. [ed.]. 1961. *Plant Growth Regulation.* Fourth International Conference on Plant Growth Regulation. The Iowa State University Press, Ames.

Laetsch, W. M., and R. E. Cleland [eds.]. 1967. *Papers on Plant Growth and Development.* Little, Brown and Company, Boston.

Leopold, A. C. 1958. "Auxin uses in the control of flowering and fruiting." *Annual Review of Plant Physiology* 9:281–310.

————. 1964. *Plant Growth and Development.* McGraw-Hill Book Company, New York.

Letham, D. S. 1967. "Chemistry and physiology of kinetin-like compounds." *Annual Review of Plant Physiology* 18:349–364.

Linskens, H. F. 1964. "Pollen physiology." *Annual Review of Plant Physiology* 15:255–270.

Loomis, W. E. [ed.]. 1953. *Growth and Differentiation in Plants.* The Iowa State College Press, Ames.

Maheshwari, P., and N. S. Rangaswamy. 1965. "Embryology in relation to physiology and genetics." *Advances in Botanical Research* 2:219–321.

Miller, C. O. 1961. "Kinetin and related compounds in plant growth." *Annual Review of Plant Physiology* 12:395–408.

Paleg, L. G. 1965. "Physiological effects of gibberellins." *Annual Review of Plant Physiology* 16:291–322.

Phinney, B. O., and C. A. West. 1960. "Gibberellins as native plant growth regulators." *Annual Review of Plant Physiology* 11:411–436.

Ray, P. M. 1958. "Destruction of auxin." *Annual Review of Plant Physiology* 9:81–118.

Rufelt, H. 1961. "Geotropism in roots and shoots." *Annual Review of Plant Physiology* 12:409–430.

Shantz, E. M. 1966. "Chemistry of naturally-occurring growth regulating substances." *Annual Review of Plant Physiology* 17:409–438.

Skoog, F. [ed.]. 1951. *Plant Growth Substances.* University of Wisconsin Press, Madison.

Steward, F. C. 1964. *Plants at Work.* Addison-Wesley Publishing Company, Inc., Reading, Mass.

Steward, F. C., and E. M. Shantz. 1959. "The chemical regulation of growth: Some substances and extracts which induce growth and morphogenesis." *Annual Review of Plant Physiology* 10:379–404.

Street, H. E. 1966. "The physiology of root growth." *Annual Review of Plant Physiology* 17:315–344.

Stuart, N. W. 1961. "Applied aspects of the gibberellins." *Annual Review of Plant Physiology* 12:369–394.

Thimann, K. V. 1965. "Toward an endocrinology of higher plants." In *Recent Progress in Hormone Research.* G. Pincus [ed.]. pp. 579–596. Academic Press, Inc., New York.

Torrey, J. G. 1967. *Development in Flowering Plants.* The Macmillan Company, New York.

van Overbeek, J. 1966. "Plant hormones and regulators." *Science* 152:721–731.

REFERENCES

Abeles, F. B. 1966. "Auxin stimulation of ethylene evolution." *Plant Physiology* 41:585–588.

Abeles, F. B., and R. E. Holm. 1966. "Enhancement of RNA synthesis. Protein synthesis and abscission by ethylene." *Plant Physiology* 41:1337–1342.

Addicott, F. T., H. R. Carns, J. W. Cornforth, J. L. Lyon, B. V. Milborrow, K. Ohkuma, G. Ryback, O. E. Smith, W. E. Thiessen, and P. F. Wareing. 1968. "Abscisic acid: A proposal for the redesignation of abscisin II (dormin)." *Biochemistry and Physiology of Plant Growth Substances* (Sixth International Conference on Plant Growth Substances).

Armstrong, D. J. 1966. "Hypothesis concerning the mechanism of auxin action." *Proceedings of the National Academy of Sciences* 56:64–66.

Arney, S. E., and P. Mancinelli. 1966. "The basic action of gibberellic acid in elongation of 'Meteor' pea stems." *New Phytologist* 65:161–175.

Bastin, M. 1966. "Root, initiation, auxin level and biosynthesis of phenolic compounds." *Photochemistry and Photobiology* 5:423–429.

Bendaña, F. E., and A. W. Galston. 1965. "Hormone-induced stabilization of soluble RNA in pea-stem tissue." *Science* 150:69–70.

Brown, C. L., R. G. McAlpine, and P. P. Kormanik. 1967. "Apical dominance and form in woody plants: A reappraisal." *American Journal of Botany* 54:153–162.

Burg, S. P., and Ellen A. Burg. 1966. "Auxin-induced ethylene formation: Its relation to flowering in the pineapple." *Science* 152:1269.

———. 1965. "Ethylene action and the ripening of fruits." *Science* 148:1190–1196.

———. 1966. "The interaction between auxin and ethylene and its role in plant growth." *Proceedings of the National Academy of Sciences* 55:262–269.

Carr, D. J., and W. J. Burrows. 1966. "Evidence of the presence in xylem sap of substances with kinetin-like activity." *Life Sciences* 5:2061–2077.

Chadwick, A. V., and S. P. Burg. 1967. "An explanation of the inhibition of root growth caused by indole-3-acetic acid." *Plant Physiology* 42:415–420.

Chrispells, M. J., and J. E. Varner. 1966. "Inhibition of gibberellic acid induced formation of α-amylase by abscisin II." *Nature* 212:1066–1067.

Chrispells, M. J., and J. E. Varner. 1967. "Hormonal control of enzyme synthesis: On the mode of action of gibberellic acid and abscisin in aleurone layers of barley." *Plant Physiology* 42:1008–1016.

Coartney, J. S., D. J. Morre, and J. L. Key. 1967. "Inhibition of RNA synthesis and auxin-induced cell wall extensibility and growth by actinomycin D." *Plant Physiology* 42:434–439.

Digby, J., and P. F. Wareing. 1966. "The relationship between endogenous hormone levels in the plant and seasonal aspects of cambial activity." *Annals of Botany* 30:607–622.

Epstein, E., and P. G. Miles. 1967. "Identification of indole-3-acetic acid in the basidiomycete *Schizophyllum commune.*" *Plant Physiology* 42:911–914.

Fan, Der-Fong, and G. A. Maclachlan. 1967. "Massive synthesis of ribonucleic acid and cellulase in the pea epicotyl in response to indoleacetic acid, with and without concurrent cell division." *Plant Physiology* 42:1114–1122.

Fox, J. E. 1966. "Incorporation of a kinin, N, 6-Benzyl-adenine into soluble RNA." *Plant Physiology* 41:75–82.

Fox, J. E., and Chong-maw Chen. 1967. "Characterization of labeled ribonucleic acid from tissue grown on ^{14}C-containing cytokinins." *Journal of Biological Chemistry* 242:4490–4494.

Goldsmith, Mary Helen M. 1966. "Maintenance of polarity of auxin movement by basipetal transport." *Plant Physiology* 41:749–754.

Hall, R. H., *et al.* 1967. "Cytokinins in the soluble RNA of plant tissues." *Science* 156:69–71.

Helgeson, J. P., and N. J. Leonard. 1966. "Cytokinins: Identification of compounds isolated from *Corynebacterium fascians.*" *Proceedings of the National Academy of Sciences* 56:59–63.

Jacobs, W. P., and C. C. McCready. 1967. "Polar transport of growth-regulators in pith and vascular tissues of *Coleus* stems." *American Journal of Botany* 54:1035–1040.

Jacobsen, J. V., and J. E. Varner. 1967. "Gibberellic acid-induced synthesis of protease by isolated aleurone layers of barley." *Plant Physiology* 42:1596–1600.

Jones, R. L., and I. D. J. Phillips. 1966. "Organs of gibberellin synthesis in light-grown sunflower plants." *Plant Physiology* 41:1381–1386.

Kefford, N. P., and P. L. Goldacre. 1961. "The changing concept of auxin." *American Journal of Botany* 48:643–649.

Kende, H. 1965. "Kinetin-like factors in the root exudate of sunflowers." *Proceedings of the National Academy of Sciences* 53:1302–1307.

Key, J. L. 1964. "Ribonucleic acid and protein synthesis as essential processes for cell elongation." *Plant Physiology* 39:365–370.

Klambt, D., Gail Thies, and F. Skoog. 1966. "Isolation of cytokinins from *Corynebacterium fascians*." *Proceedings of the National Academy of Sciences* 56:52–59.

Koshimizu, K., *et al.* 1966. "Identity of lupin inhibitor with abscisin II and its biological activity on growth of rice seedlings." *Agricultural and Biological Chemistry* 30:941–943.

Lagerstedt, H. B., and R. G. Langston. 1967. "Translocation of radioactive kinetin." *Plant Physiology* 42:611–622.

Lantican, Beatriz P., and R. M. Muir. 1967. "Isolation and properties of the enzyme system forming indoleacetic acid." *Plant Physiology* 42:1158–1160.

Leopold, A. C., and O. F. Hall. 1966. "Mathematical model of polar auxin transport." *Plant Physiology* 41:1476–1480.

Letham, D. S. 1963. "Zeatin, a factor inducing cell division isolated from *Zea mays*." *Life Sciences* 8:569–573.

Letham, D. S., and C. O. Miller. 1965. "Identity of kinetin-like factors from *Zea mays*." *Plant and Cell Physiology* 6:355–359.

Letham, D. S., and R. K. Ralph. 1967. "A cytokinin in soluble RNA from a higher plant."*Life Sciences* 6:387–394.

Lewis, L. N., R. A. Khalifah, and C. W. Coggins, Jr. 1965. "The existence of the non-indolic citrus auxin in several plant families." *Phytochemistry* 4:203–205.

Lieberman, M., and Alice T. Kunishi.1967. "Propanal may be a precursor of ethylene in metabolism." *Science* 158:938.

Loomis, R. S., and J. G. Torrey. 1964. "Chemical control of vascular cambium initiation in isolated radish roots." *Proceedings of the National Academy of Sciences* 52:3–11.

Masuda, Y., and S. Wada. 1966. "Requirement of RNA for the auxin-induced elongation of oat coleoptile." *Physiologia Plantarum* 19:1055–1063.

Mertz, D., and W. Henson. 1967. "The effect of the plant growth retardants Amo 1618 and CCC on gibberellin production in *Fusarium moniliforme*: Light stimulated biosynthesis of gibberellins." *Physiologia Plantarum* 20:187–199.

Miller, C. O. 1967. "Zeatin and zeatin riboside from a mycorrhizal fungus." *Science* 157:1055–1057.

Moore, T. C., and C. A. Shaner. 1967. "Biosynthesis of indoleacetic acid from tryptophan-^{14}C in cell free extracts of pea shoot tips." *Plant Physiology* 2:1787–1796.

Mothes, K., and L. Engelbrecht. 1961. "Kinetin-induced directed transport of substances in excised leaves in the dark." *Phytochemistry* 1:58–62.

Nicholls, P. B. 1967. "The isolation of indole-3-acetyl-2-O-myoinositol from *Zea mays*." *Planta* 72:258–264.

Nitsan, J., and A. Lang. 1966. "DNA synthesis in the elongating nondividing cells of the lentil epicotyl and its promotion by gibberellin." *Plant Physiology* 41:965–970.

Nooden, L. D., and K. V. Thimann. 1966. "Action of inhibitors of RNA and protein synthesis on cell enlargement." *Plant Physiology* 41:157–164.

Ohkuma, K., J. L. Lyon, F. T. Addicott, and O. E. Smith. 1963. "Abscisin II, an abscission-accelerating substance from young cotton fruit." *Science* 142:1592–1593.

Patterson, B. D., and A. J. Trewavas. 1967. "Changes in the pattern of protein synthesis induced by 3-indolylacetic acid." *Plant Physiology* 42:1081–1086.

Phelps, R. H., and L. Sequeira. 1967. "Synthesis of indoleacetic acid via tryptamine by a cell-free system from tobacco terminal buds." *Plant Physiology* 42:1161–1163.

Pilet, P. E. 1964. "Auxin transport in roots." *Nature* 204:559–562.

Rayle, D. L., and W. K. Purves. 1967. "Conversion of indole-3-ethanol to indole-3-acetic acid in cucumber seedling shoots." *Plant Physiology* 42:1091–1093.

———. 1967. "Isolation and identification of indole-3-ethanol (tryptophol) from cucumber seedlings." *Plant Physiology* 42:520–524.

Sarkissian, I. V., and R. G. McDaniel. 1966. "Regulation of mitochondrial activity by indoleacetic acid." *Biochimica et Biophysica Acta* 128:413–418.

Shen-Miller, J., and S. A. Gordon. 1966. "Hormonal relations in the photo-tropic response. IV. Light-induced changes of endogenous auxins in the coleoptile." *Plant Physiology* 41:831–841.

Sorokin, Helen P., and K. V. Thimann. 1964. "The histological basis for inhibition of auxiliary buds in *Pisum sativum* and the effects of auxins and kinetin on xylem development." *Protoplasma* 59:326–350.

Stonier, T., and Y. Yoneda. 1967. "Stem internode elongation in the Japanese Morning Glory (*Pharbitis nil* Choisy) in relation to an inhibitor system of auxin destruction." *Physiologia Plantarum* 20:13–19.

Sumner, D. C., and J. L. Lyon. 1967. "Effects of ($\pm$)-abscisin II on seed germination in four species of grasses." *Planta* 75:28–32.

Taylor, H. F., and T. A. Smith. 1967. "Production of plant growth inhibitors from Xanthophylls: A possible source of dormin." *Nature* 215:1513–1514.

Tester, C. F., and L. S. Deire, III. 1967. "Nucleic acid synthesis during the hormone-stimulated growth of excised oat coleoptiles." *Biochemistry* 6:2532–2538.

Thimann, K. V., and T. Sachs. "The role of cytokinins in the 'fasciation' disease caused by *Corynebacterium fascians*." *American Journal of Botany* 53:731–739.

van Overbeek, J., *et al.* 1967. "Dormin (abscisin II), inhibitor of plant DNA synthesis?" *Science* 156:1497–1499.

Wilkins, M. B., and Mary Martin. 1967. "Dependence of basipetal polar transport of auxin upon aerobic metabolism." *Plant Physiology* 42:831–839.

Winter, A. 1966. "A hypothetical route for the biogenesis of IAA." *Planta* 71:229–239.

Winter, A., and K. V. Thimann. 1966. "Bound indoleacetic acid in *Avena* coleoptiles." *Plant Physiology* 41:335–342.

Yang, S. F., H. S. Ku, and H. K. Pratt. 1967. "Photochemical production of ethylene from methionine and its analogues in the presence of flavin mononucleotide." *The Journal of Biological Chemistry* 242:5274–5280.

Zeevaart, J. A. D. 1966. "Reduction of the gibberellin content of *Pharbitis* seeds by CCC and after-effects in the progeny." *Plant Physiology* 41:856–862.

CHAPTER 22   BOOKS AND REVIEWS

Allsopp, A. 1964. "Shoot morphogenesis." *Annual Review of Plant Physiology* 15:225–254.

Brookhaven Symposia Committee [eds.]. 1964. *Meristems and Differentiation.* Brookhaven Symposia in Biology. Number 16. Biology Department, Brookhaven National Laboratory, Upton, N.Y.

Clowes, F. A. L. 1961. *Apical Meristems.* Oxford University Press, Blacksell, Oxford.

Heslop-Harrison, J. 1967. "Differentation." *Annual Review of Plant Physiology* 18:325–348.

Klein, R. M. [ed.]. 1961. *Plant Growth Regulation.* Iowa State University Press, Ames.

Knox, R. B., and L. T. Evans. 1966. "Inflorescence initiation in *Lolium temulentum* L. VIII. Histochemical changes at the shoot apex during induction." *Australian Journal of Biological Sciences* 19:233–245.

Leopold, A. C. 1964. *Plant Growth and Development.* Mc-Graw-Hill Book Company, Inc., New York.

Loomis, W. E. [ed.]. 1953. *Growth and Differentiation in Plants.* Iowa State College Press, Ames.

Näf, U. 1962. "Developmental physiology of lower archegoniates." *Annual Review of Plant Physiology* 13:507–532.

Nougarede, A. 1967. "Experimental cytology of the shoot apical cells during vegetative growth and flowering." *International Review of Cytology* 21:203–351.

Oota, Y. 1964. "RNA in developing plant cells." *Annual Review of Plant Physiology* 15:17–36.

Sachs, R. M. 1965. "Stem elongation." *Annual Review of Plant Physiology* 16:73–96.

Stange, L. 1965. "Plant cell differentiation." *Annual Review of Plant Physiology* 16:119–140.

Steward, F. C., and H. Y. Mohan Ram. 1961. "Determining factors in cell growth: Some implications for morphogenesis in plants." *Advances in Morphogenesis* 1:189–266.

Steward, F. C., and E. M. Shantz. 1959. "The chemical regulation of growth (some substances and extracts which induce growth and morphogenesis)." *Annual Review of Plant Physiology* 10:379–404.

Thompson, D. 1966. *On Growth and Form.* J. T. Bonner [ed.], abridged edition. University Press, Cambridge. (Original edition, 1942.)

Torrey, J. G. 1966. "The initiation of organized development in plants." *Advances in Morphogenesis* 5:39–91.

—————. 1967. *Development in Flowering Plants.* The Macmillan Company, New York.

REFERENCES

Avers, Charlotte, J. 1961. "Histochemical localization of enzyme activities in root meristem cells." *American Journal of Botany* 48:137–143.

Bucknall, R. A., and J. F. Sutcliffe. 1965. "The nucleic acids and cellular differentiation in the root apex of *Pisum sativum.* II. The nucleic acids and cellular development patterns." *Journal of Experimental Botany* 16:587–603.

Gifford, E. M., Jr., and K. D. Stewart. 1967. "Ultrastructure of the shoot apex of *Chenopodium album* and certain other seed plants." *Journal of Cell Biology* 33:131–142.

Gifford, E. M., and H. B. Tepper. 1962. "Histochemical and autoradiographic studies of floral induction in *Chenopodium album.*" *American Journal of Botany* 49:706–714.

Halperin, W. 1966. "Single cells, coconut milk, and embryogenesis *in vitro.*" *Science* 153:1287–1288.

Jensen, W. A. 1966. "The problem of cell development in plants." In *Plant Biology Today: Advances and Challenges.* W. A. Jensen and L. G. Kavaljian [eds.]. pp. 11–26. Wadsworth Publishing Company, Inc., Belmont, Calif.

Jensen, W. A., E. G. Pollock, P. Healey, and Mary Ashton. 1964. "Kinetin and the nucleic acid content of onion root tips." *Experimental Cell Research* 33:523–530.

Kinet, J. M., G. Bernier, and R. Bronchart. 1967. "Sudden release of the meristematic cells from G_2 as a primary effect of flower induction in *Sinapis*." *Naturwissenschaften* 13:351.

Lund, H. A., A. E. Vatter, and J. B. Hanson. 1958. "Biochemical and cytological changes accompanying growth and differentiation in the roots of *Zea mays*." *Journal of Biophysical and Biochemical Cytology* 4:87–98.

Pollock, E. G., and W. A. Jensen. 1964. "Cell development during early embryogenesis in *Capsella* and *Gossypium*." *American Journal of Botany* 51:915–921.

Thornber, J. P., and D. H. Northcote. 1961. "Changes in the chemical composition of a cambial cell during its differentiation into xylem and phloem tissue in trees. I. Main components." *Biochemical Journal* 81:449–455.

Vasil, Vimla, and A. C. Hildebrandt. 1965. "Growth and tissue formation from single, isolated cells in microculture." *Science* 147:1454–1455.

Wetmore, R. W. 1959. "Morphogenesis in plants—a new approach." *American Scientist* 47:326–340.

CHAPTER 23　　BOOKS AND REVIEWS

Briggs, W. R. 1963. "The phototropic responses of higher plants." *Annual Review of Plant Physiology* 14:311–352.

Butler, W. L. 1964. "Absorption spectroscopy *in vivo*: Theory and application." *Annual Review of Plant Physiology* 15:451–470.

Giese, A. C. [ed.]. 1964. *Photophysiology*. Academic Press, Inc., New York.

Goodwin, T. W. [ed.]. 1965. *Chemistry and Biochemistry of Plant Pigments*. Academic Press, Inc., New York.

Haupt, W. 1966. "Phototaxis in plants." *International Review of Cytology* 19:267–299.

Hillman, W. S. 1967. "The physiology of phytochrome." *Annual Review of Plant Physiology* 18:301–324.

Leopold, A. C. 1964. *Plant Growth and Development*. McGraw-Hill Book Company, Inc., New York.

Lockhart, J. A. 1963. "Photomorphogenesis in plants." *Advancing Frontiers of Plant Sciences* 7:1–43.

Mayer, A. M., and A. Poljakoff-Mayber. 1963. *The Germination of Seeds*. The Macmillan Company, New York.

Mohr, H. 1962. "Primary effects of light on growth." *Annual Review of Plant Physiology* 13:465–488.

Siegelman, H. W., and W. L. Butler. 1965. "Properties of phytochrome." *Annual Review of Plant Physiology* 16:383–392.

REFERENCES

Bonner, B. 1966. "Phytochrome and the red, far-red system." In *Plant Biology Today: Advances and Challenges*. W. A. Jensen and L. G. Kavaljian [eds.]. pp. 185–208. Wadsworth Publishing Company, Inc., Belmont, Calif.

Borthwick, H. A., and R. J. Downs. 1964. "Role of active phytochrome in control of flowering of *Xanthium pensylvanicum*." *Botanical Gazette* 125:227–231.

Borthwick, H. A., S. B. Hendricks, and M. W. Parker. 1951. "Action spectrum for inhibition of stem growth in dark-grown seedlings of albino and nonalbino barley (*Hordeum vulgare*)." *Botanical Gazette* 113:95–105.

Bottomley, W., H. Smith, and A. W. Galston. 1965. "A phytochrome mediated effect of light on the hydroxylation pattern of flavonoids in *Pisum sativum* var. 'Alaska'." *Nature* 207:1311–1312.

Briggs, W. R., and H. P. Chon. 1966. "The physiological versus the spectrophotometric status of phytochrome in corn coleoptiles." *Plant Physiology* 41:1159–1166.

Butler, W. L., H. W. Siegelman, and C. O. Miller. 1964. "Denaturation of phytochrome." *Biochemistry* 3:851–857.

Carr, D. J., and D. M. Reid. 1966. "Actinomycin-D inhibition of phytochrome-mediated responses." *Planta* 69:70–78.

Cline, M. G., and F. B. Salisbury. 1966. "Effects of ultraviolet radiation on the leaves of higher plants." *Radiation Botany* 6:151–163.

Doudney, C. O., and Betty J. Bruce. 1966. "Ultraviolet light inactivation and recovery of bacterial recombination and nucleic acid synthesis." *Radiation Research* 28:597–608.

Downs, R. J. 1955. "Photoreversibility of leaf and hypocotyl elongation of dark grown red kidney bean seedlings." *Plant Physiology* 30:468–473.

Downs, R. J., S. B. Hendricks, and H. A. Borthwick. 1957. "Photoreversible control of elongation of pinto beans and other plants under normal conditions of growth." *Botanical Gazette* 118:199–208.

Downs, R. J., H. W. Siegelman, W. L. Butler, and S. B. Hendricks. 1965. "Photoreceptive pigments for anthocyanin synthesis in apple skin." *Nature* 205:909–910.

Dring, M. J. 1967. "Phytochrome in red alga, *Porphyra tenera*." *Nature* 215:1411–1412.

Drumm, Helga, and H. Mohr. 1967. "The regulation of RNA synthesis in fern gametophytes by light." *Planta* 72:232–246.

————. 1967. "The regulation of DNA synthesis in fern gametophytes by light." *Planta* 75:343–351.

Durst, F., and H. Mohr. 1966. "Phytochrome-mediated induction of enzyme synthesis in mustard seedlings (*Sinapis alba* L.)" *Naturwissenschaften* 20:531–532.

Fondeville, J. C., H. A. Borthwick, and S. B. Hendricks. 1966. "Leaflet movement of *Mimosa pudica* L. Indicative of phytochrome action." *Planta* 69:357–364.

Galston, A. W., A. A. Tuttle, and Pauline J. Penny. 1964. "A kinetic study of growth movements and photomorphogenesis in etiolated pea seedlings." *American Journal of Botany* 51:853–858.

Hamawalt, P. C., and R. H. Haynes. 1967. "The repair of DNA." *Scientific American* 216(2):36–43.

Hartmann, K. M. 1966. "A general hypothesis to interpret 'high energy phenomena' of photomorphogenesis on the basis of phytochrome." *Photochemistry and Photobiology* 5:349–366.

Hendricks, S. B., and H. A. Borthwick. 1967. "The function of phytochrome in regulation of plant growth." *Proceedings of the National Academy of Sciences* 58: 2125–2139.

Hillman, W. S., and W. L. Koukkari. 1967. "Phytochrome effects in the nyctinastic leaf movements of *Albizzia julibrissin* and some other legumes." *Plant Physiology* 42:1413–1418.

Jaffe, M. J., and A. W. Galston. 1967. "Phytochrome control of rapid nyctinastic movements and membrane permeability in *Albizzia julibrissin.*" *Planta* 77:135–141.

Jagger, J., and R. S. Stafford. 1965. "Evidence for two mechanisms of photoreactivation in *Escherichia coli B.*" *Biophysical Journal* 5:75–88.

Jakobs, M., and H. Mohr. 1966. "Kinetical studies on phytochrome-induced protein synthesis." *Planta* 69:187–197.

Klein, R. M. 1967. "Influence of ultraviolet radiation on auxin-controlled plant growth." *American Journal of Botany* 54:904–914.

————. 1965. "Photomorphogenesis of the bean plumular hook." *Physiologia Plantarum* 18:1026–1033.

Klein, W. H., J. L. Edwards, and W. Shropshire, Jr. 1967. "Spectrophotometric measurements of phytochrome *in vivo* and their correlation with photomorphogenic responses of *Phaseolus*." *Plant Physiology* 42:264–270.

Klein, W. H., R. B. Withrow, and V. B. Elstad. 1956. "Response of the hypocotyl hook of bean seedlings to radiant energy and other factors." *Plant Physiology* 31:289–294.

Kohler, D. 1966. "Dependence of the gibberellin production of normal peas in the phytochrome system." *Planta* 69:27–33.

Lange, H., and H. Mohr. 1965. "The inhibitory effect of actinomycin-D and puromycin on the phytochrome induced synthesis of anthocyanin." *Planta* 67:107–121.

Linschitz, H., V. Kasche, W. L. Butler, and H. W. Siegelman. 1966. "The kinetics of phytochrome conversion." *Journal of Biological Chemistry* 241:3395–3403.

Lockhart, J. A. 1964. "Physiological studies on light sensitive stem growth." *Planta* 62:97–115.

————. 1958. "The response of various species of higher plants to light and gibberellic acid." *Physiologia Plantarum* 11:478–486.

Mohr, H. 1966. "Differential gene activation as a mode of action of phytochrome 730." *Photochemistry and Photobiology* 5:469–483.

Mumford, F. E., and E. L. Jenner. 1966. "Purification and characterization of phytochrome from oat seedlings." *Biochemistry* 5:3657–3662.

Nakata, S., and J. A. Lockhart. 1966. "Effects of red and far-red radiation on cell division and elongation in the stem of pinto bean seedlings." *American Journal of Botany* 53:12–20.

Naqvi, S. M., and S. A. Gordon. 1966. "Auxin transport in *Zea mays* coleoptiles. II. Influence of light on the transport of indoleacetic acid-2-^{14}C." *Plant Physiology* 42:138–143.

Rollin, P. 1966. "The influence of light upon seed germination. Possible interpretations of data." *Photochemistry and Photobiology* 5:367–371.

Schopfer, P. 1967. "The inhibition of phytochrome-mediated photomorphogenesis ('positive' photoresponses) by actinomycin D and puromycin in the mustard seedling *Sinapis alba* L.)." *Planta* 72:297–305.

Siegelman, H. W., B. C. Turner, and S. B. Hendricks. 1966. "The chromophore of phytochrome." *Plant Physiology* 41:1289–1292.

Smith, K. C., and Mary E. O'Leary. 1967. "Photoinduced DNA-protein cross-links and bacterial killing: A correlation at low temperatures." *Science* 155:1024–1026.

Spruit, C. J. P. 1966. "Thermal reactions following illumination of phytochrome." *Mededlingen Landbouwhogeschool Wageningen* 66(15):1–7.

Stafford, Helen A. 1965. "Flavonoids and related phenolic compounds produced in the first internode of *Sorghum vulgare* Pers. in darkness and in light." *Plant Physiology* 40:130–138.

Tamura, S., N. Takahashi, N. Murofuchi, and T. Yokota. 1967. "Isolation of two new gibberellins from immature seeds of *Canavalia*." *Planta* 75:279–282.

Taylor, A. O., and B. A. Bonner. 1967. "Isolation of phytochrome from the alga *Mesotaenium* and liverwort *Sphaerocarpos*." *Plant Physiology* 42:762–766.

Terry, C. E., and Jane K. Setlow. 1967. "Photoreactivating enzyme from *Neurospora crassa*." *Photochemistry and Photobiology* 6:799–803.

Thimann, K. V., and Babette S. Radner. 1962. "The biogenesis of anthocyanins. VII. The requirement for both purines and pyrimidines." *Archives of Biochemistry and Biophysics* 96:270–279.

Vince, Daphne. 1967. "Gibberellic acid and the light inhibition of stem elongation." *Planta* 75:291–308.

Vince, Daphne, and R. Grill. 1966. "The photoreceptors involved in anthocyanin synthesis." *Photochemistry and Photobiology* 5:407–411.

Wagner, E., and H. Mohr. 1966. "Kinetic studies to interpret 'high-energy phenomena' of photomorphogenesis on the basis of phytochrome." *Photochemistry and Photobiology* 5:397–406.

CHAPTER 24   BOOKS AND REVIEWS

Ashchoff, J. [ed.]. 1965. *Circadian Clocks*. North-Holland Publishing Company, Amsterdam.

Brahmachary, R. L. 1967. Physiological clocks. *International Review of Cytology* 21:65–89.

Bünning, E. 1956. Endogenous rhythms in plants. *Annual Review of Plant Physiology* 7:71–90.

Bünning, E. 1964. *The Physiological Clock*. Springer-Verlag, Berlin.

Cold Spring Harbor Symposia on Quantitative Biology. 1960. *Biological Clocks* Vol. 25.

Griffin, D. R. 1964. *Bird Migration*. Doubleday & Company, Inc., Garden City, N.Y.

Harker, Janet E. 1964. *The Physiology of Diurnal Rhythms*. Cambridge University Press, Cambridge, England.

Leopold, A. C. 1964. *Plant Growth and Development*. McGraw-Hill Book Company, Inc., New York.

Sollberger, A. 1965. *Biological Rhythm Research*. Elsevier Publishing Company, New York.

Sweeney, Beatrice M. 1963. "Biological clocks in plants." *Annual Review of Plant Physiology* 14:411–440.

Withrow, R. B. [ed.]. 1959. *Photoperiodism and Related Phenomena in Plants and Animals*. Publication No. 55 of the American Association for the Advancement of Science, Washington, D.C.

REFERENCES

Aschoff, J. 1965. "Circadian rhythms in man." *Science* 148:1427–1432.

Brown, F. A., Jr. 1957. "The rhythmic nature of life." In *Recent Advances in Invertebrate Physiology*. pp. 287–304. University of Oregon Publications, Eugene.

Brown, F. A., Jr. 1959. "The rhythmic nature of animals and plants." *American Scientist* 47:147–168.

Brown, F. A., Jr., R. O. Freeland, and C. L. Ralph. 1955. "Persistent rhythms of O_2-consumption in potatoes, carrots and the seaweed *Fucus*." *Plant Physiology* 30:280–292.

Feldman, J. F. 1967. "Lengthening the period of a biological clock in *Euglena* by cycloheximide, an inhibitor of protein synthesis." *Proceedings of the National Academy of Sciences* 57:1080–1087.

Hamner, K. 1963. "Endogenous rhythms in controlled environments." In *Environmental Control of Plant Growth*. L. T. Evans [ed.]. Chap. 13. Academic Press, Inc., New York.

Hastings, J. W. 1964. "The role of light in persistent daily rhythms." *Photophysiology* 1:333–361

Heathcote, D. G. 1966. "A new type of rhythmic plant movement: Micronutation." *Journal of Experimental Botany* 17:690–695.

Hoshizaki, T., and K. C. Hamner. 1964. "Circadian leaf movements: Persistence in bean plants grown in continuous high-intensity light." *Science* 144:1240–1241.

Karakashian, Marlene W., and J. W. Hastings. 1963. "The effects of inhibitors of macromolecular biosynthesis upon the persistent rhythm of luminescence in *Gonyaulax*." *Journal of General Physiology* 47:1–12.

Menaker, M., and A. Eskin. 1967. "Circadian clock in photoperiodic time measurement: A test of the Bünning hypothesis." *Science* 157:1182–1185.

Sargent, M. L., W. R. Briggs, and D. O. Woodward. 1966. "Circadian nature of a rhythm expressed by an invertaseless strain of *Neurospora crassa*." *Plant Physiology* 41:1343–1349.

Schweiger, E., H. G. Wallraff, and H. G. Schweiger. 1964. "Endogenous circadian rhythm in cytoplasm of *Acetabularia*: Influence of the nucleus." *Science* 146:658–659.

Sweeney, Beatrice M. 1965. "Do cells have clocks?" *Discovery* October.

———. 1966. "The measurement of time in plants." In *Plant Biology Today: Advances and Challenges*. W. A. Jensen and L. G. Kavaljian [eds.]. Wadsworth Publishing Company, Inc., Belmont, Calif.

CHAPTER 25   BOOKS AND REVIEWS

Amen, R. D. 1966. "The extent and role of seed dormancy in alpine plants." *Quarterly Review of Biology* 41:271–281.

Barton, L. V., and W. Crocker. 1948. *Twenty Years of Seed Research*. Faber & Faber, Limited, London.

Chouard, P. 1960. "Vernalization and its relation to dormancy." *Annual Review of Plant Physiology* 11:191–238.

Crocker, W., and L. V. Barton. 1957. *Physiology of Seeds*. Chronica Botanica Company, Waltham, Mass.

Evenari, M. 1949. "Germination inhibitors." *Botanical Review* 15:153–194.

Koller, D., A. M. Mayer, A. Poljakoff-Mayber, and S. Klein. 1962. "Seed germination." *Annual Review of Plant Physiology* 13:437–464.

Kramer, P. J., and T. T. Kozlowski. 1960. *Physiology of Trees.* McGraw-Hill Book Company, Inc., New York.

Langridge, J. 1963. "Biochemical aspects of temperature response." *Annual Review of Plant Physiology* 14:441–462.

Leopold, A. C. 1964. *Plant Growth and Development.* McGraw-Hill Book Company, Inc., New York.

Mayer, A. M., and A. Poljakoff-Mayber. 1963. *The Germination of Seeds.* Pergamon Press, Oxford, London, New York, Paris.

Meyer, B. S., D. B. Anderson and R. H. Böhning. 1960. *Introduction to Plant Physiology.* D. Van Nostrand Company, Princeton, N.J.

Vegis, A. 1964. "Dormancy in higher plants." *Annual Review of Plant Physiology* 15:185–224.

Wareing, P. F. 1956. "Photoperiodism in woody plants." *Annual Review of Plant Physiology* 7:191–214.

————. 1963. "The germination of seeds." *Vistas in Botany* 3:195–227.

Went, F. W. 1957. *The Experimental Control of Plant Growth.* Chronica Botanica Company, Waltham, Mass.

REFERENCES

Amen, R. D. 1967. "The effects of gibberellic acid and scarification on the seed dormancy and germination in *Luzula spicata.*" *Physiologia Plantarum* 20:6–12.

Ashford, N., and J. Levitt. 1965. "The relation of sulfhydryl groups to rest period in potato tubers." *Physiologia Plantarum* 18:229–239.

Blumenthal-Goldschmidt, S., and L. Rappaport. 1965. "Regulation of bud rest in tubers of potato *Solanum tuberosum* L. II. Inhibition of sprouting by inhibitor β complex and reversal by Gibberellin A_3." *Plant and Cell Physiology* 6:601–608.

Caspari, E. W., and R. W. Marshak. 1965. "The rise and fall of Lysenko." *Science* 149:275–278.

Chen, S. S. C., and K. V. Thimann. 1966. "Nature of seed dormancy in *Phacelia tanacetifolia.*" *Science* 153:1537–1539.

Cook, C. E., *et al.* 1966. "Germination of witchweed (*Striga lutea* Lour.): Isolation and properties of a potent stimulant." *Science* 154:1189–1190.

Cornforth, J. W., B. V. Milborrow, G. Ryback, and P. F. Wareing. 1965. "Chemistry and physiology of dormins in sycamore. Identity of sycamore dormin with abscisin II." *Nature* 205:1269–1270.

Cumming, B. G. 1963. "The dependence of germination on photoperiod, light quality and temperature on *Chenopodium* spp." *Canadian Journal of Botany* 41:1211–1233.

Eagles, C. G., and P. F. Wareing. 1964. "The role of growth substances in the regulation of bud dormancy." *Physiologia Plantarum* 17:697–709.

Ellis, R. W., and E. J. Trione. 1967. "Sulfhydryl and disulfide patterns associated with vernalization of wheat." *Physiologia Plantarum* 20:106–112.

Frankland, B., and P. F. Wareing. 1966. "Hormonal regulation of seed dormancy in hazel (*Corylus avellana* L.) and beech (*Fagus sylvatica* L.)." *Journal of Experimental Botany* 17:596–611.

Hurd, R. G., and O. N. Purvis. 1964. "The effect of gibberellic acid on the flowering of spring and winter rye." *Annals of Botany* 28:137–151.

Ikuma, H., and K. V. Thimann. 1963. "The role of the seed-coats in germination of photosensitive lettuce seeds." *Plant and Cell Physiology* 4:169–185.

Khan, A. A., and N. E. Tolbert. 1965. "Reversal of inhibitors of seed germination by red light plus kinetin." *Physiologia Plantarum* 18:437–464.

Lane, F. E., and L. F. Bailey. 1964. "Isolation and characterization studies on the β-inhibitor in dormant buds of the silver maple, *Acer saccharinum* L." *Physiologia Plantarum* 17:91–99.

Lang, A., and E. Reinhard. 1961. "Gibberellins and flower formation." *Advances in Chemistry Series* 28:71–79.

Pollock, B. M., and H. O. Olney. 1959. "Studies of the rest period. I. Growth, translocations, and respiratory changes in the embryonic organs of the after-ripening cherry seed." *Plant Physiology* 34:131–142.

Porsild, A. E., C. R. Harington, and G. A. Mulligan. 1967. "*Lupinus articus* Wats. Grown from seeds of Pleistocene age." *Science* 158:113–114.

Rollin, P., and G. Maignan. 1967. "Phytochrome and the photoinhibition of germination." *Nature* 214:741–742.

Sayers, R. L., and R. T. Ward. 1966. "Germination responses in alpine species." *Botanical Gazette* 127:11–16.

Scheibe, J., and A. Lang. 1967. "Lettuce seed germination: A phytochrome-mediated increase in the growth rate of lettuce seed radicles." *Planta* 72:348–354.

Smith, H., and N. P. Kefford. 1964. "The chemical regulation of the dormancy phases of bud development." *American Journal of Botany* 51:1002–1012.

Suge, H., and N. Yamada. 1963. "Chemical control of plant growth and development. 4. Promotion of flowering induced by uracil, uridylic acid and several growth regulators in winter wheat." *Proceedings of the Crop Science Society of Japan* 32:77–80.

————. 1965. "Flower-promoting effects of gibberellin in winter wheat and barley." *Plant and Cell Physiology* 6:147–160.

Teraoka, H. 1967. "Proteins of wheat embryos in the period of vernalization." *Plant and Cell Physiology* 8:87–95.

Tuan, Dorothy Y., and J. Bonner. 1964. "Dormancy associated with repression of genetic activity." *Plant Physiology* 39:768–772.

Vegis, A. 1963. "Climatic control of germination, bud break, and dormancy." In *Environmental Control of Plant Growth*. L. T. Evans [ed.]. Chap. 15. Academic Press, Inc., New York.

Villiers, T. A., and P. F. Wareing. 1965. "The growth-substance content of dormant fruits of *Fraxinus excelsior* L." *Journal of Experimental Botany* 16:519–531.

Wareing, P. F. 1961. "Dormancy of woody plants." In *Recent Advances in Botany*. Ninth International Botanical Congress, Montreal. pp. 1216–1219. University of Toronto Press, Toronto, Canada.

Wessen, G., and P. F. Wareing. 1967. "Light requirements of buried seeds." *Nature* 213:600–601.

CHAPTER 26   BOOKS AND REVIEWS

Doorenbos, J., and S. J. Wellensiek. 1959. "Photoperiodic control of floral induction." *Annual Review of Plant Physiology* 10:147–184.

Evans, L. T. [ed.]. 1968. *The Induction of Flowering. Some Case Histories*. In press.

Hillman, W. S. 1962. *The Physiology of Flowering*. Holt, Rinehart and Winston, Inc., New York.

Kramer, P. J., and T. T. Kozlowski. 1960. *Physiology of Trees*. McGraw-Hill Book Company, Inc., New York.

Leopold, A. C. 1964. *Plant Growth and Development*. McGraw-Hill Book Company, Inc., New York.

Meyer, B. S., D. B. Anderson, and R. H. Böhning. 1960. *Introduction to Plant Physiology*. D. Van Nostrand Company, Inc., Princeton, N.J.

Paleg, L. G. 1965. "Physiological effects of gibberellins." *Annual Review of Plant Physiology* 16:291–322.

Salisbury, F. B. 1961. "Photoperiodism and the flowering process." *Annual Review of Plant Physiology* 12:293–326.

————. 1963. *The Flowering Process*. Pergamon Press, New York.

————. 1965. "The initiation of flowering." *Endeavour* 24:74–80.

Searle, N. E. 1965. "Physiology of flowering." *Annual Review of Plant Physiology* 16:97–118.

Wareing, P. F. 1956. "Photoperiodism in woody plants." *Annual Review of Plant Physiology* 7:191–214.

Zeevaart, J. A. D. 1962. "Physiology of flowering." *Science* 137:723–731.

————. 1963. Climatic control of reproductive development.

————. In *Environmental Control of Plant Growth*. L. T. Evans [ed.]. Chap. 16. Academic Press, Inc., New York.

REFERENCES

Abeles, F. B. 1967. "Inhibition of flowering in *Xanthium pensylvanicum* Wallr. by ethylene." *Plant Physiology* 42:608–609.

Aitken, Yvonne. 1964. "Flower initiation in pasture legumes. IV. Flower initiation in *Trifolium pratense* L." *Australian Journal of Agricultural Research* 15:21–36.

Baldev, B., and A. Lang. 1965. "Control of flower formation by growth retardants and gibberellin in *Samolus parviflorus*, a long-day plant." *American Journal of Botany* 52:408–417.

Barbat, I., and C. Ochesanu. 1965. "The nature of the photoperiodical induction. The presence of a flowering-hormone or a flowering inhibitor." *Naturwissenschaften* 15:458.

Bennett, R. D., S. T. Ko, and E. Heftmann. 1966. "Effect of photoperiodic floral induction on the metabolism of a gibberellin precursor, (−)kaurene, in *Pharbitis nil*." *Plant Physiology* 41:1360–1363.

Bernier, G., and R. Bronchart. 1964. "The steps of floral induction in *Sinapis alba* L." *Naturwissenschaften* 19:469–470.

Bhargava, S. C. 1965. "A transmissible flower bud inhibitor in *Perilla crispa*." *Koninkl. Nederl. Akademie Van Wetenschappen* (Amsterdam) 68:63–68.

Bonner, J., E. Heftmann, and J. A. D. Zeevaart. 1963. "Suppression of floral induction by inhibitors of steroid synthesis." *Plant Physiology* 38:81–88.

Carr, D. J. 1967. "The relationship between florigen and the flower hormones." In *Plant Growth Regulators*. J. F. Fredrick and E. M. Weyer [eds.]. pp. 305–312. Annals of the New York Academy of Sciences, 144.

Cherry, J. H., and R. van Huystee. 1965. "Effects of 5-fluorouracil on photoperiodic induction and nucleic acid metabolism of *Xanthium*." *Plant Physiology* 40:987–993.

Collins, W. T., F. B. Salisbury, and C. Ross. 1963. "Growth regulators and flowering. III. Antimetabolites." *Planta* 60:131–144.

Cumming, B. G. 1963. "Evidence of a requirement for phytochrome-Pfr in the floral initiation of *Chenopodium rubrum*." *Canadian Journal of Botany* 41:901–926.

El-Antably, H. M. M., and P. F. Wareing. 1966. "Stimulation of flowering in certain short-day plants by abscisin." *Nature* 210:328–329.

Evans, L. T. 1960. "Inflorescence initiation in *Lolium temulentum* L. II. Evidence for inhibitory and promotive photoperiodic processes involving transmissible products." *Australian Journal of Biological Science* 13:429–440.

————. 1964. "Inflorescence initiation in *Lolium temulentum* L. VI. Effects of some inhibitors of nucleic acid, protein, and steroid biosynthesis." *Australian Journal of Biological Science* 17:24–35.

————. 1966. "Abscisin II: Inhibitory effect on flower induction in a long-day plant." *Science* 151:107–108.

Evans, L. T., H. A. Borthwick, and S. B. Hendricks. 1965. "Inflorescence initiation in *Lolium temulentum* L. VII. The spectral dependence of induction." *Australian Journal of Biological Science* 18:745–762.

Evans, L. T., and I. F. Wardlaw. 1966. "Independent translocation of ^{14}C-labelled assimilates and of the floral stimulus in *Lolium temulentum*." *Planta* 68:310–326.

Friend, D. J. C., and V. A. Helson. 1966. "*Brassica campestris* L.: Floral induction by one long day." *Science* 153:1115–1116.

Galun, E., J. Gressel, and A. Keynan. 1964. "Suppression of floral induction by actinomycin D—an inhibitor of 'messenger' RNA synthesis." *Life Sciences* 3:911–915.

Hsu, J. C. S., and K. C. Hamner. 1967. "Studies on the involvement of an endogenous rhythm in the photoperiodic response of *Hyoscyamus niger*." *Plant Physiology* 42:725–730.

Lam, S. L. 1965. "Movement of the flower stimulus in *Xanthium*." *American Journal of Botany* 52:924–928.

Lincoln, R. G., A. Cunningham, and K. C. Hamner. 1964. "Evidence for a florigenic acid." *Nature* 202:559–561.

Miller, J., and C. Ross. 1966. "Inhibition of leaf processes by p-fluorophenylalanine during induction of flowering in the cocklebur." *Plant Physiology* 41:1185–1192.

Moore, T. C. 1965. "Effects of gibberellin on the growth and flowering of intact and decotylized dwarf peas." *Nature* 206:1065–1066.

Papenfuss, H. D., and F. B. Salisbury. 1967. "Aspects of clock resetting in flowering of *Xanthium*." *Plant Physiology* 42:1562–1568.

Pharis, R. P., and W. Morf. 1967. "Experiments on the precocious flowering of western red cedar and four species of *Cupressus* with gibberellins A_3 and A_4/A_7 mixture." *Canadian Journal of Botany* 45:1519–1524.

Ray, P. M., and W. E. Alexander. 1966. "Photoperiodic adaptation to latitude in *Xanthium strumarium*." *American Journal of Botany* 53:806–816.

Reid, H. B., P. H. Moore, and K. C. Hamner. 1967. "Control of flowering of *Xanthium pensylvanicum* by red and far-red light." *Plant Physiology* 42:532–540.

Sachs, R. M., A. M. Kofranek, and S.-Y. Shyr. 1967. "Gibberellin-induced inhibition of floral initiation in *Fuchsia*." *American Journal of Botany* 54:921–929.

Salisbury, F. B. 1958. "The flowering process." *Scientific American* 198(4):109–117.

————. 1963. "Biological timing and hormone synthesis in flowering of *Xanthium*." *Planta* 59:518–534.

————. 1967. "Physiological evidence relating to the flowering hormone." In *Plant Growth Regulators*. J. F. Fredrick and E. M. Weyer [eds.]. pp. 295–314. Annals of the New York Academy of Sciences, 144.

Suge, H., and N. Yamada. 1965. "Effect of nucleic acid and its antimetabolite on induction of flowering in winter cereals." *Proceedings of the Crop Science Society of Japan* 33:324–329.

Watson, J. D., and R. E. F. Matthews. 1966. "Effect of actinomycin-D and 2-thiouracil on floral induction and nucleic acid synthesis in the bud in *Chenopodium amaranticolor*." *Australian Journal of Biological Science* 19:967–980.

Yoshida, K., K. Umemura, K. Yoshinaga, and Y. Oota. 1967. "Specific RNA from photoperiodically induced cotyledons of *Pharbitis nil*." *Plant and Cell Physiology* 8:97–108.

Zeevaart, J. A. D. 1957. "Studies on flowering by means of grafting. II. Photoperiodic treatment of detached *Perilla* and *Xanthium* leaves." *Koninkl. Nederl. Akademie Van Wetenschappen* (Amsterdam) 332–337.

————. 1966. "Inhibition of stem growth and flower formation in *Pharbitis nil* with N, N-dimethylaminosuccinamic acid (B995)." *Planta* 71:68–80.

CHAPTER 27   BOOKS AND REVIEWS

Biale, J. B. 1964. "Growth, maturation and senescence in fruits." *Science* 146:880–888.

Burg, S. P. 1962. "The physiology of ethylene formation." *Annual Review of Plant Physiology* 13:265–302.

Carns, H. R. 1966. "Abscission and its control." *Annual Review of Plant Physiology* 17:295–314.

Jacobs, W. P. 1962. "Longevity of plant organs: Internal factors controlling abscission." *Annual Review of Plant Physiology* 13:403–436.

Kramer, P. J., and T. T. Kozlowski. 1960. *Physiology of Trees*. McGraw-Hill Book Company, Inc., New York.

Leopold, A. C. 1964. *Plant Growth and Development*. McGraw-Hill Book Company, Inc. New York.

Meyer, B. S., D. B. Anderson, and R. H. Böhning. 1960. *Introduction to Plant Physiology*. D. Van Nostrand Company, Inc., Princeton, N.J.

Sax, K. 1962. "Aspects of aging in plants." *Annual Review of Plant Physiology* 13:489–506.

Varner, J. E. 1961. "Biochemistry of senescence." *Annual Review of Plant Physiology* 12:245–264.

REFERENCES

Abeles, F. B., R. E. Holm, and H. E. Gahagan. 1967. "Abscission: The role of aging." *Plant Physiology* 42:1351–1356.

Beevers, L. 1966. "Effect of gibberellic acid on the senescence of leaf discs of *Nasturtium* (*Tropaeolum majus*)." *Plant Physiology* 41:1074–1076.

Burg, S. P., and Ellen A. Burg. 1965. "Ethylene action and the ripening of fruits." *Science* 148:1190–1196.

Dennis, F. G., Jr. 1967. "Apple fruit-set: Evidence for a specific role of seeds." *Science* 156:71–73.

Fletcher, R. A., and Daphne Osborne. 1965. "Regulation of protein and nucleic acid synthesis by gibberellin during leaf senescence." *Nature* 207:1176–1177.

Holm, R. E., and F. B. Abeles. 1967. "Abscission: The role of RNA synthesis." *Plant Physiology* 42:1094–1102.

Jensen, T. E., and J. G. Valdovinos. 1967. "Fine structure of abscission zones. I. Abscission zones of the pedicels of tobacco and tomato flowers at anthesis." *Planta* 77:298–318.

Johri, M. M., and S. C. Maheshwari. 1965. "Studies on respiration in developing poppy seeds." *Plant and Cell Physiology* 6:61–72.

————. 1966. "Changes in the carbohydrates, proteins and nucleic acids during seed development in opium poppy." *Plant and Cell Physiology* 7:35–47.

Krizek, D. T., W. J. McIlrath, and B. S. Vergara. 1966. "Photoperiodic induction of senescence in *Xanthium* plants." *Science* 151:95–96.

Lyon, J. L., and O. E. Smith. 1966. "Effects of gibberellins on abscission in cotton seedling explants." *Planta* 69:347–356.

Mitchell, W. D., and S. H. Wittwer. 1962. "Chemical regulation of flower sex expression and vegetative growth in *Cucumis sativus* L." *Science* 136:880–881.

Osborne, Daphne J., and Mary Hallaway. 1964. "The auxin, 2, 4-dichlorophenoxyacetic acid, as a regulator of protein synthesis and senescence in detached leaves of *Prunus*." *The New Phytologist* 63:334–347.

Osborne, Daphne J., and Susan E. Moss. 1963. "Effect of kinetin on senescence and abscission in explants of *Phaseolus vulgaris*." *Nature* 200:1299–1301.

Rubenstein, B., and F. B. Abeles. 1965. "Relationship between ethylene evolution and leaf abscission." *Botanical Gazette* 126:255–259.

Sacher, J. A. 1967. "Senescence: Action of auxin and kinetin in control of RNA and protein synthesis in subcellular fractions of bean endocarp." *Plant Physiology* 42:1334–1342.

Scott, P. C., and A. C. Leopold. 1966. "Abscission as a mobilization phenomenon." *Plant Physiology* 41:826–830.

Scott, P. C., Lillian W. Miller, Barbara D. Webster, and A. C. Leopold. 1967. "Structural changes during bean leaf abscission." *American Journal of Botany* 54:730–734.

Seth, A. K., and P. F. Wareing. 1967. "Hormone-directed transport of metabolites and its possible role in plant senescence." *Journal of Experimental Botany* 18:65–77.

Sitton, D., C. Itai, and H. Kende. 1967. "Decreased cytokinin production in the roots as a factor in shoot senescence." *Planta* 73:296–300.

Sorokin, C. 1964. "Aging at the cellular level." *Experentia* 20:1–10.

Stoy, V. 1963. "The translocation of C^{14}-labelled photosynthetic products from the leaf to the ear in wheat." *Physiologia Plantarum* 16:851–866.

Sturani, E., and S. Cocucci. 1965. "Changes of the RNA system in the endosperm of ripening castor bean seeds." *Life Sciences* 4:1937–1944.

Yoo, B., and W. A. Jensen. 1966. "Changes in nucleic acid content and distribution during cotton embryogenesis." *Experimental Cell Research* 42:447–459.

CHAPTER 28   BOOKS AND REVIEWS

Allard, R. W. 1960. *Principles of Plant Breeding*. John Wiley & Sons, Inc., New York.

Audus, L. J. 1959. *Plant Growth Substances*. Interscience Publishers, Inc., New York.

Audus, L. J. [ed.]. 1964. *The Physiology and Biochemistry of Herbicides*. Academic Press, Inc., New York.

Cathey, H. M. 1964. "Physiology of growth-retarding chemicals." *Annual Review of Plant Physiology* 15:271–302.

Chandler, W. H. 1957. *Deciduous Orchards*. Lea and Febiger, Philadelphia.

Childers, N. F. [ed.]. 1966. *Nutrition of Fruit Crops*. Horticultural Publications, Rutgers—The State University, New Brunswick, N.J.

Clements, H. F. 1964. "Interaction of factors affecting yield." *Annual Review of Plant Physiology* 15:409–442.

Crane, J. C. 1964. "Growth substances in fruit setting and development." *Annual Review of Plant Physiology* 15:303–326.

Denison, E. L. 1958. *Principles of Horticulture.* The Macmillan Company, New York.

Dimond, A. E., and J. G. Horsfall. 1959. "Plant chemotherapy." *Annual Review of Plant Physiology* 10:257–276.

Free, M. 1961. *Plant Pruning in Pictures.* Doubleday & Company, Inc., Garden City, N.Y.

Frey, K. J. [ed.]. 1966. *Plant Breeding.* Iowa State University Press, Ames.

Hartmann, H. T., and D. E. Kester. 1959. *Plant Propagation, Principles and Practices.* Prentice-Hall, Inc., Englewood Cliffs, N.J.

Hawthorn, L. R., and L. H. Pollard. 1954. *Vegetable and Flower Seed Production.* The Blakiston Company, Inc., New York.

Hayes, H. K., F. R. Immer, and D. C. Smith. 1955. *Methods of Plant Breeding.* McGraw-Hill Book Company, Inc., New York.

Hilton, J. L., L. L. Jansen, and H. M. Hull. 1963. "Mechanisms of herbicide action." *Annual Review of Plant Physiology* 14:353–384.

Janick, J. 1963. *Horticultural Science.* W. H. Freeman & Company, Publishers, San Francisco.

Klingman, G. C. 1963. *Weed Control: As A Science.* John Wiley & Sons, Inc., New York.

Kramer, P. J., and T. T. Kozlowski. 1960. *Physiology of Trees.* McGraw-Hill Book Company, Inc., New York.

Leonard, W. H., and J. H. Martin. 1963. *Cereal Crops.* The Macmillan Company, New York.

Leopold, A. C. 1958. "Auxin uses in the control of flowering and fruiting." *Annual Review of Plant Physiology* 9:281–310.

Marshall, R. E. 1954. *Cherries and Cherry Products.* Interscience Publishers, Inc., New York.

Martin, J. H., and W. H. Leonard. 1967. *Principles of Field Crop Production.* The Macmillan Company, New York.

Moreland, D. E. 1967. "Mechanisms of action of herbicides." *Annual Review of Plant Physiology* 18:365–386.

Pearson, L. C. 1967. *Principles of Agronomy.* Reinhold Publishing Corporation, New York.

Peohlman, J. M. 1959. *Breeding Field Crops.* Henry Holt and Company, Inc., New York.

Pierre, W. H., S. A. Aldrich, and W. P. Martin. 1966. *Advances in Corn Production: Principles and Practices.* The Iowa State University Press, Ames.

Reuther, W. [ed.]. 1961. *Plant Analysis and Fertilizer Problems.* American Institute of Biological Sciences, Washington, D.C.

San Pietro, A., and F. A. Greer [eds.]. 1967. *Harvesting the Sun.* Academic Press, Inc., New York.

Shoemaker, J. S. 1955. *Small-Fruit Culture.* McGraw-Hill Book Company, Inc., New York.

————. 1956. *General Horticulture.* J. B. Lippincott Company, New York.

Stuart, N. W., and H. M. Cathey. 1961. "Applied aspects of the gibberellins." *Annual Review of Plant Physiology* 12:369–394.

Thompson, H. C., and W. C. Kelly. 1957. *Vegetable Crops.* McGraw-Hill Book Company, Inc., New York.

Tukey, H. B. 1964. *Dwarfed Fruit Trees.* The Macmillan Company, New York; Collier–Macmillan, Limited, London.

Wilsie, C. P. 1962. *Crop Adaptation and Distribution.* W. H. Freeman & Company, Publishers, San Francisco.

Winkler, A. J. 1962. *General Viticulture.* University of California Press, Berkeley and Los Angeles.

Woodford, E. K., K. Holly, and C. C. McCready. 1958. "Herbicides." *Annual Review of Plant Physiology* 9:311–358.

REFERENCES

Bonner, J. 1961. "The world's increasing population." *Federation Proceedings* 20:369–372.

Childers, N. F. 1966. "Modern fruit science." *Orchard and Small Fruit Culture.* Horticultural Publications, Rutgers—The State University, New Brunswick, N.J.

Key, J. L., C. Y. Lin, E. M. Gifford, Jr., and R. Dengler. 1966. "Relation of 2,4-D-induced growth aberrations to changes in nucleic acid metabolism in soybean seedlings." *Botanical Gazette* 127:87–94.

Ross, M. A. 1965. *Herbicides and intermediary metabolism.* Ph.D. Dissertation, Colorado State University, Fort Collins.

CHAPTER 29   BOOKS AND REVIEWS

Bernstein, L., and H. C. Hayward. 1958. "Physiology of salt tolerance." *Annual Review of Plant Physiology* 9:25–46.

Golueke, C. G., and W. J. Oswald. 1964. "Role of plants in closed systems." *Annual Review of Plant Physiology* 15:387–408.

Henckel, P. A. 1964. "Physiology of plants under drought." *Annual Review of Plant Physiology* 15:363–386.

Hiesey, W. M., and H. W. Milner. 1965. "Physiology of ecological races and species." *Annual Review of Plant Physiology* 16:203–216.

Hudson, J. P. [ed.]. 1957. *Control of the Plant Environment.* Academic Press, Inc., New York.

Kramer, P. J., and T. T. Kozlowski. 1960. *Physiology of Trees.* McGraw-Hill Book Company, Inc., New York.

Levitt, J. 1956. *The Hardiness of Plants.* Academic Press, Inc., New York.

Mirov, N. T., and R. G. Stanley. 1959. "The pine tree." *Annual Review of Plant Physiology* 10:223–238.

Olien, C. R. 1967. "Freezing stresses and survival." *Annual Review of Plant Physiology* 18:387–408.

Pittendrigh, C. S., W. Vishniac, and J. P. T. Pearman [eds.]. 1966. *Biology and the Exploration of Mars.* National Academy of Sciences–National Research Council, Publication 1296.

Prosser, C. L. 1967. *Molecular Mechanisms of Temperature Adaptation.* American Association for Advancement of Science, Washington, D.C.

Riker, A. J. 1966. "Plant pathology and human welfare." *Science* 152:1027–1032.

Salisbury, F. B. 1962. "Martian biology." *Science* 136:17–26.

Shklovskii, I. S., and C. Sagan. 1966. *Intelligent Life in the Universe.* Holden-Day, Inc., San Francisco.

Shneour, E. A., and E. A. Ottesen [eds.]. 1966. *Extraterrestrial Life: An Anthology and Bibliography.* National Academy of Sciences–National Research Council, Publication 1296A.

Sutcliffe, J. F. 1962. *Mineral Salts Absorption in Plants.* Pergamon Press, Oxford, London, New York, Paris.

Tranquillini, W. 1964. "The physiology of plants at high altitudes." *Annual Review of Plant Physiology* 15:345–362.

REFERENCES

Bunt, J. S. 1967. "Thermal energy as a factor in the biology of the polar regions." In *Thermobiology.* A. H. Rose [ed.]. pp. 555–590. Academic Press, Inc., New York.

Gates, D. M. 1965. "Energy, plants and ecology." *Ecology* 46:1–13.

————. 1965. "Heat transfer in plants." *Scientific American* 213(6):84.

Highkin, H. R., and A. Lang. 1966. "Residual effect of germination temperature on the growth of peas." *Planta* 68:94–98.

Ketellapper, H. J. 1965. "Interaction of photoperiod and cycle length in plant growth." *Physiologia Plantarum* 18:337–345.

Kohn, H., and J. Levitt. 1966. "Interrelations between photoperiod, frost hardiness and sulfhydryl groups in cabbage." *Plant Physiology* 41:792–796.

Langridge, J., and J. R. McWilliam. 1967. "Heat responses of higher plants." In *Thermobiology.* A. H. Rose [ed.]. pp. 231–292. Academic Press, Inc., New York.

Levitt, J. 1962. "A sulfhydryl-disulfide hypothesis of frost injury and resistance in plants." *Journal of Theoretical Biology* 3:355–391.

————. 1963. "Hardiness and the survival of extremes: A uniform system for measuring resistance and its two components." In *Environmental Control of Plant Growth.* L. T. Evans [ed.]. Chap. 19. Academic Press, Inc., New York.

Monk, R. W., and H. H. Wiebe. 1961. "Salt tolerance and protoplasmic salt hardiness of various woody and herbaceous ornamental plants." *Plant Physiology* 36:478–482.

Sakai, A. 1966. "Studies of frost hardiness in woody plants. II. Effect of temperature on hardening." *Plant Physiology* 41:353–359.

Sakai, A., and S. Yoshida. 1967. "Survival of plant tissue at super-low temperatures. VI. Effects of cooling and rewarming rates on survival." *Plant Physiology* 42:1695–1701.

Salisbury, F. B. 1964. "A special-purpose controlled-environment unit." *Botanical Gazette* 125:237–241.

————. 1967. "The scientist and the UFO." *Bioscience* 17:15–24.

Salisbury, F. B., and G. G. Spomer. 1964. "Leaf temperatures of alpine plants in the field." *Planta* 60:497–505.

Scholander, P. F., H. T. Hammel, Edda D. Bradstreet, and E. A. Hemmingsen. 1965. "Sap pressure in vascular plants." *Science* 148:339–346.

Went, F. W. 1964. "Growing conditions of alpine plants." *Israel Journal of Botany* 13:82–92.

Index

An italic page number indicates that a definition or important discussion may be found on that page.

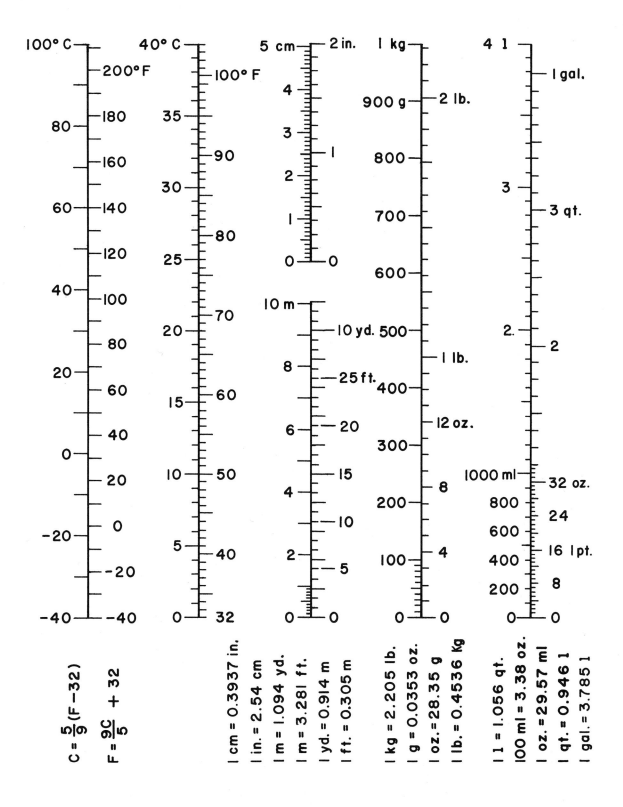